The University of Chicago School Mathematics Project

FUNCTIONS, STATISTICS, AND TRIGONOMETRY

Teacher's Edition
VOLUME 1 • CHAPTERS 1-6

Authors

John W. McConnell

Susan A. Brown

Paul J. Karafiol

Sara Brouwer

Mary Ives

Marshall Lassak

Rosa McCullagh

Natalie Jakucyn

Zalman Usiskin

The McGraw-Hill Companies

Authors

3rd EDITION AUTHORS

John W. McConnell *Lecturer in Statistics*
North Park University, Chicago, IL

Susan A. Brown *Mathematics/Science Division Chair*
York High School, Elmhurst, IL

Paul J. Karafiol *Mathematics Teacher*
Walter Payton College Prep High School, Chicago, IL

Sara Brouwer *Head of Mathematics*
The American School in London, London, England

Mary Ives *Mathematics Teacher*
University High School, Irvine, CA

Marshall Lassak *Associate Professor of Mathematics and Computer Science*
Eastern Illinois University, Charleston, IL

Rosa McCullagh *Mathematics Teacher*
University of Chicago Laboratory Schools

Natalie Jakucyn *Mathematics Teacher*
Glenbrook South High School, Glenview, IL

Zalman Usiskin *Professor of Education*
The University of Chicago

AUTHORS OF EARLIER EDITIONS

Sharon L. Senk *Professor of Mathematics*
Michigan State University, East Lansing, MI

Steven S. Viktora *Mathematics Department Chair*
New Trier Township High School, Winnetka, IL

Nils Ahbel *Mathematics Teacher*
Kent School, Kent, CT

Virginia Highstone *Mathematics Teacher*
York High School, Elmhurst, IL

David Witonsky
UCSMP

Rheta N. Rubenstein *Mathematics Department Head*
Renaissance High School, Detroit, MI

James E. Schultz *Associate Professor of Mathematics*
Ohio State University, Columbus, OH

Margaret Hackworth *Mathematics Supervisor*
Pinellas County Schools, Largo, FL

Dora Aksoy
UCSMP

James Flanders
UCSMP

Barry Kissane *Associate Professor of Education*
Murdoch University, Perth, Western Australia

Zalman Usiskin *Professor of Education*
The University of Chicago

www.WrightGroup.com

Wright Group

Printed in the United States of America.
Send all inquiries to:
Wright Group/McGraw-Hill
P.O. Box 812960
Chicago, IL 60681

ISBN-978-0-07-62140-75
ISBN-0-07-62140-79

2 3 4 5 6 7 8 9 RJE 16 15 14 13 12 11 10

The **McGraw·Hill** Companies

UCSMP EVALUATION, EDITORIAL, DESIGN, AND PRODUCTION

Director of Writing
Natalie Jakucyn

Director of Evaluation
Denisse R. Thompson
Professor of Mathematics Education
University of South Florida, Tampa, FL

Evaluation Consultant
Sharon L. Senk, *Professor of Mathematics*
Michigan State University, East Lansing, MI

Evaluation Assistants
Allison Burlock, Julian Owens

Executive Managing Editor
Clare Froemel

Editorial Staff
Gary Spencer, Carlos Encalada, Kathryn Rich,
Catherine Ballway, Carla Agard-Strickland,
Isaac Greenspan, Emily Mokros,
Currence Monson, Scott Neff

Technology Assistant
Brian Cordonnier

Design Staff
Susan Davis, Sarah Brechbill, Allison Rothmeier,
Susan Zhou

Production Coordinator
Benjamin R. Balskus

Production Assistants
Timothy Arehart, Nathan Bartlett, Gwendolyn Marks,
David McQuown, Robyn Mericle, Pamela Olson,
Tatiana Colodeeva, Samantha Fukushima,
Rachel Huddleston, Nurit Kirshenbaum, Eric Li,
Gretchen Neidhardt, Sarah Schieffer, DuanDuan Yang

Coordinator of School Relations
Carol Siegel

The following teachers and schools participated in evaluations of the third edition.

Jason Bridges
Greenwood High School
Greenwood, Arkansas

Beth Hawkins
Greenwood High School
Greenwood, Arkansas

Editha Banaban
University High School
Irvine, California

Mary Ives
University High School
Irvine, California

Brian Ray
Lindblom Math & Science Academy
Chicago, Illinois

Natalie Jakucyn
Glenbrook South High School
Glenview, Illinois

Kenneth Kerr
Glenbrook South High School
Glenview, Illinois

Chris Hayward
Cape Elizabeth High School
Cape Elizabeth, Maine

Jo Guido
Clark Montessori High School
Cincinnati, Ohio

Robert Seitz
John Adams High School
Cleveland, Ohio

James Norman
Tomahawk High School
Tomahawk, Wisconsin

The following schools participated in field studies of the first edition or second edition.

Brentwood School
Los Angeles, California

*Thornton Fractional
High School North*
Calumet City, Illinois

Kenwood Academy
Chicago, Illinois

*Thornton Fractional
High School South*
Lansing, Illinois

Niles Township High School North
Skokie, Illinois

The Culver Academies
Culver, Indiana

M. L. King High School
Detroit, Michigan

Renaissance High School
Detroit, Michigan

Southwestern High School
Detroit, Michigan

Woodward High School
Cincinnati, Ohio

Newark High School
Newark, Ohio

We wish to acknowledge the generous support of the **Amoco (now BP) Foundation** and the **Carnegie Corporation of New York** in helping to make it possible for the first edition of these materials to be developed, tested, and distributed, and the additional support of the **Amoco (now BP) Foundation** for the second edition.

UCSMP: The University of Chicago School Mathematics Project

Introduction to UCSMP

The University of Chicago School Mathematics Project (UCSMP) is a long-term project designed to improve and renovate school mathematics in grades Pre-K through 12. UCSMP began in 1983 with a six-year grant from the Amoco (now BP) Foundation. Since then, additional funding has come from the National Science Foundation, the Ford Motor Company, the Carnegie Corporation of New York, the Stuart Foundation, the General Electric (now Verizon) Foundation, GTE, Citicorp/Citibank, the Exxon Education Foundation, the Illinois Board of Higher Education, the Chicago Public Schools, from royalties, and from publishers of UCSMP materials.

UCSMP received widespread funding from business and industry because both of those communities understand the ramifications of large numbers of young adults leaving school to join the work force lacking the mathematics they need to be successful in the real world.

The UCSMP Pre-K–12 curriculum consists of two vertically articulated programs:

> The nation's leading standards-based Pre-K–6 mathematics program, *Everyday Mathematics,*® and

> The UCSMP secondary component, *UCSMP Grades 6–12.*

The entire UCSMP Pre-K–12 curriculum emphasizes problem solving, everyday applications, the use of technology, and reading in mathematics, while developing and maintaining basic skills.

Throughout the years, the following beliefs have guided the development of the UCSMP program:

> Mathematics is valuable to the average citizen.

> All students can learn a significant amount of mathematics. By spreading out the traditional four-year secondary curriculum — and more — over additional years, students are given more time to learn the content they need. This smoother pace of instruction means that the average student has a better chance of mastering the content. This keeps students in mathematics rather than weeding them out.

> The curriculum can be more efficient by spending less time on review from previous years and on outmoded content and skills.

> Calculators and computers are powerful tools that make some content more important than before, and other content less important, and allow for the introduction of new content.

UCSMP Pre-K–12 materials are currently being used by an estimated 3.5 to 4 million students in elementary and secondary schools in every state and virtually every major urban area in the United States.

Program Overview

Development and testing of University of Chicago School Mathematics Project (UCSMP) materials started in 1983. Field testing and revisions have continued ever since, resulting in the Third Editions of this comprehensive mathematics program.

The UCSMP program is unique in providing a seven-year middle school and high school curriculum. The names of the seven texts around which these years are built are:

> *Pre-Transition Mathematics*

> *Transition Mathematics*

> *Algebra*

> *Geometry*

> *Advanced Algebra*

> *Functions, Statistics, and Trigonometry*

> *Precalculus and Discrete Mathematics*

The UCSMP program emphasizes these features and benefits.

Key Program Features	Advantages	Benefits
ENRICHED CONTENT Wider scope of mathematical content than traditional programs, including more statistics in every level and transformational geometry at every level	A bridge between algebraic functions and geometric representation	Upgrades student achievement, providing continual opportunities for problem solving
PROBLEM-SOLVING Continual emphasis on problem solving with real-world application	Up-to-date curriculum which develops connections to other disciplines	Students are better prepared for jobs in computer related/ technology-based industries.
TECHNOLOGY All teachers and students in all courses will be expected to have access to graphing calculators, both in class and for assignments.	Up-to-date use of calculators and computers	Real-world experiences and greater understanding of technology
FOUR DIMENSIONS OF UNDERSTANDING The SPUR Approach: Skills, Properties, Uses, Representations	A unique four-dimensional approach to understanding	Maximizes student performance and fosters independent learning

Program Highlights

In response to various international, national, and state tests since the 1980s, combined with years of research and performance data, the UCSMP project addresses the most current issues in middle school and high school mathematics education.

Guided Instruction and Active Learning

Students learn best when classes are active and dynamic, presenting information through various modes and mediums. Students also learn at different rates and through repeated exposure to topics. Teachers guide students through lessons, activities, and projects that engage students in collaborative discovery of concepts and ideas. Continuous opportunities for review help students master concepts.

New Technology

The use of technology—including calculators, graphing calculators, dynamic geometry systems (DGS), spreadsheets, the Internet, and computer algebra systems (CAS)—is an essential component of the UCSMP Third Editions. Keeping current with modern technology will ensure that our students are well-prepared for the information age.

Real-World Applications

UCSMP uses real-world applications to introduce and develop concepts in lessons from all seven books. Skills that students learn through games and routines in *Everyday Mathematics* are put to the test through dynamic cross-curricular applications in the *UCSMP Grades 6–12* courses so students at various points of understanding can access the mathematics and continue to develop their understanding.

Reading and Writing Mathematics

Reading mathematical text is required throughout all of the UCSMP courses. Students must learn to read and write mathematical language in order to fully understand and communicate mathematical concepts. The familiarity with vocabulary and symbols that develops as students learn to read and write mathematical text will allow students to use any mathematical texts, not just their text books, as tools for understanding.

Multi-dimensional Approach to Understanding

UCSMP provides instruction which utilizes four dimensions of understanding and is unique in organizing the chapter objectives according to these dimensions. This multi-dimensional "SPUR" approach to understanding builds on differentiated instruction, providing continuous support to students despite their particular level of understanding.

SKILLS	Skills understanding means knowing a way to obtain a solution.
PROPERTIES	Properties understanding means knowing properties which you can apply. (Identify or justify the steps in obtaining answer.)
USES	Uses understanding means knowing situations in which you could apply the solving of this equation. (Set up or interpret a solution.)
REPRESENTATIONS	Representations understanding means having a representation of the solving process or a graphical way of interpreting the solution.

Read more about the SPUR approach on pages T20 and T21.

Functions, Statistics, and Trigonometry

Content

Functions, Statistics, and Trigonometry builds on the algebra and geometry students have previously studied to examine functions, statistics, and trigonometry in a unified way to help students prepare for everyday life and future courses in mathematics. Spreadsheet, graphing, and CAS technology are employed to enable students to explore and investigate, and to deal with complicated functions and data.

Functions
> Extension of student knowledge of linear, quadratic, exponential, logarithm, polynomial, and trigonometric equations and functions

> Transformations and symmetry applied in the study of the graphs of functions

> Statistical modeling of data with these functions

Statistics
> Attention given to criteria for the selection of statistical displays

> Coverage includes both population and sample statistics

> Frequency, relative frequency, and probability distributions viewed as functions and studied in detail, with emphasis on binomial and normal distributions

> Probabilities represented as areas of rectangles (in histograms) and under curves (in continuous distributions)

> Statistical inference using chi-square tests, calculation of binomial probabilities, and use of standardized data and scores

Trigonometry
> Review of the trigonometry that enables finding lengths of segments and measures of angles in any triangle given sufficient information

> Connections of trigonometry with the geometry, matrices, and complex numbers students have studied in previous years

> Use of trigonometric functions to model periodic phenomena

> Applications to a wide variety of contexts, with unique lessons devoted to obtaining the distance between cities on Earth

Use of a Variety of Tools/Technologies in an Activity-Oriented Approach
> Activities, Guided Examples, and Quiz Yourself questions throughout

> Explorations in all lessons; optional projects in all chapters

> Careful balance of mental mathematics, paper-and-pencil skills, and use of technology

> CAS, statistical, and graphing technology assumed in classroom and home use and used to develop properties, solve problems, and extend content

Part of An Articulated Curriculum

The UCSMP program is flexible, allowing schools to offer the appropriate mathematics to students regardless of their grade level. Students can enter the UCSMP program at any grade, but are advantaged by having had the previous UCSMP courses. The table below shows how *Everyday Mathematics*® and the UCSMP program can be used together beginning at Grade 5. (The percents shown are national percentiles.)

> **The UCSMP curriculum is appropriate for virtually all students, but not at the same time.**

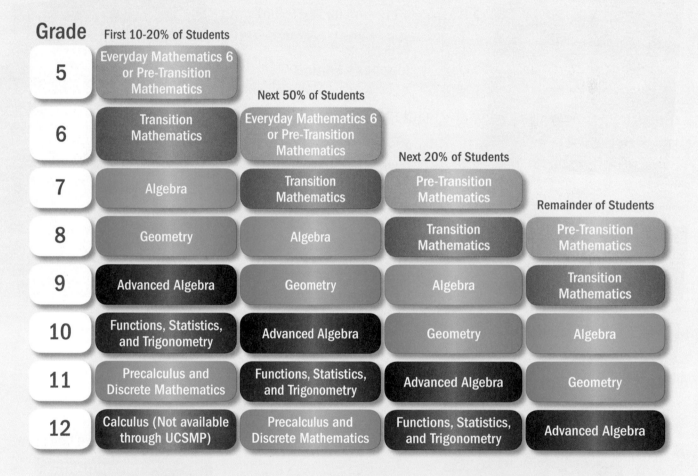

Grade	First 10-20% of Students	Next 50% of Students	Next 20% of Students	Remainder of Students
5	Everyday Mathematics 6 or Pre-Transition Mathematics			
6	Transition Mathematics	Everyday Mathematics 6 or Pre-Transition Mathematics		
7	Algebra	Transition Mathematics	Pre-Transition Mathematics	
8	Geometry	Algebra	Transition Mathematics	Pre-Transition Mathematics
9	Advanced Algebra	Geometry	Algebra	Transition Mathematics
10	Functions, Statistics, and Trigonometry	Advanced Algebra	Geometry	Algebra
11	Precalculus and Discrete Mathematics	Functions, Statistics, and Trigonometry	Advanced Algebra	Geometry
12	Calculus (Not available through UCSMP)	Precalculus and Discrete Mathematics	Functions, Statistics, and Trigonometry	Advanced Algebra

UCSMP strongly believes that its curriculum is appropriate for virtually all students, but not at the same time. No student should be deprived of the opportunity to be successful in any of the courses, but no child who is ready should have to wait a year or two to begin the curriculum. The evidence is strong that the national percentiles shown above are good predictors for readiness for the UCSMP program.

Every UCSMP course has been designed so it could be used independently of other UCSMP courses. Testing has verified that any of the UCSMP courses can be taken successfully following the typical prerequisite course in the standard curriculum. However, to take best advantage of these materials, and for them to be appropriate for the greatest number of students, it is preferable to use them in sequence.

Program Components

Each course in the UCSMP program includes the following components.

Student Edition
› Hard cover in one volume

› Online version (eSE)

› See pages T12–T15 for key features.

Teacher's Edition
› Hard cover in two volumes

› Electronic version (eTE)

› See pages T16–T17 for key features.

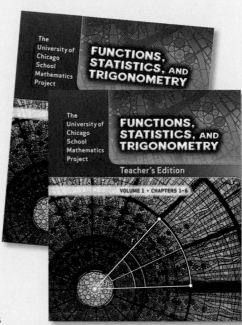

Assessment Resources
› Quizzes

› Chapter Tests

› Correlation of SPUR Objectives to Chapter Tests

› Assessment forms

Teaching Resources
› Lesson Masters

› Resource Masters

Electronic Teacher's Edition (eTE)

❯ CD-ROM of the Teacher's Edition

❯ Includes all ancillary pages and answers

❯ Includes Student Edition

❯ Includes answers and solutions to all SE problems

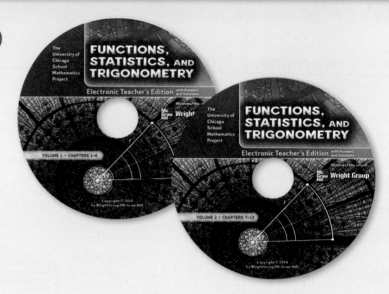

Teacher's Assessment Assistant (TAA)

❯ Sample assessment items similar to those on Chapter Test

❯ Ability to create new assessment resources

Student Edition

Hardcover Student Book

Exciting lesson features are shown below.

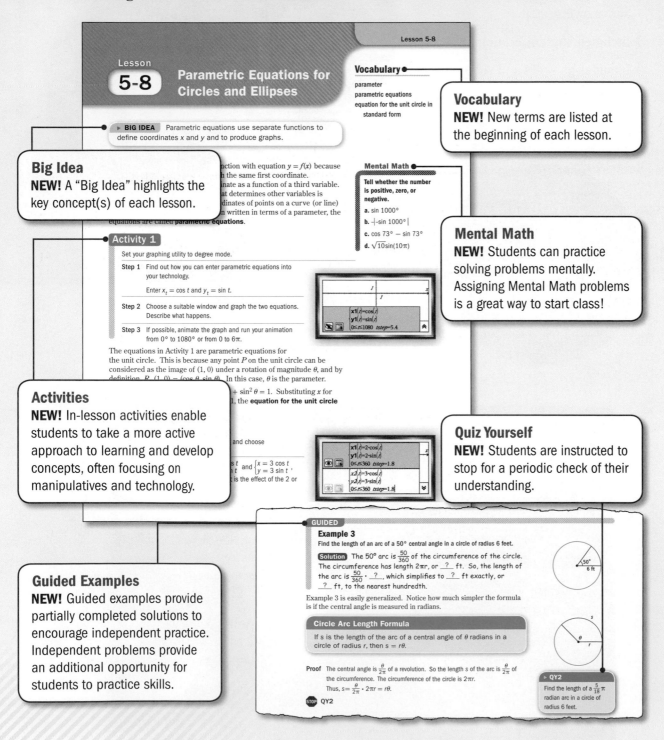

Big Idea
NEW! A "Big Idea" highlights the key concept(s) of each lesson.

Activities
NEW! In-lesson activities enable students to take a more active approach to learning and develop concepts, often focusing on manipulatives and technology.

Guided Examples
NEW! Guided examples provide partially completed solutions to encourage independent practice. Independent problems provide an additional opportunity for students to practice skills.

Vocabulary
NEW! New terms are listed at the beginning of each lesson.

Mental Math
NEW! Students can practice solving problems mentally. Assigning Mental Math problems is a great way to start class!

Quiz Yourself
NEW! Students are instructed to stop for a periodic check of their understanding.

Questions

COVERING THE IDEAS

1. Since 2003, the World Health Organization (WHO) has tracked new cases of Avian Influenza, or bird flu. The table at the right gives the number of people who have contracted the disease each year. Add columns to the table to show the total number of people who have contracted the disease at the end of each of the given years, relative frequency and cumulative relative frequency.

Year	Number of Cases
2003	4
2004	46
2005	98
2006	115
2007	88

Source: World Health Organization

2. A teacher gave a quiz which had a maximum score of 20 points. The chart below gives each score x and its frequency f.

x	7	9	12	13	14	15	16	17	18	19	20
f	1	1	2	1	3	9	16	9	4	3	1

   a. How many students took the quiz?
   b. How many students have scores less than or equal to the score at the 92nd percentile? What score is that?
   c. Use the data to draw a cumulative frequency graph.
   d. Use the data to draw a cumulative relative frequency graph.

3. a. Draw a bar graph showing the box office sales for each of the first 7 weeks of Spider-Man 3 (2007) given the tabulated cumulative values at right. (In your graph, each week's value should only reflect the sales for that week.)

Spider-Man 3 Box Office Sales

Week	Cumulative

In 9 and 10 of permuta

9. $_nP_1$
10. $_nP_n$

11. Explain why 0! is defined to equal 1.

12. Solve for $_nP_7 = 5 \cdot {}_nP_6$ for n.

APPLYING THE MATHEMATICS

13. a. Some automobile door locks use five buttons numbered 1–5. A combination consists of four different buttons pressed one at a time. How many such combinations are there?
    b. If a particular lock's combination is 2354 but you have forgotten it, what is the probability that you would guess it on the first try?

14. A student has textbooks in algebra, geometry, biology, chemistry, FST, and physics. These books are to be arranged on two shelves.
    a. How many different arrangements are possible if three books are on each shelf?
    b. How many different arrangements are possible if the three math books are on one shelf and the three science books are on another?
    c. How many different arrangements are possible if each shelf has at least one book?

Counting Strings without Replacement   **385**

REVIEW

13. A science experiment is expected to have a successful outcome 40% of the time. In 20 repetitions of the experiment, what is the expected count of the event of a failure? (**Lesson 6-8**)

14. **True or False** As Dr. Kerrich tossed his coin 100,000 times, according to the Law of Large Numbers, we would expect the relative frequency of heads to approach the probability of getting heads. (**Lesson 6-8**)

15. Suppose a person with a certain medical condition has probability 0.45 of recovering fully, if the person undergoes surgery. Also suppose that 100 surgeries for this condition are performed. Design a simulation for this situation and how you would run the simulation using technology. (**Lesson 6-7**)

16. Is the equation an identity? If not, change the right side of the equation to make it an identity. (**Lesson 4-3**)
    a. $\cos(90° - \theta) = \cos \theta$
    b. $-\cos \theta = \cos(360° - \theta)$
    c. $\sin(-\theta) = -\sin \theta$
    d. $\tan(180° + \theta) = \tan \theta$

17. For a given set of data, $\bar{x} = 22$ and $s = 9$. Find the z-score for each number. (**Lesson 3-9**)
    a. 15
    b. 24
    c. 31

EXPLORATION

18. In *A Mathematician Reads the Newspaper*, John Paulos reports that if you spin a coin on its edge, heads will occur only about 30% of the time. Perform an experiment, spinning a penny on its edge at least 150 times. Then do a chi-square test to determine whether Paulos's report seems to be correct.

Student Edition

End-of-Chapter Materials

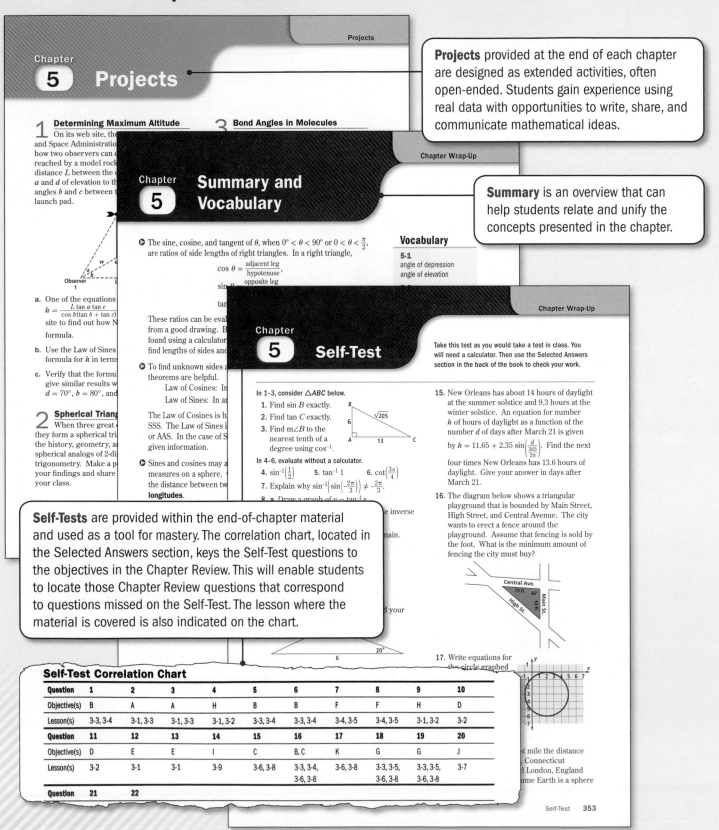

Projects

Chapter 5 Projects

> **Projects** provided at the end of each chapter are designed as extended activities, often open-ended. Students gain experience using real data with opportunities to write, share, and communicate mathematical ideas.

1 Determining Maximum Altitude
On its web site, the
and Space Administratio
how two observers can d
reached by a model rock
distance L between the
a and d of elevation to th
angles b and c between
launch pad.

Observer
1

a. One of the equations
$$h = \frac{L \tan a \tan c}{\cos b(\tan b + \tan c)}$$
site to find out how N
formula.

b. Use the Law of Sines
formula for h in terms

c. Verify that the formu
give similar results w
$d = 70°$, $b = 80°$, and

2 Spherical Triang
When three great
they form a spherical tri
the history, geometry, a
spherical analogs of 2-di
trigonometry. Make a p
your findings and share
your class.

3 Bond Angles in Molecules

Chapter Wrap-Up

Chapter 5 Summary and Vocabulary

> **Summary** is an overview that can help students relate and unify the concepts presented in the chapter.

○ The sine, cosine, and tangent of θ, when $0° < \theta < 90°$ or $0 < \theta < \frac{\pi}{2}$, are ratios of side lengths of right triangles. In a right triangle,
$$\cos \theta = \frac{\text{adjacent leg}}{\text{hypotenuse}},$$
$$\sin$$
$$\tan$$

These ratios can be eval
from a good drawing. B
found using a calculator
find lengths of sides and

○ To find unknown sides
theorems are helpful.
Law of Cosines: In
Law of Sines: In an

The Law of Cosines is h
SSS. The Law of Sines i
or AAS. In the case of S
given information.

○ Sines and cosines may a
measures on a sphere.
the distance between tw
longitudes.

Vocabulary

5-1
angle of depression
angle of elevation

Chapter Wrap-Up

Chapter 5 Self-Test

Take this test as you would take a test in class. You will need a calculator. Then use the Selected Answers section in the back of the book to check your work.

In 1–3, consider △ABC below.
1. Find sin B exactly.
2. Find tan C exactly.
3. Find m∠B to the nearest tenth of a degree using $\cos^{-1}$.

B
$\sqrt{205}$
6
A 13 C

In 4–6, evaluate without a calculator.
4. $\sin^{-1}\left(\frac{1}{2}\right)$ 5. $\tan^{-1} 1$ 6. $\cot\left(\frac{3\pi}{4}\right)$
7. Explain why $\sin^{-1}\left(\sin\left(-\frac{2\pi}{3}\right)\right) \neq -\frac{2\pi}{3}$.

15. New Orleans has about 14 hours of daylight at the summer solstice and 9.3 hours at the winter solstice. An equation for number h of hours of daylight as a function of the number d of days after March 21 is given by $h = 11.65 + 2.35 \sin\left(\frac{d}{\frac{365}{2\pi}}\right)$. Find the next four times New Orleans has 13.6 hours of daylight. Give your answer in days after March 21.

16. The diagram below shows a triangular playground that is bounded by Main Street, High Street, and Central Avenue. The city wants to erect a fence around the playground. Assume that fencing is sold by the foot. What is the minimum amount of fencing the city must buy?

Central Ave.
79 ft   86°
High St.   Main St.

> **Self-Tests** are provided within the end-of-chapter material and used as a tool for mastery. The correlation chart, located in the Selected Answers section, keys the Self-Test questions to the objectives in the Chapter Review. This will enable students to locate those Chapter Review questions that correspond to questions missed on the Self-Test. The lesson where the material is covered is also indicated on the chart.

20°
6

17. Write equations for the circle graphed

y
1
x
1 2 3 4 5 6 7
-1
-2
-3
-4
-5
-6
-7

Self-Test Correlation Chart

Question	1	2	3	4	5	6	7	8	9	10
Objective(s)	B	A	A	H	B	B	F	F	H	D
Lesson(s)	3-3, 3-4	3-1, 3-3	3-1, 3-3	3-1, 3-2	3-3, 3-4	3-3, 3-4	3-4, 3-5	3-4, 3-5	3-1, 3-2	3-2
Question	11	12	13	14	15	16	17	18	19	20
Objective(s)	D	E	E	I	C	B, C	K	G	G	J
Lesson(s)	3-2	3-1	3-1	3-9	3-6, 3-8	3-3, 3-4, 3-6, 3-8	3-6, 3-8	3-3, 3-5, 3-6, 3-8	3-3, 3-5, 3-6, 3-8	3-7
Question	21	22								

st mile the distance
, Connecticut
d London, England
ume Earth is a sphere

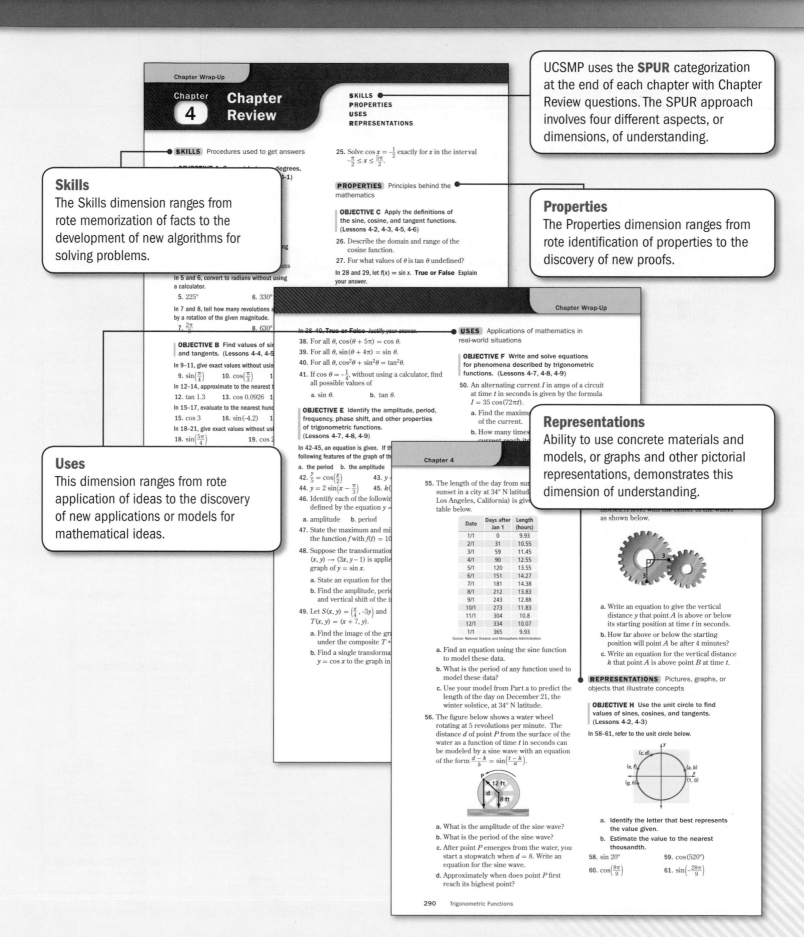

UCSMP uses the **SPUR** categorization at the end of each chapter with Chapter Review questions. The SPUR approach involves four different aspects, or dimensions, of understanding.

Skills
The Skills dimension ranges from rote memorization of facts to the development of new algorithms for solving problems.

Properties
The Properties dimension ranges from rote identification of properties to the discovery of new proofs.

Uses
This dimension ranges from rote application of ideas to the discovery of new applications or models for mathematical ideas.

Representations
Ability to use concrete materials and models, or graphs and other pictorial representations, demonstrates this dimension of understanding.

Chapter Wrap-Up

Chapter **4** **Chapter Review**

SKILLS
PROPERTIES
USES
REPRESENTATIONS

SKILLS Procedures used to get answers

25. Solve $\cos x = -\frac{1}{2}$ exactly for x in the interval $-\frac{\pi}{2} \le x \le \frac{5\pi}{2}$.

PROPERTIES Principles behind the mathematics

OBJECTIVE C Apply the definitions of the sine, cosine, and tangent functions. (Lessons 4-2, 4-3, 4-5, 4-6)

26. Describe the domain and range of the cosine function.

27. For what values of θ is $\tan \theta$ undefined?

In 28 and 29, let $f(x) = \sin x$. **True or False** Explain your answer.

In 5 and 6, convert to radians without using a calculator.

5. $225°$ 6. $330°$

In 7 and 8, tell how many revolutions a by a rotation of the given magnitude.

7. $\frac{2\pi}{3}$ 8. $630°$

OBJECTIVE B Find values of sin and tangents. (Lessons 4-4, 4-5

In 9–11, give exact values without usin

9. $\sin\left(\frac{\pi}{4}\right)$ 10. $\cos\left(\frac{\pi}{3}\right)$

In 12–14, approximate to the nearest

12. $\tan 1.3$ 13. $\cos 0.0926$

In 15–17, evaluate to the nearest hund

15. $\cos 3$ 16. $\sin(-4.2)$

In 18–21, give exact values without usi

18. $\sin\left(\frac{5\pi}{4}\right)$ 19. $\cos$

In 28–40, **True or False** Justify your answer.

38. For all θ, $\cos(\theta + 5\pi) = \cos \theta$.

39. For all θ, $\sin(\theta + 4\pi) = \sin \theta$.

40. For all θ, $\cos^2\theta + \sin^2\theta = \tan^2\theta$.

41. If $\cos \theta = -\frac{1}{4}$, without using a calculator, find all possible values of

a. $\sin \theta$.   b. $\tan \theta$.

OBJECTIVE E Identify the amplitude, period, frequency, phase shift, and other properties of trigonometric functions. (Lessons 4-7, 4-8, 4-9)

In 42–45, an equation is given. If th following features of the graph of th

a. the period   b. the amplitude

42. $\frac{y}{5} = \cos\left(\frac{x}{2}\right)$ 43. y

44. $y = 2 \sin\left(x - \frac{\pi}{3}\right)$ 45. $h($

46. Identify each of the followir defined by the equation $y =$

a. amplitude   b. period

47. State the maximum and mi the function f with $f(t) = 10$

48. Suppose the transformation $(x, y) \to (3x, y - 1)$ is applie graph of $y = \sin x$.

a. State an equation for the

b. Find the amplitude, peri and vertical shift of the i

49. Let $S(x, y) = \left(\frac{x}{4}, -3y\right)$ and $T(x, y) = (x + 7, y)$.

a. Find the image of the gr under the composite $T \circ$

b. Find a single transforma $y = \cos x$ to the graph in

USES Applications of mathematics in real-world situations

OBJECTIVE F Write and solve equations for phenomena described by trigonometric functions. (Lessons 4-7, 4-8, 4-9)

50. An alternating current I in amps of a circuit at time t in seconds is given by the formula $I = 35 \cos(72\pi t)$.

a. Find the maximu of the current.

b. How many times current reach its

Chapter 4

55. The length of the day from sunset in a city at $34°$ N latitud Los Angeles, California) is give table below.

Date	Days after Jan 1	Length (hours)
1/1	0	9.93
2/1	31	10.55
3/1	59	11.45
4/1	90	12.55
5/1	120	13.55
6/1	151	14.27
7/1	181	14.38
8/1	212	13.83
9/1	243	12.88
10/1	273	11.83
11/1	304	10.8
12/1	334	10.07
1/1	365	9.93

Source: National Oceanic and Atmospheric Administration

a. Find an equation using the sine function to model these data.

b. What is the period of any function used to model these data?

c. Use your model from Part a to predict the length of the day on December 21, the winter solstice, at $34°$ N latitude.

56. The figure below shows a water wheel rotating at 5 revolutions per minute. The distance d of point P from the surface of the water as a function of time t in seconds can be modeled by a sine wave with an equation of the form $\frac{d - k}{b} = \sin\left(\frac{t - h}{a}\right)$.

a. What is the amplitude of the sine wave?

b. What is the period of the sine wave?

c. After point P emerges from the water, you start a stopwatch when $d = 8$. Write an equation for the sine wave.

d. Approximately when does point P first reach its highest point?

labeled 71 level with the center of the wheel as shown below.

a. Write an equation to give the vertical distance y that point A is above or below its starting position at time t in seconds.

b. How far above or below the starting position will point A be after 4 minutes?

c. Write an equation for the vertical distance h that point A is above point B at time t.

REPRESENTATIONS Pictures, graphs, or objects that illustrate concepts

OBJECTIVE H Use the unit circle to find values of sines, cosines, and tangents. (Lessons 4-2, 4-3)

In 58–61, refer to the unit circle below.

a. Identify the letter that best represents the value given.

b. Estimate the value to the nearest thousandth.

58. $\sin 20°$ 59. $\cos(520°)$

60. $\cos\left(\frac{8\pi}{9}\right)$ 61. $\sin\left(-\frac{28\pi}{9}\right)$

290   Trigonometric Functions

T15

Four-Step Lesson Format

The Teacher's Edition is an extensive resource that helps address the individual needs of students. The notes within each lesson in the Teacher's Edition provide a variety of teaching ideas, organized around a four-step instructional plan.

Background provides the rationale for the inclusion of topics or approaches, provides mathematical background, and makes connections between UCSMP courses.

1 Warm-Up provides questions for students to work on as you begin class.

2 Teaching provides overall notes on how to teach and enhance the lesson, including procedures for using the Activities. This section also provides Notes on Examples and Notes on Questions to highlight important aspects of specific examples and questions. Occasionally included are Note-Taking Tips to help students study. Additional Examples, parallel to the Examples in the Student Edition, are included with each lesson for added flexibility.

3 Assignment includes suggested questions to be completed as homework, pointing out those that may be appropriate for extra credit. This section also provides suggested assignments for the next lesson, including reading the lesson and doing the Covering the Ideas section.

4 Wrap-Up includes Ongoing Assessment suggestions that give students an opportunity to informally check their understanding of concepts at the end of each lesson. These options for differentiation generally employ a quick oral and/or written activity.

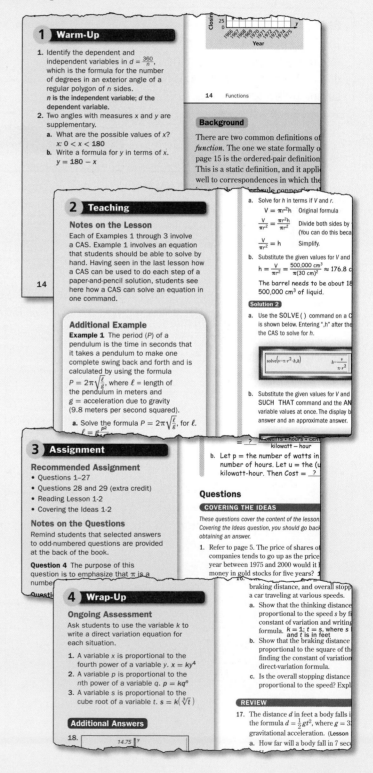

Differentiation Options

The Teacher's Edition includes many additional options for differentiation to promote universal access, including the following:

ENGLISH LEARNERS
Vocabulary Development

Gives teachers hints and instructional strategies on how to help English language learners and those with weak vocabulary skills gain access to key mathematical concepts.

Accommodating the Learner ⊕

Provides suggestions for adjusting an example, activity, or discussion to make it more accessible to students who may be struggling with a particular concept.

Accommodating the Learner ⊕

Provides suggestions for adjusting an example, activity, or discussion to make it more challenging.

Extension

May be a question, problem, activity, or outside project that extends a concept.

Clearly, all lessons contain more ideas than can be used in one class period — and there are many additional ways to teach each lesson. Depending on the background of students, a challenging activity in one class could be inappropriately easy in another. Teachers should use their professional judgment to select and sequence the activities that are appropriate for the length of a given class period and the needs of their students.

Teachers who have never used group work, manipulatives, or technology often assume that they are very time-consuming. Advanced planning and practice will help with the time management of these very worthwhile activities.

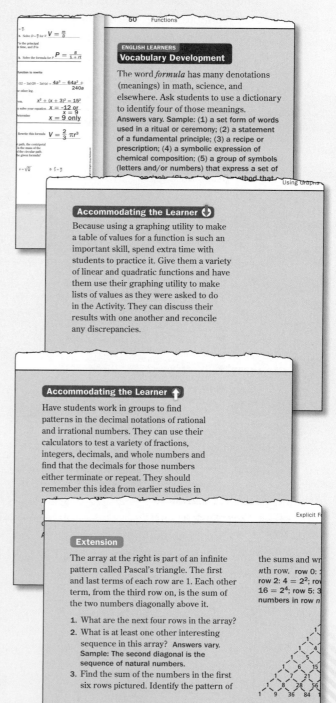

Assessment Resources

The *Assessment Resources* booklet provides guidelines for developing an effective assessment program as well as tests and quizzes for every chapter. There are also student-completed forms and teacher-completed forms for individual, group, and class activities.

❯ Two quizzes per chapter (mostly constructed-response)

❯ Chapter Tests (mostly constructed-response)

❯ Answers for all of the above

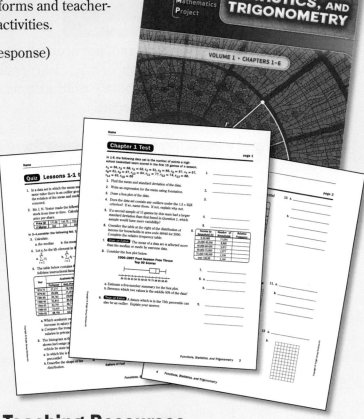

Teaching Resources

❯ Masters that teachers will want to use many times, such as Coordinate Grids, Polar Coordinate Grids, and Spreadsheet

❯ Masters with lesson Warm-Up exercises, Additional Examples, and pictures or art

❯ Lesson Masters for each lesson

❯ Answers for Lesson Masters

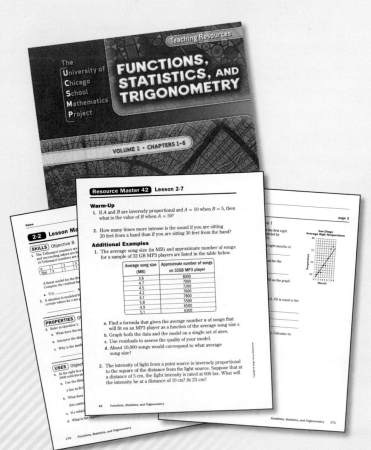

Technology

electronic Teacher's Edition, CD-Rom (eTE)

The *electronic Teacher's Edition* (eTE) comes in two volumes and includes:

> *Teacher's Edition* pages, with reduced Student Edition (SE) pages
> SE pages without overprinted answers, convenient for projecting on a screen
> *Teaching Resources*
> *Assessment Resources*
> Answer pages for all SE questions
> Worked-out Solutions for all SE questions
> TE margin with text box for writing local standards or notes

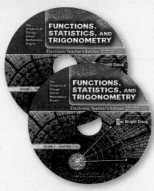

electronic Student Edition (eSE)

This is an online version of the SE. Users may access the site *UCSMPmath.com* upon purchasing the Student Edition.

Teacher's Assessment Assistant, CD-Rom (TAA)

> Build quizzes, tests, and worksheets.
> Access test items that mirror those of the Chapter Test.
> Create many more test items.
> Print worksheets for students.
> Obtain and save results automatically.

Additional Technology

The use of the latest technology has always been an outstanding feature of the UCSMP program. An essential component of UCSMP courses is the use of graphing calculators, spreadsheets, the Internet, and a computer algebra system.

Optional activity files for use with the TI-Nspire CAS are available to teachers and students at ucsmpmath.com.

Calculators

For home use and during class, students should have access to a graphing calculator and a computer algebra system (CAS).

The SPUR Approach to Understanding

Since its inception, UCSMP has been known for its SPUR approach to understanding. The SPUR approach involves four different dimensions of understanding to enable students to approach and solve problems in different ways. By approaching problems from different perspectives, students gain an appreciation of the interconnectivity among concepts in mathematics.

The four dimensions of understanding that form this unique SPUR approach are:

Skills

For some, *understanding* mathematics means simply knowing how to get an answer without help from outside sources. In classrooms, when we speak of understanding how to use technology, we mean using technology to do something for us. In *UCSMP Grades 6–12* texts, these are both aspects of the same kind of understanding, the understanding of algorithms (procedures) for getting answers. This dimension of understanding ranges from memorization of basic facts to development of new algorithms. These include doing things mentally, with paper and pencil, or with technology.

> The SPUR approach involves four dimensions of understanding to enable students to approach and solve problems in different ways.

Properties

Understanding *why* is at least as important as understanding *how.* Mathematicians often view this kind of understanding as the ultimate goal.

Uses

To the person who applies mathematics, being able to *use* the answer is most important. For example, an understanding of linear equations means being able to apply them appropriately in real situations.

Representations

Students need to be able to represent a concept and work with the concept in that representation in some way. Using concrete materials and models, or graphs and other pictorial representations, demonstrates this dimension of understanding.

Each dimension of understanding has its easy and difficult aspects. Each can be demonstrated through simple memorization or the highest level of creative thinking. UCSMP believes that the most effective teaching provides students opportunities to demonstrate all of these dimensions.

For a specific example of what understanding means in these four dimensions, consider solving $100 + 5x = 50 + 10x$ and what constitutes evidence of that understanding.

SKILLS
Skills understanding means knowing a way to obtain a solution.
Obtain x = 10 by some means.

PROPERTIES
Properties understanding means knowing properties which you can apply.
Justify the steps in obtaining the solution.

USES
Uses understanding means knowing situations in which you could apply the solving of this equation.
Set up or interpret a solution: If one person has 100 CDs and buys 5 CDs a month, and another person has 50 CDs and buys 10 CDs a month, in how many months will they have the same number of CDs?

REPRESENTATIONS
Representations understanding means having a representation of the solution or a graphical interpretation of the solution.
Graph y = 100 + 5x and y = 50 + 10x, and realize that the x-coordinate of the point of intersection is the solution.

UCSMP is unique in organizing the chapter objectives according to these dimensions. The SPUR categorization appears at the end of each chapter with the Chapter Review questions. The Self-Test for each chapter and the Lesson Masters (in the *Teacher's Resources*) are also keyed to the SPUR objectives. The categorization is meant to ensure that the book enables teachers to provide students with opportunities to gain a broader and deeper understanding of mathematics than is normally the case.

It should be noted that the SPUR approach is not a perfect sorter of knowledge; many ideas and many problems involve more than one dimension. Some types of understanding do not fit any of these dimensions exactly. What is important is that students have ample learning opportunities utilizing all four dimensions.

Assessing Student Performance in Mathematics

Effective methods of assessment offer students opportunities to demonstrate how they approach problem situations, collect and organize information, formulate and test conjectures, and communicate their mathematical insights. A good assessment program contains tasks that are appropriate to the topics students are learning and provides outcomes valuable to students. Teachers should determine an assessment program that best suits the needs of his or her students.

> ### The Assessment Principle
>
> "Assessment should support the learning of important mathematics and furnish useful information to both teachers and students."
> — NCTM *Principles and Standards for School Mathematics*, p. 22.

The assessment process should be a positive experience for students and should:

> Yield feedback on the appropriateness of instructional methods.

> Offer some clues as to how the content or pace of instruction could be modified.

> Identify for students areas for improvement and affirm their success.

> Evaluate student performance for grading purposes.

> Include a variety of assessment techniques.

> Provide opportunities for students to demonstrate their mathematical capabilities in an atmosphere that encourages maximum performance.

> Emphasize what students *do* know, *can* do, and how they think mathematically.

> Motivate students to achieve by using assessment tasks that reflect the value of students' efforts.

> Encourage students to reflect on what they have done.

Good assessment addresses higher-order thinking skills. Teachers should think about:

> Designing assessments that provide a picture of the student as a critical thinker and problem solver.

> Using assessments that identify how the student does mathematics, not just what answer he or she gets.

Assessment Options in UCSMP

The *Assessment Resources* provides a variety of assessment instruments described to the right. This resource booklet also has answers for all the quizzes and tests. The SPUR charts correlate the test items from each Chapter Test to the chapter SPUR objectives.

It should be noted that tests, quizzes, and homework assignments provide only a small picture of what a student may know. In order to help develop your students' abilities with open-ended questions or longer, more elaborate tasks, consider the Exploration questions at the end of each lesson and the Projects at the end of each chapter as part of your assessment tool kit.

Given the requirements of the high-stakes state tests, it is important that students have experiences with the types of items found on state tests, such as multiple-choice items. The multiple-choice items throughout the UCSMP texts and on the included test forms give students experience with this type of assessment.

Assessment Instruments

Chapter Quizzes, two per chapter, cover three or four lessons and contain mostly constructed-response items (items for which a student must supply requested information).

Chapter Tests assess every chapter objective in primarily constructed-response format.

Assessment Forms

Student-completed forms

Teacher-completed forms for individual, group, and class activities

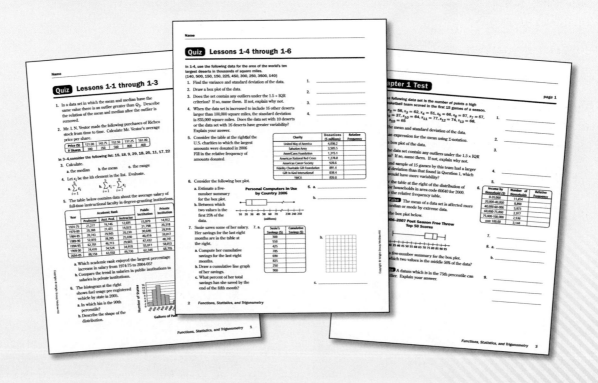

Introduction to the Research

Since 1983, the UCSMP curriculum has been carefully refined through years of field-testing and feedback from users. Teachers throughout the country have discovered that UCSMP materials provide a way for more of their students to be successful, learning more mathematics than with traditional curricula.

The research and development of the three editions of the UCSMP textbooks has involved a sequence of writing and evaluation taking 5–6 years, and three years for the new course *Pre-Transition Mathematics*. Pilot studies, formative evaluations, and national summative evaluations conducted by UCSMP staff use state-of-the-art quantitative and qualitative designs and instruments. Observations, interviews, questionnaires, and a variety of tests are used. Evaluations focus both on the characteristics of teachers, classes, schools, and districts as they implement UCSMP materials and on the performance on traditional, often standardized, and project-made tests of students who used the materials.

The timeline below summarizes the research and development for each of the three editions of UCSMP. More detailed information on the research and development of all three editions of *UCSMP Grades 6–12* and *Everyday Mathematics*® is available from Wright Group at www.wrightgroup.com.

	Pre-1989	1989	1990	1991	1992	1993	1994	1995	1996	1997	
Pre-Transition Mathematics											
Transition Mathematics	WRITE ◆ FIELD-TEST ◆ REWRITE ◆ PUBLISH			FEEDBACK ◆ WRITE ◆ FIELD-TEST ◆ PUBLISH – 2nd Ed.							
Algebra	WRITE ◆ FIELD-TEST ◆ REWRITE ◆ PUBLISH			FEEDBACK ◆ WRITE ◆ FIELD-TEST ◆ PUBLISH – 2nd Ed.							
Geometry	WRITE ◆ FIELD-TEST ◆ REWRITE ◆ PUBLISH – 1st Ed.				FEEDBACK ◆ WRITE ◆ FIELD-TEST ◆ PUBLISH – 2nd Ed.						
Advanced Algebra	WRITE ◆ FIELD-TEST ◆ REWRITE ◆ PUBLISH – 1st Ed.				FEEDBACK ◆ WRITE ◆ FIELD-TEST ◆ PUBLISH – 2nd Ed.						
Functions, Statistics, and Trigonometry	WRITE ◆ FIELD-TEST ◆ REWRITE ◆ PUBLISH				FEEDBACK ◆ WRITE ◆ FIELD-TEST ◆ PUBLISH – 2nd Ed.						
Precalculus and Discrete Mathematics	WRITE ◆ FIELD-TEST ◆ REWRITE ◆ PUBLISH				FEEDBACK ◆ WRITE ◆ FIELD-TEST ◆ PUBLISH – 2nd Ed.						

UCSMP Grades 6–12

All of the UCSMP studies mentioned were done with students having soft-cover, one-color, multi-section versions of the later published textbooks. Teachers had notes on lessons and chapter tests, but typically had none of the other ancillaries that became available later.

Over the years, UCSMP's research has been cited favorably by organizations charged with evaluating such research. For example, in its publication *On Evaluating Curricular Effectiveness: Judging the Quality of K–12 Mathematics Evaluations* (The National Academies Press, 2004), the Mathematical Sciences Education Board wrote the following in its Conclusions and Recommendations section (p. 202): "The committee was asked to review the 13 NSF-supported curricula and 6 sets of commercially generated curricula. We note that there was considerable variation in the type and extent of evaluation material provided across these 19 curricula. The database of evaluations for the NSF-supported curricula and for UCSMP greatly exceeded the database for the commercially generated materials in quantity and quality."

	1998–2003	2004	2005	2006	2007	2008	2009
			WRITE ◆ FIELD-TEST ◆ REWRITE ◆ PUBLISH – 3rd Ed.				
		WRITE ◆ FIELD-TEST ◆ REWRITE ◆ PUBLISH – 3rd Ed.					
		WRITE ◆ FIELD-TEST ◆ REWRITE ◆ PUBLISH – 3rd Ed.					
			WRITE ◆ FIELD-TEST ◆ REWRITE ◆ PUBLISH – 3rd Ed.				
			WRITE ◆ FIELD-TEST ◆ REWRITE ◆ PUBLISH – 3rd Ed.				
			WRITE ◆ FIELD-TEST ◆ REWRITE ◆ PUBLISH – 3rd Ed.				
			WRITE ◆ FIELD-TEST ◆ REWRITE ◆ PUBLISH – 3rd Ed.				

▷ Contents

VOLUME 1

Getting Started   1

Chapter 1   4
Exploring Data

Chapter 2   78
Functions and Models

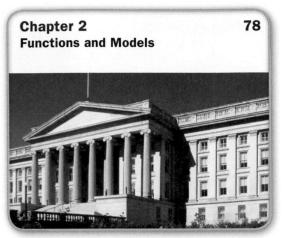

1-1	Variables, Tables, and Graphs	6
1-2	Centers of Data and Weighted Averages	14
1-3	Creating and Using Histograms	22
1-4	Box Plots	31
1-5	Cumulative Distributions	38
1-6	Measure of Spread: Variance and Standard Deviation	45
1-7	Comparing Numerical Distributions	54
1-8	Using Statistics to Solve a Mystery: The Case of the Federalist Papers	61
	Projects	67
	Summary and Vocabulary	69
	Self-Test	70
	Chapter Review	72

2-1	The Language of Functions	80
2-2	Linear Models	87
2-3	Linear Regression and Correlation	94
2-4	Exponential Functions	102
2-5	Exponential Models	110
2-6	Quadratic Models	117
2-7	Inverse Variation Models	125
2-8	Choosing a Good Model	132
	Projects	140
	Summary and Vocabulary	142
	Self-Test	144
	Chapter Review	146

Chapter 3   150
Transformations of Graphs and Data

3-1   Graphs of Parent Functions   152

3-2   The Graph-Translation Theorem   159

3-3   Translations of Data   165

3-4   Symmetries of Graphs   172

3-5   The Graph Scale
       Change Theorem   179

3-6   Scale Changes of Data   185

3-7   Composition of Functions   193

3-8   Inverses of Functions   199

3-9   z-Scores   206

   Projects   211

   Summary and Vocabulary   213

   Self-Test   215

   Chapter Review   216

Chapter 4   220
Trigonometric Functions

4-1   Magnitudes of Rotations
       and Measures of Arcs   222

4-2   Sines, Cosines, and Tangents   229

4-3   Basic Trigonometric Identities 235

4-4   Exact Values of Sines, Cosines,
       and Tangents   242

4-5   The Sine and Cosine Functions   247

4-6   The Tangent Function
       and Periodicity   252

4-7   Scale-Change Images of
       Trigonometric Functions   257

4-8   Translation Images of
       Trigonometric Functions   263

4-9   The Graph-Standardization
       Theorem   269

4-10 Modeling with Trigonometric
       Functions   276

   Projects   282

   Summary and Vocabulary   284

   Self-Test   286

   Chapter Review   288

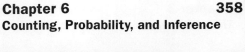

Chapter 5   292
Trigonometry

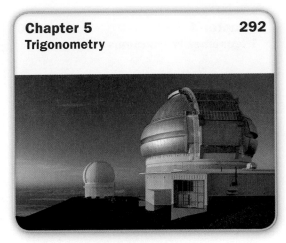

5-1	Trigonometric Ratios in Right Triangles	294
5-2	The Inverse Cosine Function	299
5-3	The Law of Cosines	304
5-4	The Inverse Sine Function	309
5-5	The Law of Sines	314
5-6	The Inverse Tangent Function	320
5-7	General Solutions to Trigonometric Equations	325
5-8	Parametric Equations for Circles and Elipses	331
5-9	The Secant, Cosecant, and Cotangent Functions	336
5-10	From New York to New Delhi	341
	Projects	349
	Summary and Vocabulary	351
	Self-Test	353
	Chapter Review	354

Chapter 6   358
Counting, Probability, and Inference

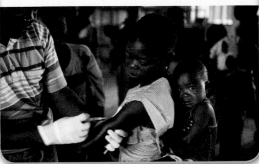

6-1	Introduction to Probability	360
6-2	Principles of Probability	367
6-3	Counting Strings with Replacement	374
6-4	Counting Strings without Replacement	381
6-5	Contingency Tables	387
6-6	Conditional Probability	395
6-7	Designing Simulations	402
6-8	Two "Laws," but Only One Is Valid	410
6-9	The Chi-Square Test	417
	Projects	426
	Summary and Vocabulary	428
	Self-Test	430
	Chapter Review	432

VOLUME 2

Chapter 7   **436**
Polynomial Functions

7-1	Characteristics of Polynomial Functions	438
7-2	Polynomial Models	446
7-3	Division and the Remainder Theorem	453
7-4	The Factor Theorem	459
7-5	Complex Numbers	465
7-6	The Fundamental Theorem of Algebra	473
7-7	Factoring Sums and Differences of Powers	481
7-8	Advanced Factoring Techniques	486
	Projects	491
	Summary and Vocabulary	493
	Self-Test	494
	Chapter Review	496

Chapter 8   **500**
Sequences and Series

8-1	Arithmetic Sequences	502
8-2	Geometric and Other Sequences	509
8-3	End Behavior of Sequences	515
8-4	Arithmetic Series	522
8-5	Geometric Series	529
8-6	How Much Does a Loan Cost?	536
8-7	Infinite Series	542
	Projects	550
	Summary and Vocabulary	552
	Self-Test	554
	Chapter Review	555

Chapter 9   **558**
Roots, Powers, and Logarithms

9-1	*n*th Roots	560
9-2	Rational Exponents	568
9-3	Logarithm Functions	575
9-4	*e* and Natural Logarithms	581
9-5	Properties of Logarithms	587
9-6	Solving Exponential Equations	594
9-7	Linearizing Data to Find Models	600
	Projects	607
	Summary and Vocabulary	609
	Self-Test	611
	Chapter Review	612

Chapter 10   **616**
Binomial Distributions

10-1	Combinations	618
10-2	Pascal's Triangle	624
10-3	The Binomial Theorem	631
10-4	Probability Distributions	637
10-5	Binomial Probabilities	645
10-6	Binomial Probability Distributions	651
10-7	Mean and Standard Deviation of a Binomial Random Variable	659
10-8	Is That Coin Fair?	666
	Projects	674
	Summary and Vocabulary	676
	Self-Test	678
	Chapter Review	679

x

Chapter 11   **684**
Normal Distributions

11-1	Normal Curves	686
11-2	Finding Probabilities Using the Standard Normal Distribution	692
11-3	Other Normal Distributions	698
11-4	The Central Limit Theorem	706
11-5	Making Inferences about Means	714
11-6	Confidence Intervals	719
11-7	Confidence Intervals in Binomial Experiments	726
	Projects	733
	Summary and Vocabulary	735
	Self-Test	737
	Chapter Review	738

Chapter 12   **742**
Matrices and Trigonometry

12-1	Matrix Multiplication	744
12-2	Matrices for Transformations	751
12-3	Matrices for Composites of Transformations	757
12-4	The General Rotation Matrix	762
12-5	Formulas for $\cos(\alpha + \beta)$ and $\sin(\alpha + \beta)$	766
12-6	Formulas for $\cos 2\theta$ and $\sin 2\theta$	771
	Projects	776
	Summary and Vocabulary	778
	Self-Test	780
	Chapter Review	781

Chapter 13 **784**
Further Work with Trigonometry

13-1 Proving Trigonometric
   Identities 786

13-2 Restrictions on
   Trigonometric Identities 792

13-3 Polar Coordinates 797

13-4 Polar Graphs 804

13-5 The Geometry of
   Complex Numbers 811

13-6 Trigonometric Form of
   Complex Numbers 817

13-7 DeMoivre's Theorem 825

 ▶ Projects 831

 ▶ Summary and Vocabulary 833

 ▶ Self-Test 835

 ▶ Chapter Review 836

VOLUME 1

Algebra Properties from
Earlier Courses T35

Geometry Properties from
Earlier Courses T37

Symbols T40

CAS T41

A Table of Random Numbers T42

Selected Answers T43

Glossary T77

Index T93

Photo Credits T107

Additional Answers T109

Welcome to UCSMP *Functions, Statistics, and Trigonometry*! We hope you enjoy this book—it was written for you.

The Themes of This Book

Functions are correspondences or mappings that relate variables. For many people, functions are the most important content of high school mathematics. In your earlier work, you have studied linear, quadratic, exponential, and logarithm functions, and perhaps also polynomial and trigonometric functions. In this book, you will review and extend ideas about these functions. Because technology has changed the ways in which people use functions, we expect you to have technology that has graphical, statistical, geometric, and algebraic capabilities. This will broaden your ability to solve problems, to make connections among mathematical ideas, and to develop generalizations.

Statistics are used by people who work in government or journalism, who have to make decisions in business, who need to interpret the results of medical or psychological studies, who are responsible for monitoring quality of environment and health, or who wish simply to understand the world. The capability of computers and networks to store, share, and analyze data has made statistics an essential subject for citizenship and careers. Statistics provides ways of extracting information from data and using that information to build knowledge that will affect your life.

Trigonometry receives special emphasis in this book because it is fundamental to higher mathematics and to many applications. Physicists, cartographers, pilots, geologists, and engineers use trigonometry to precisely measure and predict lengths, angles, and locations. Trigonometric functions link algebra with geometry. They are used as models for situations that have nothing to do with geometry or triangles: the heights of tides, the pressure of a sound wave, and the swinging of a pendulum. The fundamental ideas of trigonometry may not be new to you; in this course, you will review those ideas and extend them to new contexts and applications.

Tools Needed for This Book

In addition to the lined and unlined notebook paper, pencils, graph paper, and erasers you typically use when doing mathematics, you need a calculator or computer software that can:

- Perform numerical and algebraic computations;
- Graph functions automatically;
- Create lists and graph them;
- Display certain relations that are not functions with parametric equations;
- Graph in rectangular and polar coordinates;
- Perform operations with matrices;
- Solve equations and transform algebraic expressions;
- Generate random numbers;

1 Exploring Data

Chapter Overview

		Local Standards	Pacing (in days)		
			Average	Advanced	Block
1-1	**Variables, Tables, and Graphs** **F** Determine relationships and interpret data presented in a table.		1	1	0.5
1-2	**Centers of Data and Weighted Averages** **A** Calculate measures of center and spread for data sets. **B** Calculate averages with weights, frequencies, and relative frequencies. **C** Use Σ-notation to represent a sum or mean. **D** Describe relations between measures of center and spread.		1	1	0.5
1-3	**Creating and Using Histograms** **H** Read, interpret, and draw histograms and population pyramids from data.		1	1	0.5
	QUIZ 1		0.5	0.25	0.25
1-4	**Box Plots** **A** Calculate measures of center and spread for data sets. **E** Use statistics to draw conclusions about data. **I** Read, interpret, and draw box plots from data.		1	1	0.5
1-5	**Cumulative Distributions** **D** Describe relations between measures of center and spread. **J** Calculate and draw line graphs of cumulative frequencies and cumulative relative frequencies from tables of frequencies.		1	1	0.5
1-6	**Measures of Spread: Variance and Standard Deviation** **A** Calculate measures of center and spread for data sets. **D** Describe relations between measures of center and spread. **E** Use statistics to draw conclusions about data.		1	1	0.5
	QUIZ 2		0.5	0.25	0.25
1-7	**Comparing Numerical Distributions** **G** Use statistics to compare and contrast two data sets in the context of a situation.		1	1	0.5
1-8	**Using Statistics to Solve a Mystery:** **The Case of *The Federalist* Papers** **G** Use statistics to compare and contrast two data sets in the context of a situation.		1	1	0.5
	Self-Test		1	0.5	0.5
	Chapter Review		2	1	0.5
	Test		1	1	0.5
	TOTAL		13	11	6

Technology Resources

Teacher's Assessment Assistant, Ch. 1

Electronic Teacher's Edition, Ch. 1

Differentiated Options Universal Access

	Accommodating the Learner	Vocabulary Development	Ongoing Assessment	Materials
1-1	pp. 8, 10	p. 9	p. 13	
1-2	pp. 17, 18	p. 16	p. 21	spreadsheet application
1-3			p. 30	statistics utility
1-4		p. 32	p. 37	
1-5			p. 44	spreadsheet application
1-6	pp. 48, 49		p. 53	statistics utility
1-7		p. 57	p. 60	statistics utility
1-8	pp. 64, 65			

Objectives

	Lessons	Self-Test Questions	Chapter Review Questions
Skills			
A Calculate measures of center and spread for data sets.	1-2, 1-4, 1-6	1	1–6
B Calculate averages with weights, frequencies, and relative frequencies.	1-2	6, 13	7–12
Properties			
C Use Σ-notation to represent a sum or mean.	1-2	2	13–15
D Describe relations between measures of center and spread.	1-2, 1-5, 1-6	7, 9	16–22
Uses			
E Use statistics to draw conclusions about data.	1-4, 1-6	4, 5	23–27
F Determine relationships and interpret data presented in a table.	1-1	11	28–33
G Use statistics to compare and contrast two data sets in the context of a situation.	1-7, 1-8	15	34–35
Representations			
H Read, interpret, and draw histograms and population pyramids from data.	1-3	10, 14	36–39
I Read, interpret, and draw box plots from data.	1-4	3, 8	40–42
J Calculate and draw line graphs of cumulative frequencies and cumulative relative frequencies from tables of frequencies.	1-5	12	43, 44

Assignment Options

1. Read the Lesson; write answers to all Questions in the Lesson.
2. Write answers to Questions Applying the Mathematics, Review, and Exploration in the Lesson;
   Read the next Lesson; write answers to Questions Covering the Ideas in the next Lesson.

Resource Masters Chapter 1

None of the generic Resource Masters apply to this chapter.

Resource Master 1 Chapter 1 Opener

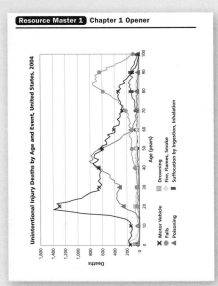

Resource Master for Chapter 1 Opener

Resource Master 3 Lesson 1-1

Resource Master 2 Lesson 1-1

Warm-up

In 1–3, give the mean, median, and mode of the data set.

1. 0, 10, 15, 20, 20, 25, 30, 30, 30, 40

2. 100, 110, 115, 120, 120, 125, 130, 130, 130, 140

3. $x, x + 10, x + 15, x + 20, x + 20, x + 25,$
   $x + 30, x + 30, x + 30, x + 40$

Additional Examples

1. Use the data from Example 1. Answer to the nearest tenth of a percent. What percent of average skaters wore less than 2 pieces of protective gear?

2. Refer to the table of income data before Example 2. How many times as likely was a family to have an income of less than $15,000 if the head of the household had some high school but no diploma rather than graduated from high school?

Resource Masters for Lesson 1-1

Resource Master 5 Lesson 1-2

Resource Master 4 Lesson 1-1

Skill Level	Amount of Protective Gear Worn			
	No gear	1 piece	2-4 pieces	Total
Beginner	188	294	227	709
Average	314	245	123	682
Advanced	372	242	140	754
Total	874	781	490	2145

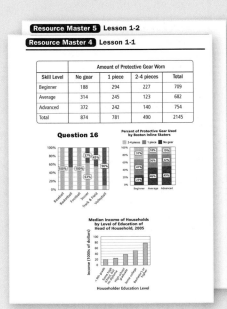

Resource Masters for Lessons 1-1 and 1-2

Resource Master 7 Lesson 1-2

Resource Master 6 Lesson 1-2

Additional Examples

3. In a college economics course, suppose that homework counts for 25%, quizzes 10%, tests 45%, and attendance 20% of each student's overall grade. Frances and her friend Adam earned the following scores during the semester. Who received the higher overall course grade?

	Frances	Adam
Homework	89	95
Quizzes	82	90
Tests	87	92
Attendance	100	70

4. To celebrate the opening of a new branch, a clothing store advertised that the first 200 customers would randomly receive free gift cards valued at $5, $15, $50, or $100. An internal memo to the new store manager contained the following sentence: "There will be 5 $100-dollar cards, 10 $50-dollar cards, 35 $15-dollar cards, and the rest will be $5-dollar cards."
   a. Calculate the total dollar value of the gift cards.
   b. Create a frequency table and calculate the weighted average as in Example 3.

Resource Masters for Lesson 1-2

Resource Master 9 Lesson 1-3

Resource Master 8 Lesson 1-3

Warm-Up

In 2000, in Columbus, Ohio, the existing houses in the city had been built at the following times:

a. In what decade was the median house in age built?
b. What percent of the houses in Columbus in 2000 were more than 40 years old?
c. Indicate two problems you would have if you were to make a histogram with these data?

Date	# of Homes
1939 or earlier	454
1940–1949	511
1950–1959	3,311
1960–1969	4,358
1970–1979	4,113
1980–1989	2,612
1990–1994	2,184
1995–1998	2,382
1999–March 2000	1,377

Source: http://www.city-data.com/xpbx/43218.html

Additional Examples

1. Use the histograms on congressional data for the following questions.
   a. About how many states have 5 to 14 representatives?
   b. What percent of states have fewer than 15 representatives?
   c. Look at the raw data set which appears before the histograms. Are you surprised that the bar spanning $0 \leq x < 5$ is the tallest? Why or why not?

2. Use the population pyramids in the lesson to answer the following questions.
   a. In 1980, which age group had the least population? Give an estimate of this population.
   b. In 2020, which group is projected to have the least population? Give an estimate of this population.
   c. Select an age group from 1980; In which age group would this segment of the population appear in the year 2020? Now, compare these two bars – are they the same length or different? If they are different, give one reason to account for this difference.

Resource Masters for Lesson 1-3

Resource Master 11 Lesson 1-3

Resource Master 10 Lesson 1-3

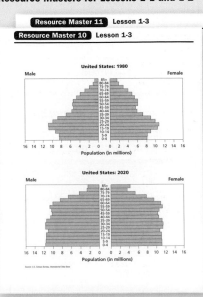

Resource Masters for Lesson 1-3

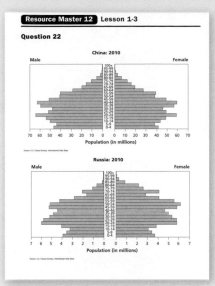

Resource Master 12 Lesson 1-3

Question 22

Resource Master for Lesson 1-3

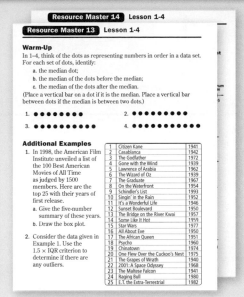

Resource Master 14 Lesson 1-4
Resource Master 13 Lesson 1-4

Warm-Up

In 1–4, think of the dots as representing numbers in order in a data set. For each set of dots, identify:
a. the median dot;
b. the median of the dots before the median;
c. the median of the dots after the median.
(Place a vertical bar on a dot if it is the median. Place a vertical bar between dots if the median is between two dots.)

Additional Examples
1. In 1998, the American Film Institute unveiled a list of the 100 Best American Movies of All Time as judged by 1500 members. Here are the top 25 with their years of first release.
   a. Give the five-number summary of these years.
   b. Draw the box plot.
2. Consider the data given in Example 1. Use the $1.5 \times$ IQR criterion to determine if there are any outliers.

1	Citizen Kane	1941
2	Casablanca	1942
3	The Godfather	1972
4	Gone with the Wind	1939
5	Lawrence of Arabia	1962
6	The Wizard of Oz	1939
7	The Graduate	1967
8	On the Waterfront	1954
9	Schindler's List	1993
10	Singin' in the Rain	1952
11	It's a Wonderful Life	1946
12	Sunset Boulevard	1950
13	The Bridge on the River Kwai	1957
14	Some Like It Hot	1959
15	Star Wars	1977
16	All About Eve	1950
17	The African Queen	1951
18	Psycho	1960
19	Chinatown	1974
20	One Flew Over the Cuckoo's Nest	1975
21	The Grapes of Wrath	1940
22	2001: A Space Odyssey	1968
23	The Maltese Falcon	1941
24	Raging Bull	1980
25	E.T. the Extra-Terrestrial	1982

Resource Masters for Lesson 1-4

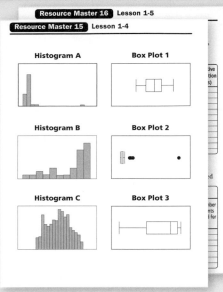

Resource Master 16 Lesson 1-5
Resource Master 15 Lesson 1-4

Histogram A   Box Plot 1
Histogram B   Box Plot 2
Histogram C   Box Plot 3

Resource Masters for Lessons 1-4 and 1-5

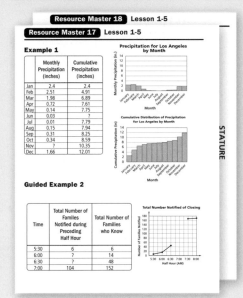

Resource Master 18 Lesson 1-5
Resource Master 17 Lesson 1-5

Example 1

	Monthly Precipitation (inches)	Cumulative Precipitation (inches)
Jan	2.4	2.4
Feb	2.51	4.91
Mar	1.98	6.89
Apr	0.72	7.61
May	0.14	7.75
Jun	0.03	?
Jul	0.01	7.79
Aug	0.15	7.94
Sep	0.31	8.25
Oct	0.34	8.59
Nov	?	10.35
Dec	1.66	12.01

Guided Example 2

Time	Total Number of Families Notified during Preceding Half Hour	Total Number of Families who Know
5:30	6	6
6:00	?	14
6:30	?	48
7:00	104	152

Resource Masters for Lesson 1-5

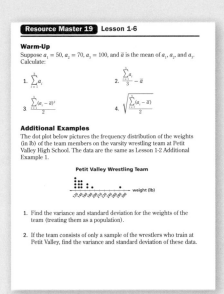

Resource Master 19 Lesson 1-6

Warm-Up

Suppose $a_1 = 50$, $a_2 = 70$, $a_3 = 100$, and $\bar{a}$ is the mean of a_1, a_2, and a_3. Calculate:

1. $\sum_{i=1}^{3} a_i$
2. $\frac{\sum_{i=1}^{3} a_i}{3} - \bar{a}$
3. $\frac{\sum_{i=1}^{3}(a_i - \bar{a})^2}{2}$
4. $\sqrt{\frac{\sum_{i=1}^{3}(a_i - \bar{a})^2}{2}}$

Additional Examples
The dot plot below pictures the frequency distribution of the weights (in lb) of the team members on the varsity wrestling team at Petit Valley High School. The data are the same as Lesson 1-2 Additional Example 1.

Petit Valley Wrestling Team

weight (lb)

1. Find the variance and standard deviation for the weights of the team (treating them as a population).
2. If the team consists of only a sample of the wrestlers who train at Petit Valley, find the variance and standard deviation of these data.

Resource Master for Lesson 1-6

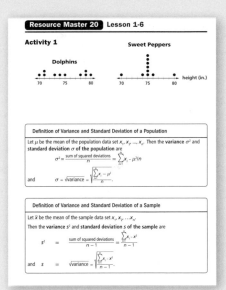

Resource Master 20 Lesson 1-6

Activity 1

Dolphins   Sweet Peppers

height (in.)

Definition of Variance and Standard Deviation of a Population

Let μ be the mean of the population data set $x_1, x_2, ..., x_n$. Then the **variance** σ^2 and **standard deviation** σ **of the population** are

$$\sigma^2 = \frac{\text{sum of squared deviations}}{n} = \frac{\sum_{i=1}^{n} x_i - \mu^2}{n}$$

and

$$\sigma = \sqrt{\text{variance}} = \sqrt{\frac{\sum_{i=1}^{n} x_i - \mu^2}{n}}.$$

Definition of Variance and Standard Deviation of a Sample

Let $\bar{x}$ be the mean of the sample data set $x_1, x_2, ... x_n$. Then the **variance** s^2 and **standard deviation** s **of the sample** are

$$s^2 = \frac{\text{sum of squared deviations}}{n-1} = \frac{\sum x_i - \bar{x}^2}{n-1}$$

and

$$s = \sqrt{\text{variance}} = \sqrt{\frac{\sum x_i - \bar{x}^2}{n-1}}.$$

Resource Master for Lesson 1-6

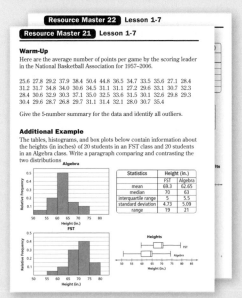

Resource Master 22 Lesson 1-7
Resource Master 21 Lesson 1-7

Warm-Up

Here are the average number of points per game by the scoring leader in the National Basketball Association for 1957–2006.

25.6 27.8 29.2 37.9 38.4 50.4 44.8 36.5 34.7 33.5 35.6 27.1 28.4
31.2 31.7 34.8 34.0 30.6 34.5 31.1 31.1 27.2 29.6 33.1 30.7 32.3
28.4 30.6 32.9 30.3 37.1 35.0 32.5 33.6 31.5 30.1 32.6 29.8 29.3
30.4 29.6 28.7 26.8 29.7 31.1 31.4 32.1 28.0 30.7 35.4

Give the 5-number summary for the data and identify all outliers.

Additional Example
The tables, histograms, and box plots below contain information about the heights (in inches) of 20 students in an FST class and 20 students in an Algebra class. Write a paragraph comparing and contrasting the two distributions.

Statistics	Height (in.)	
	FST	Algebra
mean	69.3	62.65
median	70	63
interquartile range	5	5.5
standard deviation	4.73	5.09
range	19	21

Resource Masters for Lesson 1-7

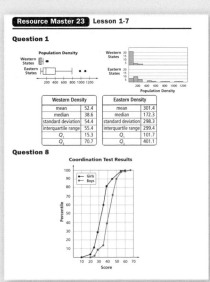

Resource Master 23 Lesson 1-7

Question 1

Population Density

	Western Density
mean	52.4
median	38.6
standard deviation	54.4
interquartile range	55.4
Q_1	15.3
Q_3	70.7

	Eastern Density
mean	301.4
median	172.3
standard deviation	298.3
interquartile range	299.4
Q_1	101.7
Q_3	401.1

Question 8

Coordination Test Results

Resource Master for Lesson 1-7

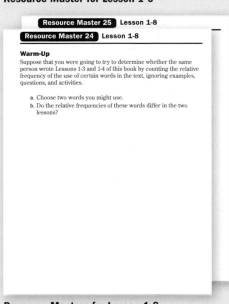

Resource Master 25 Lesson 1-8
Resource Master 24 Lesson 1-8

Warm-Up

Suppose that you were going to try to determine whether the same person wrote Lessons 1-3 and 1-4 of this book by counting the relative frequency of the use of certain words in the text, ignoring examples, questions, and activities.

a. Choose two words you might use.
b. Do the relative frequencies of these words differ in the two lessons?

Resource Masters for Lesson 1-8

Exploring Data

Pacing

Each lesson in this chapter is designed to be covered in 1 day. At the end of the chapter, you should plan to spend 1 day to review the Self-Test, 1 to 2 days for the Chapter Review, and 1 day for a test. You may wish to spend a day on projects, and possibly a day will be needed for quizzes. This chapter should therefore take 11 to 13 days. We strongly advise you not to spend more than 14 days on this chapter.

Students should be expected to do the equivalent of a complete set of Questions from a lesson nearly every day. Two Assignment Options are identified in each lesson. At times you may want to save a few questions to be done by students in class.

Overview

Before beginning this chapter, make certain that your students have read "To you, the student" so they know what materials they are expected to have. Students will also need a statistics utility (a calculator with statistics capabilities or a statistics package for a computer).

A successful implementation of the first chapter of a textbook sets the stage for an exciting and fruitful year for students. In addition to its mathematical objectives, this chapter has the following objectives:
a. Begin with content that is quite different from that of sudents' previous mathematics courses, thus requiring the students to read at the level that is necessary for success in this book;
b. Help students review important skills that will be needed in later chapters;
c. Introduce students to the technology that will be used in this course;
d. Give students experience with questions that have many possible answers and require students to use their judgment in selecting the most appropriate answer from several choices.

▶ Contents

1-1 Variables, Tables, and Graphs

1-2 Centers of Data and Weighted Averages

1-3 Creating and Using Histograms

1-4 Box Plots

1-5 Cumulative Distributions

1-6 Measures of Spread: Variance and Standard Deviation

1-7 Comparing Numerical Distributions

1-8 Using Statistics to Solve a Mystery: The Case of *The Federalist* Papers

Accidents are the fifth leading cause of death in the United States. In 2004, a reported 112,012 Americans died in accidents. Each of these deaths is particularly tragic because we think of accidental deaths as being preventable and because such deaths occur without warning. The graph on the next page displays the number of deaths from the six leading causes of accidents in the United States by age.

Looking at the graph, you can see that it would be appropriate for safety programs to target young adults to decrease motor-vehicle deaths, middle-aged people to decrease deaths from poisoning, and older people to decrease deaths from falls. In this way, the collection and display of data can be extremely important to society.

Statistics is the science of the collection, organization, analysis, and interpretation of data. For a situation like the causes of accidental deaths, statisticians decide what will constitute an accident, how the accidents will be counted, whether the data suggest particular action be taken, and how to display the data to the public. In this chapter you are asked to act like a statistician and use statistics and graphs to uncover patterns in data, compare groups, and draw conclusions.

4

Chapter 1 Overview

The main idea running through this chapter is the *distribution*. Although the term itself is not introduced until Lesson 1-3, Lessons 1-1 and 1-2 introduce common ways in which distributions are described: in tables, in graphs, and by summary statistics. We expect that most of what is in these lessons will be review for students. Lessons 1-3 and 1-4 look at histograms and box plots as pictures of distributions. In Lesson 1-8, tables and boxplots are used to analyze a non-trivial application of statistics that may

be quite appropriate to students who are simultaneously taking or who have taken a class in U.S. History.

Throughout the chapter, some common statistics are discussed. The statistics presented in this chapter are primarily *descriptive*; that is, they help to describe data sets and relations between them. They are also primarily *univariate*; that is, they deal with one variable, not with relations between variables. Measures of center (mean and median) are in Lesson 1-2.

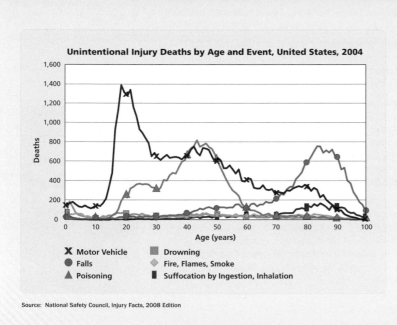

Unintentional Injury Deaths by Age and Event, United States, 2004

Legend:
- **X** Motor Vehicle
- **●** Falls
- **▲** Poisoning
- **■** Drowning
- **◆** Fire, Flames, Smoke
- **▮** Suffocation by Ingestion, Inhalation

Source: National Safety Council, Injury Facts, 2008 Edition

5

Students may begin this book with very few notions about statistics. As the study of the accidents summarized on this page indicates, collecting and displaying data can be very useful in helping devise ways to improve the quality of life. Students who are new to UCSMP books may not realize that the material on the first page of a chapter is part of the chapter. Some questions in the first lesson of a chapter may refer to these pages.

You might ask students to examine each of the causes of unintentional-injury death for the age or ages at which that cause is most prominent. Why would that be so? For instance, why are accidents due to motor vehicles most at ages 19–21? Why would poisoning be most prominent around age 40 and deaths due to falls around age 83?

A good conversation in the first days of class can demonstrate how useful statistics can be in understanding our world, and students will read material much more closely if they feel they can state opinions in class about what they have read.

Chapter 1 Projects

At the end of each chapter, you will find projects related to the chapter. At this time you might want to have students look over the projects on pages 67 and 68. You might want to have students tentatively select a project on which to work. Then, as students read and progress through the chapter, they can finalize their project choices.

Sometimes students might work alone. At other times, you might let them collaborate with classmates for a presentation and discussion. We recommend that you allow for diversity and encourage students to use their imaginations when presenting their projects. As students work on projects throughout the year, they should see many uses of mathematics in the real world.

Measures of spread (range, interquartile range, variance, and standard deviation) are in Lesson 1-6.

Distributions are also looked at as objects in themselves. Lesson 1-5 introduces cumulative distributions and percentiles and provides a way of seeing how tables and graphs of cumulative distributions differ from other distributions. In Lessons 1-7 and 1-8, distributions are compared by examining certain statistics and graphs.

Students are expected to become familiar with their statistics utility so that they can draw histograms and scatterplots and obtain the descriptive statistics mentioned above. In Chapter 2, statistics utilities are used to find equations for lines and other curves of best fit and correlations between two variables.

Lesson
1-1

Lesson
1-1 Variables, Tables, and Graphs

Vocabulary

statistic(s)

data, datum

variable

population

sample

survey

census

representative sample

categorical variable

numerical variable

▶ **BIG IDEA** Data can be presented in tables and graphs; statistics is about understanding and interpreting data to extract information and patterns.

The word *statistics* has two meanings. **Statistics** is the science of the collection, organization, analysis, and interpretation of *data*. (**Data** is the plural of **datum**, a piece of information.) Each of these activities depends on mathematics you will study in this course. A **statistic** also refers to a number used to describe a set of numbers. For example, the mean of a data set is a statistic describing a center of the data set.

Variables, Populations, and Samples

In statistics, a **variable** is a characteristic of a person or thing that can be classified, counted, ordered, or measured. For instance, some variables that describe a person are gender, religion, number of siblings, height, and family income. Some variables describing a country are population, area, major political parties, number of tons of steel produced, and birth rate.

The set of *all* individuals or objects you want to study is called the **population** for that study. If you cannot or do not collect data from the entire population, but from only a part of it, that part is called a *sample*. A **sample** is a subset of the population.

Sometimes, for reasons such as fairness or legal requirements, the entire population must be studied. For instance, to be fair, the president of a club might want to get opinions from every member of the club. Gathering facts or opinions through an interview or questionnaire is called a taking a **survey**. The U.S. Constitution requires that every ten years a **census** be taken. The U.S. census is a survey of the entire population of the United States.

Other times, for reasons such as cost, safety, or preservation of a product, it is preferable to study a sample. For instance, it might be too expensive to ask all owners of a particular make of truck whether they are pleased with the product. So the manufacturer will ask a sample of the owners. A grocer who wants to evaluate the taste of a new batch of apples cannot taste every apple (the population), because doing so would destroy the product. So instead, the grocer will taste one or two of the apples (the sample).

Mental Math

In a class of 137 girls and 126 boys, *g* girls and *b* boys signed up for the bus to go to a football game.

How many more girls than boys signed up for the bus? $g - b$

6 Exploring Data

Quiz Yourself (QY) questions help you follow the reading. You should answer each QY question before reading on. The answers to QY questions are at the end of the lesson.

 See Quiz Yourself 1 at the right.

The grocer and the medical technician use samples to draw conclusions about populations. Their chances of drawing a valid conclusion are better when their samples are **representative samples**, that is, when the samples have the same characteristics as the population. A blood sample is a representative sample of a patient's blood because the circulatory system thoroughly mixes cells, chemicals, viruses, and wastes that are present in a patient's body. If the grocer samples two or three apples from the top of the box, he may miss rotten apples in the third and fourth layers down. The grocer can make his sample more representative by taking an apple from the top layer, an apple from the bottom layer, and an apple from a middle layer.

Reading a Table

Data can come from experiments or surveys. To make sense of data, it helps to organize the data in a table or graph. In Guided Example 1 below, examine the table carefully. Look at the header information and the labels of the table's rows and columns. Try to determine the meaning of every number in the table.

A "Guided Example" is an example in which some, but not all, of the solution is shown. You should try to complete the example before reading on. Answers to Guided Examples are in the Selected Answers section at the back of the book.

> ▶ **QUIZ YOURSELF 1**
>
> A medical laboratory technician draws 10 mL of blood in order to determine the number of white blood cells in a patient's bloodstream. Identify the variable, population, and sample.

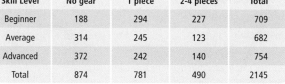

var - white blood cells
pop - all patients blood
sample - 10 mL drawn

GUIDED

Example 1

In Boston, 2145 selected inline skaters were chosen for a survey and asked to classify their ability as "Beginner," "Average," or "Advanced." They were also asked whether they wore protective gear like helmets, knee pads, shin pads, and elbow pads when skating. The data were organized in a table like that shown below.

	Amount of Protective Gear Worn			
Skill Level	No gear	1 piece	2-4 pieces	Total
Beginner	188	294	227	709
Average	314	245	123	682
Advanced	372	242	140	754
Total	874	781	490	2145

(continued on next page)

---

2 Teaching

Notes on the Lesson

The "information explosion" of the last century has produced rapidly increasing amounts of published data. In efforts to manage this abundance of data, the ability to use statistics to analyze data has become a requirement in many more professional fields. Whereas in the past, only mathematicians or statisticians were expected to be able to manipulate and interpret data, now many business professionals are expected to be able to perform this type of analysis.

You may wish to ask students to think of situations they may encounter in the future in which the ability to analyze data would be helpful.

Additional Example

Example 1 Use the data from Example 1. Answer to the nearest tenth of a percent.
What percent of average skaters wore less than 2 pieces of protective gear? 314 average skaters wore no gear and 245 wore one piece of gear for a total of 559. So 559 out of the 682 average skaters wore less than 2 pieces of gear. $\frac{559}{682} \approx 82.0\%$

Variables, populations, and samples
The use of the word *variable* in this lesson is different from that found in algebra. In this course, we use the term *variable* with both its algebraic and statistical meanings; the context makes it clear which meaning is appropriate.

1-1

Notes on the Lesson

Drawing conclusions from tables

In the table before Example 2, be sure that students understand that when the number of households is by thousands, as it is here, then the number in the table must be multiplied by 1000 to get its actual value. Questions 12–15 refer to this table.

a. Are the data based on a sample or on the entire population?

b. What variables are presented?

c. What percent of skaters wore no gear?

d. What percent of beginners wore no gear?

e. How many skaters said they were advanced?

f. How many advanced skaters wore protective gear?

Solution

a. Only selected skaters were surveyed. The data are based on a sample.

b. The variables are often named as labels of the rows and columns. In this table there are only two variables: **skill level** and __?__. Both variables are reported in categories, described by the labels of the rows and columns.

c. 874 out of the 2145 skaters wore no gear. $\frac{874}{2145} \approx 0.407$. About __?__% of the skaters wore no gear.

d. __?__ out of the __?__ beginners wore no gear. About __?__% of the beginners wore no gear.

e. You can find the total number of advanced skaters by adding the values in the three categories in the row labeled "Advanced":

$372 + \underline{?} + 140 = \underline{?}$. You can also find this total in the rightmost column of the table. __?__ skaters said they were advanced.

f. __?__ advanced skaters wore one piece of gear and __?__ wore 2 to 4 pieces of gear for a total of 382. So __?__ advanced skaters wore some protective gear.

b. amount of protective gear worn

c. 40.7

d. 188; 709; 26.5

e. 242; 754; 754

f. 242; 140; 382

The purpose of the study in Example 1 was to get information about a population of skaters. If the sample is representative of inline skaters in Boston, then about 41% of Boston skaters do not wear protective gear.

In the table of Example 1, the skill level is a **categorical variable** because the different values do not correspond to specific numbers. The number of pieces of protective gear is also reported as a categorical variable because different values are grouped into categories together. If the study had not combined 2, 3, and 4 pieces of gear into a single category, then that variable would have been a **numerical variable**. With a numerical variable, you can calculate numerical statistics such as the mean. With a categorical variable, you cannot calculate numerical statistics, though you may be able to estimate them.

Drawing Conclusions from Tables

When reading a table, you should ask three questions:

1. What variables are presented, and how?

You can usually find the variables as headings of rows and columns, but sometimes a single table will present the same variable in more than one way: by giving a value and a corresponding percentage, for example.

8   Exploring Data

Accommodating the Learner ⬇

Some students may have trouble identifying the variables from a table because they may not see a symbol that they can readily identify in the algebraic sense of the word variable. It is worthwhile for these students to discuss the use of the word *variable* in statistics. In algebra, a *variable* is a symbol that can stand for any one of a set of objects. So, in algebra we say, "Let h = the height of a person," then we mean that h stands for a number which is the height of the person.

But in statistics, h is thought to stand for the *attribute* called height. So statisticians ask questions such as, "What variable is being studied?," when they are speaking of an attribute.

2. Are the data trustworthy?

Consider the data source, the accuracy of the data, and the time when the data were collected. Ideally, the data source should be given, allowing you to verify the data if you want, and it should be reputable. The age of the data may matter; even when addressing historical issues, newer data may be more accurate, reliable, or precise than older data. Knowing when and how the data were collected helps you decide what conclusions to draw.

3. What conclusions can you draw from the table?

Some conclusions can be read directly from data in a table. Others can be drawn only after performing calculations using the data in a table, or after looking for patterns or trends in the data.

Below is a table summarizing some data collected by the U.S. Census Bureau. Before going on, read the table carefully and try to make sense of every number in it.

Income of Households by Highest Education Level of Householder in 2005

Highest Level of Education Completed by Householder	Number of Households (thousands)	Percent Distribution by Income Level								Median Income (dollars)
		Under $10,000	$10,000–$14,999	$15,000–$24,999	$25,000–$34,999	$35,000–$49,999	$50,000–$74,999	$75,000–$99,999	$100,000 and over	
Less than 9th grade	6,088	21.7	15.6	21.6	14.7	12.0	9.1	3.3	2.2	20,224
Some high school, but no diploma	9,130	17.3	12.8	20.5	15.1	14.4	11.9	4.7	3.4	24,675
High school graduate	32,345	8.8	7.8	15.8	13.3	16.7	18.9	9.4	9.3	38,191
Some college	28,874	5.7	4.8	10.6	11.7	16.8	21.1	13.2	16.1	50,412
Bachelor's degree or higher	31,153	3.0	2.2	5.0	6.5	11.6	19.9	15.6	36.2	77,179

Source: U.S. Census Bureau, Current Population Survey, 2006 Annual Social and Economic Supplement.

STOP See Quiz Yourself 2 at the right.

▶ **QUIZ YOURSELF 2**

Are the data in the table trustworthy?

Example 2

Refer to the table of income data above.

a. What variable is represented by the row headings and what kind of variable is it? What is the other variable in the table?

b. What kinds of information are presented in the columns? What columns correspond to each kind?

c. Interpret the table entry 31,153 in a sentence describing its context.

d. Write a statement relating median income to education of householder.

e. How many times as likely was a family to have an income of at least $100,000 if the head of household had graduated college rather than not started high school?

(continued on next page)

Vocabulary Development

As in all reading, vocabulary is important in the interpretation of tables. In the table of income data on page 9, the meanings of the words "householder" or "diploma" may not be clear to some students. You may wish to go down the left column, asking different students for the meaning of each row's heading. Then go through the headings for the columns. You may wish to keep an English dictionary in the classroom and encourage students to use it when they encounter an unfamiliar word.

Notes on the Lesson

Some statistical variables are numerical and others are categorical. This is a useful distinction because certain kinds of statistics are appropriate only with one type and not the other. For instance, a mean can only be calculated from data that is numerical. But when numerical data are grouped together, the result is a categorical variable. So, for instance, in the household income table, the variable "$10,000 – $14,999" is categorical, not numerical.

Example 2 Students need practice in reading complex tables such as the one in this example. Parts a–d cue students in reading strategies. Parts e and f alert students to the idea that understanding a table means more than merely parroting numbers that are in it. In this table, students may observe that the middle entries (columns 2–9) should sum to 100%.

Additional Example

Example 2 Refer to the table of income data before Example 2. How many times as likely was a family to have an income of less than $15,000 if the head of the household had some high school but no diploma rather than graduated from high school?

About 17.3% + 12.8% = 30.1% of households headed by someone with some high school had incomes less than $15,000, compared with 8.8% + 7.8% = 16.6% of households headed by high school graduates. So a household headed by someone with some high school but no diploma is almost twice as likely to have an income of less than $15,000 than a household headed by a high school graduate.

Solution

a. The row headings present the highest level of education completed by the householder, which is a categorical variable. The other variable is the annual household income. All other numbers in the table were calculated from the income data.

b. The leftmost data column gives the total number of households (in thousands) at each education level. Data columns 2-9 give the percentage of households within each education level at each income level. The rightmost column gives the median income (in dollars) for all households at each education level.

c. 31,153 occurs in the last row of the first data column, so it represents the total number of households in which the householder had a bachelor's degree or higher. Notice that values in this column are given in thousands, so we have to multiply 31,153 by 1000 to get the actual value. **In about 31,153,000 households, the householder had a bachelor's degree or higher.**

d. Examine the rightmost column. The numbers increase going down the column. **Households headed by people with higher education levels have higher median incomes.**

e. The percents of households with an income of at least $100,000 are given in the second column from the right. Families headed by someone who did not start high school are represented by the first row of level of education. **About 2.2% of households headed by someone who was not did not start high school had incomes of at least $100,000, compared with 36.2% of households headed by college graduates. Thus, a college graduate-headed household was more than 16 times as likely to have an income of at least $100,000 as a household where the head had not started high school.**

STOP See Quiz Yourself 3 at the right.

> **QUIZ YOURSELF 3**
>
> In 2005, how many households with income under $10,000 were headed by a householder with some high school but no diploma?

Bar Graphs

Conclusions can often be determined or supported by graphs. For instance, the *bar graph* at the right pictures the data from the rightmost column of the table on the previous page. It supports the conclusion in Example 2, Part e.

Bar graphs are appropriate when one variable is a categorical variable, and the other variable is numerical. One axis lists the categories, in this case householder education level. The other axis is a numerical scale, typically with counts, percents, or measurements such as income. A well-made bar graph has a descriptive title. In addition, the graph identifies the variables being described, labels the scale in equal intervals, and uses bars of equal widths for each category.

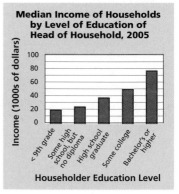

Median Income of Households by Level of Education of Head of Household, 2005

Income (1000s of dollars) vs *Householder Education Level*

Accommodating the Learner ⬆

Many online degree programs make statements quantifying the lifetime benefit of earning a degree, such as "Did you know that people who earn a bachelor's degree can earn an extra $1 million more in a lifetime than a person with just a high school diploma?"

Assume a lifetime of earning to be 40 years. Have students use the information presented in the bar graph on page 10 to make conjectures about lifetime income of households for different levels of education. What additional information would be useful when coming up with these conjectures? **Answers vary. Samples: average incomes instead of median, cost of education, inflation rates, etc.**

More complex types of bar graphs can be used to show features of data with two categorical variables. The *stacked bar graph* at the right was created from the table in Example 1 in four steps:

- First, each frequency was converted to a percentage of skaters in that experience category. For example, 188 of the 709 beginner skaters wore no gear, giving about 27%.

- At each skill level, a bar was drawn for the percentage of skaters wearing no gear.

- Bars were stacked on top of other bars by adding values. For example, because 27% of beginning skaters wore no gear and 41% wore 1 piece, the stacked bar representing 1 piece starts at 27% on the vertical axis and goes to 27% + 41% = 68% on the vertical axis.

- The parts of each stack were colored differently to distinguish them, and a legend describing each color was placed by the graph.

The stacked bar graph shows that the Average and Advanced skaters are similar in use of protective gear, and that Beginners are more likely than other skaters to wear protective gear.

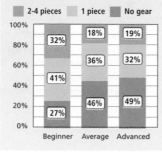

Percent of Protective Gear Used by Boston Inline Skaters

Questions

COVERING THE IDEAS

These questions cover the content of the reading. If you cannot answer a Covering the Ideas question, you should go back to the reading for help in obtaining an answer.

1. Give three examples of variables that can be used to describe a person but were not mentioned in the lesson.

2. Give three characteristics of a situation that might cause a person to study a sample rather than an entire population. **See margin.**

In 3 and 4, a situation is described. Determine the population, whether the data are based on a sample, and the variable of interest.

3. A pastry inspector counts the number of raisins per cookie in 10 oatmeal-raisin cookies in a batch fresh out of the oven.

4. A statistician computes the free-throw percentage for every player in the WNBA. **4. WNBA players; no; free-throw percentage**

In 5 and 6, refer to the National Safety Council graph on page 5.

5. What are the three most common types of accidental deaths among 80-year-olds? **5–6. See margin.**

6. Estimate the total number of accidental deaths in the U.S. in 2004.
   a. among 10-year-olds.   b. among 20-year-olds.

1. Answers vary. Sample: eye color, arm span, birth month

3. the batch of cookies; yes; number of raisins per cookie

Variables, Tables, and Graphs   **11**

Additional Answers

2. Answers vary. Sample: It is too expensive to study the entire population. It is unsafe or implausible to subject the entire population to a study, as in eating all the apples in a store to check quality. The population does not stay in one place, as in a population of animals.

5. In decreasing order: falls, motor-vehicle, and suffocation by ingestion or inhalation

6a. about 230

6b. about 1,700

Notes on the Lesson

Bar graphs In presenting stacked bar graphs, the example in the text uses relative frequency, so the bars are the same height. You may want to comment on this for two reasons: first, because some students may conclude that there are the same number of skaters in each category; second, because in the questions, they are asked to produce stacked bar graphs *both* for frequencies *and* for relative frequencies.

3 Assignment

Recommended Assignment

- Questions 1–15
- Questions 16–22
- Question 23 (extra credit)
- Reading Lesson 1-2
- Covering the Ideas 1-2 (Questions 1–12)

Notes on the Questions

For students who have not studied from UCSMP materials previously, you might want to point out the various types of Questions.

We encourage going through the questions of this lesson in order. They will cover the main ideas of the lesson.

Question 6 These can only be estimates because only the top six leading causes of accidental deaths are listed per age group.

1-1

Notes on the Questions

Question 10 This kind of question requires that a student divide one piece of data by another for its answer and tends to be more difficult than merely locating data in a table.

Additional Answers

9b. Guided Example 1d asks for the percentage of beginner skaters in the sample who wore no gear, whereas Part a asked for the percent of no gear skaters who were beginners.

14a. about 5,019 thousand households

14b. about 4.7%

15. Answers vary. Sample: The median income of households headed by someone who has at least a bachelor's degree is more than twice as high as the median income of households headed by someone with only a high school diploma.

16a. type of sport and gender

16b. boys in basketball: about 55%; girls in basketball: about 45%; boys in track and field: about 55%

16c. The percent values were rounded to the nearest 1%, so although 0.29% of baseball players are girls, that value was rounded to 0%.

16d. Answers vary. Sample: Participants in baseball and football are almost always boys and the large majority of volleyball participants are girls. The sports with more equal levels of participation between boys and girls are basketball, soccer, and track and field.

---

7. What is a *representative sample*?

In 8–10, refer to Guided Example 1.

8. a. What is the sample? b. What is the population?

9. a. What percent of skaters who wore no protective gear were beginners? **about 21.5%** 26.5%

   b. Why is your answer to Part a different from the answer to Guided Example 1 Part d? **See margin.**

10. If you were to notice a skater in Boston without any protective gear, what is the chance the skater is advanced? **about 42.6%**

11. Tell whether the variable is numerical or categorical.
    a. gender **categorical**
    b. method of transportation to school **categorical**
    c. height **numerical**
    d. distance from school **numerical**

In 12–15, refer to the table before Example 2.

12. What percent of households in 2005 were headed by people who had some college, but not a bachelor's degree? **about 26.8%**

13. What percent of households headed by high school graduates (with no college) earned at least $25,000 annually? **67.6%**

14. a. How many households headed by someone who was not a high school graduate earned less than $15,000 in 2005?

    b. What percent of the total number of households is this?

15. Write a sentence or two describing how the incomes of households headed by someone with a bachelor's degree or higher compares to the incomes of households headed by someone with a high school diploma but no college. **14–15. See margin.**

APPLYING THE MATHEMATICS

These questions extend the content of the lesson. You should study the examples and explanations if you cannot answer the question. For some questions, you can check your answers with the ones at the back of this book.

16. The *2005–2006 High School Athletics Participation Survey* of the National Federation of State High School Associations listed participation of high school students in 47 sports. The table at the right shows participation for the six sports that had the most participants. The graph on the next page displays the information in the table.
    a. What are the categorical variables in the table?
    b. Compute the missing percents on the graph.
    c. The graph shows that 100% of the participants in baseball are boys. Yet the table shows that there are girls who play baseball. Why is there a difference?

Numbers of Participants in High School Sports 2005-2006

Sport	Boys	Girls	Total
Baseball	470,671	1,382	472,053
Basketball	546,335	452,929	999,264
Football	1,071,775	1,173	1,072,948
Soccer	538,935	321,555	860,490
Track and Field	533,985	439,200	973,185
Volleyball	42,878	390,034	432,912
Total	3,204,579	1,606,273	4,810,852

16–18. See margin.

7. A representative sample is a sample that accurately reflects the important features of the population.

8a. 2,145 inline skaters in Boston

8b. Answers vary. Sample: all inline skaters in Boston

Additional Answers

17a. the age distribution of trout in a certain lake

17b. sample; The population is all of the trout in the lake. The sample is representative of the population because the trout were captured from different parts of the lake.

17c. about 14.6%

18a.

Distance to School	Elementary School	Middle School	High School	Total
2 blocks or less	72	34	12	118
2-6 blocks	132	107	89	328
6 blocks or more	80	83	108	271
Total	284	224	209	717

d. Write a few sentences about the differences between boys' and girls' participation in these sports.

17. A biologist captures 96 trout from different parts of a lake to determine the age distribution. She finds that 53 are less than six months old and 29 are between six months and one year old.

   a. What variable or variables are being studied?

   b. Is the study based on a sample or on a population? If a sample, what is the population, and what steps were taken to make the sample representative?

   c. What percent of the trout are more than one year old?

18. A school district surveys a sample of families to determine how far students must travel to school. They find that of 284 children in elementary school, 72 travel 2 blocks or less, 132 travel between 2 and 6 blocks, and 80 travel six blocks or more. Among 224 students in middle school, 34 travel 2 blocks or less and 107 travel between 2 and 6 blocks. Among 209 high school students, 12 travel 2 blocks or less and 108 travel 6 blocks or more.

   a. Create a table representing these data.

   b. Create a stacked bar graph showing the number (not percentage) of students in each grade band and, within each band, the number at each distance.

   c. Is the distance traveled a numerical or a categorical variable?

REVIEW

Each lesson contains review questions to practice ideas studied earlier.

19. **Skill Sequence** Solve each equation. (**Previous Course**)

   a. $13x = 260$ **$x = 20$**

   b. $0.13x = 260$ **$x = 2,000$**

   c. $260x = 13$ **$x = 0.05$**

   d. $260x = 0.13$ **$x = 0.0005$**

20. Identify the slope and y-intercept of the graph of the equation $y = mx + b$. (**Previous Course**) **slope: m; y-intercept: b**

21. A line has slope -3 and contains the point $(-5, 2)$. (**Previous Course**)

   a. Name two other points on the line.

   b. Find an equation for the line. **$y = -3x - 13$**

22. Find the *mean* (average) of $x + 3$, $x + 7$, and $x + 29$. (**Previous Course**) **$x + 13$**

EXPLORATION

These questions ask you to explore ideas related to the lesson. Sometimes you will need to use references found in a library or on the Internet.

23. Find an example of a bar graph in a newspaper, magazine, or other publication. Identify the variables. What conclusion(s) can you draw from the graph? **See margin.**

21a. Answers vary.
Sample: (0, -13), (1, -16)

QUIZ YOURSELF ANSWERS

1. The variable is the number of white blood cells. The population is all the patient's blood; the sample is the 10 mL of the patient's blood that is drawn.

2. Yes; the data are from the U.S. Census Bureau, a reputable source. The source is shown.

3. about $0.173 \cdot 9,130,000 \approx 1,579,490$ households

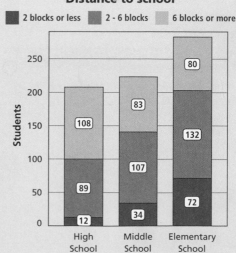
Additional Answers

23. Answers vary. Sample: The data shown below concern the State of the Union address, which the U.S. President gives annually each January to Congress. The variables are the number of times the President was applauded, the duration of applause, and the total length of the speech. One possible observation from this data is that the number of periods of applause during the speech is declining. We might conclude that the Congress was increasingly less pleased with the content of the speech.

Giving the President A Hand		Number of times	Minutes of applause	Total length of speech
Applause during the speech	2001	87	17.9	49.2
	2002	76	18.3	47.8
	2003	76	17.5	59.6
	2004	72	16.4	53.9
	2005	65	18.2	53.3
	2006	59	15.0	51.1
	2007	61	14.0	49.5

Source: The New York Times

Lesson 1-2

Lesson 1-2 Centers of Data and Weighted Averages

SPUR Objectives

A Calculate measures of center and spread for data sets.

B Calculate averages with weights, frequencies, and relative frequencies.

C Use Σ-notation to represent a sum or mean.

D Describe relations between measures of center and spread.

Materials/Resources

· Lesson Master 1-2
· Resource Masters 5, 6 and 7
· Spreadsheet application

HOMEWORK • Option 1
  • Option 2
• Questions 1–12
• • Questions 13–24
• • Question 25 (extra credit)
  • Reading Lesson 1-3
  • Covering the Ideas 1-3
    (Questions 1–10)

Local Standards

1 Warm-Up

If an A is counted as 4 points, a B as 3 points, a C as 2 points, a D as 1 point, and an F as 0 points, calculate the grade point average of a student with 3 A's, 1 B, and 2 Cs.

$$\frac{3 \cdot 4 + 1 \cdot 3 + 2 \cdot 2}{6} = \frac{19}{6} \approx 3.17$$

▶ **BIG IDEA** The mean and median are both measures of center for data.

The word "average" has more than one meaning. When people say that someone is of "average height," there is no calculation. They are saying that the person's height is somewhere in the middle range of all heights. But when people say, "The average height of the students was 162 cm," they are usually speaking of a calculated statistic, the *mean*.

Measures of Center

The **mean** of a data set is calculated by finding the sum of the numbers in the set and dividing by the number of elements. The **median** is the middle number when the set of numbers is put in increasing or decreasing order; it is the mean of the two middle numbers when the set has an even number of elements. Both the mean and median are **measures of center** or **measures of central tendency**, and at times people will use either the mean or median as the "average" of a data set.

GUIDED

Example 1

The Wacky Widget Company has 15 employees. The jobs and annual salary for each job are given in the table on the next page. A newspaper reported, "Average Wacky Widget worker earns $78,000 a year."

a. Which statistic was it reporting, the mean or the median?

b. Why might most employees be upset by the newspaper article?

Solution

a. Calculate the median salary. Since all the numbers are in thousands, ignore the thousand and consider $90,000 as 90. Put the salaries in order, smallest to largest. 24, 24, 27, 30, 30, 30, 35, 65, 65, 65, 65, 90, 90, 150, 380. The value of the middle number is __?__. So the median salary is __?__. The newspaper did not report the median. The mean is the sum of the salaries divided by __?__. The sum is __?__. So the mean is $78,000. The newspaper reported the mean. **65, $65,000; 15, $1,170,000**

b. The newspaper was reporting an average of $78,000, but __?__ of the 15 employees make less than this. **11**

14 Exploring Data

No.	Job	Salary ($1000)
1	CEO	380
2	CEO Asst	35
3	VP	150
4	VP Asst	30
5	Parts Mgr	90
6	Parts Worker	30
7	Parts Worker	30
8	Custodian	27
9	Custodian	24
10	Custodian	24
11	Sales Mgr	90
12	Sales Rep	65
13	Sales Rep	65
14	Sales Rep	65
15	Sales Rep	65

Vocabulary

mean

median

measures of center, measures of central tendency

mode

subscripted variables

Σ, sigma

index, i

summation notation, sigma notation, Σ-notation

weighted average

relative frequency

Mental Math

A store has a sale selling 5 baseball caps for a total of x. At regular price they each cost y.

How much will each of 5 individuals save if they pool their money together and buy the hats on sale?

$y - \dfrac{x}{5}$

Background

Older statistics books refer to the mean and median as measures of *central tendency*, while many newer books refer to these as measures of *center*. We use the latter term because it is becoming more preferred and because it is simpler. Although some books still call the mode a measure of center or central tendency, this is misleading because it is possible to have a data set in which the mode is an extreme value (for example, when two students score 100 on a test and no other students have identical scores).

Summation notation In this lesson the index i is used only as a subscript, to serve to enumerate the elements of a data set. Later in the course the index will be used as a variable in expressions such as $\displaystyle\sum_{i=1}^{100} i$.

Weighted averages Weighted averages arise from two different kinds of situations. If you wish to calculate the mean of a large data set of n numbers, then, to shorten the computation, you might take all the values in the data set, multiply each value by its

In Example 1, even though the newspaper accurately reported the mean salary, the president's salary alone contributes $\frac{380}{15}$ thousand dollars, or over \$25,000, toward the mean salary of employees. Reporting the mean salary in this situation is misleading. When dealing with data sets that have widely varying values, the median is often more representative of the data, and the **mode**, the most frequent value, is also often reported.

 See Quiz Yourself 1 at the right.

> ▶ **QUIZ YOURSELF 1**
>
> What is the mode salary of Wacky Widget Company employees?

Summation Notation

Calculating a mean involves finding a sum. Sums are so basic to mathematics that a shorthand notation for representing sums is commonly used. There are three parts to *summation notation*: **subscripted variables** $x_1, x_2, x_3, \ldots, x_n$ to identify each of the n data values; the Greek letter $\sum$ (**sigma**) to indicate there is a sum; and the **index i** to indicate which of the subscripted variables are being added.

To indicate the sum of the 15 salaries of the Wacky Widget Company, let x_i be the salary of the ith employee. That is, $x_1 = \$380,000$, $x_2 = \$35,000$, and so on, until $x_{15} = \$65,000$. Notice that the index subscript simply indicates the position in the list. The sum

$$x_1 + x_2 + x_3 + \ldots + x_{15} \text{ is written } \sum_{i=1}^{15} x_i$$

and is read "The sum of x-sub-i as i goes from 1 to 15." This notation is called **summation notation**, **sigma notation**, or **Σ-notation**. If you want to indicate the sum of the salaries of the three Parts workers at the Wacky Widget Company, you could write $\sum_{i=5}^{7} x_i$, which equals $x_5 + x_6 + x_7$, or \$150,000. This notation may need to be adapted when using technology. If you were to represent these 3 salaries as entries A5 to A7 in a spreadsheet, their sum would be SUM(A5:A7).

 See Quiz Yourself 2 at the right.

The mean of a data set can be expressed using sigma notation. If $\{x_1, x_2, x_3, \ldots x_n\}$ is a data set of n numbers, the mean is

$$\frac{\sum_{i=1}^{n} x_i}{n} = \frac{1}{n} \sum_{i=1}^{n} x_i.$$

> ▶ **QUIZ YOURSELF 2**
>
> Use Σ-notation to indicate the sum of the salaries of the five people in sales at Wacky Widget Company.

Example 2

A full parking lot has 46 cars. Let $p_i =$ the number of people who rode in the ith car parked in the lot.

a. What does $\sum_{i=1}^{46} p_i$ represent?

b. Use Σ-notation to express the mean number of people per car.

(continued on next page)

Centers of Data and Weighted Averages **15**

---

frequency of occurrence, and add those products to get the sum that you will divide by n. This, technically, is still a calculation of the mean, but you have weighted the values by the number of times each value occurs. The situation with concert tickets on page 17, thinking of frequencies as weights, is a weighted average of this type.

The second kind of situation is when weights are assigned to different values independent of the number of times they occur. This kind of weighted average is what is usually used in calculating a student's grade-point average (GPA), as in Example 3 and the Warm-Up.

A key idea in this lesson is that a weighted average can be calculated either from frequencies or relative frequencies. This is shown in Example 4. In the case of the GPA calculated in the Warm-Up, the student has $\frac{1}{2}$ A's, $\frac{1}{6}$ B's, and $\frac{1}{3}$ C's in relative frequencies, and the weighted average is $\frac{1}{2} \cdot 4 + \frac{1}{6} \cdot 3 + \frac{1}{3} \cdot 2$, or $\frac{19}{6}$, as it was calculated from the frequencies.

2 Teaching

Notes on the Lesson

Measures of center The measures of center should be review. Example 1 is meant to be easy and something students may have studied in middle school.

Summation notation The use of summation ($\sum$) notation is likely to be new. Summation notation is used throughout the text so emphasize it at this time. Students should be able to work with and evaluate simple expressions written with summation notation. The work with spreadsheets on pages 16 and 19 will be new for some students but likely not new for all.

Additional Example

Example 1 The chart below gives information about the weights of team members on the varsity wrestling team at Petit Valley High School.

Number of members	Weight (lbs.)
4	120
3	135
3	145
2	170
1	190
1	285

a. How many members does the team have? **14**

b. Find the mean height. **152.5**

c. Find the median height. **140**

d. Which number, the mean or the median, best describes the typical height of a member of the team? Why? **median; the mean is higher because of the outlier 285**

1-2

Notes on the Lesson

Weighted averages If your school gives weighted grades, we recommend using its weights rather than the ones in Example 3.

Additional Example

Example 2 A family-friendly beach resort has a total of 32 family suites. Let g_i = the number of guests who checked into each suite.

a. What does $\sum_{i=1}^{32} g_i$ represent?

$g_1 + g_2 + g_3 + \dots + g_{32}$, the total number of guests who checked into the beach resort

b. Use $\sum$-notation to express the mean number of guests per room.

$\dfrac{\sum_{i=1}^{32} g_i}{32}$ or $\dfrac{1}{32}\sum_{i=1}^{32} g_i$.

Example 3 In a college economics course, suppose that homework counts for 25%, quizzes 10%, tests 45%, and attendance 20% of each student's overall grade. Frances and her friend Adam earned the following scores during the semester.

	Frances	Adam
Homework	89	95
Quizzes	82	90
Tests	87	92
Attendance	100	70

Who received the higher overall course grade?

Frances' overall course grade is
$\dfrac{.25(89) + .10(82) + .45(87) + .20(100)}{1.00} = 89.6.$

Adam's overall course grade is
$\dfrac{.25(95) + .10(90) + .45(92) + .20(70)}{1.00} = 88.15.$

So Frances received the higher grade.

(In this case, the weights were given as percentages so the denominator (the sum of the weights) is 100% or 1.00.)

Solution

a. $\sum_{i=1}^{46} p_i = p_1 + p_2 + p_3 + \dots + p_{46}$. This represents the total number of people who rode in the cars parked in the lot.

b. To find the mean, divide the total number of people by the number of parking spots. $\dfrac{\sum_{i=1}^{46} p_i}{46}$ or $\dfrac{1}{46}\sum_{i=1}^{46} p_i$.

Most statistics utilities based on spreadsheets have special syntax for measures of center. For example, cell A5 in spreadsheets I and II shows the commands for the median and mean of the entries in cells A1, A2, A3, and A4 (the first four annual salaries at the Wacky Widget Company).

I   II

Weighted Averages

In some high schools and colleges, a student's grade point average (GPA) is calculated based on the weights or credits assigned to a letter grade in a specific class. In Susan's high school, AP courses are weighted as 5 credits, Honors courses are 4 credits, regular level courses are 3 credits and elective courses (like keyboarding and home economics) are 1 credit. The grading scale below is used in her school.

Letter	F	D-	D	D+	C-	C	C+	B-	B	B+	A-	A	A+
Grade Points	0.00	0.67	1.00	1.33	1.67	2.00	2.33	2.67	3.0	3.33	3.67	4.00	4.00

Susan's grades are shown on her report card in Example 3.

Example 3

Use Susan's report card at the right to find her GPA.

Solution The weights are the number of credits per course. For example, the B- Susan received in AP Calculus has a weight of 5 credits towards her GPA. To calculate Susan's GPA we use the credits per course as the weight and the grade points as the value being weighted.

Susan's GPA is $\dfrac{1(4.00) + 5(2.67) + 4(3.33) + 3(0.67) + 3(2.00)}{1 + 5 + 4 + 3 + 3}$

≈ 2.42

Susan's Report Card

Course	Credit	Letter	Grade Points
Keyboarding	1	A+	4.00
AP Calculus	5	B-	2.67
Honors English	4	B+	3.33
Regular Level Art History	3	D-	0.67
Regular Level Statistics	3	C	2.00

Vocabulary Development

It is possible for some students to become confused by the use of the words *mean* and *relative* which have other connotations outside of mathematics. In order to solidify the meanings in a mathematical context, you may wish to have them look up the definitions of these words and use each correctly within context.

In addition, some students with limited computer word processing experience may be unfamiliar with the terms *subscript* or *superscript*. Take the time to connect each term with its familiar meaning.

Susan's GPA is an example of a *weighted average*. In general,

if x_i = a value in a data set and
   w_i = the weight the value,

then the **weighted average** of the values x_i is

$$\dfrac{\sum\limits_{i}^{n} w_i x_i}{\sum\limits_{i}^{n} w_i}, \text{ which means } \dfrac{w_1 x_1 + w_2 x_2 + \ldots + w_n x_n}{w_1 + w_2 + \ldots + w_n}.$$

In Example 3, if each of Susan's courses were weighted as 1 credit, then the weighted average would be equivalent to the mean since all of the weights would be equal. In general, every mean is a weighted average in which each weight $w_i = 1$.

CAUTION: When calculating a GPA, it is common to mistake the point value for the weight. Since when calculating the weighted average, the denominator is the sum of the weights, you can see in Example 3 that the credits are the weights.

Thinking of Frequencies as Weights

You can think of frequencies as weights and calculate a mean as a weighted average as in the following situation.

Alexis wanted to buy a ticket to a concert. She saw that ticket prices were $20, $30, and $100. She wrote a letter to the concert promoters. She said, "An average price of $50 is too much for a concert for teenagers." Would you agree with Alexis that the average price of a ticket is $50?

The concert promoters responded that most of the tickets were $20. They reported that there were 1,000 $20 seats, 500 $30 seats, and only 20 $100 seats. These data are arranged in a frequency table and a bar graph below.

Ticket Price	Availability
$20	1,000
$30	500
$100	20

The calculations shown in Example 3 for the weighted average can be used to quickly calculate the mean ticket price. Computing the *mean* involves adding all the $20, $30 and $100 tickets and dividing by the sum of the frequencies:

$$\dfrac{20(1000) + 30(500) + 100(20)}{1000 + 500 + 20} = \dfrac{37000}{1520} \approx \$24.34.$$

The result is not $50, but $24.34 because there are more $20 and $30 tickets available. This means that because the $20 seats have a higher frequency of occurrence, they contribute more in computing the mean. They have more "weight" than the $100 tickets.

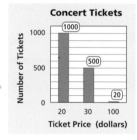

Centers of Data and Weighted Averages   **17**

Additional Example

Example 4 To celebrate the opening of a new branch, a clothing store advertised that the first 200 customers would randomly receive free gift cards valued at $5, $15, $50, or $100. An internal memo to the new store manager contained the following sentence:

"There will be 5 $100-dollar cards, 10 $50-dollar cards, 35 $15-dollar cards, and the rest will be $5-dollar cards."

a. Calculate the total dollar value of the gift cards. **$2275**

b. Create a frequency table and calculate the weighted average as in Example 3.

Card Value	Frequency
$100	5
$50	10
$15	35
$5	150

The weighted average is $11.375.

c. Create a relative frequency table and graph.

Card Value	Frequency
$100	$\frac{5}{200} = 0.025$
$50	$\frac{10}{200} = 0.05$
$15	$\frac{35}{200} = 0.175$
$5	$\frac{150}{200} = 0.75$

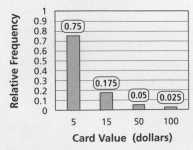

Gift Cards

d. Compute the weighted average using the relative frequency values and compare that result to the one from Part a. **$11.375; This result is identical to Part a.**

e. If there were an equal number of each gift card, what would the average be? **$42.50**

Using Relative Frequencies to Calculate Weighted Averages

The **relative frequency** is the ratio of the number of times a number or event occurs to the total number of numbers or events. The weighted average of a data set is the same whether the weights are frequencies or relative frequencies.

Example 4

a. Convert the frequency table and graph for the concert tickets to a relative frequency table and graph.

b. Compute the weighted average using the relative frequency values and compare the result with that obtained from using the frequencies.

Solution

a. Convert each frequency to a relative frequency by dividing the frequency by the total number of tickets sold. In this case, relative frequency has been rounded to two decimal places. An advantage to converting the data to a relative frequency is that it is now easy to see that about 66% of the tickets sold were $20 tickets, about 33% were $30 tickets, and about 1% were $100 tickets.

Ticket Price	Relative Frequency
$20	$\frac{1000}{1520} \approx 0.66$
$30	$\frac{500}{1520} \approx 0.33$
$100	$\frac{20}{1520} \approx 0.01$

Concert Tickets

b. The weighted average is computed by multiplying each price by its relative frequency.

$$20 \cdot \frac{100}{1520} + 30 \cdot \frac{500}{1520} + 100 \cdot \frac{20}{1520} = \frac{37000}{1520} \approx \$24.34$$

The result is identical to the weighted average computed by multiplying prices by their frequencies.

Another advantage of using relative frequencies is that the sum of the relative frequencies always equals 1 since each relative frequency is a percent of the number of tickets available.

A spreadsheet or other software can calculate the weighted average using relative frequencies.

Activity

Use software or a calculator to compute the mean of the Wacky Widget salaries as you would a weighted average. A spreadsheet and calculation split-screen are shown for one calculator. With other technology, your work may look different. **See margin.**

Step 1 Enter each of the eight salary levels in column A.

Step 2 Enter the corresponding frequencies in column B.

18   Exploring Data

Additional Answers

Activity

Steps 1–7: See the Additional Answers section at the back of the book.

5. There are two employees with salaries of $90,000 and four people with salaries of $65,000.

6a. mean = $56,428.57; median = $50,000

6b. The mean decreased by about $21,571.43 and the median decreased by $15,000.

6c. mean

8. There are 27 terms in the sum, and 27 is the subscript of the final subscripted variable, x_{27}.

Step 3 In column C, compute the product of each salary level and its corresponding frequency.

Step 4 Compute the sums of the data in columns B and C. The SUM function can be used in the spreadsheet. In cell B9, type `=SUM(B1:B8)`. Enter a corresponding function in C9 or use summation notation on the calculation screen as shown at the right.

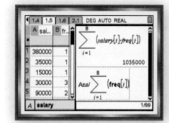

Step 5 Compute the mean using cells C9 and B9. Put the formula in cell C10.

Step 6 Compute the relative frequency of each salary. Confirm the mean using relative frequencies.

Step 7 If everyone at Wacky Widget gets a $5,000 raise, what is the new mean salary? Justify your answer using the spreadsheet or algebra.

Questions

COVERING THE IDEAS

1. What two statistics are considered measures of central tendency?

2. Express the mean of the set {3, 5, 7, 13, 17, 19} using sigma notation.

3. What is a weighted average?

4. Explain the difference between frequency and relative frequency.

In 5–7, refer to Guided Example 1 and the Activity. 5–6. See margin.

5. In one computation of the mean, why can 90 be multiplied by 2 and 65 be multiplied by 4?

6. Consider the salaries of all employees except the CEO.
   a. Find the mean and median of the salaries.
   b. Compare your answers to those in the solution on page 14. By how much has each changed?
   c. In general, which is more affected by extreme values, the mean or the median?

7. A new Parts Worker is hired. **7a.** $\frac{3}{16}$
   a. What is the new relative frequency of the Parts Worker salary?
   b. What is the new mean salary? **$75,000**
   c. What is the new median salary? **$50,000**

8. What does the number 27 indicate in the expression $\sum_{i=1}^{27} x_i$? **See margin.**

9. Write an expanded expression for $\sum_{i=4}^{8} x_i$. $x_4 + x_5 + x_6 + x_7 + x_8$

10. One teacher computes semester grades as follows: 1 grading period (GP) is equivalent to 2 semester tests (ST). One semester contains 3 grading periods and 1 semester test. Elliott's grades are as follows: GP 1: 65; GP 2: 80; GP 3: 90; ST 1: 87. What is Elliott's semester grade? **about 79.6**

1. mean and median

2. mean $= \frac{1}{6}\sum_{i=1}^{6} x_i$ where x_i is an element in the set

3. A weighted average is an average calculated when some elements in the set are assigned a larger or smaller weight.

4. The frequency of a value is the number of times some category occurs, whereas the relative frequency is the ratio of the frequency of that category to the total frequency in all categories.

Centers of Data and Weighted Averages **19**

Extension

Other variables can be used for the index, especially when each term in a list can be described algebraically. Also, the index variable can start and stop at any integer values. Consider the following.

$\sum_{j=-1}^{2} (j + 5) = (-1 + 5) + (0 + 5) + (1 + 5) + (2 + 5) = 4 + 5 + 6 + 7$

$\sum_{k=7}^{9} 3k = 3(7) + 3(8) + 3(9) = 21 + 24 + 27$

What sum does $\sum_{n=12}^{16} 2n$ represent?

$2(12) + 2(13) + 2(14) + 2(15) + 2(16) = 24 + 26 + 28 + 30 + 32$

Notes on the Lesson

Using relative frequencies to calculate weighted averages Emphasize that the bar graphs for frequencies (before Example 4) and relative frequencies (in Example 4) are identical except for the scale.

Example 4 Why is $24.34 called a weighted average?

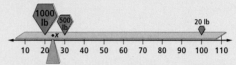

Think of the number line above as a board balanced at a pivot with coordinate x. The sum of the products of each weight and its distance from the pivot on each side must be equal. So x must satisfy the equation $(x - 20)1000 = (30 - x)500 + (100 - x)20$. Therefore $x = 24.34$

Activity This activity, rather easy using a spreadsheet program such as Excel or a calculator such as the TI-NSpire, will provide an indication of how technology-savvy your students are.

3 Assignment

Recommended Assignment

- Questions 1–12
- • Questions 13–24
- • Question 25 (extra credit)
- Reading Lesson 1-3
- (Questions 1–10)

1-2 Lesson Master

Questions on SPUR Objectives
See Student Edition pages 72–77 for objectives.

SKILLS Objective A

1. Use the data set {2, 3, 5, 8, 13, 21, 34, 55, 89}. Find each statistic.
   a. range **87** b. median **13** c. mean $\frac{230}{9} \approx 25.6$

2. The monthly rainfall in Orlando, Florida during 2005 is given in inches at the right. Find each statistic.
   a. median **3.32"**
   b. mean **about 4.53"**
   c. range **13.77"**

Jan	2.44	July	5.77
Feb	1.79	Aug	4.98
March	5.36	Sept	2.65
April	1.12	Oct	8.44
May	3.99	Nov	1.09
June	14.86	Dec	1.82

Source: City of Orlando

SKILLS Objective B

3. A person made the following purchases of stock from time to time.

Shares	5,000	10,000	7,500	6,000	11,000	8,000	10,000	5,000
Price per Share ($)	49.25	57.50	62.25	82.50	71.00	73.25	77.75	87.25

Calculate the average cost per share. $\approx$ **$69.82**

4. Ms. Field counts chapter tests as 40% of a student's grade, homework as 20%, quizzes and class work as 20%, and final exams as 20%. Lydia has an average of 89 before the final. What score must she get correct on the final to bring her grade up to 90? **94**

5. Kyle's college computes grade point averages (GPA) by assigning points for grades; A = 4.0, B+ = 3.5, B = 3.0, C+ = 2.5, C = 2.0, D = 1.0, and F = 0. It then weights the grades by the number of semester hours for each course. Compute Kyle's semester GPA based on the report at the right. $\approx$ **3.12**

Course	Grade	Hours
Writing	B+	2
Biology	C+	6
French II	A	4
Calculus	B	5

6. Mr. Vestas sells electricity from a wind turbine to his local utility. He receives 3¢ per kilowatt hour for the first 500 kilowatt hours, 2¢ per kilowatt hour for the next 1000 kilowatt hours, and 1¢ per kilowatt hour for each kilowatt hour thereafter. Mr. Vestas sold 1800 kilowatt hours last month. What was the average price per kilowatt hour the utility paid to Mr. Vestas last month, rounded to the nearest hundredth of a cent? **2.11¢**

7. The mean average monthly rainfall in Orlando, Florida for the first 5 months of 2005 was 2.94", while the mean average rainfall for the last 7 months was 5.66". Compute the weighted average monthly rainfall in Orlando for 2005. $\approx$ **4.53"**

158 *Functions, Statistics and Trigonometry*

Notes on the Questions

Question 11 Mr. Maestro is, of course, a music teacher. We assume students have seen dotplots; they are in UCSMP *Everyday Mathematics* beginning in Grade 1.

Question 12 Note that a bar graph of the relative frequencies would be quite similar in shape to the dotplot.

Questions 13–15 Notice that these are weighted average situations not involving frequencies or relative frequencies.

Questions 16 and 17 These questions are important in gaining the ability to think of the $\sum$-notation as representing a single quantity and not merely a direction to add.

[handwritten notes:] 14 a. $\frac{\$}{sh} = \frac{29176}{2100} \frac{\text{total cost}}{\text{\# of shares}} = 13.89$ 2100 111.77

b. $\frac{26876}{2100} = 12.80$ 1389 − 12.80 = $1.09

In 11 and 12, use the dotplot at the right, which shows the distribution of the number of siblings of the students in Mr. Maestro's homeroom.

11. a. How many students are in Mr. Maestro's homeroom? **28**
    b. How many students have no siblings? **4**
    c. Write a numerical expression for the mean number of siblings per student. Use your expression to calculate the mean number of siblings per student. **See margin.**

12. a. Give the relative frequencies of 0, 1, 2, 3, 4, 5, 6, and 7 siblings in Mr. Maestro's homeroom.
    b. Use the relative frequencies to calculate the mean number of siblings per student. **See margin.**

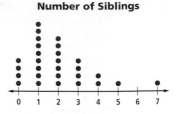

Number of Siblings

APPLYING THE MATHEMATICS

13. A science fair judge rates projects using the weighting scale shown at the right. Brendan finds out that each category can receive a rating of between 0 and 10. If he received a 7 in visual, an 8 in content and a weighted score of about 7.92, what was his score in sources to the nearest digit? **about 9**

Category	Weight
Visual	4
Content	5
Sources	3

14. Betty bought shares of Statco stock from time to time at various prices as shown below. That is, she bought 300 shares at $14.23, 200 shares at $11.55, and so on.

Number of Shares	300	200	500	100	400	200	100	300
Price ($)	14.23	11.55	12.48	13.92	16.03	15.45	14.85	13.26

[handwritten: 10.28]

[handwritten margin: 7.92 $\frac{3x + 4 \cdot 7 + 5 \cdot 8}{12}$]

a. What is Betty's average cost per share of Statco stock? **about $13.89**
b. If Betty had purchased 400 shares at $10.28 instead of $16.03, how much lower would her average cost per share have been? **about $1.09 lower**

15. Mrs. Dalloway weights the unit grades of the students in her math classes as shown in the circle graph on the right. Gyan's scores were 78 on the test, 85 on homework, and 92 in participation.

    a. What is Gyan's unit grade in Mrs. Dalloway's class? **80.45**
    b. What would Gyan's unit grade be if the three categories were equally weighted? **85**

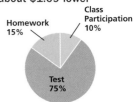

16. The stemplot at the right displays the scores of 24 students on a chemistry quiz. The first row stands for scores of 34 and 39. No student had a score in the 40s or 50s. The highest score obtained by any student was 98. **16a.–c. See margin.**

    a. What does the 7 in the row with a stem of 8 stand for?
    b. Let x_i be the score of the ith student. If the stemplot order is followed, $x_1 = 34$, $x_2 = 39$, ..., and $x_{24} = 98$. Find $\sum_{i=1}^{24} x_i$.
    c. Find $\frac{1}{24}\sum_{i=1}^{24} x_i$ and identify what you have calculated.
    d. What is the median quiz score? **81**
    e. What is the mode quiz score? **75**

stems	leaves
3	4 9
4	
5	
6	2 8
7	0 5 5 5 6 8 8
8	0 2 4 4 5 5 7
9	0 3 4 5 8 8

Additional Answers

11c. $\frac{0(4) + 1(9) + 2(7) + 3(4) + 4(2) + 5(1) + 7(1)}{28} = 1.96$

12a. $\frac{4}{28}, \frac{9}{28}, \frac{7}{28}, \frac{4}{28}, \frac{2}{28}, \frac{1}{28}, \frac{0}{28}, \frac{1}{28}$

12b. $\left(\frac{4}{28} \cdot 0\right) + \left(\frac{9}{28} \cdot 1\right) + \left(\frac{7}{28} \cdot 2\right) + \left(\frac{4}{28} \cdot 3\right) +$
$\left(\frac{2}{28} \cdot 4\right) + \left(\frac{1}{28} \cdot 5\right) + \left(\frac{0}{28} \cdot 6\right) + \left(\frac{1}{28} \cdot 7\right)$
$= \frac{55}{28} = 1.96$

16a. a score of 87

16b. 1,885

16c. about 78.5; the class average

17. Consider $\sum_{i=1}^{100}(x_i + 2)$ and $\sum_{i=1}^{100}x_i + 2$, where x_i is a positive number. Which expression has the greater value? By how much?

17. $\sum_{i=1}^{100}(x_i + 2)$, by 198

18. A bowler has averaged 164 for the first 21 games of a 90-game season. What would the bowler have to average for the rest of the season to bring his 90-game average score up to 170? **about 171.8**

19. The mean of a set of n numbers is 15. If the numbers 12 and 24 are added to the set, the mean is 16. What is n? **$n = 4$**

20. The cost to produce and deliver gasoline to consumers is displayed in the stacked bar graph at the right. **See margin.**

    a. What is the current price per gallon of gas at a gasoline station near where you live?

    b. If a person fills a tank with 12 gallons of gas, how much will be paid for marketing and distributing?

    c. If refinery costs increase by 50% but is still only 10% of the entire cost, by what percent should the total cost increase?

    d. Which should affect gas price more, a 10% tax increase or a 5% increase in the price of crude oil? Justify your answer.

What We Pay For in a Gallon of Regular Gasoline (April 2008)

Taxes 11%
Distribution & Marketing 6%
Refining 10%
Crude Oil 73%

Source: Energy Information Administration

REVIEW

In 21–23, use the table at the right below to answer the following questions for 2001. (Lesson 1-1) **See margin.**

21. About how many Black, non-Hispanic children used computers at home?

22. About how many American Indian, non-Hispanic children used computers at school?

23. What percentage of Asian, non-Hispanic children did not use computers at school?

24. **Skill Sequence** Rewrite each expression, assuming denominators do not equal zero. (**Previous Course**)

    a. $\frac{16x - x}{3x}$ **5**   b. $\frac{27y + 18y}{3y + 6y}$ **5**   c. $\frac{27z + 18}{3z + 6}$ **$\frac{9z + 6}{z + 2}$**

Computer and Internet Use by Children and Adolescents: 2001

Race/Ethnicity	Number of Children (1,000)	Percent using computers at school	Percent using computers at home
White, non-Hispanic	33,433	83.5	76.9
Black, non-Hispanic	8,275	79.8	41.0
Hispanic	8,400	71.8	40.6
Asian, non-Hispanic	2,268	76.1	75.7
American Indian, non-Hispanic	637	83.0	54.1

Source: Statistical Abstract of the United States, 2004-2005

EXPLORATION

25. Find out how weighted averages are referred to in one of the following areas. A suggestion is indicated in parentheses for each area. If you can find an example of the computation, check to see whether it matches the use of weighted average in this lesson.

    investing (average interest rate) **See margin.**
    chemistry (relative atomic mass)
    government (poverty index)
    sports (slugging percentage in baseball)

QUIZ YOURSELF ANSWERS

1. $65,000

2. $\sum_{i=11}^{15}x_i$

Question 18 This question can be solved either using arithmetic or algebra. To use algebra, think either

$21 \cdot 164 + 69 \cdot x = 90 \cdot 170$ or think

mean $= \dfrac{21 \cdot 164 + 69 \cdot x}{90} = 170$, and

solve for x. The first equation comes from applying the theorem that the product of the mean of a set of numbers and the number of numbers in the set is the sum of the numbers.

Question 19 This is a weighted average with frequencies.

4 Wrap-Up

Ongoing Assessment

Have students work with a partner to make up a data set consisting of five temperatures for which the mean is positive and the median is negative. **Answers vary. Sample: –5°, –3°, –2°, 6°, 9°; Students should demonstrate understanding of mean and median.**

Project Update

Project 4, *Graphing and Interpreting Statistical Data*, Project 5, *Class Survey*, and Project 6, *The Disputed Federalist Papers*, on page 68 relate to the content of this lesson.

Additional Answers

20a. Answers vary. Sample: $4.29

20b. Answers vary. Sample: about $3.09

20c. 5%

20d. Answers vary. Sample: A 10% tax increase would be an increase of about $0.05 and a 5% crude oil price increase would be an increase of about $0.16, so the 5% increase in the price of crude oil affects the gas price more.

21. 3,392,750

22. 528,710

23. 23.9%

25. Answers vary. Sample: In baseball, the slugging percentage is calculated as total bases earned divided by total number of at-bats. This means that a triple will count for 3 while a single will count only as 1. Although this is referred to as a weighted average, in fact, it is an arithmetic mean.

Lesson 1-3

GOAL

Examine distributions as a whole using histograms.

SPUR Objective

H Read, interpret, and draw histograms and population pyramids from data.

Materials/Resources

· Lesson Master 1–3
· Resource Masters 8–12
· Quiz 1
· Statistics utility

HOMEWORK
• Option 1
• Questions 1–10   **• Option 2**
• • Questions 11–21
• • Question 22 (extra credit)
• Reading Lesson 1-4
• Covering the Ideas 1-4
(Questions 1–6)

Local Standards

1 | Warm-Up

In 2000, in Columbus, Ohio, the existing houses in the city had been built at the following times:

1939 or earlier:	454
1940 to 1949:	511
1950 to 1959:	3,311
1960 to 1969:	4,258
1970 to 1979:	4,113
1980 to 1989:	2,612
1990 to 1994:	2,184
1995 to 1998:	2,382
1999 to March 2000:	1,377

Source: http://www.city-data.com/xips/43228.html.

a. In what decade was the median house in age built? **1970–1979**

b. What percent of the houses in Columbus in 2000 were more than 40 years old? **20.2%**

Lesson 1-3   Creating and Using Histograms

▶ **BIG IDEA**   Histograms display data and show how frequently values occur.

Joint session of Congress on January 8, 2009, to tally electoral votes

The number of representatives that each state has in the U.S. Congress depends on the population of the state. Below are the numbers of representatives from each of the 50 states in the 110th Congress (2007–2009).

```
7   7   2   4   2   1   3   5   1  11   1   5   5   3  53  13   9
6  15   3  29   5   9   9   4   1   2   7   8   3   8   4  13  18
13 19  32   8   8  25  19  10   9   2   1   2   3   6   1   1
```

This data set can be turned into a *distribution* by finding the frequency of each data value. A **distribution** is a function whose values are the frequencies, relative frequencies, or probabilities of mutually exclusive (non-overlapping) events. By graphing a distribution, you may see features of the data that are hard to see in a table. One important type of graph is a **histogram**, which is a special type of bar graph. A histogram breaks the range of a numerical variable into non-overlapping intervals of equal width, which are called **bins**. **Frequency histograms** display the number of values that fall into each interval. **Relative frequency histograms** display the percent of values that fall into each interval.

Two histograms showing the congressional data are on the next page. The histogram on the left shows frequency; the one on the right shows relative frequency.

Vocabulary

distribution
histogram
bins
frequency histograms
relative frequency histograms
skewed
symmetric
population pyramid

Mental Math

a. How many thousands are in 1 billion? **1 million**

b. How many millions are in 1 trillion? **1 million**

Background

This lesson deals with distributions and histograms. We assume that students have seen histograms, but the word *distribution* may be new. Technically, a statistical distribution is a *relation*, that is, a set of ordered pairs whose independent variable is a member of a population we are studying and whose dependent variable is a variable (in the statistical sense) we wish to study. For instance, if we speak of the distribution of test scores, the values of the independent variable are the test-takers and the values of the dependent variable are their scores.

Analyzing histograms A distribution that is skewed is unbalanced. Some books use the terms "skewed right" and "skewed left" or "right-skewed" and "left-skewed." We tried these terms in our field trials and found them to be confusing. It is much easier to understand when we say "there is a tail to the right" or "to the left."

We chose to use bins of width 5 and to make each interval include its left endpoint but not its right. For instance, on each graph the leftmost two intervals are $0 \leq x < 5$ and $5 \leq x < 10$, so a state with exactly 5 representatives is recorded in the second bar from the left.

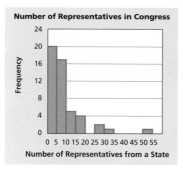

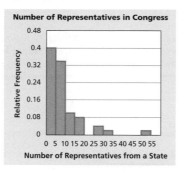

Example 1

Refer to the histograms on congressional data.

a. About how many states have 15 to 19 representatives?

b. What percent of states have 20 or more representatives?

c. In what bin does the median number of representatives fall among the 50 states?

Solution

a. Use the frequency histogram above on the left. Read the height of the bar spanning $15 \leq x < 20$. **Four states have from 15 to 19 representatives.**

b. To find the *percent* of the states rather than the *number* of states, use the relative frequency graph. Read the bars to right of $x = 20$.
$0.04 + 0.02 + 0.02 = 0.08$. **So 8% of the states have 20 or more representatives in Congress.**

c. When the 50 values are rank-ordered, the median is between the 25th and 26th values. From the frequency histogram, we conclude that there are 20 states with fewer than 5 representatives and 17 with between 5 and 10 representatives. **So the 25th and 26th values are between 5 and 10, and the median must be in the bin between 5 and 10.**

Drawing a Histogram

To make a histogram, first organize the data into non-overlapping intervals of equal width. Choosing the bin width is a matter of judgment. There is usually not a single best size. Generally, choosing 5 to 10 intervals is about right for a histogram. Too few bins will lump all the data together; too many will result in only a few numbers in each bin.

Creating and Using Histograms   **23**

c. Indicate two problems you would have if you were to make a histogram with these data?
The category "1939 or earlier" does not have a definite interval of time; the decade of the 1990s has been split, making it seem as if there were fewer houses from that decade than was the case.

2 Teaching

Notes on the Lesson

The text states that graphing a distribution may allow you to see features of the data that are hard to see in a table. You may wish to have a brief discussion of the types of features of a data set that may be easier to see in a graph such as a histogram.

Additional Example

Example 1 Use the histograms on congressional data for the following questions.

a. About how many states have 5 to 14 representatives?
17 + 5 = 22 states

b. What percent of states have fewer than 15 representatives?
0.1 + 0.34 + 0.4 = 0.84, 84%

c. Look at the raw data set which appears before the histograms. Are you surprised that the bar spanning $0 \leq x < 5$ is the tallest? Why or why not?
Answers vary. This should not be a surprise as the numbers 1, 2, 3, and 4 seem to dominate the distribution. The mode is 1.

Population Pyramids These double histograms receive their name from the shape they used to have in most countries, like that for India in 2010 in Question 16, in which there were significant numbers of deaths at all ages, so each side of the graph resembled the steps of a pyramid. Today, because deaths from childhood diseases have been greatly reduced in many countries, the graphs look more like that for the U.S. in 1980 in Example 2, where differences are due to numbers of births not to numbers of deaths.

1-3

Notes on the Lesson

Activity This Activity shows the effects of changing the bin width on a histogram.

Activity

Step 2:

Daily High Temperatures in Lincoln, Nebraska one March

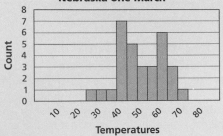

Step 3:

Daily High Temperatures in Lincoln, Nebraska one March

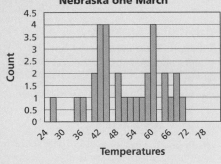

Because the bin size is so small, the labels are difficult to read for specific bars in the middle. For this reason it is important to choose reasonable size bin widths when making histograms.

Step 4:

Daily High Temperatures in Lincoln, Nebraska one March

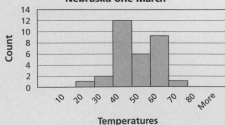

This histogram is the least detailed with too few bars. The histogram with a bin width of **5** is the best because it offers the most information without giving unnecessary detail.

Second, count the number of observations per bin and record the results in a table that gives the frequency or relative frequency for each of the bins created.

Finally, draw the histogram by first marking the horizontal axis to show the endpoints of the bins and marking the vertical axis to show the frequencies (or relative frequencies). Then, for each interval, draw a bar to represent the frequency. Unlike other bar graphs, histograms are drawn with no gaps between bars unless an interval is empty, in which case its bar has height 0. In the Activity you will make a histogram using technology.

Activity

Below are the daily high temperatures in March one year in Lincoln, Nebraska.

69, 60, 34, 41, 36, 44, 27, 45, 43, 49, 71, 67, 64, 54, 43, 40, 42, 58, 61, 68, 56, 45, 45, 64, 61, 60, 49, 51, 58, 53, 42

Step 1 Enter the temperatures into a statistical package or spreadsheet.

Step 2 Use the technology to make a histogram, using 5 as the bin width. Label your axes as shown. **2–5. See margin.**

Step 3 Change the bin width from 5 to 2. How does this affect the graph?

Step 4 Change the bin width from 2 to 10. How does this affect the graph? Which of the three bin widths (2, 5, or 10) gives the best description of the data?

Step 5 Return the bin width back to 5. Adjust the settings on your technology so that the vertical axis displays relative frequency rather than frequency. In what ways is this graph different from the one in Step 2?

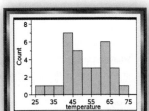

Analyzing Histograms

Histograms help you to see features of a data set that are hard to capture from a table. The graphs shown here illustrate three different shapes that are common. Histogram (A) at the right shows a **skewed** distribution. It has a cluster of high temperatures on the right side of the graph. Histogram (B) on the next page also shows a skewed distribution, but it tapers off toward the right end to form a *tail*. Histogram (C) is close to being **symmetric**, with two sides that are approximately the same shape. So, to describe the shape of a distribution, consider the following questions:

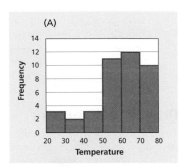
(A)

- Is the distribution skewed?
- Does the distribution have a tail? If so, at what end?
- Is the distribution symmetric?

24 Exploring Data

Activity

Step 5:

Daily High Temperatures in Lincoln, Nebraska one March

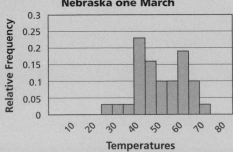

The graph looks the same; only the vertical axis has a different scale.

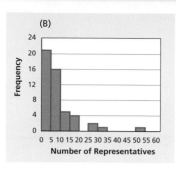

(B)

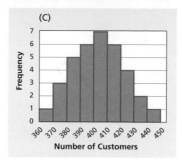

(C)

Population Pyramids

Demographers use histograms to analyze populations. One display is a double histogram called a *population pyramid*. Two examples of population pyramids are shown below.

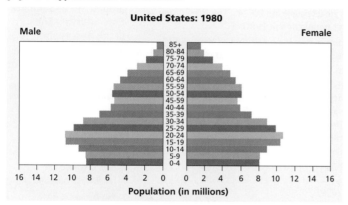

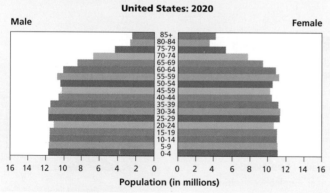

Source: U.S. Census Bureau, International Data Base

Creating and Using Histograms   **25**

Notes on the Lesson

Shapes of distributions You might take each distribution pictured in the lesson and ask whether it fits any of the special types of distribution shapes, and if it is skewed or not, and if it has a tail or not. Sometimes the answers are not definitive. Here are our opinions.

Number of Representatives (frequency)	skewed, tail to the right
Number of Representatives (relative frequency)	skewed, tail to the right
Temperature	uniform or perhaps tail to the left
Number of Customers	symmetric
Question 1	symmetric, slight tail to the right
Questions 4–8	skewed, tail to the left
Questions 9–10	symmetric

Additional Example

Example 2 Use the population pyramids in the lesson to answer the following questions.

a. In 1980, which age group had the least population? Give an estimate of this population. age 85+; 1 million males + 1.5 million females ≈ 2.5 million people age 85+

b. In 2020, which group is projected to have the least population? Give an estimate of this population. age 80–84; 2.75 million males + 3.75 million females ≈ 6.5 million people age 80–84

c. Select an age group from 1980; In which age group would this segment of the population appear in the year 2020? Now, compare these two bars – are they the same length or different? If they are different, give one reason to account for this difference. Answers vary. If 2020 bar is shorter, the population may have decreased due to deaths or emigration. If 2020 bar is longer, population may have increased due to immigration (*not* births).

3 Assignment

Recommended Assignment

- Questions 1–10
- • Questions 11–21
- • Question 22 (extra credit)
- • Reading Lesson 1-4
- • Covering the Ideas 1-4
  (Questions 1–6)

Notes on the Questions

We suggest going through the questions in order to ensure all concepts of the lesson have been covered.

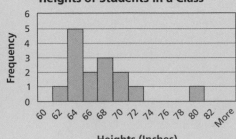

A **population pyramid** is made from two separate histograms that have been rotated 90°. The bin intervals are placed along a central vertical axis and the frequencies are on the horizontal axis. The examples on the previous page show age distributions for men and women. The first is from actual U.S. Census Bureau data. The second is a *projection*, based on what demographers expect to happen.

GUIDED

Example 2

Refer to the population pyramids on the previous page.

a. For 1980, estimate which age group had the greatest population.

b. For 2020, compare the distribution for men with the one for women. In what age groups are they most different?

c. Compare the 1980 and 2020 population pyramids. Describe three significant differences.

Solution

a. For 1980, the longest bars are for people age 20-24. The 20-24 age group had the greatest population in 1980.

b. There appears to be about the same number of men and women in most age brackets. Starting at about age __?__, there are clearly more females than males. This difference is very pronounced for the 85+ age group. **60–64**

c. First, the 1980 population pyramid has a bulge in the 15 to __?__ age range that is not as pronounced in the 2020 pyramid. Second, more people are projected to live longer in 2020. In 1980 there are __?__ million people 80 or older, while in 2020 there are __?__ million over 80 years old. Third, the total population in __?__ is bigger than the population in __?__.

🛑 **See Quiz Yourself at the right.**

Questions

COVERING THE IDEAS

In 1 and 2, the graph at the right shows the lengths of songs that Jessie has stored on an MP3 player.

1. Use two to three sentences to describe the distribution.

2. For this histogram, the bin width is 0.5. About how high would the leftmost bar be if the bin width were 1? **4**

3. Here is a list of heights (in inches) of 15 students:
   73, 66, $63\frac{3}{4}$, $68\frac{3}{4}$, 70, 69, 65, 71, 68, $80\frac{1}{2}$, 64, 67, 65, 64, $64\frac{1}{2}$.
   a. Draw a histogram of the data. **See margin.**
   b. What bin width did you use? ~~Explain your choice.~~

26   Exploring Data

Questions

1. Answers vary. Sample:The graph is sharply concentrated around the 2–3 minute time interval. The graph also seems skewed with a tail on the right.

▶ **QUIZ YOURSELF**

According to the 1980 population pyramid on the previous page, for preschool children (age 0–4), are the numbers of boys and girls equal?

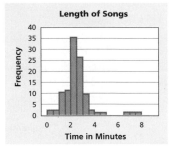

Length of Songs

Additional Answers

3a.

Heights of Students in a Class

3b. Answers vary. Sample: A bin width of 2 was used because it shows trends in the data accurately.

In 4–8, use the histogram at the right of the scores of students taking the SAT Literature Subject Test of the College Entrance Examination Board in 2007.

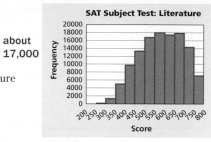

SAT Subject Test: Literature

Source: The College Board

4. About how many students scored from 500 to 549? **about 17,000**

5. What is the bin width? **50**

6. Approximately how many students took the Literature exam in 2007? **about 120,000**

7. About what percent of the students scored 700 or better? **about 18%**

8. In what interval is the median score? **550–599**

In 9 and 10, refer to the graphs of heights of African American males.

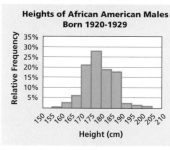

Heights of African American Males Born 1920-1929

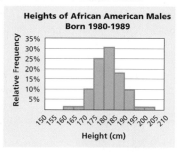

Heights of African American Males Born 1980-1989

Source: National Center for Health Statistics

9. The median height of African American males born 1920–1929 is in the 175 ≤ height < 180 cm interval and the median height of African American males born 1980–1989 is in the 180 ≤ height < 185 cm interval. The second group has the larger median height.

9. Use the histograms to estimate which bin contains the median height for each group of African American males. Which group has the larger median height?

10. a. About what percent of African American males born in 1920–1929 were at least 190 cm (about 6'3") tall? **See margin.**
    b. About what percent of African American males born in 1980–1989 were that tall?

APPLYING THE MATHEMATICS

11. At the right are some data regarding accidental deaths in the U.S. in 2004.
    a. Create a histogram of the data on drowning. **See margin**
    b. At what ages is there the highest risk of drowning?
    c. What is likely to make the histogram in Part a misleading?

In 12–14, describe a possible shape for the distribution of the variable. Explain your reasoning. **12–14. See margin.**

12. the mint dates of U.S pennies that are in a store's cash register

13. the salaries of employees in a large company

14. the scores on an easy test.

Age	Drownings
under 1 yr.	62
1–4	430
5–14	269
15–24	574
25–34	385
35–44	435

Source: National Safety Council

Notes on the Questions

Question 12 What do students think about the distributions of dates of coins? You might have students tell you the dates on the coins in their pockets, and then create a histogram from that data.

Questions 13 and 14 These questions can elicit interesting discussions.

Additional Answers

10a. About 6% of African American males born 1920-1929 were at least 190 cm tall.

10b. About 14% of African American males born 1980-1989 were at least 190 cm tall.

12 Answers vary. Sample: This graph might be skewed with a left tail because there are fewer old pennies around today.

13. Answers vary. Sample: This graph might be skewed with a right tail because most workers earn at the low end of a payroll scale. There will likely be a long, high-paid tail.

14. Answers vary. Sample: This graph might be skewed with a left tail since most scores will clump near the maximum value with a tail towards lower scores.

Additional Answers

11a.

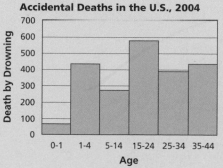

Accidental Deaths in the U.S., 2004

11b. between ages 1–4 because the number of deaths per age is the greatest.

11c. The data is organized into bins that are not all the same size.

15. Cynthia and Ralph are playing a board game. Cynthia suspects that the die they are using is biased. She decides to test the die by rolling it 100 times and counting the number of times 1, 2, 3, 4, 5, or 6 occurs. A distribution of the outcomes of this experiment is shown at the right.

a. Use two sentences to describe the distribution.

b. About what percent of the time did a 1 show up? **about 48%**

c. Do you think that the die is fair? Justify your answer.

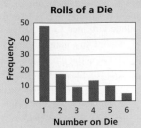

Rolls of a Die

15a. The distribution is skewed with a right tail. A roll of 1 is clearly favored.

15c. No; if the die is fair, then each number should have appeared about 17% of the time.

16. Suppose you are part of a committee to plan projects that will help India's population in the future. Using the population projections below, order these three developments in terms of importance, and explain why you have picked the order you made.

(1) Build more elementary and high schools.

(2) Stimulate development of factories and other workplaces.

(3) Build more trains and roads.

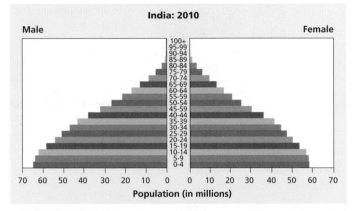

India: 2010

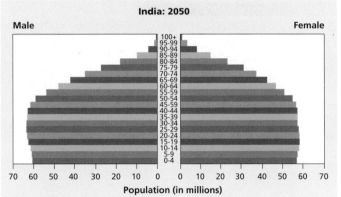

India: 2050

Source: U.S. Census Bureau, International Data Base

16. Answers vary. Sample: 3, 2, 1; the population of young people will not change much from now until 2050, so more schools do not need to be built immediately; however, creating jobs and fulfilling transportation needs are important soon since the 25 and older age groups will all grow significantly.

REVIEW

17. Monday through Friday a store averaged $2,100 a day in sales. On Saturday and Sunday the store took in $7,200 total in sales. What is the store's mean sales per day? (**Lesson 1-2**) **about $2,528.57**

18. In his Biology class, Mr. Boynton covered six chapters in the second semester. He gave two quizzes and a chapter test for each chapter, and a final at the end of the semester. Connie averaged 91 on the quizzes, 73 on the chapter tests, and 85 on the final.

  a. Mr. Boynton weights chapter tests twice as much as quizzes, and the final five times as much as each chapter test. Compute Connie's weighted average score in Biology. **about 82.88**

  b. What would Connie have had to score on the final in order to average at least 85 for the semester? (**Lesson 1-2**) **92.2**

19. If $\sum_{i=1}^{6} x_i = 15$, $\sum_{i=1}^{5} x_i = 20$, and $\dfrac{\sum_{i=1}^{7} x_i}{7} = 8$, find $x_6 \cdot x_7$. (**Lesson 1-2**) **-205**

20. Describe a situation in which the students in your school would be

  a. a sample.   **b.** a population. (**Lesson 1-1**)

21. Match the graphs to their equations. Do not use a calculator. (**Previous Course**)

a. 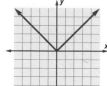 v

b. 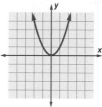 ii

c. 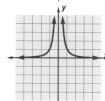 iv

d. 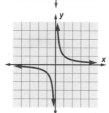 i

  i. $y = \frac{1}{x}$ **ii.** $y = x^2$ **iii.** $y = \sqrt{x}$ **iv.** $y = \frac{1}{x^2}$ **v.** $y = \sqrt{x^2}$

20. Answers vary. Samples are given.

20a. a study examining the average height of high school students in the US

20b. a study examining the average height of students in your high school

Creating and Using Histograms   **29**

Notes on the Questions
Question 17 Mr. Boynton was the biology teacher on the 1950s television series "Our Miss Brooks." Connie Brooks, the title character, was an English teacher at the school.

Question 18 This is a good question to test your students' understanding of sigma-notation.

Question 21 You should discuss students' answers to these questions.

22.

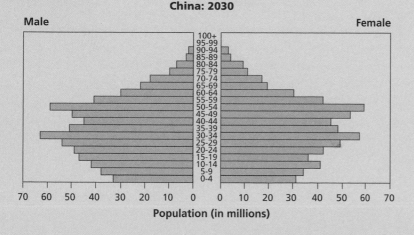

China: 2030

1-3

4) Wrap-Up

Ongoing Assessment

Have students work with a partner to complete two histograms for a set of class quiz results. Have one student draw a frequency histogram and the other a relative frequency histogram. Then have students compare their graphs, discuss the intervals they used, and correct each other's work. **Students should demonstrate that they can draw and interpret histograms.**

Administer Quiz 1 (or a quiz of your own) after students complete this lesson

Project Update

Project 1, *Automobile Survey*, Project 3, *Coin Circulation*, Project 4, *Graphing and Interpreting Statistical Data*, and Project 5, *Class Survey*, on pages 67 and 68 relate to the content of this lesson.

EXPLORATION

22. Since 1978, the People's Republic of China has had a policy that strongly encourages families to limit themselves to one child, or at most two children. In contrast, Russia is concerned about population decline and is encouraging larger families. The population pyramids below show U.S. Census Department projections for these countries in 2010. For each country make a hypothetical population pyramid for the year 2030 assuming that the government policies are successful. What long-term concerns are raised?

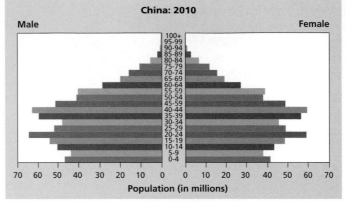

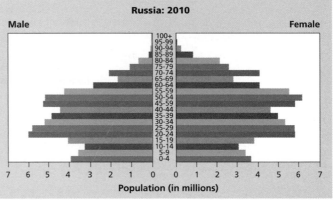

Source: U.S. Census Bureau, International Data Base

22. See margin for population pyramids. Answers vary. Sample: In the long term, China will need to be concerned with the ability of a smaller working-age population to provide health care and retirement security for a large aging population. On the other hand, Russia will need to be concerned about providing adequate education and employment opportunities for a young and expanding population.

QY ANSWERS

no

Additional Answers

22.

Russia: 2030

Male   Female

Population (in millions)

Lesson 1-4 Box Plots

▶ **BIG IDEA** Box plots are a way to display important aspects of a numerical distribution.

In this lesson you will see how a *box plot* provides a visual summary of a distribution. One advantage of a box plot is that it readily shows how the data are spread. Here is a data set of scores on an algebra test with five key numbers identified.

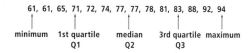

61, 61, 65, 71, 72, 74, 77, 77, 78, 81, 83, 88, 92, 94

minimum   1st quartile   median   3rd quartile   maximum
              Q1   Q2   Q3

These are the five key numbers that are shown on a box plot. Below is a box plot of the data above.

Scores on an Algebra Test

60 65 70 75 80 85 90 95

What does this plot tell us about the data? To answer that question, we must first introduce some vocabulary.

Quartiles

Box plots were invented in the 1970s by the statistician John Tukey. Five key numbers are used to create a box plot:

1. the **minimum**, the least value of the variable;
2. the **first** (or **lower**) **quartile** Q_1, the median of the numbers below the median of the distribution;
3. the **second quartile** Q_2, the median of the full distribution;
4. the **third** (or **upper**) **quartile** Q_3, the median of the numbers above the median of the distribution; and
5. the **maximum**, the largest value of the variable.

These numbers are called the **five-number summary** of a distribution.

Vocabulary

box plot, box-and-whiskers plot

minimum

first (lower) quartile

second quartile

third (upper) quartile

maximum

five-number summary

interquartile range (IQR)

whiskers

outlier

Mental Math

Five students took a make-up test in a class, scoring 83, 90, 82, 70, and 85. The teacher felt the test was hard and added 3 points to each student's score. What was the average of the scores after the 3 points were added?

85

Lesson 1-4

GOAL
Examine distributions as a whole using box plots.

SPUR Objectives

A Calculate measures of center and spread for data sets.

E Use statistics to draw conclusions about data.

I Read, interpret, and draw box plots from data.

Materials/Resources
· Lesson Master 1-4
· Resource Masters 13, 14, and 15

HOMEWORK
• **Option 1**
• Questions 1–6
• • Questions 7–14 • Option 2
• • Question 15 (extra credit)
• Reading Lesson 1-5
• Covering the Ideas 1-5 (Questions 1–5)

Local Standards

1 Warm-Up

In 1–4, think of the dots as representing numbers in order in a data set. For each set of dots, identify:

a. the median dot;

b. the median of the dots before the median;

c. the median of the dots after the median.

(Place a vertical bar on a dot if it is the median. Place a vertical bar between dots if the median is between two dots.)

1. ● ● ● ● ● ● ● ● ●
2. ● ● ● ● ● ● ● ● ● ●
3. ● ● ● ● ● ● ● ● ● ●
4. ● ● ● ● ● ● ● ● ● ● ● ●

Background

We assume that students have seen box plots before but need a thorough review.

Quartiles When a data set is ordered, the three quartiles split the data into four subsets whose size is as close as possible to one another.

Graphing and Analyzing Box Plots Which is correct, "box plots" (2 words) or "boxplots" (1 word). Neither is wrong. Both are in common use with about the same frequency. In this chapter we are not consistent; you will see both.

There are two ways in which box plots deal with outliers. Some box plots identify outliers with dots along the horizontal line of the box plot. Other box plots extend the segment to include all outliers. Some calculators follow one of these arrangements; some the other.

1-4

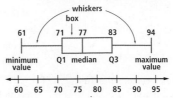

1. ● ●|● ● ●|● ●|● ●
2. ● ●|● ● ● ● ● ●|● ●
3. ● ● ● ● ● ●|● ● ● ●
4. ● ● ● ● ● ● ● ● ● ●

(Note: The answers to Parts a, b, and c are, respectively, the second quartile, the first quartile, and the third quartile of the data. All data sets follow one of these four patterns. Either 0, 1, 2, or 3 of the quartiles are members of the data set.)

2 Teaching

Notes on the Lesson

Quartiles You should be aware that some popular spreadsheet software use a different algorithm for computing quartiles. The resulting values for Q_1 and Q_3 may differ slightly from the ones that would be obtained by using the definitions given in this book. We have found this to be especially apparent in the case where the data set follows the pattern of Warm-Up 1, that is, 0 of the quartiles are members of the data set. You may wish to advise students to double-check the answers from their statistics application for Q_1 and Q_3.

Applets enabling students to move dots in a dot plot and see the effect on the box plot can be found on the internet. One such Web site is http://illuminations.nctm.org/activitydetail.aspx?ID=160

Using graphs to see outliers The idea of an outlier is defined in terms of the interquartile range (IQR). It is possible your students have never seen this statistic, which is the width of the interval containing the middle 50% of the data.

The diagram below shows how the numbers in a five-number summary are shown in a box plot. The difference $Q_3 - Q_1$ is called the **interquartile range**, or **IQR**. The IQR is the length of an interval in which you will find the middle 50% of the data. It is the length of the rectangle in the box plot.

Scores on an Algebra Test

The vertical segment in the rectangle marks the median of the distribution. The horizontal segments from the rectangle to the maximum and minimum are called **whiskers**. For this reason, a box plot sometimes is called a **box-and-whiskers plot**. Some statistics utilities also display tick marks at the end of the whiskers, as shown above.

GUIDED

Example 1

The data 29, 36, 37, 38, 40, 43, 45, 46, 47, 50 are the ages of the best actor Oscar winners from 1997 to 2006.

a. Give the five-number summary of these ages.

b. Draw the box plot.

Solution

a. There are __?__ numbers in the list. The minimum value of the data is __?__. The maximum value of the data is __?__. Recall that the median for an even number of ordered data is the mean of the middle numbers. These data have a median of $\frac{40 + 43}{2} = 41.5$. The first quartile, Q_1 is the median of the numbers below the distribution median. The first quartile is __?__. The third quartile, Q_3 is the median of the numbers above the median. The third quartile is __?__.

b. The box goes from Q_1 to Q_3, that is, from __?__ to __?__. The whiskers go from the minimum value __?__ to the maximum value __?__. Here is a plot.

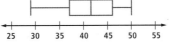

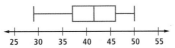

a. 10, 29, 50, 37, 46

b. 37, 46, 29, 50

STOP See Quiz Yourself at the right.

▶ **QUIZ YOURSELF**

Give the five number summary for the data set 12, 23, 23, 24, 34, 37.

32   Exploring Data

ENGLISH LEARNERS
Vocabulary Development

Be sure students do not confuse the terms *percent* and *percentile*, especially in situations involving test results. Emphasize that a score of 72% means that 72% of the questions were answered correctly. A score *s* that ranks in the 72nd percentile means that 72% of the test scores are less than or equal to *s*.

Discuss how on a very difficult exam, one could get a low score with a high percentile rank because so many students scored even

lower, while on an easy exam one might have a high score with a low percentile rank because so many students scored even higher.

Using Technology with Box Plots

You can use technology with a statistical application to find a five-number summary. Once a data set is entered into a spreadsheet, locate a menu choice for one-variable statistics calculations to show a variety of statistics, including the five-number summary. Most (but not all) technology with statistical applications can automatically generate a box plot. Below are screenshots showing the results using the age data from Guided Example 1. You will see the meanings of the symbols on the left screenshot below by the end of this chapter.

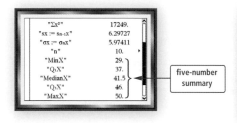

five-number summary

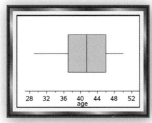

Using Graphs to See Outliers

Graphs can help you see data values that are extreme. The graph below is a histogram of the payrolls of the 30 Major League Baseball teams on opening day. Rounded to the nearest million dollars, total team payrolls were (in order) 24, 31, 37, 39, 52, 54, 58, 62, 67, 68, 69, 71, 71, 79, 82, 87, 88, 89, 90, 90, 94, 95, 100, 106, 108, 109, 109, 115, 143, and 190.

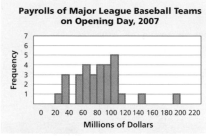

Source: USA Today

The histogram displays an extreme observation on the upper end (the payroll of the New York Yankees). Observations that are extreme are called *outliers*. But what do we mean by extreme? Is $190 million dollars an outlier? What about $143 million? A common criterion for identifying outliers is the $1.5 \times$ IQR criterion. Any number larger than $Q_3 + 1.5(\text{IQR})$ or smaller than $Q_1 - 1.5(\text{IQR})$ is considered an **outlier**.

Box Plots   33

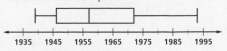

1-4

Notes on the Lesson

Comparing histograms and box plots
This is a useful exercise for developing intuition about shapes of distributions. You should be sure to discuss Example 3. You might ask students for contexts that might lead to the histograms and box plots here. Here are some possibilities:

Histogram A and Box Plot 2: A sample of 100 pedestrians in New York City asked at 4:00 p.m. how many meals they have had that day

Histogram B and Box Plot 3: A set of scores on an easy test.

Histogram C and Box Plot 1: Heights of students in the 10th grade in a school.

Additional Example

Example 2 Consider the data given in Example 1. Use the 1.5 × IQR criterion to determine if there are any outliers. There are no outliers in this data set.

Example 2

The five-number summary for the Major League Baseball payroll data (in millions of dollars) is: minimum = 24, Q_1 = 62, median = 84.5, Q_3 = 100, maximum = 190. Use the 1.5 × IQR criterion to determine if there are any outliers. If there are, identify them.

Solution
$$IQR = Q_3 - Q_1 = \underline{\ ?\ }\ \ 38$$
$$Q_3 + 1.5\,(IQR) = \underline{\ ?\ }\ \ 157$$
$$Q_1 - 1.5\,(IQR) = \underline{\ ?\ }\ \ 5$$

So, any payroll greater than $\underline{\ ?\ }$ is an outlier. **157**

Similarly, any payroll less than $\underline{\ ?\ }$ is an outlier. **5**

The New York Yankees payroll of $190 million is the only outlier.

At the right is a box plot of the Major League Baseball payroll data created by software that uses the 1.5 × IQR criterion. Typically, when the whiskers are drawn, they represent all the values except the outliers. Here the right whisker ends at $143 million, and the outlier $190 million is shown by a dot. However, when the five-number summary is calculated, all data (including outliers) are used.

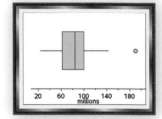

Comparing Histograms and Box Plots

A well-made histogram or a box plot can give information about the shape of a distribution and about extreme values. You can determine the general shape of one of these graphs from the shape of the other.

Example 3

Histograms and box plots of several distributions are shown below. Match the histograms with the box plots and explain your reasoning.

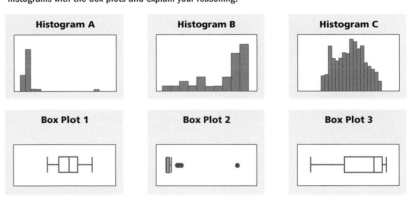

Solution In Histogram A, the extreme values on the upper end are outliers. So the histogram matches Box Plot 2.

In Histogram B, the long left tail on the histogram appears as a stretch of the lower 50% in the box plot. So it matches Box Plot 3.

Histogram C matches Box Plot 1. The histogram and box plot are both nearly symmetric.

Questions

COVERING THE IDEAS

1. **Multiple Choice** Which is not one of the numbers in the five-number summary for a set of data? **A**

   A mean   B median   C maximum   D minimum

2. The table at the right shows the mean student cost for room, board, and tuition in a public college for ten states in 2006-2007.
   a. Calculate the five-number summary for the data.
   b. Calculate the IQR for the data. **1,666**
   c. Use the 1.5 × IQR criterion to determine if any of the costs are outliers.

3. Create a box plot to fit this five-number summary. **See margin.**
   min = 45 $Q_1 = 56$ median = 66 $Q_3 = 71$ max = 87

4. In a box plot,
   a. about what percent of data should be less than Q_1?
   b. about what percent of data should fall between Q_1 and Q_3?
   c. about what percent of data should be greater than Q_3?

5. **Multiple Choice** A histogram of a distribution is shown at the right. Which of the three box plots below is a graph of this distribution? Justify your answer.

A
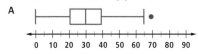

B
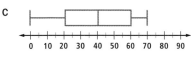

C
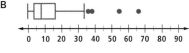

State	Cost ($)
Massachusetts	15,199
Delaware	15,201
Maryland	15,253
Illinois	15,373
Connecticut	15,457
Pennsylvania	16,263
New Hampshire	16,582
Ohio	16,919
Vermont	17,280
New Jersey	18,721

Source: 2007 Digest of Education Statistics

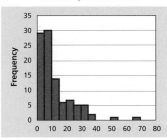

2a. minimum = 15,199; Q_1 = 15,253; median = 15,860; Q_3 = 16,919; maximum = 18,721

2c. See margin.

4a. About 25% of the data in a distribution will fall below the Q_1 value.

4b. About 50% of the data in a distribution will fall between the Q_1 value and the Q_3 value.

4c. About 25% of the data in a distribution will fall above the Q3 value.

5. B; Because the total count is 100, the median resides in the 5–10 bin. The only plot whose median is in this range is plot B.

Box Plots   35

---

③ Assignment

Recommended Assignment
- Questions 1–6
- • Questions 7–14
- • Question 15 (extra credit)
  - • Reading Lesson 1-5
  - • Covering the Ideas 1-5 (Questions 1–5)

Notes on the Questions
Question 5 This gets at the idea in Example 3.

Additional Answers

3.

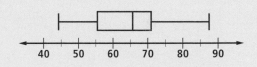

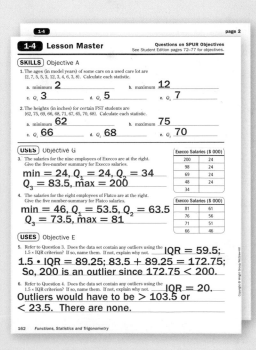

Notes on the Questions

Question 6 Here the answers can only be estimated from the box plot.

6. The following box plot displays data for the average monthly rainfall (measured in millimeters) at London Heathrow Airport between 1981 and 1991. Write the five number summary for the data. Identify outliers, if any exist. **minimum = 36; Q_1 = 44; median = 45; Q_3 = 55; maximum = 72; 72 is an outlier**

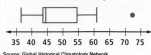

Average Rainfall at London Heathrow Airport

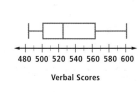

35 40 45 50 55 60 65 70 75

Source: Global Historical Climatology Network

APPLYING THE MATHEMATICS

7. The histogram and box plot below show the average 2003 SAT verbal scores for the 50 states plus Washington D.C.

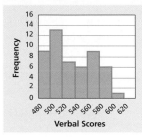

Verbal Scores

480 500 520 540 560 580 600

Verbal Scores

Source: The College Board

7a. Answers vary. Sample: the frequency of scores in each interval.

7b. Answers vary. Sample: the values of Q_1, the median, and Q_3.

a. What can you see in the histogram that you cannot see in the box plot?

b. What can you see in the box plot that you cannot see in the histogram?

8. On a 50-point history test, the median was 34 and Q_1 was 28. One student got a perfect paper and qualified as an outlier under the $1.5 \times$ IQR criterion.

a. What is the largest value Q_3 could be? **36**

b. What is the smallest value Q_3 could be? **34**

In 9 and 10, construct a set of 10 numbers whose box plot would have a shape similar to the given box plot. There are no outliers.

9.

Answers vary. Sample: {0, 0, 0, 0, 2, 2, 4, 4, 4, 8}

10.

Answers vary. Sample: {0, 0, 2, 2, 4, 4, 6, 6, 8, 8}

REVIEW

11. The graph at the right shows the distribution of the maximum waiting times in minutes of 500 customers to a telephone call center.

    a. How many customers had to wait at least 10 minutes before their call was answered? **about 53**

    b. What proportion of people were answered within 5 minutes? **about $\frac{100}{500}$ or $\frac{1}{5}$**

    c. What percent of people were answered after waiting between 5 and 10 minutes? **about $\frac{345}{500}$ or 69%**

    d. Describe the shape of the distribution and relate that to the situation. (**Lesson 1-3**)

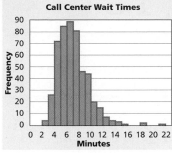

Call Center Wait Times

12. Nancy made a monthly investment in the shares of Mathco stock as shown below. That is, she bought 100 shares at $6.75, 300 shares at $7.25, and so on. (**Lesson 1-2**)

Shares	100	300	200	100	300	400	200	300	300
Cost per Share ($)	6.75	7.25	8.25	9.00	6.25	5.75	7.75	8.50	9.75

What is Nancy's average cost per share of Mathco stock?

13. At the college Grace attends, she receives grade points for each hour of class. An A+ is worth 4.3, and A is worth 4, an A- is worth 3.7, a B+ is worth 3.3, a B is worth 3, and so on. Grace has 5 hours of A, 8 hours of A-, and 3 hours of C+. (**Lesson 1-2**)

    a. What is Grace's grade point average without the 3 hours of C+?

    b. What is Grace's grade point average with the 3 hours of C+?

    c. How much lower is Grace's grade point average with the 3 hours of C+? **by about 0.28**

14. Written documents can sometimes be distinguished by the length of words used. A student, interested in how many letters are in the words English literature authors use, opened an Ernest Hemmingway novel to a random page and counted the frequency of word length for the first 250 words. Identify

    a. the population.   b. the sample.

    c. the variable of interest. (**Lesson 1-1**)

EXPLORATION

15. Suppose a data set has n elements with $n \geq 6$. As you know, if n is even, then the median of the set does not have to be an element of the set. For what values of n does the first quartile Q_1 not have to be an element of the set?

11d. Answers vary. Sample: The median wait time between 5 and 6 minutes. The range of wait times is about 19 minutes. The data is skewed with a tail on the right.

12. about $7.52

13a. about 3.82

13b. about 3.53

14a. all English literature

14b. the first 250 words of an Ernest Hemingway novel

14c. word length

15. When $n \geq 6$ and n is of the form $4k$ or $4k + 1$, where k is an integer, then Q_1 does not have to be in the set.

QY ANSWER

min = 12, Q_1 = 23,
median = 23.5,
Q_3 = 34, max = 37

4 Wrap-Up

Ongoing Assessment

Provide students with a data set of at least 20 values, such as quiz or test scores. Have them make a box plot for the data set and use the 1.5 × IQR criterion to determine if there are any outliers. **Students should demonstrate ability to draw a box plot for a data set and identify outliers.**

Project Update

Project 1, *Automobile Survey*, Project 4, *Graphing and Interpreting Statistical Data*, and Project 5, *Class Survey*, on pages 67 and 68 relate to the content of this lesson.

Lesson 1-5

Lesson 1-5

Cumulative Distributions

cumulative data

cumulative distribution

percentile, *p*th percentile

> ▶ **BIG IDEA** Cumulative distributions give the total number of values less than or equal to a particular value.

Meteorologists report rainfall in two different ways. On a day-to-day basis, rainfall affects our activities and even our mood, so the weather reports show how much rain falls each day. But in the long run, we also care about the *total* amount of rain to be sure that the soil and vegetation get enough moisture. So today's weather reports often include the total amount of precipitation that has fallen from January 1st through today. This total is an example of **cumulative data.** A function whose values are cumulative frequencies or cumulative relative frequencies is called a **cumulative distribution**.

Mental Math

Two sides of a triangle have lengths 80 and 55. What are all possible lengths of the third side?

Any number between 25 and 135.

Example 1

The table at the right and graph below show the normal precipitation in Los Angeles, California. The second column of the table shows the total, or cumulative, precipitation for the year up to and including the month. The graph is complete but some values in the table are missing.

a. Determine the missing values in the table.

b. Draw a bar graph of the cumulative precipitation by month.

c. When has half the yearly precipitation fallen?

d. When has three fourths fallen?

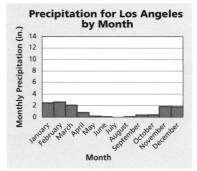

Precipitation for Los Angeles by Month

	Monthly Precipitation (inches)	Cumulative Precipitation (inches)
Jan	2.4	2.4
Feb	2.51	4.91
Mar	1.98	6.89
Apr	0.72	7.61
May	0.14	7.75
Jun	0.03	?
Jul	0.01	7.79
Aug	0.15	7.94
Sep	0.31	8.25
Oct	0.34	8.59
Nov	?	10.35
Dec	1.66	12.01

Source: National Climatic Data Center

Background

The two distributions pictured in Example 1 provide an excellent example not only of the difference between a frequency distribution and a cumulative frequency distribution, but also of the reasons a person might want each. This represents just one situation where accumulating some measure is meaningful.

Suppose a value f_i is associated with the number i. Then in a cumulative distribution, if $i < j$, then $f_i \leq f_j$. Significantly, if i can only be a nonnegative integer, then

$$f_k = \sum_{i=1}^{k-1} f_i .$$

A key aspect of a cumulative distribution is that it is an increasing function. That is, the graph either stays the same or goes up as you go to the right. In the symbolism of summation notation, if C_n is the cumulative value of the frequencies $f_1, f_2, ..., f_n$, then

$$\begin{cases} C_1 = f_1 \\ C_n = f_n + \sum_{i=1}^{n-1} f_i , n > 1 \end{cases}.$$

Lesson 1-5

GOAL

Introduce cumulative distributions and percentiles.

SPUR Objectives

D Describe relations between measures of center and spread.

J Calculate and draw line graphs of cumulative frequencies and cumulative relative frequencies from tables of frequencies.

Materials/Resources

· Lesson Master 1-5

· Resource Masters 16–19

· Spreadsheet application

HOMEWORK • Option 1
• Option 2

• Questions 1–5
• • Questions 6–17
• • Question 18 (extra credit)
  • Reading Lesson 1-6
  • Covering the Ideas 1-6
  (Questions 1–9)

Local Standards

1 ▶ Warm-Up

Suppose you have the 3rd highest score in a class of 25 on a test. In what percentile of the class are you under the definition on page 40? **23 students score less than or equal to you, so you are in the 92nd percentile.**

Solution

a. The numbers in the cumulative column are a *running total*, that is, the cumulative total amount of rainfall at the end of each month is the cumulative total from the previous month increased by the current month.

Cumulative June = June + Cumulative May =
0.03 + 7.75 = 7.78 inches.

Work backwards to find the value for November rainfall. Use an equation.

Cumulative November = November + Cumulative October
10.35 = November + 8.59
1.76 inches = November rainfall

b.

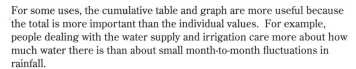

Cumulative Distribution of Precipitation for Los Angeles by Month

Notice that the bars get longer as the year progresses.

c. About 12 inches of precipitation falls in a year, so half the rain is 6 inches. This point is reached during March.

d. Three-quarters of 12 inches is 9 inches, which has usually fallen by the end of November.

For some uses, the cumulative table and graph are more useful because the total is more important than the individual values. For example, people dealing with the water supply and irrigation care more about how much water there is than about small month-to-month fluctuations in rainfall.

In the previous example, there was no maximum amount of rain possible. But in other situations there is a natural upper bound.

Cumulative Distributions **39**

Percentiles Percentiles are a special application of cumulative distributions. A percentile is a value in a *cumulative relative frequency* distribution. It tells the relative frequency (as a percent) of the values in the distribution either (1) less than, or (2) less than or equal to a particular value. Percentiles are among the most misunderstood of all statistics even though they are commonplace. One reason for misunderstanding is the fact that two definitions of percentile are in standard usage. One definition is that in the definition box on page 40. The other definition is the same, except the words "or equal to" are deleted. Under the book's definition, the highest score in a group is always at the 100th percentile (because everyone's score is either less than or equal to the highest score). The lowest score in a large data set could be at the 0th percentile if, say, it was the 1 score out of 1000 at that level; then rounded to the nearest

(continued on next page)

---

2 Teaching

Notes on the Lesson

You might begin by noting the many different places where people are interested both in frequency distributions and cumulative frequency distributions. The contexts in the lesson are precipitation, people notification, and percentiles. In the questions are people who have contracted a disease, cumulative sales, etc. The variety of these contexts can by itself indicate the importance of the idea.

Additional Example

Example 1 The table below shows the average monthly precipitation in Kansas City, Kansas.

a. Fill in the Cumulative Precipitation column.

b. Draw a bar graph of the cumulative precipitation by month.

c. When has one-fourth the yearly precipitation fallen? **during May**

d. When has half the yearly precipitation fallen? **during July**

	Monthly Precipitation (inches)	Cumulative Precipitation (inches)
Jan	1.13	1.13
Feb	1.02	2.15
Mar	2.38	4.53
Apr	3.27	7.80
May	4.55	12.35
Jun	4.73	17.08
Jul	3.61	20.69
Aug	3.62	24.31
Sep	4.17	28.48
Oct	3.28	31.76
Nov	2.30	34.06
Dec	1.45	35.51

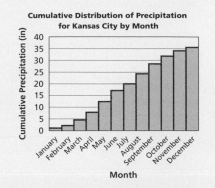

Cumulative Distribution of Precipitation for Kansas City by Month

1-5

Notes on the Lesson

On standardized tests, scores are often reported in terms of national percentiles and local percentiles. These are examples of different *populations*. You might discuss with students what it would mean if your local percentile score is lower than your national percentile score (it would mean that scores locally tend to be higher than national scores), or vice-versa.

Additional Example

Example 2 During the week preceding the start of each semester, every returning student must register for classes at Maple College. The table below shows how many of the 1350 students registered during each week-day.

a. Complete the table to show how many students registered during each day.

Summary of Registrations for Returning Students

Day	Total number of students registered during the day	Total number of students registered for class
Sun	155	155
Mon	470	625
Tue	289	914
Wed	136	1050
Thu	118	1168
Fri	97	1265
Sat	85	1350

b. Draw a line graph showing the cumulative number of students registered.

c. When had half the students registered? **Tuesday**

d. When had 75% of the students registered? **Wednesday**

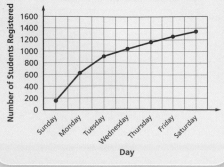

Total Number Registered for Class

GUIDED

Example 2

At 5:00 A.M. a sudden snowstorm caused Oak School to cancel classes. With no automated message-relay system, news had to spread by word-of-mouth. The table on the next page shows how many of the 170 families knew about the closing from 5 A.M. until 8 A.M.

a. Complete the table at the right to show how many families found out about the closing during each half hour.

b. Draw a line graph showing the cumulative number of families notified.

c. When had half the families been notified?

d. When had three quarters of the families been notified?

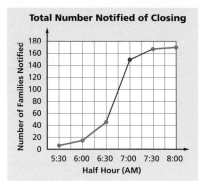

Time	Total Number of Families Notified during Preceding Half Hour	Total Number of Families who Know
5:30	6	6
6:00	?	14
6:30	?	48
7:00	104	152
7:30	?	168
8:00	2	170

Solution

a. The frequency for the half hour ending at 6:00 is Cumulative at 6:00 − Cumulative at 5:30.

   $\underline{\ ?\ } - \underline{\ ?\ } = \underline{\ ?\ }$ **14 6 8**

   The frequency for the half hour ending at 6:30 is

   $\underline{\ ?\ } - 14 = \underline{\ ?\ }$. **48 34**

   The frequency for the half hour ending at 7:30 is $\underline{\ ?\ }$. **16**

b. Fill in the points and segments from 6:30 to 7:30 A.M.

c. Half the families equals $\underline{\ ?\ }$ families. This many families have been notified by $\underline{\ ?\ }$. **85 around 6:40**

d. Three-quarters of the families equals $\underline{\ ?\ }$ families. This fraction of the families have been notified by $\underline{\ ?\ }$.

   128 around 6:55

Percentiles

In the situation of Example 2, by 8:00 A.M., 100% of the families at Oak School were notified. In a situation like this, when a cumulative frequency has a maximum of 100%, it is common to speak of *percentiles*, the value at which a certain cumulative percent has been reached.

Definition of Percentile

The *p*th **percentile** of a set of numbers is a value in the set such that *p* percent of the numbers are less than or equal to that value.

For example, if the 85th family out of 170 had been notified at exactly 6:47 and the 86th family was notified at 6:49, then the 50th percentile would be at 6:47. Some statisticians define percentiles according to the percent of numbers strictly less than the value; according to their definition, the 50th percentile would be at 6:49.

---

percentile, it would be at the 0th percentile. *However, it is common practice even with the book's definition not to report the highest score as being at the 100th percentile.* This may be a vestige of the days in which data storage on computers was restricted to a fixed number of columns of data and only two columns (for the two digits) were used for percentiles.

Without the words "or equal to," the highest score in a set of data could be well below the 100th percentile if many people

had that score. For instance, if 5 of 50 students had the highest score on a test, then 95% of the students would have scores less than those students, and those 5 students would be at the 95th percentile.

The second misunderstanding is what is known as the Lake Wobegon Effect, the mistaken notion that everyone can be above average; named after Garrison Keillor's mythical town "where the men are good looking, the women are strong, and all the children are above average." It was coined

Percentiles are commonly used for reporting results of standardized tests. You may have noticed that people are rarely said to be at the 100th percentile or 0th percentile. That is because the lowest percentile is typically reported as the 1st percentile, and the highest percentile as the 99th.

 See Quiz Yourself at the right.

▶ QUIZ YOURSELF

What percentile corresponds to Q_3, the third quartile?

Activity   See margin.

A school district administered a 30-point math test to all tenth graders in its three high schools. The student scores are in the table at the right. Construct cumulative frequency and cumulative relative frequency graphs.

Step 1 Enter the data into columns A and B of a spreadsheet. Title column A "scores" and column B "freq". In column A, replace each interval with its midpoint. For example, enter "2" instead of "1–3".

Step 2 Make the title of column C "cumfreq". Then in cell C1, enter =b1. In cell C2, enter =c1+b2. This formula adds the frequency of the current interval to a running total. Copy that formula down through cell C11.

Step 3 Display the cumulative frequency in a line graph. Your display should look like the one shown at the right below.

Without knowing how many students took the test, it is hard to tell how meaningful a particular frequency or cumulative frequency value is. Relative frequencies would be more meaningful. The percentile score is a measure of *cumulative relative frequency*.

Step 4 Make the title of column D "relfreq" (for "relative frequency"). By scrolling down through column C of the spreadsheet, you can find the total number of students who took the test. Enter a formula in cell D1 that computes the relative frequency by dividing the value in B1 by that total. Copy it down through cell D11. Which score range has the highest relative frequency, and what is its relative frequency?

Step 5 Title column E "cumrelfreq" (for "cumulative relative frequency"). Use a procedure like the one in Step 2 to compute running totals of column D.

Step 6 Make a graph of cumulative relative frequency. Use it to find the quartiles.

Step 7 Construct a box plot.

Step 8 Using either your graph or the spreadsheet, estimate
  a. the score corresponding to the 60th percentile. **about 18**
  b. the approximate percentile for a person with a score of 24. **about the 89th**

Score Interval	Frequency
0	0
1–3	3
4–6	18
7–9	54
10–12	81
13–15	148
16–18	155
19–21	162
22–24	132
25–27	89
28–30	39

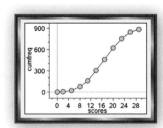

Notes on the Lesson

Activity This is how students' spreadsheets should look after completing Step 2 of the Activity.

A scores	B freq	C cumfreq
1 0	0	0
2 2	3	3
3 5	18	21
4 8	54	75
5 11	81	156
6 14	148	304

$C2 \quad =c1+b2$

Additional Answers

Activity

Steps 1–7: See the Additional Answers section at the back of the book.

in 1987 by John J. Cannell, a physician from West Virginia, when he noticed that every state in the nation reported that its elementary students had scored above average on standardized tests. This is, of course, a mathematical impossibility. If they were all above average, then the average would have to increase so that some would be below the average. What students in each state had done was to score above the average of earlier groups used to standardize the tests, groups that might purposely have been chosen to be a little weaker than typical so that schools using the test would look good overall.

The Lake Wobegon Effect reflects more striking mathematical impossibilities: Not only is it impossible for 100% of students to be above average, it is impossible for them all to be above the 25th percentile. In fact, it is impossible for 100% of students to be above the 10th percentile. By definition of percentiles, about 10% of students must be below (or below and at) the 10th percentile.

1-5

3 Assignment

Recommended Assignment

- Questions 1–5
- ● Questions 6–17
- ● Question 18 (extra credit)
- Reading Lesson 1-6
- Covering the Ideas 1-6
  (Questions 1–9)

Notes on the Questions

We suggest going through Questions 1–9 in order to cover the ideas of this lesson.

Question 2 You might discuss the following questions whose answers can generally be found from this table.

How many questions on the test were easy for a great majority of the students? **16**
How many questions were hard for a great majority? **4**
Is the distribution of scores symmetric, skewed, tail to the left, or tail to the right? **skewed slightly, tail to the left**

Question 3 Note that the sales for each week are easy to calculate from the given information. Is it true that, after the first week, each week's sales was less than the previous week? **Yes.**

Questions

COVERING THE IDEAS

1. Since 2003, the World Health Organization (WHO) has tracked new cases of Avian Influenza, or bird flu. The table at the right gives the number of people who have contracted the disease each year. Add columns to the table to show the total number of people who have contracted the disease at the end of each of the given years, relative frequency and cumulative relative frequency. **See margin.**

Year	Number of Cases
2003	4
2004	46
2005	98
2006	115
2007	88

Source: World Health Organization

2. A teacher gave a quiz which had a maximum score of 20 points. The chart below gives each score x and its frequency f.

x	7	9	12	13	14	15	16	17	18	19	20
f	1	1	2	1	3	9	16	9	4	3	1

a. How many students took the quiz? **50**
b. How many students have scores less than or equal to the score at the 92nd percentile? What score is that? **46; 18 points**
c. Use the data to draw a cumulative frequency graph.
d. Use the data to draw a cumulative relative frequency graph.

2c–d. See margin.

3. a. Draw a bar graph showing the box office sales for each of the first 7 weeks of Spider-Man 3 (2007) given the tabulated cumulative values at right. (In your graph, each week's value should only reflect the sales for that week.)
   b. Draw a cumulative relative frequency line graph for the total receipts. **a–b. See margin.**

Spider-Man 3 Box Office Sales	
Week	Cumulative
1	$151,116,516
2	$240,236,828
3	$282,379,655
4	$307,754,583
5	$318,342,110
6	$325,585,149
7	$330,021,137

Source: The Numbers–Box Office Data

4. In a class of 30 students, the scores on a test worth 50 points were recorded as: **See margin.**

32	48	34	42	26	39	44	40	39	36
45	37	39	47	34	37	38	45	38	37
46	40	43	30	38	47	42	30	48	33

a. Make a table of the data, showing the frequency and relative frequency of each score.
b. Draw a cumulative frequency line graph and a cumulative relative frequency line graph for the data.
c. Find the quartile values and construct a box plot.

5. **True or False** Consider a set of data.
   a. All data points less than or equal to the median correspond to the 50th percentile. **false**
   b. All data points in the IQR correspond to the 50th percentile. **false**
   c. If there are 12 different ordered numbers, the 3rd lowest value corresponds to the 25th percentile. **true**

Additional Answers

1., 2c–d. See the Additional Answers section at the back of the book.

3a.

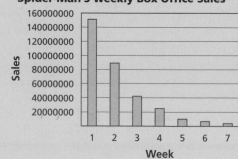

Spider-Man 3 Weekly Box Office Sales

3b.

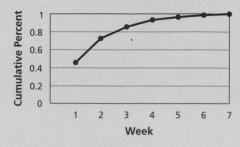

Spider-Man Cumulative Percentage of Box Office Sales

4a–c. See the Additional Answers section at the back of the book.

APPLYING THE MATHEMATICS

6–8 See margin.

6. This chart gives percentile values for the heights of boys of different ages. For example, the bottom curve shows that the 3rd percentile for a 18-year-old boy is 162.5 cm, or about 64".

   a. What is the height of a 15-year-old boy at the 75th percentile?

   b. Give the median height of a 16-year-old boy.

   c. For what age is the 75th percentile 180 cm?

   d. Make a box plot of heights for 14-year-old boys. Use the 97th and 3rd percentiles as ends of the whiskers in your box plot.

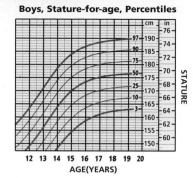

Boys, Stature-for-age, Percentiles

height

Source: National Center for Health Statistics

7. The table at the right shows the number of home runs that baseball player Roger Maris hit during his ten years in the American League.

   a. Describe a trend you see in the graph shown below.

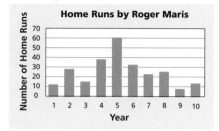

Source: Baseball Reference

Year	Home Runs
1	14
2	28
3	16
4	39
5	61
6	33
7	23
8	26
9	8
10	13

   b. Make a cumulative graph of the data. Describe how the same trend affects the cumulative graph.

8. Doctors studying a group of 240 elderly patients with Alzheimer's Disease noted six types of daily living skills in which they might be impaired. These are called impairments. The severity of Alzheimer's is measured by the total number n of impairments.

   a. For how many patients was $2 \le n \le 4$? **77**

   b. Draw a cumulative frequency line graph for the data. Highlight the segments of the graph for which $2 \le n \le 4$. **See margin.**

9. The cumulative frequency graphs in this lesson are either steady or rising. Give an example of a situation in which such a graph would both rise and fall. Explain when this would happen.

   Answers vary. Sample: A retailer's cumulative sales receipts rise during the month of December, but fall after Christmas as gifts are returned.

Number of Impairments	Number of Patients
0	100
1	43
2	36
3	17
4	24
5	9
6	11

Source: Journal of Gerontology

Cumulative Distributions **43**

Notes on the Questions

Question 9 The answer in the back of the student book is not precisely correct, since this question asks for a "cumulative frequency" situation, not merely one of accumulation. A possible situation is that of the number of items sold by a store or company. It is possible that, due to returns, the cumulative sales could decrease. For instance, the number sold by December 25 might be higher than the number sold by December 27 due to returns after Christmas.

Additional Answers

7a. Roger Maris hits more and more homeruns until he peaks in his 5th year, at which point he starts hitting fewer homeruns.

7b. The cumulative graph increases the quickest in the middle of Roger Maris' career, in agreement with the trend from Part a.

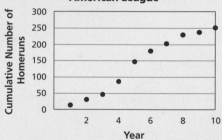

Homeruns by Roger Maris in the American League

8b.

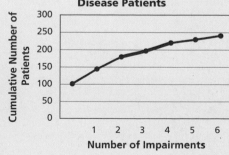

The Impairments of 240 Alzheimer's Disease Patients

Additional Answers

6a. about 175 cm or 69"

6b. about 173.5 cm or 68.5"

6c. about 17 years old

6d.

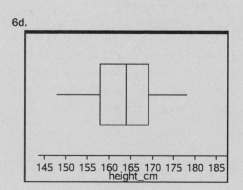

4 Wrap-Up

Ongoing Assessment
Have students work in pairs. On a separate sheet of paper, ask each student to draw up a cumulative frequency table similar to the ones in the lesson. One student should leave their frequency column blank, and the other should leave their cumulative frequency column blank. Have students exchange papers and fill in the missing values in their partner's blank column. Students should demonstrate understanding of the relationship between frequencies and cumulative frequencies.

Project Update
Project 4, *Graphing and Interpreting Statistical Data*, on page 68 relates to the content of this lesson.

REVIEW

In 10 and 11, construct a set of 12 numbers whose box plot would have a shape similar to the one given. There are no outliers. (Lesson 1-4)

10. ⬚

11. ⊢—⊣—⊣

12. A teacher is interested in comparing the reading achievement of her 16 students to that of seventh graders nationwide. The nationwide average on the reading test is 7. Her 16 students score as follows:

6	9	6	10	9	6	7	8
6	5	9	4	14	5	8	7

a. Find the mean and median for these reading scores.
b. If the mean is used as the measure of central tendency, how does the class compare to the national norm?
c. If the median is used as the measure of central tendency, how does the class compare to the national norm?
d. Using the 1.5 × IQR criterion, is the score of 14 an outlier?
e. Use a box plot to graph the distribution of scores.
(Lessons 1-4, 1-3)

13. Prudence invested in shares of Large Co. Over time she bought different numbers of shares at different prices as shown in this table. Compute Prudence's average cost per share. (Lesson 1-2)

13. $65.48 per share

Number of Shares	100	300	200	1000	700	400
Price per Share ($)	58	62	65	59	72	75

14. **Skill Sequence** Solve each equation. (Previous Course)
a. $\frac{x}{3} = 9$ $x = 27$
b. $\frac{x^2}{3} = 9$ $x = \pm 3\sqrt{3}$
c. $\frac{x^2}{3} = 9 + x$

15. Test your ability to enter a complex expression into a calculator.
Evaluate $3\pi\sqrt{\frac{(1.1 + 2.9)^2}{1.1^2 + 2.9^2}}$ to the nearest thousandth. **12.155**
(Previous Course)

16. Without graphing, tell whether the point (–48, –103) is on the line with equation $y = -2x + 7$. Justify your answer. (Previous Course)

17. If $x = -3$ and $k = 10$, compute mentally: (Previous Course)
a. $|x - k|$ **13**
b. $|k - x|$ **13**
c. $(x - k)^2$ **169**
d. $(k - x)^2$ **169**
e. $(x - k)^3$ **-2197**
f. $(k - x)^3$ **2197**

EXPLORATION

18. Pick out three characteristics about yourself that have a numerical value and about which you can find percentile information with respect to a larger group. Make your choices so that for one characteristic you have a low percentile, for one you have a high percentile, and for the third you are near the 50th percentile.
See margin.

---

10. Answers vary. Sample: {0, 0, 0, 0, 2, 2, 2, 2, 4, 4, 4, 4}

11. Answers vary. Sample: {0, 0, 2, 2, 2, 2, 2, 2, 2, 2, 4, 4}

12a. mean: 7.4375, median: 7

12b. The mean suggests that the class performed better than seventh graders nationwide.

12c. The median suggests that the class performed the same as seventh graders nationwide.

12d. yes

12e. See margin.

14c. $x = \frac{3}{2}(1 \pm \sqrt{13})$

16. -2(-48) + 7 = 103 ≠ -103, so the point (-48, -103) is not on the line with equation $y = -2x + 7$.

18. See margin.

QY ANSWER

75th percentile

Additional Answers

12e.

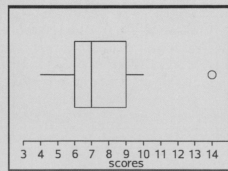

18. Answers vary. Sample: your height and weight may be compared to national averages. For instance, a 22-year-old, 74 inches tall, 155-pound male has a height in the upper percentiles and weight in the lower percentiles for that height when compared to national averages.

Measures of Spread: Variance and Standard Deviation

Vocabulary

range

deviations

population variance σ^2

population standard
deviation σ

sample variance s^2

sample standard deviation s

▶ **BIG IDEA** Variance and standard deviation depend on the mean of a set of numbers. Calculating these measures of spread depends on whether the set is a sample or population.

So far in this book you have studied the mean, the mode, the five-number summary, and the IQR. These statistics help to describe the distribution of numbers in a data set. In the Activity below you will use these statistics to compare two given data sets.

Mental Math

Lenny's average score after 3 tests is 88. What score on the 4th test would bring Lenny's average up to exactly 90? **96**

Activity 1 See margin.

The two dot plots below display frequency distributions of the height of the players on two hypothetical women's basketball teams.

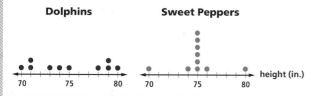

Step 1 Describe what you think is the main difference between the two dot plots from just looking at the graphs.

Step 2 Find the mean, median, mode, five-number summary, and IQR for each data set.

Step 3 Determine if any of the values from Step 2 are appropriate for distinguishing the main difference between the heights of the members of the two teams. Justify your conclusions.

In the Activity you may have concluded that the IQR helps to distinguish between the spreads of the two dot plots. It is one of the measures of *spread of a distribution*. Yet the IQR for the Sweet Peppers is 0 inches, which implies no spread. This number is not sensitive enough to indicate that there are Sweet Pepper players who are not 75" tall.

The simplest measure of the spread of a distribution is its *range*. The **range** is the difference of the maximum and minimum values of the variable. Each team has a mean height of 75" and a range of 80" − 70", or 10". In this way the distributions are quite similar. Yet the heights of the Dolphins seem more spread out than those of the Sweet Peppers.

Measures of Spread: Variance and Standard Deviation   **45**

Background

The variance and standard deviation are measures of spread based on the *mean*, whereas the interquartile range is a measure of spread related to the *median*. Thus, variance and standard deviation are more affected by a small number of extreme values than the interquartile range, which may not be affected at all.

Both the variance and standard deviation may seem to yield numbers that are unrelated to the values in the data set. To point out that there is some sense in them,

consider the numbers 30, 30, 30, 50, 50, and 50, in which each number is deviated ±10 from the mean (40). This data set has a population standard deviation of 10, which is what you would hope for. In general, if in a data set each element is deviated n from the mean, then the population variance is n^2 and the standard deviation is n.

(continued on next page)

GOAL

Introduce two of the most common measures of spread, *variance* and its square root, *standard deviation*.

SPUR Objectives

A Calculate measures of center and spread for data sets.

D Describe relations between measures of center and spread.

E Use statistics to draw conclusions about data.

Materials/Resources

· Lesson Master 1-6
· Resource Masters 19 and 20
· Quiz 2
· Statistics utility

HOMEWORK • Option 1
• Option 2
• Questions 1–9
• • Questions 10–24
• • Question 25 (extra credit)
• Reading Lesson 1-7
• Covering the Ideas 1-7 (Questions 1–5)

Local Standards

1 **Warm-Up**

Suppose $a_1 = 50$, $a_2 = 70$, $a_3 = 100$, and $\bar{a}$ is the mean of a_1, a_2, and a_3. Calculate:

1. $\displaystyle\sum_{i=1}^{3} a_i$ **220**

2. $\dfrac{\sum_{i=1}^{3} a_i}{3} - \bar{a}$ **0**

3. $\dfrac{\sum_{i=1}^{3}(a_i - \bar{a})^2}{2}$ **633.$\overline{3}$**

4. $\sqrt{\dfrac{\sum_{i=1}^{3}(a_i - \bar{a})}{2}}$ **25.2**

2 Teaching

Notes on the Lesson

Example 1 It is to a student's advantage to associate the steps in the algorithm in Example 1 with the order of operations in the formula in the definition of variance and standard deviation of a population on page 48. Spend time discussing deviation from the mean and the effect of squaring those deviations. It is important for students to understand that variance is always greater than or equal to zero.

Additional Answers

Activity 1

Step 1: The main difference between the two dot plots is that the spread of the Dolphins' heights is much greater than the spread of the Sweet Peppers' heights.

Step 2: Dolphins' mean: 75, median: 74.5, mode: 71 or 79, five-number summary: minimum = 70, Q_1 = 71, Q_2 = 74.5, Q_3 = 79, maximum = 80, IQR: 8

Sweet Peppers' mean: 75, median: 75, mode: 75, five-number summary: minimum = 70, Q_1 = 75, Q_2 = 75, Q_3 = 75, maximum = 80, IQR: 0

Step 3: The IQR is appropriate for distinguishing the main difference between the two teams' heights because the Dolphins' IQR is 8 and the Sweet Peppers' IQR is 0, which shows that the main difference is in the spread of the heights.

So we need other statistical measures to better describe the spread of the heights of the players of each team. Two measures of spread that are influenced by every data point are *variance* and *standard deviation*.

The Variance and Standard Deviation of a Population

The Dolphins can be viewed as a population of ten women. When the set of data is a population, Greek letters are used for mean, variance, and standard deviation. The mean is labeled μ (mu), variance as σ^2 (sigma-squared), and standard deviation as σ (sigma). The variance for a population is calculated from the squares of **deviations**, or differences of each data value x_i from the mean μ. The shortest Dolphin player is 70″ tall. The deviation $x_i - \mu$ for that player is $(70 - 75) = -5$ in. The square of her deviation is 25 square inches. Another of the Dolphin players is 78 inches tall. Her squared deviation is $(78 - 75)^2 = 9$ in^2.

The **population variance** is the mean of the squared deviations. That is, where n is the number of objects in a population, the variance is the sum of the squared deviations divided by n. The **population standard deviation** is the square root of the population variance. Example 1 shows how you can compute population variance and standard deviation by hand or by using a statistics utility.

Example 1

Find the variance and standard deviation for the heights of the Dolphins (treating them as a population).

Solution To find the variance and standard deviation it helps to organize the work step-by-step.

Step 1 Write the data x_i in a column. Find the mean by adding these numbers and dividing by n, the number of data points, which in this case is 10. Since the sum is 750, $\mu = 75$.

Step 2 In the next column record the result of subtracting the mean from each score, yielding $x_i - \mu$, which in this case is $x_i - 75$. Deviations are either positive, zero, or negative.

Step 3 Square each deviation and record each result in the next column.

Step 4 Add the squares of the deviations. Divide the sum of the squared deviations by n, in this case 10, to obtain the variance σ^2.

Step 5 Find the square root of the variance to get the standard deviation σ.

Results of these steps using technology are shown at the right and without using technology on the next page.

46 Exploring Data

Activity 2 The difference between the variance and standard deviation of a population (divide by n) and the variance and standard deviation of a sample (divide by $n - 1$) is due to the fact that large sets of data have slightly smaller variations than small ones. It is important that students know which keys on their calculators to use and which form of the answer to take from their computer.

After this lesson students will have studied three measures of center (mean, median, and mode) and four measures of spread (range, interquartile range, variance, and standard deviation) in this chapter. Students who have taken previous UCSMP courses may be familiar with a fifth measure of spread, the *mean absolute deviation* or *m.a.d.*, defined as

$$\text{m.a.d.} = \frac{\sum_{i=1}^{n} \left| x_i - \bar{x} \right|}{n}.$$

Height (in.) x_i	Deviation (in.) $x_i - \mu$	Square of Deviation (in²) $(x_i - \mu)^2$
70	$70 - 75 = -5$	25
71	$71 - 75 = -4$	16
71	-4	16
73	-2	4
74	-1	1
75	0	0
78	3	9
79	4	16
79	4	16
Sum 750	0	128

(handwritten annotations on table: 80 next to 79; $80-75 = 5$; 670; $0 \; -5$; $103 \; ?$; 25)

(handwritten note, top right: this example is flawed! It is missing the height = 80 in.)

The mean μ is $\frac{750}{10} = 75$ in., the variance $\sigma^2 = \frac{128}{10} = \frac{64}{5} =$ 12.8 in², and the standard deviation $\sigma = \sqrt{\frac{128}{10}} = \frac{8\sqrt{5}}{5} = \sqrt{12.8} \approx$ 3.58 in.

(handwritten note: there are only 9!)

Notice that the sum of the deviations equals 0. This is a great way to check your work. Also, notice that when the deviations are squared, values farther from the mean contribute more to the variance than values close to the mean. For instance, a height of 80 contributes $(80 - 75)^2 = 5^2 = 25$ to the sum of squared deviations, but 74 contributes only $(74 - 75)^2 = (-1)^2 = 1$. Because of this, groups with more data close to the mean generally have smaller standard deviations than groups with more data far from the mean.

Below is a picture of the Dolphins' data showing how the standard deviation of 3.58 relates to the distribution.

Dolphins

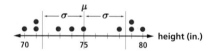

height (in.)

Basketball Beginnings
Basketball was introduced to women at Smith College in 1892, just one year after the game was invented.

You are asked to calculate the variance and standard deviation for the Sweet Peppers in Question 3.

Formulas for the variance and standard deviation are usually written using Σ-notation. For a set of n numbers $x_1, x_2, x_3, ..., x_n$ each deviation from the mean can be written as $x_i - \mu$, and the square of the deviation as $(x_i - \mu)^2$. Because the definition of the variance and standard deviation are based on the mean, they can be used only when it makes sense to calculate a mean.

Measures of Spread: Variance and Standard Deviation   **47**

(handwritten note, right margin: μ = mean; X̄ also = mean)

Students may ask "why do you square deviations?" or "why is there a separate formula for samples?" A more detailed response than the one given in this lesson can be found in Shaughnessy, J. Michael and Beth Chance, *Statistical Questions from the Classroom*, Reston, VA: National Council of Teachers of Mathematics, 2005. This small book is also useful for anticipating questions about correlation and regression that may come up in Chapter 2.

1-6

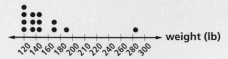
Definition of Variance and Standard Deviation of a Population

Let μ be the mean of the population data set $x_1, x_2, ..., x_n$. Then the **variance** σ^2 and **standard deviation** σ **of the population** are

$$\sigma^2 = \frac{\text{sum of squared deviations}}{n} = \frac{\sum_{i=1}^{n}(x_i - \mu)^2}{n}$$

and

$$\sigma = \sqrt{\text{variance}} = \sqrt{\frac{\sum_{i=1}^{n}(x_i - \mu)^2}{n}}.$$

Variance and Standard Deviation of a Sample

For many years statisticians only used the population formulas. Over time, mathematicians and statisticians established that dividing by n for a sample variance did not produce the best estimate of the population variance. They showed that when using a sample, dividing by $n - 1$ rather than by n provided a better estimate of population variance.

When the data is a sample, Roman letters are used for mean, variance, and standard deviation. The mean is labeled $\bar{x}$ (read "x-bar"), variance is s^2, and standard deviation is s. The only difference in the formula is that $n - 1$ is used in place of n.

Definition of Variance and Standard Deviation of a Sample

Let $\bar{x}$ be the mean of the sample data set $x_1, x_2, ...x_n$.
Then the **variance** s^2 and **standard deviation** s **of the sample** are

$$s^2 = \frac{\text{sum of squared deviations}}{n - 1} = \frac{\sum_{i=1}^{n}(x_i - \bar{x})^2}{n - 1}$$

and $s = \sqrt{\text{variance}} = \sqrt{\frac{\sum_{i=1}^{n}(x_i - \bar{x})^2}{n - 1}}.$

CAUTION: In this book most of the data come from samples, so unless directed otherwise, use the variance and standard deviation formulas for samples.

GUIDED

Example 2

According to the U.S. Department of Agriculture, ten to twenty earthworms per cubic foot is a sign of healthy soil. Mr. Green checked the soil in his garden by digging 7 one-cubic-foot holes and counting the earthworms. He found the following counts: 4, 23, 15, 10, 8, 12, 18.

48   Exploring Data

Calculate the sample variance and sample standard deviation of the numbers of earthworms per cubic foot.

Solution Follow the same steps used in Example 1, but since this data represents a sample, use the variance and standard deviation formulas for samples. The symbols x_i, $x_i - \bar{x}$, and $(x_i - \bar{x})^2$ represent the earthworm count, deviation from the mean, and squared deviation, respectively.

Count (worms) x_i	Deviation (worms) $x_i - \bar{x}$	Square of Deviation (worms squared) $(x_i - \bar{x})^2$
4	-8.86	78.5
23	_?_ 10.14	102.82
15	2.14	_?_ 4.58
10	-2.86	8.18
8	_?_ -4.86	23.62
_?_ 12	-0.86	0.74
_?_ 18	5.14	_?_ 26.42

$$\text{sum} \quad \sum_{i=1}^{7} x_i = \underline{\ ?\ }\ 90 \qquad \sum_{i=1}^{7} \frac{\ ?\ }{(x_i - \bar{x})} \approx 0 \qquad \sum_{i=1}^{7}(x_i - \bar{x})^2 = \underline{\ ?\ }\ 244.86$$

The mean $\bar{x} = \dfrac{\sum_{i=1}^{7} x_i}{7} = \dfrac{90}{7} \approx 12.86$ worms.

The variance $s^2 = \dfrac{\sum_{i=1}^{7}(x_i - \bar{x})^2}{\ ?\ } = \dfrac{\ ?\ }{\ ?\ } = \underline{\ ?\ }$ worms squared. $6; \dfrac{224.86}{6}; 40.81$

The standard deviation $s = \sqrt{\text{variance}} = \sqrt{\ ?\ } \approx \underline{\ ?\ }$ worms, to two $40.81; 6.39$ decimal places.

Wiggle, Squiggle, and Squirm In one acre of land, you can often find more than one million worms.

Because of these different formulas, some statistics utilities have two sets of symbols: s^2 and s, and σ and σ^2. Other calculators and programs use only one set of formulas for variance and standard deviation.

Activity 2

Use your calculator or statistics software to find (to the nearest tenth) the standard deviation of the following data set.

89, 79, 74, 67, 99, 91, 84, 81

If more than one standard deviation is given, record both. (You should find that the mean is 83 and both the sample and population standard deviation are between 9 and 11.)
$\sigma \approx 9.45$, $s \approx 10.10$

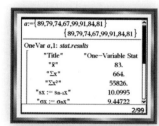

Accommodating the Learner

Ask if students have noticed that the sum of the deviations column is always zero and ask them to come up with a reason why this makes sense. Then have them use summation notation to prove that the sum of the deviations from the mean in any data set always equals 0.
(You may need to verify that the following property holds true for $\sum$-notation:
$$\sum_{i=1}^{n}(a \pm b) = \sum_{i=1}^{n} a \pm \sum_{i=1}^{n} b.)$$

$$\sum_{i=1}^{n}(x_i - \bar{x}) = \sum_{i=1}^{n} x_i - \sum_{i=1}^{n} \bar{x} = n\bar{x} - n\bar{x} = 0$$

1-6

3 Assignment

Recommended Assignment
- Questions 1–9
- • Questions 10–24
- • Question 25 (extra credit)
- • Reading Lesson 1-7
- • Covering the Ideas 1-7 (Questions 1–5)

Notes on the Questions
We suggest going through Questions 1–15 in order.

Questions

COVERING THE IDEAS

1. State whether the statistic is a measure of <u>center</u> or a measure of spread.
   a. mean **center**   b. range **spread**   c. variance
   d. interquartile range   e. standard deviation   f. median

2. **Multiple Choice** The standard deviation of a set of scores is
   A the sum of the deviations. **D**
   B the difference between the highest and lowest scores.
   C the score that occurs with the greatest frequency.
   D none of the above.

3. Use the heights of the Dolphins and Sweet Peppers.
   a. Calculate the variance and standard deviation for the heights of the Sweet Peppers using the formulas for populations.
   b. Find the difference of the means. **0**
   c. Find the difference of the ranges. **0**
   d. Find the difference of the standard deviations. **3.58 − 2.28 = 1.3**
   e. Explain in your own words what the differences in Parts b–d tell you about the two data sets.

4. What statistics change if the Dolphins and Sweet Peppers are considered samples of all women basketball players? **See margin.**

5. If the standard deviation $s = 4.5$ cm, find the sample variance. **20.25 cm^2**

In 6 and 7, the measurements refer to pulse rates of two students while jogging, in beats per minute. Use a calculator or statistical software to find the mean and sample standard deviation for each situation.

6. student A with four measurements: 100, 120, 115, 133 **6–7. See margin.**

7. student B with five measurements: 110, 120, 124, 116, 120

8. Suppose you used the formula for the sample standard deviation in Example 1. Would your answer be greater than, equal to, or less than the population standard deviation shown there? **greater than**

9. Each of the following situations produces data that can be summarized with mean and standard deviation. Which would require population formulas for variance and standard deviation rather than sample formulas? **B and D**
   A The Environmental Protection Agency measures carbon monoxide content of air at 15 locations of a metropolitan area.
   B An algebra teacher has scores from his students' final exams.
   C A consumer magazine tests four cars from each of three brands of hybrid vehicles to evaluate operating cost per mile.
   D Number of home runs per game for the Boston Red Sox in the 2008 season.

Los Angeles, CA

Margin answers (right column)
1c. spread
1d. spread
1e. spread
1f. center

3a. variance = 5.20; standard deviation ≈ 2.28

3e. The heights of the Dolphins and Sweet Peppers have the same mean and range, but the Dolphins have a greater standard deviation. Therefore the Dolphins' heights are spread out more than the Sweet Peppers' heights from the shared center, though still within the shared range.

Additional Answers

4. The variance and standard deviations would change, because they would be re-calculated using the formulas for samples.

6. $\bar{x} = 117$; $s = 13.64$

7. $\bar{x} = 118$; $s = 5.30$

Lesson Master (bottom left)

1-6 Lesson Master
Questions on SPUR Objectives
See pages 72–77 for objectives.

SKILLS Objective A

1. A table of the countries with the largest proven crude oil reserves is at the right. Calculate

Proven Crude Oil Reserves (million barrels, 2007)

Venezuela	99,377	Saudi Arabia	264,209
USSR (former)	128,254	Libya	43,663
Iran	136,150	UAE	97,800
Iraq	115,000	Nigeria	36,220
Kuwait	101,500	United States	20,972

   a. the median. **≈243,237**
   b. the mean. **≈104,315**
   c. the sample variance. **≈4,733 million barrels squared**
   d. the sample standard deviation. **≈68.802**

2. Consider the following data set {92, 103, 88, 96, 109, 77, 86, 92, 95, 90, 105}. Calculate
   a. a sample variance. **≈84.5**   b. a population variance. **≈76.8**
   c. a sample standard deviation. **≈9.19**   d. a population standard deviation. **≈8.77**

PROPERTIES   Objective D

3. Both distributions at the right have the same mean. Without calculating, determine which has the greater standard deviation. Justify your answer.
   B; B's distribution is more spread out, so it will have a greater variance and standard deviation.

USES Objective E

4. In a data set, suppose you calculate a mean and a standard deviation, and you identify all outliers using the 1.5 × IQR criterion. If you remove the outliers and calculate the new mean, and standard deviation, which of these statistics is sure to increase and which to decrease?
   The mean could increase or decrease depending on where the outliers are located, but the standard deviation will decrease.

5. Suppose the mean height of girls in one class is 63 inches with a standard deviation of 2.3 inches. The mean height of boys in another class is 65 inches with a standard deviation of 2.1 inches. Which class has more variability in height? Justify your answer.
   The class of girls has more variability because their standard deviation is greater.

Functions, Statistics and Trigonometry   165

APPLYING THE MATHEMATICS

10. Suppose you know the distance in miles each student in a class lives from school. For this data set, state the unit for each statistic.
    a. mean **miles**
    b. range **miles**
    c. variance **miles squared**
    d. standard deviation **miles**

11. Beth found the variance of a data set to be –11. Why must her answer be wrong? **The variance is always positive.**

12. Suppose two samples have the same mean, but different standard deviations s_1 and s_2, with $s_1 < s_2$. Which sample shows more variability? **The sample with standard deviation s_2.**

13. a. Consider the weights (in kilograms) of a group of deer. If the standard deviation is 7.8 kg, what is the variance? **60.84 kg²**
    b. If the variance is 19 kg², what is the standard deviation? **about 4.36 kg**

14. Use the hypothetical frequency distributions of ACT scores for groups X, Y, and Z at the right.
    a. Match each group with its best description.
       i. consistently near the mean **Group Z**
       ii. very widely spread **Group Y**
       iii. evenly distributed. **Group X**
    b. Without calculating, tell which group's ACT scores have the greatest standard deviation and which have the smallest. **14b–c. See margin.**
    c. Verify your answer to Part b with calculations.

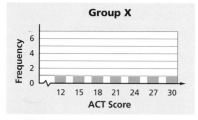

15. More than 1.3 million students in the class of 2007 took the ACT. On the mathematics section, $\mu = 21.0$ and $\sigma = 5.1$. Students receive scores rounded to the nearest whole number. What is the interval of student scores that lie within one standard deviation of the mean? **$16 \leq x \leq 26$**

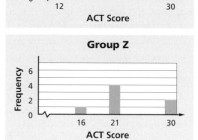

For 16 and 17, use the following data that represent the times (rounded to the nearest 5 seconds) for 20 sixth-graders to run 400 meters.

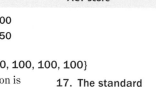

70	80	80	85	90	100	100	100	100	100
100	105	105	105	120	130	130	130	140	150

16. Find a sample of five students out of the 20 whose standard deviation for running time is as small as possible. **{100, 100, 100, 100, 100}**

17. Find a sample of four running times whose standard deviation is larger than 25 seconds. Compute the standard deviation.

    17. The standard deviation of {70, 80, 80, 150} is about 36.97.

Measures of Spread: Variance and Standard Deviation   **51**

Notes on the Questions
Question 11 You might ask students which of these statistics would be negative if all the numbers in a data set are negative.

a. mean **yes**
b. median **yes**
c. range **no**
d. variance **no**
e. standard deviation **no**

Additional Answers

14b. Group Y's scores have the greatest standard deviation and Group Z's scores have the smallest standard deviation.

14c. Group X: ≈ 6.48; Group Y: ≈ 6.80; Group Z: ≈ 5.21

1-6

19a. JAN: 187; FEB: 373; MAR: 565;

APR: 756; MAY: 949; JUN: 1144;

JUL: 1341; AUG: 1538; SEP: 1736;

OCT: 1936; NOV: 2141; DEC: 2344

U.S. Total Import Trade in Goods and Services for 2007

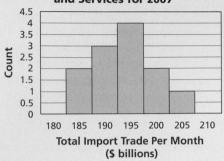

U.S. Total Import Trade in Goods and Services for 2007

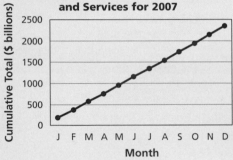

18. **Multiple Choice** A class of students is said to be *homogeneous* if the students in the class are very much alike on some measure. Here are four classes of students who were tested on a 20-point chemistry test. Which class is the most homogeneous with respect to scores on the test? Explain your answer.

A	$n = 20$	$\bar{x} = 15.3$	$s = 2.5$
B	$n = 25$	$\bar{x} = 12.1$	$s = 5.4$
C	$n = 18$	$\bar{x} = 11.3$	$s = 3.2$
D	$n = 30$	$\bar{x} = 10.4$	$s = 3.2$

18. **A** has the smallest standard deviation, so it is the most homogeneous.

REVIEW

19. Use the table below on seasonally adjusted U.S. domestic imports for 2007.

U.S. Total Imports in Goods and Services ($ billions)												
TOTAL	**JAN**	**FEB**	**MAR**	**APR**	**MAY**	**JUN**	**JUL**	**AUG**	**SEP**	**OCT**	**NOV**	**DEC**
Total (per month)	187	186	192	191	193	195	197	197	198	200	205	203
Cumulative Total	?	?	?	?	?	?	?	?	?	?	?	?

Source: U.S. Census Bureau

a. Complete the table and make both a histogram and a cumulative data line graph for imports. **See margin.**

b. What was the total cost of U.S. domestic imports for 2007? (Lessons 1-5, 1-3) **2344**

20. Two data sets of heights of people each have minimum = 50", median = 67", and maximum = 80". One data set has IQR = 15"; the other has IQR = 10".

a. Draw possible box plots for each data set. **See margin.**

b. Which data set shows more spread? (Lessons 1-4)

21. The histogram below shows the number of states receiving the number of legal permanent residents specified in each interval in 2006. Write a paragraph describing immigration in 2006. Include both specific information such as maximum, minimum, mean, or median values (when possible), and general trends such as skewness. (Lessons 1-3, 1-2, 1-1)

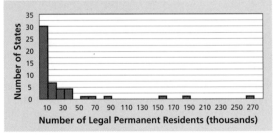

Source: U.S. Department of Homeland Security

20b. The data set with the IQR of 15 shows more spread.

21. Answers vary. Sample: The maximum influx of permanent legal residents into one state was between 260 and 270 thousand, and the minimum influx of residents was between 0 and 10 thousand; 30 states had the minimum level of influx. The mean value is between 25 and 35 thousand and the median is between 0 and 10 thousand. Most of the states are clustered in the 0 to 10 thousand interval, and the graph is skewed with a tail on the right.

20a. Answers vary. Sample:

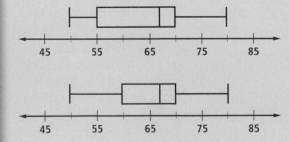

In 22 and 23, use these data on the percent of Advanced Placement Examinations in Mathematics or Computer Science taken by female high school students.

Year	1974	1979	1984	1989	1994	2004	2006	2007
Percent	26	32	35	36	43	44	45	46

Source: The College Board

22. a. **Multiple Choice** Which of the following would be an appropriate graph for representing these data? (There may be more than one correct choice.) **D**

    A box plot   B cumulative frequency graph

    C histogram   D line graph

  b. Draw such a graph, and describe trend(s) in the data. (Lessons 1-3, 1-1) **See margin.**

23. The total number of students taking AP Exams in Mathematics or Computer Science was about 121,000 in 1994 and about 311,520 in 2004.

  a. What was the average annual change in the number of women taking AP Exams in these areas during this period?

    23a. about 8,504 women/year

  b. What was the average annual increase in the number of men taking these exams in this period? **(Lesson 1-2, Previous Course)**

    23b. about 10,548 men/year

24. **Multiple Choice** $\sum_{i=1}^{n} x_i$ equals (Lesson 1-2) **D**

    A $\bar{x}.$ B $\frac{\bar{x}}{n}.$

    C $\frac{n}{x}.$ D none of these.

EXPLORATION

25. The Russian mathematician Pafnuti L. Chebychev (1821 – 1894) proved a remarkable theorem called Chebychev's Inequality: In any data set, if p is the fraction of the data that lies within k standard deviations to either side of the mean, then $p \geq 1 - \frac{1}{k^2}$.

  a. According to Chebychev's Theorem, what percent of a data set must lie within 2 standard deviations of the mean? **at least 75%**

  b. What percent must lie within 3 standard deviations? **at least 88.9%**

  c. Test Chebychev's Theorem on a data set of your choice.

    Answers vary. Sample: {20, 35, 100, 80}; $\bar{x} = 58.75$, $s = 37.5$; $\bar{x} \pm 2s$ –16.25 $\leq \bar{x} \leq$ 133.75, $\bar{x} \pm 3s$ –53.75 $\leq \bar{x} \leq$ 171.25; 75% or more and 88.9% or more of the data set does lie within 2 and 3 standard deviations to either side of the mean, respectively.

Ongoing Assessment

Have students make up 3 sets of 5 scores, each with a mean of 70, such that one data set has a standard deviation of 0, one has a standard deviation between 5 and 15, and one has a standard deviation greater than 15. Students should demonstrate understanding of standard deviation as a measure of spread by generating data sets with different standard deviations.

Administer Quiz 2 (or a quiz of your own) after students complete this lesson.

Project Update

Project 2, *Sabermetrics: The Fastest Player*, Project 3, *Coin Circulation*, and Project 5, *Class Survey*, on pages 67 and 68 relate to the content of this lesson.

Additional Answers

22b. Answers vary. Sample: The percent of female students taking AP Math or Computer Science examinations has increased from 1974 to 2007 with the greatest increase between 1989 and 1994.

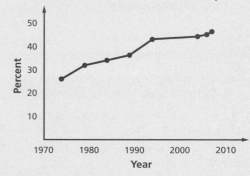

Female Students in AP Math or Comp Sci

Lesson 1-7

Lesson 1-7
Comparing Numerical Distributions

GOAL

Write descriptions of the differences between two data sets as seen from their distributions.

SPUR Objective

G Use statistics to compare and contrast two data sets in the context of a situation.

Materials/Resources

· Lesson Master 1-7
· Resource Masters 21, 22 and 23
· Statistics utility

HOMEWORK
· Option 1
· Option 2

· Questions 1–5
· · Questions 6–15
· · Question 16 (extra credit)
· Reading Lesson 1-8
· Covering the Ideas 1-8 (Questions 1–8)

Local Standards

1 Warm-Up

Here are the average number of points per game by the scoring leader in the National Basketball Association for 1957–2006.

25.6	27.8	29.2	37.9	38.4
50.4	44.8	36.5	34.7	33.5
35.6	27.1	28.4	31.2	31.7
34.8	34.0	30.6	34.5	31.1
31.1	27.2	29.6	33.1	30.7
32.3	28.4	30.6	32.9	30.3
37.1	35.0	32.5	33.6	31.5
30.1	32.6	29.8	29.3	30.4
29.6	28.7	26.8	29.7	31.1
31.4	32.1	28.0	30.7	35.4

Give the 5-number summary for the data and identify all outliers.
minimum = 25.6, Q_1 = 29.6,
median = 31.15, Q_3 = 34,
maximum = 50.4;
There are two outliers: 50.4 and 44.8.

> **BIG IDEA** A written comparison of data sets requires presentation of specific statistics as well as statements of similarities and differences.

The previous lessons used statistics to describe distributions of numerical variables and to develop cumulative distributions. This lesson asks you to compare two or more distributions. The emphasis is on clear, descriptive writing.

A written description of distributions *compares* and *contrasts* their *shapes*, *centers*, and *spreads*. The description should use the vocabulary and statistical measures you have learned in prior lessons. Although "a picture is worth a thousand words," you should not need that many words. Your description should be clear enough so that a reader who does not have graphs of the distributions can create mental images of them.

Mental Math

Multiple Choice
If an integer is divisible by 6 and by 9, then the integer must be divisible by which of the following?

A 12 **B** 15
C 18 **D** 21

C

Activity 1

Below and at the right are histograms, statistical summaries, and box plots of the distribution of heights (in inches) of all players in the National Basketball Association (NBA) and the National Football League (NFL) during the 2007–2008 season.

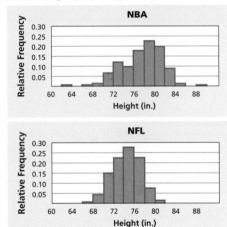

Statistics	Heights (in inches)	
	NBA	NFL
mean	79.2	74.0
median	80	74
interquartile range	5	4
standard deviation	3.63	2.58
range	25	15

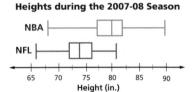

Heights during the 2007-08 Season

Background

No new statistical concepts are introduced in this lesson. The task for students is to organize their thinking and statistics they calculate and write a sensible description of how two distributions are the same and how they might differ. Teachers have found this lesson to be a good review of what students have encountered thus far in the chapter.

Activity 1 and Example 1 show how students might compare what they can learn from displays of two different data sets. Activity 2 shows how students might compare what they can learn from two different displays of the same data.

Step 1 Write a sentence about one piece of information conveyed by the statistical summaries table to compare NBA and NFL player heights.

Step 2 Write one sentence describing a comparison of NBA and NFL player heights that the box plots tell you that is not found in the table.

Step 3 Write one sentence comparing NFL and NBA player heights using a piece of information from the two histograms that is not found in either the box plots or the statistical table.

Steps 1–3. See margin.

When comparing statistical summaries, notice how many times larger one number is than another. Note where the greatest relative differences are. Besides looking at the values of the 5-number summary in the box plots, examine where a quartile in one distribution might be in the other distribution. Discuss outliers, if possible. The histograms give a better picture of the shape of the distribution.

Information from several types of displays of two distributions can help you to give a more complete comparison of them.

Example 1

Compare the distributions of the heights of the players in the NBA and in the NFL given in Activity 1.

Solution This description begins by comparing the histograms.

The distribution of heights of players in the NBA in 2007-2008 is centered around 80 inches, while the NFL distribution of heights is symmetric about the 74–76 bar. There are tails at both ends of the NBA histogram indicating very few players shorter than 72 inches or taller than 86 inches. There are no tails on the NFL histogram.

This second part of the description compares the two box plots.

The minimum heights for both the NBA and the NFL players are virtually the same, but the maximum height of the NBA players is about 9 inches higher than that of the NFL, indicating a larger spread of heights in the NBA. About 25% of the NBA players are taller than all players in the NFL. The middle 50% of the heights of the NBA players are taller than the middle 50% of the NFL players.

This description ends by comparing the statistical summary tables.

The mean and the median for the NBA are nearly the same, as is the case for the NFL. So using either statistic to describe the average for the NFL or the NBA would be appropriate. The mean and median for the NBA players are about 7% higher than the respective NFL statistics. So, on average, the NBA players are taller than the NFL players.

(continued on next page)

Comparing Numerical Distributions **55**

Additional Answers

Activity 1

Step 1: Answers vary. Sample: Both the mean and median heights of NBA players are higher than those of NFL players indicating that, on average, NBA players are taller.

Step 2: Answers vary. Sample: The tallest NBA players are much taller than the tallest NFL players and the shortest NBA players are taller than the shortest NFL players.

Step 3: Answers vary. Sample: The heights of NBA players are slightly skewed whereas the heights of NFL players are very symmetric.

2 Teaching

Notes on the Lesson

Instead of the heights given in Example 1, you may wish to collect and compare the heights of girls in your class(es) with the heights of boys.

There are at least two levels at which students can describe a graph. The lower level is to take a graph at face value, merely citing data or statistics. For instance, for Example 1, a student might write "The heights of more NBA players are in the interval $78 \leq h < 80$ than any similar 2-inch range bordered by even numbers." That shows an understanding of what the graph is about but does not give any deeper insights. However, if a student wrote, "Well over 90% of NBA players have heights from 70" to 84", that is, from 5'10" to 7'," then the student is doing something with the exhibited data. That response deserves a higher grade. Encourage students to do some analysis beyond the calculation of statistics.

1-7

Notes on the Lesson

Activity 2 The table, histogram, and box plot shown in Activity were created using the following data set: {11, 19, 25, 44, 10, 28, 34, 19, 23, 35, 22, 34, 15, 8, 22, 30, 18, 42, 35, 20}.

Additional Example

Example The tables, histograms, and box plots below contain information about the heights (in inches) of 20 students in an *FST* class and 20 students in an Algebra class. Write a paragraph comparing and contrasting the two distributions. **Answers vary. Sample:** Both distributions have similar ranges and standard deviations, though the Algebra students seem about 5"–7" shorter than the *FST* students on average. The height distribution of the *FST* class is slightly skewed, whereas the Algebra class is fairly symmetric.

Statistics		
	FST	**Algebra**
mean	69.3	62.65
median	70	63
interquartile range	5	5.5
standard devation	4.73	5.09
range	19	23

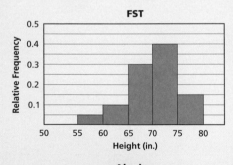

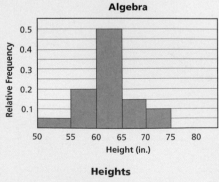

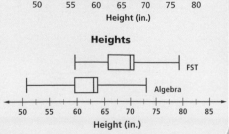

The standard deviation of the heights of the basketball players is 1 inch larger than the standard deviation for football players. This means overall there is more variability among the heights of the basketball players than of the football players. An overall difference in spread is also shown by the range of the heights of the NBA players being 10 points higher than that of the NFL players. The interquartile range for the NBA players is 5", which is slightly larger than the IQR of 4" for NFL players, indicating more spread in the heights of the middle 50% of the NBA players.

Activity 2 compares your class data with data from another sample.

Activity 2

The table, histogram, and box plot below describe the number of states visited by a sample of 20 adults in their lifetimes. A *visit* means that a person stayed for at least one night, drove or took a train through, or was in the airport. (Flying over does not count.) The count includes a person's home state.

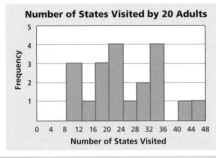

Number of States Visited				
mean	median	IQR	standard deviation	range
24.7	22.5	15.5	10.32	36

Step 1 Collect data concerning the total number of states each student in your class has visited.

Step 2 For your collected data, create a summary table, histogram, and box plot similar to those for the sample data. **See margin.**

Step 3 Compare your class data to the data from the adult sample. Use the outline below to guide your writing:

- Describe the variable involved. What is being measured in both sets of data?
- Use the five-number summary, histogram, and box plot to help you answer these questions:

  What is the shape of each data set? Are the data skewed? How can you tell?

  What is the center of each data set? Which measure is more appropriate to report: the mean or the median?

  What is the spread of each data set? Your choice of center statistic determines the spread you report.

- Explain the similarities or differences in the two data sets.

56   Exploring Data

Step 1. Answers vary. Sample: {48, 3, 11, 12, 12, 30, 27, 11, 2, 10, 35, 24, 41, 6, 15, 20, 8, 33, 22, 17}

Step 3. Answers vary. Sample: The sample data is trimodal, whereas the class data is skewed right, due to the long right whisker. The median of the class data, 16 states, is less than that of the sample, at 22.5 states. The IQR of the class data of 18 states is greater than the sample of 15.5 states, therefore the variability among the states visited is greater in the class than in the sample.

Additional Answers

Activity 2 Step 2:

mean	median	IQR	standard deviation	range
19.35	16	18	12.8893	46

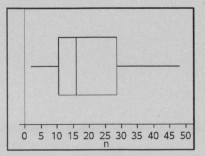

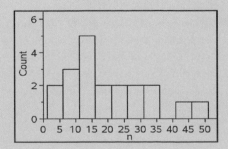

As you practice writing this kind of statistical summary, here is a checklist of things to remember.

✓ Describe the variable involved.

✓ Address all three major topics: shape, center, and spread.

✓ Give the appropriate units.

✓ Mention both data sets in your comparisons.

✓ Use words to give descriptions of your numbers. Use numbers to make your words more specific.

Questions

COVERING THE IDEAS

1. *Population density* is a measure of how crowded an area is. The information below compares Western and Eastern states in the United States in this regard. (The Mississippi River is the boundary between West and East.) Write a paragraph comparing the population densities of the Western and Eastern states.

Population Density

Western States

Eastern States

200 400 600 800 1000 1200

Source: State Master

Western Density		Eastern Density	
mean	52.4	mean	301.4
median	38.6	median	172.3
standard deviation	54.4	standard deviation	298.3
interquartile range	55.4	interquartile range	299.4
Q_1	15.3	Q_1	101.7
Q_3	70.7	Q_3	401.1

Western States 20 15 10 5
Eastern States 20 15 10 5

200 400 600 800 1000 1200
Population Density

2. Below is a list of terms you have seen in this chapter. Sort the terms into three groups: those dealing with shape, those with center, and those dealing with spread.

interquartile range   range   symmetric
standard deviation   skewed   variance
median   mean
outlier   tail

1. The variability of the Eastern states is greater than that of the Western states; the interquartile range of 299.4 is greater than 55.4. Whereas both the distributions of the Western and Eastern states have tails to the right, that of the Eastern states is longer, corresponding to its larger standard deviation of 298.3 compared to 54.4. The Eastern states also have a greater mean and median than the Western states, 301.4 and 172.3 compared to 52.4 and 38.6, respectively.

2. shape: skewed, symmetric, tail; center: mean, median; spread: interquartile range, range, outlier, standard deviation, variance

Comparing Numerical Distributions   **57**

Recommended Assignment

- Questions 1–5
- Questions 6–15
- Question 16 (extra credit)
- Reading Lesson 1-8
- Covering the Ideas 1-8 (Questions 1–8)

Notes on the Questions

Questions 1, 6, and 7 These questions require writing of the kind shown in the lesson.

ENGLISH LEARNERS
Vocabulary Development

For those students who may have struggled with some word meanings in the earlier lessons, you may wish to pay particular attention to their solution for Question 2, and if necessary, go over any terms that still may be problematic.

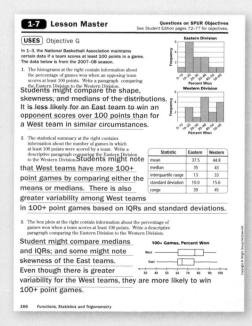

1-7

Notes on the Questions

Question 6 Go through the class, first asking volunteer students to read what they have written, then calling on others who have additional insights, and finally asking others who have not participated what they wrote. Often a student will be reluctant to put forth an answer even if it is a good one, so another strategy is to go around the class while students are doing the Warm-Up and asking students to display their answers for Questions 6 and 7.

3. In clear, descriptive writing, what three characteristics of distributions should be discussed? **Shape, center and spread**

4. Refer to the information given in Activity 1. Suppose you are told a player is in the NBA or the NFL. What can you conclude about the league to which the player belongs, and what reasons can you give for your conclusion if:
   a. the player is 82 inches tall?   b. the player is 71 inches tall?

5. The comparison in Activity 2 uses the median and IQR. Compare the same distributions using the mean and standard deviation.

APPLYING THE MATHEMATICS

6. Use these data to write a description comparing the maximum speeds on two samples of rollercoasters—wood and steel.

Maximum Speeds of Rollercoasters

Wood		Steel	
Name (Location)	Speed (mph)	Name (Location)	Speed (mph)
The Beast (OH)	64.8	Wild Thing (MN)	74.0
Balder (Sweden)	55.9	Fujiyama (Japan)	80.8
Colossos (Germany)	74.6	Goliath (GA)	70.0
The Cyclone (NY)	60.0	Incredible Hulk (FL)	67.0
El Toro (NJ)	75.0	Titan (TX)	85.0
Megafobia (UK)	48.0	Nitro (NJ)	80.0
Screamin' Eagle (MO)	62.0	Borg Assimilator (NC)	51.0
Son of Beast (OH)	78.0	Iron Dragon (OH)	40.0
Thunderbolt (PA)	55.0	Wild Mouse (PA)	28.0
The Voyage (IN)	67.4	Hypersonic XLC (VA)	80.0
Mean Streak (OH)	65.0	Corkscrew (Canada)	40.0
Giant Dipper (CA)	55.0	Dragon Khan (Spain)	65.0
Minebuster (Canada)	55.9	The Great American Scream Machine (NJ)	68.0
Colossus (CA)	62.0	Wicked Twister (OH)	72.0
Le Monstre (Canada)	59.7	The Joker's Jinx (MD)	60.0
Thunderbird (Finland)	46.6		
Thunder Road (NC)	58.0		

Source: Rollercoaster Database

Answers vary. Sample: Neither distribution is symmetrical; the distribution of the steel coasters is bimodal. The mean of the speeds of the steel roller coasters is 64.05 mph and is greater than that of the wood coasters at 61.35 mph. Additionally, the IQR of the steel coasters, 29 mph, is greater than that of the wood coasters, 10.75 mph, meaning that the variability of the speed of the steel coasters is greater than that of the wood coasters.

4a. The player is almost certainly in the NBA, because the relative frequency of the players over 80 inches in the NFL is less than 2%, while the relative frequency in the NBA is about 12%.

4b. Answers vary. Sample: A guess is difficult since 71 inches occurs in the left whisker of both graphs; however, the player is more likely in the NFL since 71 inches falls within two standard deviations of the NFL's mean, as opposed to three standard deviations of the NBA's mean.

Astroland's Cyclone rollercoaster, Coney Island, New York

5. Answers vary. Sample: The mean of the class data is 19.35 states, which is less than the mean of 24.7 for the sample. The standard deviation of the class data is 12.8893 states, which is larger than that of the sample, at 10.32 states. Again, this shows that the variability of the states visited is greater for the class.

7. The table below shows the length in meters of the 10 longest bridges in the United States and the 10 longest bridges outside of the United States. Write a descriptive paragraph comparing the length of the longest bridges in the United States to the longest bridges elsewhere in the world. **See margin.**

Longest Bridges	
U.S.	
Name	**Length (m)**
Lake Pontchartrain Causeway	38,422
Manchac Swamp Bridge	36,710
Atchafalaya Swamp Freeway	29,290
Chesapeake Bay Bridge Tunnel	24,140
Bonnet Carré Spillway	17,702
Jubilee Parkway	12,875
San Mateo-Hayward Bridge	11,265
Seven Mile Bridge	10,887
Sunshine Skyway Bridge	8,851
Twin Span	8.851
Outside U.S.	
Name	**Length (m)**
Bang Na Expressway	54,000
Yangcun Bridge of Beijing-Tianjin Intercity Rail	35,812
Hangzhou Bridge	35,673
Runyang Bridge	35,660
Donghai Bridge	32,500
King Fahd Causeway	26,000
The No. 1 Bridge of Tianjin Binhai Mass Transit	25,800
Liangshui River Bridge of Beijing-Tianjin Intercity Rail	21,563
Yongding River Bridge of Beijing-Tianjin Intercity Rail	21,133
6th October Bridge	20,500

Source: Bridgemeister

Are We There Yet?
The Donghai Bridge, in China, is 32.5 km long and links Shanghai with the Yangshan Deep Water Port.

8a. No boys score between 10 and 20, whereas about 5% of girls do.

8b. About 30% of boys score between 30 and 40, whereas about 50% of girls do.

8c. About 10% of boys score between 50 and 60, whereas about 7% of girls do.

8. The graph at the right shows results from a test of coordination that was administered to both girls and boys. The results are described with percentiles. Compare boys with girls who
   a. score between 10 and 20.
   b. score between 30 and 40.
   c. score between 50 and 60.

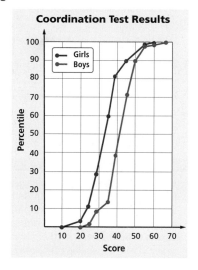

Coordination Test Results

Notes on the Questions
Question 7 After you have established the 5-number summary for each of the sets of bridges, follow the ideas of Question 6.

Additional Answers

7. Answers vary. Sample: The distribution of the sample of U.S. bridge lengths appears to be bimodal. The distribution of the sample of the outside U.S. bridge lengths appears to have an outlier on the right. Both the mean and median of the bridges outside the U.S. (30,864 m and 29,250 m, respectively) are higher than those inside the U.S. (19,889 m and 15,289 m). The IQR of bridges in the U.S. is 18,403 m, which is much bigger than the IQR of bridges outside the U.S., at 14,110 m. The standard deviation of bridges inside the U.S. is also higher with 11,479 instead of 10,255 outside the U.S.

1-7

4 Wrap-Up

Ongoing Assessment
Draw a boxplot and a histogram on the board that summarize data from two different data sets. Ask each student to write a paragraph briefly comparing the two distributions. **Students should demonstrate an ability to analyze shape, estimate measures of center and spread and discuss these characteristics for given distributions.**

Project Update
Project 2, *Sabermetrics: The Fastest Player*, Project 3, *Coin Circulation*, and Project 5, *Class Survey*, on pages 67 and 68 relate to the content of this lesson.

Additional Answers

11a.

◇	A	B	C
1	Score Interval	Frequency	Relative Frequency
2	50-59	1	0.033
3	60-69	6	0.200
4	70-79	10	0.333
5	80-89	6	0.200
6	90-99	7	0.233

11b.

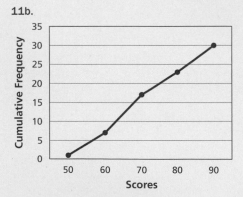

14c.

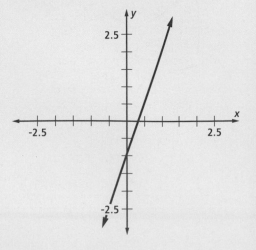

REVIEW

9. a. Consider the height in inches of a group of students. If the standard deviation is 4.3 in., what is the variance? **18.49 in^2**
   b. If the variance is 9.6 in^2, what is the standard deviation? **3.098 in**
   (**Lesson 1-6**)

10. The data in this table show how quickly 6 elevators can go from the ground floor to the top level. Let x = number of floors and y = the time in seconds. (**Lesson 1-6**)
    a. Calculate $\bar{x}$ and s_x. **$\bar{x} \approx 93.17$ floors, $s_x \approx 38.1$**
    b. Calculate $\bar{y}$ and s_y. **$\bar{y} = 32.3$ seconds, $s_y \approx 12.68$**

Building	Number of Floors	Elevator Time (sec)
Taipei 101 (Taiwan)	101	30.2
Yokohama Landmark Tower (Japan)	73	23.7
Burj Dubai (UAE)	162	55.5
Sunshine 60 (Japan)	60	24.0
John Hancock Center (USA)	100	37.6
Freshwater Place (Australia)	63	22.8

Sources: Eporis.com; Forbes.com

11. A class of 30 students received the following scores on their 100-point mid-semester physics test. (**Lesson 1-5**) **See margin.**

63	96	68	84	52	79	88	80	75	72
90	75	78	97	68	74	76	91	76	74
92	80	85	60	77	94	81	60	96	65

   a. Make a table of the data, showing the frequency and relative frequency of each score.
   b. Draw a cumulative frequency line graph for the data.

In 12 and 13, consider the following data set:
13, 27, 11, 15, 9, 16, 18, 11, 6, 8, 11. (Lesson 1-2)

12. a. Calculate $\sum_{i=1}^{11} x_i$. **145**
    b. Calculate $\bar{x}$. **about 13.18**

13. Calculate $\sum_{i=1}^{11} (x_i)^2 - \left(\sum_{i=1}^{11} x_i\right)^2$. **-18,778**

14. Consider the line with equation $y + 7 = 3(x + 2)$. (**Previous Course**)
    a. Show that $y = 3x - 1$ is an equation for the same line.
    b. What are the slope and y-intercept of the line? **$m = 3, b = -1$**
    c. Sketch a graph of the line. **See margin.**

14a. $y + 7 = 3x + 6$
$y = 3x - 1$

15. Find an equation for the line passing through $(5, 0)$ and $(0, \pi)$. (**Previous Course**) $y = -\frac{\pi}{5}x + \pi$

EXPLORATION

16. In Example 1 of this lesson, the variable studied is height, and the data come from two sets (NBA basketball players and NFL football players). The two distributions are quite different. Think of another pair of sets with distributions of a variable that you would expect to be different. Gather information about these distributions to see if your expectation is correct.

60   Exploring Data

Additional Answers

16. Answers vary. A complete answer should include a five number summary, mean, standard deviation and range for each data set. Box plots and histograms can help students compare and contrast the data sets.

Lesson 1-8

Using Statistics to Solve a Mystery: The Case of the Federalist Papers

▶ **BIG IDEA** Basic statistical analysis is used in many fields to investigate important questions.

Disputes about authorship arise in the press, the legal system, and even among historians. One such dispute was a "mystery" concerning some famous documents in United States history, *The Federalist* papers. Frequency distributions were used to investigate this mystery.

Background

The Federalist papers were written between 1787 and 1788 under the pen name "Publius" to persuade the citizens of the State of New York to ratify the Constitution. Of the 85 *Federalist* papers, 14 were known to be written by James Madison, 51 by Alexander Hamilton, 5 by John Jay, and 3 were joint works. The remaining 12 papers were called "disputed" because historians were unsure whether they were written by Hamilton or Madison.

For many years historians tried to determine which author wrote each of the disputed papers. The dispute could not be settled by comparing the ideas in the papers because the philosophies of the men were so similar. In the 1960s two statisticians, Frederick Mosteller of Harvard University and David Wallace of the University of Chicago, used computers to count the frequency of key words in documents known to have been authored by the two men: 48 papers by Hamilton and 50 papers by Madison.

Key words were chosen that were not tied too closely to either author's writing style. The words were also chosen to be independent of the context of the paper being examined. For their study, they chose to use "by," "from," and "to." Mosteller and Wallace calculated the relative frequency of the occurrence of each word. If the key word "by" occurred 32 times in a paper of 2075 words, the rate of occurrence was $\frac{32}{2075} = 0.0154$. They reported each relative frequency as the number of occurrences per 1000 words: $(0.0154) \cdot 1000 = 15.4$ occurrences per 1000 words. Note that 15.4 per 1000 equals 1.54 per 100, or 1.54%.

The table on the next page shows the frequencies of the three key words in the 48 papers by Hamilton (H) and the 50 papers by Madison (M). For example, the word "from" was used by Hamilton 5–7 times in 21 of his 48 papers. Take a few minutes to read the table before going on.

Mental Math

What is the mean of $4x + 5$ and $-8x + 2$?
$-2x + \frac{7}{2}$

James Madison (1751–1809)

GOAL

Use statistics in a historical setting and give students an opportunity to replicate a serious use of statistics quite different from the usual.

SPUR Objective

G Use statistics to compare and contrast two data sets in the context of a situation.

Materials/Resources

· Lesson Master 1-8
· Resource Masters 24 and 25

HOMEWORK	• Option 1
• Questions 1–8	• Option 2
• • Questions 9–17	
• • Question 18 (extra credit)	
• • Self-Test	

Local Standards

1   Warm-Up

Suppose that you were going to try to determine whether the same person wrote Lessons 1-3 and 1-4 of this book by counting the relative frequency of the use of certain words in the text, ignoring examples, questions, and activities.

a. Choose two words you might use. **Answers vary. Sample: "of" and "in"**

b. Do the relative frequencies of these words differ in the two lessons? **Answers vary. Sample: There are 2057 words total in Lesson 1-3, 1768 words total in Lesson 1-4. The relative frequencies of the chosen words are in the following table.**

Relative Frequency (per 1000 words)		
Word	1–3	1–4
of	61	44
in	41	20

Background

The methods used by the statisticians who studied the authorship of *The Federalist* papers are surprisingly simple. Yet they can be and have been applied to resolve the authorship of other disputed works. Furthermore, study of this lesson can be connected with virtually any course in United States history.

The lesson is about a detective story in American history, and requires a little knowledge of American history that we assume students have or are acquiring.

Before assigning the reading, it is useful to check that students know who Alexander Hamilton and James Madison were. You might share this lesson with your colleagues who teach history and other social studies. They may have additional information about this topic. In many schools, social studies teachers have been delighted to see their subject studied in a mathematics class and more than happy to supply additional information about the history.

(continued on next page)

1-8

c. Would you conclude that they were written by the same person, or by different people? **Answers vary. Sample: The relative frequencies of the words "of" and "in" for the two lessons are similar, so the lessons may have been written by the same author.**

2 Teaching

Notes on the Lesson

Many of the ideas presented in Lesson 1-1 are used in this lesson. Students need to pay careful attention to the titles and labels of the tables and graphs, keep track of the units of measure (word rates and frequencies), calculate statistics, and make inferences.

It is also useful for students to have a sense of the history behind *The Federalist* papers. You might see if anyone in your class can answer the following questions.

1. It is well known that the Declaration of Independence of the United States from England was announced in 1776. In what year was the Constitution of the United States drawn up for the original 13 states to ratify? **1787**
2. Name the first five presidents of the United States, in order.
   George Washington, John Adams, Thomas Jefferson, James Madison, James Monroe
3. When did the first president of the United States begin his first of two terms in office? **1789 or 1791, when the Constitution was finally ratified.**
4. Alexander Hamilton's portrait appears on the $10 bill. What position did he hold that provides a reason for his appearing there? **He was the first Secretary of the Treasury, from 1789 to 1795. He might have later become president, but he was killed in a duel with Aaron Burr during Jefferson's term of office.**

Additional Answers

Activity 1

Step 1:

Federalist paper	Rate per 1000 words		
	"by"	"from"	"to"
A	4.05	3.32	46.43
B	15.27	4.36	27.27
C	5.73	4.85	48.04
D	9.96	3.09	35.02

Frequency Distribution of Rate per Thousand Words of the Words "by," "from," and "to" in 48 Hamilton and 50 Madison Papers

"by"			"from"			"to"		
Rate	H	M	Rate	H	M	Rate	H	M
1-3*	2		1-3*	3	3	23-26*		3
3-5	7		3-5	15	19	26-29	2	2
5-7	12	5	5-7	21	17	29-32	2	11
7-9	18	7	7-9	9	6	32-35	4	11
9-11	4	8	9-11		1	35-38	6	7
11-13	5	16	11-13		3	38-41	10	6
13-15		6	13-15		1	41-44	8	
15-17		5				44-47	10	
17-19		3				47-50	3	
						50-53	1	
						53-56	1	
						56-59	1	
Totals	**48**	**50**	**Totals**	**48**	**50**	**Totals**	**48**	**50**

*Each interval excludes its upper endpoint. Thus a paper with a rate of exactly 3 per 100 words would appear in the count for the 3-5 interval.

🛑 See Quiz Yourself at the right.

> **▶ QUIZ YOURSELF**
>
> What word from the table does Madison use 13-15 times in 6 papers?

Activity 1 See margin.

Below are the counts for the words "by," "from," and "to" in four *Federalist* papers known to be written by either Hamilton or Madison. Follow the steps to determine the author of each of the four papers.

Federalist Paper	Frequency			Number of Words	Rate per 1000 words		
	"by"	"from"	"to"		"by"	"from"	"to"
A	11	9	126	2714	?	?	?
B	42	12	75	2750	?	?	?
C	13	11	109	2269	?	?	?
D	29	9	102	2913	?	?	?

Step 1 Complete the table and find the rate per thousand words of "by," "from," and "to" for each unknown paper.

Step 2 Determine where each of the rates calculated in Step 1 fit in the table at the top of the page.

Step 3: Based on where the rates fit into the table, conjecture as to the authorship of each of the papers A, B, C, and D. Justify your answers.

62 Exploring Data

Students do not have all of the statistics that they would need to know in order to confirm the conclusions of Mosteller and Wallace. In the lesson, we use frequency distributions and histograms. Mosteller and Wallace were able to compare *mathematically* the distributions of the words "by," "from," and "to" from Madison with the corresponding distributions of Hamilton in much the same way as statistics can be used to compare the scores of one class with the scores of another.

In this lesson, we do that comparison by sight. Sight methods can give intuition but are insufficient for coming up with the conclusions presented on page 63.

Analyzing the Frequency of the Word "by"

The table at the top of the preceding page, which analyzes papers of known authorship shows that the word "by" is used much more frequently by Madison than it is by Hamilton. The rate of its occurrence seems to distinguish between the two authors. The word "to" seems more used by Hamilton. In contrast, the use of the word "from" does not distinguish one man's writing from the other.

Based on this information, Mosteller and Wallace compared the use of the word "by" in the disputed *Federalist* papers to its use in the papers known to be authored by Hamilton and Madison. The relative frequency distributions comparing the use of the word "by" in the Hamilton papers, the Madison papers, and the disputed papers are shown at the right.

The shape of the graph for the disputed papers is clearly more like the shape of Madison's than that of Hamilton's. The median rate of occurrence of the word "by" is 11–13 for Madison's papers and for the disputed papers, and the median rate is only 7–9 for Hamilton's papers.

This evidence suggests that the disputed papers are Madison's. In fact, the full research study demonstrated that it is extremely likely that Madison authored 11 of the 12 disputed papers and probably the 12th as well.

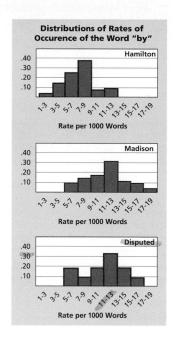

Distributions of Rates of Occurence of the Word "by"

Analyzing the Frequency of the Word "to"

Activity 2

Data about the use of the word "to" in the disputed *Federalist* papers are below.

Step 1 Complete this table and find the rate per thousand words for "to".

Federalist Paper	Frequency of "to"	Number of Words	Rate per Thousand Words
No. 49	58	1656	___?___ 35.02
No. 50	28	1113	___?___ 25.16
No. 51	50	1921	___?___ 26.03
No. 52	72	1854	___?___ 38.83
No. 53	73	2172	___?___ 33.61
No. 54	61	2005	___?___ 30.42
No. 55	78	2047	___?___ 38.10
No. 56	39	1571	___?___ 24.82
No. 57	74	2213	___?___ 33.44
No. 58	61	2093	___?___ 29.14
No. 62	80	2391	___?___ 33.46
No. 63	88	3046	___?___ 28.89

Using Statistics to Solve a Mystery: The Case of the Federalist Papers **63**

Notes on the Lesson

Students may be concerned that the distribution of the disputed papers overlaps with both the distributions of Hamilton and Madison, and therefore how could one be certain (except for the papers with high rates of the use of the word "by") that a paper was written by Madison and not Hamilton? Emphasize that these distributions were not the only data that Mosteller and Wallace had, but even with all the data, they could only come up with a probability that the disputed authorship papers were written by Madison.

Additional Answers

Activity 1

Step 2: Paper A fits into the 3–5, 3–5 and 44–47 rate categories for "by," "from" and "to," respectively. Paper B fits into the 15–17, 3–5 and 26–29 rate categories for "by," "from," and "to" respectively. Paper C fits into the 5–7, 3–5 and 47–50 rate categories for "by," "from," and "to" respectively. Paper D fits into the 9–11, 3–5 and 35–38 rate categories for "by," "from" and "to," respectively.

Step 3: Hamilton probably wrote Papers A and C, and Madison likely wrote Paper B. It is unclear who wrote Paper D. These conclusions are reached by comparing the data for A, B, C, and D to that of the papers known to be written by Hamilton and Madison and seeing which author each fits best.

1-8

3 Assignment

Recommended Assignment
- Questions 1–8
- • Questions 9–17
- • Question 18 (extra credit)
- • Self-Test

Notes on the Questions
Questions 1–10 It is essential that students read the lesson in order to answer these questions.

Additional Answers

Activity 2

Steps 2–5: See the Additional Answers section at the back of the book.

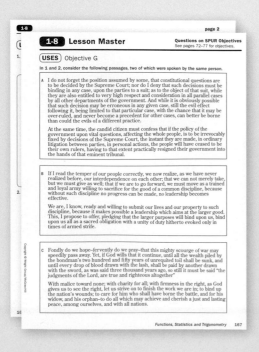

Step 2 Make a relative frequency table using the same bins that Mosteller and Wallace did in their table.

Step 3 Make a histogram from the data in the table you made in Step 2.

Step 4 Using the rate data of the word "to" from the table on page 64, make a histogram for Hamilton and one for Madison. Make sure the bin widths are the same as in your histogram from Step 3.

Step 5: Compare the histogram of the disputed Federalist papers from Step 3 to the ones you made in Step 4 for Hamilton and Madison. How do the shapes of the graphs compare? What about the median rates? Based on your evidence from the word "to", who do you believe to be the author of the disputed papers?

Steps 2–5. See margin.

Beware! Statistical reasoning is *inferential*, not deductive. That is, statistical research does not *prove* findings with certainty as in geometry or algebra. Instead, statistics gives evidence for what is *likely*, and gives a measure for a level of confidence. For example, Mosteller and Wallace reported that for the *most* disputed paper, their evidence yields odds of 80 to 1 that the author was Madison. They called these odds strong but not overwhelming. The odds were much higher and considered to be overwhelming for the other 11 papers.

Questions

COVERING THE IDEAS

1. Why were *The Federalist* papers written?

In 2–4, refer to the table on page 62.

2. a. In how many of Hamilton's papers was the word "to" used at a rate of between 38 and 41 per 1000? **10**

   b. In how many of Madison's papers was the word "to" used at a rate of between 38 and 41 per 1000? **6**

3. How many papers of Hamilton and Madison were compared to produce the table? **48 papers by Hamilton and 50 papers by Madison**

4. If a Hamilton paper uses "by" with a rate of 11 words per 1000, which bin is it in? **11–13**

In 5 and 6, refer to the histograms of the word "by" on page 63.

5. In what percent of the disputed papers was the word "by" used 11–13 times per thousand? **about 32%**

6. Would you expect fewer occurrences of the word "by" in a 1000-word essay by Hamilton or by Madison? Why?

7. What is meant by *inferential reasoning*?

8. Suppose a disputed paper has a rate of 6 uses of "from," 30 uses of "to," and 15 uses of "by," each per 1000 words. Who is the likely author, Hamilton or Madison? Explain your choice.

64 Exploring Data

1. The Federalist papers were written between 1787 and 1788 in order to persuade the citizens of the State of New York to ratify the Constitution.

6. Answers may vary. Sample: Hamilton, because the mean number of occurrences of the word "by" in papers authored by Hamilton is less than the mean in papers authored by Madison.

7. Inferential reasoning gives evidence for what is likely, but does not prove findings with certainty.

8. Madison; Although the paper's usage of 'from' does not indicate one author over the other, the usages of 'by' and 'to' indicate that Madison is the most likely author.

Accommodating the Learner ⬇

Some students might not understand why relative frequency histograms are shown on page 63 as opposed to frequency histograms. Point out that each data set reflects a different number of papers: 48 by Hamilton, 50 by Madison, and 12 that are disputed. So comparisons can only be made by converting each frequency to a relative frequency.

APPLYING THE MATHEMATICS

9. Suppose one of the disputed Federalist papers has 2107 words. The paper has 17 uses of "by," 8 uses of "from," and 97 uses of "to." Who is the likely author, Hamilton or Madison? Explain your choice.

10. Compute the weighted averages per 1000 words of the word "by" in all the papers known to be written by Hamilton and Madison. Use the median for each interval.

11. People diagnosed as ill with flu or a cold were asked questions about their illness and had their body temperatures measured. People were asked to "rate the pain in your muscles on a scale of 0–10 where 0 is no pain and 10 is very severe pain." Further, each was asked to rate their coughing on a scale of 0 (no cough) to 10 (constant coughing). CAUTION: These data are not to be used to diagnose cold or flu.

Pain Rating		
Temp	Flu	Cold
96-97	1	5
97-98	1	6
98-99	3	15
99-100	4	14
100-101	10	9
101-102	11	1
102-103	9	0
103-104	5	0
104-105	1	0
Total	45	50

Pain Rating		
Muscle	Flu	Cold
0-1	6	12
2-3	12	22
4-5	17	10
6-7	8	5
8-10	2	1
Total	45	50

Rating		
Cough	Flu	Cold
0-1	7	10
2-3	9	9
4-5	18	23
6-7	8	7
8-10	3	1
Total		

a. Marco has a temperature of 101.2. He rates his muscle pain as a 7, and cough as a 5. Which illness does Marco likely have? Explain your decision.

b. Annette rates her muscle pain as 3 and cough as 5. Her temperature is 98.3. Which illness does Annette likely have? Explain your answer.

REVIEW

In 12 and 13, describe a possible shape for the distribution of the variable. Explain your reasoning. (Lesson 1-3)

12. the prices of homes sold in the U. S. last year **See margin.**

13. the numbers of points scored by the winning team in WNBA (Women's National Basketball Association) games played last year

13. Answers vary. Sample: This is likely symmetric, centered around some average winning score.

9. This disputed paper has rates of 8.07, 3.80, and 46.04 per 1000 words for "by," "from," and "to," respectively. This pattern more closely matches Hamilton's word usage than Madison's.

10. See margin.

11a. Marco likely has the flu since two data points, especially his fever, match the data for the flu better than for a cold.

11b. Annette likely has a cold since both her temperature and the magnitude of her muscle pain match the median values for a cold better than the flu. The data about coughing is inconclusive.

Additional Answers

10.

Weighted Averages		
Rate per 1000 words	H	M
1-3	4.17	0
3-5	14.58	0
5-7	25	10
7-9	37.5	14
9-11	8.33	16
11-13	10.42	32
13-15	0	12
15-17	0	10
17-19	0	6
Total	100	100

12. Answers vary. Sample: This may be skewed with a tail on the right because fewer people can afford very expensive homes.

Accommodating the Learner ⬆

In this chapter, students have seen how displays of statistical data can sometimes be deceiving (intentionally or not). Each example below contains a statistical statement of fact from a data set followed by a conclusion. Have students explain why the conclusion might not be appropriate.

1. The average age of students at XYZ college is 26 years. Therefore the college's radio station should plan most of its programming for the over-25 crowd. **Answers vary.**

Sample: Which average was used? The mode might be more appropriate.

2. The average height for children of your child's age is 32 inches. Your child is 2 inches below normal. **Average and normal may not be the same thing.**

3. The most frequently stolen car is Brand X. Therefore, Brand X is the least secure car on the market. **Brand X may also be the most frequently sold car.**

1-8

Notes on the Questions

Question 18 Sometimes *cliometrics* means the application of statistics to history more generally than economic history.

4 Wrap-Up

Project Update

Project 6, *The Disputed Federalist Papers*, on page 68 relates to the content of this lesson.

Additional Answers

14.

Five-number Summary	U.S.	Outside U.S.
Minimum	915	1017
Q_1	946	1085
Median	998.5	1152.5
Q_3	1046	1322.5
Maximum	1451	1667

The 20 tallest buildings outside the U.S. are generally taller than the 20 tallest buildings inside the U.S. The minimum height outside the U.S. is 102 ft greater than the minimum height inside the U.S., while the maximum height outside the U.S. is 216 ft greater than inside the U.S. Likewise, the median height outside the U.S. is 154 ft greater than in the U.S. While the IQR is slightly larger outside the U.S., only the U.S. data set has outliers: 1250 and 1451.

14. The table below includes the heights in feet of the 20 tallest buildings in the U.S. and the 20 tallest buildings outside of the U.S. Compute five-number summaries for each data set. Then write a descriptive paragraph comparing the data sets. (**Lesson 1-7**) See margin.

20 Tallest Buildings							
U.S.				**Outside U.S.**			
Name	Hgt (ft)	Name	Hgt (ft)	Name	Hgt (ft)	Name	Hgt (ft)
Sears Tower	1451	Prudential Plaza	995	Taipei 101	1667	Tuntex Sky	1140
Empire State	1250	Wells Fargo	992	Petronas 1	1483	The Center	1127
Aon Center	1136	311 S Wacker	961	Petronas 2	1483	Rose Tower	1127
John Hancock	1127	AIB Building	952	Jin Mao Building	1380	Shimao Plaza	1093
Chrysler Building	1046	Key Tower	947	Two IFC	1362	Minsheng Bank	1087
NY Times Building	1046	1 Liberty Place	945	CITIC Plaza	1283	Ryugyong Hotel	1083
Bank of America, GA	1039	Columbia Center	933	Shun Hing Square	1260	Q1	1058
US Bank Tower	1018	Trump Building	927	Central Plaza	1227	Burj al Arab	1053
AT&T Corp	1007	Bank of America, TX	921	Bank of China	1205	Nina Tower	1046
Morgan/Chase	1002	Citigroup Center	915	Emirates Tower	1165	Menara Tel	1017

Source: Emporis Research

15. The frequency diagram at the right shows how many pairs of shoes each of 100 people owns. Let i = the number of pairs of shoes, and $f(i)$ = the frequency of that number. (**Lessons 1-3, 1-2**)

a. What is the mode? **3**

b. What is $f(5)$? **13**

c. Evaluate $\sum_{i=4}^{11} f(i)$. **64**

d. What does the quantity $\dfrac{\sum_{i=1}^{11}(i \cdot f(i))}{\sum_{i=1}^{11} f(i)}$ represent? **15d. the average of shoe ownership per person**

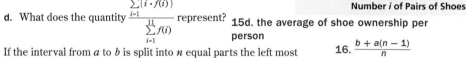

15d. the average of shoe ownership per person

16. If the interval from a to b is split into n equal parts the left most part is from a to $a + \frac{b-a}{n}$. Write the expression $a + \frac{b-a}{n}$ as a single fraction with denominator n. (**Previous Course**)

16. $\dfrac{b + a(n-1)}{n}$

17. Consider the graphs of $y = -x^2$ and $y = -|x|$. (**Previous Course**)

a. Describe several ways the graphs are alike.

b. Describe several ways the graphs are different.

17. See margin.

EXPLORATION

18. *Cliometrics* is the name given to the application of statistics to economic history. Find out how this word originated and discuss at least one thing that cliometricians have found. See margin.

QY ANSWERS

"by"

66 Exploring Data

Additional Answers

17a. Answers vary. Sample: The domain of both functions is all real numbers x and the range of both functions is $y \leq 0$. Both functions have an absolute maximum at $x = 0$.

17b. Answers vary. Sample: The slope of $y = -x^2$ changes continuously, while the slope of $y = -x$ is 1 for $x < 0$, -1 for $x > 0$ and undefined at $x = 0$.

18. Answers vary. Sample: The word cliometrics comes from the name Clio, who was the muse of history and heroic poetry in Greek mythology, and the word metrics, which refers to a standardized system of parameters for assessment. Cliometricians have corrected various inaccuracies in economic history. For example, some cliometricians argue that at the time of the Civil War, slavery was still profitable for slaveholders, and thus moral issues had a larger role in the end of slavery than historians typically believe.

Chapter 1 Projects

A project presents an opportunity for you to extend your knowledge of a topic related to the material of this chapter. You should allow time for a project than you do for typical homework questions.

1 Automobile Survey

What automobiles are most popular in your area?

a. Go to a large parking lot (near a shopping center, office building, or school) and classify at least 60 automobiles by the following criteria: style (van, truck, limousine, sports car, and so on), color, and manufacturer.

b. Report the results with at least three tables or displays. *frequency, relative freq.*

c. Write a paragraph or two summarizing and interpreting your findings.

d. Describe the differences that might have resulted if you had collected your data at a different location (e.g., senior citizens center, executive office garage, used car lot) or at a different time (church lot on Sunday, movies on a budget night).

2 Sabermetrics: The Fastest Player

Statistical means are used to compare baseball players who played at different times. For instance, data on the number of: bases stolen, times caught stealing, doubles, triples, and so on, can be used to compare the speeds of different players in order to determine who really was the fastest player. Using a baseball almanac or the Internet, investigate two players of your choosing. Devise a method and use it to determine the faster player.

3 Coin Circulation

It is common practice to collect pennies instead of spending them (thus putting them back in circulation). From a jar of pennies:

a. Choose a sample of 100 pennies. In a table, enter the frequency of pennies minted in a particular year and the relative frequencies.

b. Make a histogram of the data.

c. Do the same for nickels and compare the distributions.

d. Conjecture reasons for the differences in the distribution.

Project Rubric

Advanced	Student correctly provides all of the details asked for in the project as well as additional correct independent conclusions.
Proficient	Student correctly provides all of the details asked for in the project.
Partially proficient	Student correctly provides some of the details asked for in the project or provides all details with some inaccuracies.
Not proficient	Student correctly provides few of the details asked for in the project or provides all details with many inaccuracies.
No attempt	Student makes little or no attempt to complete the project.

Chapter 1

The projects relate to the content of the lessons of this chapter as follows:

Project	Lesson(s)
1	1-1, 1-3, 1-4
2	1-6, 1-7
3	1-1, 1-3, 1-6, 1-7
4	1-1, 1-2, 1-3, 1-4, 1-5
5	1-2, 1-3, 1-4, 1-6, 1-7
6	1-2, 1-8

1 Automobile Survey

You might wish to have students work in groups and each do the task in a different place. Then they can summarize their own data and work together to come up with a more representative answer to Part d.

2 Sabermetrics: The Fastest Player

This project may cause some impassioned debate between die-hard baseball fans. If many students select this project, try to ensure that the same players are not featured in every presentation. You may suggest that students consult an older friend or relative for ideas of prominent past players.

3 Coin Circulation

For this project you will need 100 each of pennies and nickels. Some students may have a coin collection at home which will contain sufficient quantities of each. If not, you may need to help students strategize on the best way to come up with these quantities. They may combine smaller collections, or purchase/exchange coin rolls at the bank.

4 Graphing and Interpreting Statistical Data

Many students are likely to be adept at computer word processing and graphics and should be allowed to reproduce the table so that they do not have to use the original in its original size. Stress that they should focus not just on the aesthetics of their poster but also carefully consider their interpretation of the data. The headline and displays should be informative as well as catchy.

5 Class Survey

This project is particularly suited to small-group work but may also be undertaken as a whole-class activity. We have intentionally included some area measures in anticipation of exploring non-linear relationships, and have avoided more sensitive variables such as weight, family income, and parental data. You should feel free to change the list of attributes, for you are in the best position to decide on the merits of particular variables for your class. The database constructed here should be maintained, for in the Chapter 2 Projects there is opportunity to use it.

6 The Disputed Federalist Papers

This project follows up the discussion in the lesson. As it is fairly straightforward to obtain the texts and generate word counts, you may wish to emphasize the importance of the statistical analysis part of the project. The intent is for students to use statistics to meaningfully summarize and interpret raw data so they should be able to present their findings in a report format that contains tables and graphs placed meaningfully within text.

Sample Answers for projects are in the Solution Manual in the Electronic Teacher's Edition.

4 Graphing and Interpreting Statistical Data

Obtain a copy of a recent edition of either the *Statistical Abstract of the United States* or an almanac. Pick data that you find interesting or surprising (or both) that are presented in a table. Design a poster, at least 22" × 28", that interprets the data in the table, including displays to support your interpretation. Make sure that you choose a suitable headline for your poster that will attract people's attention.

5 Class Survey

Compile a database of information about the members of your mathematics class.

a. Ask each person to complete an information sheet for the following data. Where appropriate, measure in centimeters.
   - gender
   - height
   - hand span
   - foot length
   - time spent getting ready for school each day
   - travel time to school each morning
   - time at work each day
   - time spent on homework each day
   - number of people living at home
   - language most often spoken
   - time spent on the Internet each day
   - usual mode of travel to school (school bus, walk, skateboard, bike, car, and so on)
   - time spent watching TV each day
   - time spent exercising each day

b. Construct a computer or calculator file with the class database. The database will be used again in later chapters.

c. Choose at least three variables. Use a statistics utility to display and summarize the data. For each variable decide which type of display is most appropriate (box plot, stemplot, bar graph, and so on). Whenever appropriate, calculate statistics such as the mean, median, standard deviation, percentiles, and range.

d. Write a short paragraph describing a "typical" student in your class in terms of the variables you analyzed. For numerical variables, this will involve interpreting both the center and spread of the distributions.

e. Find a variable whose value differs quite a bit by gender. Find a variable whose value doesn't differ much by gender. Justify your conclusions with statistical values or displays.

6 The Disputed Federalist Papers

Stylistic words other than those discussed in Lesson 1-8 may be used to confirm or deny the results found by Mosteller and Wallace. In a manner comparable to that carried out in Lesson 1-8, choose a stylistic word such as "of," "in," "because," "that," "and," "but," and so on, and count its occurrences in the Federalist Papers written by Hamilton and Madison, as well as the disputed papers. Confirm or deny Mosteller and Wallace's results using these data. The documents may all be found online, and words can be counted quickly using a word-processor search application.

Notes

_____

_____

_____

_____

_____

_____

_____

_____

_____

Chapter 1

Summary and Vocabulary

This page lists the most important terms and phrases for this chapter. You should be able to give a general description and a specific example of each and a precise definition for those marked with an asterisk (*).

○ Statistics is the science of the collection, organization, analysis, and interpretation of data. The set of *all* individuals or objects that could be studied is the **population**. A **sample** is a subset of the population.

○ Data can be organized and displayed in tables and graphs. Bar graphs, line graphs, box plots, dotplots, cumulative frequency graphs, and histograms are kinds of graphs studied in this chapter.

○ Summary statistics and graphs enable comparisons between data sets. Good written descriptions of data sets include discussion of shape, centers, and spreads. Measures such as the mean, median, and sometimes the mode indicate centers of the data. Measures of spread include the range, interquartile range, **variance**, and **standard deviation**. The **five-number summary** (minimum, first quartile, median (2nd quartile), third quartile, maximum) is one way to summarize the center and spread in a data set. The symbol for summation, Σ (sigma), provides a short way to write expressions for several of these measures.

○ Comparisons depend on common units. Relative frequencies, percents, rates, and percentiles in data sets are statistics useful because comparisons are not affected by the size of samples.

Vocabulary

1-1
*statistic(s)
data, datum
variable
*population
*sample
survey
census
representative sample
categorical variable
numerical variable

1-2
*mean
*median
*measures of center, measures of central tendency
mode
subscripted variables
sigma Σ
index i
summation notation, sigma notation, Σ-notation
weighted average
relative frequency

Vocabulary

1-3
distribution
histogram
bins
frequency histogram
relative frequency histogram
skewed
symmetric
population pyramid

1-4
box plot, box-and-whiskers plot
minimum
first (lower) quartile
second quartile
third (upper) quartile
maximum
*five-number summary
*interquartile range (IQR)
whiskers
outlier

1-5
cumulative data
*percentile, pth percentile

1-6
range
deviation
*population variance σ^2
*population standard deviation σ
*sample variance s^2
*sample standard deviation s

Chapter 1

Summary and Vocabulary

The Summary gives an overview of the entire chapter and provides an opportunity for students to consider the material as a whole. Thus, the Summary can be used to help students relate and unify the concepts presented in the chapter.

Vocabulary words and symbols are listed by lesson to provide a checklist of concepts that students must know. Emphasize to students that they should read the vocabulary list carefully before starting the Self-Test on pages 70–71. If students do not understand the meaning of a vocabulary word, they should refer back to the indicated lesson.

Theorems and Properties covered in the chapter are listed below the Summary with page references included to lead students back to the location in the chapter where the theorem or property is stated.

Self-Test

For the development of mathematical competence, feedback and correction, along with the opportunity for practice, are necessary. The Self-Test provides the opportunity for feedback and correction; the Chapter Review provides additional opportunities for practice. We cannot overemphasize the importance of these end-of-chapter materials. It is at this point that the material gels for many students, allowing them to solidify skills and understanding. In general, student performance should improve after these pages.

Assign the Self-Test as a one-night assignment. Worked-out solutions for all questions are in the Selected Answers section of the student book. Encourage students to take the Self-Test honestly, grade themselves, and then be prepared to discuss the test in class.

Advise students to pay special attention to those Chapter Review questions (pages 72–77) that correspond to the questions they missed on the Self-Test. These are identified in the Self-Test Correlation Chart located in the Selected Answers section at the back of the book.

Additional Answers

1. variance: $\dfrac{\sum\limits_{i=1}^{14}(x_i - \bar{x})^2}{14} \approx \dfrac{\sum\limits_{i=1}^{14}(x_i - 21.6)^2}{14}$

$\approx 195.245;$

standard deviation: $\sqrt{195.245} \approx 13.973$

2. $\dfrac{\sum\limits_{i=1}^{14} x_i}{14} \approx 21.6$

3.
High School Football Team Scores

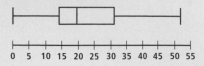

4. $Q_1 = 14$ and $Q_3 = 31$ so IQR = 17; $Q_1 - 1.5 \cdot 17 = -11.5$, $Q_3 + 1.5 \cdot 17 = 56.5$. No values in the data set are less than -11.5 or greater than 56.5, so there are no outliers.

Chapter **1** Self-Test

1–15. See margin.

Take this test as you would take a test in class. You will need a calculator. Then use the Selected Answers section in the back of the book to check your work.

In 1–5, the following data set is the number of points a high school football team scored in 14 games.

$x_1 = 14, x_2 = 21, x_3 = 0, x_4 = 45, x_5 = 20,$
$x_6 = 31, x_7 = 33, x_8 = 17, x_9 = 21, x_{10} = 7,$
$x_{11} = 6, x_{12} = 52, x_{13} = 19, x_{14} = 16.$

1. Find the variance and standard deviation of the data. Use population statistics.

2. Write an expression for the mean using Σ-notation.

3. Draw a box plot of the data.

4. Does the data set contain any outliers under the $1.5 \times$ IQR criterion? If so, name them. If not, explain why not.

5. If another data set of points scored in 14 games by a second high school football team had a smaller standard deviation than that found in Question 1, which team would have more variability in points scored?

6. Consider the table below of the number of staff positions in California public schools for 2003. Complete the table to find the relative frequency of each position.

Position	Frequency	Relative Frequency
Principals	13,340	?
Teachers	304,311	?
Aides	69,201	?
Office/Clerical	36,116	?
Counselors	6,640	?
Librarians	1,218	?
Other	109,381	?

Source: National Center for Education Statistics

7. **True or False** Extreme data affects the median of a data set less than it affects the mean.

8. Consider the box plot below.

2002–2003 Revenues for Public Schools by State (Billions of Dollars)

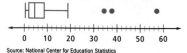

Source: National Center for Education Statistics

a. Estimate a five-number summary for the box plot.

b. Between which two values are the middle 50% of the data?

9. Tell whether each given measure of spread is directly calculated using the mean.

a. range
b. variance
c. IQR
d. standard deviation

10. All mountains in the world whose altitude is at least 8,000 meters are represented in the histogram below.

Mountains With at Least 8000 m of Altitude

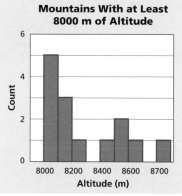

Source: The World Almanac, 2007

a. How many mountains in the world are at least 8,000 meters high?

b. Describe the shape of the distribution.

Additional Answers

5. The first team has more variability since its data have a larger standard deviation.

6.

Position	Frequency	Relative Frequency
Principals	13,340	0.025
Teachers	304,311	0.563
Aides	69,201	0.128
Office/Clerical	36,116	0.067
Counselors	6,640	0.012
Librarians	1,218	0.002
Other	109,381	0.202

7. True, because even if there are a few extreme data points in a set the median still picks out the central value. The extreme points have as much effect as non-extreme points with the mean.

8a. minimum: 1, Q_1: 2, median: 4, Q_3: 9, maximum: 57

8b. between 2 and 9 inclusive

9a. The range is not calculated using the mean.

9b. The variance is the mean of squared deviations from the mean; therefore, it is calculated using the mean.

9c. The IQR is not calculated using the mean.

11. Consider the table below about the U.S. Budget.
   a. Which source was expected to contribute the greatest amount of additional receipts in 2007 as compared to 2006? Explain how you know.
   b. Which source was expected to provide the greatest percent increase in revenues from 2007 to 2008?

Category	Actual 2006	Estimate 2007	Estimate 2008
Personal Income Taxes	1,043.9	1,168.8	1,246.6
Corporate Income Taxes	353.9	342.1	314.9
Insurance and Retirement Receipts	837.8	837.4	974.2
Excise Taxes	74.0	57.1	68.1
Estate and Gift Taxes	27.9	25.3	25.7
Customs Duties	24.8	26.8	29.2
Miscellaneous Receipts	45.0	46.7	50.7
Total Receipts	2,407.3	2,540.1	2662.5

Source: Budget of the United States Government, 2008

12. The monthly average snowfall (in inches) in Boulder, Colorado, from a recent year are shown at the right.
   a. Compute the cumulative snowfalls by month.
   b. Draw a cumulative line graph of the annual snowfall.
   c. What percent of the annual snowfall had fallen by the end of March?

Month	Snowfall (inches)
January	5.5
February	11.4
March	23.3
April	2.9
May	0.1
June	0
July	0
August	0
September	0
October	15.2
November	12.0
December	45.5

Source: National Oceanic and Atmospheric Administration

13. Carol's college computes grade point averages (GPAs) by assigning points for grades, A = 4, A− = 3.7, B+ = 3.3, B = 3, B− = 2.7, C+ = 2.3, C = 2, C− = 1.7, D+ = 1.3, D = 1, F = 0. It then weights the grade by the number of semester hours for each course. Compute Carol's first semester GPA based on the report below.

Course	Grade	Hours
Writing	B+	2
Calculus	A	4
Spanish I	C+	6
Am Lit	B	4

In 14 and 15, use the following histograms and box plots of test scores from two classes of high school students.

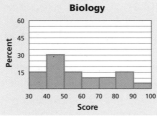

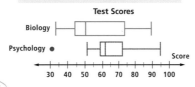

14. Use the histograms. What percent of students scored at least 80 on the psychology test?

15. Compare and contrast the two distributions using the information in the box plots.

Additional Answers

11b. For each category, subtract the estimated 2007 receipt from the estimated 2008 receipt and divide by the amount of the 2007 receipt. The greatest percentage increase is for excise taxes.

	Estimated Receipts ($ billions)		% Change
	2007	**2008**	
Personal Income Taxes	1168.8	1246.6	0.07
Corporate Income Taxes	342.1	314.9	−0.08
Insurance and Retirement Receipts	837.4	974.2	0.16
Excise Taxes	57.1	68.1	0.19
Estate and Gift Taxes	25.3	25.7	0.02
Customs Duties	26.8	29.2	0.09
Miscellaneous Receipts	46.7	50.7	0.09

12a.

Month	Cumulative Snowfall (inches)
January	5.5
February	16.9
March	40.2
April	43.1
May	43.2
June	43.2
July	43.2
August	43.2
September	43.2
October	58.4
November	70.4
December	115.9

12b.

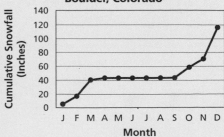

Cumulative Average Snowfall in Boulder, Colorado

12c. $\frac{40.2}{115.9} \approx 0.347$ or 34.7%

Additional Answers

9d. The standard deviation is calculated with the mean because it is the square root of the variance.

10a. 14

10b. The distribution is skewed with a tail on the right. A third of the mountains at least 8000 m high are between 8000 m and 8100 m high.

11a. Subtract the actual 2006 receipts from the estimated 2007 receipts. Personal income taxes have the largest increase: 1,168.8 − 1,043.9 = 124.9 billion dollars.

11b.–12c. See side margin.

13. $\frac{2 \cdot 3.3 + 4 \cdot 4 + 6 \cdot 2.3 + 4 \cdot 3}{2 + 4 + 6 + 4} = 3.025$

14. Adding up the last two intervals, 15% of students scored at least 80 on the psychology test.

15. The median score for Psychology is higher than for Biology, indicating that Psychology scores are generally higher than Biology. Both distributions seem to be slightly skewed with a tail on the right, especially if the outlier in Psychology is thrown out. Lastly, the spread of the Biology scores is greater, as indicated by a larger IQR.

Chapter 1 Review

Chapter Review

The main objectives for the chapter are organized in the Chapter Review under the four types of understanding this book promotes: Skills, Properties, Uses, and Representations.

Whereas end-of-chapter material may be considered optional in some texts, in UCSMP *Functions, Statistics and Trigonometry* we have selected these objectives and questions with the expectation that they will be covered. Students should be able to answer these questions with about 85% accuracy after studying the chapter.

You may assign these questions over a single night to help students prepare for a test the next day or you may assign the questions over a two-day period. If you work the questions over two days, we recommend assigning the evens for homework the first night so that students get feedback in class the next day, and then assigning the odds the night before the test because the answers are provided to the odd-numbered questions in the Selected Answers section at the back of the book.

It is effective to ask students which questions they still do not understand and use the day as a total class discussion of the material that the class finds most difficult.

Resources

- Assessment Resources: Chapter 1 Test

Technology Resources

Teacher's Assessment Assistant, Ch. 1
Electronic Teacher's Edition, Ch. 1

Chapter 1 Chapter Review

The Chapter Review questions are grouped according to the SPUR Objectives in this chapter.

SKILLS Procedures used to get answers.

OBJECTIVE A Calculate measures of center and spread for data sets. (Lessons 1-2, 1-4, 1-6)

In 1 and 2, use the data set {4, 8, 12, 14, 14, 16, 16, 18, 18, 20} for a sample. Find each statistic.

1. a. range**16**
   b. median**15**
   c. IQR**6**

2. a. mean**14**
   b. variance**24**
   c. standard deviation**$2\sqrt{6}$**

In 3 and 4, the ages in years of some of Max's relatives are {2, 12, 24, 9, 14, 29, 33, 9, 15, 61, 42, 48, 42, 56}. Calculate each statistic.

3. a. median**26.5**
   b. $\bar{x}$ about **28.3**
   c. mode**9 and 42**
   d. range**59**
   e. s about **19.1**

4. a. minimum**2**
   b. maximum**61**
   c. Q_1**12**
   d. Q_2**26.5**
   e. Q_3**42**

5. Give the five-number summary for the data set below.**See margin.**

State	Area	State	Area
Alaska	571,951	Montana	145,552
Utah	82,144	Wisconsin	54,310
California	155,959	Illinois	55,584
Rhode Island	1,045	Maine	30,862
Pennsylvania	44,817	Texas	261,797
Michigan	56,804	Florida	53,927

Source: U.S. Geological Survey

6. The median of a data set is 125, Q_1 is 99, and the IQR is 50. In this data set:
   a. what is Q_3?**Q_3 is 149.**
   b. x is an outlier. What might x be? **Data outside of the interval $24 \leq x \leq 224$ would be outliers.**

OBJECTIVE B Calculate averages with weights, frequencies, and relative frequencies. (Lesson 1-2)

7. If a city averages 70 cm of rain per month during the 5-month rainy season and 10 cm per month during the rest of the year, what is the mean amount of rain per month for the year?**35 cm per month**

8. If an A is worth 4 points and a B+ is worth 3.3 points, what is the weighted average of a student who gets 24 credits of A and 16 credits of B+?**3.72**

9. In Mrs. Clutz's physics class, 30% of girls have 3 notebooks, 20% have 5 notebooks and the rest have 7 notebooks each. On average, how many notebooks does a girl in Mrs. Clutz's class have?**5.4**

10. In a school, 3 classrooms have no computers, 14 classrooms have 1 computer, 6 classrooms have 2 computers, and 1 classroom has 3 computers. What is the average number of computers per classroom?**1.21**

11. Mr. Fisher counts tests as 60% of a student's grade, homework as 20%, and quizzes and classwork as 20%. If Mark has a test grade of 82 and a homework grade of 95, what classwork grade does he need to average 86?**89**

12. One school gives a bonus weight to Advanced Placement (AP) courses. Brian received A's in all his classes. An A was worth 4 points in a non-AP class. He took 2 AP courses and 3 non-AP courses. His grade point average was 4.2 for the semester. What is an A in an AP course worth?**4.5**

Additional Answers

5. minimum = 1,045, Q_1 = 49,372, median = 56,194, Q_3 = 150,755.5, maximum = 571,951 (all answers in square miles)

PROPERTIES The principles behind the mathematics.

OBJECTIVE C Use Σ-notation to represent a sum or mean. (Lesson 1-2)

In 13 and 14, suppose g_i equals the number of points Karen scored in the ith basketball game of this season.

$g_1 = 10 \quad g_2 = 24 \quad g_3 = 14 \quad g_4 = 12$
$g_5 = 27 \quad g_6 = 16 \quad g_7 = 20 \quad g_8 = 22$

13. a. Write an expression using Σ-notation that indicates the mean number of points Karen scored for the eight games.

   b. Evaluate the expression in Part a.**18.125**

   c. Evaluate $\sum_{i=4}^{7} g_i$.**75**

   13a. $\dfrac{\sum_{i=1}^{8} g_i}{8}$

14. a. Evaluate $\sum_{i=1}^{4} g_i - \sum_{i=5}^{8} g_i$.**-25**

   b. Explain what Part a means in this situation.**See margin.**

15. Betty bought BigCo shares each month as follows.

Month	1	2	3	4	5	6	7	8
# of Shares	100	300	200	200	300	100	200	100
$ per Share	4.25	5.75	4.50	5.25	6.00	7.50	5.75	6.50

   a. Let n_i be the number of shares and p_i be the price per share in month i. Write an expression using Σ-notation for the average price per share of Betty's BigCo buys.**See margin.**

   b. Evaluate Part a.**About $5.63**

OBJECTIVE D Describe relations between measures of center and spread. (Lessons 1-2, 1-5, 1-6)

16. Which is usually affected more by extreme values and outliers in the data set, the mean or the median?**the mean**

17. a. **True or False** The mean and mode of a data set are always equal.**false**

   b. If your answer to Part a is true, explain why. If false, give a counterexample.**See margin.**

18. **True or False** If there are 8 ordered points in a data set, the 4th lowest value corresponds to the 50th percentile. **true**

Multiple Choice In 19-21, select the best answer.

19. The Q_1, Q_2, and Q_3 statistics refer to which of the following percentiles respectively?**C**

   A 10%, 20%, 30%   B 5%, 50%, 95%
   C 25%, 50%, 75%   D 33%, 50%, 66%

20. Which statistic is used in the calculation of variance?**B**

   A median   B mean
   C interquartile range   D mode

21. If the variance of a set of n numbers is y, what is the standard deviation of the set?**C**

   A y^2 B $\dfrac{y}{n-1}$ C $\sqrt{y}$ D $\dfrac{\sqrt{y}}{n}$

22. If the mean of 50 scores is exactly 26.4, and the mean of 49 of those scores is exactly 26, what is the 50th score?**46**

USES Applications of mathematics in real-world situations **23–24. See margin.**

OBJECTIVE E Use statistics to draw conclusions about data. (Lessons 1-4, 1-6)

23. In a biology experiment, Jon recorded the number of days it took for a nest of 20 snapping turtle eggs to hatch. He obtained the sample data below.

58	63	74	60	51	51	83	48	66	50
94	53	60	74	60	78	83	82	60	83

   a. Find the five-number summary for these data.

   b. Identify all outliers using the $1.5 \times IQR$ criterion.

24. Suppose the heights of boys in one physical education class had a mean of 65 inches and a standard deviation of 3.2. The heights of boys in another physical education class had a mean of 67 inches and a standard deviation of 2.1. Which class had more variation in height? Justify your answer.

Additional Answers

14b. Karen scored 25 fewer points in the first four games than in the second four games of the season.

15a. $\dfrac{\sum_{i=1}^{9} n_i p_i}{\sum_{i=1}^{9} n_i}$

17b. Answers vary. Sample: Consider the data set $\{1, 1, 2, 3, 4, 5, 6, 6\}$. The mean is 3.5 and modes 1 and 6.

23a. minimum: 48, Q_1: 55.5, median: 61.5, Q_3: 80, maximum: 94

23b. $1.5 \cdot IQR = 36.75$; No values fall below 18.75 or above 116.75; therefore, there are no outliers.

24. The higher standard deviation of 3.2 for the first class indicates a larger variability in height.

Chapter ① Review

Notes on the Questions

The column of numbers having to do with school years completed by 2004 do not add to 215.7 because of rounding approximations. The more accurate data rounds to 215.7.

25. The table below gives the median sales price of existing single family homes during 2006 for 12 metropolitan areas. Prices are in thousands of dollars.

Area	Price	Area	Price
Akron, OH	114.6	Charleston, WV	199.4
Albuquerque, NM	184.2	Gainesville, FL	213.2
Atlantic City, NJ	254.8	Honolulu, HI	630.0
Bismarck, ND	134.9	Indianapolis, IN	119.3
Boulder, CO	366.4	Jackson, MS	147.1
Buffalo-Niagara Falls, NY	97.9	Nassau-Suffolk, NY	474.7

Source: National Association of Realtors

a. Compute the five-number summary of these data.

b. What conclusions can you make from these data regarding the price of housing in metropolitan areas in the United States? **25–27 See margin.**

26. **Fill in the Blanks** A distribution has $Q_1 = 50$, $Q_2 = 60$, $Q_3 = 80$, and no outliers. The data in the distribution must be no smaller than __?__ and no larger than __?__.

27. A canvassing organization in Austin, Texas, sent out 20 canvassers to collect money to support renewable energy resources. The amount of money each canvasser collected during the day is: 100, 68, 212, 300, 0, 90, 180, 23, 80, 440, 140, 163, 117, 140, 445, 180, 200, 140, 250, 500.

a. Find the mean, median, and sample standard deviation of the amounts collected.

b. Which amount or amounts are the outliers to the collections?

c. Removing the outliers, find the new mean, median, and standard deviation of the amounts.

Voting-Age Population, Percent Reporting Registered, and Voted								
Age, Gender, and Education	Voting-age population (millions)				Percent reporting they voted			
Year	1992	1996	2000	2004	1992	1996	2000	2004
Total	185.7	193.7	202.6	215.7	61.3	54.2	54.7	58.3
Age								
18 to 20 years old	9.7	10.8	11.9	11.5	38.5	31.2	28.4	41.0
21 to 24 years old	14.6	13.9	14.9	16.4	45.7	33.4	35.4	42.5
25 to 34 years old	41.6	40.1	37.3	39.0	53.2	43.1	43.7	46.9
35 to 44 years old	39.7	43.3	44.5	43.1	63.6	54.9	55.0	56.9
45 to 64 years old	49.1	53.7	61.4	71.0	70.0	64.4	64.1	66.6
65 years old and over	30.8	31.9	32.8	34.7	70.1	67.0	67.6	68.9
Gender								
Male	88.6	92.6	97.1	103.8	60.2	52.8	53.1	56.3
Female	97.1	101.0	105.5	111.9	62.3	55.5	56.2	60.1
Education Completed:								
8 years or less	15.4	14.1	12.9	12.6	35.1	28.1	26.8	23.6
Less than high school graduate	21.0	21.0	20.1	20.7	41.2	33.8	33.6	34.6
High school graduate or GED	65.3	65.2	66.3	68.5	57.5	49.1	49.4	52.4
Some college or associate's degree	46.7	50.9	55.3	58.9	68.7	60.5	60.3	66.1
Bachelor's or advanced degree	37.4	42.5	48.0	54.9	81.0	73.0	72.0	74.2

74   Exploring Data

Additional Answers

25a. minimum: 97.9, Q_1: 127.1,
   median: 191.8, Q_3: 310.6,
   maximum: 630
   (all answers in 1000's of dollars)

25b. Answers vary. Sample: There is a large range of home prices in U.S. metropolitan areas.

26. 5; 125

27a. mean: $188.4, median: $151.5,
   standard deviation: $138.16

27b. 440, 445, 500

27c. mean: $140.18, median: $140,
   standard deviation: $77.83

OBJECTIVE F Determine relationships and interpret data given in a table. (Lesson 1-1)

In 28–33, use the table on the previous page from the *Statistical Abstract of the United States 2007.*

28–30. See margin.

28. Which numbers in the table total 215.7?

29. Identify the variables for which data are provided in this table.

30. Explain the meaning of the number 28.4 in the seventh column, titled "2000".

31. How many women reported that they voted in the United States in 2004? **67.25 million**

32. How many high school graduates or people with a GED reported that they voted in the United States in 1992? **37.55 million**

33. In which age group did the largest percent of its members report that they voted? **65 years old and over**

OBJECTIVE G Use statistics to compare and contrast two data sets in the context of a situation. (Lesson 1-7, 1-8)

34. Use the data below of normal daily mean temperatures by month in Juneau, Alaska, and Minneapolis-St. Paul, Minnesota. Data have been rounded to the nearest degree Fahrenheit.

On average, which city shows greater variability in temperature? Use a measure of spread to justify your answer. **See margin.**

Month	Juneau, AK	Minneapolis-St. Paul, MN
January	24	12
February	28	18
March	33	31
April	40	46
May	47	59
June	53	68
July	56	74
August	55	71
September	49	61
October	42	49
November	32	33
December	27	18

Source: U.S. National Oceanic and Atmospheric Administration

35. The tables, histograms, and box plots below contain the times, to the nearest tenth of a minute, it took to run 2 miles by a class of 12 male and 12 female high school students. Write a paragraph comparing and contrasting the two distributions. **See margin.**

Statistics	Time (in minutes)	
	female	male
mean	13.8	13.6
median	13.3	13.2
interquartile range	5.0	5.7
standard deviation	3.4	3.6
range	10.8	11.6

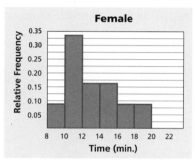

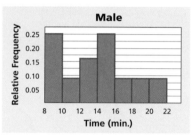

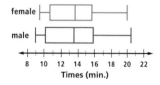

Additional Answers

28. The sum of numbers representing age group categories, gender categories, and education completed categories in 2004.

29. year, voting age population (millions), percent of voting age population reporting they voted, age, gender, education

30. 28.4% of 18–20 year-olds reported that they voted in 2000.

34. The standard deviation of the normal temperatures in Minneapolis-St. Paul is about 21.2, whereas it is 11.0 for Juneau, indicating a much greater variability in Minneapolis-St. Paul than in Juneau.

35. Answers vary. Sample: The mean, median, IQR and standard deviation differ very little between the males and females. These statistics, as well as the box plots and histograms, indicate little to no difference in the running times of males and females.

Chapter **1** Review

Additional Answers

36.

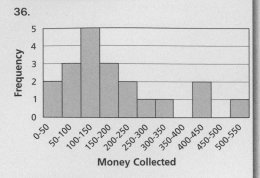

Money Collected

37.

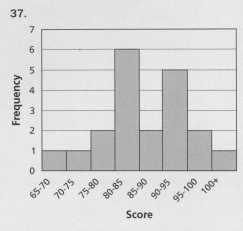

Score

38a. 45–49 age group; about 22 million

38b. 30–34 age group; about 90 million

38c. Answers vary. Sample: India has about 6 times the population of the U.S. in the age interval 0–9. In addition, age groups 0–4 and 5–9 are the largest age groups in India, while age groups 40–44 and 45–49 are the largest groups in the U.S.

38d. Answers vary. Sample: Due to rapid increases in the general standard of living and health care, India has a rapidly expanding population. The population of the U.S. is stable or declining with a greater percentage of the population in the oldest age groups. This may indicate that the standard of living and health care are at a generally high level so the rate of improvement is not as dramatic as India's.

36–38. See margin.

REPRESENTATIONS Pictures, graphs, or objects that illustrate concepts

> **OBJECTIVE H** Read, interpret, and draw histograms and population pyramids from data. (Lesson 1-3)

36. Display the data on canvassing given in Question 27 in a histogram with bin width 50.

37. The data below represent the scores of a class of 20 students on a recent geometry test. Make a histogram with the data using a bin width of 5.

80	70	100	96	84	76	94	88	91	81
79	83	89	93	91	94	65	84	97	83

38. Use the displays below, which show population pyramids of the populations of the United States and India in the year 2007 in millions.

 a. For the United States, estimate which age group had the greatest population. What is it?

 b. For India, estimate which age group had the seventh greatest population. What is it?

 c. Describe the difference between the populations of the U.S. and India in the age interval 0-9.

 d. What factors might account for such different shapes of the age structure of these two cultures?

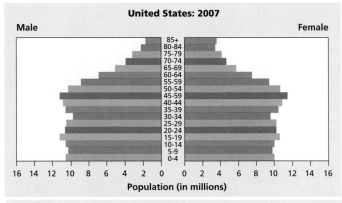

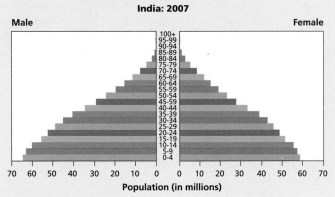

Source: U.S. Census Bureau, International Data Base

Additional Answers

41.

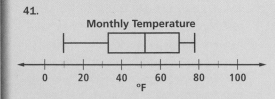

42.

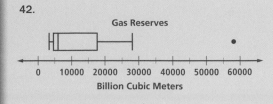

43a.

Month	Cumulative Wages
1	$3,250
2	$7,375
3	$10,125
4	$15,500
5	$20,000
6	$23,800

39. Ms. T. Chare made the following histogram of grades on her final exam in algebra.

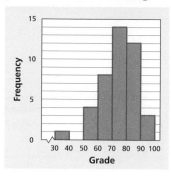

a. How many students took the exam?**42**

b. True or False The median score is between 60 and 70 points.**false**

c. What percent of her students scored more than 80 points?**about 35.7%**

OBJECTIVE I Read, interpret, and draw box plots from data. (Lesson 1-4)

40. Refer to this box plot of spending by a sample of baseball fans at a recent major league home game.

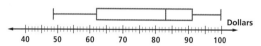

a. What is the median spending?**83**

b. What is Q_3?**91**

c. What percent of the fans spent between $62 and $91? **50%**

d. Describe the interval below Q_1.**49–62**

e. Between which quartiles is there the greatest spread?**Q_1 and Q_2**

41. Use the data below of temperatures on the 25th day of the month in St. Louis, Missouri, to create a box plot.**See margin.**

Month	1	2	3	4	5	6	7	8	9	10	11	12
°F	10	36	41	68	60	78	72	68	78	45	31	29

Source: National Oceanic and Atmospheric Administration

42. Refer to the table below describing the estimated proven natural gas reserves in billions of cubic meters in 2007 for various countries. Draw a box plot of the data in the table, identifying any outliers with dots.**See margin.**

Country	Gas Reserves
Iran	28,080
Iraq	3,170
Former USSR	58,112
Algeria	4,504
Nigeria	5,215
Saudi Arabia	7,305
United Arab Emirates	6,072
United States	5,978
Venezuela	4,838

Source: Organization of Oil Exporting Countries

OBJECTIVE J Calculate and draw line graphs of cumulative frequencies and cumulative relative frequencies from tables of frequencies. (Lesson 1-5)

43. Glenda works on commission. For the first six months of this year she earned $3,250; $4,125; $2,750; $5,375; $4,500, and $3,800.

a. Create a cumulative frequency table for Glenda's wages for the six months.

b. During which month did Glenda reach half her total sales?**month 4**

c. Draw a cumulative relative frequency line graph for her total wages for the six months.**43a, c. See margin.**

44. Below are the scores on a 10-point test in a class of 20 students.**See margin.**

3	5	3	4	7	5	6	8	10	5
6	8	7	1	6	7	8	7	8	7

a. Make a table showing the frequency and relative frequency of each score.

b. Draw a cumulative frequency line graph for the data.

Assessment

Evaluation The *Assessment Resources* provide a form of the Chapter 1 Test. Here are our recommendations for assigning a letter grade: 85–100 = A; 72–84 = B; 60–71 = C; 50–59 = D.

Feedback After students have taken the test for Chapter 1 and you have scored the results, return the tests to students for discussion. Class discussion on the questions that caused trouble for most students can be very effective in identifying and clarifying misunderstandings. You might want to have them note the items they missed and work either in groups or at home to correct them. It is important for students to receive feedback on every chapter test, and we recommend that students see and correct their mistakes before proceeding too far into the next chapter.

Suggestions for Assignment Assign Reading Lesson 2-1 and Covering the Ideas 2-1 for homework the evening of the test. It gives students work to do after they have completed the test and keeps the class moving. If you do not do this, you may cover one less chapter over the course of the year.

Additional Answers

43c.

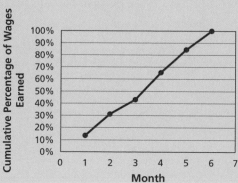

44a.

Score	Frequency	Relative Frequency
1	1	0.05
2	0	0
3	2	0.1
4	1	0.05
5	3	0.15
6	3	0.15
7	5	0.25
8	4	0.2
9	0	0
10	1	0.05

Additional Answers

44b.

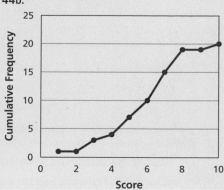

2 Functions and Models

Chapter Overview

		Local Standards	Pacing (in days)		
			Average	**Advanced**	**Block**
2-1	**The Language of Functions** **A** Work with $f(x)$ notation for function values. **C** Identify the variables, domain, and range of functions. **H** Interpret properties of relations from graphs.		1	1	0.5
2-2	**Linear Models** **B** Compute residuals from observed and predicted values. **F** Find and interpret linear models. **I** Use scatterplots and residual plots to draw conclusions about models for data.		1	1	0.5
2-3	**Linear Regression and Correlation** **D** Identify properties of regression lines and of the correlation coefficient. **F** Find and interpret linear regression and models. **I** Use scatterplots and residual plots to draw conclusions about linear models for data.		1	1	0.5
	QUIZ 1		0.5	0.25	0.25
2-4	**Exponential Functions** **E** Describe properties of exponential functions.		1	1	0.5
2-5	**Exponential Models** **F** Find and interpret exponential regression and models.		1	1	0.5
2-6	**Quadratic Models** **E** Describe properties of quadratic functions. **F** Find and interpret quadratic regression and models.		1	1	0.5
	QUIZ 2		0.5	0.25	0.25
2-7	**Inverse Variation Models** **E** Describe properties of inverse variation functions.		1	1	0.5
2-8	**Choosing a Good Model** **G** Evaluate which type of model is more appropriate for data. **I** Use scatterplots and residual plots to draw conclusions about models for data.		1	1	0.5
	Self-Test		1	0.5	0.5
	Chapter Review		2	1	0.5
	Test		1	1	0.5
	TOTAL		13	11	6

Technology Resources

Teacher's Assessment Assistant, Ch. 2

Electronic Teacher's Edition, Ch. 2

Differentiated Options Universal Access

	Accommodating the Learner	Vocabulary Development	Ongoing Assessment	Materials
2-1	pp. 83, 84	p. 83	p. 86	
2-2	pp. 89, 90	p. 89	p. 93	statistics utility
2-3	pp. 100, 98	p. 96	p. 101	statistics utility
2-4	p. 104	p. 105	p. 109	graphing calculator
2-5	p. 113		p. 116	
2-6	pp. 119, 120	p. 118	p. 124	
2-7	p. 129	p. 128	p. 131	
2-8	p. 135		p. 139	statistics utility

Objectives

	Lessons	Self-Test Questions	Chapter Review Questions
Skills			
A Work with $f(x)$ notation for function values.	2-1	1	1–4
B Compute residuals from observed and predicted values.	2-2	5, 6, 11	5–7
Properties			
C Identify the variables, domain, and range of functions.	2-1	3	8–17
D Identify properties of regression lines and of the correlation coefficient.	2-3	15	18–21
E Describe properties of quadratic, exponential, and inverse variation functions.	2-4, 2-6, 2-7	8, 9, 10	22–30
Uses			
F Find and interpret linear, quadratic, and exponential regressions and models.	2-2, 2-3, 2-5, 2-6	7, 12, 14	31–36
G Evaluate which type of model is more appropriate for data.	2-8	16	37–42
Representations			
H Interpret properties of relations from graphs.	2-1	2	43–46
I Use scatterplots and residual plots to draw conclusions about models for data.	2-2, 2-3, 2-8	4, 13	47–54

Resource Masters Chapter 2

Resource Master 151, Graph Paper, (page 151) can be used with Lesson 2-1.

Resource Master 26 Chapter 2 Opener

U.S. National Debt

Year	Amount (billions of dollars)
1965	317
1970	271
1975	533
1980	908
1985	1,823
1990	3,233
1995	4,974
2000	5,674
2005	7,933

Source: U.S. Department of the Treasury

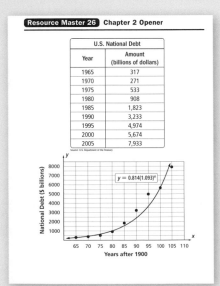

Resource Master for Chapter 2 Opener

Resource Master 28 Lesson 2-1

Resource Master 27 Lesson 2-1

Warm-up

A function f maps a number onto the square of the reciprocal of its cube.

  a. If $x = 3$, what is $f(x)$?

  b. Give a general formula for $f(x)$.

  c. Find $f\left(\frac{1}{2}\right)$.

  d. What number cannot be in the domain of f?

Additional Examples

1. The Sudoku Club at a high school needs t-shirts for their upcoming tournament. They were able to negotiate a "buy-two-get-one-free" deal from a local store. The cost for one t-shirt is $10.

  a. Which statement is true: "the cost c is a function of the number t of t-shirts" or "the number of t-shirts t is a function of the cost c?"

  b. Identify the independent and dependent variables of the function.

  c. State the domain and range of the function.

2. Consider again the cost c of buying t-shirts as given in Additional Example 1.

  a. List the ordered pairs of the function for values of t from 1 to 10.

  b. Graph the function.

3. Find the domain and range of the function with rule $y = 3(x - 5)^2 - 1$.

4. Suppose g is the function defined by $g(t) = 2t^6 - 3t - 2$ for all real numbers t.

  a. Evaluate $g(-2)$, $g(3)$, and $g(-5)$.

  b. Does $g(-2) - g(3) = g(-2 - 4)$?

  c. Evaluate $g(3p + 1)$.

Resource Masters for Lesson 2-1

Resource Master 30 Lesson 2-2

Resource Master 29 Lesson 2-2

Warm-Up

1. Explain why it is reasonable for the price of a diamond to be close to a linear function of the weight of the diamond.

2. Suppose water is in a conical-shaped funnel with a hole in the bottom that is plugged up. If the plug is removed, will the height of the water left in the funnel be a linear function of time? Why or why not?

Additional Example

The gold medal winning times for the men's 100-meter dash are listed below for the last 20 Summer Olympic Games.

  a. The data were graphed and a line fit "by eye" passed through the points (1972, 10.15) and (2004, 9.8). Find the equation of this linear model to relate the year and the winning time.

  b. Interpret the slope of your line in the context of the problem.

  c. Use the model to predict the winning time at the London 2012 Olympic Games.

  d. Usain Bolt of Jamaica won the 100-m dash at the Beijing 2008 games in a record 9.69 seconds. Based on the linear model, in which future Olympic year is it most likely that this winning time would have been run?

City	Year	Winning Time(s)
Beijing	2008	9.69
Athens	2004	9.85
Sydney	2000	9.87
Atlanta	1996	9.84
Barcelona	1992	9.96
Seoul	1988	9.92
Los Angeles	1984	9.99
Moscow	1980	10.25
Montreal	1976	10.06
Munich	1972	10.14
Mexico City	1968	9.95
Tokyo	1964	10.0
Rome	1960	10.2
Melbourne	1956	10.5
Helsinki	1952	10.4
London	1948	10.3
Berlin	1936	10.3
Los Angeles	1932	10.3
Amsterdam	1928	10.8
Paris	1924	10.6

Resource Masters for Lesson 2-2

Resource Master 31 Lesson 2-2

Page 90

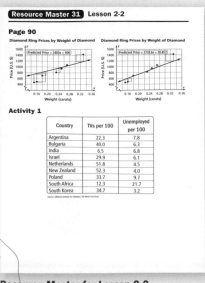

Activity 1

Country	TVs per 100	Unemployed per 100
Argentina	22.3	7.8
Bulgaria	40.0	6.3
India	6.5	6.8
Israel	29.9	6.1
Netherlands	51.8	4.5
New Zealand	52.3	4.0
Poland	33.7	9.7
South Africa	12.3	21.7
South Korea	34.7	3.2

Source: UNESCO Institute for Statistics, CIA World Fact Book

Resource Master for Lesson 2-2

Resource Master 33 Lesson 2-3

Resource Master 32 Lesson 2-3

Warm-Up

Here are some Fahrenheit-Celsius temperature equivalents: $0°C = 32°F$; $20°C = 68°F$; $37°C = 98.6°F$; $100°C = 212°F$. Find an equation for the line of best fit for these data, predicting F from C.

Additional Example

Use the data from the Additional Example in Lesson 2-2.

  a. Find a best fit linear model using a statistics utility for the relationship between the year r and the winning time t.

  b. Verify that the center of mass (1968, 10.15 seconds) is on the line.

  c. Find the sum of squared residuals for the linear regression.

  d. The 1940 and 1944 Summer Olympic Games were cancelled because of World War II. According to the regression line, what would the winning times have been in those years?

Resource Masters for Lesson 2-3

Resource Master 34 Lesson 2-3

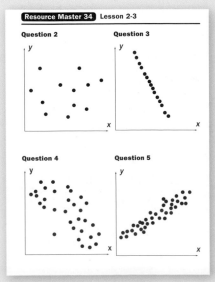

Resource Master for Lesson 2-3

Resource Master 35 Lesson 2-4

Warm-Up

A CAS will be helpful for these questions. A spreadsheet or list can also be used. Consider the number $\phi = \frac{\sqrt{5}+1}{2}$.

1. Let f be the function defined by $f(x) = \frac{\phi}{\sqrt{5}}$. Calculate $f(1)$, $f(0)$, $f(1)$, $f(2)$, $f(3)$, $f(4)$, and $f(5)$ to the nearest thousandth.
2. Graph f.

Additional Examples

1. Presently, the towns of Scarcedale and Ampleton both have approximately 8500 residents. Over the next 5 years, the population of Ampleton is expected to increase by approximately 2.3% per year, while the population of Scarcedale is expected to decrease by about 0.9% each year.
   a. Create equations to describe the population of each town as a function of time.
   b. Compare the projected populations after 5 years.
2. Jonas received a letter from his credit union stating that a 5-year CD his parents opened for him had matured and he could choose one of the following options:
   (1) Withdraw the full amount of $14,204.10.
   (2) Use the money to open a new 5-year CD with an APY of 2.81%.
   (3) Have the money deposited into his interest checking account which earns 0.95% per year.
   Assume Jonas's parents deposited $12,000 into the CD 5 years ago.
   a. What is an equation for the balance of the old CD after 5 years?
   b. Use the equation from Part a to find the annual yield of the old CD.
   c. Compare the results of options (2) and (3).
3. Compare and contrast the graphs of the three functions f, g, and h, where $f(x) = 8^x$, $g(x) = \left(\frac{1}{8}\right)^x$, and $h(x) = 8^{-x}$ for all values of x.

Resource Master for Lesson 2-4

Resource Master 36 Lesson 2-4

Example 1

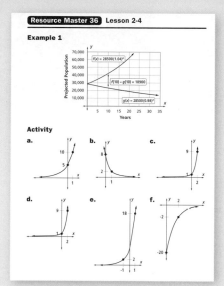

Activity

a.   b.   c.

d.   e.   f.

Resource Master for Lesson 2-4

Resource Master 37 Lesson 2-5

Warm-Up

Novelle Riche keeps track of how much money she has. In one fixed annuity investment initiated 10 years ago, she had $218,201 three years ago and she has $256,221 now.
   a. What annual yield is Novelle getting from her investment?
   b. How much did she initially invest?

Additional Examples

1. The population of a certain cell type was observed to be 100 on the second day, and 2700 on the fifth day. Assuming the growth is exponential, find the number of cells present initially, and the number of cells expected on the seventh day.

2. The National Science Foundation (NSF) publishes InfoBriefs, a newsletter containing brief reports highlighting results from recent surveys and analyses. The following data are contained in a January 2009 article about Federal R&D funding.

Fiscal year	Federal obligations for research (NSF) ($ millions)
1990	1690
1991	1785
1992	1868
1993	1882
1994	2040
1995	2149
1996	2188
1997	2249
1998	2289
1999	2506
2000	2726
2001	3044
2002	3260
2003	3609
2004	3771
2005	3743
2006	3791
2007	4051
2008	4358

   a. Use a statistics utility to graph the data and fit an exponential model of the form $f(x) = ab^x$ to the data. Use x as "years after 1990." Report the values of a and b in the exponential model to the nearest thousandth.
   b. Use your graph to describe how well the exponential curve you have modeled fits the points on the scatterplot.
   c. Calculate the residuals for 1998 and 2004.

3. A certain substance has a half-life of 24 years. If a sample of 80 grams is being observed, how much will remain in 50 years? When will only 5 grams remain?

Resource Master for Lesson 2-5

Resource Master 38 Lesson 2-5

Example 2

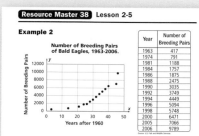

Number of Breeding Pairs of Bald Eagles, 1963-2006.

Year	Number of Breeding Pairs
1963	417
1974	791
1981	1188
1984	1757
1986	1875
1988	2475
1990	3035
1992	3749
1994	4449
1996	5094
1998	5748
2000	6471
2005	7066
2006	9789

Accomodating the Learner

Given that the points (3, 8) and (8, 89) are from a set of data that can be fit exactly by an exponential model, do the following.
   a. Find a general equation for the exponential model in the form $y = ab^x$.
   b. The complete data set consists of positive integer pairs of values of x and y. Use your equation from Part a to write down the first ten data points which correspond to $x = 1$ to 10.
   c. What do you notice about the y-values?
   d. Use your answer to Part c to write down the next two data points.

Resource Master for Lesson 2-5

Resource Master 40 Lesson 2-6
Resource Master 39 Lesson 2-6

Warm-Up

Use a CAS.
1. In what form does your CAS give the solutions to the general quadratic equation $ax^2 + bx + c = 0$?
2. Describe three different ways to find the solutions to a quadratic equation such as $2x^2 - 5x - 25 = 0$.

Additional Examples

1. Consider the function f with equation $f(x) = -3x^2 - 4x + 7$.
   a. Find the x- and y-intercepts of its graph.
   b. Tell whether the parabola has a maximum or minimum point, and find its coordinates.

2. A projectile is shot from a tower 10 feet high with an upward velocity of 100 feet per second.
   a. Approximate the relationship between height h (in feet) and time t (in seconds) after the projectile is shot.
   b. How long will the projectile be in the air?

3. A parabola contains the points (-0.1, -16.32), (2, 3), and (6, -9). Find its equation.

Resource Masters for Lesson 2-6

Resource Master 41 Lesson 2-6

Page 120

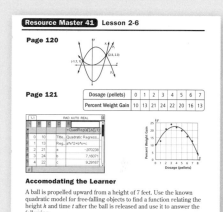

Page 121

Dosage (pellets)	0	1	2	3	4	5	6	7
Percent Weight Gain	10	13	21	24	22	20	16	13

Accomodating the Learner

A ball is propelled upward from a height of 7 feet. Use the known quadratic model for free-falling objects to find a function relating the height h and time t after the ball is released and use it to answer the following.
   a. Obtain an expression in terms of v_0 for the time t at which the ball reaches its maximum height.
   b. What must the initial velocity be in order for the ball to reach a maximum height of 350 feet?
   c. Some major league baseball pitchers can throw a ball at 100 mph. Is that fast enough to reach this height?
   d. Find a meaningful domain for t in the function used in Part b to describe the height of the ball at time t.

Resource Master for Lesson 2-6

Resource Master 42 Lesson 2-7

Warm-Up

1. If A and B are inversely proportional and $A = 10$ when $B = 5$, then what is the value of B when $A = 50$?

2. How many times more intense is the sound if you are sitting 20 feet from a band than if you are sitting 30 feet from the band?

Additional Examples

1. The average song size (in MB) and approximate number of songs for a sample of 32 GB MP3 players are listed in the table below.

Average song size (MB)	Approximate number of songs on 32GB MP3 player
3.6	8000
4.7	7000
4.5	7200
4.2	7600
4.1	7800
5.8	5500
4.9	6500
5.1	6300

   a. Find a formula that gives the average number n of songs that will fit on an MP3 player as a function of the average song size s.
   b. Graph both the data and the model on a single set of axes.
   c. Use residuals to assess the quality of your model.
   d. About 10,000 songs would correspond to what average song size?

2. The intensity of light from a point source is inversely proportional to the square of the distance from the light source. Suppose that at a distance of 5 cm, the light intensity is rated at 600 lux. What will the intensity be at a distance of 10 cm? At 23 cm?

Resource Master for Lesson 2-7

Resource Master 43 Lesson 2-7

Page 125

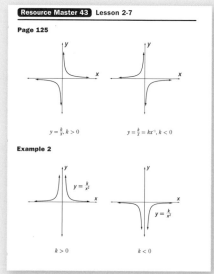

$y = \frac{k}{x}, k > 0$ $y = \frac{k}{x} = kx^{-1}, k < 0$

Example 2

$y = \frac{k}{x^2}$

$y = \frac{k}{x^2}$

$k > 0$ $k < 0$

Resource Master for Lesson 2-7

Resource Master 45 Lesson 2-8
Resource Master 44 Lesson 2-8

Warm-Up

In 2005, the top 10 breeds of dog in the U.S., as measured by American Kennel Club registrations, were:

1.	Labrador Retriever	137,867
2.	Golden Retriever	48,509
3.	Yorkshire Terrier	47,238
4.	German Shepherd Dog	45,014
5.	Beagle	42,592
6.	Dachshund	38,566
7.	Boxer	37,268
8.	Poodle	31,638
9.	Shih Tzu	28,087
10.	Miniature Schnauzer	24,144

   a. Do a linear regression on the number of registrations as a function of the rank.
   b. What does this model predict for the number of registrations for the German Shepherd?
   c. What does this model predict for the number of registrations for the 25th ranked dog, the Siberian Huskie?
   d. Examine the residuals for your model. Describe what you find.
   e. Based on Parts b, c, and d, does your model in Part a seem appropriate?

Activity 2

Year	Population (millions)	Year	Population (millions)
1790	4	1900	76
1800	5	1910	92
1810	7	1920	106
1820	10	1930	123
1830	13	1940	132
1840	17	1950	151
1850	23	1960	179
1860	31	1970	203
1870	40	1980	227
1880	50	1990	249
1890	63	2000	281

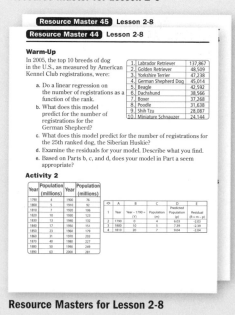

	A	B	C	D	E
1	Year	Year − 1790 (Y)	Population (m)	Predicted Population (p)	Residual (R = m − p)
2	1790	0	4	6.03	−2.03
3	1800	10	5	7.39	−2.39
4	1810	20	7	9.04	−2.04

Resource Masters for Lesson 2-8

Pacing

Each lesson in this chapter is designed to be covered in 1 day. At the end of the chapter, you should plan to spend 1 day to review the Self-Test, 1 to 2 days for the Chapter Review, and 1 day for a test. You may wish to spend a day on projects, and possibly a day will be needed for quizzes. This chapter should therefore take 13 to 15 days. We strongly advise you not to spend more than 16 days on this chapter unless your students' backgrounds with linear, exponential, and quadratic functions are particularly weak.

Students should be expected to do the equivalent of a complete set of Questions from a lesson nearly every day. Two Assignment Options are identified in each lesson. At times you may want to save a few questions to be done by students in class.

Overview

When we look for an equation that comes close to describing a set of data such as the time-series data here, we are engaging in the classic idea of mathematical modeling, namely we are searching for mathematics whose structure is as close to the real situation as we can find. We use these mathematical models for three basic reasons: to describe, to predict, and to explain.

A model of a real situation uses mathematical terminology, operations, and concepts to describe relationships among variables. Mathematical models are powerful tools in the sciences because they can be used to make predictions or can be linked to other mathematical models as part of a larger theoretical structure.

▶ Contents

2-1   The Language of Functions

2-2   Linear Models

2-3   Linear Regression and Correlation

2-4   Exponential Functions

2-5   Exponential Models

2-6   Quadratic Models

2-7   Inverse Variation Models

2-8   Choosing a Good Model

In this chapter, you will study the modeling of data involving relations between two variables. For example, the data in the table at the left from the U.S. Department of the Treasury show the United States national debt at the end of selected fiscal years. These data, graphed in the scatterplot on the next page, show that the national debt has been increasing dramatically since 1965. The table shows that in 2005 (105 years after 1900), the national debt was almost 8 trillion dollars.

To describe patterns in data, *mathematical models* are used. A **mathematical model** is a mathematical description of a real situation, usually involving some simplification and assumptions concerning the situation. Mathematical models are often used to make estimates and predictions.

U.S. National Debt

Year	Amount (billions of dollars)
1965	317
1970	371
1975	533
1980	908
1985	1,823
1990	3,233
1995	4,974
2000	5,674
2005	7,933

Source: U.S. Department of the Treasury

Chapter 2 Overview

In this chapter, we use functions as models. The idea is simple: if we graph a set of points (x, y) in which y is related to x, it is possible that there is a formula for a function of a particular kind that describes that specific relationship. We call the formula or the function a *model* for the data. Five kinds of functions are discussed in this chapter as models: linear functions (Lessons 2-2 and 2-3), exponential functions (Lessons 2-4 and 2-5), quadratic functions (Lesson 2-6), functions of inverse variation (Lesson 2-7), and functions of inverse square variation (Lesson 2-7).

The chapter begins by reviewing the language, symbolism, and properties of functions. The ideas of domain and range are critical in judging the validity and power of a model. The chapter ends with a discussion of how to choose a good model, serving to summarize the entire chapter.

If x is the number of years after 1900 and y is the debt in billions of dollars, then the relationship between x and y from 1965 to 2005 can be modeled by the exponential function with equation $y = 0.814(1.093)^x$, which is graphed on the scatterplot below.

Using this model, you might estimate the national debt in 2002 or predict its value in 2015, even though this information was not given.

In this chapter, you will study linear, quadratic, and exponential models, and see how they are used in business, government, and recreational pursuits.

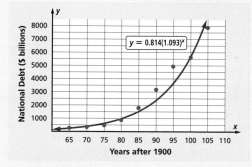

Models can emerge from theory or from observations. The idea of modeling is introduced in Lesson 2-2 visually, from data found from observations. The first linear models result from an eyeball fit to data. In Lesson 2-3 we move to the idea of a best-fitting line. This requires technology, either in the form of computer software or a statistical calculator. The goal here is to analyze the line that is computed, not the method of computation. Correlation is introduced as a measure of how well a linear model fits a data set. In Lessons 2-4 through 2-7 data are modeled by other kinds of functions.

The topics of this chapter are meaty and may lead you to want to spend a great deal of time on the lessons, but in fact much of the lessons should be review for most students and we believe an approximate lesson-a-day pace is not unreasonable.

The exponential model $y = 0.814 \cdot 1.093^x$ shown on the opening page of Chapter 2 was generated from the data given in the table using an exponential model of best fit. As was the case for the opener to Chapter 1, the accuracy of the coefficients of the terms in the model affects the degree of precision to which the model can be used as a predictor of the national debt in a given year.

Exponential models are appropriate when the percent of growth (or decay) is relatively constant. In this case, however, the size of the values of y is so large that even a point that seems to be close to the curve may represent an estimate that is off by hundreds of billions of dollars.

It is also important to note that the distance from the point to the curve is not measured in the usual geometric way as the distance to the closest point on the curve (as it would be if you wanted the distance from a point to a river), but vertically as the difference between the value given by the model and the actual value. You might ask students to calculate the difference between these values for various years using a spreadsheet or list.

Chapter 2 Projects

At the end of each chapter, you will find projects related to the chapter. At this time you might want to have students look over the projects on pages 140 and 141. You might want to have students tentatively select a project on which to work. Then, as students read and progress through the chapter, they can finalize their project choices.

Sometimes students might work alone. At other times, you might let them collaborate with classmates for a presentation and discussion. We recommend that you allow for diversity and encourage students to use their imaginations when presenting their projects. As students work on projects throughout the year, they should see many uses of mathematics in the real world.

Lesson 2-1

GOAL

Give two equivalent definitions for functions (as a set of ordered pairs and as a correspondence) and discuss the basic properties and language of functions. Discuss three representations of functions: ordered pairs, graphs, and rules such as equations.

SPUR Objectives

The SPUR Objectives for all of Chapter 2 are found in the Chapter Review on pages 146–149.

A Work with $f(x)$ notation for function values.

C Identify the variables, domain, and range of functions.

H Interpret properties of relations from graphs.

Materials/Resources

· Lesson Master 2-1
· Resource Masters 27 and 28

HOMEWORK
- Option 1
- Option 2
- Questions 1–12
- Questions 13–23
- Question 24 (extra credit)
- Reading Lesson 2-2
- Covering the Ideas 2-2 (Questions 1–8)

Local Standards

1 Warm-Up

A function f maps a number onto the square of the reciprocal of its cube.

a. If $x = 3$, what is $f(x)$? $\frac{1}{729}$

b. Give a general formula for $f(x)$.
$f(x) = \left(\frac{1}{x^3}\right)^2$ or $f(x) = \frac{1}{x^6}$ or $f(x) = x^{-6}$

c. Find $f\left(\frac{1}{2}\right)$. **64**

d. What number cannot be in the domain of f? **0**

Lesson 2-1 The Language of Functions

> **BIG IDEA** A function is a special type of relation that can be described by ordered pairs, graphs, written rules or algebraic rules such as equations.

On pages 78 and 79, nine ordered pairs of numbers are listed and graphed. The first coordinate is the number of years after 1900; the second is the U.S. national debt (in billions of dollars) for that year. Any set of ordered pairs is a **relation**. In many contexts, the second number in each ordered pair depends in some way on the first number. When this happens, the first variable in a relation is called the **independent variable** and the second variable is called the **dependent variable**. For the national debt, the number x of years after 1900 is the independent variable and the debt y in that year is the dependent variable.

What Is a Function?

When each value of the independent variable determines exactly one value of the dependent variable, the relation is called a *function*.

> **Ordered Pair Definition of Function**
>
> A **function** is a set of ordered pairs (x, y) in which each first component (x) is paired with exactly one second component (y).

For example, $f = \{(1, 2), (2, 4), (3, 7)\}$ is a function, but

$g = \{(1, 2), (2, 4), (1, 7)\}$ is not a function
because 1 is paired with both 2 and 7.

In the set of ordered pairs of a function, the set of first components is the **domain** of the function. The set of second components is the **range** of the function. The domain consists of all allowable values of the independent variable; the range is the set of possible values for the dependent variable. The domain of the function f above is $\{1, 2, 3\}$, and the range is $\{2, 4, 7\}$.

STOP QY1

For the national debt data on page 78, we can say, "The U.S. national debt is a function of the year." The domain is the set of all years the U.S. has had and will have a national debt; the range is the set of all amounts of the national debt at the end of those years.

Vocabulary

mathematical model
relation
independent variable
dependent variable
function, ordered pair definition
domain of a function
range of a function
function, correspondence definition
real function
member of a set, element of a set, $\in$
piecewise definition of a function
value of a function

Mental Math

Write each expression as a power of x.

a. $(x^{50})^3$ x^{150}

b. $x^{50} \cdot x^{-22}$ x^{28}

c. $\dfrac{x^{50}}{x^{53}}$ x^{-3}

> **▶ QY1**
>
> Give the domain and range of the function $h = \{(5, 1), (6, 3), (7, 1), (8, 3)\}$.

Background

We assume that students have studied functions in a previous course or courses, and have likely been exposed to a wide range of models for thinking about functions. It is our experience, in fact, that students at this point in their study of mathematics display a wide range of understandings of the concept of function. In this chapter we avoid the notion of a function as a mapping of one set to another, and do not emphasize a categorization of functions as *onto*, *into*, or *one-to-one*. For the purposes of this course, this categorization scheme is not necessary.

The concepts of domain and range take on new meaning in applications. In some instances, linear and quadratic functions are used to model real-world phenomena that do not have continuous domains and/or ranges. While the model might be accurate (and simpler), students need to understand that there may be restrictions on the domain and range. At other times, only certain real numbers are appropriate.

Another definition of *function* stresses the correspondence between the independent and dependent variables.

Correspondence Definition of Function

A **function** is a correspondence between two sets A and B in which each element of A corresponds to exactly one element of B.

The domain is the set A of values of the *independent variable*. The range is the set of only those elements of B that correspond to elements in A; these are the values of the *dependent variable*.

For most functions studied in this course, A and B are sets of real numbers. Functions whose domain and range are sets of real numbers are called **real functions**. Unless the domain of a function is explicitly stated, you may assume that it is the set of all real numbers for which the function is defined. Real functions have the useful characteristic that they can be pictured by a coordinate graph.

We use the symbols in the table at the right to represent sets of numbers. "z" stands for the German verb *zahlen*, "to count," and "q" stands for "quotient." These symbols can also be used in descriptions of other sets. If x is in a set A, then x is said to be a **member** or **element** of A, written $x \in A$. For instance, $3\frac{1}{2} \in \mathbb{Q}$. Similarly, every even integer can be written as $2 \cdot n$, where n is in the set of all integers. So we can write the set of even integers as $\{2n \mid n \in \mathbb{Z}\}$, read "the set of $2n$ such that n is an integer."

The symbol	represents the set of all
$\mathbb{Z}$	integers.
$\mathbb{R}$	real numbers.
$\mathbb{Q}$	rational numbers.
$\mathbb{N}$	natural numbers.

Example 1

A bakery charges \$2.00 per muffin. Customers get a \$2.00 discount for every 6 muffins purchased.

a. Which statement is true: "the cost c is a function of the number m of muffins" or "the number m of muffins is a function of the cost c?"

b. Identify the independent and dependent variables of the function.

c. State the domain and range of the function.

Solution

a. Because there is exactly one cost c for a given number of muffins, **the cost is a function of the number of muffins.** A customer who buys 5 muffins pays the same amount as one who buys 6 muffins, so the number of muffins is not a function of the cost.

b. Because c depends on m, **m is the independent variable and c is the dependent variable.**

c. The domain is the set of all possible values of m. Because "negative muffins" does not make sense and you cannot buy part of a muffin, **the domain is the set of nonnegative integers,** which can be written $\{m \mid m \in \mathbb{Z} \text{ and } m \geq 0\}$. The range is the set of all possible values of c. Any even-number cost in dollars is possible, so **the range is the set of nonnegative even integers.**

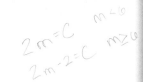

The Language of Functions   **81**

For example, a model relating the independent variable "number of dosages of a medication" to a dependent variable "cure rates" might be linear, but the domain would certainly not include negative real numbers.

It is best not to overemphasize domain and range restrictions. The point the students should get is that mathematical models are tools in the hands of the people who create them, and the tool varies depending on the needs and desires of the creator.

Technological support for the definition of function as a correspondence comes from the metaphor of a calculator as a "function machine." A calculator provides a hands-on version of the metaphor. The following is a list of similar characteristics to share with your class.

(continued on next page)

---

e. Notice from Part a that $f(3) < 3$, and from Part c that $f\left(\frac{1}{2}\right) > \frac{1}{2}$. Is there any number for which $f(x) = x$? If so, what is that number? **1**

2 Teaching

Notes on the Lesson

The terms independent and dependent are related to model-building; we think of the independent variable as coming first and the dependent variable as second. Usually the context tells us which of the two variables is independent. However, determining which is the independent variable is not automatic. For instance, in as simple a situation as buying items of the same type, where the price p per item is constant, one could use the formula $C = pn$ (cost equals number of items times the price per item) in which it is usually understood that n is the independent variable and C the dependent variable. But if one wished to know how many items n can be bought for a particular amount C, then the formula would be $n = \frac{C}{P}$, and now the dependent and independent variables have switched.

What is a function? Of the two definitions of *function*, the first is static: a set of ordered pairs in which each first element is paired with exactly one second element. The second definition is dynamic: a correspondence which makes use of one value to obtain another value. Both aspects of function are important and both are used throughout this book. With our definition of function (a rather standard definition), there is no such thing as a multi-valued function.

Example 1 Students may consider the questions posed in Example 1 as trivial, but do not underestimate their value. They introduce important vocabulary and make the point that the formal language of functions is related to realistic applications.

Guided Example 2: Answers vary. Sample:

n	Sample set (ordered)	Count of numbers larger than the median
2	{2, 5}	1
3	{24, 46, 68}	1
4	{13, 24, 35, 47}	2
5	{1, 2, 3, 4, 5}	2
6	{1, 2, 4, 6, 7, 9}	3
7	{2, 5, 6, 8, 9, 10, 15}	3
8	{1, 3, 4, 5, 7, 9, 10, 12}	4
9	{3,4,5,7,8,10,11,12,20}	4
10	{1,2,5,6,8,11,13,17,21,30}	5

Additional Examples

Example 1 The Sudoku Club at a high school needs t-shirts for their upcoming tournament. They were able to negotiate a "buy-two-get-one-free" deal from a local store. The cost for one t-shirt is $10.

a. Which statement is true: "the cost *c* is a function of the number *t* of t-shirts" or "the number of t-shirts *t* is a function of the cost *c*?" **Cost is a function of the number of t-shirts.**

b. Identify the independent and dependent variables of the function. **t is the independent variable and c is the dependent variable.**

c. State the domain and range of the function. **The domain is the set of nonnegative integers; the range is the set of nonnegative integer multiples of 10.**

Example 2 Consider again the cost *c* of buying t-shirts as given in Additional Example 1.

a. List the ordered pairs of the function for values of *t* from 1 to 10. **(1, 10), (2, 20), (3, 20), (4, 30), (5, 40), (6, 40), (7, 50), (8, 60), (9, 60), (10, 70)**

b. Graph the function.

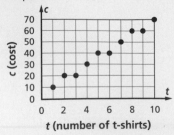

Descriptions of Functions

Functions can be described in many ways. Some frequently-used descriptions are (1) tables or lists of ordered pairs, (2) rules expressed in words or equations, and (3) coordinate graphs. You should know how to recognize functions described in each of these ways, and how to convert from one description to another.

GUIDED

Example 2 See margin for table.

Let *n* be an integer with $n \geq 2$. Graph the function that shows how many elements of an ordered set of *n* different integers are greater than the median of that set.

Solution Copy and complete a table similar to the one below with possible sets for the values of *n* from 2 to 10. Circle and count the elements greater than the median. Call this count *C*. Make a scatterplot of the points (*n*, *C*) for *n* from 2 to 10.

n	Sample set (ordered)	Count C of numbers greater than the median
2	{2,⑤}	1
3	{24, _?_, ⑥⑧ }	1
4	{13, _?_, ㉟, _?_ }	_?_
5	{ _?_ , _?_ , _?_ , _?_ , _?_ }	_?_
⋮	⋮	⋮

Each ordered pair of this function is of the form (*n*, *C*) where *n* is the number of elements in the set and *C* is the number of elements greater than the median. So for integer values of *n* from 2 to 10, the ordered pairs of the function were found in the table: (2, 1), (3, 1), (4, _?_), (5, _?_), (6, _?_), (7, _?_), (8, _?_), (9, _?_), and (10, _?_). The ordered pairs are graphed at the right. Notice that we do not connect the dots, because the values of *n* are *discrete*. Also notice that pairs of *n*-values share the same count or frequency, *C*. **2; 2; 3; 3; 4; 4; 5**

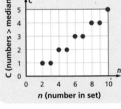

STOP QY2

In Example 2, the function is described in a table and a graph. Another description of the function in Example 2 combines two rules, one when *n* is even, and the other when *n* is odd.

$$C = \begin{cases} \frac{n}{2}, & \text{when } n \text{ is even} \\ \frac{n-1}{2}, & \text{when } n \text{ is odd} \end{cases}$$

For instance, when $n = 13$, *n* is odd, so $C = \frac{13-1}{2} = 6$. This type of description of a function is called a **piecewise definition** because it breaks the domain into pieces, and there is a rule for each piece.

▶ **QY2**

In Example 2, for what value(s) of *n* does $C = 7$?

Calculator	Function
1. number entered (input)	1. argument or independent variable *x*
2. output of a calculation on display	2. value of the function or dependent variable *f(x)*
3. inputs which do not lead to an error message	3. domain of the function *f*
4. all possible numerical outputs	4. range of the function *f*
5. each input has exactly one output	5. each first element is paired with exactly 1 second element
6. input not in domain generates an error message	6. argument not in domain means the function is not defined for that argument

Often the domain and range of a function can be determined solely from a graph or an equation.

Example 3

A rule for the function graphed at the right is $y = 2^x - 4$. Find the domain and range of the function.

Solution The domain is the set of x-values for which $2^x - 4$ is defined, which is the **set $\mathbb{R}$ of all real numbers**. From the graph, the range appears to be the set of all real numbers greater than -4, which can be written as $\{y \mid y > -4\}$.

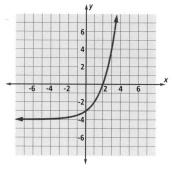

In a function, there is only one member of the range paired with each member of the domain. So, in a graph using rectangular coordinates, if y is a function of x, no vertical line will intersect the graph at more than one point. This is often referred to as the *vertical line test* for determining whether a relation is a function. You can see how this works on the two graphs of relations shown below. Only the relation graphed at the left is a function.

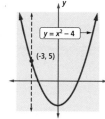

y is a function of x:
no vertical line intersects the
graph more than once.

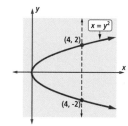

y is not a function of x:
there is at least one vertical line that
intersects the graph more than once.

Naming Functions and Their Values

A function is usually named by a single letter such as f or g. For a function f, the symbol $f(x)$, which is read "f of x," indicates the value of the dependent variable when the independent variable is x. $f(x)$ is also called the **value** of the function at x. This symbol was first used by the mathematician Leonhard Euler (pronounced "oiler") in the 18th century. Euler's notation is particularly useful when evaluating functions at specific values of the independent variable. This notation is also used when defining functions on a computer algebra system (CAS).

The Language of Functions   **83**

2-1

3 Assignment

Recommended Assignment

- Questions 1–12
- • Questions 13–23
- • Question 24 (extra credit)
- • Reading Lesson 2-2
- • Covering the Ideas 2-2
  (Questions 1–8)

Additional Example

Example 4 Suppose g is the function defined by $g(t) = 2t^2 - 3t - 2$ for all real numbers t.

a. Evaluate $g(-2)$, $g(3)$, and $g(-5)$.
 12; 7; 63

b. Does $g(-2) - g(3) = g(-2 - 4)$? **no**

c. Evaluate $g(3p + 1)$. $\mathbf{18p^2 + 3p - 3}$
 or $\mathbf{3(3p - 1)(2p + 1)}$

Example 4

Suppose f is the function defined by the rule $f(x) = 4 \cdot \left(\frac{1}{2}\right)^x$ for all real numbers x.

a. Evaluate $f(5)$.
b. Does $f(-2 + 3) = f(-2) + f(3)$?
c. Evaluate $f(q + 1)$.

Solution 1 Use paper and pencil.

a. Substitute 5 for x: $f(5) = 4 \cdot \left(\frac{1}{2}\right)^5 = 4 \cdot \frac{1}{32} = \frac{1}{8}$.

b. Evaluate the left side. Work within parentheses first.
$$f(-2 + 3) = f(1) = 4 \cdot \left(\frac{1}{2}\right)^1 = 2$$
Evaluate the right side.
$$f(-2) + f(3) = 4\left(\frac{1}{2}\right)^{-2} + 4\left(\frac{1}{2}\right)^3 = 16 + \frac{1}{2} = 16\frac{1}{2}$$
So, $f(-2 + 3) \neq f(-2) + f(3)$.

c. Substitute $q + 1$ for x in the rule.
$$f(q + 1) = 4 \cdot \left(\frac{1}{2}\right)^{q+1}$$

Solution 2 Define the function f on a CAS.

a. Input $f(5)$.

b. Input $f(-2 + 3)$. Input $f(-2) + f(3)$. The screenshot verifies the calculations in Solution 1.

c. The screenshot at the right indicates that
$f(q + 1) = 2 \cdot 2^{-q}$. Yet our answer in Solution 1 was
$f(q + 1) = 4 \cdot \left(\frac{1}{2}\right)^{q+1}$. To show that these two forms are equivalent, convert one answer to the other. We write
4 and $\frac{1}{2}$ as powers of 2.
$$4 \cdot \left(\frac{1}{2}\right)^{q+1} = 2^2 \cdot (2^{-1})^{q+1} \qquad x^{-n} = \frac{1}{x^n}$$
$$= 2^2 \cdot 2^{-q-1} \qquad \text{Power of a Power Property}$$
$$= 2^1 \cdot 2^{-q} \qquad \text{Product of Powers Property}$$
The result can be verified using a CAS.

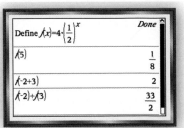

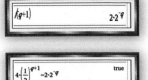

Part b of Example 4 illustrates that, in general, $f(a + b) \neq f(a) + f(b)$. That is, there is no general distributive property for functions over addition.

Questions

COVERING THE IDEAS

In 1–3, identify the independent variable and the dependent variable.

1. A parent bases a child's allowance on the number of chores completed by the child.
2. The participation grade in a class is calculated, in part, by the student's attendance.
3. Trees grow from sunlight and water.

1. independent variable: number of chores completed; dependent variable: allowance earned

2. independent variable: attendance dependent variable: participation grade

3. independent variable: sunlight and water; dependent variable: tree growth

---

Accommodating the Learner ⬇

Although students have studied functions previously, some might still be confused about the distinction between *relations* and *functions*. Point out that *any* set of ordered pairs is a relation. A function is a special type of relation, one in which there is exactly one output (*y*-value) for each input (*x*-value).

You may wish to use some non-mathematical relationships to solidify these concepts. For example, for any person x, that person can have only one biological mother, M. So the relation between x and M is a function $M(x)$. Ask students if $B(x)$, the relationship between a person x and their brother, B, is a function.

No it is not, because a person can have more than one brother. This would be an example of a one-to-many relation.

In 4 and 5, give a definition of the term.

4. domain 　　　　5. range

6. An online photo lab usually charges $0.25 per print to make a color print from a digital file. During a special promotion, customers receive a $0.50 discount if 12 or more prints are made.
    a. Which is true, "the cost c is a function of the number n of prints made" or "the number n of prints made is a function of the cost c?"
    b. What is the cost of making 20 color prints from digital files?
    c. List all the ordered pairs (n, c) for $0 \le n \le 16$.
    d. Graph the relation in Part c for $0 \le n \le 16$. See margin.
    e. Write a piecewise formula for c in terms of n.

7. Consider the function defined by $y = f(x)$. What symbol represents each of the following?
    a. the function f 　　b. the dependent variable y
    c. the value of the function $f(x)$ 　d. the independent variable x

8. Let g be the function defined by $g(t) = t^2 - 5$.
    a. Compute $g(-7)$. **44**
    b. Find the value(s) of t such that $g(t) = 12$. $\pm \sqrt{17}$
    c. Find the domain of g. $\{t \mid t \in \mathbb{R}\}$
    d. Find the range of g. $\{y \mid y \ge -5\}$
    e. Evaluate $g(p + 3)$. $p^2 + 6p + 4$

9. Consider $h(x) = \sqrt{x + 3}$.
    a. Evaluate $h(q - 1)$. $\sqrt{q + 2}$
    b. For what value of q does $h(q - 1) = 3$? **7**

In 10–12, a relation is graphed on a rectangular coordinate grid. Tell whether the relation is a function.

10.
not a function

11.
function

12.
not a function

APPLYING THE MATHEMATICS

13. Refer to the graph of $y = f(x)$ at the right.
    a. Determine the domain and range of f. See margin.
    b. Find $f(2)$. **-0.4**
    c. When does $f(x) = 1.2$? $x = 0$ or $x = 4$

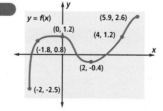

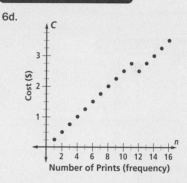

4. The domain is the set of all allowable values for the independent variable.

5. The range is the set of all possible values for the dependent variable.

6a. The cost c is a function of the number n of prints made.

6b. $4.50

6c. (0, 0), (1, 0.25), (2, 0.50), (3, 0.75), (4, 1.00), (5, 1.25), (6, 1.50), (7, 1.75), (8, 2.00), (9, 2.25), (10, 2.50), (11, 2.75), (12, 2.50), (13, 2.75), (14, 3.00), (15, 3.25), (16, 3.50)

6e. $C =$
$\begin{cases} 0.25n \text{ for } 0 \le n < 12 \\ 0.25n - 0.5 \text{ for } n \ge 12 \end{cases}$

Notes on the Questions
Question 8e You might have students compare the answer to $g(p) + g(3)$ to emphasize that the Distributive Property does not apply here.

Questions 10–12 These questions assume that the graph of the function is on a rectangular coordinate system and that we are thinking of y as a function of x. With parametric equations, the graph in Question 12 can be the function of a single variable t. In polar coordinates, that graph can be a function of θ.

Additional Answers
6d.

13a. domain: $\{x \mid -2 \le x \le 5.9\}$
range: $\{y \mid -2.5 \le y \le 2.6\}$

The Language of Functions　**85**

Extension

Review the concepts of dependent and independent variables. Point out that very often in science, time is the independent variable. Ask students to think of situations in which time is the dependent variable.
Answers vary. Sample: Measuring the time it takes to travel certain set-distance intervals.

2-1

Notes on the Questions

Question 14 This question is extended in Question 24.

Questions 22 and 23 These questions are preparation for the discussion of linear functions in the next lesson.

4) Wrap-Up

Ongoing Assessment

Write three functions on the board. Have students identify the independent variable, the dependent variable, domain, range, and state in words the rule of each function.

Additional Answers

15.

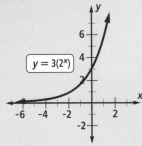

$y = 3(2^x)$

Yes, this relation passes the vertical line test and is therefore a function.

domain: $\{x \mid x \in \mathbb{R}\}$; range: $\{y \mid y > 0\}$

16.

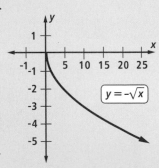

$y = -\sqrt{x}$

Yes, this relation passes the vertical line test and is therefore a function.

domain: $\{x \mid x \geq 0\}$; range: $\{y \mid y \leq 0\}$

17.

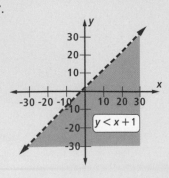

$y < x + 1$

---

14. Refer to the national debt model, $y = 0.814(1.093)^x$, on page 79.
   a. According to the model, what was the national debt in 1995? How close is this to the actual value?
   b. According to the graph of the model, in what year was the national debt first one trillion dollars?

In 15–17, consider the relation defined by each sentence. Sketch a graph. Tell if the sentence defines a function. If so, give its domain and range.

15. $y = 3 \cdot 2^x$ 16. $y = -\sqrt{x}$ 17. $y < x + 1$

18. At the right is the graph of a function whose equation is $f(t) = 3 + 2 \cdot (3)^{-t}$.
   a. Find the domain and range of the function.
   b. Use the graph to approximate $f\left(\frac{1}{2}\right)$.
   c. Use the graph to estimate the value of t such that $f(t) = 3.5$.

REVIEW

In 19 and 20, suppose that six used cars of a particular make and model are advertised in the newspaper for the following prices: $14,950; $15,250; $14,500; $14,700; $14,250; $14,900. (Lessons 1-6, 1-2)

19. Let $c_i =$ the cost of the ith used car advertised.
   a. Evaluate $\dfrac{\sum\limits_{i=1}^{6} c_i}{6}$. about $14,758.33
   b. Which statistical measure is represented by the quantity in Part a? **mean**

20. a. Without calculating, tell why the standard deviation of this data set will be less than 500. **See margin.**
   b. Calculate the standard deviation to verify your answer to Part a.

21. **Skill Sequence** Find the missing expression. (**Previous Course**)
   a. $x^2 - 12x + \underline{\ ?\ } = (x - 6)^2$ b. $x^2 + \underline{\ ?\ } + 25 = (x + 5)^2$
   c. $x^2 + 22x + 121 = (\underline{\ ?\ })^2$ d. $x^2 + 2ax + a^2 = (\underline{\ ?\ })^2$

22. Without graphing, determine whether the point (3, -4) is on the line with equation $y = 3x - 5$. (**Previous Course**) $3 \cdot 3 - 5 = 4 \neq -4$

23. Write an equation for the line with slope $-\frac{3}{2}$ that passes through (-6, 4). (**Previous Course**) $y - 4 = -\frac{3}{2}(x + 6)$

EXPLORATION

24. Find out the size of the U.S. national debt for a date as close as possible to today's date. What does the equation on page 79 predict for the national debt on the date you have? Calculate the percent error of the prediction. **See margin.**

14a. about $3,798 billion, which is about 23.6% less than the observed value of $4,974 billion.

14b. 1979

15-17. See margin.

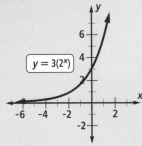

18a.

domain: $\{t \mid t \in \mathbb{R}\}$

range: $\{y \mid y > 3\}$

18b. Answers vary. Sample: about 4.2

18c. Answers vary. Sample: about 1.3

20b. about 354.14

21a. 36

21b. 10x

21c. $x + 11$

21d. $x + a$

QY ANSWERS

1. domain $\{5, 6, 7, 8\}$; range $\{1, 3\}$.

2. $n = 14$ and $n = 15$

Additional Answers

17. No, this relation does not pass the vertical line test. For example, there are infinitely many values that satisfy the expression for $x = 0$.

18a. domain: $\{t \mid t \in \mathbb{R}\}$; range: $\{y \mid y > 3\}$

18b. Answers vary. Sample: about 4.2

18c. Answers vary. Sample: about 1.3

20a. The range between the highest and lowest value is 1000. Since standard deviation measures the spread from the mean of a given set, the measure of spread from the mean will necessarily be smaller than 500.

24. Answers vary. Sample: As of July 9, 2008, the national debt was 9,633 billion dollars. According to the exponential model, $D(x)$, the predicted value in 2008 is about 12,067 billion dollars. This amounts to about a 25% error.

Lesson 2-2 Linear Models

▶ **BIG IDEA** The sum of squared deviations is a statistic for determining which of two lines fits the data better.

A **linear function** is a set of ordered pairs (x, y) satisfying an equation of the form $y = mx + b$, where m and b are constants. Recall that the graph of every such function is a line with slope m and y-intercept b.

Fitting a Line to Data

When data in a scatterplot lie near a line, we can create a **linear model** for the data, that is, a model of one variable as a linear function of the other. Even if the linear function does not contain all of the data points, it may still be useful in describing the overall trend of the data or in predicting values of either the dependent or independent variable.

In this lesson and the next, you will learn several techniques for constructing linear models. One technique is to fit a line to data "by eye," that is, to draw a line that seems close to the data.

GUIDED

Example 1

Jewelers emphasize that the price of a diamond is determined by cut, carat weight, color and clarity. The table at the right gives carat weights and approximate prices in U.S. dollars for twenty diamond rings sold at a recent auction in Singapore. All rings are of the same quality gold and contain a single diamond. The data are graphed below.

Prices of Diamond Rings Sold in Singapore

Weight (carats of diamonds)

Weight x	Price y (U.S. $)
0.18	702.00
0.17	517.50
0.25	963.00
0.29	1290.00
0.27	1080.00
0.15	484.50
0.20	747.00
0.25	1017.00
0.21	724.50
0.17	529.50
0.35	1629.00
0.33	1417.50
0.26	994.50
0.16	513.00
0.12	334.50
0.18	664.50
0.15	430.50
0.16	507.00
0.16	498.00
0.23	829.50

Source: Journal of Statistics Education

Linear Models **87**

Vocabulary

linear function
linear model
interpolation
extrapolation
observed values
predicted values
residual
sum of squared residuals

Mental Math

What is the sum of a set 25 elements whose mean is 300? **7500**

GOAL

Discuss the idea of a line of fit and the use of the sum of squared residuals as a measure of that fit.

SPUR Objectives

B Compute residuals from observed and predicted values.

F Find and interpret linear models.

I Use scatterplots and residual plots to draw conclusions about models for data.

Materials/Resources

· Lesson Master 2-2
· Resource Masters 29–31

HOMEWORK • Option 1 • Option 2

- • Questions 1–8
- • • Questions 9–14
- • • Question 15 (extra credit)
  - • Reading Lesson 2-3
  - • Covering the Ideas 2-3 (Questions 1–12)

Local Standards

1 Warm-Up

1. Explain why it is reasonable for the price of a diamond to be close to a linear function of the weight of the diamond. **If the value of the diamond per carat is constant, the price will be an exact linear function of the weight of the diamond.**

2. Suppose water is in a conical-shaped funnel with a hole in the bottom that is plugged up. If the plug is removed, will the height of the water left in the funnel be a linear function of time? Why or why not? **No, the volume of the water per unit height is greater the farther the water is from the hole. The height will go down slowly at first and then gradually increase.**

Background

In teaching modeling, it is often instructive to distinguish three types of models: the *exact model*, where the mathematics gives the precise value (as is often found in dealing with money); the *almost exact theory-based model* (such as in describing the path of a projectile); and what might be called the *impressionistic model*, where there is little basis to predict the model, but the data fit it (such as with using lines of fit for test scores).

In this lesson, the diamond weight-price data of Example 1 are an almost exact theory-based model (we would expect price to vary directly as weight, except that larger diamonds are rarer than smaller ones). The TV-unemployment data of the Activity are an impressionistic model because we should not expect these variables to be linearly related.

(continued on next page)

2-2

2 Teaching

Notes on the Lesson

Example 1 Use Warm-Up 1 to begin the discussion of Example 1. The data set was chosen to be close to linear in order to facilitate modeling with a line. The slope of the line of fit is an estimate of the average price per carat.

Be sure to emphasize that a linear model does not have to pass through any of the data points. Students tend to want to "rig" the line and make it go through a data point in the "middle" of the set. Yet, in one sense, that thinking is on the right track. As is pointed out in the next lesson, the line of best fit does contain the center of gravity of the data set. But the center of gravity does not have to be (and usually is not) one of the given points.

Measuring how well a line models data Make sure students understand the terms *observed values*, *predicted values*, and *residuals*. The line of best fit minimizes the sum of the squared residuals. The definition of *residual* is important; it is the *vertical* difference between the data point and the corresponding point on the line of best fit. Students sometimes confuse residual with the perpendicular distance to the line. The following diagram clarifies this misconception.

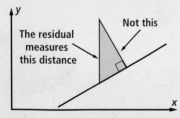

When a point is not on the line and the line is not horizontal, the vertical distance is always larger than the perpendicular distance.

The linear model is based on the weight of the diamond used. Although the data are not collinear, the line through (0.18, 600) and (0.32, 1400) seems close to the points. It has been added to the graph. An equation of this graphed line is one linear model for these data. Is the size alone a good predictor of price?

a. Find an equation of the graphed line which relates weight and price.

b. Interpret the slope of the line in the context of the problem.

c. Use the model to estimate the price of a 0.3-carat diamond ring.

d. Why is the model not good for predicting the cost of a 0.05-carat diamond ring?

e. Why is the set of data not a function?

Solution

a. We use the points (0.18, 600) and (0.32, 1400) to find an equation of the line:

$$m = \frac{y_2 - y_1}{x_2 - x_1} = \frac{\underline{\quad?\quad}}{\underline{\quad?\quad}} \approx \underline{\quad?\quad} \quad \frac{1400 - 600}{0.32 - 0.18}; \textbf{5714.29}$$

Substitute $m = 5714.29$ and (0.18, 600) into the point-slope form of the equation for a line.

$$y - y_1 = m(x - x_1)$$
$$y - \underline{\quad?\quad} = 5714.29(x - \underline{\quad?\quad})\ \textbf{600; 0.18}$$
$$y = \underline{\quad?\quad}\ \textbf{5714.29}x - \textbf{428.57}$$

b. The slope is the rate of change. The cost increases by about $\underline{\quad?\quad}$ **5714.29** dollars for every 1-carat increase in weight.

c. To predict the cost from the weight, substitute $x = 0.3$ and solve for y. When $x = 0.3$, $y = \underline{\quad?\quad}$. According to the model, the cost of **1285.72** a 0.3-carat diamond ring will be about $\underline{\quad?\quad}$. **$1285.72**

d. Substitute 0.05 for x and solve for y. The model predicts that a 0.05-carat diamond ring will cost $\underline{\quad?\quad}$. This means that the **–$142.86** seller would pay you to take the ring! This is not plausible, so the model is not a good predictor.

e. There is at least one x-value that does not have a unique y-value. **There are two diamonds at 0.17 carats that have different prices, so the data set is not a function.**

In this example, known diamond weights range from 0.12 to 0.35 carats. If you use the model to predict the price of a 0.3-carat diamond, you are making a prediction *between* known values. Prediction between known values is called **interpolation.** If you calculate the price of a diamond weighing 0.05 carats, you are making a prediction *beyond* known values. Prediction beyond known values is called **extrapolation.** Extrapolation is usually more hazardous than interpolation, because it depends on an assumption that a relationship will continue past the known data. In this case, a diamond much smaller than those in the sample might be inexpensive, but it will not be free.

Hard Rock
The largest rough diamond ever found weighed 3106 carats.

Students who have studied from UCSMP *Algebra* or *Advanced Algebra* should have experience with linear models. For them, the new idea will be the use of residuals to gauge the fit of a model.

We expect all students to be able to

1. "fit" (by eye) a line to a scatterplot,

2. find an equation of the form $y = mx + b$ for the line (in this equation m is the rate of change and b is the initial value of y),

3. use their model to predict, by interpolation or extrapolation, values of y for different values of x, and

4. calculate residuals from their predictions and use the sum of the squares of residuals to compare how lines fit.

Lesson 2-3 follows naturally from this lesson; in it, students learn that the *line of best fit* is the one with the least sum of squared residuals. Some teachers have taught these two lessons together.

Measuring How Well a Line Models Data

In Chapter 1, you studied the sample variance, which was computed as the sum of the squared deviations from the mean divided by $n - 1$. A similar statistic, the *residual*, tells how far away data are from your chosen model. At the right is a table showing a smaller sample of the diamond ring data on page 87. These data, collected from sources such as experiments or surveys, are called **observed values**. Below, the scatterplot of these data is shown together with the graph of the line with equation $y = 2400x + 400$. This equation seems to be a pretty good model for the data. However, is it the best model? To compare models, we calculate *residuals*. The values predicted by a model are called **predicted values**. The observed value minus the predicted value is the **residual**. A residual is positive when the observed value is higher than what is predicted by the model. A residual is negative when the observed value is lower than what the model predicts.

For instance, a 0.16-carat diamond ring sold for $507.00. This is lower than the price predicted by the model.

$$\text{predicted price} = 2400 \cdot (0.16) + 400$$
$$= \$784$$

The residual, or error, is

$$\text{residual} = \text{observed value} - \text{predicted value}$$
$$= 507 - 784$$
$$= -277.$$

The actual cost was $277 less than predicted. On the graph, we see that the observed value is 277 units below the linear model $y = 2400x + 400$. That is why the residual is negative. Every data point has a residual, so n data points provide n residuals. The absolute value of a residual is the length of the vertical segment from the data point to the corresponding point on the linear model.

Diamond Ring Prices by Weight of Diamond	
Weight	Price (U.S. dollars)
0.15	484.50
0.16	507.00
0.18	702.00
0.25	963.00
0.27	1080.00
0.33	1417.50
0.23	829.50

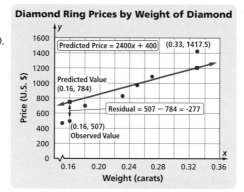

Diamond Ring Prices by Weight of Diamond

Predicted Price = 2400x + 400 (0.33, 1417.5)

Predicted Value (0.16, 784)

Residual = 507 − 784 = −277

(0.16, 507) Observed Value

 QY

> **QY**
>
> What is the residual for the 0.33-carat diamond?

Linear Models **89**

ENGLISH LEARNERS
Vocabulary Development

The word *residual* is related to the word *residue*, what is left after some process has taken place.

Accommodating the Learner ⬇

Point out to students that when they attempt to fit a line to data by eye, more than one line is possible. The slopes of all the lines that closely fit the data should be approximately equal, as should be the y-intercepts. You may wish to demonstrate this by comparing the equations for the lines different students have drawn by eye for a particular data set.

Additional Example

Example 1 The gold medal winning times for the men's 100-meter dash are listed below for the last 20 Summer Olympic Games.

City	Year	Winning Time(s)
Beijing	2008	9.69
Athens	2004	9.85
Sydney	2000	9.87
Atlanta	1996	9.84
Barcelona	1992	9.96
Seoul	1988	9.92
Los Angeles	1984	9.99
Moscow	1980	10.25
Montreal	1976	10.06
Munich	1972	10.14
Mexico City	1968	9.95
Tokyo	1964	10.0
Rome	1960	10.2
Melbourne	1956	10.5
Helsinki	1952	10.4
London	1948	10.3
Berlin	1936	10.3
Los Angeles	1932	10.3
Amsterdam	1928	10.8
Paris	1924	10.6

a. The data were graphed and a line fit "by eye" passed through the points (1972, 10.15) and (2004, 9.8). Find the equation of this linear model to relate the year and the winning time. $t = -0.01r + 29.84$

b. Interpret the slope of your line in the context of the problem. **Answers vary. Sample: The athletes' times are improving at a rate of approximately 1 hundredth of a second every year, which would shave 4 hundredths of a second off the winning time every Summer Olympic Games.**

c. Use the model to predict the winning time at the London 2012 Olympic Games. **9.72 seconds**

d. Usain Bolt of Jamaica won the 100-m dash at the Beijing 2008 games in a record 9.69 seconds. Based on the linear model, in which future Olympic year is it most likely that this winning time would have been run? **2016. Substituting $t = 9.69$ gives us $r = 2015$, so 2016 is the closest Olympic year.**

2-2

Notes on the Lesson

The squares in the graphs of linear models 1 and 2 also emphasize that each residual is the (directed) vertical distance between the point and the line.

Caution: Since all of the residual is in the direction of the dependent variable, the residuals for a line of fit of Y on X are typically different from that of X on Y. A line of fit might perhaps be better called a "line of prediction."

Emphasize that none of the examples in this lesson involves the line of best fit. Lines of best fit are introduced in Lesson 2-3.

On the graphs below, this line and another linear model are drawn to fit the seven points. Recall that when you compute variance, you add the squared deviations from the mean. Similarly, when modeling data with a line, we can measure the variation from the line by adding the squares of the residuals. You can use spreadsheets to calculate residuals and the sum of squared residuals, as shown below.

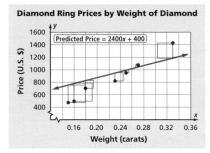 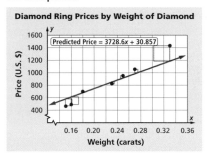

You can also think of (residual)^2 as the area of a geometric square whose side has length equal to the absolute value of the residual. These geometric sqares are drawn on the graphs below.

Linear Model 1

Squares are shown for a line that does not go through any data points.

Diamond Ring Prices by Weight of Diamond

Predicted Price = 2400x + 400

Total area of the squares ≈ 237,800

Linear Model 2

Squares are shown for a line through two of the data points.

Diamond Ring Prices by Weight of Diamond

Predicted Price = 3728.6x + 30.857

Total area of the squares ≈ 59,870

The second line is a better model of the data because it has a smaller total area of the squares. The total area is the **sum of squared residuals**.

Definition of Sum of Squared Residuals

Sum of squared residuals $= \sum_{i=1}^{n} (\text{observed } y_i - \text{predicted } y_i)^2$

Accommodating the Learner

The *sum of squared residuals* is referred to as a similar statistic to the *variance*, which was studied in Chapter 1. Ask students to explain how the two statistics are similar and how they are different. **Answers vary. Sample: Both statistics take a measure of how far the actual data points deviate from a particular value or line. For these calculations, we have to square and then sum these deviations or residuals. The variance compares each of the data points to their mean; these deviations always sum to zero. The residual compares each observed value to the one predicted by a linear model; these residuals do not always sum to zero. We can calculate the variance for one variable from a data set, but we need to compare two variables and a line of fit before we can calculate the sum of squared residuals.**

The sum of squared residuals is a statistic that measures lack of fit. If you compare two lines, the one with the larger sum of squared residuals is not as good a model as the one with the smaller sum of squared residuals. If you have many possible lines you could use to model data, compute the sum of squared residuals for each model. The line that gives the smallest value provides the best fit to the data.

Activity

See margin.

This table shows the number of televisions per 100 people in 1997 and the number of unemployed per 100 people in 2008 for nine countries from around the world. Some people suggest that increased TV viewing leads to a less productive workforce. Are these statistics related?

Country	TVs per 100	Unemployed per 100
Argentina	22.3	7.8
Bulgaria	40.0	6.3
India	6.5	6.8
Israel	29.9	6.1
Netherlands	51.8	4.5
New Zealand	52.3	4.0
Poland	33.7	9.7
South Africa	12.3	21.7
South Korea	34.7	3.2

Source: UNESCO Institute for Statistics, CIA World Fact Book

Step 1 Use a statistics utility to create a scatterplot with number of TVs on the x-axis and number of unemployed people on the y-axis.

Step 2 Add a movable line to the scatterplot.

Step 3 Move the line as close to $y = -0.3x + 17$ as you can. Your screen should look similar to the one at the right. Record the sum of squared residuals.

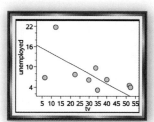

Step 4 Move the line so that it goes through the points for Bulgaria and the Netherlands. Record the equation. Record the sum of squared residuals.

Step 5 Tell which line is the better model of the data. Explain your choice.

Step 6 Move the line until you get the smallest sum of squares that you can. Record the equation and the sum of squared residuals.

Questions

COVERING THE IDEAS

1. Define *linear function*.

2. Refer to the diamond price data in Example 1.
   a. Find an equation for the line that passes through the data points (0.35, 1629) and (0.12, 334.50).
   b. Write a sentence that states how cost increases for every carat increase in weight according to your equation.
   c. Use your line to predict the price of a 0.17-carat diamond.
   d. Is this interpolation or extrapolation?

3. **Fill in the Blanks** For a data set, residuals are the differences between ___?___ values and ___?___ values. **observed; predicted**

1. A linear function is a set of ordered pairs (x, y) which can be described by an equation of the form $y = mx + b$, where m and b are constants.

2a. $y = 5628.26x - 340.89$

2b. The cost of a diamond ring increases by \$5628.26 for every one-carat increase in weight.

2c. \$615.91

2d. interpolation

Linear Models   **91**

2-2

3 Assignment

Recommended Assignment
- Questions 1–8
- Questions 9–14
- Question 15 (extra credit)
- Reading Lesson 2-3
- Covering the Ideas 2-3 (Questions 1–12)

Additional Answers

Step 5: The second line is a better fit because its sum of squared residuals is smaller. This means that the data points are closer to the second model, on average, than the first.

Step 6: $y = -0.203x + 14.18$, sum of squared residuals ≈ 166.56

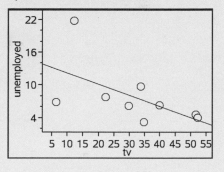

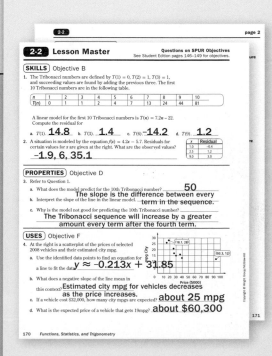

Additional Answers

Steps 1–3: Answers vary. Sample: sum of squared residuals ≈ 185.5

Step 4: $y = -0.15x + 12.3$, sum of squared residuals ≈ 172.6

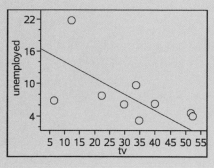

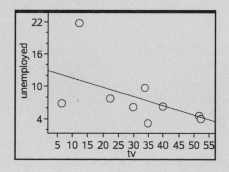

2-2

Notes on the Questions

Questions 9c and 10c In preparation for Lesson 2-3, you should compare the sums of the squared residuals for these two models. You might point out that we will be looking for the line for which this sum is minimized and see if students can find a better line (just as Question 16 asks for Question 11).

4. When a residual is positive, is the observed value higher or lower than the predicted value? **higher**

In 5 and 6, a diamond speculator used the line with equation $y = 5000x - 250$ to estimate the price of diamond rings.

5. a. What would the speculator predict for the price of the 0.29-carat diamond ring? **$1200**
   b. According to the data in Example 1, what is the residual for the 0.29-carat diamond ring? **$90**

6. a. What would the speculator predict as a price for the 0.21-carat diamond ring? **$800**
   b. What is the residual for this diamond ring? **–$75.50**

7. Does the phrase "sum of squared residuals" mean "first sum the residuals and then square the sum" or "first square each residual and then sum the squares?"

7. "first square each residual and then sum the squares"

8. Consider the linear model $f(x) = 5.2x - 3$.
   a. Given a residual of –0.2 at $x = 1$, find the observed value. **2**
   b. Given a residual of 2.1 at $x = 4$, find the observed value. **19.9**
   c. Given a residual of 0 at $x = 3$, find the observed value. **12.6**

APPLYING THE MATHEMATICS

In 9 and 10, suppose Jane asked members of her family how many states they had visited. Her data are in the table at the right.

9. Jane plotted the data and drew a line through the points for Ed and Grandma. She found its equation to be $y = 0.55x + 3.5$.
   a. What is the slope of this line and what does it represent?
   b. Complete the spreadsheet below to calculate the residuals for this model.
   c. What is the sum of squared residuals for Jane's model?
   d. Jane used her equation to predict how many states she will have visited at age 30. Is this interpolation or extrapolation?
   e. What is Jane's prediction from Part d?

Family Member	Age	States Visited
Jane	16	15
Cousin Xia	16	18
Dad	40	27
Grandma	70	42
Brother Ed	10	9
Uncle Ralph	45	19

◇	A	B	C	D
1	Age	States Visited	Predicted	Residual²
2	16	15	12.3	7.29
3	16	18	**12.3**	**32.49**
4	40	27	25.5	2.25
5	70	42	42.0	0
6	10	9	**9.0**	**0**
7	45	19	28.25	85.56

9a. 0.55; The number of states visited increases by 0.55 for every one year increase in age.

9c. 127.59

9d. interpolation

9e. 20 states

10. Xia thought that drawing the line through the points for Ed and Dad would look better because then there would be two points above the line and two below the line. Her line has equation $y = 0.6x + 3$.

92   Functions and Models

a. What is the residual for Grandma using Xia's model? **–3**

b. What is the squared residual for Dad using Xia's model? **0**

c. Calculate the sum of squared residuals for Xia's model. **164.92**

d. Xia uses the equation to predict how many states Grandma will have visited when she reaches 100. Is this interpolation or extrapolation? **extrapolation**

e. What is Xia's prediction from Part d? **63**

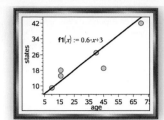

11. The table at the right gives expected life spans and gestation periods for selected animals. *Gestation* for mammals is development time in the mother's uterus until birth. For humans, the mean time is 266 days. **See margin.**

a. Make a scatterplot with Life Span as the independent variable.

b. Draw the line through the points for Lion and Elephant. Do you think this line fits the data well?

c. Find an equation for the line in Part b in slope-intercept form.

d. Interpret the slope of the line in Part b.

e. What is the residual for the Moose under this model?

f. Use the line in Part b to predict the gestation period for the Blue Whale, which has an estimated life span of 80 years. (The actual gestation period is estimated at 11-12 months.) Is this interpolation or extrapolation?

g. What is the sum of squared residuals for the line?

Animal	Expected Life Span (years)	Mean Gestation (days)
Black Bear	20	215
Camel	40	390
Elephant	55	660
Gorilla	50	251
Gray Squirrel	9	42
Hippopotamus	45	240
Lion	12	100
Moose	27	240
Wolf	10	63

Source: BBC

REVIEW

12. Consider the function $\{(-2, 8), (-1, 8), (0, 8), (3, 8), (8, 8)\}$. (Lesson 2-1)

a. State its domain.   b. Give its range.

In 13 and 14, a sample of five math test scores is given. (Lesson 1-6)

a. Find the standard deviation of the data set.

b. Explain a conclusion you can draw about the spread of the data set by just looking at it. **13 and 14. See margin.**

13. 63, 77, 81, 83, 92

14. 94, 95, 95, 96, 100

12a. $\{-2, -1, 0, 3, 8\}$

12b. $\{8\}$

EXPLORATION

15. Use statistical software to draw a line that has the smallest sum of squared residuals for the data in the table in Question 11.

a. What is the equation? $y = 8.65x - 13.06$

b. What is the sum of squared residuals? **about 93,233.2**

Notes on the Questions
Questions 11 and 16 In general, larger animals have longer gestation periods. The use of functions to model the data takes that generalization and makes it more specific. Question 16 asks students to explore better lines than the one used in Question 11.

4 Wrap-Up

Ongoing Assessment
Present a new set of (roughly linear) data to the class, similar to those in the Example and Additional Example (Olympic and other sports-related data are easily found on the Internet). Have students work in small groups to plot the data, eyeball a line of best fit, find its equation, and calculate the sum of squared residuals. Then have each group compare their sum with other groups to see whose line fit the data the best.

Additional Answers

13a. about 10.59

13b. Because there are only five data points and the range is 29, the spread is large.

14a. about 2.35

14b. Because the data falls in a small range of 6 points, the spread is small.

Additional Answers

11a–b. This line appears to model the data fairly well

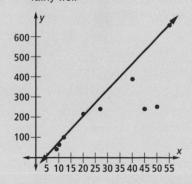

11c. $y = \frac{560}{43}x - \frac{2420}{43}$

11d. The average gestation period increases by about 13.0 days for every increase of one year in an animal's expected life span.

11e. –55.35

11f. about 986 days; extrapolation

11g. about 211,453

Lesson 2-3

Lesson 2-3

Linear Regression and Correlation

Vocabulary

method of least squares
line of best fit, least squares
   line, regression line
center of mass
correlation coefficient
perfect correlation
strong correlation
weak correlation

GOAL

Discuss data which, when graphed, show a roughly linear pattern of growth. Explain how to use technology to find an equation for the line of best fit and to determine the closeness of fit, as measured by the (linear) correlation coefficient.

SPUR Objectives

D Identify properties of regression lines and of the correlation coefficient.

F Find and interpret linear regression and models.

I Use scatterplots and residual plots to draw conclusions about linear models for data.

Materials/Resources

· Lesson Master 2-3
· Resource Masters 32–34
· Quiz 1

HOMEWORK

· Option 1
· Option 2

- Questions 1–12
- · Questions 13–25
- · Question 26 (extra credit)
- Reading Lesson 2-4
- Covering the Ideas 2-4 (Questions 1–6)

Local Standards

1 Warm-Up

Here are some Fahrenheit-Celsius temperature equivalents: 0°C = 32°F; 20°C = 68°F; 37°C = 98.6°F; 100°C = 212°F. Find an equation for the line of best fit for these data, predicting F from C. $F = 1.8C + 32$; the fit is exact.

▶ **BIG IDEA** The regression line is the line of best fit to data. The correlation coefficient measures the strength and direction of a linear pattern in data.

The sum of squared residuals can be used to determine which of two lines is the better fit to a specific set of data. When data are fairly linear, like the diamond weights and prices in Lesson 2-2, you are likely to find a good model quickly. When there is a large spread of data points on a scatterplot, you might have to try several equations. Even if you pick the equation with the smallest sum of squared residuals, there is likely another line with an even smaller sum of squared residuals that you did not try. How can you find the best model?

The Line of Best Fit

The problem of finding the best linear model for a set of data emerged from studies of astronomy, geography, and navigation in the late 1700s and early 1800s. A method for finding the line of best fit was first published by the French mathematician Adrien Legendre in 1805. His approach to the problem is called the **method of least squares**, because he used the Sum of Squared Residuals to determine the linear equation of best fit.

The **line of best fit**, also known as the **least squares line** or **regression line**, has three important properties:

1. It is the line that minimizes the sum of squared residuals, and it is unique. There is only one line of best fit for a set of data.

2. It contains the **center of mass** of the data, that is, the point $(\bar{x}, \bar{y})$ whose coordinates are the mean of the x-values and the mean of the y-values.

3. Its slope and intercept can be computed directly from the coordinates of the given data points.

Although the formula for the slope of the least squares line uses only addition, subtraction, squaring, and division, it is too complex for computation by hand. Every statistics utility contains a *regression* routine that will take the coordinates of a set of data points and compute the slope and y-intercept of the line of best fit.

Suppose you thought the price of a new car was going to be $19,000. Instead, it was $20,000. By what percent of the actual price were you off?

5 percent

A sextant is an instrument used to determine latitude and longitude, using angle measures.

Background

This lesson follows naturally from Lesson 2-2. The lesson discusses the statistical line of best fit, which is the line that minimizes the sum of squared residuals from the points to the line and which is called the least squares or regression line. Students should be able to use a statistical utility to draw a line of best fit on a scatterplot of data and use the computer-generated equation of that line to make predictions about the population which the line models. We do not expect students to be able to calculate a line of best fit by hand. However, students should know what is meant by the method of least squares.

In statistics, *regression* refers to a measure of the extent to which two variables increase together linearly, or how one decreases as the other increases linearly. The idea was first described by Sir Francis Galton in 1877 to explain results in an experiment with sweet peas. Offspring were normally distributed about a population average, not their parents' average.

Example

a. Use a statistics utility to find a line of best fit for the data about the weight in carats and the price of diamond rings from Lesson 2-2.

b. According to the regression line, how much will a 0.5-carat diamond ring cost?

c. Verify that the center of mass (0.212, $793.65) is on the line.

d. Find the sum of squared residuals for the linear regression.

Solution

a. Enter the entire data set from Lesson 2-2 into a statistics utility. Label the weight as *x* and the price as *y*. Use the linear regression feature to find an equation for *y* as a function of *x*. **The linear regression model is y = 5501.53x − 372.67.**

b. Substitute 0.5 for *x* and calculate *y*.

$$y = 5501.53(0.5) − 372.67 ≈ 2378.1$$

According to the linear regression model, the price would be $2378.10.

c. Substitute the coordinates of the center of mass for *x* and *y* in the regression equation.

$$y = 5501.53x − 372.67$$

Does $793.65 = 5501.53(0.212) − 372.67$?

Yes. It checks.

d. On many statistics utilities, once the regression equation is given, the residuals are calculated and stored until the next regression is found. In the screenshot at the right, the residuals are stored under the name Resid. So the sum of the squared residuals is 41842.9.

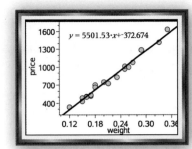

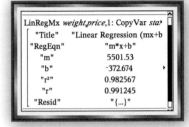

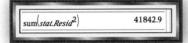

 QY1

Correlation

For the diamond ring data, the regression line is the best linear model for these data. But how good is "best?"

To measure the strength of the linear relation between two variables, a *correlation coefficient* is used. The correlation coefficient is often denoted by the letter *r*. The terms "co-relation" and "regression" were introduced by the English researcher Sir Francis Galton in the 1880s in a study comparing the heights of children with the heights of their parents. The statistic we now use for correlation was given a mathematical foundation by the English statistician Karl Pearson in 1896. Statisticians today use Pearson's formula, which can be evaluated automatically with a statistics utility.

> **QY1**
>
> Use the least-squares regression line to estimate the price of a diamond ring weighing 0.17 carats.

Linear Regression and Correlation   **95**

(Normal distributions are studied in Chapter 11.) Galton called this "reversion," or going back to the population mean. In 1885 he used the word *regression* in describing a similar phenomenon among heights of children in relation to their parents' heights.

The line of best fit Of the three properties listed here of the line of best fit, the key property is the first, since it is the only one that determines a unique line. There are many lines through the center of mass and there are many ways one could compute slopes and intercepts from coordinates of the data points.

2-3

Notes on the Lesson

Correlation What we call correlation is short for *linear correlation*. Thus, the line below might be the *line* of best fit for the given data points, but no line fits well.

This situation has all the points at both ends below the line and it would be modeled better by a quadratic function.

Particular nonlinear models will be discussed in Lessons 2-4 (exponential), 2-6 (quadratic), and 2-7 (inverse variation) in this chapter and in Chapters 5 (trigonometric), 7 (higher-degree polynomial), and 9 (logarithmic).

Some students may want a strict criterion for determining when a correlation is strong and when a correlation is weak. There is no single criterion; the strength depends on the situation.

> **Definition of Correlation Coefficient (Pearson's Formula)**
>
> The **correlation coefficient** for a population with n elements is
> $$r = \frac{1}{n}\sum_{i=1}^{n}\left(\frac{x_i - \bar{x}}{s_x}\right)\left(\frac{y_i - \bar{y}}{s_y}\right).$$
> $\frac{1}{n}$ is replaced by $\frac{1}{n-1}$ for data from a sample.

Unlike the sum of squared residuals, which can be measured for any line modeling a set of data, the correlation coefficient describes fit and direction for the regression line only.

It can be proved that, regardless of the data set, the correlation coefficient r is always a number between –1 and 1. Some data sets and the corresponding values of r are shown in the scatterplots below.

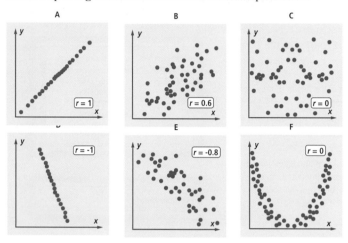

You should use your statistics utility to calculate the value of r. However, you should be able to interpret the value of r in the context of your data. In general, the sign of r indicates the *direction* of the relation between the variables, and its magnitude indicates the *strength* of the relation. Positive values of r indicate a positive association between the variables. That is, larger values of one variable are associated with larger values of the other. Negative values of r indicate a negative association between the variables. That is, larger values of one variable are associated with smaller values of the other.

The extreme values of 1 and -1 indicate a perfect linear relation, as in scatterplots A and D. That is, all data points lie on a line. Thus, a situation in which $r = \pm1$ is sometimes called a **perfect correlation**.

Vocabulary Development

Though we define the word *regression* for this course, be aware that it is possible that students have encountered the word *regression* in other contexts, and these uses of the word are different from its meaning in statistics. In astronomy, regression refers to a westward shifting in the moon's orbit. In biology, it refers to an organism's reversion to another type—commonly an earlier or simpler type. In medicine, it is the gradual disappearance of a disease.

In psychology, it is a reversion to more infantile behavior. So most of the uses of the word regression impart the notion of going backward, which is the generic definition of the word.

A relation for which most of the data fall close to a line (scatterplot E) is called a **strong correlation**. A **weak correlation** is one for which, although a linear trend can be seen, many points are not very close to the line (scatterplot B). A value of r close or equal to 0 (scatterplots C and F) indicates that the variables are not related by a linear model. Note, however, that as indicated in scatterplot F, if $r = 0$, the variables might be strongly related in some other way as denoted by the pattern. A number line below summarizes these relations.

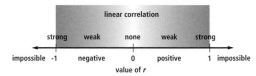

There are no strict rules about how large a correlation must be to be considered strong. In some cases, $|r| = 0.5$ is considered fairly strong, and in others it might be considered moderate or weak.

STOP QY2

Without calculating the correlation coefficient, you can get a sense of its value by looking at the numerical data or at a scatterplot of the data.

Activity

Set 1		Set 2		Set 3		Set 4		Set 5	
x	**y**	**x**	**y**	**x**	**y**	**x**	**y**	**x**	**y**
10	30	4	10	250	3	3	250	-3	9
11	40	8	9	300	9	9	300	-2	4
15	80	13	2	500	11	11	500	0	0
12	50	11	5	750	10	10	750	2	4
14	70	8	4	600	12	12	600	3	9

Step 1 Look at the pattern in each data table and predict what the correlation coefficient might be for that data set.

Step 2 Draw a scatterplot of each data set. Use the scatterplot to predict the correlation coefficient, altering your prediction from Step 1 if necessary.

Step 3 Use a statistics utility to determine the regression line and correlation coefficient for each data set. Compare your prediction from Step 2 to the actual correlation coefficient. **Steps 2, 3. See margin.**

Some statistics utilities give values of r^2 rather than of r. This is because r^2 is used in advanced statistical techniques. You can calculate r by taking the square root of r^2, and then determine the sign of correlation according to the direction in the scatterplot.

STOP QY3

> **QY2**

Multiple Choice
In the graph below, which of the values is a reasonable value for r?

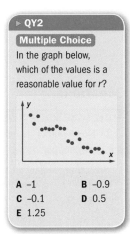

A -1	B -0.9
C -0.1	D 0.5
E 1.25	

Activity Step 1:

Answers vary. Sample: set 1: $r = 1$; set 2: $r = -0.8$; set 3: $r = 0.62$; set 4: $r = 0.6$; set 5: $r = 0$

> **QY3**

An r^2 value of 0.6 yields what possible values for r, to the nearest tenth?

Linear Regression and Correlation   **97**

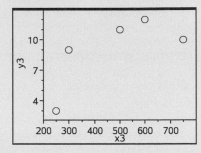
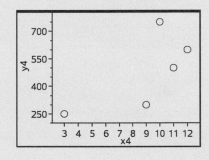
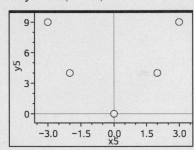
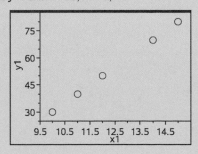
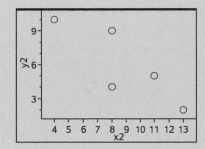

2-3

Notes on the Lesson

Cautions about correlation The principle *correlation does not imply causation* is a mantra in statistics. This principle is often violated in political arguments and even sometimes in scientific discourse. You might ask each student to think of an example different from the ones in the book and compile these into a long list available for students to read.

3 Assignment

Recommended Assignment

- Questions 1–12
- Questions 13–25
- Question 26 (extra credit)
- Reading Lesson 2-4
- Covering the Ideas 2-4 (Questions 1–6)

Cautions about Correlation

It is important to note that while *r* provides a mathematical measure of *linearity*, it does not provide information about *cause and effect*. For instance, there is a large positive correlation between shoe size and reading level of children. But this does not mean that learning to read better causes your feet to grow or that wearing bigger shoes improves your reading.

It is up to the people who analyze and interpret the data to determine why two variables might be related. In the case of shoe size and reading level, the correlation is strong because each variable is related to age. Older children generally have both larger feet and higher reading skills than younger children. Similarly, the data in the Activity in Lesson 2-2 give a relationship between TVs and unemployment. The correlation is –0.8, which is strong, but it does not imply that unemployment can be reduced by providing a country with more TVs. This idea is sometimes summarized as *correlation does not imply causation*.

Another caution about correlation and regression: watch out for influential points. Outliers in either the *x*- or *y*-coordinate can have a strong impact on the values of slope, *y*-intercept, and correlation of the least squares line.

Questions

COVERING THE IDEAS

1. Give two other names for the regression line.

In 2–5, match the scatterplot with the best description.

| A | strong negative correlation | B | weak negative correlation |
| C | strong positive correlation | D | almost no correlation |

2.
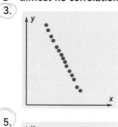

3.

4.

5.

1. least squares line, line of best fit

2. D

3. A

4. B

5. C

Accommodating the Learner

Have students write a brief explanation of why the correlation coefficient for the line containing the points (–3, 16), (7, –34), and (11, –54) is –1. **Answers vary. Sample:** By comparing the slopes of two pairs from these points, we can tell that they are collinear, so $r = 1$ or –1. Since larger values of the first coordinate are associated with smaller values of the second coordinate, there is a negative relation between the variables. Thus, $r = -1$.

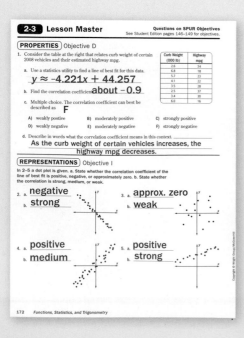

2-3 Lesson Master

Questions on SPUR Objectives
See Student Edition pages 146–149 for objectives.

PROPERTIES Objective D

1. Consider the table at the right that relates curb weight of certain 2008 vehicles and their estimated highway mpg.

Curb Weight (000 lb)	Highway mpg
2.6	34
6.8	18
5.7	23
4.1	22
3.5	28
2.5	37
3.4	30
6.0	16

a. Use a statistics utility to find a line of best fit for this data.
$y \approx -4.221x + 44.257$

b. Find the correlation coefficient. **about –0.9**

c. Multiple choice. The correlation coefficient can best be described as **F**

A) weakly positive   B) moderately positive   C) strongly positive
D) weakly negative   E) moderately negative   F) strongly negative

d. Describe in words what the correlation coefficient means in this context.
As the curb weight of certain vehicles increases, the highway mpg decreases.

REPRESENTATIONS Objective I

In 2–5 a dot plot is given. a. State whether the correlation coefficient of the line of best fit is positive, negative, or approximately zero. b. State whether the correlation is strong, medium, or weak.

2. a. **negative**   b. **strong**

3. a. **approx. zero**   b. **weak**

4. a. **positive**   b. **medium**

5. a. **positive**   b. **strong**

172   *Functions, Statistics, and Trigonometry*

In 6–8, refer to the Activity.

6. Why is the correlation coefficient 1 for Set 1?

7. The x- and y-values in Sets 3 and 4 are swapped. How does this affect r? Does this make sense?

8. The line of best fit for Set 5 has a slope of 0 and r of 0. However, there is a definitive pattern. What other type of model would fit these data? **quadratic model**

9. What point must be on the line of best fit?

10. Draw a scatterplot showing perfect positive correlation.

11. Suppose for some data set, $r^2 = 0.4$. Find all possible values of r.

12. **True or False** A negative value of r implies a negative slope for a linear regression line.

APPLYING THE MATHEMATICS

13. Make up a data set in which all the data lie on a single horizontal line, as shown at the right. Calculate the correlation coefficient for your set. Explain the result that you get.

In 14 and 15, state whether you think the correlation coefficient is positive, negative, or almost zero. Explain your answer.

14. number of putts sunk in golf and the distance of ball from hole

15. a person's height and the distance he/she lives from school

16. Heavy metals can enter the food chain when metal-rich discharges from mines contaminate streams, rivers, and lakes. The table shows the lead and zinc contents in milligrams of metal per kilogram of fish (mg/kg) for 10 whole fish (4 rainbow trout, 4 large scale suckers, and 2 mountain whitefish) taken from the Spokane River during July, August, and October of 1999. **16a-b. See margin.**

	Rainbow Trout				Large Scale Sucker				Mountain Whitefish	
Lead (mg/kg)	0.73	1.14	0.60	1.59	4.34	1.98	3.12	1.80	0.65	0.56
Zinc (mg/kg)	45.3	50.8	40.2	64.0	150.0	106.0	90.8	58.8	35.4	28.4

Source: Quantitative Environmental Learning Project, Seattle Central Community College

a. Use a statistics utility to find an equation of the least squares line to predict the amount of zinc from the amount of lead.

b. Use a statistics utility to find an equation of the least squares line to predict the amount of lead from the amount of zinc.

c. Are your answers to Parts a and b the same? **no**

d. Use an appropriate equation to predict the amount of zinc in a fish that has $2\,\frac{mg}{kg}$ of lead. $y = 28.73(2) + 19.54 = 77\,\frac{mg}{kg}$

17. A regression line for a set of data is $y = 10x + 4$. If the sum of squared residuals is 0, what is the correlation coefficient? $r = 1$

6. All of the data fit the line of best fit exactly.

7. This does not affect r because swapping the data does not affect its degree of correlation.

9. $(\bar{x}, \bar{y})$

10. See margin.

11. $r \approx \pm 0.6325$

12. true

13. Answers vary. Sample: {(1, 4), (3, 4), (4, 4), (5, 4), (5.5, 4), (6, 4), (9, 4)}. The correlation is undefined. This is because in the equation for computing the correlation coefficient, s_y appears in the denominator, and for the chosen data set $s_y = 0$ and division by 0 is undefined.

14. Negative; as the distance from the hole increases, it is less and less likely the golfer will sink the putt.

15. Zero; there is no correlation between a person's height and how far he/she lives from school.

Notes on the Questions

Question 13 The answer to this question may trouble many of your students. Using the formula for correlation, points on a horizontal line should have an undefined correlation because the standard deviation of the y-values is 0 in the formula for the correlation coefficient. But some students will feel that the correlation should be 1, since there is a perfect fit with a line. Other students may feel that the correlation should be 0, since the horizontal is halfway between a line with positive slope (and a correlation of 1) and a line with negative slope (and a correlation of –1), or because there is no variation in the dependent variable. Calculators themselves differ: we have seen some give 0 as the correlation while others give 1. For this reason, in this book we do not define the idea of linear correlation when all the values of the dependent variable are the same.

Questions 16, 20, and 26 These are the questions in the question set for which students are asked to find an equation for the line of best fit.

Question 16 You should be certain to assign this question. The point of Parts a and b is that the line that best predicts Z from L is not necessarily the same as (and usually different from) the line that best predicts L from Z.

Additional Answers

10. Answers vary. Sample:

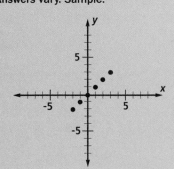

16a. $y = 28.73x + 19.54$; $r = 0.941$

16b. $y = 0.031x - 0.411$; $r = 0.941$

2-3

Notes on the Questions

Question 20 In this context, we expect that cars with better fuel economy would have lower levels of greenhouse emissions. So we expect that there will be a negative correlation.

18. The scatterplot at the right shows the engine size (in liters) of 14 models of cars and their respective fuel economies (in miles per gallon).

    a. Is the association positive or negative? Explain your answer.
    b. Is the correlation coefficient positive or negative? Explain your answer.

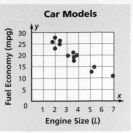

Car Models

Source: United States Department of Energy

19. There is a 0.8 correlation between the total sales tax collected in Florida each year from 1960–2000 and the numbers of shark attacks in those years. Does this mean the more sales tax, the more shark attacks? Explain why or why not.

20. The data set below gives the greenhouse emissions and fuel economy for five car models.

Car Model	City MPG	Greenhouse Emissions (tons per year)
A	21	8.0
B	11	14.1
C	19	8.7
D	16	9.6
E	24	6.8

    a. Use a statistics utility to calculate the regression line and the correlation coefficient. Use city mpg as the independent variable.
    b. It can be proven that the slope of the regression line is given by the formula $slope = r \cdot \frac{s_y}{s_x}$, where r is the correlation coefficient, s_y is the standard deviation of the dependent variable n, and s_x is the standard deviation of the independent variable. Confirm that this formula gives you the same answer as you found in Part a.
    c. Compute the values of $\bar{x}$ and $\bar{y}$.
    d. Show that the point $(\bar{x}, \bar{y})$ lies on the least squares line.

REVIEW

21. A rule of thumb on body measurement is "arm span is equal to height." Selena and Luis used data on 15 adult men to write an equation expressing arm span y as a function of height x. Selena used the rule of thumb. She found the sum of squared residuals for the model $y = x$ was 3050. Luis fit a line on the scatterplot. His line had equation $y = 0.9x + 0.2$. His sum of squared residuals was 4109. Which line had the better fit? (**Lesson 2-2**) $y = x$

22. Suppose $h(x) = \sqrt{x + 9}$. (**Lesson 2-1**)
    a. Find $h(16)$. **5**
    b. What is the domain of h? $\{x \mid x \geq -9\}$
    c. Give the range of h. $\{y \mid y \geq 0\}$

18a. Negative; larger values of one variable are associated with smaller values of the other.

18b. Negative; there is a negative relation between the variables.

19. No; both likely correlate with Florida's increasing population, but an increase in the rate of sales tax would not cause an increased in shark attacks.

20a. $y = -0.545x + 19.358$; $r \approx -0.968$

20b. $s_x \approx 4.97$, $s_y \approx 2.80$, $r \cdot \frac{s_x}{s_y} \approx -0.545$

20c. $\bar{x} = 18.2$, $\bar{y} = 9.44$

20d. $-0.545 \cdot 18.2 + 19.358 \approx 9.44$

Accommodating the Learner

Some students believe that when they fit a line to data by eye, the more data points on the line, the better the fit. To show that this is not the case, have them plot this set of data: $\{(1, 2), (2, 4), (3, 6), (4, 8), (5, 11)\}$. The line with equation $y = 2x$ passes through the first four points. The line of best fit determined with a statistics utility has equation $y = 2.2x - 0.4$ and passes through one point. Have students calculate the sum of squared residuals for each equation.

Students should find that for $y = 2x$, the sum is 1, while for $y = 2.2x - 0.4$, the sum is 0.4.

23. Suppose $g(t) = t^2 - 6t - 6$. For what value(s) of t does $g(t) = 0$? (Lesson 2-1) $t = 3 \pm \sqrt{15}$

24. Let $y = 5x^2 + 2x$. Is y a function of x? Why or why not? (Previous Course)

25. **Skill Sequence** Rewrite each expression without fractions. (Previous Course)

 a. $\frac{t}{\frac{1}{5t}}$ $5t^2$ b. $\frac{4x}{\frac{x}{y}}$ $4y$ c. $\left(\frac{r}{\frac{1}{5}}\right)^2$ $25r^2$

EXPLORATION

26. In Parts a–d, use or modify the data as indicated. Then use a statistics utility to compute the regression line and the correlation coefficient for the data. Record your results.

 a. Use the unemployment and TV data from Lesson 2-2.

 b. Use the data in Part a but replace the data for South Africa with that of Nicaragua: 6.8 TVs per 100 people and 3.9 unemployed per 100 people.

 c. Leave Nicaragua in the data set. Replace the Netherlands with Spain, which has 40.2 TVs per 100 people and 13.9 unemployed per 100 people.

 d. Change the Spain data to the extreme situation of 80 TVs per 100 people and unemployment of 50 per 100 people. (No country has these statistics.)

 e. Write a paragraph summarizing what you have found.

24. Yes, there exists a unique value of y for every possible value of x.

26a. $y = -0.203x + 14.181$; $r = -0.576$

26b. $y = -0.025x + 6.582$; $r = -0.198$

26c. $y = 0.031x + 5.935$; $r = 0.143$

26d. $y = 0.483x - 5.570$; $r = 0.741$

26e. The variables in the data set have strong negative correlations. This correlation becomes weakly positive when South Africa and the Netherlands are replaced by Nicaragua and Spain. The correlation becomes strongly positive when Spain is replaced by the fictional, extreme data point.

Linear Regression and Correlation   **101**

Notes on the Questions

Question 26 Because it is rather automatic to calculate linear regression, it is possible for students to do all the required calculations more quickly than it might seem at first glance.

4 Wrap-Up

Ongoing Assessment

See Questions 14 and 15. Have students come up with three of their own situations, similar to these, illustrating each a positive, negative, and almost zero correlation coefficient. Have students present their situations to the class. **Answers vary. Check students' work.**

Administer Quiz 1 (or a quiz of your own) after students complete this lesson.

Project Update

Project 1, *Temperature vs. Latitude*, Project 2, *Class Survey Data Revisited*, and Project 3, *Five Years From Now*, on pages 140 and 141 relate to the content of this lesson.

Lesson 2-4

GOAL
Review the properties of exponential functions that we assume students have studied in previous courses.

SPUR Objectives
E Describe properties of exponential functions.

Materials/Resources
· Lesson Master 2-4
· Resource Masters 35 and 36

HOMEWORK
• Option 1
• Option 2
• Questions 1–6
• • Questions 7–18
• • Question 19 (extra credit)
• Reading Lesson 2-5
• Covering the Ideas 2-5
(Questions 1–7)

Local Standards

1 Warm-Up

A CAS will be helpful for these questions. A spreadsheet or list can also be used.

Consider the number $\phi = \frac{\sqrt{5} + 1}{2}$.

1. Let f be the function defined by $f(x) = \frac{\phi^x}{\sqrt{5}}$. Calculate $f(-1)$, $f(0)$, $f(1)$, $f(2)$, $f(3)$, $f(4)$, and $f(5)$ to the nearest thousandth. **0.276, 0.447, 0.724, 1.171, 1.894, 3.065, 4.960**

2. Graph f.

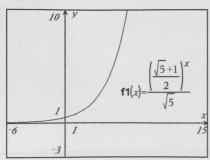

Lesson 2-4 — Exponential Functions

Vocabulary
growth factor
exponential function with base b
exponential growth function
exponential growth curve
exponential decay function
asymptote

> ▶ **BIG IDEA** Exponential functions describe quantities that grow or decay by a constant factor.

Linear functions exhibit an additive pattern of change. As the value of x increases by 1, the value of $f(x) = mx + b$ increases by a constant amount m, which is the slope of the graph of the function f. *Exponential functions* are based on multiplication rather than addition. In an exponential function f with equation $f(x) = ab^x$, increasing x by 1 causes the function value to be multiplied by a constant amount b, the *growth factor*. Sometimes the growth factor is not given directly, but instead is described as a percent of change.

Mental Math
Suppose you earn $1000 on a job and 10% is taken out for income tax. Then your employer gives you a 10% raise. How much will you have after the raise and tax? **$990**

Exponential Growth and Decay

One common application of exponential functions is to describe changes in population.

Example 1
The town of Centerburg is suffering from a decline in population. A demographer has predicted that, under current conditions, the current population of 28,500 will decrease by 2% each year over the next decade. However, a manufacturer claims that a new factory will reverse the trend and cause the population to grow by 4% annually instead.

a. Create equations to describe the population of Centerburg as a function of time under these two conditions:

Function f: the population of 28,500 increases by 4% each year (with the new factory)

Function g: the population of 28,500 decreases by 2% each year (with no new factory)

b. Compare the projected populations after 10 years.

Solution

a. An annual growth rate of 4% means that each year the population is 1.04 times larger than the previous year's population. In contrast, if the population shrinks 2% each year, then each year it is multiplied by 0.98. Equations for the two functions can be written as
$f(x) = 28500(1.04)^x$ and $g(x) = 28500(0.98)^x$.

Background

Students who have taken UCSMP *Algebra* and *Advanced Algebra* have seen exponential functions twice, though only in the latter course are non-integer exponents discussed.

When b is positive and x is irrational, the real power b^x can be estimated by calculating or estimating b^r for rational estimates r of x. This property enables the defining of exponential functions $f(x) = ab^x$ with positive base $b \neq 1$ and $a \neq 0$, where x may be any real number. Properties and

graphs of exponential functions are described in this lesson, with applications to growth situations ($b > 1$), though decay situations ($b < 1$) are also included.

Common features of exponential functions Exponential functions have even more in common than is stated here. In the next UCSMP course, *Precalculus and Discrete Mathematics*, we prove that for all values of a, the graphs of $y = ab^x$ are congruent. Thus, letting $a = 1$, they are all congruent to the graph of $y = b^x$.

b. Evaluate these two functions when $x = 10$ years.
$f(10) = 28500(1.04)^{10} \approx 42{,}190$
$g(10) = 28500(0.98)^{10} \approx 23{,}290$

One way to compare is to subtract to find out how much the two projections $f(10)$ and $g(10)$ differ.

$$f(10) - g(10) = 42{,}190 - 23{,}290 = 18{,}900$$

Under the assumption that the factory is built and there is an annual growth rate of 4%, the population in ten years will be about 42,190. If, however, there is no change and there is an annual decrease of 2%, then the population in ten years will be about 23,290. The manufacturer claims that building the factory will lead to 18,900 more people living in Centerburg than would otherwise be there.

A second way to compare is by graphing the functions.

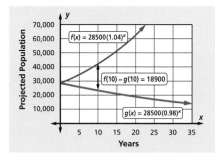

The graphs show that the populations differ by over 15,000 in 10 years and differ by about 30,000 in 15 years.

Each function in Example 1 has an equation of the form $y = ab^x$ in which the initial population a is repeatedly multiplied by the **growth factor** b. This is true of all exponential functions.

Definition of Exponential Function

An **exponential function with base b** and initial value a is a function with an equation of the form
$$f(x) = ab^x,$$
where $a \neq 0$, $b > 0$, and $b \neq 1$.

When an exponential function has a growth factor that is greater than 1, as in the situation in which the factory is built in Centerburg, the function is called an **exponential growth function**, and its graph is called an **exponential growth curve**.

(See the Extension for this lesson.) In general, this result follows because when $a > 0$ and $a \neq 1$, then a can itself be written as a power of b. In particular, $a = b^{\log_b a}$. So when $y = ab^x$, then also $y = b^{\log_b a} \cdot b^x = b^{x + \log_b a}$ which is an equation of the form $y = b^{x + k}$.

Furthermore, for all bases b and c, the graphs of $y = b^x$ and $y = c^x$ are similar. This is because c can be written as $b^{\log_b c}$. This result, too, is demonstrated in *Precalculus and Discrete Mathematics*.

As a result of these properties, graphs of all exponential functions look alike.

---

3. Let F_n be the nth term of the Fibonacci sequence 1, 1, 2, 3, 5, 8, 13, … where each term after the second is the sum of the preceding two terms. Find the differences between the values of F_n and $f(n)$ for $n = 1, 2, 3, 4, 5, 10,$ and 15.
0.2764, –0.1708, 0.1056, –0.0652, 0.0403, –0.0036, 0.0003

This last question illustrates that the exponential function f is a good approximation for the Fibonacci sequence, especially for large n.

---

2 Teaching

Notes on the Lesson

The exponential model of the Centerburg (a fictional city) population which begins this lesson is an example of applying a continuous model to a discrete situation — populations are whole numbers only.

Example 1 The formulas in Part a give the population in terms of years after now. To give the population in year x, the graph must be translated the year number of units to the right. For instance, if the year is 2011, replace x by $x - 2011$. The result is
$f(x) = 28{,}500(1.04)^{x - 2011}$
$g(x) = 28{,}500(0.98)^{x - 2011}$.

Students who have taken UCSMP *Advanced Algebra* have seen this kind of substitution. Students in this course will encounter it in Chapter 3.

You might ask students why certain restrictions are needed to define an exponential function. **If the coefficient a or the base b in $y = ab^x$ is zero, $f(x) = 0$ for all x. If the base $b = 1$, then $f(x) = a$ for all x. These are constant functions, not exponential functions.** You might ask what the graph of $f(x) = ab^x$ looks like if $b = 1$. **The graph is a horizontal line with equation $y = a$.**

2-4

Notes on the Lesson

Guided Example 2 Students who have had previous UCSMP courses will have seen compound interest twice, in *Algebra* and *Advanced Algebra*, and the ideas in this example will be review.

The roles of the constants *a* and *b* in *f(x) = abˣ* By now it should be clear to students that the equation $y = ab^x$ with $a > 0$ models situations of growth if $b > 1$, since as x increases, b^x increases. If $0 < b < 1$, exponential decay occurs, because as x increases, b^x decreases. The Activity is designed to help students visualize the properties of exponential functions.

Additional Example

Example 1 Presently, the towns of Scarcedale and Ampleton both have approximately 8500 residents. Over the next 5 years, the population of Ampleton is expected to increase by approximately 2.3% per year, while the population of Scarcedale is expected to decrease by about 0.9% each year.

a. Create equations to describe the population of each town as a function of time. Let the populations of Scarcedale and Ampleton be $s(t)$ and $a(t)$ respectively. $s(t) = 8500(0.991)^t$; $a(t) = 8500(1.023)^t$

b. Compare the projected populations after 5 years. When $t = 5$ years, $s(5) = 8500(0.991)^5 \approx 8124$ residents and $a(5) = 8500(1.023)^5 \approx 9524$ residents. Scarcedale's population would have dropped by 376 over the 5 years, while Ampleton's increased by 1024 over the same time period. The two towns will differ in population by about 1400 residents.

In contrast, in a situation like Centerburg's population without the factory, the growth factor is between 0 and 1 and the function is called an **exponential decay function**. The word "decay" comes from the fact that these exponential functions model situations, such as radioactive decay, in which a quantity is diminishing by a constant factor. (Note that we still call b a growth factor, even though the function is decreasing.)

 QY1

Note that in an exponential function, the independent variable is in the exponent. Thus, the function f with equation $f(x) = x^2$ is *not* exponential, even though it involves an exponent.

Another example of exponential growth is the value of an investment earning compound interest. Suppose you deposit P dollars in an account which pays an annual percentage yield r. If you make no deposits or withdrawals, each year your balance is multiplied by $1 + r$. After t years, your balance A is given by $A = P(1 + r)^t$. The function f with equation $A = f(r) = P(1 + r)^t$ is an exponential function with base $1 + r$.

▶ QY1

When $a = 400$ and $b = 2.5$, tell whether $f(x) = ab^x$ describes a growth or decay function, and why.

GUIDED

Example 2

$2500 is invested in an account with a 5.3% annual yield.

a. What is the yearly growth factor?

b. What is the equation for the balance A after t years?

c. What is the balance after 7 years?

d. What value is associated with $t = -2$? What does $t = -2$ mean?

Solution

a. $r = 0.053$. So the yearly growth factor is $(1 + r) = \underline{?}$. 1.053

b. The initial value is $\underline{?}$ and the growth factor is $\underline{?}$, so $A = \underline{?}$. 2500; 1,053; $2500(1.053)^t$

c. $A = 2500(\underline{?})^7 = \underline{?}$. 1.053; 3588.71

d. $A = 2500(\underline{?})^{-2} = \underline{?}$. If the account had been started 1.053; 2254.67 2 years ago, an investment of $\underline{?}$ would have produced $2254.67 $2500 this year.

The Roles of the Constants *a* and *b* in *f(x) = abˣ*

Examples 1 and 2 show that the value of a in $f(x) = ab^x$ represents the initial value, and the value of b determines whether f models exponential growth or exponential decay. But how do the values of a and b affect the graph of the function?

Accommodating the Learner ⊕

Some students may have trouble identifying the value b of the base, when the growth *rate* of a population is given. Since b is the number by which the population is multiplied each year, students must add 1 to the growth rate to determine b. Have students refer to the solution in Example 1 on page 102, where the growth rate is 4% and the value of b is $1 + 0.04 = 1.04$. To get the growth factor for a declining population, we make the growth rate negative and add 1. In this example, $1 + (-2\%) = 1 - 2\% = 1 - 0.02 = 0.98$.

Accommodating the Learner ⬆

Most savings accounts accumulate interest daily or monthly at a nominal rate instead of annually. The quoted APY is obtained by compounding this nominal rate for the corresponding number of periods. Have students use the General Compound Interest Formula, $A = P\left(1 + \frac{r}{n}\right)^{nt}$, to calculate the nominal rate compounded daily which corresponds to the APY of Example 2. **5.16%**

Activity

Experiment with your graphing technology to find values of a and b in $f(x) = ab^x$ that produce each graph below. Write an equation for each function. Be sure that your graphs contain the points marked on the graphs shown. Use trace or a table to check values of each function, as shown at the right.

a.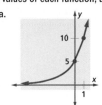

b.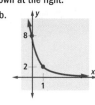

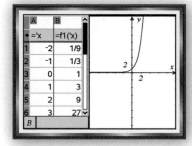

c.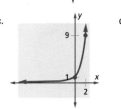

d.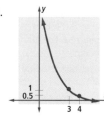

e.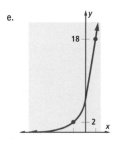

f.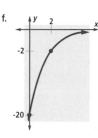

Activity

a. $y = 5(2)^x$

b. $y = 8(0.25)^x$

c. $y = 3^x$

d. $y = 8(0.5)^x$

e. $y = 6(3)^x$

f. $y = -20(0.31623)^x$

Common Features of Exponential Functions

The six graphs in the Activity have much in common. For Parts a, c, and e, as you move to the left on the graph, the values of y get closer and closer to 0 and the curve approaches the x-axis. On the other hand, for Parts b, d, and f, moving to the right produces y-values that get closer and closer to 0. In all cases, the x-axis is a horizontal *asymptote* of the function. An **asymptote** is a line that the graph of a function $y = f(x)$ approaches as x approaches a fixed value or increases or decreases without bound. Note that the asymptote is not actually part of the graph.

 QY2

▶ **QY2**

Use the graphs in the Activity.

a. Which functions are increasing?

b. Which functions have a range that is the set of positive real numbers?

Additional Example

Example 2 Jonas received a letter from his credit union stating that a 5-year CD his parents opened for him had matured and he could choose one of the following options:

(1) Withdraw the full amount of $14,204.10.

(2) Use the money to open a new 5-year CD with an APY of 2.81%.

(3) Have the money deposited into his interest checking account which earns 0.95% per year.

Assume that Jonas's parents deposited $12,000 into the CD 5 years ago.

a. What is an equation for the balance of the old CD after 5 years?
$14{,}204.10 = 12{,}000(1 + r)^5$

b. Use your equation from Part a to find the annual yield of the old CD.
3.43%

c. Compare the results of options (2) and (3). **Answers vary. Sample: At the end of 5 years, option (2) would mature to $14{,}204.10(1.0281)^5 \approx$ $16{,}315.13. If he does not spend any of it, option (3) would give him $14{,}891.74 after 5 years. Option (2) yields considerably more money than option (3).**

Additional Example

Example 3 Compare and contrast the graphs of the three functions f, g, and h, where $f(x) = 8^x$, $g(x) = \left(\frac{1}{8}\right)^x$, and $h(x) = 8^{-x}$ for all values of x. Function f is an exponential growth function; g and h are exponential decay functions. Functions g and h are identical, so they have the same graph. That graph is the reflection image of f over the y-axis.

GUIDED

Example 3

For each function characteristic, compare and contrast the linear function $f(x) = 2x + 8$ with the exponential function $g(x) = 8 \cdot 4^x$.

a. domain and range
b. y-intercept and x-intercept
c. asymptote
d. increasing or decreasing

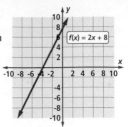

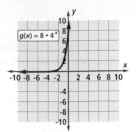

Solution

Look for similarities between the functions and ways in which they differ.

a. The two functions have the same domain, which is
   ___?___. But the range of f is the set of all real numbers, **all real numbers**
   while the range of g is ___?___. **positive real numbers**

b. Both functions have a y-intercept of ___?___. **8**
   The x-intercept of the graph of $f(x) = 2x + 8$ is –4 since
   $f(-4) = 0$. However, since $8 \cdot 4^x$ is positive for all real
   numbers x, function g has no x-intercept.

c. Function f does not have an asymptote, but the line with
   equation ___?___ is an asymptote for function g. **y = 0**

d. Both functions are ___?___ over their entire domain. **increasing**

The definition of an exponential function f places restrictions on the values allowed for a and b in $f(x) = ab^x$. The base b must be a positive number other than 1, and $a \neq 0$. All these exponential functions have the following properties:

    (1) The domain is the set of real numbers.

    (2) If $a > 0$, then the range is the set of positive real numbers.
        If $a < 0$, then the range is the set of negative real numbers.

    (3) The graph contains the point $(0, a)$.

    (4) The x-axis is an asymptote for the graph.

    (5) For positive values of a, if $b > 1$, then the function is
        increasing. If $0 < b < 1$, then the function is decreasing.
        For negative values of a, which are used less often, this
        situation is reversed.

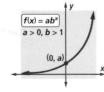 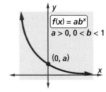

Extension

If students have had UCSMP *Advanced Algebra*, you can ask them to prove that the graph of g in Example 3 is congruent to the graph of $y = 4^x$. Proof: $g(x) = 8 \cdot 4^x = 4^{1.5} \cdot 4^x = 4^{x+1.5}$. Consequently, by the Graph-Translation Theorem found in that course, the graph of $g(x) = 8 \cdot 4^x$ is the image of the graph of $y = 4^x$ under the horizontal translation 1.5 units to the left. Since figures and their translation images are congruent, the two graphs are congruent. In this course, the Graph-Translation Theorem is found in Chapter 3.

Additional Answers

2a. exponential; $a = 11$, $b = 4$

2b. not exponential

2c. not exponential

2d. exponential; $a = 1$, $b = 0.6$

Questions

COVERING THE IDEAS

1. In 2008, the population of Ireland was 4,156,119, with an average annual growth rate of 1.13%. Assume this growth rate continues. $Y = 4156119 (1.0113)^x$
   a. Estimate, to the nearest thousand, the population of Ireland in 2009. **4,203,000**
   b. Express the population P as a function of n, the number of years after 2008.
   c. Estimate, to the nearest thousand, Ireland's population in the year 2020. **4,756,000**

Cobh, a seaport on the south coast of Ireland

2. Tell whether the equation describes an exponential function. If it does, give the values of a and b in $f(x) = ab^x$. **See margin.**
   a. $g(m) = 11 \cdot 4^m$ b. $s(t) = 6$ c. $j(z) = z^2$ d. $w(x) = 0.6^x$

1b. $P(n) = 4156119(1.0113)^n$

3. On your 21st birthday, $4000 is invested for you at an annual yield of 8%. You do not withdraw any money from the account.
   a. Write a formula for A, the balance in the account after t years.
   b. What will be the balance in the account when you are 65?
   c. How much money would have to have been invested when you were 17 at the same yield to get the same result as in Part b?

3a. $A = 4,000(1.08)^t$
3b. about $118223.89
3c. about $2940.12

4. Find values of a and b so that the exponential function f with $f(x) = ab^x$ produces the graph shown at the right. $a = 3, b = 2$

5. Consider the exponential equation $f(x) = ab^x$.
   a. **True or False** The initial value of the function is $f(1)$. **false**
   b. If $0 < b < 1$, what type of exponential function is f? **decay**

6. Let $f(x) = 3^x$ and $g(x) = \left(\frac{1}{3}\right)^x$.
   a. Graph the functions f and g on one set of axes for $-3 < x < 3$.
   b. Compare and contrast these two functions.
   c. Which function, f or g, represents exponential decay? **g**

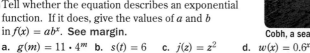

6a.
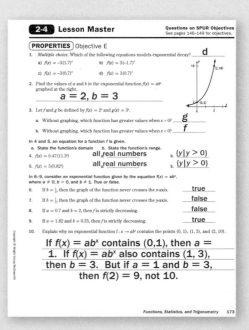

APPLYING THE MATHEMATICS

7. Consider $f(x) = 4^x$ and $g(x) = 5^x$.
   a. Without graphing, tell which function has greater values when $x > 0$. **g**
   b. Without graphing, tell which function has greater values when $x < 0$. **f**
   c. Check your answers to Parts a and b by graphing f and g on the same set of axes. **See margin.**

8. On the same axes, graph $f(x) = 2 \cdot 3^x$ and $g(x) = 3 \cdot 2^x$.
   a. Which function has the greater y-intercept? **g**
   b. For what value of x is $f(x) = g(x)$? Explain how you found your answer. **See margin.**
   c. For what values of x is $f(x) < g(x)$? $x < 1$

6b. The graphs have the same domain, range and y-intercept. f is increasing, but g is decreasing. The graphs are reflections of each other over the y-axis.

Exponential Functions **107**

Additional Answers

7c.
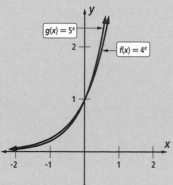

8b. $x = 1$; This is the x-value where the graphs intersect.

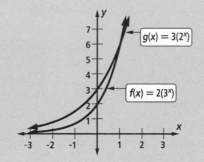

2-4

Additional Answers

9b. $y = 12$ when $x = 0$ is the initial value. The growth factor is $\frac{1}{2}$ because as x increases by 1, y is divided by 2.

13. False, correlation does not mean causation. For instance, both a and b may be causally related to a third variable c, and thus correlate to each other without being directly related.

14. False, a correlation coefficient r is stronger the closer it is to ± 1

15c. False; $f(1) + f(2) = -1 + 0 = -1$, but $f(1 + 2) = f(3) = \frac{3}{5}$.

15d. False; The domain is $\{x \mid x \neq -2\}$, while the range is $\{y \mid y \neq 3\}$.

---

9. a. Multiple Choice Which equation describes the function defined by the table given at the right? **B**

   A $y = 48\left(\frac{1}{2}\right)^x$ **B** $y = 12\left(\frac{1}{2}\right)^x$

   C $y = 3(2)^x$ **D** $y = 12(2)^x$

  b. Explain how the initial value and growth factor from your answer to Part a are seen in the table. **See margin.**

x	y
-2	48
-1	24
0	12
1	6
2	3
3	1.5

10. a. In 2007, China's population was estimated to be about 1,322,000,000. Its average annual growth rate was about 0.6%. If this growth rate continues, what will be the population of China in the year 2015? $y = 1322000000\,(1.006)^x$

  b. In the year 2000, the annual growth rate of China was 0.9%. Using this growth rate and the 2007 population of China, what would be the projected population in 2015? How much greater is this than your answer to Part a? $y = 1322000000\,(1.009)^x$

10a. 1,368,805,000

10b. about 1,420,237,000; this is 33,432,000 greater than the answer to Part a.

11. A gardener recycles yard waste in a compost bin in which each month 90% of the previous month's material is still present.

  a. How much of an initial 20 cubic feet of material would remain after 1, 2, and 3 months? **18, 16.2, and 14.58 cubic feet**

$y = a(.9)^x$

$y = 20(.9)^x$

  b. After n months, how much of an initial 20 cubic feet of material would remain? $20(0.9)^n$

  c. True or False After six months, more than half the material will have decayed. **false**

12. Compare the functions $y = x^2$ and $y = 2^x$. Mention each feature.

  a. type of function   **b.** range   **c.** y-intercept   **d.** asymptote

REVIEW

13. True or False If a and b have a correlation coefficient of 1, then either a causes b or b causes a. Explain your answer. **(Lesson 2-3) See margin.**

14. True or False The correlation coefficient $r = -0.85$ indicates a weaker relation than the correlation coefficient $r = 0.65$. Explain your answer. **(Lesson 2-3) See margin.**

15. Let $f(x) = \frac{3x - 6}{x + 2}$. **(Lesson 2-1)**

  a. Evaluate $f(1)$. **–1**

  b. If $f(x) = 0$, find x. **2**

  c. True or False $f(1) + f(2) = f(1 + 2)$. Justify your answer.

  d. True or False The domain and range of f are equal. Justify your answer. **15 c–d. See margin.**

  e. Evaluate $f(p - 3)$. $f(p - 3) = \frac{3p - 15}{p - 1}$

12a. $y = x^2$ is a quadratic function and $y = 2^x$ is an exponential function.

12b. The range of $y = x^2$ is the set of nonnegative real numbers, and the range of $y = 2^x$ is the set of positive real numbers.

12c. The y-intercept of $y = x^2$ is 0, and the y-intercept of $y = 2^x$ is 1.

12d. $y = x^2$ has no asymptotes, and $y = 2^x$ has one asymptote, the x-axis.

16. The box plot at the right pictures a data set that has no outliers.
    a. What is the percentile of A? **25th percentile**
    b. What is the percentile of B? **50th percentile**
    c. What is the percentile of C? **75th percentile**
    d. In what percentile range does D fall?
       (Lessons 1-5, 1-4) **Between the 75th and 99th percentile**

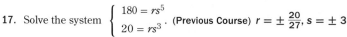

17. Solve the system $\begin{cases} 180 = rs^5 \\ 20 = rs^3 \end{cases}$. (Previous Course) $r = \pm\frac{20}{27}, s = \pm 3$

18. Here are the world record times for the Men's outdoor 1500-meter run between 1957 and 1983.
    a. Enter the data into a statistics utility. Let the number of years after 1957 be the independent variable. Find the correlation coefficient between the number of years after 1957 and the record time. **–0.95**
    b. What does the value of the correlation coefficient tell you about the relation between the two variables? **See margin.**
    c. Find an equation for the line of best fit predicting world records for this event. **See margin.**
    d. Using your model, predict what the record might have been in 2008. The actual record was 3.43 minutes. What does the comparison between your prediction and the actual time indicate about the strength of your model in extrapolation? (Lessons 2-3, 2-2) **See margin.**

Year	Runner and Country	Time (seconds)
1957	Jungwirth (Czech)	218.1
1958	Elliott (Australia)	216.0
1960	Elliott (Australia)	215.6
1967	Ryun (U.S.)	213.1
1974	Bayi (Tanzania)	212.2
1979	Coe (U.K.)	212.1
1979	Ovett (U.K.)	212.1
1980	Ovett (U.K.)	211.36
1983	Maree (U.S.)	211.23
1983	Ovett (U.K.)	210.28

Source: The Fascination of Statistics; IAAF

EXPLORATION

19. a. Explain why a city whose population is growing at 5% per year does not grow twice as fast as a city whose population is growing at 2.5% per year. **See margin.**
    b. City A grows 10% in 2011 and 2% in each year from 2012 to 2020. City B grows 2% in each year from 2011 to 2019 and then 10% in 2020. Compare the total percentage increase from 2011 to 2020 for the populations of these cities. **See margin.**
    c. Generalize the result of Part b. **See margin.**

Sebastian Coe, shown here in the 1980 Olympics 1500-meter run, co-held the world record of 3 min 31.36 sec at the time.

QY ANSWERS

1. $f(x) = 400 \cdot 2.5^x$ describes an exponential growth function because $2.5 > 1$.
2. a. a, c, e, f
   b. a, b, c, d, e

Exponential Functions **109**

Lesson

2-5

Exponential Models

Vocabulary

exponential regression
half-life

GOAL

Construct mathematical models of situations which are exponential in nature. Given two points of such a model, find an equation of the form $y = ab^x$ by solving a system of two equations with two unknowns.

SPUR Objectives

F Find and interpret exponential regression and models.

Materials/Resources

· Lesson Master 2-5
· Resource Masters 37 and 38

HOMEWORK • Option 1

• Questions 1–7 • Option 2
• • Questions 8–18
• • Question 19 (extra credit)
• Reading Lesson 2-6
• Covering the Ideas 2-6
(Questions 1–10)

Local Standards

1 Warm-Up

Novelle Riche keeps track of how much money she has. In one fixed annuity investment initiated 10 years ago, she had $218,201 three years ago and she has $256,221 now.

a. What annual yield is Novelle getting from her investment? **5.5%**

b. How much did she initially invest? **$150,000**

▶ **BIG IDEA** Exponential models are used in many fields in which data follow some kind of natural growth or decay. Exponential regression is used to fit exponential models to data.

Mental Math

Veronica is preparing a study plan for a biology test. She plans to study for four days, and each day she plans to study 50% longer than the previous day. On the first day she plans to study for 24 minutes. How many hours and minutes total will she study? **3 hr 15 min**

Finding an Exponential Function Using a System of Equations

Exponential models describe situations in diverse fields such as biology, paleontology, sociology, physics, and economics.

Populations very often grow at a constant rate, at least in the short run. Therefore, it is natural to fit an exponential model to population data. The average population growth rate in the U.S. is about 0.883%, but in areas that are growing quickly, the rate can be much higher.

Example 1

Huntley, Illinois had been a small farming town. But when a large housing development was built, the population growth pattern changed. Two special censuses gave village planners the data in the table at the right.

Year	Population
2003	12,270
2005	16,719

Source: The Village of Huntley

a. Find an exponential model for the data. Let $p(t)$ be the population t years after 2000.

b. Predict the population of Huntley in the year 2015.

Solution

a. A general equation for the model is $p(t) = ab^t$. From the table, $p(3) = 12,270$ and $p(5) = 16,719$. Substitute these values into the general equation to get a system.

$$\begin{cases} 12{,}270 = ab^3 \\ 16{,}719 = ab^5 \end{cases}$$

Divide the second equation by the first. This can be done because $a \neq 0$ and $b \neq 0$.

$$\frac{16{,}719}{12{,}270} = b^2$$

Because the base b must be positive, take the positive square root.

$$b = \sqrt{\frac{16{,}719}{12{,}270}} \approx 1.1673$$

This is the growth factor. The population was growing about 17% per year.

Huntley, IL

Background

Because it takes three noncollinear points to determine a circle, and three to determine a quadratic function, students may be surprised to read that an exponential curve is determined by just two points. The theoretical justification for this does not come until Chapter 8, when the exponential equation is seen as equivalent to a linear equation in the logs of the variables.

Correlation coefficients obtained in exponential models can be quite high even when the data are not particularly exponential. This is because even when differences between numbers are great, the differences in their logarithms may be small. An r-value of 0.95 is not particularly high under these circumstances. For example, consider the data points in the following table.

To find a, substitute this value of b into one of the two equations in the system. Using the first equation,

$$12{,}270 = a(1.1673)^3$$

$$a \approx \frac{12{,}270}{(1.1673)^3} \approx 7714.$$

According to this model, the initial population of Huntley in 2000 was 7714. The full exponential model is $p(t) = 7714(1.1673)^t$.

Check Use a CAS to solve the system of equations. A partial solution is shown at the right. The negative answers are not valid in this context.

solve$(12270 = a \cdot b^3$ and $16719 = a \cdot b^5, a, b)$
$a = -7714.29$ and $b = -1.1673$ or $a = 7714.2\blacktriangleright$

b. The model predicts the population in 2015 to be
$p(15) = a \cdot b^{15} = 7714(1.1673)^{15} \approx 78{,}500.$
Actually, demographers expect this growth rate to slow before then, but the model describes what would happen based on the two special census years.

Exponential Regression

The model for the population of Huntley was derived from just two data points. Two points are enough to algebraically determine an exponential function that is a perfect fit for those two points. If there are more than two data points, there may not be a model that fits all the data perfectly. However, if many data points follow an approximately exponential pattern, a statistics utility will find an **exponential regression** curve that models the pattern well.

1: Actions   REAL
1: One-Variable Statistics
2: Two-Variable Statistics
3: Linear Regression (mx+b)
4: Linear Regression (a+bx)
5: Median–Median Line
6: Quadratic Regression
7: Cubic Regression
8: Quartic Regression
9: Power Regression
A: Exponential Regression
B: Logarithmic Regression
C: Sinusoidal Regression
D: Logistic Regression (d=0)

GUIDED

Example 2

Bald eagles were once threatened with extinction. In the 48 contiguous states, their numbers were at an all-time low of 417 in 1963. But protection programs helped them rebound. In 2007, they were removed from the list of endangered species kept by the U.S. Fish and Wildlife Services.

a. Use a statistics utility to fit an exponential model of the form $f(x) = ab^x$ to the data. Let x be "years after 1960." Report the values of a and b in the table on the next page to the nearest thousandth.

b. Superimpose the graph of the exponential model on the scatterplot and describe how well the exponential curve fits the data.

c. Identify the initial amount and the growth factor and explain their meanings.

d. Find the residuals for the model's predicted values for 2000 and 2005.

(continued on next page)

Bald eagles have a wing span of 6 to 8 feet.

Exponential Models   **111**

2 Teaching

Notes on the Lesson

Example 1 In solving linear systems, students have been accustomed to adding and subtracting equations. Here the situation is exponential, and a variable is eliminated by dividing the equations in the system. This provides a clue to the fact that subtracting linear expressions has something in common with dividing exponential expressions, a consequence of the relationship between numbers and their logarithms.

The population figures shown here were obtained directly from the Village Clerk of Huntley, IL while UCSMP was securing a photo. They may conflict with those displayed on The Village of Huntley, IL Website.

Example 2 These data provide a nice example of the success of conservation efforts with respect to the bald eagle. You might have students eyeball the data in the graph on page 112 and compare the equation for an exponential curve through those two points with the equation given by exponential regression.

Additional Example

Example 1 The population of a certain cell type was observed to be 100 on the second day, and 2700 on the fifth day. Assuming the growth is exponential, find the number of cells present initially, and the number of cells expected on the seventh day. 11 on the first day; 24,300 on the seventh day

x	1	2	3	4	5	6	7	8	9	10
y	1	2	3	4	5	6	7	8	9	11

Linear regression shows the line of best fit has equation $y \approx 1.0545x - 0.2$, with a very high $r \approx 0.996$, as expected. Exponential regression shows the equation $y = 1.2512 \cdot 1.2657^x$, with what still seems to be a high $r \approx 0.958$.

2-5

Example 2 The National Science Foundation (NSF) publishes InfoBriefs, a newsletter containing brief reports highlighting results from recent surveys and analyses. The following data are contained in a January 2009 article about Federal R&D funding.

Fiscal year	Federal obligations for research (NSF) ($ millions)
1990	1690
1991	1785
1992	1868
1993	1882
1994	2040
1995	2149
1996	2188
1997	2249
1998	2289
1999	2506
2000	2726
2001	3044
2002	3260
2003	3609
2004	3771
2005	3743
2006	3791
2007	4051
2008	4358

a. Use a statistics utility to graph the data and fit an exponential model of the form $f(x) = ab^x$ to the data. Use x as "years after 1990." Report the values of a and b in the exponential model to the nearest thousandth. **$a \approx 1625.160$; $b \approx 1.056$; $f(x) = 1625.160(1.056)^x$**

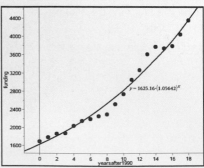

b. Use your graph to describe how well the exponential curve you have modeled fits the points on the scatterplot. **Answers vary. Sample: The model is very close to most points of the scatterplot.**

c. Calculate the residuals for 1998 and 2004. **−224.087; 286.095**

Year	Number of Breeding Pairs
1963	417
1974	791
1981	1188
1984	1757
1986	1875
1988	2475
1990	3035
1992	3749
1994	4449
1996	5094
1998	5748
2000	6471
2005	7066
2006	9789

Source: U.S. Fish and Wildlife Services

Solution

a. A statistics utility gives $a \approx 296.177$ and $b \approx 1.079$. Therefore, $f(x) \approx \underline{\ ?\ }$. **296.177 (1.079)^x**

b. Your graph should look similar to the screenshot at the right. The model is close to most of the points of the scatterplot. See margin.

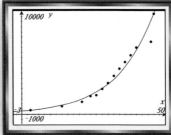

c. The initial value of the exponential model is about $\underline{\ ?\ }$ breeding pairs, which corresponds to the year $\underline{\ ?\ }$. The growth factor is $\underline{\ ?\ }$. This means that during the years 1963 through 2006, the eagle population had a growth rate of about $\underline{\ ?\ }$ % per year. **296; 1960; 1.079; 7.9**

d. In 2000, the predicted number of breeding pairs is $f(40) \approx \underline{\ ?\ }$ pairs. So for 2000, **6200** residual = observed value − predicted value = $\underline{\ ?\ } - \underline{\ ?\ } = \underline{\ ?\ }$. In 2005, the predicted number of **6471; 6200; 271** breeding pairs is $\approx \underline{\ ?\ }$ pairs. For 2005, error = $\underline{\ ?\ } - \underline{\ ?\ }$ = $\underline{\ ?\ }$. **9068; 7066; 9068; −2002**

Letting x = years after 1960 makes a difference in the model. If the actual year is used as the independent variable, the statistics utility model is $f(\text{year}) = (9.181 \cdot 10^{-63}) \cdot (1.079)^{\text{year}}$. The exponents are so large that a small change in the growth factor due to rounding, for example, would create a large difference in the predicted values. This is a consideration for exponential models. However, with linear and quadratic models, it often does not make a difference whether you use the year as it is or use the number of years from a given point in time.

STOP QY

▶ **QY**

a. Without a calculator, estimate the value of $1.077^{1963} - 1.076^{1963}$.

b. Estimate the value in Part a with a calculator.

c. How close was your estimate to the actual value?

Additional Answers

Guided Example 2b.

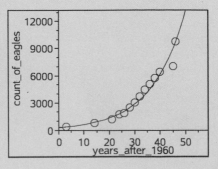

Half-Life and Exponential Decay

Radioactive elements are useful in situations involving detective work, such as diagnosing health problems with barium x-rays or finding the age of archeological artifacts with carbon dating.

The **half-life** of a radioactive element is the amount of time it takes an original quantity to decay to half that amount. If you know the half-life of a radioactive element and the amount of the substance at one point in time, you can find the original amount.

In 2007, the element polonium was in the news when London police detectives investigated the poisoning of former Russian KGB agent Alexander Litvinenko. Since polonium had never been known to be used in a poisoning, the authorities did not look for evidence of it until weeks after the crime had taken place. As a consequence, they had to work backwards from the evidence to calculate the amount of polonium used on the victim. They made use of the fact that the half-life of polonium is 138 days.

Example 3

Detectives in the Litvinenko investigation found polonium on a cup in a hotel that he had visited. Suppose that 4 micrograms were found, and it had been 30 days since Litvinenko was there.

a. Find how much polonium was on the cup originally.

b. Derive a model for this situation.

Solution

a. Let t represent the number of days since a micrograms of polonium were placed on the cup. Then $f(t) = ab^t$ is the amount of polonium remaining. First, find the daily decay factor b. The half-life tells us that it takes 138 days for a micrograms of polonium to decay to $\frac{1}{2}a$ micrograms. So when $t = 138$, we know that $f(t) = \frac{1}{2}a$. Substitute these values into $f(t) = ab^t$.

$$\frac{1}{2}a = ab^{138}$$

$$\frac{1}{2} = b^{138} \qquad \text{Divide both sides by } a.$$

$$\left(\frac{1}{2}\right)^{\frac{1}{138}} = (b^{138})^{\frac{1}{138}} \qquad \text{Raise each side to the } \frac{1}{138}\text{th power.}$$

$$b \approx 0.995$$

The decay factor is about 0.995. The polonium decay function is $f(t) = a(0.995)^t$. Now use the information that there were 4 micrograms after 30 days. Again, substitute.

$$4 \approx a(0.995)^{30}$$

$$a \approx 4.649$$

There were about 4.65 micrograms of polonium originally.

2-5

3 Assignment

Recommended Assignment
- Questions 1–7
- • Questions 8–18
- • Question 19 (extra credit)
- Reading Lesson 2-6
- Covering the Ideas 2-6
  (Questions 1–10)

Notes on the Questions

Question 3 This question utilizes the relationship of exponential models to population growth.

Questions 4 and 10 These questions involve the use of exponential models in an impressionistic situation, that is, a situation for which there is no underlying reason for the relationship to be exponential.

Questions 5, 6, and 9 These questions involve half-life.

Question 5 The model assumes that the body does not digest or dispose of the barium, and that the change in the amount is due solely to radioactive decay.

---

b. Substitute the values of a and b into $f(t) = ab^t$.
After t days, there are $f(t) = 4.65(0.995)^t$ micrograms of polonium remaining.

Check

Graph $f(x) = 4.65(0.995)^t$. Trace to see that $(0, 4.65)$ and $(30, 4.00)$ are on the graph.

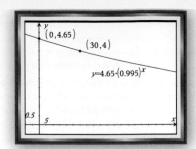

Questions

COVERING THE IDEAS

1. Suppose an exponential function with equation $f(t) = ab^t$ contains the two points $(3, 20)$ and $(10, 156)$. **See margin.**
   a. Write the system of equations that results from substituting the two points into the equation.
   b. Solve the system to yield an equation for the function. Round your values for a and b to the nearest thousandth.
   c. Check your equation for the two points $(3, 20)$ and $(10, 156)$.

2. The graph at the right shows two ordered pairs that lie on the graph of an exponential function. Find an equation for the exponential function that contains the two points. $y = 5(3)^x$

3. In a study of the change in an insect population, there were about 170 insects four weeks after the study began, and about 320 after two more weeks. Assume an exponential model of growth.
   a. Find an equation relating the population to the number of weeks after the study began. $y = 47.979(1.372)^x$
   b. Estimate the initial number of insects. **about 48**
   c. Predict the number of insects five weeks after the study began. **233**

4. The prices of some diamonds of different sizes are given in the table at the right.
   a. Find an exponential regression model for this data.
   b. According to your model, what would be the price of a 2-carat diamond?

5. The half-life of barium, which is used in CAT scans for medical diagnosis, is 2.6 minutes. Suppose a patient swallows a drink containing 10 units of barium prior to getting a CAT scan.
   a. Find an exponential model for the amount of barium left in the patient's system as a function of the number of minutes that have passed since drinking the barium. $y = 10(0.766)^x$
   b. Find the amount of barium left after an hour.

   about 0.000001 units

Weight (carats)	Price
0.25	$504
0.40	$1,040
0.55	$1,925
0.80	$3,680
1.25	$10,000
1.65	$18,150

4a. $y = 391.354(11.917)^x$

4b. about $55,578.09

Additional Answers

1a. $\begin{cases} 20 = ab^3 \\ 156 = ab^{10} \end{cases}$

1b. $f(t) = 8.293(1.341)^t$

1c. $8.293 \cdot 1.341^3 \approx 20$;
$8.293 \cdot 1.341^{10} \approx 156$

---

6. Safety engineers monitor workplaces to see that workers are not exposed to unsafe levels of hazardous chemicals. Suppose that one chemical has a half-life of 7 days. If a worker currently has 18 units of this chemical in his body and was exposed 5 days ago, how much was the initial dose in his body? **about 29.53 units**

7. The table at the right shows how the number of U.S. cell-phone subscribers has grown since 1985.
   a. Create an exponential regression model for the number of subscribers t years after 1985. Report your value of a rounded to the nearest integer and b rounded to the nearest thousandth.
   b. Describe how well the model fits the data.
   c. Determine the year in which the value predicted by the model differs by the greatest *percent* from the actual value.

Year	Number of Cell-Phone Subscribers (thousands)
1985	340
1987	1,231
1989	3,509
1991	7,557
1993	16,009
1995	33,786
1997	55,312
1999	86,047
2001	128,375
2003	158,722

Source: CTIA - The Wireless Association

APPLYING THE MATHEMATICS

8. Benjamin Franklin specified in his will that "1000 pounds sterling" were to be given to the town of Boston for the purposes of providing loans at interest to apprentices. He expected the loans to be repaid and unused money to be well invested. He predicted, "If this plan is executed, and succeeds as projected without interruption for one hundred years, the sum will then be one hundred and thirty-one thousand pounds...." What annual yield did Franklin expect on his gift to Boston? **5%**

9. Radium has a half-life of 1620 years. Suppose 3 g of radium is present initially.
   a. Complete the table below for this situation.

Number of Half-Lives	0	1	2	3
$t =$ Number of Years After Start	0	1620		
$f(t) =$ Amount of Radium Present (grams)	3			

   b. Give an exponential model for the amount of radium left as a function of time t.
   c. How much radium would you expect to find after 4000 years?

10. A tour guide noticed that larger groups took more time to assemble for an event. The guide collected the data below. **See margin.**

Number of People	2	3	4	5	6	7	8	9	10
Time to Assemble (minutes)	2	2.6	3.4	4.4	5.7	7.4	9.7	12.5	16.3

   a. Make a scatterplot of the data.
   b. Find the linear regression model and graph it.
   c. Find the exponential regression model and graph it.
   d. Which of the two models seems to fit the data better? Why?

7a.

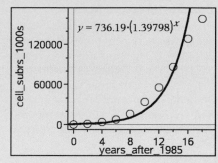

$y = 736.19 \cdot (1.39798)^x$

7a. $a \approx 736$, $b \approx 1.398$; $y = 736(1.398)^t$

7b. The model increases much more quickly than the data in the years after 1997, but otherwise fits well.

7c. 1985

9a.

Number of half lives	t	$f(t)$
0	0	3
1	1620	1.5
2	3240	0.75
3	4860	0.375

9b. $y = 3(0.9995722)^x$

9c. about 542 mg

10a. and b.

$y = 1.7083x - 3.1389$

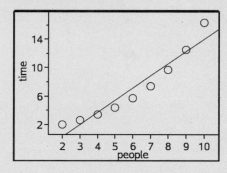

10c. $y = 1.1863(1.2995)^x$

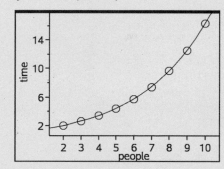

10d. The exponential model; it passes through all the data points.

4 Wrap-Up

Ongoing Assessment

Have students repeat Question 10b by using a system of two equations as in Example 1. Then ask them to write a paragraph that compares this model to the one found using technology. Students demonstrate that they can find and compare exponential models using technology and using a system of equations.

Project Update

Project 3, *Five Years From Now*, on page 141 relates to the content of this lesson.

11. Consider $f(x) = 7^x$ and $g(x) = 8^x$. Without graphing, which function has greater values when:

    a. $x > 0$. **g**

    b. $x < 0$ (Lesson 2-4) **f**

In 12 and 13, **Fill in the Blank**. (Lesson 2-4)

12. All functions with equations of the form $y = a \cdot b^x$ contain the point ___?___. **(0, a)**

13. The graph of every function in the form $y = b^x$ where $b > 0$ and $b \neq 1$ is always above the ___?___. **x-axis**

14. Use the Huntley data from Example 1. (Lesson 2-2)

    a. Find a linear model determined by the data for 2003 and 2005.

    b. What does the linear model predict for the 2015 population?

In 15 and 16, give an example of a function satisfying the given condition. In each case, give a domain and a rule. (Lesson 2-1)

15. The range is the set of all negative real numbers.

16. The range is the set of all nonnegative real numbers.

17. In 2004, of the 50 countries in the Western Hemisphere that consume petroleum, the mean consumption was about 608 thousand barrels per day per country. (Lesson 1-2) See margin.

    a. Find the total number of barrels consumed per day by all 50 countries.

    b. The United States consumed 20,731 thousand barrels per day in 2004. What would the mean be if the U.S. was not included?

    c. What percentage of the Western Hemisphere consumption is due to the U.S. consumption?

    d. Explain why mean consumption for all 50 countries is misleading given the U.S. consumption.

18. Consider an isosceles right triangle. (Previous Course)

    a. If the legs have length s, how long is the hypotenuse? $s\sqrt{2}$

    b. If the hypotenuse has length h, how long are the legs? $h\dfrac{\sqrt{2}}{2}$

19. Find out what happened to Alexander Litvinenko.

Answers vary. Sample: Alexander Valterovich Litvinenko was a member of the Committee for State Security (KGB) in the Soviet Union. In 1998, Litvinenko publicly accused his superiors of various crimes committed during his time in the KGB. After taking asylum in Great Britain, Litvinenko became suddenly ill in 2006, dying shortly after from lethal poisoning by radioactive polonium-210. It is unknown who poisoned Litvinenko.

14a. $y = 2{,}224.5x + 5{,}596.5$ where x is years after 2000.

14b. 38,964

15. Answers vary. Sample: $y = -3^x$; domain: all real numbers

Over a barrel?
In 2007, the U.S. imported 3,437,000 barrels of petroleum per day.

16. Answers vary. Sample: $y = 2^x$; domain: all real numbers

a. Answers vary.

b. about $1.455 \cdot 10^{63}$, a number with 64 digits in base 10

c. Most people estimate a much smaller difference.

Additional Answers

17a. about 30,400 thousand barrels per day

17b. about 197.3 thousand barrels per day

17c. about 67.5%

17d. The U.S. petroleum consumption is an extreme data point.

Lesson
2-6 Quadratic Models

Vocabulary

quadratic model
quadratic regression

▶ **BIG IDEA** Quadratic models are appropriate to consider when you think data will increase to a peak and then drop, or when data will decrease to a low point and then come back.

Linear functions are appropriate for modeling situations involving a constant amount of change. Exponential functions model situations involving a constant percent of change. In this lesson, we focus on **quadratic models**, that is, models based on quadratic functions.

Properties of Quadratic Functions

A *quadratic function* is a function with an equation that can be put into the form $f(x) = ax^2 + bx + c$, where $a \neq 0$. Recall that the graph of a quadratic function is a *parabola*. If $a > 0$, the parabola opens up and has a *minimum point*, as shown at the left below. If $a < 0$, the parabola opens down and has a *maximum point*, as shown at the right below. The existence of these extrema distinguishes quadratic functions from linear and exponential functions.

Mental Math

The identity
$(x + y)^2 =$
$x^2 + 2xy + y^2$
shows how to calculate
$(x + 1)^2$ **from** x^2. **Use it to find:**

a. 41^2, since $40^2 = 1600$.

b. 101^2.

a. **1681**

b. **10,201**

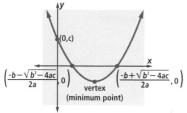
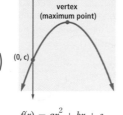

$$f(x) = ax^2 + bx + c$$
$$a > 0$$
$$b^2 - 4ac > 0$$

$$f(x) = ax^2 + bx + c$$
$$a < 0$$
$$b^2 - 4ac < 0$$

The domain of a quadratic function is the set of all real numbers. When $a < 0$, the range is the set of all real numbers less than or equal to the maximum value. When $a > 0$, the range is the set of all real numbers greater than or equal to the minimum value. The *y*-intercept is the *y*-coordinate of the point where $x = 0$:

$$f(0) = a \cdot 0^2 + b \cdot 0 + c = c.$$

So, regardless of the value of a, c is the *y*-intercept.

Quadratic Models **117**

Background

UCSMP students should be quite familiar with quadratic functions, having studied them both in *Algebra* and in *Advanced Algebra*. There is quadratic modeling in *Advanced Algebra*, including the idea of using quadratic regression to find the quadratic function through three given points.

Example 2 This context (projectile motion) involves an almost-exact, theory-based model. That is, we expect a quadratic to fit the data because the

principles of physics imply that paths of projectiles are quadratic.

Example 3 Example 3 is an exact model because there is at most one quadratic function through three non-collinear points. (If two of the points lie on the same vertical line, there is no function possible.)

Fitting a quadratic model through more than three points The last application (weight gain for given dosage) gives a situation which leads to an impressionistic model.

GOAL

Review the general quadratic equation $y = ax^2 + bx + c$, its graph, and the Quadratic Formula. Review or introduce quadratic modeling and use technology to determine the best fitting parabola.

SPUR Objectives

E Describe properties of quadratic functions.

F Find and interpret quadratic regression and models.

Materials/Resources

· Lesson Master 2-6
· Resource Masters 39–41
· Quiz 2

HOMEWORK • **Option 1**

• Questions 1–10 **• Option 2**
• • Questions 11–20
• • Question 21 (extra credit)
• Reading Lesson 2-7
• Covering the Ideas 2-7
(Questions 1–7)

Local Standards

1 **Wary-Up**

Use a CAS.
1. In what form does your CAS give the solutions to the general quadratic equation $ax^2 + bx + c = 0$?
Answers vary. Many split up the fractions. Sample: $x = \dfrac{\sqrt{b^2 - 4ac} - b}{2a}$
or $x = \dfrac{-(\sqrt{b^2 - 4ac} + b)}{2a}$
2. Describe three different ways to find the solutions to a quadratic equation such as $2x^2 - 5x - 25 = 0$.
Answers vary. Sample: Graph $y = 2x^2 - 5x - 25$ **and look for** x-**intercepts; Factor** $2x^2 - 5x - 25$ **into** $(2x + 5)(x - 5)$ **and solve** $(2x + 5)(x - 5) = 0$; **Use the Quadratic Formula.**

2 Teaching

Notes on the Lesson

Do not spend time having students draw careful graphs of quadratics; a sketch is all that is expected here, and that can be gotten from a graphing utility. Do make certain, however, that students are fluent in reading the coordinates of vertices and intercepts from a given graph and that they can determine the window that will show a graph.

Additional Example

Example 1 Consider the function f with equation $f(x) = -3x^2 - 4x + 7$.

a. Find the x- and y-intercepts of its graph. **x-intercepts are $-\frac{7}{3}$ and 1; y-intercept is 7**

b. Tell whether the parabola has a maximum or minimum point, and find its coordinates. **maximum; $\left(-\frac{2}{3}, \frac{25}{3}\right)$**

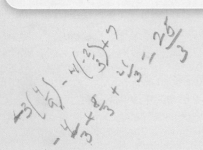

The x-intercepts are the x-coordinates of the points where $y = 0$. The x-intercepts exist only when $b^2 - 4ac \geq 0$, and then can be found by solving the quadratic equation $ax^2 + bx + c = 0$. From the Quadratic Formula, the x-intercepts are

$$\frac{-b + \sqrt{b^2 - 4ac}}{2a} \text{ and } \frac{-b - \sqrt{b^2 - 4ac}}{2a}.$$

The maximum or minimum point of any quadratic function occurs at the x-value that is the mean of the solutions to the equation $f(x) = 0$, that is, when $x = -\frac{b}{2a}$.

GUIDED

Example 1

Consider the function f with equation $f(x) = 2x^2 - 3x - 2$.

a. Find the x- and y-intercepts of its graph.

b. Tell whether the parabola has a maximum or minimum point, and find its coordinates.

Solution 1

a. Since $f(0) = \underline{\ ?\ }$, the y-intercept is –2. **–2**

To find the x-intercepts, let $f(x) = 0$ and solve for x.

$$2x^2 - 3x - 2 = 0$$

$$x = \frac{\underline{\ ?\ } \pm \sqrt{\underline{\ ?\ }^2 - 4 \cdot \underline{\ ?\ } \cdot \underline{\ ?\ }}}{2 \cdot \underline{\ ?\ }} \quad \text{3; –3; 2; –2; 2}$$

$$= \frac{\underline{\ ?\ } \pm \sqrt{\underline{\ ?\ }}}{\underline{\ ?\ }} \quad \text{3; 25; 4}$$

$$= 2 \text{ or } -\frac{1}{2}$$

The x-intercepts are 2 and $-\frac{1}{2}$.

b. Because the coefficient of x^2 is $\underline{\ ?\ }$, the vertex is a minimum **positive** point. Since parabolas are symmetric, the x-coordinate of the minimum (or maximum) point occurs at the mean of the two x-intercepts.

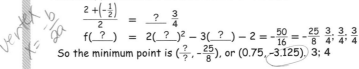

$$\frac{2 + \left(-\frac{1}{2}\right)}{2} = \underline{\ ?\ } \quad \frac{3}{4}$$

$$f(\underline{\ ?\ }) = 2(\underline{\ ?\ })^2 - 3(\underline{\ ?\ }) - 2 = -\frac{50}{16} = -\frac{25}{8} \quad \frac{3}{4}; \frac{3}{4}; \frac{3}{4}$$

So the minimum point is $\left(\frac{\underline{\ ?\ }}{\underline{\ ?\ }}, -\frac{25}{8}\right)$, or $(0.75, -3.125)$. **3; 4**

Solution 2

Use a CAS to find the x- and y-intercepts.

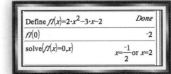

ENGLISH LEARNERS

Vocabulary Development

As in Chapter 1 with A_i, the initial velocity v_0 and initial height h_0 should be read as v-sub-zero and h-sub-zero.

QY

Using Known Quadratic Models

In the 17th century, extending earlier work of Galileo, Isaac Newton showed that the height h of an object at time t after it has been thrown with an initial velocity v_0 from an initial height h_0 satisfies the formula

$$h = -\frac{1}{2}gt^2 + v_0 t + h_0,$$

where g is the acceleration due to gravity. Recall that velocity is a rate of change of distance with respect to time; it is measured in units such as miles per hour or meters per second. Acceleration is the rate at which velocity changes, so it is measured in units such as miles per hour *per hour* or meters per second². Near the surface of Earth, g is approximately $32 \frac{\text{ft}}{\text{sec}^2}$ or $9.8 \frac{\text{m}}{\text{sec}^2}$.

Taking a dive
The world record for the highest dive is 53.90 meters. It took place in Villers-le-Lac, France.

> **▶ QY**
> What is the domain of the function in Example 1?

GUIDED

Example 2

A ball is thrown upward from a height of 15 m with initial velocity $20 \frac{\text{m}}{\text{sec}}$.

a. Find the relation between height h and time t after the ball is released.

b. How high is the ball after 3 seconds?

c. When will the ball hit the ground?

Solution

a. The conditions satisfy Newton's equation. Here $v_0 = \underline{\ ?\ } \frac{\text{m}}{\text{sec}}$, and **20**
$h_0 = \underline{\ ?\ }$ m. Use the metric system value $g = 9.8$. **15**

$$h = -\frac{1}{2}(\underline{\ ?\ })t^2 + \underline{\ ?\ }t + 15 \quad \textbf{9.8; 20}$$
$$h = -4.9t^2 + 20t + 15$$

b. Here $t = 3$ and you are asked to find h.

$$h = -4.9(3)^2 + 20 \cdot 3 + 15 = \underline{\ ?\ } \quad \textbf{30.9}$$

After 3 seconds, the ball is $\underline{\ ?\ }$ meters high. **30.9**

c. At ground level, $h = \underline{\ ?\ }$. Solve $0 = -4.9t^2 + 20t + 15$ for t. Use a **0**
CAS to get $t \approx \underline{\ ?\ }$ or $t \approx \underline{\ ?\ }$. The negative value of t does not make **–0.65; 4.73**
sense in this situation, so we use the positive value. **The ball will hit the ground after** $\underline{\ ?\ }$ **seconds. 4.73**

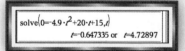

$$\text{solve}\left(0 = -4.9 \cdot t^2 + 20 \cdot t + 15, t\right)$$
$$t = -0.647335 \text{ or } \quad t = 4.72897$$

Accommodating the Learner ⬇

Remind students that when the data points all lie on a single parabola, any three data points can be used to determine the quadratic equation. However, when the data points show a quadratic trend, but not an exact quadratic fit, different triples of points will usually determine somewhat different quadratic equations. As pointed out previously, a statistics utility can determine the best-fitting model.

Notes on the Lesson

Example 2 Students who have studied from UCSMP *Algebra* and *Advanced Algebra* have twice seen quadratic models for projectile motion. Some of your students may have also encountered the relevant formulas in physics. You should probe to see how many have seen this model before. Point out the difference between an equation of the path of the ball and an equation for the height of the path over time (as in this example). Both equations are quadratic, and both graphs are parabolas, but they are not describing the same phenomenon. In the equation of the path, both x and y stand for distances. If the scales on the axes are the same, the graph looks like the path. In the equation of the height of the ball over time, x stands for time and y stands for a distance. The graph is not a picture of the path even though it has the same shape.

You might mention that in baseball, when a long home run is hit, occasionally there is the question of how far the ball would have traveled had it not hit a wall, or the bleachers, or some other object. The mathematics puts together ideas from Examples 2 and 3: from TV tape of the baseball game, an attempt is made to determine a few points on the flight of the ball. Then quadratic regression (appropriate because the ball is a projectile) is used to fit the best parabola to those points, and that parabola is examined to determine where it hits ground level again.

Additional Example

Example 2 A projectile is shot from a tower 10 feet high with an upward velocity of 100 feet per second.

a. Approximate the relationship between height h (in feet) and time t (in seconds) after the projectile is shot. $h = -16t^2 + 100t + 10$

b. How long will the projectile be in the air? ≈ 6.3 seconds

Notes on the Lesson

Example 3 You might have students pick a 4th point on this parabola and run a quadratic regression again, including that point. The same parabola will result. Then have students pick a point not on the parabola and run the quadratic regression with the original 3 points and the new point. Now the result will be a quadratic function that likely does not contain any of the 4 points (but is close to them).

Additional Example

Example 3 A parabola contains the points (–0.1, –16.32), (2, 3), and (6, –9). Find its equation.
$y = -2x^2 + 13x - 15$

Finding the Quadratic Model through Three Points

The picture at the right shows that two points do not determine a parabola. To compute a unique quadratic model, you need a minimum of three noncollinear points.

One way to fit a quadratic model to data is to identify specific points on the model and set up a system of equations. The system must allow you to solve for the values of a, b, and c in the equation $y = ax^2 + bx + c$.

Alternately, you can use *quadratic regression*, a calculation available in many statistics packages. **Quadratic regression** is a technique, similar to the method of least squares, that finds an equation for the best-fitting parabola through a set of points.

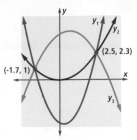

There are many parabolas that pass through the two points (–1.7, 1) and (2.5, 2.3).

Example 3

The parabola at the right contains points (1, –9), (6, –4), and (–0.2, 12.12). Find its equation.

Solution 1 Because the ordered pairs (x, y) are solutions of the equation $y = ax^2 + bx + c$, substitute to get 3 linear equations, each with a, b, and c as unknowns.

$$\begin{aligned}
f(1) &= -9 = a(1)^2 + b(1) + c \\
f(6) &= -4 = a(6)^2 + b(6) + c \\
f(-0.2) &= 12.12 = a(-0.2)^2 + b(-0.2) + c
\end{aligned}$$

This produces a system of three equations.

$$\begin{cases}
-9 = a + b + c \\
-4 = 36a + 6b + c \\
12.12 = 0.04a - 0.2b + c
\end{cases}$$

Use the `solve` command on a CAS. An equation for the parabola that contains these three points is
$f(x) = 3x^2 - 20x + 8$.

Solution 2 Use quadratic regression. You are asked to do this in Question 8.

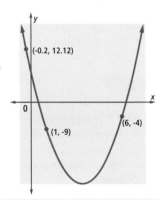

Check Substitute the points into the equation.
Does $3(1)^2 - 20(1) + 8 = -9$?   Yes.
Does $3(6)^2 - 20(6) + 8 = -4$?   Yes.
Does $3(-0.2)^2 - 20(-0.2) + 8 = 12.12$?   Yes, it checks.

When data points all lie on a single parabola, as in Example 3, the system strategy will yield an exact model. The model found by solving a system will be identical to the model formed by using quadratic regression. However, if the data show a quadratic trend, but not an exact quadratic fit, then the two solution strategies may yield slightly different equations.

Accommodating the Learner

A ball is propelled upward from a height of 7 feet. Use the known quadratic model for free-falling objects to find a function relating the height h and time t after the ball is released and use it to answer the following.
$h = -16t^2 + v_0 t + 7$

a. Obtain an expression in terms of v_0 for the time t at which the ball reaches its maximum height. $t = \frac{v_0}{32}$

b. What must the initial velocity be in order for the ball to reach a maximum height of 350 feet? **about 148 ft/sec**

c. Some major league baseball pitchers can throw a ball at 100 mph. Is that fast enough to reach this height? **Not quite; 148 ft/sec is about 101 mph.**

d. Find a meaningful domain for t in the function used in Part b to describe the height of the ball at time t. $0 \le t \le 9.3$

Fitting a Quadratic Model through More Than Three Points

The following table contains data that might be collected by farmers interested in increasing the weight of their pigs. Suppose twenty-four randomly selected pigs were each given a daily dosage (in pellets) of a food supplement. Each group of three pigs received a dosage from 0 to 7 pellets, and the average percent weight gain for each group was recorded. The table below shows the average percent weight gain for each group of three pigs in relation to the number of pellets they were given daily.

Dosage (pellets)	0	1	2	3	4	5	6	7
Percent Weight Gain	10	13	21	24	22	20	16	13

The data show that more is not necessarily better. The pigs' bodies start rejecting the supplement when the dosage is too high. So there is a peak in the data and a quadratic model might be appropriate. A scatterplot of the data and the graph of the quadratic regression model $y = -1.0x^2 + 7.2x + 9.3$ are shown below. With the exception of the point $(3, 24)$, the data points lie fairly close to the parabola.

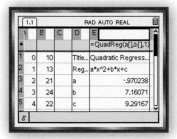 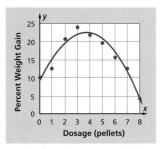

There is something quite different about this application when compared to the application in Example 2. There is no theory that links dosage with percent weight gain as there is with projectile motion. Models such as this one are called *impressionistic models* or *non-theory-based models*, because no theory exists that explains why the model fits the data. This is different from Example 2, where the well-established theory of gravity and all sorts of real data have verified that the height of a projectile is a quadratic function of time.

Notes on the Lesson

Fitting a quadratic model through more than three points It is important that students understand why a linear fit is not appropriate for the pig-weight problem. Not only do the data appear to fall on a curve, but if a line were used, all the data points on the far left and far right would fall above the line. This kind of pattern often indicates that a curvilinear model is more appropriate. Emphasize the danger of extrapolating from an impressionistic quadratic model. The model is reasonable for only a small range of dosages.

$y = -.97 + 7.16x + 9.3$

$R^2 = .911$

or $y = -1.0x^2 + 7.2x + 9.3$

Extension

Have students explain why the following statement is true: "The maximum or minimum point of the graph of any quadratic function occurs at the x-value that is the mean of the solutions to the equation $f(x) = 0$." From the Quadratic Formula, the solutions to any quadratic equation $ax^2 + bx + c = 0$ are $x_1 = \dfrac{-b + \sqrt{b^2 - 4ac}}{2a}$ and $x_2 = \dfrac{-b - \sqrt{b^2 - 4ac}}{2a}$. The mean of x_1 and x_2 is $\dfrac{x_1 + x_2}{2} = \dfrac{-2b}{4a} = -\dfrac{b}{2a}$. This is the general form of the x-coordinate of the vertex of a parabola.

2-6

3 Assignment

Recommended Assignment

- Questions 1–10
- • Questions 11–20
- • Question 21 (extra credit)
- • Reading Lesson 2-7
- • Covering the Ideas 2-7
  (Questions 1–7)

Notes on the Questions

We suggest going through Questions 1–14 in order.

Questions 4, 6, and 9 Unlike some texts, we do not control quadratics so that almost all solutions are rational numbers. When dealing with real data, solutions with rational numbers rarely occur. Fortunately, calculators do arithmetic with decimal approximations as easily as they do arithmetic with whole numbers, and a CAS can give exact values.

Question 10 Typically, students' estimates of the location of the vertex are not as far from the x-axis as the actual vertex is. You can use Part c to review the Pythagorean Distance Formula between two points in the coordinate plane.

Questions

COVERING THE IDEAS

1. What is the general form of an equation of a quadratic function?

2. What values of x are the solutions to $ax^2 + bx + c = 0$?

3. What is the range of the function f in Example 1?

4. Consider the graph of the function f with $f(x) = 2x^2 - x - 4$.
   a. Give its y- and x-intercepts.
   b. Sketch the part of the graph where $-3 \leq x \leq 3$.
   c. Give the coordinates of the minimum point. $\left(\frac{1}{4}, -\frac{33}{8}\right)$

5. Tell whether the graph of the equation has a maximum point, a minimum point, or neither.
   a. $y = 8x^2 - 3x - 7$ **minimum**   b. $y = 2x + 4x^2$ **minimum**
   c. $y = 6 - 2x^2$ **maximum**   d. $y = -x^2 + 5x + 177$ **maximum**

6. Repeat Example 2 as if the ball were on the moon. Acceleration due to gravity on the moon is $1.6 \frac{m}{s^2}$.

In 7 and 8, refer to Example 3.

7. Using the quadratic model, show that $f(4) = -24$.

8. Find the quadratic model by using quadratic regression.

9. Refer to the data about weight gain in pigs on page 121.
   a. What does the model predict for the percent weight gain for pigs fed 4.5 pellets daily?
   b. Is the prediction in Part a extrapolation or interpolation?

10. A parabola contains the points $(0, 1)$, $(4, 5)$, and $(8, 7)$. **See margin.**
    a. Graph these points and estimate the coordinates of the vertex.
    b. Find an equation for the parabola by setting up and solving a system of equations.
    c. Check your estimate in Part a.

APPLYING THE MATHEMATICS

11. The table below shows the largest number of pieces $f(n)$ into which a pizza can be cut by n straight cuts.

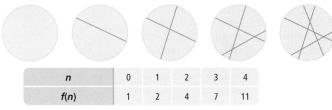

n	0	1	2	3	4
$f(n)$	1	2	4	7	11

   a. Fit a quadratic model to these data using regression.
   b. Use your model to find the greatest number of pieces produced by 5 straight cuts. Check your answer by drawing a diagram.

Answer column (right margin)

1. $f(x) = ax^2 + bx + c$

2. $x = \frac{-b \pm \sqrt{b^2 - 4ac}}{2a}$

3. $\{y | y \geq -3.125\}$

4a. y-intercept: -4

x-intercepts:
$\frac{1 - \sqrt{33}}{4}, \frac{1 + \sqrt{33}}{4}$

4b.
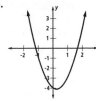

6a. $h = -0.8t^2 + 20t + 15$

6b. for $t = 3$, $h = 67.8$ m

6c. for $h = 0$, $t = 25.73$ seconds

7. $3(16) - 20(4) + 8 = -24$

8. $f(x) = 3x^2 - 20x + 8$

9a. 21.45%

9b. interpolation

11a. $f(n) = 0.5n^2 + 0.5n + 1$

11b. $f(5) = 16$

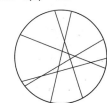

Lesson Master (bottom left)

Additional Answers

10a. Answers vary. Sample: (10, 8)

10b. $y = -\frac{1}{16}x^2 + \frac{5}{4}x + 1$

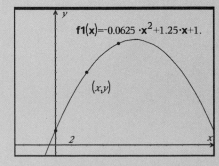

f1(x)=-0.0625 ·x² +1.25·x+1.

10c. The vertex is (10, 7.25).

12. A piece of an artery or a vein is approximately the shape of a cylinder. The French physiologist and physician Jean Louis Poiseuille (1799–1869) discovered experimentally that the velocity v at which blood travels through arteries or veins is a function of the distance r of the blood from the axis of symmetry of the cylinder. For example, for a wide arterial capillary, the following formula might apply: $v = 1.185 - (185 \cdot 10^4)r^2$, where r is measured in cm and v in $\frac{cm}{sec}$.

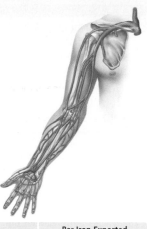

a. Find the velocity of blood traveling on the axis of symmetry of this capillary. **1.185 $\frac{cm}{sec}$**

b. Find the velocity of blood traveling $6 \cdot 10^{-4}$ cm from the axis of symmetry. **0.519 $\frac{cm}{sec}$**

c. According to this model, where in the capillary is the velocity of the blood 0? **0.0008 cm from axis of symmetry**

d. What is the domain of the function mapping r onto v?

e. Sketch a graph of this function. **12 d-e. See margin.**

13. Use the table at the right showing the amount of bar iron exported to England from the American Colonies from 1762 to 1774. Bar iron is measured in "old" tons of 2240 pounds. **13 a, b, d. See margin.**

a. Construct a scatterplot for these data with the independent variable as years after 1762.

b. Find the quadratic regression model for these data.

c. Use your quadratic model to predict the amount of bar iron exported in 1776. (The actual value was 28 old tons.) **$f(14) = -526.9$**

d. Why is extrapolation to 1776 inappropriate?

Year	Bar Iron Exported (old tons)
1762	110
1763	310
1765	1079
1768	1990
1770	1716
1771	2222
1773	838
1774	639

Source: U.S. Census Bureau

14. The Center for Disease Control studies trends in high school smoking. The percent of students in grades 9 through 12 who reported smoking cigarettes on 20 of the 30 days preceding the administration of the National Youth Risk Behavior Survey (frequent cigarette use) increased in the 1990s, but decreased after 1999.

Years after 1990	1	3	5	7	9	11	13	15
% of Frequent Cigarette Use = y	12.7	13.8	16.1	16.7	16.8	13.8	9.7	9.4

a. Construct a scatterplot for these data.

b. Calculate the sum of squared residuals for the quadratic model $y = -0.2x^2 + 2x + 11$. **about 267.04**

c. Find the quadratic regression model for the data. Calculate the sum of squared residuals for this model.

d. Which model has a smaller sum of squared residuals?

e. Using the regression model, predict the cigarette use in 2006 and 2010. Do you think the predictions are reasonable?

14a. See margin.

14c. $f(x) = -0.118x^2 + 1.581x + 10.970$; sum of squared residuals ≈ 7.57

14d. the quadratic regresssion model

14e. $f(16) = 6.17$; $f(20) = -4.43$; The prediction for 2006 is reasonable, but the prediction for 2010 is not because the count cannot negative.

Question 11 As with Example 3 in the reading, you might point out that the arithmetic reason the data fit a quadratic model exactly is because the differences between successive values of $f(n)$ form a linear sequence. The geometric reason that the data are quadratic is that it deals with the number of intersections of lines, and if the number of lines increases linearly, then the number of intersections increases as the product of a linear with a linear, that is, as a quadratic.

Questions 13 and 14 The quadratics here are impressionistic models.

Question 14 This is the only question in which we compare one quadratic model to a second quadratic model found by quadratic regression.

Additional Answers

13b. $f(x) = -46.393x^2 + 620.48x - 120.6$; x is the number of years after 1762

13d. The negative value indicates that the colonies were importing bar iron from England in 1776. However, in 1776 the colonies declared war on England and active trade between the colonies and England stopped.

14a.

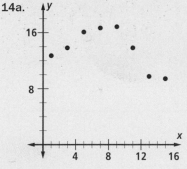

Additional Answers

12d. $0 \leq r < 0.0008$

12e. Velocity of Blood Through Capillaries with Respect to Capillary Radius

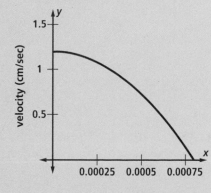

13a. Bar Iron Exports to England from American Colonies (1762–1774)

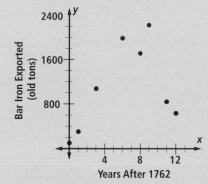

2-6

Notes on the Questions

Question 20 This graph is fundamental to the content of Lesson 2-7, so should be discussed.

4 ▶ Wrap-Up

Ongoing Assessment

Have students work in pairs. Each student should write down coordinates of three noncollinear points, then give their paper to their partner. Students should then find an equation of a parabola through the three given points, and present their work to their partner. **Answers vary. Check students' work.**

Administer Quiz 2 (or a quiz of your own) after students complete this lesson.

Additional Answers

20.

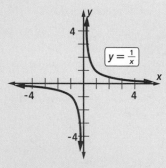

21a. $(-2, -3)$, $\left(-\frac{3}{2}, -\frac{5}{4}\right)$, $(-1, 0)$, $\left(-\frac{1}{2}, \frac{3}{4}\right)$, $(0, 1)$, $\left(\frac{1}{2}, \frac{3}{4}\right)$, $(1, 0)$, $\left(\frac{3}{2}, -\frac{5}{4}\right)$, $(2, -3)$

21b.

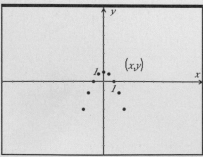

21c. $f(x) = -x^2 + 1$

21d. Since the vertex of each parabola occurs at $x = \frac{-b}{2a}$ and a is now 2 instead of 1, each point will be half its prior distance to the y-axis. The new quadratic model is $f(x) = -2x^2 + 1$.

REVIEW

15. The half-life of Th-232 (Thorium) is 14.05 billion years. Suppose a sample contains 100 grams of pure thorium. **(Lesson 2-5)**
  a. Find an equation for the amount of Th-232 left as a function of the number of billions of years that have passed. $f(t) = 100(0.952)^t$
  b. Find the amount left after 13.7 billion years, the estimated age of our atmosphere. $f(13.7) \approx 50.87$ g

In 16 and 17, Sri Lanka and Madagascar are two island nations in the Indian Ocean. In 2007, the population of Sri Lanka was about 20.9 million people and the population of Madagascar was about 19.4 million people. In 2007, the population of Sri Lanka was growing at a rate of about 0.98% annually, while the population of Madagascar was growing at a rate of about 3.01% annually. Let the function $S(x) = ab^x$ represent the population (in millions) of Sri Lanka x years after 2007, and let the function $M(x) = cd^x$ represent the population (in millions) of Madagascar x years after 2007.

Kandy
A town in the center of Sri Lanka

16. a. Determine a, b, c, and d and write formulas for $S(x)$ and $M(x)$.
  b. Assuming constant growth rates, use your formulas from Part a to estimate the populations of Sri Lanka and Madagascar in 1997.
  c. Graph $y = S(x)$ and $y = M(x)$ on the same set of axes for $0 \leq x \leq 50$.
  d. Make a prediction about how the future populations of Sri Lanka and Madagascar will compare if current trends continue. **(Lesson 2-4)**

17. When the function S is used to predict the population of Sri Lanka in 2008, the residual is 2.848. What was the observed population? **(Lesson 2-2)** about 23,953,000

18. What are the maximum and minimum possible values for a correlation coefficient? **(Lesson 2-3)** –1, 1

19. *Skill Sequence* Solve for x. **(Previous Course)**
  a. $(5x - 10)(x - 3) = 0$ b. $3x^2 = 1 - 2x$ c. $3x^4 = 1 - 2x^2$

20. Sketch the graph of $y = \frac{1}{x}$. **(Previous Course) See margin.**

EXPLORATION

21. a. Find the vertices for the family of quadratic functions **See margin.** $y = x^2 + bx + 1$ for $b = \{-4, -3, -2, -1, 0, 1, 2, 3, 4\}$.
  b. Graph all of your collected vertices in a scatterplot.
  c. Find an exact quadratic model for the data.
  d. If you had started this question with $y = 2x^2 + bx + 1$, what would you predict the quadratic model of the vertex data to be? Why?

16a. $a = 20.9$, $b = 1.0098$, $c = 19.4$, $d = 1.0301$; $S(x) = 20.9(1.0098)^x$, $M(x) = 19.4(1.0301)^x$

16b. $S(-10) = 18.96$ million, $M(-10) = 14.42$ million

16c. See margin.

16d. Since the population is an exponential growth model and Madagascar's growth rate is larger, Madagascar's population will become larger than Sri Lanka's.

19a. $x = 2$ or $x = 3$

19b. $x = -1$ or $x = \frac{1}{3}$

19c. $x = \pm\frac{\sqrt{3}}{3}$

Lesson 2-7

Inverse Variation Models

▶ **BIG IDEA** Inverse and inverse square functions model many physical situations.

Inverse Variation

Suppose you have 6 pounds of ground meat to make into hamburger patties of equal weight. The more patties you make, the less each patty will weigh. More specifically, the weight W of each patty is related to the number N of patties produced by the equation

$$W = \frac{6}{N}.$$

In this situation, the weight per patty *varies inversely as* (or *is inversely proportional to*) the number of patties.

 QY1

In general, we say that y **varies inversely as** x (or y **is inversely proportional to** x) whenever $y = \frac{k}{x}$. The parameter k is called the **constant of variation** (or **constant of proportionality**), and cannot be 0. In the hamburger situation, it is impossible for either N or W to be negative, but in other situations the domain and range may include negative values. Graphing $y = \frac{k}{x}$ for both positive and negative values of x shows that there are two basic types of graphs, depending on the value of k. Sometimes you will see the expression $\frac{k}{x}$ written as kx^{-1}.

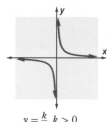

$y = \frac{k}{x}, k > 0$

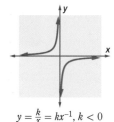

$y = \frac{k}{x} = kx^{-1}, k < 0$

Activity   See margin.

Step 1   Graph $y = \frac{k}{x}$ for different positive values of k. On some graphing utilities, you can use a slider for k as shown on the next page. How does increasing the value of k affect the graph?

(continued on next page)

Inverse Variation Models   **125**

Vocabulary

varies inversely as, is inversely proportional to
constant of variation, constant of proportionality
inverse-square relationship
varies inversely as the square of, is inversely proportional to the square of
power function

Mental Math

Rewrite the expression as a power of a single variable, if possible.

a. $\frac{1}{x}$ x^{-1}
b. $\frac{1}{y^2}$ y^{-2}
c. $(z^{-3})^5$ z^{-15}
d. $(\sqrt{w})^{24}$ w^{12}

▶ **QY1**

Using the relationship above, make a table of the weight W per patty for $N = 12, 24, 36,$ and 48 patties. Will the weight ever equal zero?

Lesson 2-7

GOAL
Review inverse variation functions as models in a variety of situations.

SPUR Objectives
E Describe properties of inverse variation functions.

Materials/Resources
· Lesson Master 2-7
· Resource Masters 42 and 43

HOMEWORK   • Option 1
•   Questions 1–7   • Option 2
• • Questions 8–15
• • Questions 16 and 17 (extra credit)
    • Reading Lesson 2-8
    • Covering the Ideas 2-8 (Questions 1–7)

Local Standards

1   **Warm-Up**

1. If A and B are inversely proportional and $A = 10$ when $B = 5$, then what is the value of B when $A = 50$?
$B = 1$

2. How many times more intense is the sound if you are sitting 20 feet from a band than if you are sitting 30 feet from the band? $\frac{9}{4}$ **or 2.25 times as intense**

Additional Answers

Activity
See the side margin of page 126.

Background

We assume that students have seen the ideas of direct and inverse variation in a previous course such as UCSMP *Advanced Algebra*. The two types of functions used as models in this lesson, the inverse variation functions with equations $y = \frac{k}{x}$ and the inverse square variation functions with equations $y = \frac{k}{x^2}$, are both found in a wide variety of situations.

Inverse variation   Any situation in which there is a constant product gives rise to an inverse variation function. The example that starts the lesson is about having a fixed amount of ground meat with which to make hamburger patties; the product of the amount of meat in each patty and the number of patties is constant. Another example is a rectangle with fixed area. As one dimension grows, the other must shrink accordingly in order for the area to stay the same.

(continued on next page)

2-7

2 Teaching

Notes on the Lesson

Use the Warm-Up questions to begin the class in order to assess how much your students have remembered from the time when they studied direct and inverse variation.

Example 1 Here we expect the relationship between pressure and volume to fit an inverse-square relationship. It is a theory-based model and only measurement error and other errors that creep in keep it from being an exact model.

Inverse-square relationships Find out if any of your students have taken enough science to know the inverse-square laws in physics. Students who have studied from UCSMP *Advanced Algebra* will have seen both types of variation from this lesson early in that course.

Example 2 This, too, is a theory-based model.

Additional Answers

Activity

Step 1

If $k > 0$, then increasing k increases the distance between the vertices of the graph and the origin.

Step 2

Decreasing k when $k < 0$ increases the distance between the vertices and the origin. The asymptotes are unaffected by increasing/decreasing k.

Step 3

For $k = 1$, as x gets closer to 0 from the right, y approaches positive infinity.

Step 4

For $k = 1$, as x gets closer to 0 from the left, y approaches negative infinity.

Step 2 Graph $y = \frac{k}{x}$ for different negative values of k. How does the sign of k affect the graph? Which features of the graph are invariant, that is, which features do not depend on the value of k?

Step 3 Fix a particular positive value of k and pick a point on the graph with $x > 0$. Then trace the graph, moving to the left. As x gets closer to 0, what happens to the y-coordinate?

Step 4 Now pick to a point on the graph with $x < 0$. Then trace the graph, moving to the right. As x gets closer to 0, what happens to the y-coordinate?

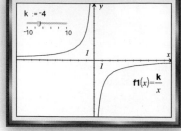

The graphs suggest that there are points on the graph of $y = \frac{k}{x}$ corresponding to all real values of x except $x = 0$, and to all real values of y except $y = 0$. The domain of the function with equation $y = \frac{k}{x}$ is therefore $\{x \mid x \neq 0\}$ and the range is therefore $\{y \mid y \neq 0\}$.

The graphs in the activity are *hyperbolas*. Both hyperbolas have a *horizontal asymptote* at $y = 0$. In numerical terms, as x gets larger, y gets closer and closer to 0. In the hamburger situation, this means that with a fixed amount of meat, as the number of hamburgers increases, the weight of each burger decreases until, with enough burgers, the weight of each can be as small as you wish.

In addition, both graphs have a *vertical asymptote* at $x = 0$, because as x gets closer to 0, y gets larger and larger (or more and more negative) without ever reaching a bound.

Determining the Constant of Variation

When one quantity varies inversely as another, you can determine the constant of variation from one data point. Inverse variation is common in the physical world. For instance, according to Boyle's Law, the volume of a gas varies inversely as the pressure. Pressure is measured in kilopascals (kPa) and volume is measured in milliliters (mL).

GUIDED

Example 1

In a chemistry lab, you collect data on the pressure and volume of a gas.

Volume (mL)	20	30	40	50	60	70	80	90	100
Pressure (kPa)	253.3	160.5	120.9	101.6	84.6	70.9	64.2	53.8	49.3

a. Find a formula relating the pressure and volume of the gas sample you studied in the lab.
b. Graph both the data and the model on a single set of axes.
c. Use residuals to assess the quality of your model.
d. What volume corresponds to a pressure of 40 kPa?

126   Functions and Models

Activity The graphs of inverse-variation functions are all rectangular hyperbolas whose asymptotes are the axes. They are called "rectangular" hyperbolas because their asymptotes are perpendicular. The graphs of all inverse-variation functions are geometrically similar; they have the same shape. An instance is seen in Guided Example 1.

Inverse-square relationships The most common inverse-square relationships are the following.

1. The intensity of light hitting an object is proportional to the inverse square of the distance between the light source and the object.

2. The first relationship also applies to radiation coming from a source to an object.

3. The first relationship also applies to sound intensity.

4. The force of attraction between two objects with mass is inversely

Solution

a. The model is of the form $P = \frac{k}{V}$. We start by selecting a "typical" point in the middle of the data set: $(V, P) = (60, 84.6)$.

Set $84.6 = \frac{k}{\boxed{?}}$ and solve for k. **60**

$k = (\underline{\ ?\ })(\underline{\ ?\ }) = 5076$. **84.6; 60**

Therefore, $P = \underline{\ ?\ }$. $\frac{5076}{V}$

b. Enter the data into two columns of a spreadsheet. Generate a scatterplot and superimpose a graph of the model. The graph is shown at the right.

c. Add a third column that computes the predicted values and a fourth that computes the difference between the observed values and the predicted values as shown at the right.

There are more negative than positive residuals, so we might consider __?__ (increasing/decreasing) the value of k we derived, but the residuals are not large and do not show a clear pattern that would suggest a different model shape. **The low absolute values of the residuals and the lack of a clear pattern suggest that the model is fairly accurate. decreasing**

d. Substitute 40 for P in the equation from Part a:

$40 = \frac{5076}{V}$. Then solve for V: $V = \underline{\ ?\ }$ mL. **126.9**

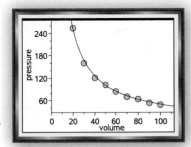

A vol...	B pres...	C model	D residual
		=5076./volu	
1 20	253.3	253.0	-0.5
2 30	160.5	169.2	-8.7
3 40	120.9	126.9	-6.
4 50	101.6	101.52	0.08
5 60	84.6	84.6	0.
6 70	70.9	72.5143	-1.61429
D1 =b1−c1			

Inverse-Square Relationships

In science contexts, the relationship $y = \frac{k}{x^2} = kx^{-2}$ is very common. Such relationships are called **inverse-square relationships**, and we write **y varies inversely as the square of x** (or **y is inversely proportional to the square of x**). In many respects, inverse-square relationships are similar to inverse-variation situations.

Example 2

The force exerted by the electrical field between two charged objects is inversely proportional to the square of the distance between them. At a distance of 1.5 meters, you measure a force of 30 newtons. What will be the force at a distance of 3.0 meters? At 15 meters?

Solution First compute the constant of variation, then substitute the known distances to find the unknown force.

Because $F = \frac{k}{d^2}$, we can write $30\ N = \frac{k}{(1.5\ m)^2}$ and solve for k.

$k = 30\ N \cdot 1.5^2\ m^2 = 67.5\ N \cdot m^2$.

Then use the equation $F = \frac{67.5\ N \cdot m^2}{d^2}$, substituting 3.0 m and 15 m for d.

When $d = 3.0$ m, the force is 7.5 N; when $d = 15$ m, the force is 0.3 N.

proportional to the square of the distance between them.

5. The force of attraction or repulsion between two electrically charged particles, in addition to being directly proportional to the product of the electric charges, is inversely proportional to the square of the distance between them; this is Coulomb's law. An instance is seen in Example 2.

Reciprocals of power functions Both inverse-variation functions and inverse-square functions can be thought of as power functions with negative exponents or as reciprocals of power functions with positive exponents. Inverse-variation functions with equations $y = \frac{k}{x} = kx^{-1}$ and inverse-square variation functions with equations $y = \frac{k}{x^2} = kx^{-2}$ are odd or even functions as their exponents are odd or even.

Additional Examples

Example 1 The average song size (in MB) and approximate number of songs for a sample of 32 GB MP3 players are listed in the table below.

Average song size (MB)	Approximate number of songs on 32GB MP3 player
3.6	8000
4.7	7000
4.5	7200
4.2	7600
4.1	7800
5.8	5500
4.9	6500
5.1	6300

a. Find a formula that gives the average number n of songs that will fit on an MP3 player as a function of the average song size s.
Answers vary. Sample: The model is of the form $n = \frac{k}{s}$. Pick a "typical point," (4.9, 6500), so $k = 31{,}850$.
$n = \frac{31850}{s}$ makes sense since the samples have capacity 32 GB.

b. Graph both the data and the model on a single set of axes.
Answers vary. Sample:

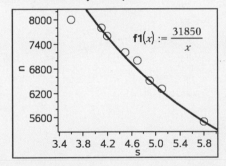

$f1(x) := \frac{31850}{x}$

c. Use residuals to assess the quality of your model.
Answers vary. Sample:

A s	B n	C model	D
		=31850/(a[])	=b[]−c[]
1 3.6	8000	8847.22	-847.222
2 4.7	7000	6776.6	223.404
3 4.5	7200	7077.78	122.222
4 4.2	7600	7583.33	16.6667
5 4.1	7800	7768.29	31.7073
C model:=$\frac{31850}{a\boxed{}}$			

(continued on next page)

2-7

Graphs of $y = \frac{k}{x^2}$ share many of the features of the graphs of $y = \frac{k}{x}$.

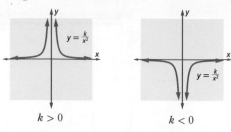

$$k > 0 \qquad\qquad k < 0$$

Asymptotes: Both types of graphs have horizontal asymptotes at $y = 0$ and have vertical asymptotes at $x = 0$.

Domain: Because $\frac{k}{x^2}$ is defined for all values of x except when $x = 0$, the domain of $y = \frac{k}{x^2}$ is $\{x \mid x \neq 0\}$. $y = \frac{k}{x}$ has the same domain.

Range: The graphs above suggest that the range of $y = \frac{k}{x^2}$ depends on the value of k: for $k > 0$, the range is $\{y \mid y > 0\}$, while for $k < 0$, the range is $\{y \mid y < 0\}$. The inverse variation function has range $\{y \mid y \neq 0\}$. As with $y = \frac{k}{x}$, making the absolute value of k larger moves the graph of $y = \frac{k}{x^2}$ further away from the origin.

Note also that as $|x|$ increases, y gets close to zero much more quickly for $y = \frac{k}{x^2}$ than for $y = \frac{k}{x}$.

STOP QY2

Reciprocals of Power Functions

Recall that a **power function** is a function with an equation of the form $y = ax^n$, where n is an integer greater than 1. In this case we say that y varies directly as x^n. The reciprocal of a power function is a function of the form $y = \frac{1}{ax^n}$, or alternatively, $y = bx^{-n}$, where the coefficient $b = \frac{1}{a}$. In these cases, we say that y varies inversely as x^n. Inverse-variation functions are the reciprocals of direct-variation functions. Properties of these functions are summarized in the tables below.

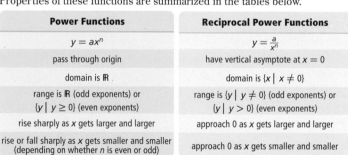

Power Functions	Reciprocal Power Functions
$y = ax^n$	$y = \frac{a}{x^n}$
pass through origin	have vertical asymptote at $x = 0$
domain is $\mathbb{R}$	domain is $\{x \mid x \neq 0\}$
range is $\mathbb{R}$ (odd exponents) or $\{y \mid y \geq 0\}$ (even exponents)	range is $\{y \mid y \neq 0\}$ (odd exponents) or $\{y \mid y > 0\}$ (even exponents)
rise sharply as x gets larger and larger	approach 0 as x gets larger and larger
rise or fall sharply as x gets smaller and smaller (depending on whether n is even or odd)	approach 0 as x gets smaller and smaller

▶ **QY2**

Consider $f(x) = \frac{6}{x}$ and $g(x) = \frac{6}{x^2}$. Compare $f(10)$ and $g(10)$, $f(100)$ and $g(100)$, $f(1000)$ and $g(1000)$. For each pair, which value is closer to zero?

Questions

COVERING THE IDEAS

1. **Multiple Choice** In which equation does W vary inversely as the square of g? **C**

   A $W = \frac{k}{g}$ B $W = kg^2$ C $W = \frac{k}{g^2}$ D $W = k\sqrt{g}$

2. **Multiple Choice** Which of the following is *not* a characteristic of the function $y = \frac{k}{x}$ or its graph? **A**

   A domain is the set of all real numbers

   B horizontal asymptote at $y = 0$

   C vertical asymptote at $x = 0$

   D shape is a hyperbola

3. Suppose that y varies inversely as x, and that $y = 45$ when $x = 10$.
   a. Compute the constant of variation. **$k = 450$**
   b. Find y when $x = 2$. **225**

4. Suppose 240 hot dogs were ordered for a picnic, and x people finished them all.
   a. Write a formula for y, the mean number of hot dogs each person ate. $y = \frac{240}{x}$
   b. Graph the relation you found in Part a.
   c. Your graph has a horizontal asymptote. Find its equation, and ~~explain its meaning in the context of the problem.~~

5. What kind of variation is described by $y = 11.1x^{-2}$?

6. Refer to Example 2. When two electrically-charged particles are 0.4 m apart, the force between them is 12 N. What will the force be when they are 0.2 m apart? **48 N**

7. In a chemistry experiment, the data in the table below were collected on the pressure and volume of a sample of gas. According to Boyle's Law, the pressure varies inversely as the volume.

V (mL)	200	220	240	260	280	300	320
P (kPa)	142.5	131.2	119.6	112.9	101.7	103.2	95.4

   a. Use the data point (240, 119.6) to compute the constant of proportionality.
   b. Write a formula for P in terms of V using your value from Part a.
   c. Graph the data and the formula you found in Part b on the same set of axes.
   d. Compute the sum of squared residuals for this model.

4a. $y = \frac{240}{x}$

4b.
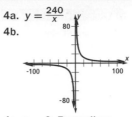

4c. $y = 0$; Regardless of the number of people, everyone will get some portion of hot dog. The horizontal asymptote means that as the number of people increase, the portion gets closer to 0.

5. an inverse-square variation

7a. $k = 28{,}704$ kPa • mL

7b. $P = \frac{28{,}704}{V}$

7c.
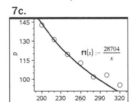

$f1(x) := \frac{28704}{x}$

7d. about 97.52

Accommodating the Learner ⬇

The unit of force in the International System of Units (SI) is the newton, N, which is defined as a kilogram-meter per second squared (kg-m/s²). Be sure that students do not think that N is a variable in Example 2.

3 Assignment

Recommended Assignment

- Questions 1–7
- Questions 8–15
- Questions 16 and 17 (extra credit)
- Reading Lesson 2-8
- Covering the Ideas 2-8 (Questions 1–7)

Notes on the Questions

Question 7 Here we know that an inverse-variation function is the appropriate model, so errors will tend to be measurement errors or errors in the purity of the experiment (for example, a gas leak). This is the only data-centered question for this lesson in this set, so it should be discussed in detail.

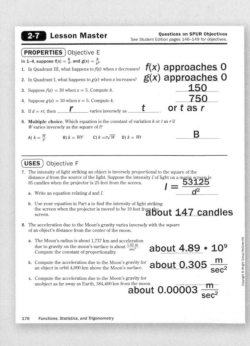

2-7

Notes on the Questions

Questions 10–14 These questions represent a good review of many of the important ideas of the chapter.

Question 11 Students may be confused by the negative value given for a distance in the table. In this situation, the wrecking ball's distance from the building can be considered negative after it breaks through the wall. Drawing a diagram may help clarify this for students.

Question 14 The equation of a line of best fit can be affected by (1) the level of accuracy of the data input and (2) the level of accuracy to which the slope is reported. To illustrate (1), you might first input the data using the year as the independent variable and record the line of best fit and the prediction for Parts b and d. Having done that, input the data defining x as the number of years since 1900, in effect applying a horizontal translation of the graph by 1900 units, and again record the line of best fit and the prediction for Parts b and d. Notice that the slope remains the same but the y-intercept changes. In the latter case, only two digits are needed for the years, and this line of best fit will be more accurate than the first. Also, defining the independent variable as years since 1900 will translate the data closer to the axes and the line of best fit will have a much more workable y-intercept. Regarding (2), if the slope of the line of best fit is calculated to too few decimal places, any prediction is likely to be poor. The level of accuracy of the values of m and b affects all statistics that depend on those values. In general, it is better not to round until the end of all computations.

Additional Answers

10a.

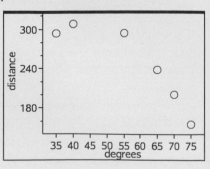

APPLYING THE MATHEMATICS

8. **True or False** The time it takes you to walk a certain distance is inversely proportional to your average speed. **true**

9. The acceleration of a falling object due to Earth's gravity varies inversely as the square of the object's distance from the center of Earth.
   a. Earth's radius at sea level is about 6378 km and the acceleration due to gravity on Earth's surface is about $9.8 \frac{m}{s^2}$. Compute the constant of proportionality.
   b. Compute the acceleration due to Earth's gravity for an object in orbit 10,000 km above Earth's surface.
   c. Compute the acceleration due to Earth's gravity for an object as far away as the Moon, 384,400 km from Earth's center.

REVIEW

10. Data records show the distance a ball traveled when hit at various angles at a constant bat velocity of 100 mph. **(Lesson 2-6)**

Angle (degrees)	35	40	55	65	70	75
Distance (reached feet)	294	308	294	239	201	156

   a. Construct a scatterplot for these data.
   b. Find a quadratic model for these data.

11. A wrecking ball swings to knock down a building. The following data were collected giving the height of the ball during its swing at various distances from the building. **(Lesson 2-6)**

Distance (feet)	100	75	50	25	0	-25
Height reached (feet)	601	536	499	501	510	554

   a. Find a quadratic regression model for these data.
   b. Determine the sum of squared residuals for your model.

12. Consider the function $r: t \to 5(0.83)^t$. **(Lesson 2-5)**
   a. Give the domain of r. $\{t | t \in \mathbb{R}\}$
   b. Give the range of r. $\{r | r > 0\}$
   c. State equations for any asymptotes of the graph of r. $y = 0$

13. Henry looked at the census data for Iowa City, Iowa, for the years 1960, 1970, 1980, 1990 and 2000 and used it to create a linear model of population growth. You do not need to have the data to answer these questions. **(Lesson 2-4)**
   a. Henry used his model to predict the population of Iowa City in 1984. Was his prediction a result of interpolation or extrapolation?
   b. Henry also used his model to predict the population of Iowa City in 2016. Would you expect his prediction for 1984 or his prediction for 2016 to have a larger error? Explain your answer.

9a. about 3.987 • $10^8 \frac{m^3}{s^2}$

9b. about $1.49 \frac{m}{s^2}$

9c. about $0.00270 \frac{m}{s^2}$

10a. See margin.

10b. $y = -0.17x^2 + 15x - 28$

11a. $y = 0.021x^2 - 1.2x + 511$

11b. sum of squared residuals ≈ 78.2969

13a. interpolation

13b. The 2016 prediction would probably have a larger error since it is a result of extrapolation.

14. The table at the right shows the winning jumps in the men's long jump event at the Olympic games. **(Lesson 2-3) See margin.**

   a. Make a scatterplot of these data.

   b. Find the line of best fit predicting the winning jump for a given year.

   c. What does the slope of the line tell you about the average rate of change in the length of the winning long jump from 1896 to 2004?

   d. Use the line of best fit to predict the winning jump for the Beijing Olympics in 2008.

   e. What is residual for in the prediction? (The actual jump by Irving Jahir Saladino Aranda was 8.34 m.)

   f. Which data points seem to be outliers here? Give a plausible explanation for why those outliers might have occurred.

Dwight Phillips (right) with John Moffitt, silver medalist

Year	Gold Medalist	Jump
1896	Ellery Clark, United States	6.34 m
1900	Alvin Kraenzlein, United States	7.19 m
1904	Myer Prinstein, United States	7.34 m
1908	Francis Irons, United States	7.48 m
1912	Albert Gutterson, United States	7.60 m
1920	William Pettersson, Sweden	7.15 m
1924	DeHart Hubbard, United States	7.45 m
1928	Edward B. Hamm, United States	7.74 m
1932	Edward Gordon, United States	7.64 m
1936	Jesse Owens, United States	8.06 m
1948	Willie Steele, United States	7.82 m
1952	Jerome Biffle, United States	7.57 m
1956	Gregory Bell, United States	7.83 m
1960	Ralph Boston, United States	8.12 m
1964	Lynn Davies, Great Britain	8.07 m
1968	Robert Beamon, United States	8.90 m
1972	Randy Williams, United States	8.24 m
1976	Arnie Robinson, United States	8.35 m
1980	Lutz Dombrowski, East Germany	8.54 m
1984	Carl Lewis, United States	8.54 m
1988	Carl Lewis, United States	8.72 m
1992	Carl Lewis, United States	8.67 m
1996	Carl Lewis, United States	8.50 m
2000	Ivan Pedroso, Cuba	8.55 m
2004	Dwight Phillips, United States	8.59 m

Source: Athletics Weekly 2008

15. a. Which is generally least affected by outliers in the data set, the mean or median? **median**

   b. If a data set is skewed with a tail to the left, then which is larger: the mean or median? **(Lessons 1-3, 1-2) median**

EXPLORATION

16. According to the mathematics in the lesson, it is never possible to entirely escape Earth's gravity: since gravitational force varies inversely as the square of the distance, no matter how large the distance gets, the force of gravity from Earth never actually equals zero. Yet astronomical missions such as the Voyager continue to travel away from Earth, without burning rockets continually. Research the concept of escape velocity and explain why such missions are possible. **See margin.**

17. In Question 7, you used a data point to determine an inverse-variation model for the data. Experiment with different data points to see if you can find a model with a lower sum of squared residuals. **See margin.**

QY ANSWERS

1. no;

N	12	24	36	48
W	$\frac{1}{2}$	$\frac{1}{4}$	$\frac{1}{6}$	$\frac{1}{8}$

2. $g(x)$ is closer to zero than $f(x)$ for $x = 10$, 100, and 1000

Inverse Variation Models **131**

4 Wrap-Up

Ongoing Assessment

Have students work in pairs to come up with five real-world situations involving inverse variation that are not mentioned in this lesson. Encourage students to share their ideas with the class. **Answers vary. Check students' work.**

Project Update

Project 4, *Light Intensity,* on page 141 relates to the content of this lesson.

Additional Answers

14a.

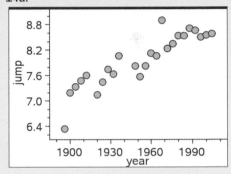

14b. $y = 0.0163x - 23.9$

14c. It changes by 0.0163 meters every year.

14d. about 8.83 m

14e. −0.49 m

14f. Answers vary. Sample: The 1968 point appears to be an outlier. While there is the general trend of higher jumps every Olympics, some athletes excel beyond this trend.

16. Answers vary. Sample: Escape velocity is the speed where the kinetic energy of an object (the energy associated with its motion) is equal to its gravitational potential energy, of the form $U = -\frac{Gm_1 m_2}{r}$, from a point an infinite distance away. Additionally, while an object never leaves Earth's gravitational field, it enters that of other astronomical bodies.

17. The middle point (260, 112.9) gives a sum of squared residuals of about 82.5. The inverse variation model in this case is $\frac{29354}{x}$.

Lesson 2-8

GOAL

Introduce the notion of *residual plots* to test for the suitability of a model.

SPUR Objectives

G Evaluate which type of model is more appropriate for data.

I Use scatterplots and residual plots to draw conclusions about models for data.

Materials/Resources

· Lesson Master 2-8A
· Resource Masters 44 and 45

HOMEWORK • Option 1 • Option 2

• Questions 1–7
• • Questions 8–14
• • Question 15 (extra credit)
• • Self-Test

Local Standards

---

1 Warm-Up

In 2005, the top 10 breeds of dog in the U.S., as measured by American Kennel Club registrations, were as follows:

1.	Labrador Retriever	137,867
2.	Golden Retriever	48,509
3.	Yorkshire Terrier	47,238
4.	German Shepherd Dog	45,014
5.	Beagle	42,592
6.	Dachshund	38,566
7.	Boxer	37,268
8.	Poodle	31,638
9.	Shih Tzu	28,087
10.	Miniature Schnauzer	24,144

Source: American Kennel Club, New York, NY, as reported in *The World Almanac and Book of Facts 2007*, p. 292.

a. Do a linear regression on the number of registrations as a function of the rank.

Lesson 2-8 Choosing a Good Model

Vocabulary

residual plot

▶ **BIG IDEA** The residual plot can help you choose a model for a given data set.

You have seen how to fit linear, exponential, quadratic, and inverse variation models to data. One aspect of modeling, however, is worthy of further discussion: *How do you know you have found a good model?* If two models appear to fit the data equally well, it is usually wise to pick the simpler of the two, but how can you tell how well data fit a model? One measure of how well a model fits the data is the correlation coefficient, but this applies only to linear models.

Another method to determine how well a model fits data is to analyze the residuals. When you evaluate a model at the x-value for a particular data point, you are likely to get a predicted y-value that is different from the observed y-value. Recall that the residual is the difference.

residual = error = observed y-value − predicted y-value

Mental Math

Name the figure that is the graph of the equation.

a. $3xy = 4$ **hyperbola**

b. $3x + y = 4$ **line**

c. $3x^2 + y = 4$ **parabola**

d. $y = 3 \cdot 4^x$ **exponential curve**

Residual Plots

The graph at the left below shows a scatterplot and linear regression model for a data set. The graph at the right below shows the *residual plot* for that model. The point (9, 5.22) marked on the scatterplot has its corresponding point marked on the residual plot, (9, 0.96). This means that the data point $x = 9$ has an observed value of 5.22 and a residual value of 0.96 under the linear regression model.

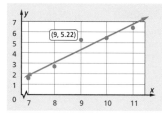 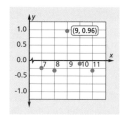

STOP QY

▶ **QY**

What is the predicted value for $x = 9$?

Background

Often in this chapter, students are asked to critique the use of a model. What assumptions or simplifications are needed for the model? Should all the data points be used, or are some outliers? Can the model be used to predict events, through interpolation or extrapolation, or is it best treated as a good description of observed data? These questions are important facets of intelligent use of mathematical models.

In comparing various models, this lesson provides the opportunity to review the ideas of linear, exponential, quadratic, inverse-variation and inverse-square function models and serves as a summary for the chapter as a whole. This lesson should be done through its activities.

A **residual plot** pairs each x-value from the data set with its residual. If the residuals are clustered around the x-axis, as shown in the leftmost diagram below, the model is likely to be a good fit for the data. If, however, the residuals have a different pattern, then a better model can probably be found. The second and third graphs below show patterns of residuals indicating that both models need improvement.

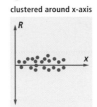

Residual Pattern:	clustered around x-axis	same side of axis at ends	shaped like funnel
Residual Plot:	good model	weak model	weak model

Analyzing Residuals for a Linear Model

> **Activity 1**   See margin.

The table at the right shows the length L of each day (sunrise to sunset) computed at a city in the Northern Hemisphere every 10 days for 100 days beginning on August 31st. D is the number of days after this date.

Step 1 Use a statistics utility to create the scatterplot of the data.

Step 2 Find the regression line and correlation coefficient for these data. What does the correlation coefficient indicate about a linear model for these data?

Step 3 Reproduce the spreadsheet below. Then use your calculated regression line to fill in both the predicted day lengths and the associated residuals. A few entries have already been filled in.

◇	A	B	C	D
1	Days (D)	Computed Day Length (L)	Predicted Day Length (p)	Residual (R = L – p)
2	0	793	786.05	6.95
3	10	766	761.53	4.47
4	20	739		
5	30	711		-1.49
6	40	684		
7	50	657		
8	60	631		
9	70	607		
10	80	586		
11	90	568		
12	100	556		

(continued on next page)

D (days)	L (minutes)
0	793
10	766
20	739
30	711
40	684
50	657
60	631
70	607
80	586
90	568
100	556

Sunset on Lake Franklin in the Chequamegon-Nicolet Forest in Northern Wisconsin

In Lesson 2-3, students encountered the correlation coefficient as a measure of the closeness of fit of the line of best fit to data. But the correlation coefficient does not indicate whether another model might be better. By looking for patterns in the residuals, that is, the errors made by models, we can both compare models with each other and fine tune them. There are other measures of how well a model fits data, but they are not discussed in this course.

If your available technology does not automatically calculate residuals, it is easy to calculate them using a spreadsheet program. Enter the data in two columns as you would into a calculator. Then, for a third column, calculate the values predicted by the particular regression equation. Finally, for a fourth column, subtract the values in the third column from those in the first column. The values in the fourth column give you the residuals you need.

(continued on next page)

$y = -7707.42x + 90,483.13$

b. What does this model predict for the number of registrations for the German Shepherd? **59,653 registered German Shepherds**

c. What does this model predict for the number of registrations for the 25th ranked dog, the Siberian Huskie? **–102,202; (The actual number is 9452.)**

d. Examine the residuals for your model. Describe what you find. **The residuals resemble a quadratic. They start positive, become negative in the middle, and then become positive again. They are all quite large in absolute value.**

e. Based on Parts b, c, and d, does your model in Part a seem appropriate? **The linear model is a poor model.**

2 ▶ Teaching

Notes on the Lesson

Be sure to point out that the residual is a signed value. See Accommodating the Learner (Down) on page 135 for further discussion.

Additional Answers

Activity 1

Step 1

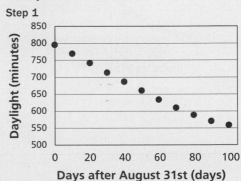

Step 2

$y = 786.045 - 2.452x$; $r = -0.996$; $|r|$ is very close to 1, therefore a linear model seems like a good fit for the data. A negative r indicates that L decreases as D increases.

Steps 3–5

See the Additional Answers section at the back of the book.

2-8

Notes on the Lesson

Analyzing residuals from an exponential model The second set of data in the lesson is the familiar census data of the United States. Here the exponential model is close but wanders from the data.

Residuals from a quadratic model
Examination of the residuals shows a pattern that suggests that from 1790 to 1860, or perhaps to 1880, the single exponential model is fine, but from that time on there is another long-term trend. Surprisingly, a quadratic model, which might be used just to work with the period from 1860 to 2000, works quite well for the entire time period. Its disadvantage is that there is no theory to suggest that population should grow quadratically.

Additional Answers

Activity 2

Step 1

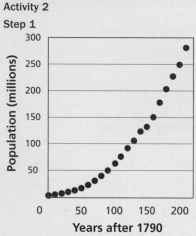

Years after 1790

Step 2

$$y = (6.0332)1.02043^x$$

Steps 3–5

See the Additional Answers section at the back of the book.

Step 4 Plot the residual set of points (D, R) on the same axes as the scatterplot in Step 1.

Step 5 Based on the residual plot, what do you conclude about a linear model for these data?

Activity 1 tested the theory that the number of minutes of daylight decreases in a linear fashion. Even though the correlation coefficient in Step 2 indicates that a line is a good model, the residuals show that there is a better model. Therefore, the researcher must seek another theory or more realistic model to explain the manner in which daylight decreases.

One way to seek a better model is to gather more data. In Activity 1, the hours of sunlight were provided for about 3 months of the year. This is not the full domain of the situation. Data for two or more years would show a periodic wavy pattern that requires functions you will study in later chapters of these book.

Analyzing Residuals for Other Models
Exponential Model

Activity 2 See margin.

Step 1 Use a statistics utility to create a scatterplot of the U.S. Census data shown at the right. Use years after 1790 as the independent variable.

Step 2 Compute the exponential regression model for these data.

Step 3 Using the exponential regression model, compute the predicted populations and residuals. Organize the data in a spreadsheet like the one shown below.

Step 4 Plot the set of residual points (Y, R).

Step 5 Based on the residual plot, why is the exponential model not a good fit for these data?

Year	Population (millions)	Year	Population (millions)
1790	4	1900	76
1800	5	1910	92
1810	7	1920	106
1820	10	1930	123
1830	13	1940	132
1840	17	1950	151
1850	23	1960	179
1860	31	1970	203
1870	40	1980	227
1880	50	1990	249
1890	63	2000	281

Source: U.S. Census Bureau

◇	A	B	C	D	E
1	Year	Year − 1790 = (Y)	Population (m)	Predicted Population (p)	Residual (R = m − p)
2	1790	0	4	6.03	-2.03
3	1800	10	5	7.39	-2.39
4	1810	20	7	9.04	-2.04

Activity 2 suggests that although exponential regression models are useful for modeling population growth, they frequently break down over time. Limited resources and other factors prohibit populations from growing indefinitely.

134   Functions and Models

Activity 1 In theory, the data are part of a sine wave. So, if the particular 11 points lie on a line, it must be either that they are on a part of the wave that is approximately linear, or they are so close together on the sine wave that the curve of the wave does not present itself, or they are so far apart on the sine wave that they happen to hit the wave when it repeats (as would be the case if the length L were calculated on the same day each year for 10 years). In this case, it happens that a linear model is not a bad fit because from August 31 to December 9 (100 days later), the length of a day decreases consistently. We would never know that the linear model was a bad fit without either theory or a look at the residual plot. The residual plot has enough of a pattern to let us know that some other function might work.

Activity 2 Here we have the converse situation from Example 1. The usual model for population growth is exponential, but it does not fit well!

A graph of the quadratic regression model of the U.S. population data, $y = 0.007x^2 - 0.1138x + 6.1097$, is shown at the left below. It turns out that this quadratic model is a much better fit than the exponential model. The residuals are relatively small and they cluster in a horizontal band centered around the x-axis. However, the quadratic model is an impressionistic model of population growth because there is no theory that supports a quadratic relationship between year and population.

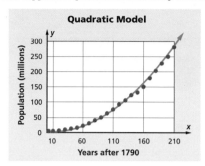

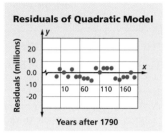

As mentioned in earlier lessons, extrapolation is risky business. This is particularly true when there is no theory to support the model. The quadratic model is a very good model for the population of the U.S. from 1790 to 2000, but there is no assurance that the model will make accurate predictions for years outside the data set. An even better model than the quadratic model might be a piecewise function, with each piece chosen to best fit a portion of the domain.

Careful Modeling

You should consider at least five things when building a model from data. Assuming that your data are a representative sample of the population of interest, you should:

1. Build a model from theory, if possible. Some real-world situations suggest certain models.

2. Graph the data on a scatterplot. Draw the model on the same graph. A good model should follow any pattern or trend in the data.

Choosing a Good Model   **135**

2-8

Notes on the Lesson

Sometimes there is no good model The Dow Jones industrial average grew quite steadily during the years 1987–1999. This provides no indication that such growth will continue. The average started going down just before 2000 and plummeted in 2001. It then grew rather consistently until the end of 2007, when it plummeted back to levels from many years before.

3. Graph the residuals. If the residual plot does not fall within a relatively narrow horizontal band centered around the *x*-axis or if there is a pattern to the residuals, you may have to change your theory or look for a better model.

4. Use the correlation coefficient to check whether a linear model is appropriate.

5. In all cases, be aware of the model's ability or limitation for interpolation and extrapolation.

Sometimes There Is No Good Model

Everyone who invests in the stock market wants to buy stocks when their prices are low and sell when their prices are high. The difficulty is that when you buy today because you think the price is low, you have no guarantee that the price tomorrow will be higher. In many cases the price goes down and your investment loses value. In the same way, you might sell a stock today because you think prices are high and likely to go down, only to find out that the prices are even higher tomorrow. No model has been developed that can accurately predict changes in the stock market, but many people make a living by developing models that work for a short time or in special situations.

The graph below shows the Dow Jones industrial average from July, 2001 to March, 2009.

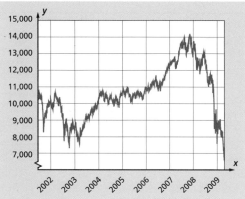

Source: Yahoo! Finance 2008

The graph shows many individual trends, but no overall, consistent trend. There are many fluctuations. Catastrophic events often cause significant changes in the graph.

136   Functions and Models

Additional Answers

3b.

Days (d)	Predicted Day Length (p)	Computed Day Length (L)	Residual
0	792.63	793	0.37
10	763.88	766	2.12
20	736.17	739	2.83
30	709.47	711	1.53
40	683.73	684	0.27
50	658.93	657	-1.93
60	635.03	631	-4.03
70	611.99	607	-4.99
80	589.79	586	-3.79
90	568.40	568	-0.40
100	547.78	556	8.22

One example of this was the destruction of the World Trade Center on September 11, 2001, which initiated a drop in the stock market. (See if you can locate the drop in the Dow-Jones average due to September 11 on the graph.) Even the most sophisticated stock traders with powerful statistical models were caught off guard by this event.

Questions

COVERING THE IDEAS

1. What characterizes a residual plot of a good model?

2. **Multiple Choice** Look at the residual plots below. Which indicates the best model? Explain your answer.

A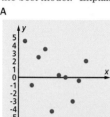

B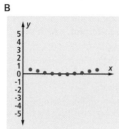

C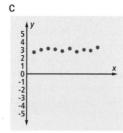

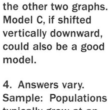

3. a. An exponential regression model for the length L of the Dth day in Activity 1 is $L \approx 792.63(0.996312)^D$. Compute a table of predicted values using this model. **3a–c. See margin.**

   b. Compute a table of residual values using the results from Part a.

   c. Create a plot of the residuals from Part b and explain if the exponential regression model is a good model for this data.

In 4–6, refer to Activity 2.

4. Why is it reasonable to expect that an exponential model is an appropriate theoretical model for the population data?

5. a. Find an exponential regression model for the population data using only the years from 1790 to 1880. $y = (3.99866)1.0292^x$

   b. Make a spreadsheet with year, census population, predicted population, and residual. **See margin.**

   c. Plot the residuals. **See margin.**

   d. Is an exponential model appropriate for the 1790–1880 time period? Explain your decision. **See margin.**

6. a. Use the quadratic regression equation to predict the 1900 population to the nearest million. **74 million**

   b. Use the value in Part a to calculate the residual for the 1900 population. **2 million**

7. Why do you think no good model has been found for predicting the future prices of stocks? **Answers vary. Sample: The prices of stocks fluctuate based on many factors that cannot be accurately forecasted or predicted.**

Choosing a Good Model **137**

1. The residuals are clustered around the *x*-axis.

2. B; The residuals in B are closer to 0 than the other two graphs. Model C, if shifted vertically downward, could also be a good model.

4. Answers vary. Sample: Populations typically grow at an exponential rate for a certain amount of time. However, this may change due to environmental conditions, resources, and other factors.

2-8

3 Assignment

Recommended Assignment

- Questions 1–7
- • Questions 8–14
- • Question 15 (extra credit)
- • Self-Test

Notes on the Questions

We suggest going through Questions 1–7 in order.

Additional Answers

5b. See the Additional Answers section at the back of the book.

5c.

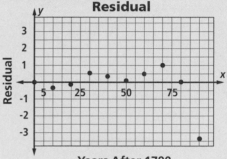

5d. It seems to be appropriate for the time period because the residuals are scattered closely about the *x*-axis. However, the data for 1880 diverges unexpectedly, so this model probably should not be used to extrapolate into the future.

Additional Answers

3a.

Days (*d*)	Predicted Day Length (*p*)
0	792.63
10	763.88
20	736.17
30	709.47
40	683.73
50	658.93
60	635.03
70	611.99
80	589.79
90	568.40
100	547.78

3c.

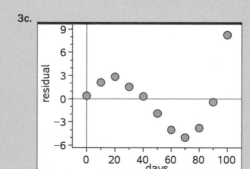

The exponential model is not a good fit for this data because there is a distinct pattern in the residual plot.

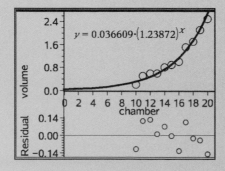

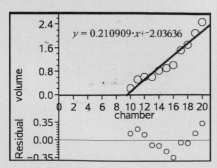

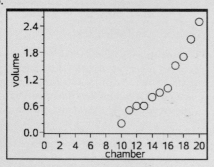

2-8

Notes on the Questions

Question 8 The inside of the shell of the chambered nautilus is certainly one of the most beautiful examples of a mathematical spiral found in nature. The spiral can be modeled closely by the graph of the powers of a complex number in the complex plane.

Question 10 The lack of a pattern does not mean that there are no patterns to unemployment. It just means that the year is not a good predictor. But some other variable more tied to economics, such as the profits of companies in the preceding year, might be a good predictor.

Additional Answers

8a. Answers vary. Sample: Looking at the picture, it would seem an exponential model might be the appropriate theoretical model because intuitively the rate of change of volume increase will grow rapidly as chambers increase.

8b.

Answers vary. Sample: From the scatterplot, it appears that an exponential growth function would fit the data well.

8c. Linear:

$y = 0.210909x - 2.03636$

$r = 0.96$; The linear model is quite strong although there is a pattern in the residuals.

APPLYING THE MATHEMATICS

8. The chambered nautilus is a cephalopod mollusk, a relative of octopuses and squids. It creates a spiral shell that has inspired mathematicians and poets for centuries. As it grows, the animal partitions off increasingly larger cells to inhabit. The table below gives the volume (in cubic centimeters) of chambers 10 through 20 of a nautilus. **See margin.**

Chamber number	10	11	12	13	14	15	16	17	18	19	20
Volume (cm³)	0.2	0.5	0.6	0.6	0.8	0.9	1	1.5	1.7	2.1	2.5

Source: Paleobiology

a. Is a linear or exponential function the more appropriate theoretical model for the data? Give a reason for your answer.

b. Make a scatterplot of the data, using chamber number as the independent variable. From the scatterplot, which model seems more appropriate?

c. Determine whether the linear or exponential regression model better fits the data using residual plots as well as the value of the linear model's correlation coefficient.

d. Write a sentence indicating which model you would choose, and why.

9. The table at the right shows how many millions of miles motor vehicles drove in the U.S. in certain years. **See margin.**

a. Is any theoretical model appropriate? If so, what kind and why?

b. Make a scatterplot of the data. What kind of model seems appropriate?

c. Sketch the residual plots for the linear, exponential, and quadratic regression models.

d. Write a sentence indicating which model you would choose and why.

Year	Miles (millions)
1920	47,600
1930	206,320
1940	302,188
1950	458,246
1960	718,762
1970	1,109,724
1980	1,527,295
1990	2,144,362
2000	2,746,925

Source: Historical Statistical Abstract

10. Seasonally-adjusted U.S. unemployment figures for June of each year are given in the table below. **See margin.**

Year	1997	1998	1999	2000	2001	2002	2003	2004	2005	2006	2007	2008
Unemployed (thousands)	6799	6212	5951	5651	6484	8393	9266	8280	7536	7017	6997	8499

Source: Bureau of Labor Statistics

a. Make a scatterplot of the data, plotting the number of years after 1997 as the independent variable.

b. Which, if any, of a linear, exponential, or quadratic function seems to model these data? Justify your answer.

Additional Answers

8c. (continued)

Exponential:

$y = 0.036609(1.23872)^x$

From the residual plot, most of the points are closer to zero than the linear model's residual plot. The residual plots alone indicate that the exponential model is the better fit.

8d. Answers vary. Sample: The theoretical model and the scatterplot eyeballing of the data points both suggest an exponential model. Although the correlation coefficient and residual plot were relatively strong fits for the linear model, the exponential model still had a residual plot closer to zero. It seems apparent that the exponential model is the

REVIEW

11. Recall that the force between electrical fields is inversely proportional to the square of the distance between them. When two electrically charged particles are 0.8 m apart, the force between them is 5 N. What will the force between them be when they are 0.1 m apart? **(Lesson 2-7)** **320 N**

12. **Multiple Choice** If grades g in school vary inversely as the number t of hours spent watching TV every day, then which of the following describes the relationship between g and t? **(Lesson 2-7)** **B**

    A $g = kt^2$ B $g = \frac{k}{t}$

    C $g^2 = \frac{k}{t}$ D $g = \frac{k}{t^2}$

13. The population of Florida from 1950 to 2000 is given in the table below. **(Lesson 2-6)**

Year	1950	1960	1970	1980	1990	2000
Population (thousands)	2,771	4,952	6,791	9,747	12,938	15,982

Source: Historical Statistical Abstract

  a. Make a scatterplot of the data, plotting number of years after 1950 as the independent variable.

  b. Find a quadratic regression model for the data.

  c. Use your model to predict the population of Florida in 2015.

14. A 6″ diameter frozen personal cheese pizza lists its total calories as 590. About how many calories are in a single 2-square-inch bite of pizza? **(Previous Course)** **about 41.73 calories**

EXPLORATION

15. Find population data over a number of years for your city or state. Find the linear, quadratic, or exponential model that best fits the data. Use your model to predict the population of your city or state in the year 2050. Do you believe this a reasonable prediction? Explain your response.

Answers vary. Sample: The table shows the population of the city of Chicago (excluding metropolitan suburbs) for the years 1970 to 2000. We might use an exponential model to approximate this data set, for example: $y = 3{,}253{,}200(0.9947^x)$ where x is years after 1970. According to this model, in 2050 the central city of Chicago will have a population of 2.131 million people. This is probably not a reasonable prediction. Though Chicago's population, like that of many other urban metropolitan areas, has shifted towards the suburbs, its population will likely stabilize at a higher population than the model predicts. Demographic changes are quite dynamic, and models must be updated continually in order to forecast population shifts.

13a.

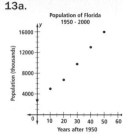

Population of Florida
1950 - 2000

13b. $y = 1.736x^2 + 178.813x + 2801.61$

13c. **21,760 thousand people**

Tampa, Florida

Year	Population
1970	3,366,957
1980	3,005,072
1990	2,783,726
2000	2,896,016

QY ANSWER

4.26

Choosing a Good Model   **139**

Notes on the Questions

Question 14 A quadratic model closely fits the relationship between the diameter of a pizza and the number of total calories in it.

4 Wrap-Up

Ongoing Assessment

Have each student present his or her work for Question 8, 9, or 10, including the graphs of the residuals. Ask the student to explain what the graphs suggest about the appropriateness of each model. **Students show understanding of how to interpret a scatterplot of residuals.**

Project Update

Project 3, *Five Years From Now*, on page 141 relates to the content of this lesson.

Additional Answers

10a.

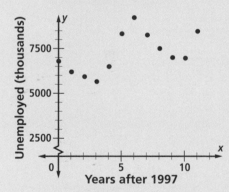

U.S. Unemployment
June 1997 - June 2008

10b. Answers vary. Sample: There appears to be no simple theory between time and the unemployment rate. None of the three standard models fit the scatterplot well. The residual plots for all of the models are far from the x-axis and lie in the same pattern of the data itself, indicating that these types of models are not applicable to the data.

Additional Answers

model to choose.

9a. Answers vary. Sample: The amount of driving and motor vehicle ownership generally depends on the population. So theoretically an exponential model might be a good fit. However, because there seems to be no immediate relationship behind time and miles driven in motor vehicles, this would most likely be considered impressionistic and therefore have no theoretical basis.

9b–d. See the Additional Answers section at the back of the book.

Chapter

2

The projects relate to the content of the lessons of this chapter as follows:

Project	Lesson(s)
1	2-3
2	2-3
3	2-3, 2-5, 2-8
4	2-7

1 Temperature vs. Latitude

Data for cities other than those listed here can be found on the Internet or in almanacs. Students might wish to examine whether cities in the southern hemisphere behave differently from cities at the corresponding distance from the equator in the northern hemisphere.

1 Temperature vs. Latitude

At the right are the latitude (in degrees North) and the average daily maximum temperature in October for various cities in North America.

a. Use a statistics utility to draw a scatterplot with latitude on the *x*-axis and average daily maximum temperature on the *y*-axis.

b. Find a linear regression model for these data. Interpret the sign and magnitude of the slope of the regression line.

c. Over what domain do you expect the regression line to fit the data well?

d. Predict the average daily October maximum temperature for these cities:

　　Detroit, MI　　42°22′ N
　　Tampa, FL　　27°49′ N

e. The actual average daily high temperature in October is 62°F for Detroit and 84°F for Tampa. Find the residual for each of your predicted values in Part d.

f. Which cities appear to be outliers? Give plausible reasons why these cities might have a different relation between latitude and temperature than the others.

g. Find the latitude and average daily maximum temperatures in cities in other parts of the world, e.g., in Africa, Asia, or Europe. Explain any big differences between the regression lines you find for these areas and the one found in Part b.

Place	Latitude	Temperature (°F)
Caribou, ME	46.87	51
Chicago, IL	41.98	64
Denver, CO	39.77	68
Great Falls, MT	47.48	58
Juneau, AK	58.3	47
Kansas City, MO	39.32	69
Mexico City, Mexico	19.42	72
New Orleans, LA	29.98	80
Ottawa, Canada	45.43	55
Salt Lake City, UT	40.78	65
San Francisco, CA	37.62	70
Seattle, WA	47.45	60
Washington, DC	38.85	68

Source: National Climatic Data Center

Project Rubric

Advanced	Student correctly provides all of the details asked for in the project as well as additional correct independent conclusions.
Proficient	Student correctly provides all of the details asked for in the project.
Partially proficient	Student correctly provides some of the details asked for in the project or provides all details with some inaccuracies.
Not proficient	Student correctly provides few of the details asked for in the project or provides all details with many inaccuracies.
No attempt	Student makes little or no attempt to complete the project.

2 Class Survey Data Revisited

Use the class database constructed as a project at the end of Chapter 1. Some people claim that many high school students spend too much time watching TV or surfing the Internet.

a. Make a scatterplot of time spent watching TV versus time spent doing homework. Make a second scatterplot of time spent surfing the Internet versus time spent doing homework. Find the lines of best fit for each scatterplot.

b. Are there any outliers? Remove these data from the set and obtain an equation for a new regression line.

c. From the data, do you think students generally spend too much time watching TV or surfing the Internet? Why or why not?

3 Five Years From Now

The U.S. Bureau of Labor Statistics computes the Consumer Price Index "CPI" as a gauge of inflation.

a. Visit the BLS website and find data for the CPI in January for each year since 1982.

b. Plot the data on a scatterplot. Use a linear model to find an equation for the line of best fit for the data.

c. Find an exponential regression model for the same data.

d. Which model better fits the data?

e. Pick a new car you would like to own and find out how much it costs. Use the model you selected to calculate the cost of the car five years from now.

4 Light Intensity

The amount of energy given off by a flashlight is constant. If you aim a flashlight at a wall and then step back, the area illuminated by the flashlight will get larger. Since the intensity of the light is measured by the amount of light energy that strikes a given area, the intensity decreases as you step back. In this project, assume that your flashlight is the standard of measure, so its energy coefficient is 1.

a. Enter a dark room and place the flashlight 1 foot from a wall. Measure the diameter of the region that is illuminated by the light and calculate the area of illumination. Repeat the process, moving the flashlight back at one-foot intervals until you have gathered at least ten data points.

b. Make a scatterplot of your distance and illumination data. Does the scatterplot suggest how distance from the wall is related to the area of illumination?

c. Use a statistics utility to find the equation for a line of best fit for your data. Plot this regression line on your scatterplot. How well does the regression line seem to model the data? Does this mathematical model support the theory in Part b? If not, try another model to see if you can improve the fit using the sum of squared residuals.

2 Class Survey Data Revisited

In Part b there is a reference to discarding outliers. Some people feel that outliers should not be discarded. Obviously, in some contexts, discarding outliers is warranted, for instance, if data are improperly fed into a computer. In other contexts, one would not wish to discard outliers and would treat them simply as random events. Good statistical practice dictates that a person indicate any reasons for discarding outliers.

Answers to Part c should not be approached from an idealistic standpoint but should be an analysis of the results from the regressions. Some students may argue that such a judgment cannot be made without additional data on academic performance to judge the impact of time spent on homework.

Notes

_____

_____

_____

_____

_____

_____

_____

_____

_____

_____

_____

_____

_____

_____

_____

_____

_____

_____

Chapter 2

Summary and Vocabulary

Summary and Vocabulary

The Summary gives an overview of the entire chapter and provides an opportunity for students to consider the material as a whole. Thus, the Summary can be used to help students relate and unify the concepts presented in the chapter.

Vocabulary words and symbols are listed by lesson to provide a checklist of concepts that students must know. Emphasize to students that they should read the vocabulary list carefully before starting the Self-Test on pages 144–145. If students do not understand the meaning of a vocabulary word, they should refer back to the indicated lesson.

Theorems and Properties covered in the chapter are listed below the Summary with page references included to lead students back to the location in the chapter where the theorem or property is stated.

○ Any set of ordered pairs is a relation. **Functions** are those relations in which no two ordered pairs have the same first component. A function can also be viewed as a correspondence between two sets A and B, which relates each element of A (the function's **domain**) to exactly one element of B. Functions can be defined by giving a rule for the correspondence, a graph, a table, or a description in words, and by indicating the domain of the function.

○ In this chapter, sets of data are modeled by linear, quadratic, and exponential functions. Scatterplots can be used to represent the data and to determine the type of relationship and the feasibility of a particular model. Some models are theory-based, as when a known law of physics is behind the mathematics. Other models are impressionistic in that there is no known theory to explain why the model should fit. Even if the model looks like a good fit, a plot of residuals may reveal that the model needs improvement.

○ Linear functions model constant increase or constant decrease. A linear model can be approximated by drawing a line close to all the data points. The **line of best fit** minimizes the sum of the squared residuals between observed and predicted values, and can be found with a statistics utility.

○ The strength of a linear relation between two variables is measured by the **correlation coefficient**, r. The sign of the correlation coefficient indicates the direction of the relation between the variables, and its magnitude indicates the strength of the linearity. Although perfect correlations ($r = \pm 1$) are rare, an r with an absolute value close to 1 indicates a strong linear relation. Strong correlations indicate a linear relationship between variables, but correlation does not necessarily imply causation. An r-value close to zero indicates that the variables are not related linearly.

○ **Exponential functions with base b**, which are of the general form $y = ab^x$ with $a > 0$, $b > 0$, and $b \neq 1$ model exponential growth (when $b > 1$) and decay (when $0 < b < 1$). Quadratic models of the form $y = ax^2 + bx + c$ include theory-based models for projectile motion. Most statistics utilities can find exponential and quadratic models of best fit. Many physical situations are modeled by functions of inverse variation with equations of the form $y = \frac{k}{x}$ or by functions of inverse-square variation with equations of the form $y = \frac{k}{x^2}$. The graphs of these functions have vertical and horizontal asymptotes.

Vocabulary

2-1
mathematical model
relation
independent variable
dependent variable
function, ordered pair
  definition
domain of a function
range of a function
function, correspondence
  definition
real function
member of a set, element
  of a set, $\in$
piecewise definition of a
  function
value of a function

2-2
linear function
linear model
interpolation
extrapolation
observed values
predicted values
residual
sum of squared residuals

2-3
method of least squares
line of best fit, least
  squares line, regression
  line
center of mass
correlation coefficient
perfect correlation
strong correlation
weak correlation

○ Choosing a good model requires both an analysis of the data set and an understanding of how the data were obtained. **Residuals**, the differences between the observed values and the values predicted by the model, can be used to judge the quality of a model. If the residuals are large or if there is a pattern to the residuals, the model may be inadequate and another should be sought. Piecewise functions may provide a composite model that fits better than any function based on a single rule.

○ Function models can produce very reasonable predictions for intervals over which the original data were observed. However, one should use caution when making predictions outside the domain of observed values. Interpolation is safer than extrapolation.

Vocabulary

2-4
growth factor
exponential function with base b
exponential growth function
exponential growth curve
exponential decay function
asymptote

2-5
exponential regression
half-life

2-6
quadratic model
quadratic regression

2-7
varies inversely as, is inversely proportional to
constant of variation, constant of proportionality
inverse-square relationship
varies inversely as the square of, is inversely proportional to the square of
power function

2-8
residual plot

Properties and Theorems

Pearson's Formula for Linear Correlation (p. 96)

Self-Test

For the development of mathematical competence, feedback and correction, along with the opportunity for practice, are necessary. The Self-Test provides the opportunity for feedback and correction; the Chapter Review provides additional opportunities for practice. We cannot overemphasize the importance of these end-of-chapter materials. It is at this point that the material gels for many students, allowing them to solidify skills and understanding. In general, student performance should improve after these pages.

Assign the Self-Test as a one-night assignment. Worked-out solutions for all questions are in the Selected Answers section of the student book. Encourage students to take the Self-Test honestly, grade themselves, and then be prepared to discuss the test in class.

Advise students to pay special attention to those Chapter Review questions (pages 146–149) that correspond to the questions they missed on the Self-Test. These are identified in the Self-Test Correlation Chart located in the Selected Answers section at the back of the book.

Additional Answers

1a. $f(2) = -9.8(2)^2 - 5.2(2) + 12.7 = -39.2 - 10.4 + 12.7 = -36.9$

1b. $g(2n) = 5(2n)^2 - 3 = 20n^2 - 3$

2. Any number can go into this function so domain: $\{x | x \in \mathbb{R}\}$; the function is never less than or equal to 1 so range: $\{y | y > 1\}$.

3. x can be any real number except 0 so domain: $\{x | x \neq 0\}$; the function can be any real number except 0 so range: $\{y | y \neq 0\}$.

4a. D and E; the points with greater x-values have smaller y-values.

4b. C and F; C has no pattern to the data points and F is a quadratic relation.

4c. A and D; all of the points are on a line.

5. residual = observed − predicted, so observed = 17,000 + $3{,}424{,}000(1.013)^{15} \approx 4{,}172{,}999$ people.

Take this test as you would take a test in class. You will need a calculator. Then use the Selected Answers section in the back of the book to check your work.

See margin for Self-Test answers.

1. a. Evaluate $f(2)$ to the nearest tenth when $f(x) = -9.8x^2 - 5.2x + 12.7$.
   b. Evaluate $g(2n)$ if $g(x) = 5x^2 - 3$.

2. The line with equation $y = 1$ is a horizontal asymptote to the graph below. Give the domain and range of the graphed function.

3. What are the domain and range of p when $p(x) = -\frac{2}{x}$?

4.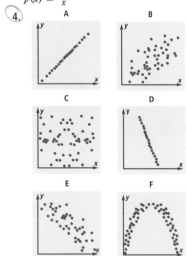

   a. Which scatterplots indicate a negative association between variables?
   b. Which scatterplots indicate a correlation coefficient close to zero?
   c. Which correlation coefficient(s) equal 1?

5. The equation $P = 3{,}424{,}000(1.013)^x$ can be used to model the population P of New Zealand x years after 1993. In 2008, this model produced a residual of 17,000 rounded to the nearest thousand. What was the actual population in 2008?

6. Stephen and Chris fit different lines to a scatterplot by eye. The sum of squared residuals was 34 for Stephen's line and was 576 for Chris's line. Use the sum of squared residuals to explain which of their models is a better fit to the data.

7. Suppose a ball is thrown upward at a velocity of 44 $\frac{ft}{sec}$ from a cliff 200 feet above a dry riverbed. Use the formula $h = -\frac{1}{2}gt^2 + v_0 t + h_0$ where $g = 32 \frac{ft}{sec^2}$.
   a. Write an equation for the height h (in feet above the riverbed) of the ball after t seconds.
   b. At what time will the ball hit the riverbed?

In 8 and 9, suppose that $y = 60$ when $x = 10$. For each situation,
   a. compute the constant of variation.
   b. find y when $x = 3$.

8. when y varies inversely as x

9. when y varies inversely as the square of x

10. Does the function f with $f(x) = 105(1.2)^x$ model exponential decay or exponential growth? How do you know?

11. A movie studio uses the regression equation $y = 2.51x + 471.10$ to predict how much money a movie will earn based on the cost of making the movie. Here, $y =$ world revenues in millions of dollars and $x =$ the movie's budget in millions of dollars. The movie "Regression without a Cause" had a budget of $115 million and earned $524 million. What is the residual?

Additional Answers

6. The larger the sum of the squared residuals, the further the points are from the line. Because Stephen's line has a smaller sum of squared residuals it is a better fit for the data.

7a. Filling in the initial velocity, initial height, and gravitational acceleration we get $h = -16t^2 + 44t + 200$.

7b. Use the Quadratic Formula.
$$\frac{-44 \pm \sqrt{44^2 - 4(-16)(200)}}{2(-16)} \approx 1.375 \pm 3.793 \approx$$
5.168 seconds

8a. The form is $y = \frac{k}{x}$ and $60 = \frac{k}{10}$, so $k = 600$.

8b. Substitute $x = 3$. $y = \frac{600}{3} = 200$

9a. The form is $y = \frac{k}{x^2}$ and $60 = \frac{k}{100}$, so $k = 6000$.

9b. Substitute $x = 3$. $y = \frac{6000}{3^2} = \frac{2000}{3}$

10. The growth factor is greater than 1 (and a is positive) so the function models exponential growth.

11. Use 115 for x and evaluate. $y = 2.51(115) + 471.1 = \$759.75$ million; The residual is observed − predicted = $524 − 759.75 = -\$235.75$ million.

12. Find the growth rate by using the half-life. $\frac{a}{2} = ab^{30}$ so $b \approx 0.0977$. The initial value a is 10 so the equation is $y = 10(0.0977)^x$. When $x = 20$ the function equals ≈ 6.3 g.

12. Cesium-137 has a half life of 30 years. How much of a 10-gram sample will be left after 20 years?

13. The residuals for a linear and inverse-square model are graphed below. What do these graphs tell you about the appropriateness of each model?

Linear Model

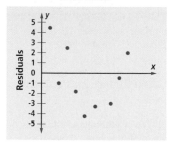

Inverse-Square Model

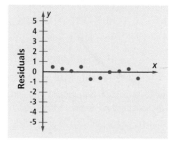

14. The table below shows the height h in feet of a ball above ground level t seconds after being thrown off the top of a building.

t	1	2	3	4	5	6
h	298	302	277	219	128	8

a. Fit a quadratic model to the data.

b. Is this a theory-based model or is it an impressionistic model?

c. From your model, what is the height of the ball 4 seconds after it was thrown?

15. The table below lists the percent of U.S. citizens aged 18–24 who voted in midterm elections from 1974 to 2002.

Year	Percent 18-24 Year-Olds Who Voted
1974	25.4
1978	25.1
1982	26.6
1986	23.9
1990	22.9
1994	22.2
1998	18.5
2002	19.4

Source: Center for Information and Research on Civic Learning and Engagement

a. Using the line of best fit with the number of years after 1974 as the independent variable, what does the slope tell you about voter turnout in midterm elections among 18–24 year olds?

b. Find the correlation coefficient. What does the correlation coefficient tell you about the relationship between the year and voter turnout in midterm elections among 18–24 year olds?

16. Sonia researched the number of fast-food restaurants in her city in several years and recorded the data in the table below.

Years after 2000	Number of Restaurants
1	31
2	36
3	39
4	48
5	53
6	63
7	71

a. Make a scatterplot of the data. Which model appears appropriate for the data?

b. Plot the residuals for the regression equations for various models.

c. Write a sentence or two explaining your choice of best fit model.

16a. Answers vary. Sample: A quadratic model looks appropriate for the data.

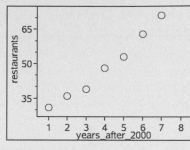

16b. Linear: $y = 6.71429x + 21.8571$ with correlation coefficient of about 0.99

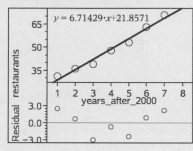

Quadratic: $y = 0.5x^2 + 2.71429x + 27.8571$

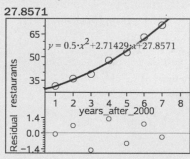

Exponential: $y = 26.7905(1.14995)^x$

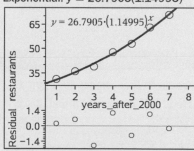

16c. Answers vary. Sample: Neither theory nor an eyeball of the residual plot lead to any particular model. The linear residual plot has an almost parabolic pattern with larger residuals than the quadratic and exponential regressions. Both the quadratic and exponential regressions have very similar residual plots, so either model could be chosen based on the criteria in the chapter.

---

13. By the graphs of the residuals, the linear model seems to be unfit because the residuals are in a pattern and are far from the x-axis. The inverse-square model seems to fit the data very well because the residuals are clustered near the x-axis and don't seem to make a pattern. Therefore, the inverse-square model is more appropriate.

14a. Use a quadratic regression on a calculator with t as the independent variable and h as the dependent variable. $h = -15.786t^2 + 52.5t + 261$

14b. This is a theory-based model because it is based on the theory of gravity.

14c. Substitute 4 for t and evaluate. $h = -15.786(4)^2 + 52.5(4) + 261 \approx 218.4$ feet

15a. To find the line of best fit, use linear regression on a calculator. The slope, –0.265 means that the percent of 18-24 year-olds who vote has decreased by an average of 0.265% per year.

15b. The correlation coefficient, –0.905, indicates that there is a strong negative correlation between the year and the percent of young people who vote.

Chapter Review

The main objectives for the chapter are organized in the Chapter Review under the four types of understanding this book promotes: Skills, Properties, Uses, and Representations.

Whereas end-of-chapter material may be considered optional in some texts, in UCSMP *Functions, Statistics, and Trigonometry* we have selected these objectives and questions with the expectation that they will be covered. Students should be able to answer these questions with about 85% accuracy after studying the chapter.

You may assign these questions over a single night to help students prepare for a test the next day or you may assign the questions over a two-day period. If you work the questions over two days, we recommend assigning the evens for homework the first night so that students get feedback in class the next day, and then assigning the odds the night before the test because the answers are provided to the odd-numbered questions in the Selected Answers section at the back of the book.

It is effective to ask students which questions they still do not understand and use the day as a total class discussion of the material that the class finds most difficult.

Resources
- Assessment Resources:
  Chapter 2 Test

Technology Resources

Teacher's Assessment Assistant, Ch. 2
Electronic Teacher's Edition, Ch. 2

Additional Answers

3b. no; $(4^3 + 2) - (2^3 + 2) = 56 \neq$
  $2^3 + 2 = 10$

Chapter **2** Chapter Review

SKILLS
PROPERTIES
USES
REPRESENTATIONS

SKILLS Procedures used to get answers

OBJECTIVE A Work with $f(x)$ notation for function values. (Lesson 2-1).

In 1 and 2, let $f(x) = 4^x$.

1. Evaluate.
   a. $f(1)$ **4**   b. $f(-1)$ $\frac{1}{4}$ c. $\frac{f(6)}{f(3)}$ **64**

2. **True or False** Justify your answer.
   a. $f(2) + f(-2) = 0$ **false;** $16 + \frac{1}{16} \neq 0$
   b. $f(2) \cdot f(3) = f(5)$ **true;** $4^2 \cdot 4^3 = 4^5$

3. Let $g(x) = x^3 + 2$.
   a. If $g(x) = 3$, find x. $x = 1$
   b. Does $g(4) - g(2) = g(2)$? Justify your answer. **See margin.**

4. Suppose $p(x) = 5x - 2$.
   Evaluate $p(n + 1) - p(n)$. **5**

OBJECTIVE B Compute residuals from observed and predicted values. (Lesson 2-2)

In 5–7, let $F(n)$ be the nth Fibonacci number as in the following table for $1 < n < 9$.

n	1	2	3	4	5	6	7	8	9
F(n)	1	1	2	3	5	8	13	21	34

5. a. The line of best fit for these nine ordered pairs is $F(n) = 3.65n - 8.47$. Calculate the residuals for the first 9 Fibonacci numbers. **5a-b. See margin.**
   b. The 16th Fibonacci number is 987. Calculate the residual for this number.
   c. Calculate the sum of squared residuals for the first 9 Fibonacci numbers for the linear model. **210.206**

6. An exponential model for these 9 Fibonacci numbers is $F(n) = 0.4935(1.594)^x$. Calculate the residual for the 16th Fibonacci number for the exponential model. **129.7643**

7. a. Calculate the residuals for the quadratic model for these 9 Fibonacci numbers, $F(n) = 0.787x^2 - 4.218x + 5.952$. **See margin.**
   b. The residual for the 15th Fibonacci number is 490.288. What is the 15th Fibonacci number? **610**

PROPERTIES Principles behind the mathematics

OBJECTIVE C Identify the variables, domain, and range of functions. (Lesson 2-1)

In 8–11, a function is described by an equation.
   a. State its domain.   b. Give its range.

8. $f(x) = -2x^2 + 10x - 12$ $\{x | x \in \mathbb{R}\}$; $\{y | y \leq 0.5\}$

9. $r(t) = 4 \cdot 3^t$ $\{t | t \in \mathbb{R}\}$; $\{y | y > 0\}$

10. $j(x) = \frac{3}{-x}$ $\{x | x \neq 0\}$; $\{y | y \neq 0\}$

11. $I = \frac{1}{d^2}$ $\{d | d \neq 0\}$; $\{I | I > 0\}$

In 12 and 13, a function is described by an equation. Identify the independent and dependent variables.

12. $P = (x - 3)^4 x$; **P**   13. $y = f(t)$ **t; y**

14. Ruth has $23, and n friends join her for coffee. Coffee cost $2 per cup. The rule $R(n) = 2(n + 1)$ describes the amount $R(n)$ in dollars that Ruth will spend on coffee. What is a reasonable domain and range for the function R? $\{n | 0 \leq n \leq 10\}$; $\{y | 2 \leq y \leq 22\}$

In 15–17, tell if the statement is true or false.

15. The line of best fit is the linear model with the least sum of squared residuals. **true**

16. The correlation coefficient r is measured in the same unit as the slope of the regression line. **false**

17. Correlation does not imply causation. **true**

Additional Answers

5a.

n	F(n)	model	residuals
1	1	–4.82	5.82
2	1	–1.17	2.17
3	2	2.48	–0.48
4	3	6.13	–3.13
5	5	9.78	–4.78
6	8	13.43	–5.43
7	13	17.08	–4.08
8	21	20.73	0.27
9	34	24.38	9.62

5b. 937.07

7a.

n	F(n)	model	residuals
1	1	2.521	-1.521
2	1	0.664	0.336
3	2	0.381	1.619
4	3	1.672	1.328
5	5	4.537	0.463
6	8	8.976	–0.976
7	13	14.989	-1.989
8	21	22.576	-1.576
9	34	31.737	2.263

OBJECTIVE D Identify properties of regression lines and of the correlation coefficient. (Lesson 2-3)

In 18–21, r represents a correlation coefficient.

18. **Multiple Choice** $r = 0.05$ indicates what? **B**

   A a strong positive association

   B a weak positive association

   C a weak negative association

   D a strong negative association

19. What value of r indicates a perfect positive association? $r = 1$

20. For a set of data, the line of best fit is given by $y = 8.4 - 3.6x$ and $r^2 = 0.60$. What is r?

21. Explain what is meant by a strong positive correlation. **20–21. See margin.**

OBJECTIVE E Describe properties of quadratic, exponential, and inverse variation functions. (Lessons 2-4, 2-6, 2-7)

22. Consider the function f with $f(x) = ab^x$ with $b > 0$ and $a > 0$. **22–24. See margin.**

   a. Under what conditions is f decreasing?

   b. Under what conditions is f increasing?

23. Which of the functions, $a: t \to 0.8(1.1)^t$ or $b: t \to 1.1(0.8)^t$, models exponential growth and which models exponential decay?

24. Without graphing, how can you tell whether the graph of $f(x) = 5x^2 + 2x + 1$ has a maximum or minimum point?

In 25 and 26, identify the quadrants in which the graph of each equation appears.

25. a. $y = \frac{1}{x}$ **I, III**   b. $y = \frac{1}{-x}$ **II, IV**

26. a. $y = \frac{1}{x^2}$ **I, II**   b. $y = \frac{1}{-x^2}$ **III, IV**

In 27–30, suppose $f(x) = \frac{k}{x}$ and $g(x) = \frac{k}{x^2}$, with $k > 0$.

27. In Quadrant I, what happens to $f(x)$ as x increases? **$f(x)$ decreases**

28. In Quadrant II, what happens to $g(x)$ as x increases? **$g(x)$ increases**

29. Suppose $f(x) = 40$ when $x = 10$. Compute k. **400**

30. Suppose $g(x) = 40$ when $x = 10$. Compute k. **4000**

USES Applications of mathematics in real-world situations

OBJECTIVE F Find and interpret linear, quadratic, and exponential regressions and models. (Lessons 2-2, 2-3, 2-5, 2-6)

31. As part of a biology lab, Ben recorded the population of Drosophila (fruit flies) over a five-week period as follows: 2, 13, 74, 482, and 2793.

   a. Find the exponential regression equation of best fit for these data. $y = 0.335(6.108)^x$

   b. Calculate the residual for the week the population was 74. **–2.34**

32. The table below shows the height h in feet of a ball above ground level t seconds after being thrown off the top of a building.

t	1	2	3	5	6
h	279	291	271	135	19

   a. Find the quadratic model of best fit for these data. $h = -16t^2 + 60t + 235$

   b. Use your model to predict the height of the ball after 4 seconds. **219 feet**

   c. Is your prediction in Part b extrapolation or interpolation? **interpolation**

In 33 and 34, the heights (in inches) and shoes sizes of seven boys are recorded below.

Height (in.)	75	66	72	68	71	69	70
Shoe Size	13	$8\frac{1}{2}$	11	9	12	$10\frac{1}{2}$	10

33. a. Using the maximum and minimum height points, fit a linear model to the data by eye. $s = 0.5h - 24.5$

   b. Calculate the sum of squared residuals. **2**

34. a. Find the line of best fit for predicting shoe size from height. $s = 0.510h - 25.19$

   b. Find the sum of squared residuals for the line of best fit in Part a. **1.996**

   c. Why should the sum in Part b be less than your answer for Question 33b? **See margin.**

35. Actinium-226 has a half-life of 29 hours. If 100 mg of actinium-26 remain after 34 hours, how many mg were there originally?

Additional Answers

20. $r \approx -0.775$

21. Most of the observed data fall close to a linear model with positive slope; this indicates that the two variables have a strong positive relationship.

22a. $0 < b < 1$

22b. $b > 1$

23. a models exponential growth, b models exponential decay.

24. The coefficient of the leading term is positive, so the parabola opens up. Therefore, it has one minimum point and no maximum points.

34c. The best-fit line has the lowest possible sum of squared residuals.

35. 225.4 mg

Notes on the Questions

Question 42 The precipitous decline in the population of New Orleans from 2005 to 2006 was due to the devastation of Hurricane Katrina. Function models of the type discussed in this chapter are particularly poor at allowing for natural disasters.

Additional Answers

37. exponential; Population growth is often described by exponential growth equations.

38. quadratic; Quadratic models describe motion with respect to gravity.

39. linear; Peoples' body parts are proportional to each other, so their measurements can be described by a linear model.

40. no model; Prices of rare metals are subject to unpredictable events in markets around the world.

41a. Answers vary. Sample: Cell division splits or doubles the amount of cells after each division. Exponential growth models describe this type of process.

41b. The scatterplot appears to be exponentially growing. The rate of change of bacteria per hour is increasing.

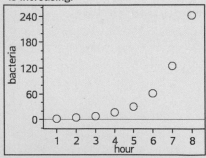

41c. Exponential: $y = 1.01688(1.98128)^{x_i}$
    The residual plot supports the choices made in Parts a and b.

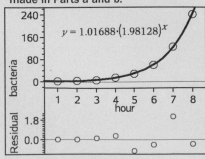

41d. The theory, the scatterplot, and the residual plot all support the choice of an exponential model.

37–42. See Margin.

36. The intensity I of light striking an object is inversely proportional to the square of the distance d from the source of the light. The intensity of light on a movie screen is 75 candles when the projector is 20 feet away.
    a. Create a model for this situation. $I = \dfrac{30,000}{d^2}$
    b. Use your model to predict the intensity of light striking the screen when the projector is 25 feet away. **48 candles**

| **OBJECTIVE G** Evaluate which type of model is more appropriate for data. (Lesson 2-8)

In 37–40, a situation is described. State whether a linear, exponential, or quadratic model is most appropriate for the situation. If no model is appropriate, say so. Explain your answer.

37. In 1859, Thomas Austin released 24 gray rabbits in Australia. The rabbits multiplied so quickly that within 20 years they were referred to as the "gray carpet."

38. In a physics experiment, Tim rolled a marble down an inclined plane and timed how long it took the marble to cover a given distance. Tim observed that the marble kept going faster and faster due to gravitational acceleration.

39. A tailor wanted to reduce the amount of time it took to make measurements, so he decided to make a model to predict the length of inseams based on sleeve length.

40. Jim knew that if he could accurately predict the price of gold, he would become rich.

41. Susie is developing a model for cell division in bacteria. She uses a microscope to count the number of bacteria present in a Petri dish at the end of each hour for eight hours. Her data are shown below.

End of Hour	1	2	3	4	5	6	7	8
Bacteria	2	4	8	16	30	61	124	241

   a. Is any theoretical model appropriate for the data? If so, what theory and why?
   b. Make a scatterplot. Which model appears appropriate for the data? Why?
   c. Confirm your choice from Parts a and b by plotting the residuals.

148 Functions and Models

---

42. Estimates of the population of New Orleans county from 2000 to 2005 are listed below.
    a. Make a scatterplot. Which model appears appropriate for the data?
    b. Plot the residual plots for the linear, quadratic, and exponential regression models. Do the plots give a clear choice of the best model?
    c. Calculate the correlation coefficient for the linear model.
    d. Write a paragraph explaining your choice of best fit model.
    e. According to the model, what population would you expect in 2006?
    f. The actual population in 2006 was 210,198. What is the residual?
    g. Explain why your model is so far off.

Year	Estimated Population
2000	484,674
2001	477,548
2002	472,085
2003	466,767
2004	460,556
2005	453,726

Source: U.S. Census Bureau

REPRESENTATIONS Pictures, graphs, or objects that illustrate concepts

| **OBJECTIVE H** Interpret properties of relations from graphs. (Lesson 2-1)

In 43–46, state whether the graph represents a function mapping x to y. If the relation is a function, determine its domain and range.

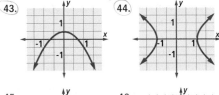

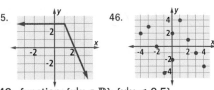

43. function; $\{x|x \in \mathbb{R}\}$; $\{y|y \leq 0.5\}$
44. not a function; The relation fails the vertical line test.
45. function; $\{x|x \in \mathbb{R}\}$; $\{y|y \leq 3\}$
46. not a function; (0, 2) and (0, –2) are both points on the relation.

Additional Answers

42a.

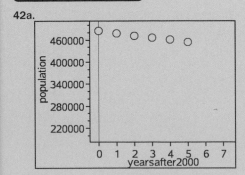

Answers vary. Sample: A linear regression appears to be a good fit.

42b. The residual plots do not indicate that one model is better than any other.

Linear: $y = -6029.54x + 484300$

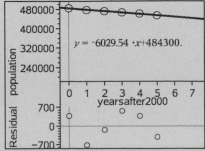

OBJECTIVE I Use scatterplots and residual plots to draw conclusions about models for data. (Lessons 2-2, 2-3, 2-8)

In 47–50, use the displays below. They show the number of hours 12 students spent studying for a test and their scores on the test. Both linear and quadratic models have been fit to the data and the regression equations are given.

$$y = 1.887x + 60.762$$

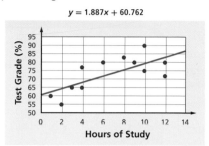

$$y = -0.455x^2 + 7.979x + 46.775$$

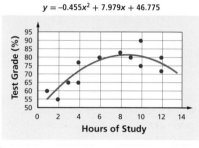

47. Consider the quadratic model and the student who studied eight hours for the test.
   a. What is the observed y-value? **83%**
   b. What is the predicted y-value? **82%**
   c. What is the residual? **1%**

48. Repeat Question 47 for the linear model and the student who studied eight hours for the test. **83%; 76%; 7%**

49. According to the quadratic model, what is the ideal amount of time to study in order to achieve a maximum score? Does this make sense? Explain why or why not.

49–50. See Margin.

50. The residuals for each model are graphed below. What do these graphs tell you about the appropriateness of each model?

Linear Model

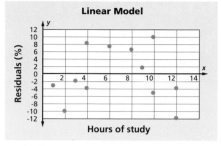

Hours of study

Quadratic Model

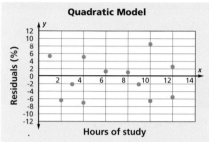

Hours of study

In 51–54, a scatterplot is given. State whether the correlation coefficient is likely to be positive, negative, or approximately zero.

51.
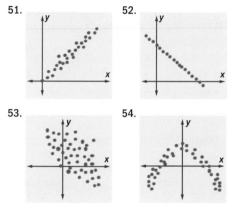

52.

53.

54.

51. positive   52. negative
53. negative   54. ≈ zero

Assessment

Evaluation The *Assessment Resources* provide a form of the Chapter 2 Test. Here are our recommendations for assigning a letter grade: 85–100 = A; 72–84 = B; 60–71 = C; 50–59 = D.

Feedback After students have taken the test for Chapter 2 and you have scored the results, return the tests to students for discussion. Class discussion on the questions that caused trouble for most students can be very effective in identifying and clarifying misunderstandings. You might want to have them note the items they missed and work either in groups or at home to correct them. It is important for students to receive feedback on every chapter test, and we recommend that students see and correct their mistakes before proceeding too far into the next chapter.

Suggestions for Assignment Assign Reading Lesson 3-1 and Covering the Ideas 3-1 for homework the evening of the test. It gives students work to do after they have completed the test and keeps the class moving. If you do not do this, you may cover one less chapter over the course of the year.

Additional Answers

42c. $r \approx -0.999$

42d. Answers vary. Sample: There is no theoretical support for any model, nor do the residual plots give a clear choice. The scatterplot and the correlation coefficient are strong reasons for choosing a linear model.

42e. 448,123

42f. –237,925

42g. Answers vary. Sample: At the end of August 2005, Hurricane Katrina, a Category 5 storm, hit the Gulf coast. Thousands of people were displaced, and the mayor of New Orleans ordered the first ever mandatory evacuation of the city.

49-50. See the Additional Answers section at the back of the book.

Additional Answers

Quadratic: $y = -27x^2 - 5894.54x + 484210$

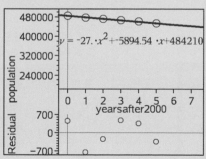

Exponential: $y = 484434(0.987227)^x$

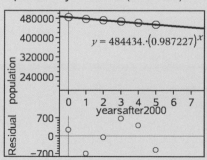

Chapter Overview

	Local Standards	Pacing (in days)		
		Average	Advanced	Block
3-1 Graphs of Parent Functions **E** Describe and identify symmetries and asymptotes of graphs. **I** Recognize functions and their properties from their graphs.		1	1	0.5
3-2 The Graph-Translation Theorem **C** Use the Graph-Translation Theorem to find transformation images. **D** Describe the effects of translations on functions and their graphs. **J** Apply the Graph-Translation Theorem to make or identify graphs.		1	1	0.5
3-3 Translations of Data **H** Use translations to describe and analyze data and statistics.		1	1	0.5
QUIZ 1		0.5	0.25	0.25
3-4 Symmetries of Graphs **D** Describe the effects of translations on functions and their graphs. **E** Describe and identify symmetries and asymptotes of graphs. **I** Recognize functions and their properties from their graphs.		1	1	0.5
3-5 The Graph Scale-Change Theorem **C** Use the Graph Scale-Change Theorem to find transformation images. **D** Describe the effects of translations and scale changes on functions and their graphs. **J** Apply the Graph-Translation Theorem or the Graph Scale-Change Theorem to make or identify graphs.		1	1	0.5
3-6 Scale Changes of Data **H** Use scale changes to describe and analyze data and statistics.		1	1	0.5
QUIZ 2		0.5	0.25	0.25
3-7 Composition of Functions **A** Find equations for and values of composites of functions. **F** Identify properties of composites of functions.		1	1	0.5
3-8 Inverses of Functions **B** Find inverses of functions. **F** Identify properties of inverses of functions. **I** Recognize functions and their properties from their graphs. **K** Graph inverses of functions.		1	1	0.5
3-9 z-Scores **G** Identify properties of z-scores. **H** Use z-scores to describe and analyze data and statistics.		1	1	0.5
Self-Test		1	0.5	0.5
Chapter Review		2	1	0.5
Test		1	1	0.5
TOTAL		14	12	6.5

Technology Resources

Teacher's Assessment Assistant, Ch. 3
Electronic Teacher's Edition, Ch. 3

Differentiated Options Universal Access

	Accommodating the Learner	Vocabulary Development	Ongoing Assessment	Materials
3-1	pp. 154, 155		p. 158	
3-2	pp. 162, 163	p. 161	p. 164	graph variation application
3-3	p. 167		p. 171	
3-4	p. 174		p. 178	
3-5	pp. 182, 183		p. 184	graph variation application
3-6			p. 192	
3-7	pp. 195, 196	p. 195	p. 198	
3-8	pp. 201, 202	p. 201	p. 205	
3-9	pp. 208, 209		p. 210	

Objectives

		Lessons	Self-Test Questions	Chapter Review Questions
Skills				
A	Find equations for and values of composites of functions.	3-7	10	1–6
B	Find inverses of functions.	3-8	7, 8	7–9
Properties				
C	Use the Graph-Translation Theorem or the Graph Scale-Change Theorem to find transformation images.	3-2, 3-5	2, 12	10–17
D	Describe the effects of translations and scale changes on functions and their graphs.	3-2, 3-4, 3-5	3	18–24
E	Describe and identify symmetries and asymptotes of graphs.	3-1, 3-4	1, 14	25–30
F	Identify properties of composites and inverses of functions.	3-7, 3-8	11, 16	31–37
G	Identify properties of z-scores.	3-9	13	38–41
Uses				
H	Use translations, scale changes, or z-scores to describe and analyze data and statistics.	3-3, 3-6, 3-9	5, 6, 17	42–47
Representations				
I	Recognize functions and their properties from their graphs.	3-1, 3-4, 3-8	15	48–57
J	Apply the Graph-Translation Theorem or the Graph Scale-Change Theorem to make or identify graphs.	3-2, 3-5	4	58–65
K	Graph inverses of functions.	3-8	9	66–69

Resource Masters Chapter 3

Resource Master 152, Four Quadrant Graph Paper, (page 152) can be used with Lessons 3-1 through 3-5, and 3-8.

Resource Master 46 Lesson 3-1

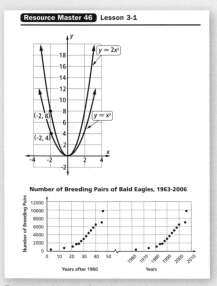

Number of Breeding Pairs of Bald Eagles, 1963-2006

Resource Master for Chapter 3 Opener

Resource Master 48 Lesson 3-1

Resource Master 47 Lesson 3-1

Warm-Up
Have students graph $y = x^3$ with a graphing utility using the default window.
1. Describe the default window.
2. Change the x-scale on the window so that the graph goes into the corners of the window.
3. Revert to the original window and change the equation so that the graph looks like Graph (2).

Additional Example 1
a. Display the graph of $h(x) = -(x - 20)\,2 + 17$ in an appropriate window.
b. State the domain and range of the function.

Additional Example 2
Graph the real function h with $h(x) = -9 - \sqrt{5 - x}$ in a window that shows important features. State the domain and range.

Additional Example 3
Tony makes a free throw in basketball practice. From its point of release, 6 ft in the air, the ball goes directly into the hoop which is 13 ft away and 10 ft high. An equation modeling the height $b(x)$ of the ball in feet at time x in seconds is $b(x) = -13.5x^2 + 19.5x + 6$.
a. Create a graph that would be helpful in determining the maximum height of the ball and how long it lasts.
b. What is the domain and range of b within the context of this situation?

Resource Masters for Lesson 3-1

Resource Master 50 Lesson 3-2

Resource Master 49 Lesson 3-2

Warm-Up
1. Under a translation, the image of (0, 0) is (12, 25).
a. Find a rule for this translation.
b. Find the image of (-2, -8) under this translation.
2. a. Compare the graphs of $y = x^3$ and $y - 25 = (x - 12)^3$.
b. Find the coordinates of a point on each graph.

Additional Example 1
Under a translation, the image of (0, 0) is (-12, 5).
a. Find a rule for this translation.
b. Find the image of (6, -10) under this translation.

Additional Example 2
a. Compare the graphs of $y = x^3 + 1$ and $y = (x + 4.2)^3 - 5$.
b. Find the coordinates of a point on one graph and its corresponding image on the second graph.
c. What is the image of (0, 0) under the translation that maps the first graph onto the second graph?

Additional Example 3
If the graph of $y = -\frac{1}{2x^2}$ is translated 8 units up and 17 units to the left, what is an equation for its image?

Resource Masters for Lesson 3-2

Resource Master 51 Lesson 3-2

Page 161

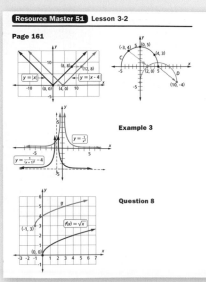

Example 3

Question 8

Resource Master for Lesson 3-2

Resource Master 53 Lesson 3-3

Resource Master 52 Lesson 3-3

Warm-Up
1. Find the mean of the data set: 101, 102, 103, 104, 105, 106, 107, 108, 109, 110.
2. Find the mean of the data set: 136, 137, 138, 139, 140, 141, 142, 143, 144, 145.
3. Explain how the answer to Warm-Up 1 can be used to determine the answer to Warm-Up 2.

Additional Example
At a martial arts tournament, the 20 fighters weighed in before the tournament. All the fighters made weight and a statistician computed the following statistics:
mean = 191.125 lb,
standard deviation = 29.7 lb,
median = 194.5 lb,
IQR = 35.5 lb.
After finishing her calculations, it was brought to the statistician's attention that the scales were not correctly calibrated. The starting weight was set at 0.25 lb, not 0. Find the correct values for the mean, standard deviation, median, and interquartile range for the 20 fighters.

Accommodating the Learner
Let $\{x^1, x^2, x^3, ..., x^n\}$ be a data set, and k a constant.

a. Prove that $\sum_{i=1}^{n} (x_i + k) = \sum_{i=1}^{n} x_i + nk$.

b. Prove that $\sum_{i=1}^{n} (x_i - \bar{x}) = 0$, where $\bar{x}$ is the mean of the set.
(Hint: Apply the result of Part a.)

Resource Masters for Lesson 3-3

Resource Master 55 Lesson 3-4

Resource Master 54 Lesson 3-4

Warm-Up
1. How many symmetry lines does a square have?
2. How many centers of symmetry does a square have?
3. How many symmetry lines does an isosceles trapezoid have?
4. How many centers of symmetry does an isosceles trapezoid have?
5. Draw a figure with more than one center of symmetry.

Additional Example 1
Prove that the graph of $y = \sqrt{36 - x^2}$ is symmetric to the y-axis.

Additional Example 2
Determine whether the function $f(x) = x^3 - 5x$ is odd, even, or neither. If it appears to be even or odd, prove it.

Additional Example 3
Consider the function H with $y = H(x) = \frac{3}{x - 8} + 9.5$.
a. Give equations for the asymptotes of its graph.
b. Describe any lines or points of symmetry.

Resource Masters for Lesson 3-4

Resource Masters for Lesson 3-5

Resource Master 57 Lesson 3-5
Resource Master 56 Lesson 3-5

Warm-Up

1. If you multiply a number by 0.8, you can get back to the original number either by multiplying the product by ___ or dividing the product by ___.

2. If you divide a number by 30, you can get back to the original number either by multiplying the quotient by ___ or dividing the quotient by ___.

3. Multiple Choice When $a \neq 0$, $\frac{\frac{x}{a}}{a} =$

   A ax B $\frac{x}{a}$ C $\frac{\frac{x}{a}}{a}$ D $\frac{a}{x}$

Additional Example 1
Sketch and compare the graphs of $y = |x|$ and $\frac{y}{4} = |6x|$. Describe the transformation that maps the first graph onto the second.

Additional Example 2
The line $41x - 29y = 700$ contains the points $(39, 31)$ and $(10, -10)$. Use this information to obtain two points on the line with equation $20.5x - 87y = 700$.

Accommodating the Learner
Try this question, which can be tricky. Let G be the graph of $y = x^2$. Let H be the graph of $y = 0.01x^2$. Find an equation for a transformation T that maps G onto H if T is a
   a. vertical scale change.
   b. horizontal scale change.
   c. size change.

Resource Masters for Lesson 3-5

Resource Master 59 Lesson 3-5
Resource Master 58 Lesson 3-5

Example 2

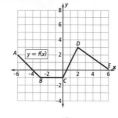

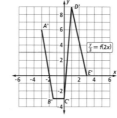

x	f(x)
-6	2
-3	-1
0	-1
2	3
6	0

Resource Master for Lesson 3-6

Resource Master 60 Lesson 3-6

Warm-Up
From 1995 to 2005 in U.S. cities, on the average, prices of food went up 25.1%, prices of medical care rose 46.6%, and rents went up 37.8%. Estimate the 2005 price of the following items, whose 1995 prices are given.
   1. a carton of cereal that cost $3.39
   2. rent that was $850/month
   3. a hospital room that was $1000 for one night

Additional Example 1
In 1990, the CPI was 391.4. In 2005, the CPI was 585.0. Suppose an oven cost $450 in 1990. What might you expect a similar oven to have cost in 2005?

Additional Example 2
To give an approximate conversion from kilograms to pounds, you can multiply the number of kilograms by 2.2. A local grocery store gets a shipment of cheese imported from France. Each pre-packaged piece is labeled with the weight in kilograms, and must be relabeled with the weight in pounds. What will be the effect of changing from kilograms to pounds on:
   a. the upper quartile of the data?
   b. the variance of the data?
   c. the standard deviation of the data?

Resource Masters for Lesson 3-6

Resource Master 62 Lesson 3-6
Resource Master 61 Lesson 3-6

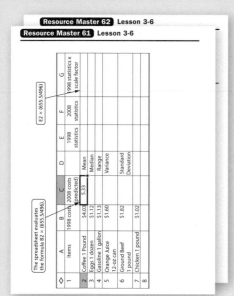

Resource Master for Lesson 3-6

Resource Master 63 Lesson 3-6

Questions 15-18

Resource Master for Lesson 3-7

Resource Master 64 Lesson 3-7

Warm-Up
Every person has 2 biological parents, 4 biological grandparents, 8 biological great-grandparents. Call these your first-generation, second-generation, and third-generation ancestors. Suppose two of your great-grandparents were second cousins, meaning that they themselves had one pair of great-grandparents in common. If no others of your recent ancestors were related, how many ancestors would you have in the third- through eighth-generation ancestors.

Additional Example 1
Let $f(x) = x^2$ and $g(x) = \frac{1}{3x + 1}$. Evaluate:
   a. $f(g(4))$.
   b. $g(f(4))$.
   c. $(f \circ g)(4)$.

Additional Example 2
Use the functions f and g of Additional Example 1.
   a. Derive a formula for $(f \circ g)(x)$.
   b. Give a simplified formula for $(g \circ f)(x)$.
   c. Verify that $f \circ g \neq g \circ f$ by graphing.

Additional Example 3
Use the functions f and g of Additional Example 1. Find the domain of $f \circ g$.

Additional Example 4
Let $s: (x, y) \rightarrow (x, \frac{y}{2})$ and $T: (x, y) \rightarrow (x - 1, y - 2)$.
   a. Describe S and T in words.
   b. Write a simplified formula for the composite $(T \circ S)(x, y)$ and describe it in words.
   c. Write a simplified formula for the composite $(S \circ T)(x, y)$ and describe it in words.

Resource Masters for Lesson 3-8

Resource Master 66 Lesson 3-8
Resource Master 65 Lesson 3-8

Warm-Up
Indicate how you could undo each operation or composite of operations.
   1. turning left and walking 30 yards, then turning around and walking 15 yards
   2. multiplying a number by $1\frac{2}{3}$
   3. adding 40 to a number, then dividing the result by one-half
   4. taking the fifth power of a positive number, then taking its positive square root

Additional Example 1
Let $h = \{(1, 1), (2, 4), (3, 9), (4, 16)\}$.
   a. Describe the inverse of h.
   b. Is the inverse a function?
   c. Describe h and its inverse in words.

Additional Example 2
   a. Describe the graph of the function $y = 2(x + 5)^2 - 1$.
   b. Give an equation for the inverse of the function $y = 2(x + 5)^2 - 1$.
   c. Based on your answer to Part a, describe the graph of the inverse of the function. Is the inverse a function?

Additional Example 3
   a. Give an equation for the inverse of the function with equation $y = \frac{5}{x + 8 - 1}$.
   b. Is the inverse a function?

Additional Example 4
   a. Use the Inverse of Functions Theorem to determine whether f and g, defined by $f(x) = \frac{3x + 1}{5 - x}$ and $g(x) = \frac{3x - 1}{x + 3}$, are inverses.
   b. Verify your result in Part a by examining the graphs of f and g.

Resource Master for Lesson 3-9

Resource Master 67 Lesson 3-9

Warm-Up
   1. Calculate the mean and the standard deviation for these scores:
      63, 71, 84, 90, 97.
   2. The score of 63 is how many standard deviations below the mean?
   3. The score of 90 is how many standard deviations above the mean?

Additional Example 1
Ned scored 5.8 on a pop quiz on which the mean score is 6.4 and the standard deviation is 0.9. What is his z-score and how far is his score from the mean?

Additional Example 2
Monique scored 81 on a test with a mean of 90 and a standard deviation of 6. She scored 73 on a test on which the mean was 75 and the standard deviation was 5. On which test did Monique perform better compared to her classmates?

Resource Master for Lesson 3-9

Resource Master 68 Lesson 3-9

Page 206

Food Production	Protective Services	Construction	Education
$8.24	$16.11	$17.57	$20.47

Healthcare	Architecture/Engineering	Management
$26.17	$31.14	$40.60

L_1	8.24	16.11	17.57	20.47	26.17	31.14	40.60
L_2	-14.66	-6.79	-5.31	-2.43	3.27	8.24	17.70
L_3	-1.4	-0.6	-0.5	-0.2	0.3	0.8	1.7

Question 18

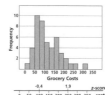

Chapter

3 **Transformations of Graphs and Data**

Pacing

Each lesson in this chapter is designed to be covered in 1 day. However, well-prepared students may be able to do Lessons 3-2 and 3-3 in a single day and skip Lesson 3-7. At the end of the chapter, you should plan to spend 1 day to review the Self-Test, 1 to 2 days for the Chapter Review, and 1 day for a test. You may wish to spend a day on projects, and possibly a day will be needed for quizzes. This chapter should therefore take 12 to 15 days. We strongly advise you not to spend more than 16 days on this chapter.

Students should be expected to do the equivalent of a complete set of Questions from a lesson nearly every day. Two Assignment Options are identified in each lesson. At times you may want to save a few questions to be done by students in class.

Overview

For many students, a graph of a function is a picture of its equation. As a picture, the graph is not viewed as a geometric object and it is not seen to have geometric properties. This chapter is based on a quite different view of graphs: they are geometric objects, made up of sets of points.

The graph of $y = 2x^2$ (an offspring) is obtained from the graph of $y = x^2$ (its parent) by multiplying each y-coordinate of each point $y = x^2$ by 2. Geometrically, the distance of the point from the x-axis has been doubled. This abstract example of a scale change involves functions with no real context. In contrast, the data on the breeding pairs of eagles is very concrete. In the chapter, students will learn that although it may be clearer to associate the year with the number of breeding pairs, in doing some of the statistics, it may be more realistic to translate the data so that 0 is the image of the year 1960. Here the "parent" is the graph of the data on the right and the image is the graph on the left.

▶ **Contents**

3-1   Graphs of Parent Functions

3-2   The Graph-Translation Theorem

3-3   Translations of Data

3-4   Symmetries of Graphs

3-5   The Graph Scale-Change Theorem

3-6   Scale Changes of Data

3-7   Composition of Functions

3-8   Inverses of Functions

3-9 z-Scores

A *transformation* is a one-to-one correspondence between sets of points. Two important transformations are translations and scale changes. A translation of data occurs, for example, if you add the same number to every student's score on a test. A scale change occurs when you change raw scores into percents. In this chapter you will learn to apply these transformations to graphs of functions that are defined algebraically and to graphs of data sets. In the graphs at the right, the transformation doubles each vertical coordinate of the preimage to create the image. It is an example of a scale change.

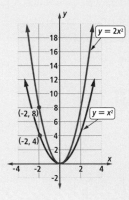

Chapter 3 Overview

This chapter discusses a topic common to statistics and to the study of functions, namely the transformation of a set of data or a set of points into a more convenient form to be studied. The idea is simple: sometimes information is presented in a form that is unwieldy for further study; sometimes it can be transformed into a more convenient form.

Conversely, by studying information in its simplest form and studying the effects of transformations on that information, we can obtain results about information that is not given in such a convenient form.

Two transformations are considered in this chapter: translations (adding a constant to all values of a variable) and scale changes (multiplying each value of a variable by a constant). The inverses of these transformations are found by subtracting and dividing the constant.

Lesson 3-1 reviews some parent functions and the effects of changing windows on their graphs. What we know about the

An example of a figure and its *translation* image is shown below. As mentioned in Lesson 2-5, it is common to let the independent variable be years after a starting year in to minimize differences in residuals. In this case, the original data is translated so that time is measured in *years after 1960*.

Translations and scale changes can be described by algebraic formulas. In this chapter you will study these descriptions and the effects of these transformations on equations of functions and on statistical measures.

Number of Breeding Pairs of Bald Eagles, 1963-2006

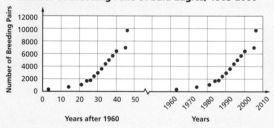

151

graph of a parent function or relation can be applied to transformation images of that graph. What we know about the equation of a relation can be applied to determine an equation for the transformation image. The primary objectives of Lessons 3-2 and 3-5 are for students to gain an understanding of how transformations affect important features of graphs and how those effects are represented in the changes in equations for the relations. Lessons 3-3 and 3-6 ask students to transfer this understanding to data sets and to predict the effects of the

same kinds of transformations on measures of center and spread. If the graphs of functions appear to be symmetric over the *y*-axis or through the origin (see the graphs on page 173), then students are asked in Lesson 3-4 to prove algebraically that the function is even or odd, respectively. In Lessons 3-7 and 3-8, the techniques of graphing and proof are applied to study composition and inverses of functions. The composite of a translation and a scale change of data to standardize the data gives rise to *z*-scores, which close the chapter.

The graphs epitomize the main theme of the chapter: if you know properties of a parent function and know how certain transformations affect those properties, then you have power to analyze a host of offspring of the parent.

Using Pages 150–151

This is a time to explore your students' understanding of congruence and similarity. Remind students that parabolas extend without end, so a graph can show only a part of a parabola. Then ask: Do you think the two parabolas pictured are congruent? **No.** Similar? **Yes, all parabolas are similar. The parent can be mapped onto the offspring by the size change that maps (x, y) onto (0.5x, 0.5y).** The following general definitions of congruence and similarity are found in UCSMP materials: two figures are *congruent* if and only if one can be mapped onto the other by an isometry (i.e., a composite of reflections – or equivalently, a composite of reflections, rotations, and translations). Two figures are *similar* if and only if one can be mapped onto the other by a similarity transformation (a composite of isometries and size changes).

The two parts of the data graph are congruent because one part is the image of the other under a translation

Chapter 3 Projects

At the end of each chapter, you will find projects related to the chapter. At this time you might want to have students look over the projects on pages 211 and 212. You might want to have students tentatively select a project on which to work. Then, as students read and progress through the chapter, they can finalize their project choices.

Sometimes students might work alone. At other times, you might let them collaborate with classmates for a presentation and discussion. We recommend that you allow for diversity and encourage students to use their imaginations when presenting their projects. As students work on projects throughout the year, they should see many uses of mathematics in the real world.

GOAL

Introduce concepts and language associated with certain relations and their graphs, and allow students to become familiar with the ways in which graphing utilities deal with these concepts.

SPUR Objectives

The SPUR Objectives for all of Chapter 3 are found in the Chapter Review on pages 216–219.

E Describe and identify symmetries and asymptotes of graphs.

I Recognize functions and their properties from their graphs.

Materials/Resources

· Lesson Master 3-1
· Resource Masters 47 and 48

HOMEWORK · Option 1
· Option 2

- Questions 1–10
- Questions 11–23
- · Question 24 (extra credit)
  - Reading Lesson 3-2
  - Covering the Ideas 3-2
    (Questions 1–11)

Local Standards

---

1 Warm-Up

Have students graph $y = x^3$ with a graphing utility using the default window.

1. Describe the default window.
   Answers vary. Sample: $-10 \leq x \leq 10$; $-10 \leq y \leq 10$
2. Change the x-scale on the window so that the graph goes into the corners of the window. **Answers vary. Sample: On a TI-89, about $-2.2 \leq x \leq 2.2$; $-10 \leq y \leq 10$.**
3. Revert to the original window and change the *equation* so that the graph looks like Graph (2). **Answers vary. Sample: On a TI-89, about $y = \frac{x^3}{100}$.**

Graphs of Parent Functions

▶ **BIG IDEA** Knowledge of the features and graphs of parent functions helps in analyzing more complex functions.

Parent Functions

Many useful functions cluster in families. The **parent function** of the family is usually the member that has the simplest equation. For example, the parent of all linear functions has equation $f(x) = x$. The parent of the quadratic function g with $g(x) = -4.9x^2 + 31x + 5$ has equation $f(x) = x^2$. Eight important parent functions are graphed below.

Mental Math

Describe the shape of the graph of each equation.

a. $3x - 4y = 7$

b. $3x^2 - 4y = 7$

c. $3x \cdot 4y = 7$

a. line

b. parabola

c. hyperbola

| $f(x) = x$ | $f(x) = x^2$ | $f(x) = x^3$ | $f(x) = \sqrt{x}$ |
| (linear) | (quadratic) | (cubic) | (square root) |

| $f(x) = \frac{1}{x}$ | $f(x) = \frac{1}{x^2}$ | $f(x) = |x|$ | $f(x) = 2^x$ |
| (inverse variation) | (inverse square) | (absolute value) | (exponential growth) |

STOP QY1

Tell which parent functions have each characteristic.
   a. The domain does not include 0.
   b. The graph contains the origin.

Background

Before this chapter, students have used graphing utilities in this course to store data and to graph. Here we begin a more in-depth analysis of the graphs made by these utilities. Students should be able to use a graphing utility to display functions, change viewing windows, read coordinates of points from the display, and recognize the possibility of asymptotes and discontinuities. Students need to know the graphs of what should be familiar functions so that they can concentrate on using the

features of their graphing utilities properly and efficiently.

We try to be consistent in our language, but not pedantic. You should, in speaking, try to distinguish between:

1. *f*, a function (a correspondence).

2. an equation for *f* (one way of describing the function).

3. the graph of *f* (a set of points, a picture of the function, usually found by graphing its equation).

4. $f(x)$, a value of the function.

Choosing Windows of Graphs

When you display an image on a computer screen, its appearance can be changed by zooming in and out and by scrolling left and right or up and down. These changes affect what is displayed on the screen. At the left below is a document as it appears when it is opened. If you zoom out, then scroll up and left, you might see the picture at the right below.

lish Justice, insure dome:
uility, provide for the co
:e, promote the general
re, and secure the Blessin
:y to ourselves and our Po
p ordain and establish thi
:tution for the United St:

We the People of the United States, in Order to form a more perfect Union, establish Justice, insure domestic Tranquility, provide for the common defence, promote the general Welfare, and secure the Blessings of Liberty to ourselves and our Poster-ity, do ordain and establish this Constitution for the United States of America.

Similarly, when you plot a function on graph paper or with a graphing utility, you want to choose the viewing **window** that shows important aspects of the function. Graphing utilities have a standard window that is used as a default for plotting functions. The standard window is usually appropriate for parent functions but often misses important features of graphs of their offspring. Your knowledge of the parent graphs can help you choose a good window. On graphing utilities, the window is described by identifying the least and greatest values of x and y that will be shown, $\texttt{xmin}$, $\texttt{xmax}$, $\texttt{ymin}$, and $\texttt{ymax}$.

Example 1

a. Display the graph of $g(x) = |x + 25| - 10$ in an appropriate window.

b. State the domain and range of the function g.

Solution

a. The graph of $g(x) = |x + 25| - 10$ in a standard window as shown at the right does not display important features of g. The parent of the function is the absolute value function, with equation $f(x) = |x|$. A key feature of the graph of the absolute value function is its vertex. The vertex is the minimum point of the graph.
The smallest value of $f(x) = |x|$ is when $x = 0$. For $f(x) = |x + 25| - 10$, the **minimum value occurs when** $|x + 25| = 0$, **or when $x = -25$. Since $f(-25) = -10$, the vertex is (-25, -10).** Choose $\texttt{xmin}$, $\texttt{xmax}$, $\texttt{ymin}$, and $\texttt{ymax}$ to include (–25, –10). The window **-55 ≤ x ≤ 5,** **–20 ≤ y ≤ 30** displays the important features of the graph, showing the vertex and the x- and y- intercepts and vertex.

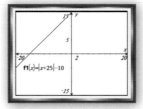

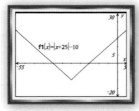

(continued on next page)

In later lessons, we transform graphs of functions by substitutions into their equations.

The key concept for students to realize is that because graphing utility screens are discrete sets of points, even a graph that looks continuous only has as many points as the horizontal window will allow and will fit on the vertical window used. By using the trace function to trace along the graph, the student can see which points have been graphed.

2 Teaching

Notes on the Lesson

The examples and most of the questions are devoted to developing the skills of displaying a graph and changing the size of the viewing window to see important features of the graph, including its domain, range, and asymptotes.

This lesson considers the eight parent functions that appear at the start of the lesson and some of their offspring, but at this point we do not expect students to be able to describe algebraically the transformations that take parents into offspring. We expect that students have seen the parent graphs before. You may want to have students find the coordinates of a point or two on each graph to make certain that they make a connection between the equations and the curves.

Parent functions A parent function is the simplest form of the equation for a certain type of function. Functions whose graphs are the images of a parent function by a composite of simple transformations are referred to as "offspring." However, the meaning of "simple transformation" is not always consistent. With the scale transformations and translations of this chapter, every quadratic with equation $y = ax^2 + bx + c$ is an offspring of $y = x^2$, every absolute value function with equation $y = a|x - h| + k$ is an offspring of $y = |x|$, and every sine wave with horizontal translation symmetry is an offspring of $y = \sin x$.

However, we often think of $y = x^3$ as the parent of every cubic polynomial even though not every cubic has a graph that is an offspring. Ironically, we do not think of the graph of $f(x) = 3^x$ as an offspring of the graph of $y = 2^x$ even though the latter can be mapped onto the former by a composite of scale changes and translations. So, sometimes the "parent" is a simple representative of a class of functions and the offspring another representative whose equation or graph looks like that of the parent.

On the other hand, you might notice that the graphs of the exponential growth and exponential decay functions with equations $y = 2^x$ and $y = 2^{-x}$ are reflection images of each other over the y-axis, so you could easily consider the graph of $y = 2^x$ to be the parent and the graph of $y = 2^{-x}$ to be an offspring.

Notes on the Lesson

Choosing windows of graphs The website http://www.ourdocuments.gov allows you to view the originals of documents such as the U.S. Constitution and the Gettysburg Address in a viewing window much like that which opens this lesson.

You can work through the examples during class with individual students or small groups of students using graphing utilities. Most students with graphing utilities probably will not have the capability to print hard copies of their graphs, so encourage them to make neat, accurate sketches when necessary.

Example 1 The Graph-Translation Theorem is studied both in UCSMP Algebra and UCSMP Advanced Algebra. Students familiar with this theorem (studied in Lesson 3-2) will realize that the graph of g is the image of the graph of $y = |x|$ under the translation 25 units to the left and 10 units down. This determines the vertex of the angle that is the graph.

Example 2 Emphasize that sketches should include all important features. For example, unless specifically asked to use a particular window or restrict values to a particular domain, the graph of a quadratic function should appear to be symmetric. A sketch of a quadratic function such as the one shown below does not make clear whether the student understands symmetry. Also, all relative maximum and minimum points of polynomial functions should be included in sketches of the function.

Additional Example

Example 1

a. Display the graph of $h(x) = -(x - 20)^2 + 17$ in an appropriate window. **Answers vary. Check students' work. A key feature of the graph is its maximum point (20, 17).**

b. State the domain and range of the function. **The domain is the set of all real numbers, $\mathbb{R}$. The range is $\{y \mid y \leq 17\}$.**

---

b. Any value of x produces a value of $f(x)$, so the domain is the set of all real numbers, $\mathbb{R}$. Since the minimum y-coordinate on the graph is –10, the range is $\{y \mid y \geq -10\}$.

STOP QY2

▶ **QY2**

Identify $\mathtt{xmin}$, $\mathtt{xmax}$, $\mathtt{ymin}$, and $\mathtt{ymax}$ in the window of the second graph of Example 1.

Example 2

Graph the real function g with equation $g(x) = \sqrt{x - 8} + 5$ in a window that shows the graph's important features. State the domain and range.

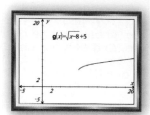

Solution In the real number system, square roots can only be evaluated for nonnegative numbers. Thus, $\sqrt{x - 8}$ is defined only when $x - 8 \geq 0$ or $x \geq 8$. When $x = 8$, $g(x) = 5$. When $x \geq 8$, $g(x) \geq 5$. So pick a window that shows the axes, the point (8, 5), and points to the right and above (8, 5). We chose $\mathtt{xmin} = -5$, $\mathtt{xmax} = 20$, $\mathtt{ymin} = -5$, and $\mathtt{ymax} = 20$.

The graph shows that the domain is $\{x \mid x \geq 8\}$ and the range is $\{y \mid y \geq 5\}$.

When functions are used to model real-world phenomena, the domain may be restricted. In Example 3, the quadratic for falling bodies works well while the object is in air, but not while the object is in water.

Example 3

Stephen, who is 1.7 m tall, dives off a 3 m springboard. An equation modeling his height $h(x)$ in meters above the water at time x in seconds is

$$h(x) = -4.9x^2 + 4.5x + 4.7.$$

a. Create a graph that would be helpful for determining the maximum height of his dive and how long it lasts.

b. What is the domain and range of h within the context of this situation?

Solution

a. The parent function has equation $y = x^2$, so we know the graph of h is a parabola. In this situation, the equation only applies to the time from when Stephen leaves the board to when he enters the water, which from the standard window graph, shown at the left at the top of the next page, we see is between $x = 0$ and $x = 1.5$. Even though negative values of x do not have meaning in this situation, it is still useful to include negative values for the window settings in order to see the intercepts. You may need to modify the vertical window settings to include the vertex. The graph at the right on the next page is shown on the window $-1 \leq x \leq 5, -1 \leq y \leq 7$.

Accommodating the Learner ⬇

Some students might have trouble indicating the correct window and scale on the hard copy or sketch of their graph. As they zoom in and zoom out, the window and scales change from that of the first window. When students have found the view of the graph they wish to copy, remind them to check the window dimensions and scale.

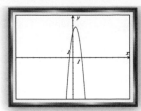
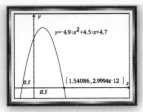

b. The maximum height is about 5.73 meters and the dive lasts about 1.5 seconds. The TRACE function on your calculator can help find these maximum x- and y- values. **The diver's fall through air has domain close to $\{x \mid 0 \leq x \leq 1.5\}$. The range is about $\{h(x) \mid 0 \leq h(x) \leq 5.73\}$.**

Asymptotes

The parent functions with equations $y = \frac{k}{x}$ and $y = \frac{k}{x^2}$, pictured on page 152, each have the x- and y-axes as asymptotes. As x moves closer and closer to 0, the curve approaches the y-axis, so the y-axis is a vertical asymptote. The curve approaches the horizontal asymptote, which is the x-axis, when x increases or decreases without bound. Asymptotes exist on all graphs of offspring of the parents $y = \frac{k}{x}$ and $y = \frac{k}{x^2}$.

How are asymptotes marked on a graph if they are not the axes? Consider the function f with equation $f(x) = \frac{1}{x-5}$. At the vertical asymptote, the graph appears to "jump" as shown at the right. This *discontinuity* occurs when $x = 5$, since $f(5) = \frac{1}{5-5} = \frac{1}{0}$ and division by 0 is undefined. The vertical asymptote of $x = 0$ (the y-axis) for the graph of the parent function $h(x) = \frac{1}{x}$ has moved to $x = 5$ for its offspring $f(x) = \frac{1}{x-5}$. While points on the vertical asymptote are not actually part of the graph, the asymptote helps to explain the behavior of the function. So we mark the asymptote, showing it with a dashed line. The x-axis is still a horizontal asymptote even though you will not necessarily see dashed line notation appear over the x-axis.

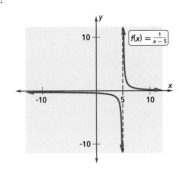

Some graphing utilities handle discontinuous graphs in misleading ways. A vertical line may appear where there should be a vertical asymptote. Therefore it is important to both know what a good graph looks like, and to know the limitations of whatever graphing technology you are using. A good graph meets the following criteria:

- Axes are labeled appropriately, with the scales shown.

- The window is chosen so that the characteristic shape of the graph can be seen.

- The intercepts are shown.

Graphs of Parent Functions   **155**

Notes on the Lesson

Example 3 Students should know from their algebra study that the x-coordinate of the vertex of the graph of $y = ax^2 + bx + c$ is $-\frac{b}{2a}$. Here, $\frac{-4.5}{2(-4.9)} \approx 0.46$, and substituting this value for x yields $y \approx 5.73$. You might use the trace function or other command on the graphing utility to verify that $f(0.46)$ is very close to a maximum. If you use this function, note that on many graphing utilities the points traced are not necessarily those with convenient coordinates. The vertex even may not be graphed. Some graphing utilities have a feature that displays the coordinates of any point on a graph indicated by the user. Therefore, if a student reports that the vertex of a parabola is slightly off, there is reason to expect that the student is reading directly from the screen and has not realized that the coordinates themselves are of a point that might not be the vertex, but is near the vertex.

Asymptotes We assume students have seen asymptotes before.

Discontinuities Infinite and jump discontinuities are examples of essential discontinuities. Essential discontinuities cannot be eliminated by defining a value of a function at a particular point. In contrast, removable discontinuities are those that can be removed (as their name implies) by the appropriate definition of the function at a point of discontinuity. For example, the function g defined by $g(x) = \frac{x^2 - 25}{x + 5}$ has a graph that is exactly like the graph of $h(x) = x - 5$, except that g has a discontinuity at $x = -5$, where it is not defined. So the graph has a hole in it at the point $(-5, -10)$. By defining $g(-5) = -10$, that discontinuity can be removed, so the discontinuity is removable.

Emphasize that none of the properties of a function change when you change the window. You are just looking at the function from a different viewpoint. It is just like viewing a house or other object from different places.

Accommodating the Learner ⬆

Have students enter the function $y = x^3 + 5x^2 + 4x$ in their graphing utility and answer the following questions.

1. Describe what the graph looks like on each of the following windows.
  a. $-0.01 \leq x \leq 0.1$; $-0.01 \leq y \leq 0.1$
    A straight line
  b. $-1 \leq x \leq 1$; $-1 \leq y \leq 1$ **A parabola**
  c. $-10 \leq x \leq 10$; $-10 \leq y \leq 10$ **A cubic**

2. What type of function is this? Explain why a function such as this one cannot have any vertical asymptotes or points of discontinuity. **cubic polynomial; Answers vary. Sample: The domain of a polynomial function is the set of all real numbers and there are no gaps.**

3-1

Additional Examples

Example 2 Graph the real function h with $h(x) = -9 - \sqrt{5 - x}$ in a window that shows important features. State the domain and range. **Answers vary. Check students' work. The domain is $\{x \mid x \leq 5\}$ and the range is $\{y \mid y \leq -9\}$.**

Example 3 Tony makes a free throw in basketball practice. From its point of release, 6 ft in the air, the ball goes directly into the hoop which is 13 ft away and 10 ft high. An equation modeling the height $b(x)$ of the ball in feet at time x in seconds is $b(x) = -13.5x^2 + 19.5x + 6$.

a. Create a graph that would be helpful in determining the maximum height of the ball and how long it lasts. **Answers vary. Check students' work.**

b. What is the domain and range of b within the context of this situation? **The domain is close to $\{x \mid 0 \leq x \leq 1.7\}$. For this domain, the range is about $\{y \mid 0 \leq y \leq 13.04\}$.**

Additional Answers

6a.

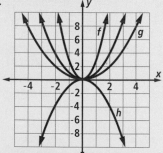

7a.

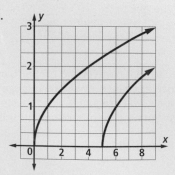

- Any endpoints are indicated as included (•) or excluded (◦).
- Asymptotes are shown with dotted lines. (An exception is when the *x*- or *y*-axis is an asymptote since the axes already appear.)

If you are not careful in choosing a window, what you see on your screen may appear to be in the family of one parent function when the function you are considering actually belongs to another family of functions. Consider the graph of $f(x) = x^3$ in the two windows below. At the left, the function appears to be linear. At the right, its true cubic nature is shown.

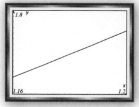
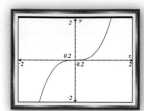

Questions

COVERING THE IDEAS

In 1–3, refer to the parent functions at the beginning of the lesson.

1. Name the functions whose graphs pass through Quadrant III.
2. Name the functions whose range is the set of all real numbers.
3. Name the functions for which the *y*-axis is a line of symmetry.
4. Consider the function f with $f(x) = 3^x - 5$. Give equations for any asymptotes of its graph. $y = -5$
5. Give the domain and range of h with $h(x) = |x + 30| + 12$.
6. Let three functions f, g, and h be defined by $f(x) = 3x^2$, $g(x) = 0.5x^2$, and $h(x) = -x^2$. **6a–b. See margin.**
   a. Graph f, g, and h in the same window on a graphing utility.
   b. Graph $y = x^2$ in the same window. Describe how each graph in Part a is related to the graph of the parent function.

In 7 and 8, equations for two functions are given. **7–8a. See margin.**
   a. Sketch graphs of each pair of functions on the same set of axes.
   b. How are the two graphs related?
7. $y = \sqrt{x}$, $y = \sqrt{x - 5}$
8. $y = |x|$, $y = |4x|$
9. State the dimensions of the default window of your graphing utility.

1. linear, cubic, inverse variation

2. linear, cubic

3. quadratic, inverse square, absolute value

5. domain: $\{x \mid x \in \mathbb{R}\}$; range: $\{y \mid y \geq 12\}$

6b. All graphs have the same vertex. The graph of f is a horizontal shrinking of the parent graph; the graph of g is a horizontal stretch of the parent graph. The graph of h is the reflection image of the parent graph.

7b. The graph of $y = \sqrt{x - 5}$ is the image of the graph of $y = \sqrt{x}$ under the translation 5 units to the right.

8b. The graph of $y = |4x|$ is a horizontal shrink of the graph of $y = |x|$ by a factor of $\frac{1}{4}$.

9. Answers vary. Sample: $-10 \leq x \leq 10$, $-10 \leq y \leq 10$

Additional Answers

8a.

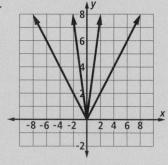

10a. See the Additional Answers section at the back of the book.

11a.

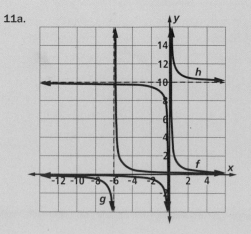

10. a. Graph the function f with $f(x) = x^3 - x$ on the given windows.
   i. $-1 \le x \le 1, -1 \le y \le 1$ ii. $-5 \le x \le 5, -5 \le y \le 5$
   iii. $-10 \le x \le 10, -10 \le y \le 10$ iv. $-100 \le x \le 100, -100 \le y \le 100$
   b. Which window provides the most useful graph? Why?

APPLYING THE MATHEMATICS

11. a. Graph $f(x) = \frac{1}{x}$, $g(x) = \frac{1}{x+6}$, and $h(x) = \frac{1}{x} + 10$
   on the same set of axes.
   b. At what value(s) of x is each of f, g, and h
   discontinuous? **11a–d. See margin.**
   c. Give an equation of the vertical asymptote of
   each curve.
   d. How is each of g and h related to f?

12. The graph at the right shows the function f with
   $f(x) = \frac{3x}{4 - x^2}$. Find a window for which the visible
   portion of the graph looks like the graph of
   a. a cubic function. **See margin for graphs.**
   b. a square root function.

13. Let f be the function with $f(x) = \sqrt{x^2 + 30x + 200}$.
   a. What is the domain of f?
   b. Choose an appropriate window and sketch a graph. **See margin.**

14. The relationship between the wrist circumference and neck
   circumference in humans is modeled by $y = 1.92x + 4.23$, where x is
   the wrist circumference (cm) and y is the neck circumference (cm).
   What is a reasonable domain in this context? **See margin.**

15. a. Use your graphing utility to sketch the graphs of $f(x) = \frac{1}{x^2}$ and
   $g(x) = \frac{4}{x^2}$ on the same set of axes. Choose a window that allows
   you to compare the two functions. **15a, c. See margin.**
   b. **True or False** For all x, $f(x) < g(x)$. **true**
   c. Justify your response to Part b both algebraically (by using the
   formulas) and geometrically (by using the graphs).

REVIEW

16. Consider the function $r : t \rightarrow 5(0.83)^t$. **(Lesson 2-4) See margin.**
   a. Give the domain of r.
   b. Give the range of r.
   c. State equations for any asymptotes of the graph of r.

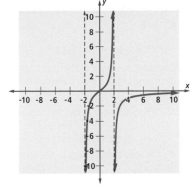

Graphs of Parent Functions   157

10a. See margin.

10b. The window
in Part ii offers
the best graph
because it graphs
all the function's
characteristics without
distorting them.

12a. Answers vary.
Sample: $-2 \le x \le 2$,
$-4 \le y \le 4$

12b. Answers vary.
Sample: $2.5 \le x \le 8$,
$-2 \le y \le 0$

13a. domain:
$\{x \mid x \le -20 \text{ or } x \ge -10\}$

---

3 Assignment

Recommended Assignment
- Questions 1–10
- Questions 11–23
- Question 24 (extra credit)
- Reading Lesson 3-2
- Covering the Ideas 3-2
  (Questions 1–11)

Notes on the Questions
Questions 7 and 8 At this point,
students may need to work by sight,
though students who have studied from
UCSMP Algebra or Advanced Algebra
texts should recognize the relation
between the graphs in both of these
Questions.

Questions 7 and 11 These questions are
precursors to Lesson 3-2.

Questions 8 and 12 These questions are
precursors to Lesson 3-6.

Question 14 Some people would say
the domain is the set of positive real
numbers so as to impose no arbitrary
upper limit on x.

Additional Answers

15a, c. See the Additional Answers section at
   the back of the book.
16a. $\{t \mid t \in \mathbb{R}\}$
16b. $\{r \mid r > 0\}$
16c. $r = 0$

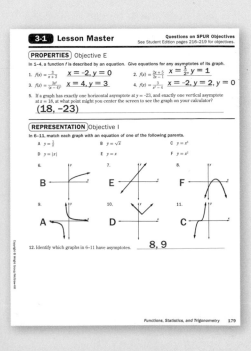

Additional Answers

11b. $x = 0, -6$, and 0 for f, g, and h, respectively
11c. $x = 0$, $x = -6$, and $x = 0$ for f, g, and
   h, respectively
11d. g is a translation of f 6 units to the left and h
   is a translation of f 10 units up.
12. See the Additional Answers section at the
   back of the book.
13a. domain: $\{x \mid x \le -20 \text{ or } x \ge -10\}$

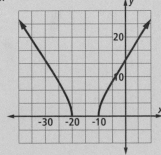

13b.

14. Answers vary. Sample: $\{x \mid 4 \le x \le 40\}$

3-1

Notes on the Questions

Questions 17–20 At this point we have discussed only rectangular coordinates. In polar coordinates, the graph in Question 17 is the graph of a constant function.

Question 25 This exploration will go more quickly if students use the window-change applet to adjust the window. You might have students share their responses with the rest of the class.

4 Wrap-Up

Ongoing Assessment

Have each student produce the graph of $f(x) = x^2 + 10$ in three different windows. Ask the student to show you each graph and describe the window. Then have him or her explain which of the three windows is the most useful and why. **Students should demonstrate their skill using a graphing utility and explain the merits of various windows.**

Additional Answers

21.

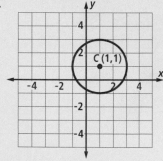

22a. minimum: 134.4; Q_1: 149.3; median: 230.2; Q_3: 401.1; maximum: 736.8

22b. Answers vary. Sample: There is a fairly large spread in housing costs in large U.S. metropolitan areas.

22c. There are no outliers.

22d. mean: 290.623; standard deviation: 178.913

23a.

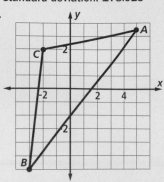

In 17–19, state whether the graph represents a function. **(Lesson 2-1)**

17.

18.

19.

17. not a function

18. function

19. function

21–24. See margin.

20. **Skill Sequence** Simplify. **(Previous Course)**

a. $\frac{1}{\frac{1}{6}}$ 6

b. $\frac{1}{\frac{1}{n}}$ n

c. $\left(\frac{1}{n}\right)^{-1}$ n

21. Sketch the graph of $(x - 1)^2 + (y - 1)^2 = 4$. **(Previous Course)**

22. Consider the table at the right. Prices are in thousands of dollars. **(Lessons 1-6, 1-4)**

a. Compute the five-number summary.

b. What conclusion can you draw from these data regarding the price of housing in large metropolitan areas in the United States?

c. Identify any outliers in the data.

d. Remove any outliers and find the mean and standard deviation for the remaining data.

Median Sales Price Existing Single-Family Homes, 2006			
Atlanta	171.8	New York	469.3
Chicago	273.5	Philadelphia	230.2
Cleveland	134.4	St. Louis	148.4
Dallas	149.5	San Francisco	736.8
Detroit	151.7	Seattle	361.2
Houston	149.1	Washington, D.C.	431.0
Miami	371.2		

Source: National Association of Realtors

23. a. Draw $\triangle ABC$ with $A = (5, 3)$, $B = (-3, 4)$, and $C = (-2, 2)$.

b. Draw $\triangle A'B'C'$, the triangle whose x-coordinates are 6 more than the corresponding coordinates in $\triangle ABC$.

c. How are $\triangle ABC$ and $\triangle A'B'C'$ related? **(Previous Course)**

EXPLORATION

24. a. Graph the function f with equation $f(x) = \frac{5x^2 - 271x + 3600}{(x - 24)(x - 30)} + 20$.

Set your window to $10 \leq x \leq 40$, $10 \leq y \leq 40$. A window-change applet may be provided by your teacher.

b. Find a window that shows only a portion of the graph that looks like a parabola. Record the viewing window.

c. Find a window that shows only a part of the graph that looks like a line.

d. Find a window that shows a graph that may have inverse-square as a parent.

e. See how many of the other parent functions you can mimic by zooming in on part of the graph of f.

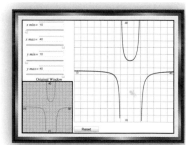

QY ANSWERS

1. a. inverse variation, inverse square

b. all except inverse variation, inverse square, and exponential growth

2. –55; 5; –20; 30

Additional Answers

23b.

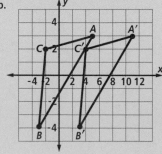

23c. $\triangle A'B'C'$ is the image of $\triangle ABC$ under the translation of 6 units to the right.

24. See the Additional Answers section at the back of the book.

Lesson 3-2

The Graph-Translation Theorem

Vocabulary

transformation
preimage
image
translation

▶ **BIG IDEA** When the graph of a function is translated vertically or horizontally, its equation changes in a related way.

The Translation Image of a Graph

A **transformation** is a one-to-one correspondence between sets of points. Another term for "correspondence" is "mapping." We say that one set, the **preimage**, is mapped onto the other set, the **image**. One type of transformation is a **translation**, which shifts the graph horizontally or vertically. You can quickly describe and interpret translation images of functions of common parent functions. Below, the graph of the parent function f is the preimage. The graph of g is its image under a *vertical translation*.

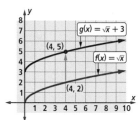

x	f(x)	g(x)
1	1	4
2	$\sqrt{2}$	$\sqrt{2}+3$
3	$\sqrt{3}$	$\sqrt{3}+3$
4	2	5
5	$\sqrt{5}$	$\sqrt{5}+3$

This translation can also be written as $T(x, y) = (x, y + 3)$ or $T: (x, y) \rightarrow (x, y + 3)$, which is read "$(x, y)$ is mapped onto $(x, y + 3)$." The graph of $g(x) = \sqrt{x} + 3$ is the translation image of the graph $f(x) = \sqrt{x}$.

The general translation of the plane translates figures horizontally and vertically at the same time.

Definition of Translation

A **translation** in the plane is a transformation that maps each point (x, y) onto $(x + h, y + k)$, where h and k are constant.

Background

A *translation* is the mathematical name for a slide. Translations are caused by adding a constant to a variable; the resulting graph is an image congruent to the original.

The Graph-Translation Theorem is one of two related theorems about graphing studied in this chapter. It is a powerful theorem, as it is applicable to all relations. The idea is a strong one: it says that algebraic substitutions have geometric counterparts. In later chapters, it is applied to the phase shift of trigonometric functions

and to the graphs of conics not in standard position. For example, the graph of $y = \sin (x - b)$ is the image of the graph of $y = \sin x$ under the horizontal translation $(x, y) \rightarrow (x + b, y)$. A vertical translation of that magnitude maps the graph of $y = mx$ onto the graph of $y = mx + b$. By writing the second equation as $y - b = mx$, we can see the substitution of $y - b$ for y that causes the translation.

(continued on next page)

Lesson 3-2

GOAL
Show that the substitution of $x - h$ for x and $y - k$ for y in an equation for a relation has the effect of translating a graph h units to the right and k units up.

SPUR Objectives

C Use the Graph-Translation Theorem to find transformation images.

D Describe the effects of translations on functions and their graphs.

J Apply the Graph-Translation Theorem to make or identify graphs.

Materials/Resources
· Lesson Master 3-2
· Resource Masters 49, 50, and 51
· Graph variation application

HOMEWORK • Option 1
• Option 2
• Questions 1–11
• • Questions 12–18
• • Question 19 (extra credit)
• Reading Lesson 3-3
• Covering the Ideas 3-3 (Questions 1–8)

Local Standards

Mental Math

Consider the data set {2, 2, 3, 4, 6}.

a. Find the mean, median, and mode of the data set.

b. Which measure is least descriptive of the center of the data set?

a. mean $= \frac{17}{5} = 3.4$; median $= 3$; mode $= 2$

b. mode

1 Warm-Up

1. Under a translation, the image of $(0, 0)$ is $(12, 25)$.
   a. Find a rule for this translation. $T(x, y) = (x + 12, y + 25)$
   b. Find the image of $(-2, -8)$ under this translation. **(10, 17)**
2. a. Compare the graphs of $y = x^3$ and $y - 25 = (x - 12)^3$. **The second graph is 12 units to the right and 25 units above the first.**

(continued on next page)

b. Find the coordinates of a point on each graph. **Answers vary. Sample: (–2, –8) is on the first graph, so (10, 17) is on the second graph. Notice that the translation is the same as in Warm-Up 1.**

3. If the graph of $y = |x|$ is translated 2 units up and 3 units to the left, what is an equation for its image? **$y - 2 = |x + 3|$**

2 Teaching

Notes on the Lesson

Teachers continually remind us of the impact that having studied transformations in geometry has on student ability to understand graphs of functions. If your students have studied from previous UCSMP texts, then they should be familiar with this content and find this lesson to be very easy. If your students have never studied transformations before, they are at a disadvantage. This lesson may require 2 days for such students, for you will need to review translations with them. In particular, you will want to emphasize for these students:

- A translation is one type of transformation.
- Every translation in the plane can be described by a formula of the form $(x', y') = (x + h, y + k)$.
- A translation is a distance-preserving transformation; that is, the distance between two points equals the distance between their images.
- A figure and its translation image are congruent. That is because one general definition of congruence is that any figure and its image under a distance-preserving transformation are congruent.
- A line and its translation image are parallel. Consequently, translations preserve tilt.

Additional Example

Example 1 Under a translation, the image of (0, 0) is (–12, 5).

a. Find a rule for this translation. **$T(x, y) = (x - 12, y + 5)$**

b. Find the image of (6, –10) under this translation. **(–6, –5)**

Example 1

The graph of $y = x^2$ is shown at the right, together with its image under a translation T. The point (0, 0), which is the vertex of the preimage, maps onto the vertex (–3, 1) of the image.

a. Find a rule for the translation T.

b. Find the image of (2, 4) under this translation.

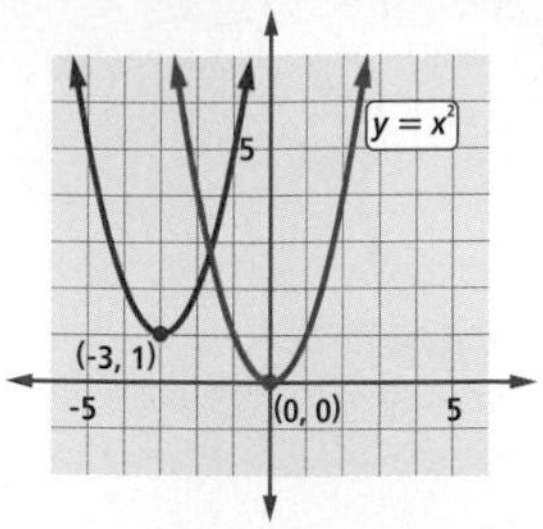

Solution

a. The second graph has been obtained from the graph of $y = x^2$ by a translation 3 units to the left and 1 unit up. Thus,
$T(x, y) = (x - 3, y + 1)$.

b. $T(2, 4) = (2 - 3, 4 + 1) = (-1, 5)$

STOP QY1

> **QY1**
> What is the range of the image function in Example 1?

You can use technology to explore translations.

Activity

MATERIALS Graph variation application supplied by your teacher or the Internet

Consider $f1(x) = \sqrt{x}$. The graph of $f2$ is the image of the graph of $f1$ under a translation of h units horizontally and k units vertically. Points (0, 0) and (1, 1) are on the preimage graph, and P and Q are their images.

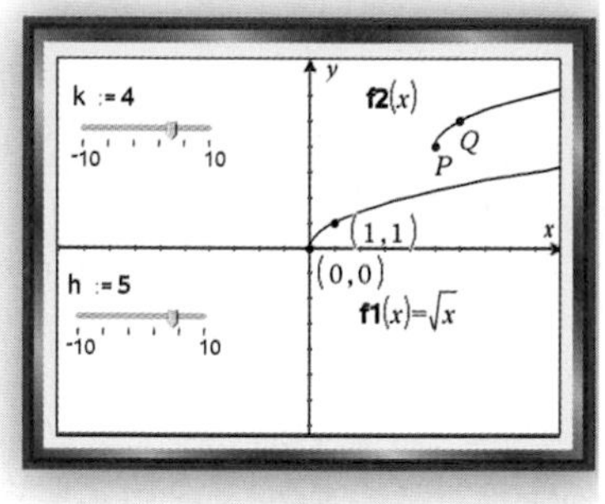

Step 1 The screen at the right shows the instance in which h is 5 and k is 4. Give the coordinates of P and Q. **$P = (5, 4)$; $Q = (6, 5)$**

Step 2 Adjust the sliders so that $h = -3$ and $k = 2$. Give the coordinates of P and Q on the image. **Step 2: $P = (-3, 2)$; $Q = (-2, 3)$**

Step 3 Find values of h and k so that the endpoint of the image is at (8, –6). **$h = 8, k = -6$**

The Graph-Translation Theorem

Graphed in blue at the right is the circle with equation $x^2 + y^2 = 25$ and one point that lies on it, (3, –4). When they are translated 10 units right and 2 units down, the images are the circle with equation $(x - 10)^2 + (y + 2)^2 = 25$ and the point (13, –6), which are shown in red. The preimage point (3, –4) and its image (13, –6) satisfy the equations of their respective circles.

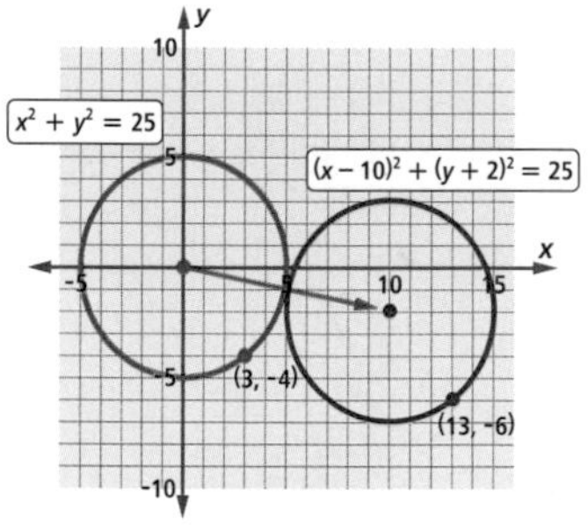

Students who have studied from UCSMP *Advanced Algebra* should be familiar with translations and the Graph-Translation Theorem. Many students may be familiar with translations but not with their algebraic applications. The notation that A' is the image of A, and $(x' y')$ is the image of (x, y) will also be familiar to some students. The prime notation gives a way of explaining the Graph-Translation Theorem.

In the theorem,

$$T: (x, y) \rightarrow (x + h, y + k).$$

Write this as

$$T: (x, y) \rightarrow (x', y').$$

Then $x' = x + h$, so $x' - h = x$. Similarly, $y' - k = y$, as presented in the lesson. The equation of the image of the equation $x^2 + y^2 = 25$ is $(x' - 10)^2 + (y' + 2)^2 = 25$ under the transformation $T: (x, y) \rightarrow (x + 10, y - 2)$. In this case, the image figure is a circle that is centered at (10, -2) with radius 5 in the same coordinate system. Its equation must be the image equation without the primes.

If we let T stand for this translation, then $T: (x, y) \rightarrow (x + 10, y - 2)$. Name the image point (x', y'). Then $x' = x + 10$ and $y' = y - 2$. Solving for x and y gives $x' - 10 = x$ and $y' + 2 = y$. Substitute in the equation $x^2 + y^2 = 25$ and you get $(x' - 10)^2 + (y' + 2)^2 = 25$. It is customary to write the image circle equation without the primes.

There is a direct relationship between replacing a variable expression in an equation and finding the image of a graph under a transformation. Consider the graphs of $f(x) = |x|$ and $g(x) = |x - 4|$ at the right. As the arrow from the point $(8, 8)$ to $(12, 8)$ indicates, the graph of $g(x) = |x - 4|$ is the image of the graph of $f(x) = |x|$ under the translation 4 units to the right, or $(x, y) \rightarrow (x + 4, y)$. Note that adding 4 to each x-coordinate corresponds to replacing x by $x - 4$ in the equation of the preimage. This leads to an important generalization.

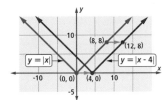

Graph-Translation Theorem

Given a preimage graph described by a sentence in x and y, the following two processes yield the same image:
(1) replacing x by $x - h$ and y by $y - k$ in the sentence;
(2) applying the translation $(x, y) \rightarrow (x + h, y + k)$ to the preimage graph.

That is, for $T(x, y) = (x + h, y + k)$, an equation of the image of $y = f(x)$ is $y - k = f(x - h)$.

The Graph-Translation Theorem can be applied to write an equation if a graph is given, and to sketch a graph if an equation is given. Translations also occur in situations that might not be described with an equation.

GUIDED

Example 2 See margin.

At the right are graphs of the function $y = C(x) = \sqrt{25 - x^2}$ and its image $y = D(x)$ under the translation $(x, y) \rightarrow (x + 5, y - 4)$. Both are semicircles. Find an equation for the image.

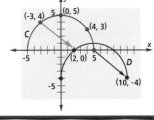

Solution Because the translation is 4 units down, replace y with __?__. Because the translation is 5 units to the right, replace x with __?__. This gives the equation __?__. Solve for y. $y = $ __?__

Check 1 The point $(-3, 4)$ is on C. According to the translation, the image of $(-3, 4)$ is $(\underline{?}, \underline{?})$. Show that this image point checks in your equation for D.

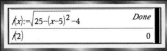

Check 2 Use a graphing utility to plot C and D on the same axes.

The Graph-Translation Theorem **161**

Notes on the Lesson

Even experienced students may still be unsure that replacing x by $x - h$ translates a graph to the right rather than the left. Students often need practice both with the relationship between graph transformations and replacements in equations, and with the simple mechanics of doing the replacements. Because students tend to find translations simpler than scale changes, Lesson 3-2 is an appropriate time for a classroom activity that would give students practice and instant feedback on this algebra. For example, you could use individual student whiteboards and have students flash answers to questions like: Start with the equation $x^2 + 4x + 2y^2 = 4$ and write the equation that yields the image under (1) a translation 4 units to the left; (2) a translation up 2 units, etc. It is particularly important to use equations that have multiple occurrences of x, or that are solved for y.

At this point students should know the parent graphs for the absolute value, square root, squaring, cubing, reciprocal, and inverse square functions. They should be able to focus on issues having to do with translations and not be stymied by the parent functions.

Additional Example
Example 2
a. Compare the graphs of $y = x^3$ and $y = (x + 4.2)^3 - 5$.
   The second graph is 4.2 units to the left and 5 units below the first.

b. Find the coordinates of a point on one graph and its corresponding image on the second graph.
   Answers vary. Sample: $(1, 1)$ is on the first graph, so $(-3.2, -4)$ is on the second graph.

c. What is the image of $(0, 0)$ under the translation that maps the first graph onto the second graph?
   $(-4.2, -5)$

Additional Answers

Example 2:
$y + 4$; $x - 5$; $y + 4 = \sqrt{25 - (x - 5)^2}$;
$\sqrt{-x^2 + 10x - 4}$; 2; 0
$0 + 4 = \sqrt{-(2^2) + 10 \cdot 2}$
$4 = \sqrt{16}$
$4 = 4$

3-2

Additional Example

Example 3 If the graph of $y = -\frac{1}{2x^2}$ is translated 8 units up and 17 units to the left, what is an equation for its image? $y = -\frac{1}{2(x + 17)^2} + 8$

3 Assignment

Recommended Assignment

- Questions 1–11
- • Questions 12–18
- • Question 19 (extra credit)
- • Reading Lesson 3-3
- • Covering the Ideas 3-3
  (Questions 1–8)

Additional Answers

10b.

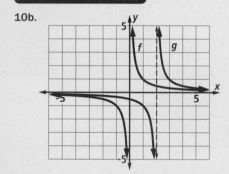

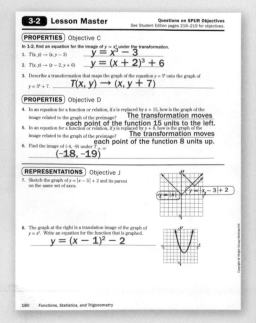

162   Chapter 3

STOP QY2

Example 3
Sketch a graph of $y = \frac{1}{(x + 1)^2} - 4$.

Solution First rewrite the sentence in the form $y - k = \frac{1}{(x - h)^2}$ to see the replacements in relation to the function $y = \frac{1}{x^2}$.

$$y - 4 = \frac{1}{(x + 1)^2} = \frac{1}{(x - -1)^2}$$

In the equation $y = \frac{1}{x^2}$, y has been replaced by $y - -4$ and x has been replaced by $x - -1$. Thus, by the Graph-Translation Theorem, the graph of $y - -4 = \frac{1}{(x - -1)^2}$ is the image of the graph of $y = \frac{1}{x^2}$ under the translation $T(x, y) = (x - 1, y - 4)$. Therefore, its graph is translated 1 unit to the left and 4 units down from the graph of the parent inverse-square function. In particular, its asymptotes are $x = -1$ and $y = -4$. With this knowledge, its graph can be sketched. The graphs of the parent function and the given equation are drawn at the right.

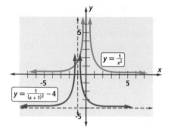

Questions

COVERING THE IDEAS

In 1–3, find the image of each point under the given translation.

1. $(2, -5)$, move left 3 units and up 6 units **(–1, 1)**
2. $(-14, -7)$, horizontal translation of 2 units and a vertical translation of –3 units **(–12, –10)**
3. (p, q), horizontal translation of a units and vertical translation of b units **(p + a, q + b)**

In 4 and 5, find the image of the point under $T: (x, y) \to (x - 3, y + 4)$.

4. $(1, -2)$ **(–2, 2)**   5. (r, s) **(r – 3, s + 4)**

6. **Multiple Choice** Which rule is for a translation T that has the effect of sliding a graph 3 units down and 7 units to the left? **D**
   A $T(x, y) = (x - 3, y - 7)$ B $T(x, y) = (x + 3, y + 7)$
   C $T(x, y) = (x - 7, y + 3)$ D $T(x, y) = (x - 7, y - 3)$

7. Suppose $y = \frac{1}{x}$ and $T(x, y) = (x + 3, y + 4)$.
   a. Find the images of $(1, 1)$, $(-1, -1)$, and $(0.5, 2)$ under T.
   b. Verify that the three images under T satisfy $y - 4 = \frac{1}{x - 3}$.

7a. (4, 5), (2, 3), (3.5, 6)

7b. $5 - 4 = 1 = \frac{1}{4 - 3}$;
$3 - 4 = -1 = \frac{1}{2 - 3}$;
$6 - 4 = 2 = \frac{1}{3.5 - 3}$.

162   Transformations of Graphs and Data

Lesson Master 3-2

PROPERTIES Objective C

In 1-2, find an equation for the image of $y = x^3$ under the transformation.
1. $T(x, y) \to (x, y - 3)$ $y = x^3 - 3$
2. $T(x, y) \to (x - 2, y + 6)$ $y = (x + 2)^3 + 6$
3. Describe a transformation that maps the graph of the equation $y = 5^x$ onto the graph of $y = 5^x + 7$. $T(x, y) \to (x, y + 7)$

PROPERTIES Objective D

4. In an equation for a function or relation, if x is replaced by $x + 15$, how is the graph of the image related to the graph of the preimage? **The transformation moves each point of the function 15 units to the left.**
5. In an equation for a function or relation, if y is replaced by $y + 8$, how is the graph of the image related to the graph of the preimage? **The transformation moves each point of the function 8 units up.**
6. Find the image of $(-4, -9)$ under T. **(–18, –19)**

REPRESENTATIONS Objective J

7. Sketch the graph of $y = |x - 3| + 2$ and its parent on the same set of axes.

8. The graph at the right is a translation image of the graph of $y = x^2$. Write an equation for the function that is graphed. $y = (x - 1)^2 - 2$

Accommodating the Learner

For students who have limited experience with transformations, it may be worthwhile to give them a brief in-class exercise to reinforce the effects of a translation on its preimage. Students should be able to associate a translation with its notation, meaning, and effect on the equation of a function. You may ask several questions phrased in the following way:

What effect does the translation $(x, y) \to (x + 3, y - 7.5)$ have on a graph?
The image would be 3 units to the right and 7.5 units down.

How would you change the equation of the preimage to accomplish this translation?
Replace x by $(x - 3)$, and y by $(y + 7.5)$.

What translation is equivalent to replacing x by $(x + 3.25)$ and y by $(y - 1)$ in the equation of the preimage?
Shift left 3.25 units, and up 1 unit.

8. The graph of $f(x) = \sqrt{x}$ is shown at the right, together with its image under a translation T. The image of $(0, 0)$ on the graph is the point $(-1, 3)$.

a. Find a rule for the translation T. $T(x, y) = (x - 1, y + 3)$

b. Find the image of $(9, 3)$ under this translation. $(8, 6)$

c. Find an equation for the image g. $g(x) = \sqrt{x + 1} + 3$

9. Use the Graph-Translation Theorem to find an equation of the image of $y = |x|$ under $T(x, y) = (x - 4, y + 6)$. $y = |x + 4| + 6$

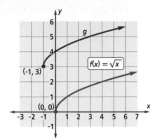

In 10 and 11, rules for two functions are given.
a. State a rule for a translation that maps f onto g.
b. Graph f and g on the same set of axes. See margin.

10. $f(x) = \frac{1}{x}; g(x) = \frac{1}{x - 2}$

11. $f(x) = x^2; g(x) = (x + 2)^2 + 1$

APPLYING THE MATHEMATICS

12. a. Graph f and g, where $f(x) = \frac{1}{x}$ and $g(x) = \frac{1}{x + 3} - 2$, on the same set of axes. See margin.

b. Find equations for the asymptotes of g. How are they related to the asymptotes of f?

c. Give the domain and range of f and g.

13. The parabola $y = (x - 3)^2 + 5$ is the image of the parabola $y = (x + 2)^2 + 7$ under a translation $T: (x, y) \rightarrow (x + h, y + k)$. What are the values of h and k? $h = 5, k = -2$

14. **Multiple Choice** A circle has radius 4 and center $(2, -3)$. Which of the following might be an equation for the circle? **C**

A $(x + 2)^2 + (y + 3)^2 = 16$ B $(x - 2)^2 + (y - 3)^2 = 16$
C $(x - 2)^2 + (y + 3)^2 = 16$ D $(x + 2)^2 + (y - 3)^2 = 16$

15. The formula $N = 0.82(1.09)^t$ gives the approximate current U.S. national debt (in billions of dollars), t years after 1900.

a. Compute the estimated national debt for 2007.

b. Convert the formula to one that maps the actual year y onto the debt. **15a. about $8,288,000,000,000**

REVIEW

16. Consider the equation $y = \frac{1}{x - 1}$. **(Lesson 3-1)**

a. Identify the parent equation. $y = \frac{1}{x}$

b. Graph the equation and its parent on the same axis. See margin.

10a. $T(x, y) = (x + 2, y)$

11a. $T(x, y) = (x - 2, y + 1)$

12b. $x = -3, y = -2$; they are images of $x = 0$ and $y = 0$ under the translation 3 units to the left and 2 units down.

12c. The domain of f is $\{x | x \neq 0\}$ and the domain of g is $\{x | x \neq -3\}$. The range of f is $\{y | y \neq 0\}$ and the range of g is $\{y | y \neq -2\}$.

15b. $N = 6.36 \cdot 10^{-72} (1.09)^y$

Notes on the Questions

Questions 10 and 11 Encourage students to replace $f(x)$ and $g(x)$ with y and then use the Graph-Translation Theorem.

Question 11 Although graphing utilities usually require y to be isolated on one side of the equation, the Graph-Translation Theorem is most easily understood if the constant associated with vertical shift to is grouped with y. Thus encourage your students to rewrite the equation as $g(x) - 1 = (x + 2)^2$ or $y - 1 = (x + 2)^2$ before applying the Graph-Translation Theorem.

Question 14 This illustrates that the circle with equation $(x - h)^2 + (y - k)^2 = r^2$ is h units to the right and k units up from the circle with equation $x^2 + y^2 = r^2$.

Question 15 Notice that this conversion is a translation of the independent variable even though the variable is named y.

Question 16 Students could graph this equation by realizing that its graph is 1 unit to the right of the graph of $y = \frac{1}{x}$. From this, the asymptotes of the graph are easily seen to have equations $y = 0$ and $x = 1$.

Additional Answers

12a.

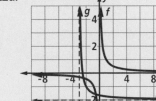

16b.

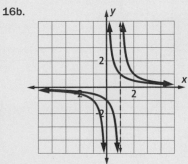

Accommodating the Learner

Ask students to prove that every translation is a distance-preserving transformation. Let the translation map (x, y) onto $(x + h, y + k)$. Let $P = (a, b)$ and $Q = (c, d)$ be any two points, and P' and Q' their respective images under the translation. We wish to show that the distance $P'Q'$ equals the distance PQ. From the formula, $P' = (a + h, b + k)$ and $Q' = (c + h, d + k)$. So, $P'Q' = \sqrt{((a + h) - (c + h))^2 + ((b + k) - (d + k))^2} = \sqrt{(a - c)^2 + (b - d)^2} = PQ$.

Additional Answers

11b.

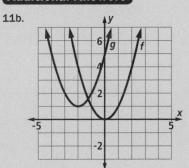

3-2

4 Wrap-Up

Ongoing Assessment

Have students each translate one of the parent functions shown on page 152 and write an equation for the image. Then have students exchange just their image equation with a partner and sketch a graph of the partner's equation. Students should demonstrate an understanding of the Graph-Translation Theorem by writing the equation and sketching a graph for the image of a function under a translation.

17. Use the mean lengths of largemouth bass of various ages given below. (Lesson 2-3)

Age (years)	1	2	3	4	5	6	7	8	9	10
Length (inches)	6.3	9.0	11.6	13.5	15.8	17.4	18.9	19.8	20.3	20.7

Source: Illinois Department of Natural Resources

a. Find an equation of the line of best fit for predicting length from age.

b. Interpret the slope of the line.

c. Use the line to predict the length of a twelve-year-old largemouth bass in Illinois.

d. Suggest a reason for being cautious about your prediction in Part c.

e. Find the correlation coefficient r between the age of the fish and its mean length.

f. Interpret the sign of r.

18. **Skill Sequence** Factor. (Previous Course)

a. $k^2 - 9$ b. $9 - 16t^2$ c. $(p + 4)^2 - 25$

EXPLORATION

19. a. Consider the linear equation $f(x) = 3x - 5$. Find an equation for the image of the graph of f under the following transformations.

    i. $T(x, y) = (x + 1, y + 3)$

    ii. $T(x, y) = (x + 2, y + 6)$

    iii. $T(x, y) = (x - 4, y - 12)$

    iv. $T(x, y) = (x + 1, y + 5)$

b. Make a conjecture based on the results of Part a.

c. Prove your conjecture in Part b.

d. Generalize this problem to any line of the form $y = mx + b$.

19a. i. $y - 3 = 3(x - 1) - 5$ or $y = 3x - 5$
ii. $y - 6 = 3(x - 2) - 5$ or $y = 3x - 5$
iii. $y + 12 = 3(x + 4) - 5$ or $y = 3x - 5$
iv. $y - 5 = 3(x - 1) - 5$ or $y = 3x - 3$

19b. Answers vary. Sample: The image of $y = 3x - 5$ under $T(x, y) = (x + h, y + 3h)$ is $y = 3x - 5$.

19c. Substitute $x - h$ for x and $y - 3h$ for y: $y - 3h = 3(x - h) - 5$; $y = 3x - 5$.

19d. Answers vary. Sample: The image of $y = mx + b$ under $T(x, y) = (x + h, y + mh)$ is $y = mx + b$.

The world-record largemouth bass, caught in 1932 in Georgia, was 32.5 inches long and 28.5 inches in girth.

17a. $y = 1.621x + 6.413$

17b. For every year that a largemouth bass ages, it grows 1.621 inches.

17c. about 25.87 inches

17d. Answers vary. Sample: extrapolation may not be appropriate in this context, because largemouth bass may stop growing in length when they are 10 years old.

17e. 0.97

17f. Age and length are positively correlated for the largemouth bass.

18a. $(k + 3)(k - 3)$
18b. $(3 - 4t)(3 + 4t)$
18c. $(p + 9)(p - 1)$

QY ANSWERS

1. $\{y \mid y \geq 1\}$
2. For C, $-5 \leq x \leq 5$.
For D, $0 \leq x \leq 10$.

164   Transformations of Graphs and Data

Lesson 3-3 Translations of Data

Vocabulary

invariant

▶ **BIG IDEA** Adding or subtracting the same value to every number in a data set adds or subtracts that value to measures of center but does not affect measures of spread.

Translating Data

The 2007 United States Open Golf Championship was played at the Oakmont Country Club in Pennsylvania. In golf, *par* is a predetermined number of strokes that a good golfer should require to complete a hole. For the Oakmont course, pars on the 18 holes totaled 70 strokes, so the course was considered to be a par-70 course. A golfer's progress through the 18 holes of a golf course is tracked by how many strokes the golfer is above or below par. For example, in his first round of the Open, Tiger Woods took 71 strokes, which was one over par, or +1. Angel Cabrera, the eventual champion, took 69 strokes, which was one under par, or –1, for the round.

The dimples on a golf ball make the ball travel farther.

▶ **Mental Math**

Calculate the average score for five basketball games that had scores of 92, 93, 94, 98, and 98.
95

News reports give both the raw scores, 71 and 69, and the scores relative to a par, 1 and –1. Notice that if a player's score is *s*, then his score in relation to par is $s - 70$. This is an example of a *translation of data*. Translations of data produce distributions that have predictable shapes, centers, and spreads.

 QY

A translation of a set of data $\{x_1, x_2, ..., x_n\}$ is a transformation that maps each x_i to $x_i + h$, where h is some constant. If T is the translation, then this transformation can be described as

$$T: x \rightarrow x + h \text{ or } T(x) = x + h.$$

The number $x + h$, or the point it represents, is the translation image of x. In the U.S. Open, the transformation T mapping each number of strokes onto its image has the rule $T(x) = x - 70$.

▶ **QY**

A golf course is rated at par 72. If a player's stroke score is *x*, what is his score relative to par?

Background

Many people apply the skill of translating to find a mean in day-to-day routines without being aware that they are doing so. It is intuitively sensible that averaging 105, 108, and 103 can be done mentally by averaging 5, 8, and 3, and then adding 100. This lesson shows that such a strategy works for all data sets. A translation by *h* of a data set moves the display *h* units and increases each measure of center by *h*.

However, all measures of spread (range, interquartile range, variance, standard deviation) remain unchanged, as do percentiles.

(continued on next page)

GOAL

Emphasize the parallel ideas of translating graphs and translating data. Investigate the effects of adding a constant to each data value on the displays of those values, on measures of center, and on measures of spread.

SPUR Objectives

H Use translations to describe and analyze data and statistics.

Materials/Resources

· Lesson Master 3-3
· Resource Masters 52 and 53
· Quiz 1

HOMEWORK   • Option 1
• Option 2

• Questions 1–8
• • Questions 9–17
• • Question 18 (extra credit)
   • Reading Lesson 3-4
   • Covering the Ideas 3-4
     (Questions 1–11)

Local Standards

1 Warm-Up

1. Find the mean of the data set: 101, 102, 103, 104, 105, 106, 107, 108, 109, 110. **105.5**
2. Find the mean of the data set: 136, 137, 138, 139, 140, 141, 142, 143, 144, 145. **140.5**
3. Explain how the answer to Warm-Up 1 can be used to determine the answer to Warm-Up 2. **Since each element in the data set of Warm-Up 2 is 35 greater than an element of Warm-Up 1, the mean will be 35 greater.**

3-3

2 Teaching

Notes on the Lesson

Measures of center and spread of translated data The two theorems (Centers of Translated Data and Spreads of Translated Data) are the basis for the strategy used in this lesson, and they should be discussed thoroughly. Help students work through the mathematical symbols used in justifying the theorems. (Question 12 asks them to prove two of the more basic theorems of summation notation.) They need to stay familiar with summation notation, as it is used in later chapters.

Additional Answers

Activity

Step 2:

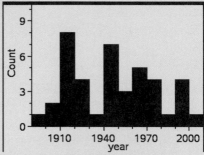

Step 5: mean: 27, median: 27, mode: –2, 27, range: 112 years, IQR: 50.5 years, standard deviation: 29.16; the range, IQR, and standard deviation are the same; the mean, mode, and median have changed.

Step 6: The histogram has the same shape and counts, but the *x*-axis is translated 1920 units to the left. The histogram bars stay the same, no matter how you change the slider.

Activity

In the United States, the passage of the 19th amendment to the Constitution in 1920 gave women the right to vote. This activity compares the year in which women earned the right to vote in the U.S. to the year women achieved that right in other countries.

Step 1 Enter the years below into a statistics utility. Label the column `year`.

1893	New Zealand	1920	United States	1949	China	1974	Jordan
1902	Australia	1921	Sweden	1950	India	1976	Portugal
1906	Finland	1928	Britain	1954	Colombia	1989	Namibia
1913	Norway	1928	Ireland	1957	Malaysia	1990	Western Samoa
1915	Denmark	1931	Spain	1962	Algeria	1993	Kazakhstan
1917	Canada	1944	France	1963	Iran	1993	Moldova
1918	Austria	1945	Italy	1963	Morocco	1994	South Africa
1918	Germany	1947	Argentina	1964	Libya	2005	Kuwait
1918	Poland	1947	Japan	1967	Ecuador		
1918	Russia	1947	Mexico	1971	Switzerland		
1919	Netherlands	1947	Pakistan	1972	Bangladesh		

Source: New York Times

Step 2 Make a histogram of the data. Use bin size 10. Compute the mean, median, mode, range, IQR, and standard deviation for the data.

Step 3 To compare the year in which women got the right to vote in different countries to the U.S., subtract 1920, the U.S. or *baseline* value, from all data points. To do this, first create a slider called "baseline" that takes on values from 0 to 2000. Title a second column `newyear`. In the formula line, enter = `year` – `baseline`.

Step 4 Adjust your slider so that baseline = 1920. What is the adjusted value for Libya? For Finland? Interpret each in a sentence.

Step 5 Compute the mean, median, mode, range, IQR, and standard deviation for the adjusted data. Which values are the same as the original data? Which are different? **Steps 5–8. See margin.**

Step 6 Now make a histogram of the adjusted data. Use bin size 10. How does it compare to the histogram for the original data? What happens to the histogram bars when you move the slider?

Step 7 Make box plots of both the original and the adjusted data. Again, move the slider around. Describe how the box plot changes as you change the data.

Step 8 Which numbers in the five-number summary are affected by translating the data, and which ones are unaffected by the translation?

Step 2: See margin for histogram. mean: 1947, median: 1947, mode: 1918, 1947, range: 112 years, IQR: 50.5 years, standard deviation: 29.16

Step 4: The adjusted value for Libya is 44, therefore Libyan women got the right to vote 44 years after American women. The adjusted value for Finland is –14, therefore Finnish women got the right to vote 14 years before American women.

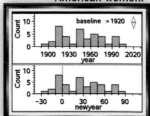

Translating data Whenever data is considered above or below a par value, it has been translated. For instance, in golf, scores are often translated. That is, if a round is par 72 and a person shoots 75, he or she might say "I shot 3 over par." Someone who shoots 71 would say, "I shot 1 under." In sports sections in newspapers, both the actual scores and the scores in relation to par are given. Subtracting par from the actual scores gives the amount of the translation, so that the score of a person who shoots under par is identified with a negative number.

Measures of spread for translated data The theorem (Spreads of Translated Data) could be restated as: Measures of spread are invariant under translations.

Measures of Center of Translated Data

Some of the results in the Activity are generalized in this theorem.

> **Theorem (Centers of Translated Data)**
>
> Adding h to each number in a data set adds h to each of the mean, median, and mode.

Proof Let $\{x_1, x_2, \ldots, x_n\}$ be a data set. Consider the translation in which x_i is mapped to $x_i + h$. To find the mean of the image set, you must evaluate

$$\frac{\sum_{i=1}^{n} (x_i + h)}{n}.$$

By definition of Σ, this expression represents

$$\frac{\overset{n \text{ terms}}{\overbrace{(x_1 + h) + (x_2 + h) + (x_3 + h) + \cdots + (x_n + h)}}}{n}.$$

Using the Associative and Commutative Properties of Addition, we rewrite the expression as

$$\frac{(x_1 + x_2 + x_3 + \cdots + x_n) + \overset{n \text{ terms}}{\overbrace{(h + h + h + \cdots + h)}}}{n}$$

$$= \frac{\left(\sum_{i=1}^{n} x_i\right) + nh}{n}$$

$$= \frac{\sum_{i=1}^{n} x_i}{n} + \frac{nh}{n}$$

$$= \frac{\sum_{i=1}^{n} x_i}{n} + h = \bar{x} + h.$$

Thus under a translation by h, the mean of the image set of data is h units more than the mean of the original set of data. It also can be shown that after a translation of h units, the median and mode of the image set are also increased by h units.

Measures of Spread for Translated Data

In the Activity, you saw that the range of the distributions, the IQR, and the standard deviation before and after the translation remain unchanged. To see that this is true in general for a data set $\{x_1, x_2, \ldots, x_n\}$ under a translation by h, first recall that range = maximum − minimum. Because a translation does not change the relative positions of the data points, the minimum value of the translated data is the image of the original minimum, and the maximum value of the translated data is the image of the original maximum.

Translations of Data   **167**

Additional Answers

Activity

Step 7: The shape of the box plot and relative distribution of the summary data does not change, but the x-axis changes.

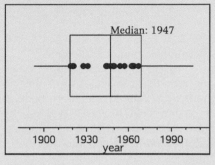

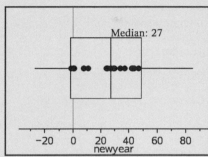

Step 8: All of the numbers (minimum, Q_1, median, Q_3, maximum) change with a translation, but the IQR and range are unaffected. Thus the box plot has the same appearance.

Let $\{x_1, x_2, x_3, \ldots, x_n\}$ be a data set, and k a constant.

a. Prove that $\sum_{i=1}^{n} (x_i + k) = \sum_{i=1}^{n} x_i + nk$.

b. Prove that $\sum_{i=1}^{n} (x_i - \bar{x}) = 0$, where $\bar{x}$ is the mean of the set.
(Hint: Apply the result of Part a.)

a. $\sum_{i=1}^{n} (x_i + k) = (x_1 + k) + (x_2 + k) + \ldots + (x_n + k)$
$= (x_1 + x_2 + \ldots + x_n) + nk$
$= \sum_{i=1}^{n} x_i + nk$

b. $\sum_{i=1}^{n} (x_i - \bar{x}) = \sum_{i=1}^{n} x_i - n\bar{x}$
$= n\bar{x} - n\bar{x}$
$= 0$

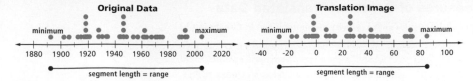

3-3

Original Data

minimum · maximum

1880 1900 1920 1940 1960 1980 2000 2020

segment length = range

Translation Image

minimum · maximum

-40 -20 0 20 40 60 80 100

segment length = range

Under a translation of h units, the minimum m is mapped to $m + h$ and the maximum M is mapped to $M + h$. The range of the translated data is

$$(M + h) - (m + h) = M - m,$$

which is the range of the original data. Therefore the range remains unchanged after the translation.

In the calculation of the variance and standard deviation of image data under a translation by h, the mean $\bar{x}$ becomes $\bar{x} + h$. So, each new deviation equals $(x_i + h) - (\bar{x} + h) = x_i - \bar{x}$, which is the original deviation. Because each individual deviation stays the same under a translation, the variance and standard deviation also stay the same.

Theorem (Spreads of Translated Data)

Adding h to each number in a data set does not change the range, interquartile range, variance, or standard deviation of the data.

Because the measures of spread of a data set do not vary under a translation, they are said to be **invariant** under a translation.

The preceding theorems can be used to compute measures of center or spread when data are increased or decreased.

Guided Example: 3 oz; 3 oz; 3 lb 5 oz; 3 oz; 3 oz; 3 lb 3.4 oz; 8 oz; 1 lb

GUIDED

Example

In a local produce store, cantaloupes sell for 99¢ per pound. A clerk weighed 30 melons and computed the following statistics: mean = 3.5 lb, standard deviation = 8 oz, median = 3.4 lb, and IQR = 1 lb. After finishing his task, the clerk noticed that the scales were not correctly calibrated. The scale was set at 3 oz as its starting weight, not 0. Find the correct values for the mean, standard deviation, median, and interquartile range for the 30 melons.

Solution The clerk recorded the weight of each cantaloupe as 3 ounces too heavy. The data need to be translated 3 ounces smaller. The mean and the median will therefore be decreased by 3 ounces.

Mean = 3.5 lb − _?_ = 3 lb 8 oz − _?_ = _?_

Median = 3.4 lb − _?_ = 3 lb 6.4 oz − _?_ = _?_

But the standard deviation and IQR will be unchanged.

Standard deviation = _?_ and IQR = _?_

Questions

COVERING THE IDEAS

1. A transformation that maps a number x to $x + h$ is called a(n) __?__.

   1. translation

2. The box plots at the right show the distribution of December salaries for 10 employees in a start-up company before and after their year-end bonus was added. How much was the bonus? **$1000**

   December Salary

3. Kayla withdrew the 5 amounts shown below from an ATM while visiting her sister in another town.

   Withdrawal amounts:
   $50 $100 $80 $120 $100.

   a. Find the following statistics for the five withdrawals.

   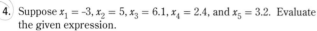

i. range **$70**	ii. mode **$100**
iii. median **$100**	iv. mean **$90**
v. variance **$700**	vi. standard deviation **$26.46**

   b. Since Kayla was not using her own bank's ATM, she was charged a fee of $1.50 for each transaction. Use your answers to Part a to compute the same statistics for the amounts withdrawn including the transaction fees.

4. Suppose $x_1 = -3$, $x_2 = 5$, $x_3 = 6.1$, $x_4 = 2.4$, and $x_5 = 3.2$. Evaluate the given expression.

   a. $\sum_{i=1}^{5} (x_i + 8)$ **53.7**

   b. $\sum_{i=1}^{5} x_i + 8$ **21.7**

5. For a set of n test scores, the mean was x and the standard deviation was s. Later, every score was increased by b bonus points.

   a. What is the mean of the translated scores? **$\bar{x} + b$**

   b. What is the standard deviation of the translated scores? **s**

6. Name four statistical measures that are invariant under a translation. **range, standard deviation, variance, IQR**

7. A set of data is translated. Find the missing values in the table.

	Original Data	Transformed Data
cases	10	__?__ **10**
mean	__?__ **63.5**	53
standard deviation	8.03	__?__ **8.03**
median	70	59.5
range	23	__?__ **23**
IQR	12	12

3b. i. $70
b. ii. $101.50
b. iii. $101.50
b. iv. $91.50
b. v. $700
b. vi. $26.46

3 Assignment

Recommended Assignment

- Questions 1–8
- Questions 9–17
- Question 18 (extra credit)
- Reading Lesson 3-4
- Covering the Ideas 3-4
  (Questions 1–11)

Notes on the Questions

Question 3a You may wish to remind students that in this book most of the data come from samples, so unless directed otherwise use the variance and standard deviation formulas for samples.

Question 3b This question can be done by either computing (50 + 1.50) + (100 + 1.50) + (80 + 1.50) + (120 + 1.50) + (100 + 1.50) or by computing (50 + 100 + 80 + 120 + 100) + 5(1.50). The generalization is found in Part a of the Accommodating the Learner (up) for this lesson.

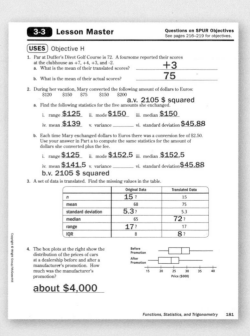

Additional Answers

8a.

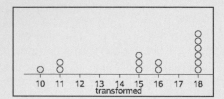

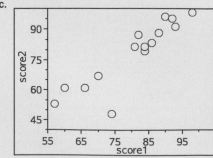

9a.

	score1	score2		
	84	79		
	84	81		
	66	61		
	98	98		
	70	67		
	86	83		

A | **score1**

9b.

	$\overline{x}$	s
score 1	80.33	12.34
score 2	77.93	16.10

9c.

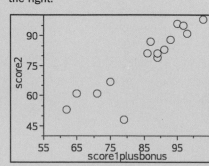

9d. 0.899

9e. $y = 1.173x - 16.333$

---

8. Consider the two frequency distributions below.

Original Scores	Frequency
2	1
3	2
7	3
8	2
10	6

Transformed Scores	Frequency
10	1
11	2
15	3
16	2
18	6

8a. See margin.

8b. $T(x) = x + 8$

a. Make a dot-frequency diagram showing the two sets of scores.
b. Identify the transformation used to get the transformed scores.
c. Find the interquartile range, mode, mean, and median for the original scores. **IQR: 3; mode: 10; mean: 7.5; median: 8**
d. Use the theorems of the lesson and your answers to Parts b and c to give the IQR, mode, mean, and median for the transformed data. **IQR: 3; mode: 18; mean: 15.5; median: 16**

APPLYING THE MATHEMATICS

In 9 and 10, consider the data at the right, which give the scores from the first two tests in a class of 15 students taking *FST*. See margin.

Test 1	Test 2
84	79
84	81
66	61
98	98
70	67
86	83
74	48
60	61
88	88
93	91
81	81
90	96
82	87
57	53
92	95

9. a. Enter these data into a statistics utility, naming the lists *score 1* and *score 2*.
   b. Find the means and standards deviation of *score 1* and *score 2*.
   c. Draw a scatterplot with *score 1* on the horizontal axis and *score 2* on the vertical axis.
   d. Find the correlation coefficient.
   e. Find the line of best fit for predicting *score 2* from *score 1*.
   f. Suppose the teacher decided to add 5 bonus points to each score on the first test. Add 5 to each *score 1*. Draw a new scatterplot. How is this scatterplot different from the one in Part c?
   g. Compute the correlation coefficient and the least squares regression equation for the new scores on test 1 and the scores on test 2. Compare your answers to those in Parts d and e. What value(s) are invariant under this transformation? What value(s) have changed?
   h. Suppose the teacher made an error when computing the scores for the second test and to correct his error he subtracted 3 points from each score. Draw a scatterplot with the *score 1 plus bonus* on the horizontal axis and *score 2 minus 3* on the vertical axis. How is this scatterplot different from those drawn in Parts c and f?
   i. Compute the correlation coefficient and the least squares regression equation for the transformed scores.
   j. Compare the correlation coefficient, slope and intercepts. What value(s) are invariant under these transformations? What value(s) have changed?

Counting on a calculator

Additional Answers

9f. The points are shifted on the *x*-axis 5 units to the right.

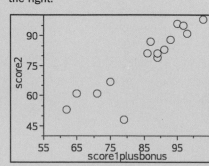

9g. $r = 0.899$, $y = 1.173x - 22.2$; The correlation coefficient and slope of the regression line are invariant; the y-intercept changed.

9h. For any point (x, y) in Part c, the point is translated to $(x + 5, y - 3)$. For the point (x, y) in Part f, the point is translated to $(x, y - 3)$. Screenshot at the right.

10. **Multiple Choice** Generalize the results of Question 9. If bivariate data are translated, which (if any) of the following are invariant? **B, D, E**
    A means of the two variables
    B standard deviations of the two variables
    C intercept of the line of best fit
    D slope of the line of best fit
    E correlation coefficient between the two variables

11. Mentally calculate the mean of the heights of the starters on a basketball team: 6′, 6′2″, 6′3″, 6′4″, 6′6″. **6′3″**

12. Let $\{x_1, x_2, x_3, ..., x_n\}$ be a data set with median m, and h a constant.
    a. Suppose that n is odd. Explain why the median of the set $\{x_1 + h, x_2 + h, ..., x_n + h\}$ is $m + h$.
    b. Explain why the median of the translated set is also $m + h$ when n is even.

REVIEW

13. Consider the equation $y + 3 = \frac{1}{x + 2}$. **(Lesson 3-2)**
    a. Graph the equation using paper and pencil.
    b. Check your work with a graphing utility.
    c. Give a rule for the translation that maps the graph of $y = \frac{1}{x}$ onto the graph in Parts a and b. $T(x, y) = (x - 2, y - 3)$

14. Suppose the translation $T: (x, y) \longrightarrow (x - 8, y + 13)$ is applied to the graph of the function with equation $y = \frac{1}{x^2}$. **(Lesson 3-2)**
    a. Find an equation for the image. $y - 13 = \frac{1}{(x + 8)^2}$
    b. Sketch graphs of the image and preimage. **See margin.**

15. Let a real function f be defined by $f: x \longrightarrow \sqrt{x + 99}$. What is the domain of f? **(Lesson 3-1)** $\{x \mid x \geq -99\}$

16. **Skill Sequence** Solve for t. **(Previous Course)**
    a. $rt = 18$ b. $rt = 7 + r$ c. $r = \frac{5}{t}$ d. $r + 4 = \frac{1}{t}$

17. a. Draw $\triangle ABC$ with $A = (0, 2)$, $B = (3, 0)$, and $C = (4, 4)$.
    b. Let r be the transformation that maps each point (x, y) onto $(2x, 3y)$. Draw $A'B'C' = r(\triangle ABC)$. **17a–b. See margin.**
    c. What transformation is r? **(Previous Course)** the scale change $S_{2,3}$

EXPLORATION

18. Give an example of a situation other than an athletic event where data are often translated, and explain why the translated data are used. **See margin.**

12a. If n is odd, in the set there is some i such that x_i is the median m. Since a translation maps each x_i to $x_i + h$, it maps the median to $m + h$.

12b. If n is even, there is no i in the set such that x_i is the median. The median is defined as the mean of the two middle values when the set is arranged in increasing order. For example $m = \frac{x_a + x_b}{2}$. Since a translation maps each x_i to $x_i + h$, it maps the median to
$$\frac{(x_a + h) + (x_b + h)}{2}$$
$$= \frac{(x_a + x_b) + (2h)}{2} =$$
$$\frac{(x_a + x_b)}{2} + h = m + h.$$

13a–b.

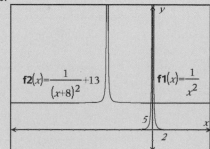

16a. $t = \frac{18}{r}$

16b. $t = \frac{7}{r + 1}$

16c. $t = \frac{5}{r}$

16d. $t = \frac{1}{r + 4}$

QY ANSWER

$x - 72$

Translations of Data **171**

3-3

Notes on the Questions
Question 17 This question reviews scale changes in anticipation of Lesson 3-5.

4 Wrap-Up

Ongoing Assessment
Write a problem like Question 7 on the board. Ask students to copy and complete the table. **Answers vary. Check students' work.**

Administer Quiz 1 (or a quiz of your own) after students complete this lesson.

Project Update
Project 1, *Sports Handicaps*, Project 3, *Transformation Groups*, and Project 5, *Class Survey Revisited, Yet Again*, on pages 211 and 212 relate to the content of this lesson.

Additional Answers

17a.

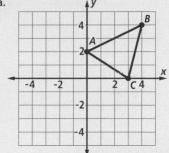

17b.

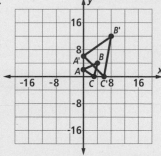

18. Answers vary. Sample: Conversions between different scales of measurement can be understood as translations of data. For example, the conversion between Celsius and Kelvin is a translation on the x-axis. We often consider data in more than one scale because the scales can highlight different aspects of the data. For instance, the temperature 0°C is the freezing temperature of water, whereas the temperature 0 K is absolute zero.

Additional Answers

9h.

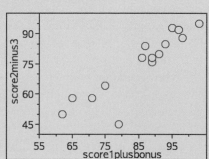

9i. $r = 0.899$, $y = 1.173x - 25.2$

9j. The correlation coefficient and slope are invariant; the y-intercept changed.

14b.

f2(x) = $\frac{1}{(x+8)^2}$ + 13   f1(x) = $\frac{1}{x^2}$

Lesson 3-4

Lesson 3-4

GOAL

Review the ideas of reflection and rotation symmetry, apply them to graphs of functions, and to the ideas of even and odd functions.

SPUR Objectives

D Describe the effects of translations on functions and their graphs.

E Describe and identify symmetries and asymptotes of graphs.

I Recognize functions and their properties from their graphs.

Materials/Resources

· Lesson Master 3-4
· Resource Masters 54 and 55

HOMEWORK

• Option 1
• Option 2

• Questions 1–11
• • Questions 12–25
• • Question 26 (extra credit)
• Reading Lesson 3-5
• Covering the Ideas 3-5 (Questions 1–11)

Local Standards

1 Warm-Up

1. How many symmetry lines does a square have? **4**
2. How many centers of symmetry does a square have? **1**
3. How many symmetry lines does an isosceles trapezoid have? **1**
4. How many centers of symmetry does an isosceles trapezoid have? **0**
5. Draw a figure with more than one center of symmetry. **Answers vary. Samples: sine wave, line.**

Symmetries of Graphs

Lesson 3-4

Vocabulary

reflection-symmetric
axis of symmetry
line of symmetry
symmetric about a point
point symmetry
even function
odd function

▶ **BIG IDEA**   Rules for functions can be used to determine symmetries of graphs and vice versa.

Recall from your previous courses that a figure is **reflection-symmetric** if and only if the figure can be mapped onto itself by a reflection over some line *l*. The reflecting line *l* is called the **axis** or **line of symmetry** of the figure. A line of symmetry can be any line in the plane. Similarly, a figure is **symmetric about point** *p* or has **point symmetry** if and only if the figure can be mapped onto itself under a rotation of 180° around *P*. The point *P* is called a **center of symmetry**.

Because graphs are sets of points, these definitions apply to graphs. Any symmetry of a figure implies that one part of the figure is congruent to another part. So when a graph has symmetry, the symmetry shortens the time in drawing the graph and helps in studying it.

Mental Math

What is the least number of symmetry lines the figure can have?

a. parabola **1**

b. rectangle **2**

c. equilateral triangle **3**

d. circle **infinite**

Activity 1

The diagram at the right shows half of a graph.

Step 1 Copy the diagram. Draw the other half of the graph so that the result is point-symmetric about the origin. Label this half A.

Step 2 Draw the other half of the original graph so that the result is symmetric with respect to the *y*-axis. Label this half B.

Step 3 Draw the other half of the original graph so that it is symmetric over the *x*-axis. Label the graph C.

Step 4 What symmetries does the union of graphs A, B, and C and the original graph possess?

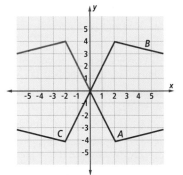

Recall also that the reflection image of (x, y) over the *x*-axis is $(x, -y)$ and the reflection image of (x, y) over the *y*-axis is $(-x, y)$. Also the image of (x, y) under a rotation of 180° about the origin is $(-x, -y)$. Combining these facts with the definitions of reflection, symmetry, and point symmetry yields three theorems.

Step 4: The union of these graphs is reflection-symmetric over both axes and is point-symmetric about the origin.

Background

Symmetry is at once one of the easiest ideas in mathematics and the most important. If we know that a figure (such as the graph of a relation) is symmetric, then we need only deal with a part of the figure to know the whole. In this lesson, all symmetries of graphs assume that these graphs are on a rectangular coordinate grid. There are theorems corresponding to those on page 173 for graphs in polar coordinates, but they are different.

A figure is considered to be symmetric if it coincides with its image under some non-trivial isometry. The first paragraph of the lesson reviews reflection symmetry and one type of rotation symmetry. But there is also translation symmetry, when a figure coincides with its image under a translation. Students will encounter this type of symmetry in the study of graphs of trigonometric functions, for every sine wave and its translation and scale change images is translation-symmetric.

Theorem (Symmetry over y-axis)

A graph is symmetric with respect to the y-axis if and only if for every point (x, y) on the graph, $(-x, y)$ is also on the graph.

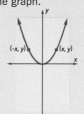

Theorem (Symmetry over x-axis)

A graph is symmetric with respect to the x-axis if and only if for every point (x, y) on the graph, $(x, -y)$ is also on the graph.

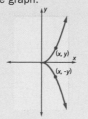

Theorem (Symmetry about the Origin)

A graph is symmetric to the origin if and only if for every point (x, y) on the graph, $(-x, -y)$ is also on the graph.

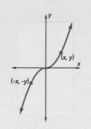

Proving That a Graph Has Symmetry

One point can be a counterexample that shows a graph does not have a certain type of symmetry. But one point cannot determine that a general relationship holds. The graphs of $f(x) = x^2$ and $g(x) = \frac{10}{3x^2 + 1}$ seem symmetric with respect to the y-axis. But this is not a proof.

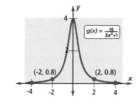

To show that the graph of an equation is symmetric, you use algebra and test the general point (x, y).

Example 1

Prove that the graph of $f(x) = \frac{1}{x^2 + 1}$ is symmetric to the y-axis.

Solution To show that the graph of f is symmetric to the y-axis, you need to show that for all (x, y) on the graph, $(-x, y)$ is also on the graph. In other words, you need to prove $f(x) = f(-x)$ for all x in the domain of f.

$$f(x) = \frac{10}{3x^2 + 1}$$

$$f(-x) = \frac{10}{3(-x)^2 + 1} = \frac{10}{3x^2 + 1}$$

So $f(x) = f(-x)$. Therefore the graph of $f(x) = \frac{10}{3x^2 + 1}$ is symmetric to the y-axis.

2 Teaching

Notes on the Lesson

All of the material in this lesson may be review for students who have studied from UCSMP *Advanced Algebra*.

Be sure to point out the difference between *point symmetry* and *rotation symmetry*. A figure has *rotation symmetry* (as defined in UCSMP *Geometry*) if it can be mapped onto itself by a rotation of any magnitude between 0° and 360°. *Point symmetry* requires that the magnitude be 180°.

Students may have difficulty with the notation in the definitions of symmetry and of even and odd functions. When confronted with x and –x in the same setting, students tend to think that x must be positive and –x must be negative. To counter this, you might say "In even functions, any two opposite x-values give the same y-values." Keep appealing to symmetry: if (x, y) and $(-x, y)$ are on a graph, the points are reflection images of each other over the y-axis.

Additional Example

Example 1 Prove that the graph of $y = \sqrt{36 - x^2}$ is symmetric to the y-axis. For all x, $f(-x) = \sqrt{36 - (-x)^2} = \sqrt{36 - x^2} = f(x)$, therefore the graph of $y = \sqrt{36 - x^2}$ is symmetric to the y-axis.

When $n \neq 0$, the graph of $y = ax^n$ is symmetric with respect to the y-axis when n is even and is symmetric with respect to the origin when n is odd, whether or not n is positive or negative. So, for instance, $y = \frac{1}{x}$ can be interpreted as $y = x^{-1}$, which indicates it is an odd function symmetric to the origin. More generally, if the equation for a graph contains only odd powers of the independent variable, then the graph is point-symmetric with respect to the origin (Activities 1 and 2). If the equation for a graph contains only even powers of the independent variable, then the graph is reflection-symmetric with respect to the y-axis (Example 1).

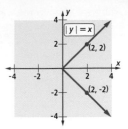

Notes on the Lesson

The lesson mentions that even and odd functions get their names from the power functions. Students should understand that even power functions are only a subset of the set of even functions, and odd power functions are a subset of the odd functions. Example 2 shows an odd function even though it is not a power function.

A graphing utility makes the identification of odd or even functions a much less conceptual task than used to be the case because the classification is visual rather than analytical. At the same time, however, emphasize that a graph can only give an indication of the odd or even status of a function. Even if the odd or even property looks to be satisfied, a proof of the property is required to demonstrate it. A graph can, on the other hand, suggest a counterexample with specific points to show that a function is not odd or not even.

Some students think that a function is even or odd when they manage to provide just one numerical example that meets the condition. The difference between a specific example and proving something true for all values in the domain may need clarification. To show that one numerical example does not suffice, you can consider the function f with $f(x) = x^3 - 4x + 1$. The points $(2, 1)$ and $(-2, 1)$ are on the graph of f, but the function is not an even function.

Some students might not see symmetry to the origin as resulting from a 180° rotation. They may, however, see that an odd function maps onto itself if it is reflected over the x-axis and then the image is reflected over the y-axis (or vice versa). That the composite of two reflections over intersecting lines is a rotation is a theorem deduced in UCSMP *Geometry* and has been discussed also in UCSMP *Advanced Algebra* and will appear again in this course. To see the 180° rotation, have students turn the page upside down. If a figure looks the same upside down as it does originally, then it has point symmetry over some point. Examples with letters of the alphabet are Z, N, and S, but not C or K.

Using Symmetry to Aid in Graphing

The ideas of symmetry apply to graphs of relations that are not functions. For instance, the graph of $x = |y|$ is symmetric to the x-axis, since if $x = |y|$, then $x = |-y|$.

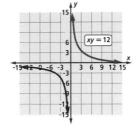

Even and Odd Functions

In previous courses and Lesson 2-7, you studied power functions with equations such as $y = x^2$, $y = x^3$, or $y = x^4$. The power functions f with $f(x) = ax^n$, where $a \neq 0$ and n is even, can all be proved to be symmetric over the y-axis. For this reason, any function whose graph is symmetric with respect to the y-axis is called an *even function*.

Definition of Even Function

A function is an **even function** if and only if for all values of x in its domain, $f(-x) = f(x)$.

By the method of Example 1, the graphs of the power functions f with $f(x) = ax^n$, where $a \neq 0$ and n is odd, can all be proved to be symmetric about the origin. For this reason, a function whose graph is symmetric about the origin is called an *odd function*.

Definition of Odd Function

A function f is an **odd function** if and only if for all values of x in its domain, $f(-x) = -f(x)$.

🛑 **QY**

If you are not sure if a function is even, odd, or neither, then a graphing utility or CAS may help you decide.

Step 1: The function is $f(x) = \frac{12}{x}$. $f(-x) = -\frac{12}{x}$ $\neq f(x)$, $-f(x) = -\frac{12}{x}$ $\neq f(x)$ but $-f(-x) = \frac{12}{x}$ $= f(x)$, so the equation is only symmetric with respect to the origin.

▶ **QY**

Look at the graphs for the theorems on page 173 of this lesson.

a. Which graph shows an even function?

b. Which graph shows an odd function?

174   Transformations of Graphs and Data

Accommodating the Learner ⬇

If some students are having trouble with the geometry in this lesson, you might give them a variety of graphs to sketch, such as the following:

1. Sketch the graph of a function which is symmetric over the y-axis, but does not contain the origin.

2. Sketch the graph of a quadratic function that is symmetric over the line $x = -7$.

3. Sketch the graph of an odd function that contains the point $(3, 20)$.

4. Sketch the graph of an even function that contains the point $(3, 20)$

Answers vary. Check students' work.

Example 2

Determine whether the function $f: x \rightarrow 4x - 2x^3$ is odd, even, or neither. If it appears to be even or odd, prove it.

Solution 1 Draw a graph to see if f appears to be even or odd.
A graph of f is shown at the right.

The graph appears to be symmetric about the origin, so f seems to be an odd function. To prove this, suppose (x, y) is on the graph. That is, $y = f(x) = 4x - 2x^3$. Now consider $f(-x)$.

$$f(-x) = 4(-x) - 2(-x)^3$$
$$= -4x + 2x^3$$
$$= -(4x - 2x^3)$$

Thus, $f(-x) = -f(x)$ for all x, so f is an odd function.

Solution 2 Define $f(x) = 4x - 2x^3$ on a CAS. Evaluate $f(-x)$ and $-f(x)$, as shown at the right. The expression for $f(-x)$ is the same as for $-f(x)$. For all x, $f(-x) = -f(x)$, so f is odd.

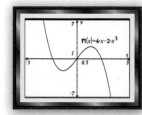

Using the Graph-Translation Theorem to Find Symmetries

You have seen graphs with symmetry related to the x-axis, the y-axis, and the origin. However, a line or point of symmetry may be located in other positions. If the graph is the translation image of a familiar graph, the symmetry of the known graph can give information about symmetry in the image.

Example 3

Consider the function F with $y = F(x) = \dfrac{1}{(x + 3)^2} - 7$.

a. Give equations for the asymptotes of its graph.
b. Describe any lines or points of symmetry.

Solution

a. Rewrite the equation as $y + 7 = \dfrac{1}{(x + 3)^2}$. This shows that, by the Graph-Translation Theorem, the graph of F is the image of the graph of $y = \dfrac{1}{x^2}$ under the translation $T(x, y) = (x - 3, y - 7)$. The graph of the parent function has asymptotes $x = 0$ and $y = 0$. Each asymptote is translated 3 units to the left and 7 units down. So, the asymptotes of F are $x = -3$ and $y = -7$.

b. Since the graph of $y = \dfrac{1}{x^2}$ is symmetric to the y-axis, the graph of F is symmetric over the vertical line $x = -3$. Indeed, this line is the translation image of $x = 0$ under $T: (x, y) \rightarrow (x - 3, y - 7)$.

Check Sketch a graph of F.

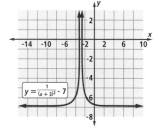

$$y = \frac{1}{(x+3)^2} - 7$$

Notes on the Lesson

Example 3 Point out that although the graph of the function has line symmetry, it is not an even function. For an even function, the graph must be symmetric with respect to the y-axis. Similarly, it is possible for a graph to have point symmetry but not be an odd function, when the center of symmetry is not the origin.

Additional Examples

Example 2 Determine whether the function $f(x) = x^3 - 5x$ is odd, even or neither. If it appears to be even or odd, prove it. **Odd; for all x, $f(-x) = (-x)^3 - 5(-x) = -x^3 + 5x = -(x^3 - 5x) = -f(x)$.**

Example 3 Consider the function H with $y = H(x) = \dfrac{3}{x - 8} + 9.5$.

a. Give equations for the asymptotes of its graph. **$x = 8$ and $y = 9.5$**

b. Describe any lines or points of symmetry. **the graph of H is symmetric to the point $(8, 9.5)$**

3 Assignment

Recommended Assignment
- Questions 1–11
- •. Questions 12–25
- • Question 26 (extra credit)
- • Reading Lesson 3-5
- • Covering the Ideas 3-5
  (Questions 1–11)

Notes on the Questions
You might have students discuss their work on these questions in small groups of 2–4, as we think it would take a long time to discuss all the questions with the entire class. Then you might summarize the main points of these questions.

Question 5 The graph of $y = x \cdot |x|$ looks quite a bit like the graph of $y = x^2$. Can students see why?
(When $x \geq 0$, $x \cdot |x| = x^2$; when $x < 0$, $x \cdot |x| = x \cdot (-x) = -x^2$. So when $x \geq 0$, the two graphs are identical. When $x < 0$, the graphs are reflection images of one another over the x-axis.)

Properties of Graphs of Translation Images

In general, if f is a function and each point (x, y) on its graph is mapped to $(x + h, y + k)$, then the graph of the image is congruent to the graph of the preimage, and all key points and lines are also mapped under this translation. Specifically, lines of symmetry map to lines of symmetry, maxima to maxima, minima to minima, vertices to vertices, symmetry points to symmetry points, and asymptotes to asymptotes.

This chart summarizes the characteristics of even and odd functions.

	Even Function	Odd Function
Symmetry	symmetric over y-axis	symmetric about about the origin
Transformation	$(x, y) \rightarrow (-x, y)$	$(x, y) \rightarrow (-x, -y)$
Function Notation	$f(-x) = f(x)$	$f(-x) = -f(x)$
Sample Graph and Equation	 $y = x^2$	$y = x^3$

Questions

COVERING THE IDEAS

1. The part of a graph that is in Quadrant II is shown. The graph is symmetric over to the x-axis and passes through only two quadrants.
   a. Copy the graph and complete it.
   b. The point $(-6, 5)$ is on the graph. Use symmetry to to find another point on the graph. $(-6, -5)$

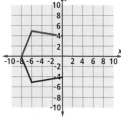

In 2–4, suppose z is a relation function that includes $(4, -2)$. What other point must be included in the relation if z has the stated property?

2. z is odd. $(-4, 2)$ 　　　　3. z is even. $(-4, -2)$

4. The graph of z is symmetric with respect to the x-axis. $(4, 2)$

5. The point $(-3, -9)$ satisfies the equation $y = x \cdot |x|$. Use this point to test whether the graph of $y = x \cdot |x|$ appears to be symmetric
   a. over the y-axis. 　　b. over the x-axis. 　　c. about the origin.

6. Prove that the function f defined by $f: x \rightarrow 6x^{-1}$ is an odd function.

5a. $-9 \neq 3\,|3|$; the graph is not symmetric with respect to the y-axis.

5b. $9 \neq -3\,|-3|$; the graph is not symmetric with respect to the x-axis.

6. $f(-x) = \dfrac{6}{-x} = -\dfrac{6}{x} = -f(x)$

Additional Answers

5c. $9 = 3\,|3|$; the graph could be symmetric with respect to the origin.

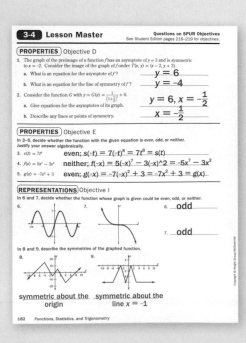

7. The part of the graph of $y = \dfrac{8}{2 + x^2}$ that lies in Quadrant I is at the right. Test for symmetry with respect to the y-axis, x-axis, and origin. Then, complete the graph.

8. For each type of function in the left column, name two properties from the right column which match.

a. even function   i. The graph is symmetric about the origin.

b. odd function   ii. If (x, y) is in the function, so is $(-x, y)$.

8a. ii, iv

8b. i, iii

iii. If (x, y) is in the function, so is $(-x, -y)$.

iv. The graph is symmetric over to the y-axis.

v. The graph is symmetric over to the x-axis.

vi. If (x, y) is in the function, so is $(x, -y)$.

In 9 and 10, an equation of a function is given. Tell if the function is odd, even, or neither.

9. $f(x) = -246x$ **odd**

10. $g(x) = \frac{1}{2}x^3 + 3$ **neither**

11. Consider the function $f: x \to \dfrac{1}{x - 6} + 1$.

a. Sketch a graph of $y = f(x)$. **See margin.**

b. Give equations for the asymptotes of the graph. $x = 6, y = 1$

c. How are these asymptotes related to the asymptotes of the parent function?

APPLYING THE MATHEMATICS

12. At the right is the graph of a function f that is point-symmetric with respect to the origin. Sketch the graph that is the translation image of the graph of f with $(-6, 4)$ for a center of symmetry. **See margin.**

13. Give a counterexample to prove that the function f with $f(t) = t^3 - 2$ is not an even function.

In 14 and 15, one quadrant of the graph of the given equation is shown. Use symmetry to complete the graph.

14. $x^2 + 4y^2 = 16$

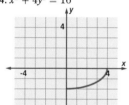

15. $|x| + |y| = 3$ **See margin.**

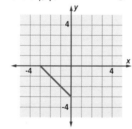

16. Recall from geometry that a circle whose center is at the origin has an equation of the form $x^2 + y^2 = r^2$. Prove algebraically that the circle with equation $x^2 + y^2 = 9$ has all three types of symmetry discussed in this lesson. **See margin.**

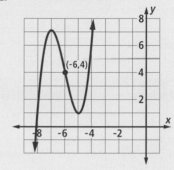

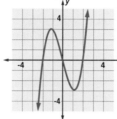

7. $f(-x) = \dfrac{8}{2 + x^2} = f(x)$,

$-f(x) = -\dfrac{8}{2 + x^2} \neq f(x)$,

and $-f(-x) =$

$-\dfrac{8}{2 + x^2} \neq f(x)$, so f is only symmetric with respect to the y-axis. See margin for graph.

11c. They are translated 6 units to the right and 1 unit up.

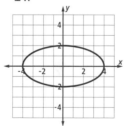

13. Answers vary. Sample: The point $(2, 6)$ is on the graph but the point $(-2, 6)$ is not, so f cannot be even.

14.

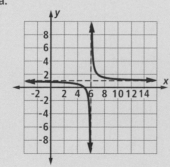

Notes on the Questions

Question 11 Ask students for an equation of the parent function. $y = \frac{1}{x}$

Question 13 f is not an odd function either, but its graph is point-symmetric with respect to $(0, -2)$.

Additional Answers

12.

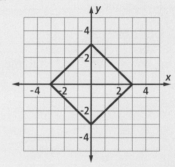

15.

16. Suppose that (x, y) is a point on the circle. Then $x^2 + y^2 = 9$. Test

$(-x, y)$: $(-x)^2 + y^2 = x^2 + y^2 = 9$

$(x, -y)$: $x^2 + (-y)^2 = x^2 + y^2 = 9$

$(-x, -y)$: $(-x)^2 + (-y)^2 = x^2 + y^2 = 9$

The circle has all three types of symmetry.

Symmetries of Graphs   **177**

Additional Answers

7.

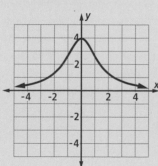

11a.

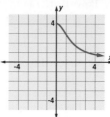

3-4

Notes on the Questions

Question 26a If the function is continuous, the answer is No. But if the function has discontinuities, then it is possible for it to have any amount of rotation symmetry. For example, consider this piecewise-defined function with three jump discontinuities:

$$f(x) = \begin{cases} x - 1 \text{ if } 1 < x < 2 \\ -x - 1 \text{ if } 0 < x < 1 \\ -x + 1 \text{ if } -1 < x < 0 \\ x + 1 \text{ if } -2 < x < -1 \end{cases}$$

The graph of f has 90° rotation symmetry about the origin.

4 ▶ Wrap-Up

Ongoing Assessment

Have students write a paragraph describing the symmetries of the graphs of odd and even functions, giving an example and graph of each. **Answers vary. Check students' work.**

Project Update

Project 2, *Facial Symmetry and Asymmetry*, on page 211 relates to the content of this lesson.

---

17. Prove that if f and g are odd functions, so is $f + g$. *Hint:* Consider $(f + g)(x)$ and $(f + g)(-x)$.

18. Use the function g with $g(x) = x^3$ as a parent function. The functions h and j with $h(x) = -x^3$ and $j(x) = x^3 + 2$ are related to it.
    a. Sketch the graphs of all three functions. **See margin.**
    b. Determine if each function is odd, even, or neither.
    c. Describe a transformation that maps g onto h.
    d. Describe a transformation that maps g onto j. **See margin.**
    e. Describe the symmetries of the three graphs. If there is reflection symmetry, give the equation of the line of symmetry. If there is point symmetry, give the coordinates of the center of symmetry.

REVIEW

19. The class results of a test on *Moby Dick* in American Literature were $\bar{x} = 67$ and $s = 13$. The teacher decides to add 4 points to each score. (**Lesson 3-3**)
    a. What is the class mean after this transformation? $\bar{x} = 71$
    b. What is the class standard deviation after this transformation? $s = 13$

A whale of a tale
Moby Dick was a sperm whale.

20. **Skill Sequence** If $t_1 = 10$, $t_2 = -1$, $t_3 = 16$, and $t_4 = 6$, evaluate the expression. (**Lessons 3-3, 1-5**)
    a. $\sum_{i=1}^{4} t_i - 2$ **29**
    b. $\sum_{i=1}^{4} (t_i - 2)$ **23**
    c. $-2\sum_{i=1}^{4} t_i$ **-62**

21. Suppose the translation $T: (x, y) \rightarrow (x + 2, y - 5)$ is applied to the graph of $y = x^5$. (**Lesson 3-2**)
    a. Find an equation for the image. $y = (x - 2)^5 - 5$
    b. Are the graphs of the preimage and image congruent? Explain why or why not. **yes; translations preserve length and angle measure**

In 22–25, use the circle at the right. $P = (a, b)$ and Q is the image of P under a 180° rotation around O. Express each of the following in terms of a and b. (**Previous Course**)

22. OF a

23. OP $\sqrt{a^2 + b^2}$

24. x-coordinate of Q $-a$

25. y-coordinate of Q $-b$

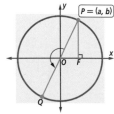

EXPLORATION

26. a. Can the graph of a function be mapped onto itself by a rotation whose magnitude is not 180° or 360°? If so, give some examples. If not, explain why not.
    b. Consider the question of Part a for graphs of relations which are not functions. **See margin.**

---

17. Suppose $f(x)$ and $g(x)$ are odd functions, then $f(-x) = -f(x)$ and $g(-x) = -g(x)$. Let $h(x) = f(x) + g(x)$. Then $h(-x) = f(-x) + g(-x) = -f(x) - g(x) = -(f(x) + g(x)) = -h(x)$ i.e. $h(x)$ is odd. Thus, the sum of two odd functions is odd.

18b. g and h are odd, j is neither

18c. $(x, y) \rightarrow (-x, y)$

18e. g and h both have point symmetry about the origin and j has point symmetry about $(0, 2)$.

QY ANSWER

a. the graph with symmetry over the y-axis

b. the graph with symmetry about the origin

Additional Answers

18a.

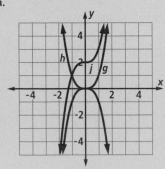

18d. $(x, y) \rightarrow (x, y + 2)$

26a. Yes; for example, the graph of the function $\{(1, 3), (-3, 1), (-1, -3), (3, -1)\}$ is mapped onto itself by rotations of 90° and 270°.

26b. Yes; for instance, the graph of a square centered at the origin can be mapped onto itself by a rotation of 90° about the origin.

Lesson 3-5

The Graph Scale-Change Theorem

Vocabulary

horizontal and vertical scale change

scale factor

size change

▶ **BIG IDEA** The graph of a function can be scaled horizontally, vertically, or in both directions at the same time.

Vertical Scale Changes

Consider the graph of $y = f1(x) = x^3 + 3x^2 - 4x$ shown both in the graph and function table at the right. What happens when you multiply all the y-values of the graph by 2? What would the resulting graph and table look like? Activity 1 will help you answer these questions.

Mental Math

What is $R_{270°}$ (1, 0)?

$(0, -1)$

Activity 1 See margin.

MATERIALS Graphing utility or slider graph application from your teacher

Step 1 Graph $f1(x) = x^3 + 3x^2 - 4x$ with window $-11 \leq x \leq 13$ and $-10 \leq y \leq 40$.

Step 2 Graph $f2(x) = 3(x^3 + 3x^2 - 4x) = 3 \cdot f1(x)$ on the same axes. Fill in the table of values for $f1(x)$ and $f2(x)$ only. Describe how the $f2(x)$ values relate to the $f1(x)$ values.

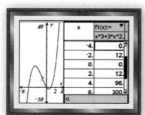

x	$f1(x)$	$f2(x)$	$0.5 \cdot f1(x)$	$1.5 \cdot f1(x)$	$2 \cdot f1(x)$
-4	?	?	?	?	?
2	?	?	?	?	?
7	?	?	?	?	?
10	?	?	?	?	?

Step 3 Repeat Step 2 with $f3(x) = b(x^3 + 3x^2 - 4x)$ and use a slider to vary the value of b. Set the slider to 0.5, 1.5, and then 2. For each of these b-values, use a function table to fill in a column of the table in Step 2. Describe how the $f3(x)$ values relate to the corresponding values of $f1(x)$.

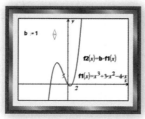

In Step 2 of Activity 1, we say that the graph of $f2$ is the image of the graph of $f1$ under a *vertical scale change* of magnitude 3. Each point on the graph of $f2$ is the image of a point on the graph of f under the mapping $(x, y) \rightarrow (x, 3y)$. You can create the same change by replacing y by $\frac{y}{3}$ in the equation for $f1$, because $\frac{y}{3} = x^3 + 3x^2 - 4x$ is equivalent to $y = 3(x^3 + 3x^2 - 4x)$, or $y = 3f1(x)$ in function notation. Similarly, if you replace y by $2y$ in the original equation, you would obtain $2y = x^3 + 3x^2 - 4x$, which is equivalent to $y = \frac{1}{2}(x^3 + 3x^2 - 4x)$ or $y = \frac{1}{2}f(x)$.

The Graph Scale-Change Theorem **179**

Background

The development in this lesson parallels the one in Lesson 3-3 of the Graph-Translation Theorem, and so does the mathematics. Just as replacing x by $x - h$ added h to the x-coordinates of points which satisfy a relation, so replacing x by $\frac{x}{a}$ multiplies the x-coordinates by a.

The Graph Scale-Change Theorem

Here is a proof of this theorem. If a preimage graph undergoes a scale change by a horizontal factor a and vertical factor b, then $x' = ax$ and $y' = by$. Therefore $x = \frac{x'}{a}$

and $y = \frac{y'}{b}$. Substituting gives an equation in $\frac{x'}{a}$ and $\frac{y'}{b}$. This equation, because it involves x' and y', is an equation for the image graph.

The Graph Scale-Change Theorem is applied in later chapters to determine the amplitude and period of trigonometric functions and to the graphs of ellipses (see Example 1). Students should be able to sketch graphs of equations that are scale changes of parent functions and write equations for scale change images.

(continued on next page)

GOAL

Apply the Graph Scale-Change Theorem to all relations.

SPUR Objectives

C Use the Graph Scale-Change Theorem to find transformation images.

D Describe the effects of translations and scale changes on functions and their graphs.

J Apply the Graph-Translation Theorem or the Graph Scale-Change Theorem to make or identify graphs.

Materials/Resources

· Lesson Master 3-5
· Resource Masters 56–59
· Graph variation application

HOMEWORK • Option 1
• • Option 2

• Questions 1–11
• • Questions 12–22
• • Question 23 (extra credit)
• Reading Lesson 3-6
• Covering the Ideas 3-6 (Questions 1–7)

Local Standards

1 **Warm-Up**

1. If you multiply a number by 0.8, you can get back to the original number either by multiplying the product by __?__ or by dividing the product by __?__. 1.25; 0.8

2. If you divide a number by 30, you can get back to the original number either by multiplying the quotient by __?__ or dividing the quotient by __?__. 30; $\frac{1}{30}$

3. **Multiple Choice** When $a \neq 0$, $\frac{x}{\frac{1}{a}} = $ **A**

A ax. **B** $\frac{x}{a}$. **C** $\frac{\frac{x}{1}}{a}$. **D** $\frac{a}{x}$.

Additional Answers

Activity 1. See page 180.

3-5

2 Teaching

Notes on the Lesson

When $a > 1$, students may think that replacing x by $\frac{x}{a}$ in an equation shrinks the graph of the equation. Use a graphing utility to verify the graphs on the first page of the lesson, and to illustrate that the result is really a stretch.

Additional Answers

Activity 1, Step 1:

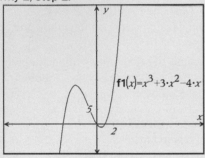

$f1(x){=}x^3{+}3{\cdot}x^2{-}4{\cdot}x$

Step 2:

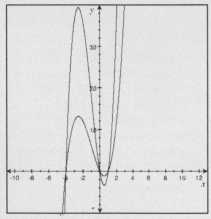

x	f1(x)	f2(x)
–4	0	0
2	12	36
7	462	1386
10	1260	3780

The values of f2 are those of f1 multiplied by 3.

Step 3:

x	f1(x)	0.5 · f1(x)	1.5 · f1(x)	2 · f1(x)
–4	0	0	0	0
2	12	6	18	24
7	462	231	693	924
10	1260	630	1890	2520

The new values are b times larger than the values of f.

STOP QY

Horizontal Scale Changes

Replacing the variable y by ky in an equation results in a vertical scale change. What happens when the variable x is replaced by $\frac{x}{2}$? By $4x$?

> **QY**
>
> Replacing y by $\frac{y}{4}$ in the equation for f1 yields an equation equivalent to $y = $ __?__ . What is the effect on the graph of f ?

Activity 2   See margin.

MATERIALS Graphing utility or slider graph application provided by your teacher.

Step 1 Consider the graph of f1 in Activity 1. Complete the table at the right.

x	f1(x)
–4	?
–1	?
2	?

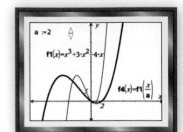

Step 2 If $f4(x) = f1\left(\frac{x}{a}\right)$, then $f4(x) = \left(\frac{x}{a}\right)^3 + 3\left(\frac{x}{a}\right)^2 - 4\left(\frac{x}{a}\right)$. Graph f4 and use a slider to vary the value of a.

Step 3 a. What are the x- and y-intercepts of f1?
b. How do the intercepts of f4 change as a changes?

The graph of f4 in Activity 2 is the image of the graph of f1 under a *horizontal scale change* of magnitude a. Each point on the graph of f4 is the image of a point on the graph of f1 under the mapping $(x, y) \rightarrow (ax, y)$. Replacing x by $\frac{x}{2}$ in the equation doubles the x-values of the preimage points while the corresponding y-values remain the same. Accordingly, the x-intercepts of the image are two times as far from the y-axis as the x-intercepts of the preimage.

The Graph Scale-Change Theorem

In general, a **scale change** centered at the origin with **horizontal scale factor** $a \neq 0$ and **vertical scale factor** $b \neq 0$ is a transformation that maps (x, y) to (ax, by). The scale change S can be described by

$$S: (x, y) \rightarrow (ax, by) \quad \text{or} \quad S(x, y) = (ax, by).$$

If $a = 1$ and $b \neq 1$, then the scale change is a **vertical scale change**. If $b = 1$ and $a \neq 1$, then the scale change is a **horizontal scale change**. When $a = b$, the scale change is called a **size change**. Notice that in the preceding instances, replacing x by $\frac{x}{2}$ in an equation for a function results in the scale change $S: (x, y) \rightarrow (2x, y)$ and replacing y by $\frac{y}{3}$ leads to the scale change $S: (x, y) \rightarrow (x, 3y)$. These results generalize.

Sometimes, scale changes with magnitudes greater than 1 are called *stretches*, and scale changes with magnitudes less than 1 are called *shrinks*. A scale change with the same vertical and horizontal magnitude is a size change or size transformation, and the image under it is similar to the preimage.

Additional Answers

Activity 2, Step 1:

x	f1(x)
–4	0
–1	6
2	12

Step 3a: $x = -4, 0, 1$

Step 3b. The y-intercepts do not change, but the x-intercepts do: As the absolute value of a increases, the absolute values of the x-intercepts get larger. As the absolute value of a decreases, the absolute values of the x-intercepts get smaller.

Graph Scale-Change Theorem

Given a preimage graph described by a sentence in x and y, the following two processes yield the same image graph:
(1) replacing x by $\frac{x}{a}$ and y by $\frac{y}{b}$ in the sentence;
(2) applying the scale change $(x, y) \rightarrow (ax, by)$ to the preimage graph.

try $y = x^2$
$y = 2x^2$
$y = \frac{1}{2}x^2$

Proof Name the image point (x', y'). So $x' = ax$ and $y' = by$. Solving for x and y gives $\frac{x'}{a} = x$ and $\frac{y'}{b} = y$. The image of $y = f(x)$ will be $\frac{y'}{a} = f\left(\frac{x'}{a}\right)$. The image equation is written without the primes.

Unlike translations, scale changes do not produce congruent images unless $a = b = 1$. Notice also that multiplication in the scale change corresponds to division in the equation of the image. This is analogous to the Graph-Translation Theorem in Lesson 3-2, where addition in the translation $(x, y) \rightarrow (x + h, y + k)$ corresponds to subtraction in the image equation $y - k = f(x - h)$.

GUIDED

Example 1 See margin.
The relation described by $x^2 + y^2 = 25$ is graphed at the right.
a. Find images of points labeled A–F on the graph under $S: (x, y) \rightarrow (2x, y)$.
b. Copy the circle onto graph paper; then graph the image on the same axes.
c. Write an equation for the image relation.

Solution

a. Copy and complete the table below.
b. Plot the preimage and image points on graph paper and draw a smooth curve connecting the image points. A partial graph is drawn below.
c. According to the Graph Scale-Change Theorem, an equation for an image under $S: (x, y) \rightarrow (2x, y)$ can be found by replacing x by __?__ in the equation for the preimage. The result is the equation __?__ .

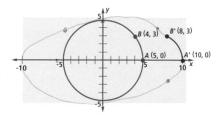

Point	Preimage x	Preimage y	Image $2x$	Image y
A	5	0	10	0
B	?	?	?	?
C	?	?	?	?
D	?	?	?	?
E	?	?	?	?
F	?	?	?	?

The Graph Scale-Change Theorem   **181**

Notes on the Lesson

Emphasize that scale change images are generally not congruent and not similar to preimages and that the limitations of graphing utilities do not account for differences in shape. However, in the special case where $a = b$, a size change results, and size changes do produce images which are similar to preimages.

Example 1 Be sure to show the image curve from Part b so that students see that the image points seem to lie on an ellipse. Some (but not all) properties of ellipses can be derived from this relationship between ellipses and circles. For instance, scale changes can be used to derive the area formula $A = \pi ab$ for an ellipse with axes of length $2a$ and $2b$. But scale changes do not affect lengths uniformly, so cannot be used to determine part or all of the circumference of an ellipse.

Additional Example
Example 1 Sketch and compare the graphs of $y = |x|$ and $\frac{y}{4} = |6x|$. Describe the transformation that maps the first graph onto the second. **Check students' work.** The graph of the second relation is the image of the graph of the first under a horizontal scale change of magnitude $\frac{1}{6}$, and a vertical scale change of magnitude 4. It is an angle with vertex (0, 0) and sides containing (1, 24) and (–1, 24). The transformation is a scale change $S: (x, y) \longrightarrow (\frac{x}{6}, 4y)$.

Additional Answers

Example 1

a.

Point	Preimage x	Preimage y	Image $2x$	Image y
A	5	0	10	0
B	4	3	8	3
C	3	4	6	4
D	0	5	0	5
E	–3	4	–6	4
F	4	–3	8	–3

b.

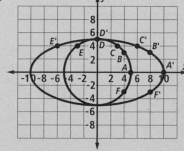

c. $\frac{x}{2}$; $\left(\frac{x}{2}\right)^2 + y^2 = 25$

3-5

Notes on the Lesson

Negative scale factors The argument here shows that a reflection can be thought of as a special type of scale change. This is not as strange as it might seem at first. Changes in units of currency are scale changes, e.g., if there are 200 yen to the dollar, then a price in yen is 200 times the price in dollars. When you pay, you think of this cost as negative. But the person receiving the money thinks of the cost as positive. This change in point of view is the reflection.

3 Assignment

Recommended Assignment

- Questions 1–11
- • Questions 12–22
- • Question 23 (extra credit)
- Reading Lesson 3-6
- Covering the Ideas 3-6
  (Questions 1–7)

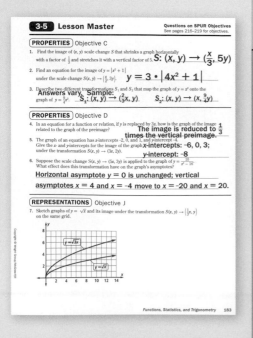

Example 2

A graph and table for $y = f(x)$ are given at the right. Draw the graph of $\frac{y}{3} = f(2x)$.

x	f(x)
-6	2
-3	-1
0	-1
2	3
6	0

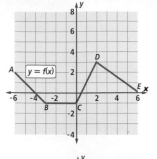

Solution Rewrite $\frac{y}{3} = f(2x)$ as $\frac{y}{3} = f\left(\frac{x}{\frac{1}{2}}\right)$. By the Graph Scale-Change Theorem, replacing x by $\frac{x}{\frac{1}{2}}$ and y by $\frac{y}{3}$ is the same as applying the scale change $(x, y) \rightarrow \left(\frac{1}{2}x, 3y\right)$.

So,

$A = (-6, 2) \Rightarrow (-3, 6) = A'$

$B = (-3, -1) \Rightarrow (-3/2, -3) = B'$

$C = (0, -1) \Rightarrow (0, -3) = C'$

$D = (2, 3) \Rightarrow (1, 9) = D'$

and $E = (6, 0) \Rightarrow (3, 0) = E'$.

The graph of the image is shown at the right.

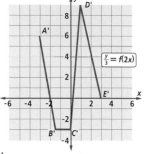

Negative Scale Factors

Notice what happens when a scale factor is –1. Consider the horizontal and vertical scale changes H and V with scale factors equal to –1.

$$H: (x, y) \rightarrow (-x, y) \text{ and } V: (x, y) \rightarrow (x, -y)$$

In H, each x-value is replaced by its opposite, which produces a reflection over the y-axis. Similarly, in V, replacing y by $-y$ produces a reflection over the x-axis. More generally, a scale factor of $-k$ combines the effect of a scale factor of k and a reflection over the appropriate axis.

Questions

COVERING THE IDEAS

1. **True or False** Under every scale change, the preimage and image are congruent. **false**

2. Under a scale change with horizontal scale factor a and vertical factor b, the image of (x, y) is __?__. **(ax, by)**

3. Refer to the Graph Scale-Change Theorem. Why are the restrictions $a \neq 0$ and $b \neq 0$ necessary?

4. If S maps each point (x, y) to $\left(\frac{x}{2}, 6y\right)$, give an equation for the image of $y = f(x)$ under S. **$y = 6 \cdot f(2x)$**

3. If $a = 0$, every x-coordinate is mapped to 0, which maps the graph to a subset of the y-axis; if $b = 0$, every y-coordinate is mapped to 0, which maps the graph to a subset of the x-axis.

Accommodating the Learner ⬇

Some students may become confused by scale changes that stretch or shrink the graph both horizontally *and* vertically. You might want to encourage these students to use one of two strategies to simplify the process.

(1) Choose individual points on the preimage and transform these coordinates to obtain the corresponding points on the image, as in Example 1.

(2) Think of the transformation as a two-step process that composes the horizontal scale change and the vertical scale change. Performing each scale change individually might provide a better understanding of this type of transformation.

3-5   Lesson Master

Questions on SPUR Objectives
See pages 216–219 for objectives.

PROPERTIES Objective C

1. Find the image of (x, y) scale change S that shrinks a graph horizontally with a factor of $\frac{1}{3}$ and stretches it with a vertical factor of 5. **$S: (x, y) \rightarrow \left(\frac{x}{3}, 5y\right)$**

2. Find an equation for the image of $y = |x^2 + 1|$ under the scale change $S(x, y) \rightarrow \left(\frac{x}{2}, 3y\right)$. **$y = 3 \cdot |4x^2 + 1|$**

3. Describe two different transformations S_1 and S_2 that map the graph of $y = x^2$ onto the graph of $y = \frac{9}{4}x^2$. **Answers vary. Sample:** $S_1: (x, y) \rightarrow \left(\frac{2}{3}x, y\right)$ $S_2: (x, y) \rightarrow \left(x, \frac{9}{4}y\right)$

PROPERTIES Objective D

4. In an equation for a function or relation, if y is replaced by $3y$, how is the graph of the image related to the graph of the preimage? **The image is reduced to $\frac{1}{3}$ times the vertical preimage.**

5. The graph of an equation has x-intercepts –2, 0, and 1, and y-intercept –4. Give the x- and y-intercepts for the image of the graph under the transformation $S(x, y) \rightarrow (3x, 2y)$. **$x$-intercepts: –6, 0, 3; y-intercept: –8**

6. Suppose the scale change $S(x, y) \rightarrow (5x, 3y)$ is applied to the graph of $y = \frac{10}{x^2 - 16}$. What effect does this transformation have on the graph's asymptotes? **Horizontal asymptote $y = 0$ is unchanged; vertical asymptotes $x = 4$ and $x = -4$ move to $x = -20$ and $x = 20$.**

REPRESENTATIONS Objective J

7. Sketch graphs of $y = \sqrt{x}$ and its image under the transformation $S(x, y) \rightarrow \left(\frac{1}{2}x, y\right)$ on the same grid.

5. Consider the function $f1$ used in Activities 1 and 2.
   a. Write a formula for $f1\left(\frac{x}{3}\right)$.
   b. How is the graph of $y = f1\left(\frac{x}{3}\right)$ related to the graph of $y = f1(x)$?

6. **Multiple Choice** Which of these transformations is a size change? **A**
   A $(x, y) \rightarrow (3x, 3y)$
   B $(x, y) \rightarrow (3x, y)$
   C $(x, y) \rightarrow (x + 3, y + 3)$
   D $(x, y) \rightarrow \left(\frac{x}{3}, y\right)$

7. Functions f and g with $f(x) = -2x^2 + 5x + 3$ and $g(x) = \frac{1}{2}f(x)$ are graphed at the right.
   a. What scale change maps the graph of f to the graph of g? $S(x, y) = \left(x, \frac{1}{2}y\right)$
   b. The x-intercepts of f are at $x = -\frac{1}{2}$ and $x = 3$. Where are the x-intercepts of g? $x = -\frac{1}{2}, 3$
   c. How do the y-intercepts of f and g compare?
   d. The vertex of the graph of f is (1.25, 6.125). What is the vertex of the graph of g? **(1.25, 3.0625)**

8. Consider the parabola with equation $y = x^2$. Let $S(x, y) = \left(2x, \frac{y}{7}\right)$. **See margin.**
   a. Find the images of (–3, 9), (0, 0), and $\left(\frac{1}{2}, \frac{1}{4}\right)$ under S.
   b. Write an equation for the image of the parabola under S.

9. The graph of a function f is shown at the right. **See margin.**
   a. Graph the image of f under $S(x, y) = \left(\frac{1}{2}x, 3y\right)$.
   b. Find the x- and y-intercepts of the image.
   c. Find the coordinates of the point where the y-value of the image of f reaches its maximum. **(1, 9)**

10. Give another name for the horizontal scale change of magnitude –1. **a reflection with respect to the y-axis**

11. Describe the scale change that maps the graph of $y = \sqrt{x}$ onto the graph of $y = \sqrt{\frac{x}{12}}$. **horizontal scale change of magnitude 12**

APPLYING THE MATHEMATICS

12. Refer to the parabolas at the right. The graph of g is the image of the graph of f under what
   a. horizontal scale change?
   b. vertical scale change?
   c. size change? $S(x, y) = (16x, 16y)$

13. Write an equation for the image of the graph of $y = x + \frac{1}{x}$ under each transformation.
   a. $S(x, y) = (2x, 2y)$
   b. $S(x, y) = \left(\frac{x}{3}, -y\right)$

14. A scale change maps (10, 0) onto (2, 0) and (–5, 8) onto (–1, 2). What is the equation of the image of the graph of $f(x) = x^3 - 8$ under the scale change? $y = \frac{125}{4}x^3 - 2$

The Graph Scale-Change Theorem **183**

5a. $f1\left(\frac{x}{3}\right) = \frac{1}{27}x^3 + \frac{1}{3}x^2 - \frac{4}{3}x$

5b. $f1\left(\frac{x}{3}\right)$ is the image of $f(x)$ stretched horizontally by a factor of 3.

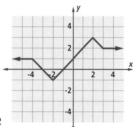

7c. The y-intercept of g is $\frac{1}{2}$ the value of the y-intercept of f.

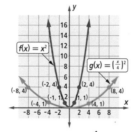

12a. $S(x, y) = (4x, y)$
12b. $S(x, y) = \left(x, \frac{y}{16}\right)$

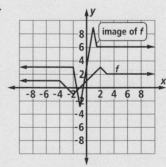

13a. $y = x + \frac{4}{x}$
13b. $y = -3x - \frac{1}{3x}$

Additional Example
Example 2 The line $41x - 29y = 700$ contains the points (39, 31) and (10, –10). Use this information to obtain two points on the line with equation $20.5x - 87y = 700$. **The second line is the image of the first under a scale change $S(x, y) = \left(2x, \frac{y}{3}\right)$, so two points on that line are $\left(78, \frac{31}{3}\right)$ and $\left(20, -\frac{10}{3}\right)$.**

Notes on the Questions

Question 8 This question is a good one to go through in detail if students are having difficulty understanding the Graph Scale-Change Theorem.

Question 12 This question is tricky for many students because they have to think in two different ways about scale transformations. In general, there are infinitely many size changes that map f onto g. The parabola with equation $y = x^2$ can be mapped onto the parabola with equation $y = ax^2$ by any scale change S of the form $S(x, y) = (kx, ak^2y)$. When $k = \frac{1}{a}$, the scale change has equation $S(x, y) = \left(\frac{1}{a}x, \frac{1}{a}y\right)$, so the scale change is a size change and the parabolas are shown to be similar.

Additional Answers

8a. $(-3, 9) \rightarrow \left(-6, \frac{9}{7}\right)$, $(0, 0) \rightarrow (0, 0)$, $\left(\frac{1}{2}, \frac{1}{4}\right) \rightarrow \left(1, \frac{1}{28}\right)$

8b. $y = \frac{1}{7}\left(\frac{x}{2}\right)^2$

9a.

9b. $x = -1.5, -0.5; y = 3$

Accommodating the Learner ↑

Try this question, which can be tricky. Let G be the graph of $y = x^2$. Let H be the graph of $y = 0.01x^2$. Find an equation for a transformation T that maps G onto H if T is a

a. vertical scale change. $T(x, y) = (x, 0.01y)$

b. horizontal scale change. $T(x, y) = (0.1x, y)$

c. size change. $T(x, y) = (100x, 100y)$

Extension

Have students prove the statement in the teacher notes for Question 12.

3-5

4 Wrap-Up

Ongoing Assessment

Have students write a paragraph explaining a vertical scale change and a horizontal scale change. **Answers vary. Check students' work. Students' writings should demonstrate an understanding of scale change.**

Project Update

Project 3, *Transformation Groups*, on page 212 relates to the content of this lesson.

In 15 and 16, give a rule for a scale change that maps the graph of *f* onto the graph of *g*.

15.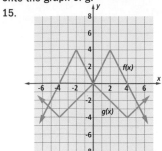

16.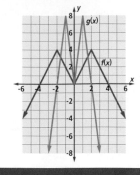

15. $S(x, y) = (2x, -y)$

16. $S(x, y) = \left(\frac{x}{2}, 2y\right)$

REVIEW

In 17 and 18, an equation for a function is given. Is the function odd, even, or neither? If the function is odd or even, prove it. **(Lesson 3-4)**

17. $f(x) = (5x + 4)^3$ **neither**

18. $g(x) = 5x^4 + 4$

19. If $f(x) = -g(x)$ for all *x* in the common domain of *f* and *g*, how are the graphs of *f* and *g* related? **(Lesson 3-4)**

20. One of the parent functions presented in Lesson 3-1 has a graph that is not symmetric to the *x*-axis, *y*-axis, or origin. It has the asymptote $y = 0$. Which is it? **(Lesson 3-1)**

21. The table at the right shows the number of injuries on different types of rides in amusement parks in the U.S. in 2003, 2004, and 2005. Use the table to explain whether each statement is supported by the data. **See margin.**

	2003	2004	2005
Total	1954	1648	1713
Children's Rides	277	219	192
Family and Adult Rides	1173	806	1131
Roller Coasters	504	613	390

Source: National Safety Council

a. Injuries on children's rides decreased slightly each year.

b. The number of injuries on roller coasters decreased from 2003 to 2004.

c. Roller coasters are not as safe as children's rides. **(Lesson 1-1)**

22. Pizza π restaurant made 300 pizzas yesterday; 64% of the pizzas had no toppings, 10% of the pizzas had two toppings, and 26% had more than two toppings. How many pizzas had at least two toppings? **(Previous Course)** **108 pizzas had at least two toppings**

EXPLORATION

23. a. Explore $g(x) = b(x^3 + 3x^2 - 4x)$ for $b < 0$. Explain what happens to the graph of *g* as *b* changes.

b. Explore $h(x) = \left(\frac{x}{a}\right)^3 + 3\left(\frac{x}{a}\right)^2 - 4\left(\frac{x}{a}\right)$ for $a < 0$. Explain what happens to the graph of *h* as *a* changes. **See margin.**

18. even; $g(-x) = 5(-x)^4 + 4 = 5x^4 + 4 = g(x)$

19. They are reflections of each other over the *x*-axis.

20. exponential function

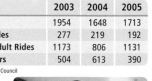

QY ANSWER

$4(x^3 + 3x^2 - 4x)$; a vertical scale change of magnitude 4

Additional Answers

21a. The table confirms this statement: the number of injuries on children's rides decreased from 277 in 2003 to 219 to 192.

21b. The table refutes this statement: There were 613 injuries on roller coasters in 2004, more than the 504 injuries in 2003.

21c. The table partially confirms this statement: Roller coasters had more injuries than children's rides in every year. On the other hand, the table cannot say whether the chance of being injured is higher on a roller coaster or on a children's ride.

23a. A negative value of *b* reflects the graph of *g* over the *x*-axis. As *b* becomes more negative, the graph of *g* stretches vertically by a factor of *b*.

23b. A negative value of *a* reflects the graph of *h* over the *y*-axis. As *a* becomes more negative, the graph of *h* stretches horizontally by a factor of *a*.

Lesson 3-6

Scale Changes of Data

Lesson 3-6

Vocabulary

scale change of a data set
scale factor
scale image

▶ **BIG IDEA** Multiplying every number in a data set by k multiplies all measures of center and the standard deviation and range by k, while the variance is multiplied by k^2.

Scale changes can also be applied to data sets. A useful example to consider is the Consumer Price Index (CPI), a measure of inflation. To calculate the CPI, the cost of a specified basket of goods is totaled in a particular base year, then scaled so the cost equals 100. Costs in later years are then compared to the base year cost.

The table at the right gives the CPI at five-year intervals beginning at 1950, with 1967 as the base year.

Scaling allows prices in any year to be compared to prices in any other year. Just solve a proportion.

Year	CPI
1950	72.1
1955	80.2
1960	88.7
1965	94.5
1970	116.3
1975	161.2
1980	298.8
1985	322.2
1990	391.4
1995	456.5
2000	515.8
2005	585.0
June 2008	655.5

Mental Math

Find the x-intercept(s) of the graph of the equation.

a. $y = |x + \pi||$ $(-\pi, 0)$

b. $y = |x - \pi||$ $(\pi, 0)$

c. $y = |x| + \pi$

d. $y = |x| - \pi$

c. No x-intercepts

d. $(-\pi, 0)$ and $(\pi, 0)$

Example 1

Suppose a refrigerator cost $800 in 1995. What might you expect the cost of a similar refrigerator to be in June 2008?

Solution Set up a proportion.

$$\frac{\text{cost in June 2008}}{\text{cost in 1995}} = \frac{\text{CPI in June 2008}}{\text{CPI in 1995}}$$

Let x = cost of a refrigerator in June 2008. Substitute, using the CPI values given in the table.

$$\frac{x}{\$800} = \frac{655.5}{456.5}$$

Solve the proportion.

$$x = 800 \cdot \frac{655.5}{456.5} = \$1148.74\ldots \approx \$1150$$

The cost of a similar refrigerator in June 2008 was probably about $1150.

Scale Changes of Data   **185**

GOAL

Investigate the effects of scaling data on the display, the measures of center, and the measures of spread.

SPUR Objectives

H Use scale changes to describe and analyze data and statistics.

Materials/Resources

· Lesson Master 3-6
· Resource Masters 60–63
· Quiz 2

HOMEWORK   • **Option 1**

• Questions 1–7   • **Option 2**
• • Questions 8–24
• • Question 25 (extra credit)
  • Reading Lesson 3-7
  • Covering the Ideas 3-7
    (Questions 1–11)

Local Standards

1 Warm-Up

From 1995 to 2005 in U.S. cities, on the average, prices of food went up 25.1%, prices of medical care rose 46.6%, and rents went up 37.8%. Estimate the 2005 price of the following items, whose 1995 prices are given.

1. a carton of cereal that cost $3.39 **$4.24**

2. rent that was $850/month **$1,171.30**

3. a hospital room that was $1000 for one night **$1,466.00**

Background

In the same way that Lesson 3-3 on translating data followed Lesson 3-2 on translating graphs, this lesson on scaling data immediately follows the lesson on scaling graphs. Students should see scaling graphs and scaling data as parallel concepts.

Scaling data and scale changes of graphs of functions are not only mathematically based on the same idea, but they often occur together. When lengths or masses are changed from metric to customary, or when time is changed from minutes to seconds, or when costs are scaled by the CPI (as in the lesson's Activity and in the Warm-Up here), graphs too are scaled.

(continued on next page)

2 Teaching

Notes on the Lesson

Example 1 The question discusses the cost of a "similar refrigerator," but few refrigerators on the market in 1995 were still on the market in 2008. The more recent refrigerators tend to be energy efficient and may have features (e.g., ice cube makers) that many older refrigerators did not have. Any detailed discussion of how prices have changed over the years needs to consider whether the object being purchased has also changed.

Activity This is a straightforward activity whose results may be predicted by many students. However, even those students can be helped in their understanding of the effects of scaling by going through the calculations.

Additional Example

Example 1 Use the data from Example 1. Suppose an oven cost $450 in 1990. What might you expect a similar oven to have cost in 2005? **about $673**

Additional Answers

Activity

Steps 2–5: See the Additional Answers section at the back of the book.

Step 6: For mean, median, standard deviation, and range, multiplying by the scale factor accurately finds the 2008 stats. Multiplying by the scale factor does not work for the variance.

The ratio $\frac{655.5}{456.5}$ in Example 1 is a *scale factor*. In this case, $\frac{655.5}{456.5} \approx$ 1.436, indicating there was about a 43.6% increase in prices from 1995 to June 2008. By multiplying the 1995 price by 1.436, you can estimate what the June 2008 price of an item would be if the cost kept pace with inflation.

🛑 **QY**

A **scale change** of a set of data $\{x_1, x_2, \ldots, x_n\}$ is a transformation that maps each x_i to ax_i, where a is a nonzero constant. That is, S is a scale change if and only if there is a nonzero constant a with

$$S: x \to ax, \text{ or } S(x) = ax.$$

The number a is called the **scale factor** of the scale change. The number ax or the point it represents is called the **scale image** of x.

In the situation above, the 1995 cost x of an item can be mapped onto the estimated June 2008 cost via the scale change

$$S: x \to 1.436x, \text{ or } S(x) = 1.436x.$$

Scaling and Measures of Center

Scale changes of data, like translations, affect statistical measures derived from the data.

Activity   Steps 2-5. See margin.

The CPI in 1998 was about 496. Here are average prices of some grocery items in that year.

Year	Coffee 1 pound	Eggs 1 dozen	Gasoline 1 gallon	Orange Juice 12-oz can	Ground Beef 1 pound	Chicken 1 pound
1998	4.03	1.12	1.13	1.60	1.82	1.02

Source: Bureau of Labor Statistics

Step 1 Calculate the scale factor needed to predict costs of items in 2008 from 1998 prices. $\frac{655.5}{496} = 1.322$

Step 2 Enter the price data for 1998 into a spreadsheet like the one on page 187.

Step 3 Use the scale factor from Step 1 to compute the predicted June 2008 prices of the same items. Record these costs in a new column.

Step 4 Calculate the mean, median, range, variance, and standard deviation of each set of prices. Record the results to the nearest hundredth in another column.

Step 5 Multiply the 1998 statistics by the scale factor from Step 1 and place the results in an additional column. Your spreadsheet should look similar to the one on the next page.

▶ **QY**

If a person earned $2,500 a month in 1995, what would the person need to have earned in June 2008 to keep up with inflation?

Example 2 Technically this is not a scale change because the multiplier is the rate $\frac{\$2.50}{\text{box}}$, not a scalar, but the mathematical properties of the multiplication are the same. The context would be a scale change if there was some percentage increase in the cost of a box of candy, as in Question 4.

Box plots provide a very nice picture of the effects of scale changes. The position of the center of the box (the median of the data), the width of the box (the IQR), and the lengths of the whiskers are multiplied by the scale factor.

Step 6 Compare the results of Step 5 to those of Step 4. Which of the 2008 statistics can be found by scaling the corresponding 1998 statistics, rather than by calculating from the costs of the groceries?
See margin.

| The spreadsheet evaluates the formula B2 × (655.5/496). |

| E2 × (655.5/496) |

◇	A	B	C	D	E	F	G
1	Items	1998 costs	2008 costs (predicted)		1998 statistics	2008 statistics	1998 statistics x scale factor
2	Coffee 1 Pound	$4.03	5.33	Mean			
3	Eggs 1 dozen	$1.12	1.48	Median			
4	Gasoline 1 gallon	$1.13	1.49	Range			
5	Orange Juice 12-oz can	$1.60	2.12	Variance			
6	Ground Beef 1 pound	$1.82	2.41	Standard Deviation			
7	Chicken 1 pound	$1.02	1.35				
8							

The Activity shows how scaling data affects statistics for measures of center and spread. These ideas are applied in Example 2.

Example 2

As a fund-raiser, club members sell candy for $2.50 per box. The number of boxes each of the 17 members sold is given below.

27, 30, 32, 32, 34, 35, 35, 37, 38, 39, 40, 41, 41, 43, 44, 44, 50

a. Compute the mean, median, standard deviation, and IQR of the numbers of boxes sold.

b. Find the amount of money each member collected.

c. Compute the mean, median, standard deviation, and IQR of the amounts of money collected by scaling the values in Part a.

Solution

a. For the number of boxes, mean = 37.8, median = 38, standard deviation = 5.89, and IQR = 9.

b. Apply the transformation $x_i \rightarrow 2.5x_i$ to each value.
The number of dollars each member collected are 67.50, 75, 80, 80, 85, 87.50, 87.50, 92.50, 95, 97.50, 100, 102.50, 102.50, 107.50, 110, 110, and 125.

c. For the money collected, mean = 37.8 · 2.5 = 94.5, median = 38 · 2.5 = 95, standard deviation = 5.89 · 2.5 = 14.73, and IQR = 9 · 2.5 = 22.5.

The first two theorems in this lesson can be written in one sentence: A scale change of a data set by a factor of a multiplies the range and measures of central tendency by a, the standard deviation by $|a|$, and the variance by a^2.

It is not uncommon to combine scale changes and translations. Examples are found in Lesson 3-9 with z-scores and in Chapter 4 with graphs of trigonometric functions.

Notes on the Lesson

Assist students to work through the mathematical symbols in the proof of the two theorems of this lesson as students need to be comfortable using sigma notation. You may find it easier to write $\sum$ for $\sum_{i=1}^{n}$ throughout to focus students' attentions on what is being added. State each line in words. For instance, in the proof of the Centers of Scale Changes of Data Theorem regarding the mean, in the first line we multiply each of the data by a, and then add. In the second line, the result is shown to be equal to adding all the data before multiplying. That same idea is found on line 3 of the derivation of the Spreads of Scale Changes of Data Theorem, but here the multiplication is by a^2.

Scaling and measures of spread In lines 1 and 2 of the derivation of the Spread of Scale Changes of Data Theorem, point out that all of the manipulation is going on inside the summation and amounts to showing that $(ax - ay)^2 = a^2(x - y)^2$.

Ask students why, in the Spread of Scale Changes of Data Theorem, the standard deviation is multiplied by $|a|$. **Possible answer: The variance of the image data is a^2 times the original variance, and since standard deviation is the positive square root of the variance, the standard deviation must be $\sqrt{a^2 S^2}$ $|a| \cdot S$, which is $|a|$ times the original standard deviation.**

Box plots of the numbers of candy boxes sold and amounts collected illustrate the effects of scaling on the data values, the center (mean and median), and the spread (range, IQR, and standard deviation).

As you saw in the Activity and Examples, scale changes not only affect the data, they affect measures of center as well. This effect is stated in the theorem below.

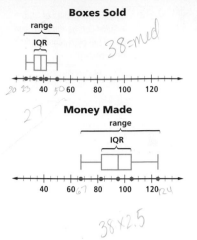

Boxes Sold

38=med

27

Money Made

38×2.5

Theorem (Centers of Scaled Data)

Multiplying each element of a data set by the factor a multiplies each of the mode, mean, and median by the factor a.

Proof We prove the mean part of the theorem here; it can also be proved that the median and mode are multiplied by a (see Question 9 for the median). To describe the effect of a scale change on statistical measures for a general data set, represent the set as $\{x_1, x_2, x_3, ..., x_n\}$. Under a scale change with scale factor a, the image data set is

$$\{ax_1, ax_2, ax_3, ..., ax_n\} = \{x_1', x_2', ..., x_n'\}.$$ Let $\bar{x}$ be the mean of the original data set and $\bar{x}'$ be the mean of the image set.

The mean $\bar{x}' = \dfrac{\sum_{i=1}^{n} (ax_i)}{n}$.

By definition of $\sum$,

$$\bar{x}' = \frac{ax_1 + ax_2 + ax_3 + \cdots + ax_n}{n}$$
$$= \frac{a(x_1 + x_2 + x_3 + \cdots + x_n)}{n}$$
$$= \left(\frac{a\sum_{i=1}^{n} x_i}{n}\right) = a\left(\frac{\sum_{i=1}^{n} x_i}{n}\right).$$

Thus $\bar{x}' = a\bar{x}$. So, under a scale change, the mean of a set of data is mapped to the mean of the image set of data.

Scaling and Measures of Spread

The Activity and Example 2 show that measures of spread in a scale-change image data set are predictable. Both the range and standard deviation can be found by multiplying by the scale factor.

Extension

Ask students what happens if each value in a data set is modified in ways other than adding or multiplying by a constant. For instance, suppose each value in a data set with positive numbers is squared. What happens to the mean, mode, variance, and standard deviation? **The median and mode are squared. The mean, variance and standard deviation are changed but not in any simple way.** Then have students choose and experiment with other functions applied to each value in a data set.

The predicted variance can also be found using the scale factor in a different way. These effects are described in the following theorem.

Theorem (Spreads of Scaled Data)

If each element of a data set is multiplied by $a > 0$, then the variance is a^2 times the original variance, the standard deviation is a times the original standard deviation, and the range is a times the original range.

Proof Consider the data set $\{x_1, x_2, ..., x_n\}$ and its image $\{ax_1, ax_2, ..., ax_n\}$ under a scale change of magnitude a. By the Centers of Scaled Data Theorem, the mean of the image data set is $a\bar{x}$, where $\bar{x}$ is the mean of the original data set. So the variance of the image data is given by

$$\frac{\sum_{i=1}^{n} (ax_i - a\bar{x})^2}{n-1} = \frac{\sum_{i=1}^{n} [a(x_i - \bar{x})]^2}{n-1} \qquad \text{Distributive Property}$$

$$= \frac{\sum_{i=1}^{n} [a^2(x_i - \bar{x})^2]}{n-1} \qquad \text{Power of a Product Property}$$

Applying the Distributive Property,

$$\sum_{i=1}^{n} [a^2(x_i - \bar{x})^2] = a^2 \sum_{i=1}^{n} (x_i - \bar{x})^2.$$

Hence, the variance of the image data is given by

$$\frac{a^2 \sum_{i=1}^{n} (x_i - \bar{x})^2}{n-1} = a^2 \left(\frac{\sum_{i=1}^{n} (x_i - \bar{x})^2}{n-1} \right) = a^2 s^2,$$

where s^2 is the variance of the original data set. Thus, the variance of the image data is a^2 times the variance of the original data.

To get the standard deviation of the image data, take the square root of the variance. Thus, the standard deviation of the image data is $|a| \cdot s$, which is $|a|$ times the standard deviation of the original data set. It can also be proved that the range and IQR of the image data are $|a|$ times the range and IQR, respectively, of the original data set.

Questions

COVERING THE IDEAS

1. Define *scale change* of a set of data.

2. A Rambler, a small car, cost about $2000 in 1965. What would a comparable car have cost in 2005? **about $12,381**

3. In what 5-year period from 1950 to 2005 was there the greatest percent increase in CPI, and what was that percent?

---

3 **Assignment**

Recommended Assignment

- • Questions 1–7
- • • Questions 8–24
- • • Question 25 (extra credit)
- • Reading Lesson 3-7
- • Covering the Ideas 3-7
  (Questions 1–11)

1. A scale change of a set of data is a transformation that maps each x_i to ax_i, where a is a nonzero constant.

3. Between 1975 and 1980, the CPI increased by 85.36%.

2. $\dfrac{\text{cost in 2005}}{\text{cost in 1965}} = \dfrac{CPI\ 2005}{CPI\ 1965}$

$\dfrac{\$8}{\$2000} = \dfrac{585}{94.5}$

$x = \$12,381$

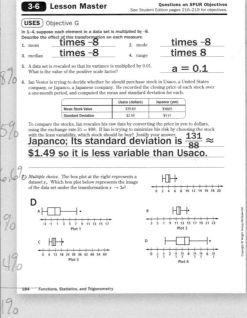

3-6

Notes on the Questions

Question 10 Of course, when housing prices rise 2%, it does not mean that the cost of every house has risen 2%. In fact, typically there is little overlap between the sales of houses one year and the sales of houses the next; that is, the same house usually does not get sold in consecutive years. Furthermore, there is a tendency for houses to have more adornments and get "nicer" year after year, so a 3-bedroom house in 1990 might not look the same as a 3-bedroom house in 2010. Even so, it is reasonable that the distribution of housing prices would look much the same except for a translation and a scale change.

Additional Answers

4b.

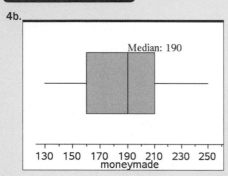

Median: 190

130 150 170 190 210 230 250
moneymade

5b.

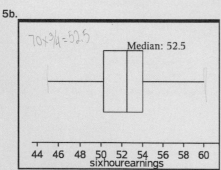

$70 \times 3/4 = 52.5$

Median: 52.5

44 46 48 50 52 54 56 58 60
sixhourearnings

9. For odd n, the median is the middle number when the set of numbers is put in increasing or decreasing order. If a set is $\{x_1, x_2, x_3, \ldots, x_n\}$, then under a scale change with scale factor a, the set becomes $\{ax_1, ax_2, ax_3, \ldots, ax_n\}$. Therefore, if the median of a set is x_m, the median of the set subject to the scale change is ax_m. For even n, using the same data set, the median is the mean of the middle two numbers, $\frac{x_j + x_k}{2}$. For the scaled set the median is $\frac{ax_j + ax_k}{2} = a\left(\frac{x_j + x_k}{2}\right)$, which satisfies the Centers of Scale Changes of Data Theorem.

10. median: $263,364; IQR: $82,620

---

4. Consider the candy sales in Example 2. Suppose that a box costs $5 instead of $2.50.
   a. For the money collected, calculate each statistic.
      i. range   ii. mode   iii. median
      iv. mean   v. variance   vi. standard deviation
   b. Draw a box plot of the amounts of money collected.

5. A restaurant employs 11 workers, whose individual earnings for an 8-hour day are summarized by this box plot. Suppose that each employee begins working 6 hours instead of 8. Assume employees earn the same hourly wage, regardless of the number of hours worked.

   Original Earnings

   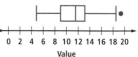

   Dollars

   a. What scale factor would be used to find each person's new daily earnings? $\frac{3}{4}$
   b. Draw a boxplot of the earnings for the 6-hour work day.

6. Suppose all elements of a data set are multiplied by x. Explain why the variance is multiplied by x^2.

7. **Multiple Choice** The box plot at the right represents a data set D. Which box plot below represents the image of D under the transformation $x \to \frac{1}{3}x$? **C**

   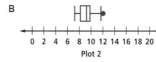

   0 2 4 6 8 10 12 14 16 18 20
   Value

   A
   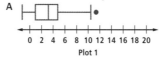

   0 2 4 6 8 10 12 14 16 18 20
   Plot 1

   B
   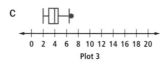

   0 2 4 6 8 10 12 14 16 18 20
   Plot 2

   C
   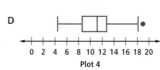

   0 2 4 6 8 10 12 14 16 18 20
   Plot 3

   D

   0 2 4 6 8 10 12 14 16 18 20
   Plot 4

APPLYING THE MATHEMATICS

8. Suppose $Y_1 = 11$, $Y_2 = -3$, $Y_3 = -2$, $Y_4 = 7$, $Y_5 = 5$, $Y_6 = 4$. Evaluate each expression.
   a. $\displaystyle\sum_{i=1}^{6} 10Y_i$ **220**
   b. $\displaystyle\sum_{i=1}^{6} rY_i$ **22r**
   c. $\displaystyle\sum_{i=1}^{6} \left(\frac{Y_i}{m}\right)$ $\frac{22}{m}$
   d. $\displaystyle\sum_{i=1}^{6} (Y_i + 2)$ **34**

9. Prove the Centers of Scale Changes of Data Theorem for medians. **See margin.**

10. For a large city, the median house price one year was $258,200 with an interquartile range of $81,000. Assume that house prices rise 2% over the next year. What would be the median and IQR for house prices in the next year? **See margin.**

4a. i. $115
     ii. $160, $175, $205, and $220
     iii. $190
     iv. $188.82
     v. $867.28
     vi. $29.45

4b. See margin.

5b. See margin.

6. A data set $\{y_1, y_2, y_3, \ldots, y_n\}$ multiplied by x has a variance of
$$\frac{\displaystyle\sum_{i=1}^{n} (xy_i - x\bar{y})^2}{n-1} = \frac{\displaystyle\sum_{i=1}^{n} x^2(y_i - \bar{y})^2}{n-1} = \frac{x^2\displaystyle\sum_{i=1}^{n} (y_i - \bar{y})^2}{n-1}.$$

11. Let $\bar{x}$ = the mean and s = the standard deviation of scores on a test for a class of n students. Suppose everyone's score is multiplied by r, and then increased by a bonus b. For the new scores, find the
    a. mean.   b. variance.   c. standard deviation.

12. Let M represent the maximum value of a data set and let m represent the minimum value.
    a. Write an expression for the range r of the data set.
    b. After a scale change with scale factor $d > 0$, what are the maximum and minimum values of the image data set?
    c. Write and simplify an expression for the range of the image data.
    d. How would your answers to Parts a–c change if $d < 0$?

13. Consider the following data, which give the height h in cm and weight w in kg of twelve students.

h (cm)	144	168	140	157	153	162	160	160	166	166	173	165
w (kg)	68	86	69	77	85	74	78	84	84	83	82	82

    a. Enter these data into a statistics utility. Create a scatterplot with h on the horizontal axis. **See margin.**
    b. Find the line of best fit for predicting weight from height.
    c. Compute the correlation coefficient. $r = 0.7499$
    d. Use a statistics utility to convert the height to inches (1 in. = 2.54 cm) and weight to pounds (1 lb = 0.454 kg). Draw a new scatterplot. How is the scatterplot different from that in Part a?
    e. Compute the correlation coefficient and the regression equation for predicting weight from height in Part d.
    f. Which of the following statistics remain invariant under scale changes of the data?
        i. correlation coefficient   **invariant**
        ii. slope of the regression line   **not invariant**
        iii. y-intercept of the regression line   **not invariant**

REVIEW

14. Consider the functions f and g with $f(x) = x$ and $g(x) = 7x$.
    a. Describe a scale change that maps the graph of f onto the graph of g.   **vertical stretch by a factor of 7**
    b. Describe a scale change that maps the graph of g onto the graph of f. (Lesson 3-5)   **vertical shrink by a factor of $\frac{1}{7}$**

11a. $\bar{x}r + b$
11b. $(rs)^2$
11c. rs
12a. $r = M - m$
12b. dM, dm
12c. $dM - dm =$
$d(M - m) = dr$
12d. Part a: no changes;
Part b: minimum $= dM$ and maximum $= dm$;
Part c: $d(M - m) = |d|r$

13b. w = 3.628 + 0.4746h

13d. The scatterplot appears the same but the scale of the axes is different.

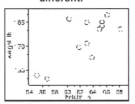

13e. w = 7.991 + 2.655h

Notes on the Questions

Question 11 This question summarizes the main ideas of the lesson and anticipates the discussion of z-scores.

Question 12 This question is an important one to discuss.

Question 13 This question illustrates that a change in units can be viewed as a scale change if only the numbers are considered and the units ignored.

Additional Answers

13a.

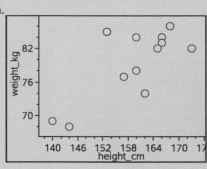

Notes on the Questions

Question 24c Do not accept $7(x + \frac{5}{7}\pi)$ as a correct answer. Because the general form has a subtraction, so should a special case.

Question 25 By "statistics" is meant measures of spread and measures of center.

4   Wrap-Up

Ongoing Assessment

Refer to Example 2 in the lesson. Ask students to compute the mean, median, standard deviation, and IQR of the amounts of profit made on the candy, if they originally cost the club $1.75 per box. **mean = 28.32; median = 28.5; standard deviation = 4.42; IQR = 6.75**

Administer Quiz 2 (or a quiz of your own) after students complete this lesson.

Project Update

Project 3, *Transformation Groups*, and Project 4, *CPI/Rate of Inflation*, on page 212 relate to the content of this lesson.

In 15–18, match the equation with its graph. **(Lessons 3-5, 3-2)**

15. $f(x) = |x + 5|$ **B**

16. $g(x) = |3x|$ **C**

17. $h(x) = \frac{1}{3}|x|$ **A**

18. $j(x) = |x - 5|$ **D**

A   B   C   D

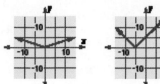

19. Name all the functions in Questions 15–18 that are even functions. **(Lesson 3-4)** $g(x) = |3x|, h(x) = \frac{1}{3}|x|$

20. A certain hyperbola H is a translation image of the graph of $y = \frac{1}{x}$ and has asymptotes $x = 2$ and $y = -5$. Give an equation for H. **(Lessons 3-2, 3-1)** $y + 5 = \dfrac{1}{x - 2}$

In 21–23, if possible, factor the given expression. **(Previous Course)**

21. $6x^3 - 18x^2$ 22. $9m^2n^2 - 49$ 23. $3r^2 - 2r - 5$

24. **Skill Sequence** Rewrite each of the following in the form $a(x - h)$. **(Previous Course)**

    a. $7x - 21$ b. $21x - 7\pi$ c. $7x + 5\pi$

EXPLORATION

25. Take a data set of positive values and take the square root of each value. Which statistics, if any, are invariant? Which are affected in predictable ways?

For a one-variable data set, the 5-number summary of the data set (minimum, maximum, etc) is affected predictably; each statistic after the transformation is the square root of the original statistic. The measures of spread, including variance, mean, and standard deviation are affected, but their definitions need to be used to trace this; simply taking the square root of the original statistic is not correct. The number of elements in the data set is invariant. For a two-variable data set, the y-intercept of the regression equation after the transformation is the square root of the prior y-intercept. The other statistics (the correlation coefficient and the slope of the regression line) must be calculated from their definitions.

---

21. $6x^2(x - 3)$

22. $(3mn - 7) \cdot (3mn + 7)$

23. $(3r - 5)(r + 1)$

24. a. $7(x - 3)$

    b. $21\left(x - \frac{\pi}{3}\right)$

    c. $7\left(x - \left(-\frac{5\pi}{7}\right)\right)$

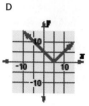

QY ANSWER

$3,590

Lesson
3-7 Composition of Functions

Vocabulary

composite
function composition

▶ **BIG IDEA** Following one process by another process creates a composite that itself can be viewed as a single process.

The presidents of the United States from 1989–1992 and 2001–2008 were George H.W. Bush and his son. This was not the first time that a father and son had been presidents. The 2nd and 6th presidents, John Adams and John Quincy Adams, were also father and son. Here is part of John Quincy Adams's family tree. It shows that John Adams and Abigail Smith are John Quincy Adams's parents. Because President John Adams had the same name as his father, we call the father "Sr." and the son "Jr." here even though they never used those names.

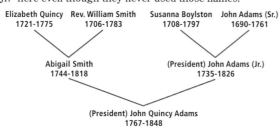

Elizabeth Quincy 1721-1775   Rev. William Smith 1706-1783   Susanna Boylston 1708-1797   John Adams (Sr.) 1690-1761

Abigail Smith 1744-1818   (President) John Adams (Jr.) 1735-1826

(President) John Quincy Adams 1767-1848

Functions can be used to describe the relationships between members of this tree. For example, suppose m is the function defined by

$$m(x) \text{ is the mother of } x,$$

and f is the function defined by

$$f(x) \text{ is the father of } x.$$

Then $m(\text{John Quincy Adams}) = \text{Abigail Smith}$, $m(\text{Abigail Smith}) = \text{Elizabeth Quincy}$, $f(\text{John Quincy Adams}) = \text{John Adams Jr.}$, and so on.

Functions can be combined so that the value of one function becomes the argument of another. For example, since

$$m(\text{John Quincy Adams}) = \text{Abigail Smith},$$
$$\text{and} \qquad f(\text{Abigail Smith}) = \text{Rev. William Smith},$$

this combination can be written

$$f(m(\text{John Quincy Adams})) = f(\text{Abigail Smith}) = \text{Rev. William Smith}.$$

In words, this equation says that the father of the mother of John Quincy Adams is Rev. William Smith.

Mental Math

Start with a number *n*.

a. Subtract 4 from it. Then multiply the difference by 3. What number results?

b. Multiply it by 3. Then subtract 4 from the product. What number results?

a. $3(n-4)$ or $3n-12$

b. $3n-4$

John Adams

John Quincy Adams

Composition of Functions **193**

Background

Composition is the most important operation with functions. Notice that we distinguish between the operation, *composition*, and the result of the operation, the *composite*. Many people call both of these "composition"; we think that is confusing to students.

We place composition of functions here for two reasons. First, it provides a mathematical basis for the discussion of inverse functions and relations in Lesson 3-8 (which in turn provides language to discuss inverses of trigonometric, exponential and logarithmic functions in later chapters.) Second, the idea of composition of *transformations* has already been employed in this chapter. It is natural to think of combining two transformations into one;

(continued on next page)

GOAL
Formalize the concept of composition of functions by defining composition and introducing the ∘ symbol.

SPUR Objectives

A Find equations for and values of composites of functions.

F Identify properties of composites of functions.

Materials/Resources
· Lesson Master 3-7
· Resource Master 64

HOMEWORK • **Option 1**
• Questions 1–11 • Option 2
• • Questions 12–24
• • Question 25 (extra credit)
• Reading Lesson 3-8
• Covering the Ideas 3-8 (Questions 1–10)

Local Standards

1 Warm-Up

Every person has 2 biological parents, 4 biological grandparents, 8 biological great-grandparents. Call these your first-generation, second-generation, and third-generation ancestors. Suppose two of your great-grandparents were second cousins, meaning that they themselves had one pair of great-grandparents in common. If no others of your recent ancestors were related, how many ancestors would you have in the third-through eighth-generation ancestors. **8, 16, 30, 60, 120, 240 (Everyone has to have many ancestral couples that were related to each other because otherwise someone would have more ancestors than there have ever been people on Earth.)**

3-7

Notes on the Lesson

This lesson may be review for many students. You might wish to ask how many of your students have studied composition of functions. Those who have studied from UCSMP *Geometry* will be familiar with composition of transformations. Those who have studied from UCSMP *Advanced Algebra* should be familiar with all the content in this lesson.

The non-numerical example of composition using the Adams family emphasizes the idea of a function of a function. Be careful if you extend the example to students' families, as in real life the delineation of people and their roles may not be as clear, or the same for everyone. Adoptions and surrogate parents are common and the discussion could be uncomfortable for some students. However, the mathematics of the situation can be clarified by always thinking of the "biological" parents, whomever they might be, regardless of whether students know them. You can justify this use by noting that these are the people doctors are interested in when tracing genetically-transmitted diseases.

You might note that we could not define a function *b* for "brother of" or *s* for "sister of" because a function must have a unique value. This could be solved by defining "oldest brother of" or "youngest sister of," but that does not have the same simplicity as biological mother or father.

There is no universal way that *f* ∘ *g* is read. Some people read *f* ∘ *g* as "*g* followed by *f*"; others read "the composite of *f* with *g*." In some contexts one of these readings will be more natural than the other; for instance, in the Adams family example, the language of composites is better than the language of "followed by" because in *f* ∘ *m*, *f* precedes m in time. Another way is to read both $(f \circ g)(x)$ and $f(g(x))$ as "*f* of *g* of *x*," and think of them as applying *g*, then *f*. Students who are uncomfortable with what seems to be a reversal of order could be reminded that we always work with nested parentheses from the inside out.

We say that *m* and *f* have been *composed* to make a new function, which we could call the "maternal grandfather" function. We denote this function by the symbol *f* ∘ *m*, read as "the *composite* of *f* with *m*."

> **Definition of Composite Function**
>
> Suppose *f* and *g* are functions. The **composite** of *g* with *f*, written **g ∘ f**, is the function defined by
> $$(g \circ f)(x) = g(f(x)).$$
> The domain of *g* ∘ *f* is the set of values of *x* in the domain of *f* for which *f*(*x*) is in the domain of *g*.

The composite *g* ∘ *f* can be written without parentheses when applied to an argument, as in *g* ∘ *f*(*x*). Parentheses make it easier to see that there is one composite function applied to the argument, as in the following.

$$(f \circ m)(\text{John Quincy Adams}) = f(m(\text{John Quincy Adams}))$$
$$= f(\text{Abigail Smith})$$
$$= \text{Rev. William Smith}$$

Composition of Functions Is Not Commutative

The operation that yields the composite of two functions is called **function composition**. Order makes a difference in function composition.

$$(m \circ f)(\text{John Quincy Adams}) = m(f(\text{John Quincy Adams}))$$
$$= m(\text{John Adams Jr.})$$
$$= \text{Susanna Boylston}$$

The mother of the father of John Quincy Adams is Susanna Boylston. The function *m* ∘ *f* might be called the "paternal grandmother" function.

Notice that the two functions *f* ∘ *m* and *m* ∘ *f* are different functions. The range of *f* ∘ *m* contains only men, while the range of *m* ∘ *f* contains only women. This illustrates that *composition of functions is not commutative*. The next two examples show this with functions of real numbers.

Example 1

Let *f* and *g* be defined by $f(x) = 2x^2 + 3x$ and $g(x) = x - 7$. Evaluate.
a. $(f \circ g)(-2)$ b. $(g \circ f)(-2)$

Solution

a. To evaluate $(f \circ g)(-2)$, first evaluate $g(-2)$.
$$g(-2) = -2 - 7 = -9$$
Then use this output as the input to *f*. So
$$f(g(-2)) = f(-9)$$
$$= 2(-9)^2 + 3(-9) = 135.$$

---

already there has been the combination of a horizontal and a vertical translation into one two-dimensional translation, and horizontal and vertical scale changes into one scale change, and then the composite of a scale change and a translation in the calculation of *z*-scores.

Composites of transformations Students who have had UCSMP *Geometry* and UCSMP *Advanced Algebra* will be familiar with this idea and should have no trouble thinking of the composite of two functions as a single function. But in this lesson, the discussion centers around functions of a single variable.

b. $g \circ f(-2) = g(f(-2)) = g(2(-2)^2 + 3(-2))$
$= g(2)$
$= 2 - 7 = -5$

It can be tedious to evaluate points for composites of functions. An alternative is to find a formula for the composite.

GUIDED

Example 2

Let $f(x) = 2x^2 + 3x$ and $g(x) = x - 7$.

a. Derive a formula for $(f \circ g)(x)$.
b. Give a simplified formula for $(g \circ f)(x)$.
c. Verify that $f \circ g \neq g \circ f$ by graphing.

Solution

a. In $(f \circ g)(x) = f(g(x))$, first substitute $x - 7$ for $g(x)$.

$$f(g(x)) = f(x - 7)$$

Now use $x - 7$ as the input to function f. $\quad x - 7; x - 7;$

$$f(x - 7) = 2(\underline{})^2 + 3(\underline{}) \quad x^2; 14x$$
$$= 2(\underline{} - \underline{} + 49) + 3x - 21$$
$$= \underline{} \quad 2x^2 - 25x + 77$$

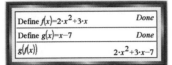

Define $f(x) = 2 \cdot x^2 + 3 \cdot x$ *Done*
Define $g(x) = x - 7$ *Done*
$g(f(x))$ $2 \cdot x^2 + 3 \cdot x - 7$

b. To find a formula for $(g \circ f)(x)$, substitute the expression for $f(x)$ first, or use a CAS. Define the functions on your CAS and evaluate the composite directly.

c. Graph the two functions, $f \circ g$ and $g \circ f$, using a graphing utility. You can see that the graphs are different. So the functions are different.

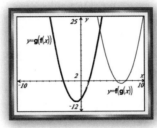

Notice that although $f \circ g$ and $g \circ f$ are **not** the same function, there is at least one value of x at which they have the same y-value. This is the x-value at the point of intersection of the two parabolas.

 QY

Finding the Domain of a Composite Function

The domain of a composite function $g \circ f$ is the set of all elements for which $g \circ f$ is defined. So, to be in the domain of $g \circ f$, a number x must be in the domain of f, and the corresponding $f(x)$ value must be in the domain of g.

▸ **QY**

True or False $f \circ g$ is the image of the graph of f under a translation 7 units to the right.

Composition of Functions   **195**

Notes on the Lesson

Although we often place parentheses around the composite to emphasize it, as in $(f \circ g)(x)$, this is not necessary.

Examples 1 and 2 These examples demonstrate the calculation of values and formulas for composite functions. That composition of functions is not commutative is shown implicitly in Example 1 and overtly in Example 2.

Additional Examples

Example 1 Let $f(x) = x^2$ and $g(x) = \dfrac{1}{3x + 1}$. Evaluate:

a. $f(g(4))$. $\dfrac{1}{169}$
b. $g(f(4))$. $\dfrac{1}{49}$
c. $(f \circ g)(4)$. $\dfrac{1}{169}$

Example 2 Use the functions f and g of Additional Example 1.

a. Derive a formula for $(f \circ g)(x)$. $f(g(x)) = \dfrac{1}{(3x + 1)^2}$
b. Give a simplified formula for $(g \circ f)(x)$. $g(f(x)) = \dfrac{1}{3x^2 + 1}$
c. Verify that $f \circ g \neq g \circ f$ by graphing. The graphs have only two points in common, when $x = 0$ and when $x = -1$.

ENGLISH LEARNERS
Vocabulary Development

Recent practice is careful to distinguish the word "composition" (the operation) from "composite" (the result). For the sake of clarity, we strongly encourage you to follow this practice as we do in this book. This distinction is analogous to the discussion of multiplication, for which we distinguish "multiplication" (the operation) from "product" (the result).

Accommodating the Learner ⬇

Some students may be uncomfortable with what seems to be a reversal of order when evaluating a composite function, $(f \circ g)(x) = f(g(x))$. It may be useful for them to think of a composite function in layers and identify an "inside function," which should be applied first, and an "outside function," which should be applied next. As in their previous mathematical experience, they will be simplifying the nested parentheses from the inside out.

3-7

Notes on the Lesson

Example 3 This example shows that one needs to be careful when looking at the domain of the composite of two functions. Go back to the definition of *composite* on page 194 so that students see why the domain of $g \circ f$ is the set of values of x in the domain of f for which $f(x)$ is in the domain of g. Other values simply would not allow the composite to be calculated.

Additional Examples

Example 3 Use the functions f and g of Additional Example 1. Find the domain of $f \circ g$.
the set of all real numbers except $-\frac{1}{3}$.

Example 4 Let $S: (x, y) \rightarrow (x, \frac{y}{3})$ and $T: (x, y) \rightarrow (x - 1, y - 2)$.

a. Describe S and T in words.
   S is a vertical scale change of magnitude $\frac{1}{3}$, and T is a translation 1 unit left and 2 units down.

b. Write a simplified formula for the composite $(T \circ S)(x, y)$ and describe it in words.
   $(T \circ S)(x, y) = (x - 1, \frac{y}{3} - 2)$.
   $T \circ S$ is a vertical scale change of magnitude $\frac{1}{3}$, followed by a translation 1 unit left and 2 units down.

c. Write a simplified formula for the composite $(S \circ T)(x, y)$ and describe it in words.
   $(S \circ T)(x, y) = (x - 1, \frac{y - 2}{3})$.
   $S \circ T$ is a translation 1 unit left and 2 units down, followed by a vertical scale change of magnitude $\frac{1}{3}$.

Example 3

Let f and g be real functions defined by $f(m) = \sqrt{m}$ and $g(m) = \frac{2}{m - 3}$. Find the domain of $g \circ f$.

Solution 1 Because f is a real function, the domain of f is the set of all nonnegative real numbers. The domain of g is the set of all real numbers but 3, so all values of $f(m)$ except when $\sqrt{m} = 3$ are in the domain of g. Thus, the domain of $g \circ f$ is the set of real numbers m with $m \geq 0$ and $m \neq 9$.

Solution 2 Find a formula for $g \circ f$ and analyze the domain.
$(g \circ f)(m) = g(f(m)) = g(\sqrt{m}) = \frac{1}{\sqrt{m} - 3}$
$\sqrt{m}$ is defined in the real number system only for $m \geq 0$.
$\sqrt{m} - 3 = 0$ when $m = 9$. So, the domain of $g \circ f$ is $\{m: m \geq 0 \text{ and } m \neq 9\}$.

Check Use a graphing utility to graph $g(f(x)) = \frac{1}{\sqrt{x} - 3}$. You should get a graph like the one at the right with an asymptote at $x = 9$.

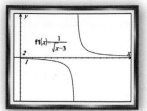

Example 3 shows that the domain of the composite can be different from the domain of either of the component functions.

Composition of Transformations

Because transformations are functions, they can be composed. Like other functions, composition of transformations is not commutative.

GUIDED

Example 4

Let $S: (x, y) \rightarrow (2x, y)$ and let $T: (x, y) \rightarrow (x + 4, y - 3)$.

a. Describe S and T in words.

b. Write a formula for the composite $(T \circ S)(x, y)$ and describe it in words.

c. Write a formula for the composite $(S \circ T)(x, y)$ and describe it in words.

Solution

a. S is a horizontal scale change of magnitude __?__ and T is a __?__. translation 4 units to the right and 3 units down

b. $(T \circ S)(x, y) = T(S(x, y)) = T(2x, y) = (2x + 4, y - 3)$.
   $T \circ S$ is a horizontal scale change of magnitude 2, followed by a translation 4 units right and 3 units down.

c. $(S \circ T)(x, y) = S(T(x, y)) = S(\underline{?}, \underline{?}) = (2(\underline{?}), \underline{?}) = (\underline{?}, \underline{?})$. $T \circ S$ is a translation 4 units right and 3 units down, followed by a horizontal scale change of magnitude 2.

$x + 4; y - 3; x + 4; y - 3; 2x + 8; y - 3$

Accommodating the Learner

Prove that the composite $L_2 \circ L_1$ of the two linear functions $L_1: x \rightarrow mx + b$ and $L_2: x \rightarrow nx + c$ is a linear function and find the slope and y-intercept of the composite function. Use this information to determine whether composition of linear functions is commutative.

Extension

Choose two functions f and g, in order to investigate the following. Does the value of the composite of these functions ever equal the product of the values of the functions? That is, does $f(g(x)) = f(x) \cdot g(x)$? Does the value of the composite of these functions ever equal the sum of the values of the functions? That is, does $f(g(x)) = f(x) + g(x)$? **The answers depend on which functions you choose, but these values are seldom the same.**

Questions

COVERING THE IDEAS

In 1 and 2, consider John Quincy Adams's family tree.

1. What biological relation does the composite $m \circ m$ represent?
2. John Quincy Adams married Louisa Catherine Johnson. Suppose they have a child, x. **2a. $(m \circ f)(x)$ = Abigail Smith**
   a. Evaluate $(m \circ f)(x)$. b. Explain why $(f \circ m)(x) \neq (m \circ f)(x)$.

In 3 and 4, refer to the functions f and g of Examples 1 and 2.

3. Verify that $f(g(0)) \neq g(f(0))$. **$f(g(0)) = f(-7) = 77$; $g(f(0)) = g(0) = -7$**
4. **True or False** a. $f(g(6)) = g(f(6))$ b. $f(g(3)) = g(f(3))$ **true**
5. Let $M(t) = 2t - 1$ and $N(t) = \frac{3}{t+1}$. **5a. $(M \circ N)(t) = \frac{6}{t+1} - 1$**
   a. Find a formula for $(M \circ N)(t)$. b. State the domain of $M \circ N$.
6. **True or False** Composition of functions is commutative. **false**

In 7 and 8, let $f(x) = (x + 1)^2$ and $g(x) = x - 2$.

7. Evaluate $f(g(-5))$ and $g(f(-5))$. **36; 14**
8. Show that $g \circ f \neq f \circ g$ by graphing. **See margin.**

In 9 and 10, $f(x) = 2x^3 - 1$ and $g(x) = 3x$.

9. Evaluate each expression.
   a. $f(g(-1))$ **-55** b. $(f \circ g)(0)$ **-1**
10. a. Find a formula for $(f \circ g)(x)$. **$(f \circ g)(x) = 54x^3 - 1$**
    b. State the domain of $f \circ g$. **all real numbers**
    c. For what value of x does $(f \circ g)(x) = (g \circ f)(x)$?
11. Let T be a transformation that translates each point right 3 and up 1; let S be a vertical scale change of magnitude $\frac{1}{4}$.
    a. **Fill in the Blanks** T: $(x, y) \to$ (__?__, __?__) and S: $(x, y) \to$ (__?__, __?__). **$x + 3$; $y + 1$; x; $\frac{y}{4}$**
    b. Find a formulas for $T \circ S$ and $S \circ T$.

APPLYING THE MATHEMATICS

12. Consider the sets A, B, and C at the right.
    a. Evaluate $g(f(3))$. **2**
    b. The composite $g \circ f$ maps 4 to what number? **$\sqrt{5}$**
    c. If $f(x) = x + 1$ and $g(x) = \sqrt{x}$, write a formula for $g(f(x))$.
    d. If the domain of f is extended to the set of all reals, what is the domain of $g \circ f$? **$\{x \mid x \geq -1\}$**

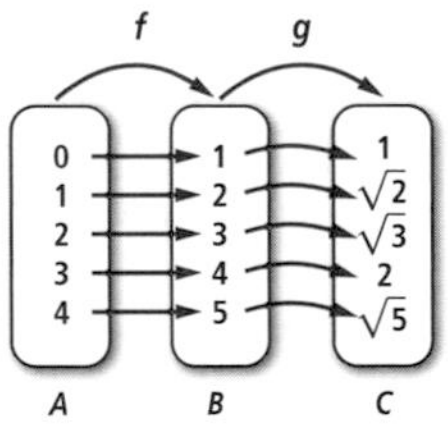

13. If $S(x, y) = (-y, x)$, find a formula for $S \circ S$. **$(S \circ S)(x, y) = (-x, -y)$**
14. If $T(x, y) = (x + 6, 2y)$, find a formula for $T \circ T$. **$(T \circ T)(x, y) = (x + 12, 4y)$**

In 15–17, suppose $D(x) = 0.9x$ and $R(x) = x - 100$.

15. Explain why it is appropriate to call D a discount function and R a rebate function.

1. maternal grandmother
2b. Louisa Catherine Johnson's father is not John Quincy Adams's mother.
4a. false
5b. all real numbers except -1
10c. $x = \sqrt[3]{-\frac{1}{24}} \approx -0.3467$
11b. $(T \circ S)(x, y) = \left(x + 3, \frac{y}{4} + 1\right)$; $(S \circ T)(x, y) = \left(x + 3, \frac{y + 1}{4}\right)$
12c. $(g \circ f)(x) = \sqrt{x + 1}$
15. Discounts are usually based on some percentage of the original price and rebates are usually a fixed dollar amount reduction in price.

Additional Answers

8.

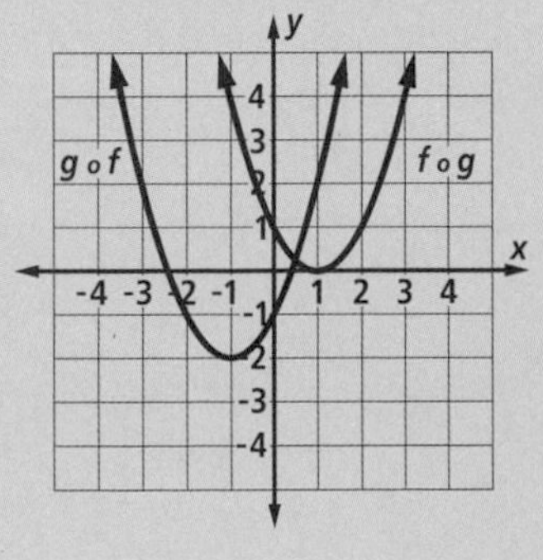

3-7

3 Assignment

Recommended Assignment

- Questions 1–11
- Questions 12–24
- Question 25 (extra credit)
- Reading Lesson 3-8
- Covering the Ideas 3-8 (Questions 1–10)

Notes on the Questions

Questions 1 and 2 You might ask how many students s in your class can tell you the name of $m \circ m(s)$? (Almost all should be able to do this.) What about $f \circ m(s)$? What about $f \circ m \circ m(s)$. Can any students trace back many many generations? A nice activity is to have students identify all the ancestors they know using function composition notation. If adopted, students can use their adopted parents' ancestors.

Question 4b Point out that even though the composite values are equal for the argument 3, the functions $f \circ g$ and $g \circ f$ are not equal.

Question 12 The use of arrows in this way is a common representation of function composition, but be careful that students realize that f, the first function here, is on the left.

Questions 15–17 In UCSMP *Advanced Algebra*, this context is used to introduce composition of functions, so it may be familiar to students. If both the discount and rebate were percents of the price, then the composite of the functions would be commutative. As is, this is a translation and a scale change.

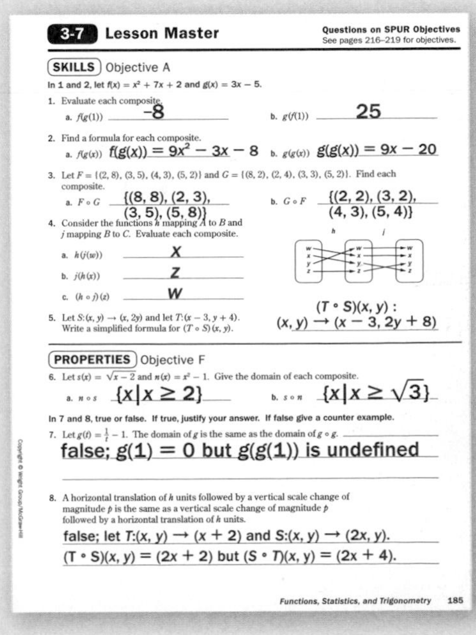

3-7 Lesson Master — Questions on SPUR Objectives. See pages 216–219 for objectives.

SKILLS Objective A

In 1 and 2, let $f(x) = x^2 + 7x + 2$ and $g(x) = 3x - 5$.

1. Evaluate each composite.
   a. $f(g(1))$ **-8** b. $g(f(1))$ **25**
2. Find a formula for each composite.
   a. $f(g(x))$ **$f(g(x)) = 9x^2 - 3x - 8$** b. $g(g(x))$ **$g(g(x)) = 9x - 20$**
3. Let $F = \{(2, 8), (3, 5), (4, 3), (5, 2)\}$ and $G = \{(8, 2), (2, 4), (3, 3), (5, 2)\}$. Find each composite.
   a. $F \circ G$ **{(8, 8), (2, 3), (3, 5), (5, 8)}** b. $G \circ F$ **{(2, 2), (3, 2), (4, 3), (5, 4)}**
4. Consider the functions h mapping A to B and j mapping B to C. Evaluate each composite.
   a. $h(j(w))$ **x**
   b. $j(h(x))$ **z**
   c. $(h \circ j)(z)$ **w**
5. Let $S: (x, y) \to (x, 2y)$ and let $T: (x - 3, y + 4)$. Write a simplified formula for $(T \circ S)(x, y)$. **$(T \circ S)(x, y)$: $(x, y) \to (x - 3, 2y + 8)$**

PROPERTIES Objective F

6. Let $s(x) = \sqrt{x - 2}$ and $n(x) = x^2 - 1$. Give the domain of each composite.
   a. $n \circ s$ **$\{x \mid x \geq 2\}$** b. $s \circ n$ **$\{x \mid x \geq \sqrt{3}\}$**

In 7 and 8, true or false. If true, justify your answer. If false give a counter example.

7. Let $g(t) = \frac{1}{t} - 1$. The domain of g is the same as the domain of $g \circ g$.
   false; $g(1) = 0$ but $g(g(1))$ is undefined
8. A horizontal translation of h units followed by a vertical scale change of magnitude p is the same as a vertical scale change of magnitude p followed by a horizontal translation of h units.
   false; let $T:(x, y) \to (x + 2)$ and $S:(x, y) \to (2x, y)$. $(T \circ S)(x, y) = (2x + 2)$ but $(S \circ T)(x, y) = (2x + 4)$.

Functions, Statistics, and Trigonometry 185

3-7

Notes on the Questions

Question 19 The difficult part of this question is to identify the variables. Many students will name each unit as a variable, rather than realize that the functions are determined by conversion factors.

Question 25 A function that satisfies this equation is its own inverse. So you can use this question to lead into Lesson 3-8.

4 Wrap-Up

Ongoing Assessment

Have students work with a partner. Ask one student to define a function f and the other to define a function g. Then have one student find a formula for $f(g(x))$, and have the other student find a formula for $g(f(x))$. **Answers vary. Check students' work.**

Project Update

Project 3, *Transformation Groups*, on page 212 relates to the content of this lesson.

---

16. a. Evaluate $D(R(1200))$ and $R(D(1200))$. **990; 980**
    b. If you are buying a flat screen TV for $1200, is it better to apply the discount after the rebate or before the rebate? **before**

17. Find rules for $D \circ R(x)$ and for $R \circ D(x)$. Prove that $D \circ R \neq R \circ D$.

18. From these tables, evaluate each expression, if possible.

x	-5	-3	-1	0	1	2	3	4	5
f(x)	-5	-4	-3	0	3	2	1	0	-1

x	0	1	4	9	16	25
g(x)	0	1	2	3	4	5

a. $f(g(4))$ **2**   b. $g(f(4))$ **0**   c. $f(g(1))$ **3**   d. $g(f(1))$ **not possible**

19. a. One mile is 5280 feet. Write a formula for a function m that converts number of feet to number of miles.
    b. One mile is exactly 1.609344 kilometers. Write a formula for a function k that converts number of miles to number of kilometers.
    c. Write a rule for a composite function that converts feet to kilometers.
    d. How many feet is 5 kilometers?

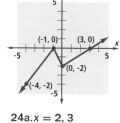

20. Let f and g be real functions with $f(x) = \frac{1}{x}$ and $g(x) = x + 4$.
    a. Give equations for all asymptotes of the graph of $f \circ g$.
    b. Give equations for all asymptotes of the graph of $g \circ f$.

REVIEW

21. The graph of $y = f(x)$ is drawn at the right. Draw the graph of $y = 2f(3x)$. (**Lesson 3-5**) **See margin.**

22. Prices of pies at Benny's Bakery have a mean of $13.58 and a variance of 2.18. Assuming that customers do not change their purchasing pattern, what will be the effect on the mean and standard deviation under each circumstance? (**Lessons 3-6, 3-3**)
    a. The price per pie increases by 50 cents. **See margin.**
    b. The price per pie increases by 5%. **See margin.**

23. Find an equation for the image of the graph of $f(x) = x^2$ under the transformation S: $(x, y) \rightarrow \left(\frac{x}{4}, y\right)$. (**Lessons 3-5, 3-2**) $y = 16x^2$

24. **Skill Sequence** Find all real solutions. (**Previous Course**)
    a. $(5x - 10)(x - 3) = 0$ b. $3x^2 = 1 - 2x$ c. $3x^4 = 1 - 2x^2$

EXPLORATION

25. Find a function f such that $f(f(x)) = x$ yet $f(x) \neq x$.

    Answers vary. Sample: $f(x) = \frac{1}{x}$

17.
$(D \circ R)(x) = 0.9x - 90;$
$(R \circ D)(x) = 0.9x - 100;$
$0.9x - 90 \neq 0.9x - 100$
19a. $m(x) = \frac{x}{5280};$
19b. $k(x) = 1.609344x$
19c. $(k \circ m)(x) = 0.0003048x$
19d. 16,404.2 feet

20a. $x = -4, y = 0$
20b. $x = 0, y = 4.$

24a. $x = 2, 3$
24b. $x = -1, \frac{1}{3}$
24c. $x = \pm \frac{\sqrt{3}}{3}$

QY ANSWER
true

Additional Answers

21.

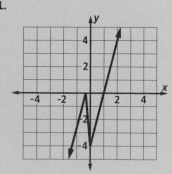

22a. The mean increases by 50 cents and the standard deviation stays the same.
22b. Both the mean and standard deviation increase by 5%.

Lesson 3-8

Inverses of Functions

Vocabulary

inverse of a function
identity function

Lesson 3-8

▶ **BIG IDEA** Descriptions of inverses of functions can be determined from the function itself, represented by ordered pairs or an equation, or its graph.

The volume of a cube is $V = e^3$, where e is the length of an edge. Considering V as a function of e, we can write $V = f(e)$, and f is the *cubing* function. For example, the volume of a cube with 7-cm edges is $f(7) = 7^3 = 343$ cm^3. However, sometimes you know the volume of a cube and need to find the edge length. Suppose a cube has a volume of 250 cm^3. Solve for the edge length by finding the cube root of 250; $e = \sqrt[3]{250} \approx 6.3$ cm. In general, $e = \sqrt[3]{V}$. Considering e as a function of V, we can write $e = g(V) = \sqrt[3]{V}$. The functions $f: e \to e^3$ and $g: V \to \sqrt[3]{V}$ are examples of *inverse functions*.

Mental Math

What operation undoes each action?

a. adding $\frac{2}{3}$ to a number

b. multiplying a number by $\frac{\pi}{2}$

c. squaring a positive number

a. subtracting $\frac{2}{3}$

b. dividing by $\frac{\pi}{2}$ or multiplying by $\frac{2}{\pi}$

c. taking the square root

Finding the Inverse of a Function

Recall that a function can be considered as a set of ordered pairs in which each first element is paired with exactly one second element. If you switch coordinates in the pairs, the resulting set of ordered pairs is called the **inverse** of the function.

Example 1

Let $f = \{(-3, -5), (-2, 0), (-1, 3), (0, 4), (1, 3), (2, 0), (3, -5)\}$.
Describe the inverse of f. Is the inverse a function?

Solution

Let g be the inverse of f. The ordered pairs in g are found by switching the x- and y-coordinates of each pair in f.

$g = \{(-5, -3), (0, -2), (3, -1), (4, 0), (3, 1), (0, 2), (-5, 3)\}$

The inverse is not a function because there are ordered pairs in which the same first element is paired with different second elements, such as $(-5, -3)$ and $(-5, 3)$.

Inverses of Functions **199**

GOAL

Define inverse of a function, discuss how to determine an inverse of a function from its graph or by graphing, and then examine the skill of finding an equation of an inverse.

SPUR Objectives

B Find inverses of functions.

F Identify properties of inverses of functions.

I Recognize functions and their properties from their graphs.

K Graph inverses of functions.

Materials/Resources

· Lesson Master 3-8
· Resource Masters 65 and 66

HOMEWORK • Option 1

- Questions 1–10 • Option 2
- • Questions 11-25
- • Question 26 (extra credit)
  - Reading Lesson 3-9
  - Covering the Ideas 3-9 (Questions 1–9)

Local Standards

1 Warm-Up

Indicate how you could undo each operation or composite of operations.

1. turning left and walking 30 yards, then turning around and walking 15 yards **Answers vary. Sample: continue walking 15 yards and turn left**

2. multiplying a number by $1\frac{2}{3}$ **Answers vary. Sample: divide the result by 5 and multiply by 3**

(continued on next page)

Background

This lesson combines all of the aspects of SPUR. There are skills, properties, uses, and representations. The objectives involve all but uses, but uses are found in the first paragraph of the lesson and in Questions 11, 12, and 17. Students should be able to write an equation for the inverse of a given function, graph one function given the graph of the other, and use the Inverse Function Theorem.

Finding the inverse of a function Like most college texts, we define the inverse of a function as the relation in which the components of all ordered pairs of the function are switched. Under this definition, every function has an inverse, but of course not all inverses are functions. Some books only allow a relation to be called the inverse of a function if the relation itself is a function.

(continued on next page)

3-8

3. adding 40 to a number, then dividing the result by one-half **Answers vary. Sample: multiply the result by $\frac{1}{2}$ and subtract 40**

4. taking the fifth power of a positive number, then taking its positive square root **Answers vary. Sample: square the result and take its positive fifth root**

---

2 | Teaching

Notes on the Lesson

Students should be able to think of inverse functions in two ways. One is that *they undo each other*. For example, the halving function $f(x) = \frac{x}{2}$ undoes the doubling function $g(x) = 2x$. This way leads to the notion that the composite of two inverse functions is the identity function. This is what is proved in the theorem in this lesson about inverse functions. Some books take this as the definition of inverse functions.

The other way of thinking of inverse functions is that the elements of *their ordered pairs* (their domain and range) *are switched*. This way is most useful in comparing the graphs of a function and its inverse, and in finding an equation for the inverse of a function. In this book, this is the way we define inverse functions.

In this book, the notation f^{-1} is reserved only for inverses which are functions. This is not the case in some other books, and if you wish to use the notation more generally, be certain to mention your choice with your students.

Be sure that your students understand that $f^{-1}(x) \neq \frac{1}{f(x)}$. Some students confuse the algebraic exponent –1 with the notation for inverse functions. Although the multiplicative inverse of a real number is its reciprocal, the inverse of a function under composition is not. Note that when f and f^{-1} are inverse functions, then for all x, $f(f^{-1}(x)) = f^{-1}(f(x))$. Therefore, the composition of inverse functions *is* commutative.

If the original function is described by an equation, then switching the variables in the equation gives an equation for its inverse. This has the same effect as switching the coordinates of every ordered pair.

Example 2

a. Give an equation for the inverse of the function described by $y = -x^2 + 4$.

b. Sketch a graph of $y = -x^2 + 4$ and the inverse on the same set of axes.

c. Is the inverse a function?

Solution

a. To form an equation for the inverse, switch x and y. **The inverse is described by the equation $x = -y^2 + 4$.**

b. The graphs of $y = -x^2 + 4$ and $x = -y^2 + 4$ its inverse are drawn at the right.

c. The graph of the inverse contains ordered pairs with the same first coordinate but different second coordinate and fails the vertical-line test. **So $x = -y^2 + 4$ is not an equation of a function.**

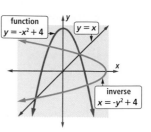

At the right are tables with some ordered pairs of each relation in Example 2. Notice that the ordered pairs, from the function to the inverse, follow the mapping $(x, y) \rightarrow (y, x)$. This mapping can be seen graphically as a reflection over the line $y = x$. So, the graphs of a function and its inverse are reflection images of each other over the line $y = x$.

function $y = -x^2 + 4$		inverse $x = -y^2 + 4$	
x	y	x	y
-2	0	0	-2
-1	3	3	-1
0	4	4	0
1	3	3	1
2	0	0	2
3	-5	-5	3
4	-12	-12	4

STOP QY1

Activity

Step 1 Let $a(x) = \frac{1}{x - 3} + 4$. Describe in words what the function does to a number x according to the order of operations.

Step 2 Now describe in words how to "undo" the process you described in Step 1. Call this function b and write a formula for $b(x)$.

Step 3 Check your answers to Steps 1 and 2 by choosing a value for x, inputting that x-value into the formula for $a(x)$, and then substituting that output into the formula for $b(x)$. What was your result?

The Activity shows that when one function undoes the effects of another function, the original input x results. When two functions are comprised of the operations of each other in reverse order, they are inverse functions of each other. Sometimes it is more convenient to switch the x- and y-coordinates of the original function first and then perform the inverse operations to arrive at the inverse of the original function.

200 Transformations of Graphs and Data

> **QY1**
> If (3,12.5) is a point on the graph of a function, what point is on the graph of its inverse?

Step 1: Subtract 3, take the reciprocal, and add 4.

Step 2: Subtract 4, take the reciprocal, and add 3. $b(x) = \frac{1}{x - 4} + 3$

Step 3: Pick $x = 5$. $a(5) = \frac{1}{5 - 3} + 4 = \frac{9}{2}$. $b\left(\frac{9}{2}\right) = \frac{1}{\frac{9}{2} - 4} + 3 = 5$.

You get the original x-value back.

Under either characterization, the inverse of a function f is a function if and only if f is one-to-one, and the Horizontal Line Test is valid. A function is one-to-one if and only if $f(x_1) = f(x_2)$ implies that $x_1 = x_2$.

Activity The function a in the activity can be viewed as the composite $h \circ g \circ f$ of the three functions with formulas $f(x) = x - 3$, $g(x) = \frac{1}{x}$, and $h(x) = x + 4$. The general idea is that the inverse of $h \circ g \circ f$ is $f^{-1} \circ g^{-1} \circ h^{-1}$. That is, the inverse of a composite of functions is the composite of the inverses, in the reverse order. The idea of "undoing" is one that is quite familiar to students: the inverse of putting on socks and then putting on shoes is taking off the shoes first, then taking off the socks.

Example 3

Consider the function f with $f(x) = \frac{1}{x-3} + 4$.

a. Give an equation for the inverse of f.

b. Graph f and its inverse on the same set of axes.

Solution 1

a. Let $y = \frac{1}{x-3} + 4$. Switch x and y to find an equation for the inverse.

$$x = \frac{1}{y-3} + 4$$

This equation answers the question, but we usually solve for y.

$$x - 4 = \frac{1}{y-3} \qquad \text{Subtract 4.}$$

$$y - 3 = \frac{1}{x-4} \qquad \text{Take reciprocals.}$$

From this equation, by the Graph Translation Theorem, you can see that the graph of the inverse is the image of the graph of $y = \frac{1}{x}$ under the translation $(x, y) \rightarrow (x + 4, y + 3)$.

$$y = \frac{1}{x-4} + 3 \qquad \text{Add 3.}$$

b. The graphs of $y = \frac{1}{x-3} + 4$ and of $y = \frac{1}{x-4} + 3$ are shown at the right. To check that they are inverses, we also graphed $y = x$. Notice that each branch of the inverse is the image of one of the branches of the original hyperbola under a reflection over $y = x$.

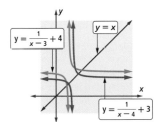

Solution 2 Use the `solve` command on a CAS. Notice that the solution given here is in a different form than Solution 1. The CAS rewrote $\frac{1}{x-4} + 3$ using common denominators.

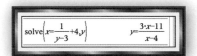

STOP QY2

Examples 2 and 3 demonstrate a significant feature of inverses. That is, not all inverses are functions. Looking at the graph and applying the definition of function reveals that the inverse from Example 2 is not a function, while the inverse from Example 3 is a function.

When the inverse of a function f is a function, it is denoted by the symbol f^{-1}, read "f inverse." With this notation, the rule for the inverse of f in Example 3 can be written $f^{-1}(x) = \frac{3x-11}{x-4}$. *Caution:* Note that f^{-1} does not denote the reciprocal of f, which is $\frac{1}{f}$.

STOP QY3

> **QY2**
>
> Show that
> $$\frac{1}{x-4} + 3 = \frac{3x-11}{x-4}.$$

> **QY3**
>
> a. What is the vertical asymptote of the graph of f in Example 3?
> b. What is the vertical asymptote of the graph of f^{-1}?

Additional Examples

Example 1 Let $h = \{(1, 1), (2, 4), (3, 9), (4, 16)\}$.

a. Describe the inverse of h. **Let g be the inverse of h. $g = \{(1, 1), (4, 2), (9, 3), (16, 4)\}$.**

b. Is the inverse a function? **Yes.**

c. Describe h and its inverse in words. **h is a squaring function; its inverse g is a positive square root function.**

Example 2

a. Describe the graph of the function $y = 2(x + 5)^2 - 1$. **The graph is a parabola opening up with minimum point (–5, –1).**

b. Give an equation for the inverse of the function $y = 2(x + 5)^2 - 1$. **$x = 2(y + 5)^2 - 1$**

c. Based on your answer to Part a, describe the graph of the inverse of the function. Is the inverse a function? **The graph of the inverse is a parabola opening right. Its leftmost point is (–1, –5). No, the inverse is not a function because there are two points on the graph with the same first coordinate.**

Example 3

a. Give an equation for the inverse of the function with equation $y = \frac{5}{x+8} - 1$. **$y = \frac{5}{x+1} - 8$**

b. Is the inverse a function? **Yes.**

Inverse Functions and Composition of Functions

Because the inverse of a function is found by switching the x- and y-coordinates, the domain and range of the inverse are found by switching the domain and range of the original function. Thus, the domain of f^{-1} is the range of f, and the range of f^{-1} is the domain of f. Hence, if f is a function whose inverse is also a function, $f(f^{-1}(x))$ and $f^{-1}(f(x))$ can always be calculated.

For example, for the function in Example 3,

$$f(f^{-1}(2)) = f\left(\frac{1}{2 - 4} + 3\right) = f(2.5) = \left(\frac{1}{2.5 - 3} + 4\right) = 2,$$

and $\quad f^{-1}(f(2)) = f^{-1}\left(\frac{1}{2 - 3} + 4\right) = f^{-1}(3) = \left(\frac{1}{3 - 4} + 3\right) = 2.$

As you will see in Example 4, for these functions, $f \circ f^{-1}(x) = f^{-1} \circ f(x) = x$ for all values of x for which the composites are defined. This is why f^{-1} is called the inverse of f; f^{-1} undoes the effect of f. This property of the composition of inverses is an instance of the following theorem.

Inverses of Functions Theorem

Given any two functions f and g, f and g are inverse functions if and only if $f(g(x)) = x$ for all x in the domain of g, and $g(f(x)) = x$ for all x in the domain of f.

When f and g are inverse functions, then $f = g^{-1}$ and $g = f^{-1}$. The theorem states that two functions are inverses of each other if and only if $f \circ g$ and $g \circ f$ are the function I with $I(x) = x$, a function which is called an **identity function**. The Inverses of Functions Theorem enables you to test whether two functions are inverse functions even if you have not derived one from the other.

Example 4

a. Use the Inverses of Functions Theorem to determine whether f and g, defined by $f(x) = \dfrac{2x - 4}{x + 1}$ and $g(x) = \dfrac{x - 1}{2x + 4}$, are inverses.

b. Verify your result in Part a by graphing f and g.

Solution

a. Define both relations on a CAS. Use the CAS to evaluate $f(g(x))$

Because $(f \circ g)(x) \neq x$, the functions are not inverses.

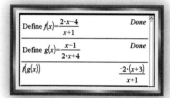

Accommodating the Learner

Have students prove that if the inverses of f and g are functions, then the inverse of $f \circ g$ is the function $g^{-1} \circ f^{-1}$. (Hint: consider $g^{-1} \circ f^{-1} \circ f \circ g(x)$ and $f \circ g \circ g^{-1} \circ f^{-1}(x)$ and apply the Inverse Function Theorem.)

b. Graph f, g, and $y = x$. The graph of g is shown using a bold line. Note that the graphs of f and g are not reflection images of each other over $y = x$.

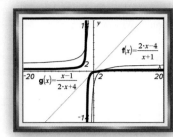

Questions

COVERING THE IDEAS

1. Define *inverse of a function*.

2. Let $f = \{(1, -4), (2, -6), (3, -8), (4, -10)\}$.
   a. Find g, the inverse of f. $\{(-4, 1), (-6, 2), (-8, 3), (-10, 4)\}$
   b. Graph f and g on the same set of axes.
   c. What transformation relates the graphs of f and g?

3. a. Suppose $f(x) = -2x^2$. Graph f and its inverse on the same axes.
   b. Explain why the inverse of f is not a function.

4. Give an example, different from those in the lesson, of a function whose inverse is not a function. **Answers vary. Sample: $y = \dfrac{1}{x^2}$**

In 5–7, write an equation for the inverse of the function with the given equation. Solve your equation for y. Is the inverse a function?

5. $y = 2x - 4$ 6. $y = -x^3$ 7. $y = \sqrt{x}$

8. A rule for a function h is given. Is the inverse of h a function?
   a. $h(x) = |x + 2|$ no   b. $h(x) = x + 2$ yes

In 9 and 10, determine if f and g are inverses by finding $g \circ f(x)$ and $f \circ g(x)$. Then check your conclusion by graphing the functions.

9. $f(x) = x^3$; $g(x) = \sqrt[3]{x}$ 10. $f(x) = \dfrac{2}{x} - 5$; $g(x) = \dfrac{2}{x + 5}$

APPLYING THE MATHEMATICS

11. At one point in the summer of 2008, one U.S. dollar was worth 10.033 Mexican pesos. Let $M(x)$ be the cost in pesos of an item priced at x U.S. dollars and $U(x)$ be the cost in dollars of an item priced at x Mexican pesos. **See margin.**

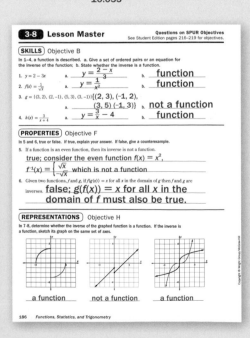

   a. Write expressions for $M(x)$ and $U(x)$.
   b. What was the U.S. price of an item which cost 20,000 pesos?
   c. Are M and U inverses of each other? Justify your answer.

Inverses of Functions   **203**

---

1. The relation found by switching the x- and y-coordinates of all points.

2b.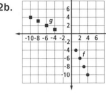

2c. g is the reflection image of f over the line $y = x$.

3a.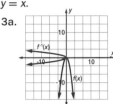

3b. $f^{-1}(x)$ is equivalent to the relation $y = \pm\sqrt{-\dfrac{x}{2}}$; therefore some x-values are assigned two y-values, which is not allowed in a function.

5. $x = 2y - 4$; $y = \dfrac{x}{2} + 2$; yes

6. $x = -y^3$; $y = -\sqrt[3]{x}$; yes

7. $x = \sqrt{y}$; $y = x^2$ for $x \geq 0$; yes

9–10. See margin.

---

3 Assignment

Recommended Assignment
- Questions 1–10
- • Questions 11-25
- • Question 26 (extra credit)
- • Reading Lesson 3-9
- • Covering the Ideas 3-9 (Questions 1–9)

Notes on the Questions
We suggest going through Questions 1–11 in order.

Questions 9 and 10 These should be assigned together. Ask students for various ways to know why one function has an inverse that is a function, while the other does not. (One way is through the graphs of the given functions; another is through the definition of inverse as switching the components of the ordered pair; still another way is to ask whether the operations undo each other.)

Question 10 Notice that f is the composite of the function $r: x \to \dfrac{2}{x}$ followed by $s: x \to x - 5$. Its inverse is the function that is the composite of the inverses of these functions in reverse order: $s^{-1}: x \to x + 5$ followed by $r^{-1}: x \to \dfrac{2}{x}$, which is g.

Additional Answers

11a. $M(x) = 10.033x$, $U(x) = \dfrac{x}{10.033}$

11b. $1,993.42

11c. yes, $M(U(x)) = \dfrac{10.033x}{10.033} = x$ for all real x, $U(M(x)) = \dfrac{10.033x}{10.033} = x$ for all real x

Additional Answers

9. $g(f(x)) = x$ for all x, $f(g(x)) = x$ for all x, therefore the functions are inverses.

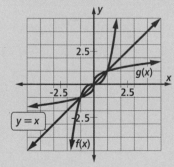

10. $f(g(x)) = x$ for all $x \neq -5$, $g(f(x)) = x$ for all $x \neq 0$; the functions are inverses.

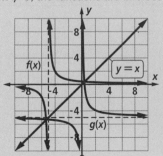

Additional Answers

13a.

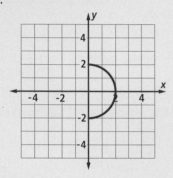

14a.

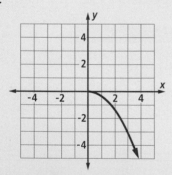

16a. $f^{-1}(x) = \frac{x-b}{m} = \frac{1}{m}x - \frac{b}{m}$

16b. false; The inverse of a linear function $y = b$ for all x is $x = b$, which is not a function.

20a. $C = \frac{5}{9}(F - 32)$; $K = C + 273.15$

20b. $K = \frac{5}{9}(F - 32) + 273.15 = \frac{5}{9}F + 255.37$; The composite rule converts from Fahrenheit to Kelvin.

21a. $p(x) = -|x| + 7$, so $p(-x) = -|-x| + 7 = -x + 7 = p(x)$. Therefore p is an even function.

21b. The graph is symmetric over the y-axis.

12. The rule for converting from degrees Fahrenheit to degrees Celsius is "subtract 32, then multiply by $\frac{5}{9}$."
   a. Determine the rule for converting Celsius to Fahrenheit.
   b. Do the two rules represent inverse functions? Why or why not?

In 13 and 14, a graph is given.
   a. Sketch the graph of the inverse of the function.
   b. State whether or not the inverse is a function.

13.   b. no   14. b. yes

15. If h is the reciprocal function defined by $h(p) = \frac{1}{p}$, show that $h(p) = h^{-1}(p)$ for all $p \neq 0$. That is, h is its own inverse.

16. a. Let $f(x) = mx + b$, where $m \neq 0$. Find a formula for $f^{-1}(x)$.
   b. **True or False** The inverse of every function whose graph is a line is a function whose graph is a line. If false, give a counterexample. **See margin.**

17. An empty box weighs 11 ounces. It is filled with bolts weighing 8 oz each. The total weight in ounces of the box is given by $w(n) = 11 + 8n$ where n is the number of bolts. Write a formula for the inverse function which finds the number of bolts given the total weight. $n(w) = \frac{w - 11}{8}$

REVIEW

In 18 and 19, let $v(t) = 39t$ and $r(t) = t + 17$. (Lesson 3-7)

18. Evaluate each composite.
   a. $(r \circ v)(-1)$ -22 b. $r \circ r(-1)$ **33**

19. Find a formula for each function.
   a. $v \circ r$ b. $v \circ v$

20. Consider the Fahrenheit to Celsius rule in Question 12 and the rule to convert from Celsius to Kelvin of "add 273.15." (Lesson 3-7)
   a. Write equations for functions that convert from Fahrenheit to Celsius and from Celsius to Kelvin.
   b. Find the composite function. What does this function do? **See margin.**

21. a. Prove that the function p defined by $p(x) = -|x| + 7$ is an even function.
   b. What type of symmetry does the graph of $y = p(x)$ have? (Lesson 3-4) **See margin.**

12a. $F = \frac{9}{5}C + 32$

12b. yes; The composites of the functions are equal to x.

13a. See margin.

14a. See margin.

15. To find the inverse, $h^{-1}(p)$, switch p and $h(p)$:
   $p = \frac{1}{h(p)}$,
   $h^{-1}(p) = \frac{1}{p}$;
   $h^{-1}(h(p)) = \frac{1}{\frac{1}{p}} = p$
   for all $p \neq 0$, therefore the function is its own inverse.

19a. $39(t + 17) = 39t + 663$

19b. $39(39t) = 1521t$

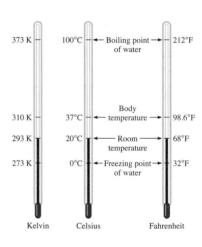

In 22 and 23, use the data in the table at the right that contains the number of cell phone subscribers (in thousands) and the average length of local calls.

	Subscribers	Min/Call
1985	340	n/a
1990	5,283	2.20
1995	33,786	2.15
2000	109,478	2.56
2005	207,896	3.00

Source: CTIA - The Wireless Association

22. a. Graph the data for subscribers for a given year.
    b. Find the best exponential model relating the year to the number of subscribers.
    c. Use the model to predict the number of cell phone subscribers in 2010. **(Lesson 2-5)**

23. a. Graph the data for the average call length for a given year.
    b. Find a good model relating the year to the call length.
    c. Use the model to predict the average length of a cell phone call in 2010. **(Lesson 2-3)**

24. The table below contains average hourly earnings of production workers in the U.S. by month in 2006. **(Lesson 2-3)**
    The line of best fit for this data set is $y = 0.06x + 16.38$.

Month	1	2	3	4	5	6	7	8	9	10	11	12
Hourly Wage	16.43	16.49	16.55	16.63	16.66	16.73	16.79	16.84	16.88	16.94	16.99	17.07

Source: Bureau of Labor Statistics

    a. Use the line of best fit to predict the hourly wage for April 2008.
    b. Use a spreadsheet to find the deviation and squared deviation for each month. **See margin.**
    c. What is the sum of the squared deviations? What conclusion can you draw about that number?

25. Rewrite $p_1q_1 + p_2q_2 + \ldots + p_nq_n$ using Σ-notation. **(Lesson 1-2)**

EXPLORATION

26. The field of cryptology relies on inverses. Research the Caesar cipher to find out what it is and how it relates to inverse functions.

22a. See margin.

23a. See margin.

26. Answers vary. Sample: The Caesar cipher is a well-known encryption method where every letter of the message is translated to a letter a fixed number of positions away in the alphabet. This cipher is related to inverse functions because the function or method to perform the encryption is the inverse of the function or method to perform the decryption. One such method is using modular arithmetic. If we encrypt the message using the function $f(x) = (x + n)$ mod 26, because there are 26 letters in the alphabet, then we decrypt this message using the inverse function $f^{-1}(x) = (x - n)$ mod 26.

22b. $y = (1.2517 \cdot 10^{-207}) \cdot 1.276^x$

22c. 946,388

23b. $y = 0.0049x^2 - 19.5193x + 19441.1$

23c. 3.79 min

24a. $18.06
     c. 0.008; This is the smallest possible sum of squared deviations because it is based on deviations from the line of best fit.

25. $\displaystyle\sum_{i=1}^{n} p_iq_i$

Inverses of Functions   205

4 Wrap-Up

Ongoing Assessment
Have students define two different functions, one whose inverse is a function and one whose inverse is not a function. For each function, the student should give an equation for the inverse and graph the function and inverse on the same set of axes. **Answers vary.** **Check students' work.**

Project Update
Project 3, *Transformation Groups*, on page 212 relates to the content of this lesson.

Additional Answers

22a.
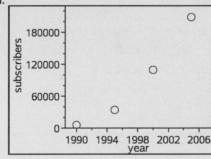

23a.
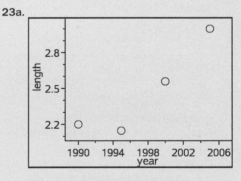

Additional Answers

24b.

◇	A	B	C	D
1	data	model	deviation	sqdev
2	16.43	16.44	-.01	.0001
3	16.49	16.5	-.01	.0001
4	16.55	16.56	-.01	.0001
5	16.63	16.62	-.01	.0001
6	16.66	16.68	-.02	.0004
7	16.73	16.74	-.01	.0001
8	16.79	16.8	-.01	.0001
9	16.84	16.86	-.02	.0004
10	16.88	16.92	-.04	.0016
11	16.94	16.98	-.04	.0016
12	16.99	17.04	-.05	.0025
13	17.07	17.1	-.03	.0009

Lesson

3-9

Lesson

3-9 z-Scores

GOAL

Recognize the role of z-scores and use them in standardizing data.

SPUR Objectives

G Identify properties of z-scores.

H Use z-scores to describe and analyze data and statistics.

Materials/Resources

· Lesson Master 3-9
· Resource Masters 67 and 68

HOMEWORK
· Questions 1–9
· · Questions 10–26
· · Question 27 (extra credit)
· · Self-Test

· **Option 1**
· **Option 2**

Local Standards

---

1 Warm-Up

1. Calculate the mean and the standard deviation for these scores: 63, 71, 84, 90, 97.
   Mean = 81; s.d. ≈ 13.9

2. The score of 63 is how many standard deviations below the mean?
   About 1.3 s.d. below the mean

3. The score of 90 is how many standard deviations above the mean?
   About 0.6 s.d. above the mean

Vocabulary

z-score
raw data
standardized data

▶ **BIG IDEA**   z-scores enable a score to be compared to other scores in the same data set.

What is a z-Score?

Sometimes a person wants to know how his or her score or salary compares to a group as a whole. One way to do this is to compute a percentile. Another way is to analyze how many standard deviations the score or salary is above or below the mean.

The U.S. Bureau of Labor Statistics tracks the median hourly wages for 22 general occupational categories. The 2007 median wages for certain occupations are listed in the table below. The mean of the 7 median hourly wages is $\bar{x} = \$22.90$ and the standard deviation is $s = \$10.70$.

Food Production	Protective Services	Construction	Education	Healthcare	Architecture/ Engineering	Management
$8.24	$16.11	$17.57	$20.47	$26.17	$31.14	$40.60

In general, the transformation that maps each wage x to the score $\frac{x - \bar{x}}{s} = \frac{x - 22.90}{10.70}$ tells you how many standard deviations that wage is above or below the mean. For example, the median wage for Management is $\frac{40.60 - 22.90}{10.70} \approx 1.7$ standard deviations above the mean, while the median wage for Food Production is $\frac{8.24 - 22.90}{10.70} \approx -1.4$ standard deviations above, or 1.4 standard deviations below, the mean.

In the table below, row L_1 is the original set of wages, L_2 is the image of L_1 under the translation T where $T(x) = x - \bar{x} = x - 22.90$, and L_3 is the image of L_2 under the scale change S where $S(x) = \frac{x}{s} = \frac{x}{10.70}$.

L_1	8.24	16.11	17.57	20.47	26.17	31.14	40.60
L_2	-14.66	-6.79	-5.31	-2.43	3.27	8.24	17.70
L_3	-1.4	-0.6	-0.5	-0.2	0.3	0.8	1.7

The transformation that maps the original data set L_1 onto L_3 is the composite $S \circ T$, where $S \circ T(x) = S(T(x)) = S(x - 22.90) = \frac{x - 22.90}{10.70}$. $S \circ T(x)$ is called the *z-score* for the value x. The z-score for Protective Services is -0.6; this means that $16.11 is 0.6 standard deviations below the mean. In the same way, the 0.8 z-score for Architecture/Engineering means that $31.14 is 0.8 standard deviations above the mean.

Mental Math

Suppose the mean of a set of scores is 486 and the standard deviation is 37. What number is:

a. 1 standard deviation above the mean? (remember – this is mental math!) **523**

b. 1 standard deviation below the mean? **449**

c. 2 standard deviations above the mean? **560**

d. 2 standard deviations below the mean? **412**

Background

Two purposes are served by z-scores. The first purpose is to indicate how far out in a distribution of scores a score x is. The z-score uses the standard deviation as its unit. A z-score of 1 means the score was 1 standard deviation above the mean. A z-score of -1 means the score is 1 standard deviation below the mean. The situation that begins the lesson has to do with wages. Example 1 is of this type and uses test scores.

The second purpose of z-scores is to provide a way to compare a value in one data set with a value in another data set when the data sets are not directly comparable. Example 2 is of this type.

Suppose one class scores much higher than other classes on a particular test. How much of an outlier is the class's score? We may say "The class's score was 2.3 standard deviations above the mean." In so doing, we have taken the class's score x, subtracted the mean $\bar{x}$ from it, and divided by the

The preceding discussion can be generalized in the following definition.

Definition of z-Score

Suppose a data set has mean $\bar{x}$ and standard deviation s. The **z-score** for a member x of this data set is

$$z = \frac{\text{deviation}}{\text{standard deviation}} = \frac{x - \bar{x}}{s}.$$

A positive z-score tells how many standard deviations the score is above the mean. A negative z-score tells how far below the mean the score is.

 QY

Example 1

Nancy scored 87 on a math quiz on which the mean score was 70 and the standard deviation of the scores was 8. Find her z-score and tell how far her score was from the mean.

Solution Her z-score is
$$z = \frac{87 - 70}{8} \approx 2.1,$$
so her score was 2.1 standard deviations above the mean.

Sometimes the original data are called **raw data** or raw scores, and the results of the transformation are called **standardized data** or standardized scores. In Example 1, a raw score of 87 corresponds to a standardized score of 2.1.

Properties of z-Scores

What happens to the mean and standard deviation of a data set if each score is converted to a z-score? Refer again to the median wages shown in row L_1 of the table on page 206. Because adding (or subtracting) the number h to every number in a data set adds (or subtracts) h to the mean, the mean of the data set in L_2 is $22.90 - 22.90 = 0$. Under a translation of a data set, the standard deviation is invariant. Thus, the standard deviation of the data set in L_2 is still 10.70. Because the scale change S with $S(x) = ax$ multiplies both the mean and standard deviation by a, the mean of the data set in L_3 is $\frac{1}{10.70} \cdot 0 = 0$ and the standard deviation is $\frac{1}{10.70} \cdot 10.70 = 1$. Thus, the z-scores in L_3 have mean 0 and standard deviation 1. In general, we have the following theorem.

Theorem (Mean and Standard Deviation of z-Scores)

If a data set has mean $\bar{x}$ and standard deviation s, the mean of its z-scores will be 0, and the standard deviation of its z-scores will be 1.

> **QY**
>
> Find the z-score for $20.47 in the table and describe what it means.

2 Teaching

Notes on the Lesson

Properties of z-scores In the formula for a z-score, the translation occurs first, and then the scale change. That is, first $\bar{x}$ is subtracted from the score, and then the subtracted score is divided by s. The transformations could be done in reverse order. Then you would first divide all scores by s to cause the standard deviation to be 1. The resulting mean would be $\frac{\bar{x}}{s}$. Subtracting that new mean from each value would create the same final data set, with mean 0 and standard deviation 1, and the same z-scores.

Additional Example

Example 1 Ned scored 5.8 on a pop quiz on which the mean score is 6.4 and the standard deviation is 0.9. What is his z-score and how far is his score from the mean? **About –0.7; Ned's score is about 0.7 standard deviations below the mean.**

standard deviation s, and found the result to be 2.3. We have mentally calculated the z-score of that class relative to the set of classes. That is, z-scores have as their unit the standard deviation of the data set, and their mean is 0. This makes it possible to determine percentiles from z-scores using a table.

The calculation of the z-score is similar. We subtract the mean of the data set from all the data and work with our new data set. This makes 0 the mean of the new data set. Now we divide the transformed data by the standard deviation of the data. The resulting data is scaled and has a standard deviation of 1 but its mean stays the same, at 0.

(continued on next page)

Notes on the Lesson

Question 9 provides a setting in which costs from different years are compared using z-scores. You might ask students to think of other situations where this kind of comparison might be reasonable. Here is one possibility: In 1790 Virginia was the most populous state in the United States. Was Virginia more of an outlier in population than California is today?

You could obtain the heights of all students in your class or classes. Is the height of the tallest boy or the tallest girl more of an outlier in height compared to his classmates of the same gender?

Additional Example

Example 2 Monique scored 81 on a test with a mean of 90 and a standard deviation of 6. She scored 73 on a test on which the mean was 75 and the standard deviation was 5. On which test did Monique perform better compared to her classmates? **The second test, since her z-score is higher.**

3 Assignment

Recommended Assignment

- Questions 1–9
- • Questions 10–26
- • Question 27 (extra credit)
- • Self-Test

Using z-Scores to Make Comparisons

Standardized scores, or z-scores, make it easier to compare different sets of numbers.

GUIDED

Example 2

Mark scored 78 on a history test on which the mean was 71 and the standard deviation was 10. He scored 68 on a chemistry test on which the mean was 62 and the standard deviation was 6. Use z-scores to determine on which test he performed better compared to his classmates.

Solution His z-scores are:

history: $\frac{? - 71}{10} = \underline{\ ?\ }$ 78, 0.7

chemistry: $\frac{68 - ?}{?} = \underline{\ ?\ }$. 62, 6, 1

Because his z-score on the $\underline{\ ?\ }$ test is higher, Mark **chemistry** performed better on that test compared to his classmates.

In Example 2 you should notice that Mark scored above the mean on both tests, but the z-scores provide more information. The z-scores are sensitive to the fact that the scores on the history test are more spread out than those on the chemistry test.

Questions

COVERING THE IDEAS

In 1–3, refer to the data sets in rows L_2 and L_3 on page 206.

1. By computing directly, find the mean and standard deviation of each data set.

2. What does the z-score of -0.2 mean?

3. Which median wage is 0.5 standard deviations below the mean?

4. Find the z-score for a test score of 84 for each situation.
   a. mean = 89; standard deviation = 6.1
   b. mean = 67; standard deviation = 8.8

5. In which situation, 4a or 4b, is the test score better compared to others who took the test?

6. What is a standardized score?

7. A data set has a mean of 19 and a standard deviation of 4.3. How can the data set be transformed so that the mean is 0 and the standard deviation is 1? **for all data points x, $\frac{x - 19}{4.3}$**

8. Refer to Example 2. Mary scored 54 on the history test and 47 on the chemistry test. Use z-scores to determine on which test she did better compared to her classmates.

---

1. L_2 mean = 0.0029, L_2 standard deviation = 10.7, L_3 mean = 0.014, L_3 standard deviation = 1.019

2. A z-score of -0.2 means the wage is 0.2 standard deviations below the mean.

3. $17.57 ，

4. a. $z = \frac{84 - 89}{6.1} \approx$ -0.82
   b. $z = \frac{84 - 67}{8.8} \approx$ 1.93

5. Part 4b's test score of 84 is better compared to others who took the test.

6. A standardized score is a transformed data point, which allows one to compare different sets of numbers.

8. Mary did better on the history test since she was 1.7 standard deviations below the mean, while for chemistry, she was 2.5 standard deviations below the mean.

Because they use population statistics where we use sample statistics, in the formula for z-scores, some books use μ where we use $\bar{x}$ and σ where we use s. Then the formula for the z-score is $z = \frac{x - \mu}{\sigma}$. Students will encounter this expression later in the book along with the study of normal distributions. At that time, the z-score will be used to determine the probability that an event occurs.

Accommodating the Learner ↑

Refer students to Example 2. Ask them to find a single score which would indicate the same performance on both tests. **48.5; this score is 2.25 standard deviations below the mean for both tests**

9. In 2007, Colorado high school students' average ACT scores were: English, 19.7; Math, 20.1; Reading, 20.8; and Science, 20.4. Jennie's scores were: English, 24; Math, 21; Reading, 18; and Science, 20. Find Jennie's z-score for each section assuming that each section had a standard deviation of 1.8.

APPLYING THE MATHEMATICS

In 10 and 11, the mean boys' time for a one-mile race was 6 minutes 6 seconds with a standard deviation of 16 seconds. The mean girls' time was 8 minutes 15 seconds with a standard deviation of 24 seconds.

10. Who is faster relative to others of his or her gender, a boy who runs a mile in 5 minutes 34 seconds, or a girl who runs a mile in 7 minutes 35 seconds?

11. Suppose a girl runs the race in 8 minutes 30 seconds. What boy's time would have the same z-score? **6 minutes 16 seconds**

12. A student got a z-score of 1.33 on a test with a mean of 73 and a standard deviation of 9. What was the student's raw score? **≈85**

13. The graph at the right shows how much customers spend at a grocery store. The costs have mean $125 and standard deviation $65. Copy the horizontal axis as shown.
    a. Change each value labeled on the axis to a z-score. Values for 100 and 250 are shown.
    b. Locate the points on the axis that correspond to z-scores of 0, 1, and –1.

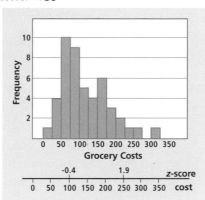
Grocery Costs

14. A teacher tells a class that the mean raw score on a test was 58. Alex has a raw score of 73 and a z-score of 1.25. What was the standard deviation on the test? **12**

15. Considering the data sets in L_1 and L_3 at the start of the lesson, use the translation $T(x) = x - \bar{x}$ and the scale change $S(x) = \frac{x}{s}$.
    a. Find $(T \circ S)(x)$. $\frac{x}{s} - \bar{x}$
    b. Apply $T \circ S$ to the data set in L_1. What are the mean and standard deviation of this new data set?
    c. Are these the same mean and standard deviation as for the data set in L_3? Explain why or why not.

In 16–19, use the table at the right with the scores from two tests.

16. How many standard deviations above the mean is Fiona's score on the physics test? **3.48**

17. On which test did Raj do better compared to others who took the test? **Physics**

	Physics	Mathematics
Fiona	84	64
Raj	70	76
Test Statistics	mean: 60 standard deviation: 6.9	mean: 70 standard deviation: 10.7

z-Scores **209**

---

9. English: 2.39
   Math: 0.5
   Reading: –1.56
   Science: –0.22

10. The boy, since his z-score is further below the mean and the lower your time is the better.

13.
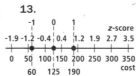

15b. 0, 1 mean ≈ –20.76; standard deviation ≈ 1

15c. See margin.

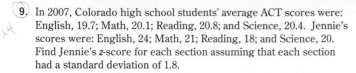

Notes on the Questions
Question 13 You might ask students for other possible contexts in which amounts of money might be compared. Here is one possibility: Who was richer for his time compared to the average person – John D. Rockefeller or Bill Gates?

Additional Answers

15c. No; The mean is different because $T \circ S \neq S \circ T$. The standard deviation is the same because it is invariant under translations.

9. $\bar{x} = 20.25$
   $s = 1.8$
   a. Eng $\frac{24 - 19.7}{1.8} = 2.39$
   b.
   c.
   d.

10.

11. $\frac{8.5 - 8.25}{24} =$

Accommodating the Learner ⬇

If your students are having trouble understanding z-scores, you might point out the application of z-scores to the question: Who was the most powerful driver in golf? A professional golfer today can typically drive a ball more than 300 yards whereas few golfers 35 years ago could do that. Does that mean that today's golfers are all more powerful than golfers of 35 years ago? No, because the equipment has changed. The golf clubs are different and so are the golf balls. Thus it is unfair to compare the length of a drive of a person 35 years ago with the length of today's drives. Enter z-scores. If we have a distribution of performances in the two different eras, we can use z-scores to say "for the time in which golfer X played, he was better compared to his contemporaries than golfer Y was in the time that golfer Y played."

3-9

Ongoing Assessment
Refer students to Example 2. Change Mark's scores to 65 on both tests. Have students work in pairs to complete the example, one partner computing the History z-score and the other the Chemistry z-score.

Project Update
Project 5, *Class Survey Revisited, Yet Again*, on page 212 relates to the content of this lesson.

---

18. Simon had a 58 on the physics test. He scored equally well (in terms of z-score) on the mathematics test. What was his raw score on the mathematics test? ≈67

19. Andrea had the same raw score on each test, and she also had the same z-score on each test. What raw score did she get? ≈42

REVIEW

20. a. Write an equation for the inverse of g where $g(t) = \sqrt{t + 4}$.
    b. Is the inverse of g a function? **(Lesson 3-8) yes**

21. **True or False** Let $f(x) = x^3$ and $g(x) = x^{-3}$. **(Lessons 3-8, 3-7)**
    a. For all x, $f(g(x)) = g(f(x))$. **true**   b. f and g are inverses.

In 22 and 23, **true or false**. If false, give a counterexample. **(Lessons 3-8, 3-4)**

22. The inverse of an even function is a function.

23. The inverse of an odd function is a function. **See margin.**

24. Consider a 15% discount function D where $D(x) = 0.85x$ and a 7% total-with-tax function T where $T(x) = 1.07x$. **(Lesson 3-7)**
    a. If you buy an item with a list price of x dollars, what will it cost you after this discount and tax? **0.91x**
    b. Which is better to take first, the discount or the tax? Explain.

25. **Multiple Choice** A transformed set of data has a variance three times that of the original set. How were the data transformed? **(Lesson 3-6) B**

    A translated by 3   B multiplied by $\sqrt{3}$
    C multiplied by 3   D multiplied by 9

26. **Multiple Choice** The graph of which relation has point symmetry? **(Lesson 3-4) C**

    A $y = |x|$ B $y = x^2$
    C $y = x^3$ D $y = \frac{1}{x^2}$

EXPLORATION

27. In each of the 22 general occupation categories tracked by the U.S. Bureau of Labor Statistics (BLS), there are a number of more specific occupation descriptions. Visit the BLS website and identify a specific occupation description that interests you.
    a. Calculate a mean and standard deviation for the median wages of the specific occupations within the general category.
    b. Calculate the z-scores for the highest and lowest median wages in the general occupation category. What do these z-scores tell you about the range and distribution of wages within this group?
    c. Calculate the z-score for the occupation you have chosen. Describe how the wage for your occupation compares to the other wages within the category.

20a. See margin.
21b. false
22. false, $f(x) = x^2$ is even, $f^{-1}(x) = \pm\sqrt{x}$ is not a function as it doesn't pass the vertical line test.

24b. It's the same either way: $D(T(x)) = 0.85(1.07x) = 0.91x$ and $T(D(x)) = 1.07(0.85x) = 0.91x$

27a. Answers vary. Sample: the following are statistics for the Legal Occupations category: $\bar{x} = 29.37$ and the standard deviation $= 13.46$

27b–c. See margin.

QY ANSWER

The median wage for Education is 0.2 standard deviations below the average median wage for the seven occupations.

Additional Answers

20a. $g^{-1}(t) = t^2 - 4$, domain: $\{t \mid t \geq 0\}$

23. False; $f(x) = x^3 - x$ is odd, but its inverse is not a function.

27b. 1.65, –0.86, respectively. The variability within the Legal Occupations is relatively low.

27c. The z–score for the wages of lawyers = 1.61, which is the second highest within the category.

Chapter 3 Projects

1 Sports Handicaps

To enable a wide variety of players to play against one another in golf and bowling, players are given handicaps which are taken from or added to their scores.

a. Obtain the full data set of raw scores for a golfer or bowler for a season. Use these to determine the handicap for this athlete.

b. Calculate the descriptive statistics you studied in Chapter 1 for this data set.

c. Apply the handicap of this person to these scores and calculate the same descriptive statistics for the image set.

d. Show how the results that you found in Parts b and c agree with theorems stated in this chapter.

e. Discuss whether you think the handicap was too small, just about right, or too large. In your discussion, you might wish to consider the following questions: Would this handicap enable the person to compete with a professional? With a good high school athlete? What handicap do you think you would need?

Got a moment to spare?
Bowling pins are 15 inches high, the same as the circumference of the pin.

2 Facial Symmetry and Asymmetry

According to researchers such as Paul Ekman, spontaneous emotional reactions elicit more symmetrical facial expressions than deliberate emotional reactions. According to Ekman, of the 10,000 facial expressions the 42 facial muscles can form, only about 3000 are relevant to emotion.

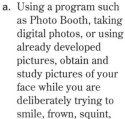
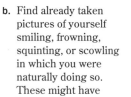
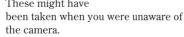

a. Using a program such as Photo Booth, taking digital photos, or using already developed pictures, obtain and study pictures of your face while you are deliberately trying to smile, frown, squint, and scowl.

b. Find already taken pictures of yourself smiling, frowning, squinting, or scowling in which you were naturally doing so. These might have been taken when you were unaware of the camera.

c. Compare the pictures. Do you agree with Ekman that spontaneous expressions are more symmetrical?

d. Take a straight-on picture of your face and then use Photo Booth's Mirror tool and the left half of your face to create a picture of you that is vertically symmetrical. Compare this picture to the original. What do you notice?

The projects relate to the content of the lessons of this chapter as follows:

Project	Lesson(s)
1	3-3
2	3-4
3	3-3, 3-5, 3-6, 3-7, 3-8
4	3-6
5	3-3, 3-9

1 Sports Handicaps

In bowling, handicaps are made so that professionals will beat amateurs most of the time. In golf, the handicaps make the playing field more even.

Project Rubric

Advanced	Student correctly provides all of the details asked for in the project as well as additional correct independent conclusions.
Proficient	Student correctly provides all of the details asked for in the project.
Partially proficient	Student correctly provides some of the details asked for in the project or provides all details with some inaccuracies.
Not proficient	Student correctly provides few of the details asked for in the project or provides all details with many inaccuracies.
No attempt	Student makes little or no attempt to complete the project.

3 Transformation Groups
We call the composite of a scale change and a translation a *rubberband transformation*. The set of rubberband transformations also forms a group but it is not commutative.

5 Class Survey Revisited, Yet Again

This is a straightforward project. If data in centimeters is transformed to data in inches, then the mean and standard devatiation are changed in predictable ways. For students who wish to extend this project, you might have them construct z-scores for the students in the class on one or more of the variables. They could show that the z-scores are the same whether the data are in inches or centimeters.

Sample answers for projects are in the Solution Manual in the Electronic Teacher's Edition.

3 Transformation Groups
The set of all scale changes under composition forms a mathematical structure called a *commutative group*. The properties of this commutative group are listed here.

  i. Closure: If S_1 and S_2 are scale changes, then so is $S_2 \circ S_1$.

  ii. Commutativity: $S_1 \circ S_2 = S_2 \circ S_1$.

  iii. Associativity: $(S_3 \circ S_2) \circ S_1 = S_3 \circ (S_2 \circ S_1)$

  iv. Identity: There is a scale change I such that $S \circ I = I \circ S = S$.

  v. Inverses: For every scale change S there is an inverse scale change S^{-1} such that $S \circ S^{-1} = S^{-1} \circ S = I$.

Each of these properties can be proven. For instance, for property ii, let $S_1(x, y) = (ax, by)$ and $S_2(x, y) = (cx, dy)$. Then
$$(S_2 \circ S_1)(x) = S_2(S_1(x, y))$$
$$= S_2(ax, by) = (cax, dby).$$
$$(S_1 \circ S_2)(x) = S_1(S_2(x, y))$$
$$= S_1(cx, dy) = (acx, bdy).$$
Because multiplication of real numbers is commutative, $ac = ca$ and $bd = db$. So $S_1 \circ S_2 = S_2 \circ S_1$.

  a. Prove the remaining properties for scale changes.

  b. Does the set of all translations form a commutative group under composition?

4 CPI/Rate of Inflation
The U.S. Bureau of Labor Statistics (BLS) is responsible for gathering the data for the Consumer Price Index (CPI). Visit the BLS database website at www.bls.gov/data. Search the "Average Price Data" for your region or type of city and create a basket of 10 goods that includes gasoline, electricity, and various foods and beverages. Make sure that the goods you have selected have data available for a ten-year period.

  a. Use your basket of goods to create a CPI for your area for the ten-year period.

  b. Ask someone who is at least ten years older than you to look at your list of goods and estimate the percentage increase in cost of each item over the ten-year period. Use this information to create a "subjective CPI."

  c. Compare the actual CPI for the ten-year period to your CPI and the subjective CPI. Which is a more accurate estimation of the actual CPI, your CPI or the subjective CPI? Why do you think one is better than the other?

  d. Research the items that are included in the basket of goods used to calculate the actual CPI. Argue why this basket is or is not a good indication of the cost of living for a family in your neighborhood.

5 Class Survey Revisited, Yet Again
Use the class survey database constructed as a project in Chapter 1. Consider the variables which involve units, for example, height, hand span, foot length, etc.

  a. Convert these measurements to other units (for example, if the data were originally in centimeters, change to inches). Apply transformations to create new data sets from the original data.

  b. Drop the units from both the original and the image data. Compare the descriptive statistics of the image with those of the original data to confirm the results of Lesson 3-3.

  c. Examine some relations between pairs of original variables (e.g., between height and foot length) and between their images under these transformations. What statistics are invariant under these transformations?

Notes

_____ _____

_____ _____

_____ _____

_____ _____

_____ _____

_____ _____

_____ _____

Chapter 3

Summary and Vocabulary

○ Equations, graphs of functions, and data can be transformed in similar ways. Two such **transformations** – **translations** and **scale changes** – are studied in this chapter. When graphs of functions are translated or scaled, the **images** resemble the graphs of the **preimages**, or original **parent functions**. Translations slide graphs, whereas scale changes stretch or shrink them horizontally and vertically.

○ Connections among transformations, function equations, and graphs are given by the Graph-Translation and Graph Scale-Change Theorems. By the Graph-Translation Theorem, a translation (x, y) $\rightarrow (x + h, y + k)$ transforms the graph of $y = f(x)$ to a graph of $y - k = f(x - h)$. The Graph Scale-Change Theorem asserts that scaling the graph of $y = f(x)$ by **horizontal scale factor** a and **vertical scale factor** b, $(x, y) \rightarrow (ax, by)$, produces the graph of $\frac{y}{b} = f\left(\frac{x}{a}\right)$. Some features of graphs can be predicted if just the equation is given, and equations can be written if just the graph is given.

○ Symmetries of graphs can be determined from their equations. **Odd functions** have **point symmetry** around the origin; **even functions** are **reflection-symmetric** over the y-axis.

○ Asymptotes, discontinuities, and other features of functions can be identified from a graph of the function. Knowing the parent function of a transformed function can assist in this identification.

○ Under a translation of magnitude h, measures of center for a data set are translated by h, while measures of spread are unaffected. In contrast, when data are multiplied by a factor $a > 0$, measures of center, the standard deviation, and the range are multiplied by a, and the variance is multiplied by a^2.

○ **Composites** of functions are formed by letting one function g operate on those outputs of another function f that are in g's domain. The composite of f followed by g is written as $g \circ f$, and is defined by $(g \circ f)(x) = g(f(x))$. In general, **function composition** is not commutative. That is, $f \circ g$ and $g \circ f$ are usually different functions.

○ The **inverse** of a function $f: x \rightarrow y$ can be obtained by switching x's and y's in its equation or by switching x- and y-coordinates in a set of ordered pairs. When the resulting relation is a function, it is denoted by f^{-1}. The graphs of a function and its inverse are reflection images of each other with respect to the line $y = x$. Another characteristic property of inverse functions is that the composite of a function f and its inverse f^{-1} is the **identity function** I. That is, for all x in the domain of the composite, $f(f^{-1}(x)) = f^{-1}(f(x)) = I(x) = x$.

Vocabulary

3-1
window
parent function

3-2
transformation
preimage
image
translation

3-3
invariant

3-4
reflection-symmetric
axis of symmetry
line of symmetry
symmetry about a point
point symmetry
center of symmetry
even function
odd function

3-5
horizontal and
    vertical scale
    change
horizontal and
    vertical scale
    factor
size change

3-6
scale change of a
    data set
scale factor
scale image

3-7
composite
function composition

Summary and Vocabulary

The Summary gives an overview of the entire chapter and provides an opportunity for students to consider the material as a whole. Thus, the Summary can be used to help students relate and unify the concepts presented in the chapter.

Vocabulary words and symbols are listed by lesson to provide a checklist of concepts that students must know. Emphasize to students that they should read the vocabulary list carefully before starting the Self-Test on page 215. If students do not understand the meaning of a vocabulary word, they should refer back to the indicated lesson.

Theorems and Properties covered in the chapter are listed below the Summary with page references included to lead students back to the location in the chapter where the theorem or property is stated.

○ Suppose a data set has mean $\bar{x}$ and standard deviation s. A **z-score** is the result of a composite of a specific translation $(T(x) = x - \bar{x})$ followed by a scale change $(S(x) = \frac{x}{s})$ of the translated data. The z-score, $z = \frac{x - \bar{x}}{s}$, corresponding to the raw score x, tells how many standard deviations x is above or below the mean. A data set transformed in this way has mean 0 and standard deviation 1. Using z-scores makes it possible to compare scores from different data sets.

Vocabulary

3-8
inverse of a function
identity function

3-9
z-score
raw data
standardized data

Properties and Theorems

Graph-Translation Theorem (p. 161)
Theorem (Centers of Translated Data) (p. 167)
Theorem (Spreads of Translated Data) (p. 168)
Theorem (Symmetry over the y-axis) (p. 173)
Theorem (Symmetry over the x-axis) (p. 173)
Theorem (Symmetry about the Origin) (p. 173)
Graph Scale-Change Theorem (p. 181)
Theorem (Centers of Scaled Data) (p. 188)
Theorem (Spreads of Scaled Data) (p. 189)
Inverses of Functions Theorem (p. 202)
Theorem (Mean and Standard Deviation of z-scores) (p. 207)

Chapter 3 Self-Test

Take this test as you would take a test in class. You will need a calculator. Then use the Selected Answers section in the back of the book to check your work.
1–17 See margin.

1. Give equations for the asymptotes of the graph of the function $h: x \rightarrow \dfrac{1}{x-7} - 9$.

In 2 and 3, let the translation $T: (x, y) \rightarrow (x + 4, y - 2)$ be applied to the graph of $y = x^2$.

2. Write an equation for the image.

3. What are the coordinates of the vertex of the image?

4. The graph of a function f is below. Sketch a graph of its image under the transformation S when $S(x, y) = (2x, -y)$.

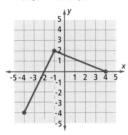

In 5 and 6, suppose a chemistry student finds masses of different samples of potassium chloride (KCl) and subtracts 150 from each value before computing the statistics below.

mean: 4.2 g	standard deviation: 1.3 g
minimum: 0.4 g	maximum: 13.6 g
median: 3.8 g	Q_1: 3.6 g Q_3: 4.6 g

5. For the actual sample masses, give the
   a. median.   b. range.   c. IQR.

6. For the actual sample masses, give each statistic from Question 5 in ounces using 1 gram ≈ 0.035 ounces.

In 7–9, let f be a real function with $f(x) = 4\sqrt[3]{x} + 2$.

7. Find an equation for the inverse of f.

8. Is the inverse of f a function? Support your answer.

9. Sketch graphs of f and its inverse.

In 10 and 11, let m and n be real functions with $m(x) = 16 - 5x$ and $n(x) = x + \sqrt{x}$.

10. Write an expression for $n(m(x))$.

11. Give the domain of $n \circ m$.

12. Suppose the scale change $S(x, y) = \left(3x, \dfrac{y}{2}\right)$ is applied to the graph of $y = \dfrac{1}{x^2}$. Write an equation for the image.

13. A data set has a mean of 83 and a standard deviation of 7. What transformation should be applied so that the image set has a mean of 0 and a standard deviation of 1?

14. Tell whether the function j with equation $j(x) = x^2 - 5$ is even, odd, or neither. Support your answer with algebra.

15. The graph below of a function g is an angle.

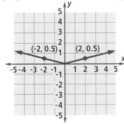

   a. What is the parent function of g?
   b. Find an equation for g.
   c. What symmetries does the graph of g have?
   d. Give the range of g.

16. Give a rule for the reflection over the line $y = x$.

17. Suppose a population of mice has a mean weight of 30 g and a standard deviation of 3.4 g. A population of moose has a mean weight of 910 lb and a standard deviation of 185 lb. Which animal is heavier relative to its population, a 37-g mouse or a 1260-lb moose? Explain your answer.

Self-Test

For the development of mathematical competence, feedback and correction, along with the opportunity for practice, are necessary. The Self-Test provides the opportunity for feedback and correction; the Chapter Review provides additional opportunities for practice. We cannot overemphasize the importance of these end-of-chapter materials. It is at this point that the material gels for many students, allowing them to solidify skills and understanding. In general, student performance should improve after these pages.

Assign the Self-Test as a one-night assignment. Worked-out solutions for all questions are in the Selected Answers section of the student book. Encourage students to take the Self-Test honestly, grade themselves, and then be prepared to discuss the test in class.

Advise students to pay special attention to those Chapter Review questions (pages 216–219) that correspond to the questions they missed on the Self-Test. These are identified in the Self-Test Correlation Chart located in the Selected Answers section at the back of the book.

Additional Answers

See the Additional Answers section at the back of the book.

Chapter Review

The main objectives for the chapter are organized in the Chapter Review under the four types of understanding this book promotes: Skills, Properties, Uses, and Representations.

Whereas end-of-chapter material may be considered optional in some texts, in UCSMP *Functions, Statistics, and Trigonometry* we have selected these objectives and questions with the expectation that they will be covered. Students should be able to answer these questions with about 85% accuracy after studying the chapter.

You may assign these questions over a single night to help students prepare for a test the next day or you may assign the questions over a two-day period. If you work the questions over two days, we recommend assigning the evens for homework the first night so that students get feedback in class the next day, and then assigning the odds the night before the test because the answers are provided to the odd-numbered questions in the Selected Answers section at the back of the book.

It is effective to ask students which questions they still do not understand and use the day as a total class discussion of the material that the class finds most difficult.

Resources

• Assessment Resources: Chapter 3 Test

Technology Resources

Teacher's Assessment Assistant, Ch. 3
Electronic Teacher's Edition, Ch. 3

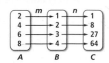

Chapter 3 Chapter Review

SKILLS
PROPERTIES
USES
REPRESENTATIONS

SKILLS Procedures used to get answers

OBJECTIVE A Find equations for and values of composites of functions. (Lesson 3-7)

In 1 and 2, consider the functions m mapping A to B, and n mapping B to C, as shown at the right.

1. What is $n(m(6))$? **27**

2. Find $(n \circ m)(2)$. **1**

In 3 and 4, let $f(t) = 7t - 9$ and $g(t) = t^2 - t$.

3. Evaluate each composite.

   a. $f(g(-2))$ **33**   b. $g(f(-2))$ **552**

4. Find a formula for $f(f(t))$. **See margin.**

In 5 and 6, let $\frac{4}{x}$ and $g(x) = x - 8$.

5. Evaluate each composite.

   a. $(f \circ g)(-8)$ $-\frac{1}{4}$ b. $(g \circ g)(-8)$ **-24**

6. Find an equation for $g \circ f$. **See margin.**

OBJECTIVE B Find inverses of functions. (Lesson 3-8). **7–9. See margin.**

In 7–9, a function is described.

a. Describe the inverse using a set of ordered pairs or an equation.

b. State whether the inverse is a function.

7. $f(x) = |x|$ 8. $\ell(x) = \frac{4}{x-3}$

9. $g = \{(3, 4), (4, 12), (5, 9), (6, 0), (7, 11)\}$

PROPERTIES Principles behind the mathematics

OBJECTIVE C Use the Graph-Translation Theorem or the Graph Scale-Change Theorem to find transformation images. (Lessons 3-2, 3-5)

10. **Multiple Choice** Which scale change **D** stretches a graph horizontally by a factor of 4 and shrinks it vertically by a factor of 11?

   A $S(x, y) = (4x, 11y)$ B $S(x, y) = \left(\frac{x}{4}, 11y\right)$

   C $S(x, y) = \left(\frac{x}{4}, \frac{y}{11}\right)$ D $S(x, y) = \left(4x, \frac{y}{11}\right)$

11. **Multiple Choice** Which translation has the effect on a graph of moving each point 5 units down and 9 units to the right?

   A $T(x, y) = (x - 5, y + 9)$ **B**

   B $T(x, y) = (x + 9, y - 5)$

   C $T(x, y) = (x - 9, y + 5)$

   D $T(x, y) = (x + 5, y - 9)$

In 12 and 13, find an equation for the image of the graph of $y = x^2$ under the transformation.

12. $T: (x, y) \to (x - 2, y + 7)$ $y = (x + 2)^2 + 7$

13. $S: (x, y) \to \left(\frac{x}{2}, 3y\right)$ $y = 3(2x)^2$

In 14 and 15, suppose $f(x) = |x|$. Find an equation for the image of the graph of f under the transformation.

14. $S(x, y) = \left(5x, \frac{y}{4}\right)$ $y = \frac{1}{4}\left|\frac{1}{5}x\right|$

15. $T(x, y) = (x - 1, y)$ $y = |x + 1|$

16. Describe a transformation that maps the graph of $\sqrt{x}$ onto the graph of $\sqrt{5x}$.

17. Describe a transformation that maps the graph of $y = 8^x$ onto the graph of $y = 8^x + 4$. **16–20. See margin.**

OBJECTIVE D Describe the effects of translations and scale changes on functions and their graphs. (Lessons 3-2, 3-4, 3-5)

In 18–21, describe how the graph of the image is related to the graph of the preimage when the given change is made in the equation for a function or relation.

18. x is replaced by $x - 90$.

19. y is replaced by $y + 15.3$.

20. x is replaced by $3x$.

Additional Answers

4. $f(f(t)) = 49t - 72$

6. $g \circ f = \frac{4}{x} - 8$

7a. $x = |y|$

7b. The inverse is not a function.

8a. $y = \frac{4}{x} + 3$

8b. The inverse is a function.

9a. $\{(4, 3), (12, 4), (9, 5), (0, 6), (11, 7)\}$

9b. The inverse is a function.

16. $S:(x, y) \to \left(\frac{x}{5}, y\right)$

17. $T:(x, y) \to (x, y + 4)$

18. The graph of the image is translated 90 units to the right.

19. The graph of the image is translated 15.3 units down.

20. The graph of the image is shrunk by a factor of 3 horizontally.

21, 22, 24–28, 40, 41, 42b., 42d. See margin.

21. y is replaced by $\frac{y}{8}$.

22. Match each general transformation with one of Questions 18–21 above.

   a. $T: (x, y) = (x, y + k)$ **b.** $T: (x, y) \rightarrow (x, by)$

   c. $T: (x, y) = (ax, y)$ **d.** $T: (x, y) \rightarrow (x + h, y)$

23. True or False Under a translation, asymptotes of the preimage are mapped to asymptotes of the image. **true**

24. Give a rule for a scale change that has the effect of reflecting the graph over the x-axis.

OBJECTIVE E Describe and identify symmetries and asymptotes of graphs. (Lessons 3-1, 3-4)

In 25–28, a function is described by an equation. Determine if the function is odd, even, or neither.

25. $k(t) = |3t + 4|$ **26.** $j(m) = 10m^3$

27. $f(x) = 3|x| + 1$ **28.** $s(y) = 7y^2 - 3y^4$

29. Consider the function f with $f(x) = \frac{1}{2x - 1}$. Give equations for any asymptotes of its graph. $x = \frac{1}{2}, y = 0$

30. If a graph has a horizontal asymptote at $y = 3$ and a vertical asymptote at $x = -2$, around what point might you center the screen to see the graph on your calculator? **(−2, 3)**

OBJECTIVE F Identify properties of composites and inverses of functions. (Lessons 3-7, 3-8)

31. If f and g are real functions with $f(x) = \sqrt{x}$ and $g(x) = x - 2$, what is the domain of $f \circ g$? $\{x \mid x \geq 2\}$

32. If two relations are inverses of each other, what transformation maps the graph of one onto the graph of the other? $(x, y) \rightarrow (y, x)$

In 33–37, true or false.

33. If f is a function with an inverse f^{-1}, then $f^{-1}(x) = \frac{1}{f(x)}$. **false**

34. If $f(x) = x^2$ and $g(x) = \sqrt{x} + 2$, for all x, $f \circ g(x) = g \circ f(x)$. **false**

35. If f is a function, then $f(f^{-1}(x)) = x$ for all x in the domain of f^{-1}. **true**

36. For all real functions f and g, $f \circ g = g \circ f$. **false**

37. A scale change with magnitude a followed by a translation of h units is the same as a translation of h units followed by a scale change with magnitude a. **false**

OBJECTIVE G Identify properties of z-scores. (Lesson 3-9)

In 38 and 39, a new data set is formed by taking the z-scores from raw scores with mean $\bar{x}$ and standard deviation s.

38. What is the standard deviation of the standardized data set? **1**

39. What is the mean of the standardized data set? **0**

In 40 and 41, a z-score is given. Explain what it tells you about the original data point in terms of the mean and standard deviation of the original data set.

40. $z = 0.04$ **41.** $z = -1.3$

USES Applications of mathematics in real-world situations

OBJECTIVE H Use translations, scale changes, or z-scores to describe and analyze data and statistics. (Lessons 3-3, 3-6, 3-9)

In 42 and 43, consider the table below.

Raw Scores	Scaled Scores	Frequency
4	16	1
5	20	3
6	24	2
8	32	7
9	36	2

42. a. Find the mode, mean, and median of the raw data. **mode: 8, mean: 7, median: 8**

   b. Identify the transformation used to scale the scores.

   c. Find the mode, mean, and median of the scaled scores.

   d. What theorem of translated data is shown in Parts b and c?

Additional Answers

21. The graph of the image is stretched by a factor of 8 vertically.

22a. Question 19

22b. Question 21

22c. Question 20

22d. Question 18

24. $S:(x, y) \rightarrow (x, -y)$

25. neither

26. odd

27. even

28. even

40. The data point is 0.04 standard deviations more than the mean.

41. The data point is 1.3 standard deviations less than the mean.

42b. The raw scores were multiplied by a scale change of 4.

42c. mode: 32, mean: 28, median: 32

42d. Centers of Scaled Data Theorem

Additional Answers

43c. Spread of Scale Changes of Data
Theorem

45a. 46.2 mm

45b. 68.8 mm

45c. 136.52 mm²

46. He did better on the English test
compared to his classmates.

47. The porpoise is heavier relative to its
group.

48. Yes, each output has one input.

49. No, some outputs have more than one
input, for example, $y = 0$.

58.

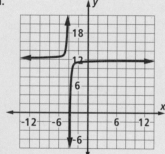

59a.

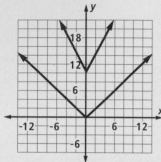

59b. $x = -4$, $y = 12$

59c. $\left(-\frac{23}{6}, 0\right)$

43c., 45–49, 58, 59. See margin.

43. a. What is the range of the raw scores? **5**
    b. What is the range of the scaled scores? **20**
    c. What theorem of translated data is shown
       in Parts a and b?

44. Use a translation to mentally calculate the
    average of these bowling scores: 103, 114,
    107, 101, 105. **106**

45. For a sample of a certain butterfly species,
    a scientist found a mean length of 1.82
    inches with a range of 2.71 inches and a
    standard deviation of 0.46 inches. If the
    data are converted to millimeters (1 inch =
    25.4 mm), give the following statistics of the
    resulting data set.

    a. mean   b. range   c. variance

46. Ken scored 83 on an *FST* test on which the
    mean was 77 and the standard deviation
    was 4.1. His score on an English test was
    63. On the English test, the mean was 54
    and the standard deviation was 5.3. On
    which test did he do better compared to
    his classmates?

47. A pod of porpoises has a mean weight of
    163 kg and a standard deviation of 29 kg.
    A school of yellow fin tuna has a mean
    weight of 83 lb and a standard deviation of
    17 lb. Which animal is heavier relative to its
    group, a porpoise which weighs 207 kg or a
    tuna which weighs 107 lb?

REPRESENTATIONS Pictures, graphs, or
objects that illustrate concepts

| **OBJECTIVE I** Recognize functions and their
properties from their graphs. (Lessons 3-1,
3-4, 3-8)

In 48 and 49, determine whether the function graphed
seems to have an inverse which is a function. Give a
reason for your answer.

48. 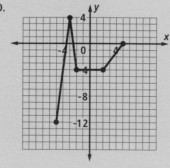   49.

In 50–55, match each graph with the equation of its
parent function.

A $y = |x|$ B $y = \sqrt{x}$ C $y = x$

D $y = \frac{1}{x}$ E $y = x^3$ F $y = x^2$

50. 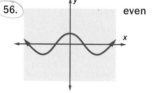   51.   52.

53. 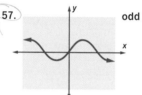   54.   55.

In 56 and 57, classify the function graphed as possibly
odd, possibly even, or neither.

56.   even

57.   odd

| **OBJECTIVE J** Apply the Graph-Translation
Theorem or the Graph Scale-Change Theorem
to make or identify graphs. (Lessons 3-2, 3-5)

58. Sketch the graph of $y = |2x| + 10$ and its
    parent function on the same set of axes.

59. Let $k(x) = 12 - \frac{2}{x + 4}$.
    a. Sketch a graph of the function k.
    b. Give equations of any asymptotes.
    c. Give the coordinates of the x-intercepts.

Additional Answers

60.

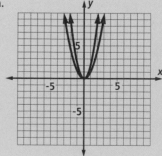

62a.

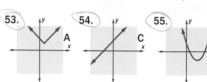

60. The graph of $y = f(x)$ is drawn below. Draw the graph of $y = 4f(-x)$.

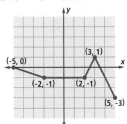

61. Give an equation for the transformation that maps the graph of f onto the graph of g.

$$T:(x, y) \rightarrow (x + 3, y + 2)$$

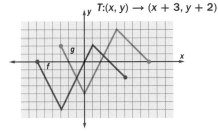

62. a. Graph $f(x) = x^2$ and $g(x) = 2x^2$ on the same set of axes.

b. True or False g is the image of f under the transformation $S: (x, y) \rightarrow (2x, y)$. **false**

In 63–65, the graph is a translation or a scale-change image of the graph of the given parent function. Write an equation for the function that is graphed.

63. parent: $y = x^2$ $y = (x + 2)^2 + 5$

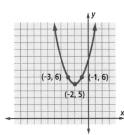

(-3, 6) (-1, 6)
(-2, 5)

64. parent: $y = \sqrt{x}$ $y = \sqrt{2x}$

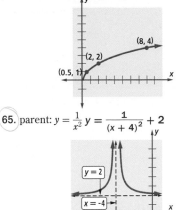

(8, 4)
(2, 2)
(0.5, 1)

65. parent: $y = \dfrac{1}{x^2}$ $y = \dfrac{1}{(x + 4)^2} + 2$

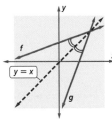

$y = 2$
$x = -4$

OBJECTIVE K Graph inverses of functions. (Lesson 3-8)

In 66–68, a rule for a function is given.
a. Find an equation for its inverse.
b. Graph the function and its inverse.
c. Determine if the inverse is a function.

66. $y = -2x^3$ **67.** $h(x) = \dfrac{2}{x}$ **68.** $j(x) = -x^2 + 4$

69. Tell whether or not f and g graphed below are inverses of each other. Explain your reasoning.

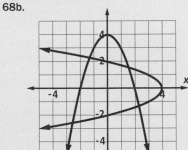

$y = x$

69. They are inverses of each other. We can tell because they are symmetric over the line $y = x$, which implies that $f(g(x)) = g(f(x)) = x$.

60, 62a., 66–68. See margin.

Chapter Review **219**

Assessment
Evaluation The *Assessment Resources* provide a form of the Chapter 3 Test. Here are our recommendations for assigning a letter grade: 85–100 = A; 72–84 = B; 60–71 = C; 50–59 = D.

Feedback After students have taken the test for Chapter 3 and you have scored the results, return the tests to students for discussion. Class discussion on the questions that caused trouble for most students can be very effective in identifying and clarifying misunderstandings. You might want to have them note the items they missed and work either in groups or at home to correct them. It is important for students to receive feedback on every chapter test, and we recommend that students see and correct their mistakes before proceeding too far into the next chapter.

Suggestions for Assignment Assign Reading Lesson 4-1 and Covering the Ideas 4-1 for homework the evening of the test. It gives students work to do after they have completed the test and keeps the class moving. If you do not do this, you may cover one less chapter over the course of the year.

Additional Answers

68a. $y = \pm \sqrt{4 - x}$

68b.

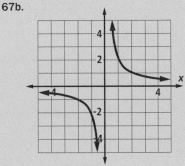

68c. The inverse is not a function.

Additional Answers

66a. $y = \left(-\dfrac{x}{2}\right)^{\frac{1}{3}}$

66b.

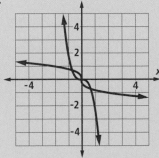

66c. The inverse is a function.

67a. $y = \dfrac{2}{x}$

67b.

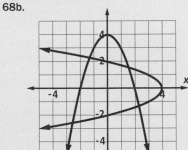

67c. The inverse is a function.

Trigonometric Functions

Chapter Overview

	Local Standards	Average	Advanced	Block
4-1 Magnitudes of Rotations and Measures of Arcs **A** Convert between degrees, radians, and revolutions.		1	1	0.5
4-2 Sines, Cosines, and Tangents **C** Apply the definitions of the sine, cosine, and tangent functions. **H** Use the unit circle to find values of sines, cosines, and tangents.		1	1	0.5
4-3 Basic Trigonometric Identities **C** Apply the definitions of the sine, cosine, and tangent functions. **D** Apply theorems about sines, cosines, and tangents. **H** Use the unit circle to find values of sines, cosines, and tangents.		1	1	0.5
QUIZ 1		0.5	0.25	0.25
4-4 Exact Values of Sines, Cosines, and Tangents **B** Find values of sines, cosines, and tangents.		1	1	0.5
4-5 The Sine and Cosine Functions **B** Find values of sines and cosines. **C** Apply the definitions of the sine and cosine functions. **I** Draw or intepret graphs of the parent sine and cosine functions in degrees or radians.		1	1	0.5
4-6 The Tangent Function and Periodicity **C** Apply the definition of the tangent function. **D** Apply theorems about sines, cosines, and tangents. **I** Draw or interpret graphs of the parent tangent function in degrees or radians.		1	1	0.5
QUIZ 2		0.5	0.5	0.25
4-7 Scale-Change Images of Trigonometric Functions **E** Identify the amplitude, period, frequency, phase shift, and other properties of trigonometric functions. **F** Write and solve equations for phenomena described by trigonometric functions. **J** Graph and describe transformation images of graphs of trigonometric functions.		1	1	0.5
4-8 Translation Images of Trigonometric Functions **E** Identify the amplitude, period, frequency, phase shift, and other properties of trigonometric functions. **F** Write and solve equations for phenomena described by trigonometric functions. **J** Graph and describe transformation images of graphs of trigonometric functions.		1	1	0.5
4-9 The Graph-Standardization Theorem **E** Identify the amplitude, period, frequency, phase shift, and other properties of trigonometric functions. **F** Write and solve equations for phenomena described by trigonometric functions. **J** Graph and describe transformation images of graphs of trigonometric functions.		1	1	0.5
4-10 Modeling with Trigonometric Functions **G** Find equations of trigonometric functions to model periodic phenomena.		1	1	0.5
Self-Test		1	0.5	0.5
Chapter Review		2	1	0.5
Test		1	1	0.5
TOTAL		15	13	7

Technology Resources

Teacher's Assessment Assistant, Ch. 4

Electronic Teacher's Edition, Ch. 4

Differentiated Options Universal Access

	Accommodating the Learner	Vocabulary Development	Ongoing Assessment	Materials
4-1	p. 225	p. 224	p. 228	
4-2		p. 231	p. 234	compass, protractor, graph paper
4-3		p. 239	p. 241	compass, protractor, graph paper or DGS
4-4	p. 244		p. 246	
4-5	p. 248		p. 251	
4-6	p. 254		p. 256	
4-7	pp. 258, 259	p. 260	p. 262	
4-8	p. 264		p. 268	
4-9	p. 272		p. 275	sinusodial graph applet
4-10			p. 281	statistics utility

Objectives

		Lessons	Self-Test Questions	Chapter Review Questions
Skills				
A	Convert between degrees, radians, and revolutions.	4-1	1, 2, 3	1–8
B	Find values of sines, cosines, and tangents.	4-4, 4-5	4, 5, 6	9–25
Properties				
C	Apply the definitions of the sine, cosine, and tangent functions.	4-2, 4-3, 4-5, 4-6	8	26–31
D	Apply theorems about sines, cosines, and tangents.	4-3, 4-6	11, 14	32–41
E	Identify the amplitude, period, frequency, phase shift, and other properties of trigonometric functions.	4-7, 4-8, 4-9	7, 16	42–49
Uses				
F	Write and solve equations for phenomena described by trigonometric functions.	4-7, 4-8, 4-9	17, 20	50–53
G	Find equations of trigonometric functions to model periodic phenomena.	4-10	18	54–57
Representations				
H	Use the unit circle to find values of sines, cosines, and tangents.	4-2, 4-3	9, 10	58–65
I	Draw or interpret graphs of the parent sine, cosine, and tangent function in degrees or radians.	4-5, 4-6	12	66–70
J	Graph and describe transformation images of graphs of trigonometric functions.	4-7, 4-8, 4-9	13, 15, 19	71–78

Resource Masters Chapter 4

Resource Master 152, Four Quadrant Graph Paper, (page 152) can be used with Lessons 4-2 through 4-9.

Resource Master 70   Lesson 4-1

Resource Master 69   Lesson 4-1

Warm-Up
In 1–5, give the length of the arc of a unit circle whose degree measure is as given.

1. 360°, the full circle
2. 180°
3. 45°
4. 120°
5. 213°
(Each answer is the radian measure equivalent to the degree measure.)

Additional Examples
1. a. Convert 42° to radians exactly.
   b. Convert 42° to the nearest hundredth of a radian.
2. Convert 28.8 radians to the nearest degree.
3. Find the length of a 200° arc in a circle of radius 10.5 ft.
4. Refer to Example 4 in the lesson. The swing height can be adjusted to accommodate a taller person by shortening the length of the ropes to 7 ft. How far would the seat of the swing travel if it moves through an angle of 1.5 radians at this shorter length?

Resource Masters for Lesson 4-1

Resource Master 72   Lesson 4-2

Resource Master 71   Lesson 4-2

Warm-Up
Give the exact coordinates of as many points on the unit circle as you can.

Additional Examples
1. Evaluate $\cos -4\pi$ and $\sin -4\pi$.
2. a. Evaluate $\tan -4\pi$.
   b. Evaluate $\tan(450°)$.
3. a. Find, to the nearest thousandth, the coordinates of the image of $(1, 0)$ under a rotation of $-\frac{10\pi}{9}$.
   b. Based on your answer to Part a, tell whether $\tan\left(-\frac{10\pi}{9}\right)$ is positive or negative.
4. A large clock with rotating hour and minute hands is on a building such that its center is 20 meters above the ground. The length of the hour hand is 1.5 meters and the length of the minute hand is 2 meters.
   a. Draw a sketch of the clock at time 8:20 and use it to determine the magnitude of rotation from the 3:00 direction of each hand.
   b. Use your answer to Part a to give the height off the ground of the tip of each hand at 8:20.

Resource Masters for Lesson 4-2

Resource Master 74   Lesson 4-3

Resource Master 73   Lesson 4-3

Warm-Up
In 1–5, one coordinate of a point on the unit circle is given. Find all possible values of the other coordinate.

1. $(0, a)$
2. $\left(\frac{1}{2}, b\right)$
3. $\left(c, -\frac{\sqrt{3}}{2}\right)$
4. $(d, 0.28)$
5. $(e, 0.9)$

Additional Examples
1. If $\sin\theta = \frac{8}{17}$, find $\cos\theta$.

2. Given that $\sin 172° \approx 0.1392$, find a value of x other than 172° and between 0° and 360° for which $\sin x = 0.1392$.

3. If $\sin x = 0.681$, compute the values of the following.
   a. $\cos x$
   b. $\tan x$
   c. $\sin(-x)$
   d. $\sin(\pi - x)$
   e. $\cos(\pi + x)$

Resource Masters for Lesson 4-3

Resource Master 75   Lesson 4-3

Pages 238, 239

Supplements Theorem			
For all θ,	$\sin(180° - \theta)$	$= \sin\theta$	$= \sin(\pi - \theta)$
	$\cos(180° - \theta)$	$= -\cos\theta$	$= \cos(\pi - \theta)$
	and $\tan(180° - \theta)$	$= -\tan\theta$	$= \tan(\pi - \theta)$

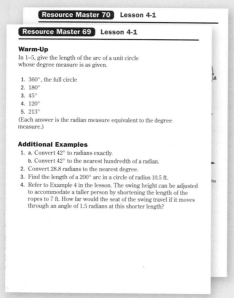

$(\cos(180° - \theta), \sin(180° - \theta))$
$= (-\cos\theta, \sin\theta) = Q$ $P = (\cos\theta, \sin\theta)$
$(-1, 0) = B$ $A = (1, 0)$

Complements Theorem		
For all θ,	$\sin(90° - \theta) = \cos\theta$	$= \sin\left(\frac{\pi}{2} - \theta\right)$
and	$\cos(90° - \theta) = \sin\theta$	$= \cos\left(\frac{\pi}{2} - \theta\right)$

Questions 17–21

17.
18.
19.
20.
21.

Resource Master for Lesson 4-3

Resource Master 77   Lesson 4-4

Resource Master 76   Lesson 4-4

Warm-Up
In 1–4, give the coordinates of the indicated image to the nearest thousandth.

1. $R_{30}(1, 0)$
2. $R_{45}(1, 0)$
3. $R_{60}(1, 0)$
4. $R_{120}(1, 0)$

Additional Examples
1. Using a sketch like the one in Example 1, compute the exact values of $\cos -45°$ and $\sin -45°$.
2. Derive the exact values of $\cos -60°$ and $\sin -60°$.
3. Find the exact value of $\tan -60°$.
4. Without using technology, find the exact values of $\cos 300°$, $\sin 300°$, and $\tan 300°$.
5. Without using technology, compute the exact value of each trigonometric function below.
   a. $\sin\frac{7\pi}{6}$
   b. $\tan\frac{5\pi}{4}$
   c. $\cos 2\pi$

Accommodating the Learner
Let θ be an angle formed by the longest diagonal of a cube and a diagonal of a face of the cube. Find θ exactly.

Resource Masters for Lesson 4-4

Resource Master 79   Lesson 4-5

Resource Master 78   Lesson 4-5

Warm-Up
Without using a calculator, given that $\sqrt{2} \approx 1.414$ and $\sqrt{3} \approx 1.732$, approximate to the nearest hundredth:

1. $\frac{\sqrt{2}}{2}$
2. $\frac{\sqrt{3}}{2}$
3. $\frac{\sqrt{3}}{3}$
4. $\left(\sqrt{2}\right)^2$

Page 247

θ (degrees)	0°	30°	45°	60°	90°	120°	135°	150°	180°
θ (radians)	0	$\frac{\pi}{6}$	$\frac{\pi}{4}$	$\frac{\pi}{3}$	$\frac{\pi}{2}$	$\frac{2\pi}{3}$	$\frac{3\pi}{4}$	$\frac{5\pi}{6}$	π
$\sin\theta$ (exact)	0	$\frac{1}{2}$	?	$\frac{\sqrt{3}}{2}$	?	?	?	?	?
$\sin\theta$ (approx.)	0	?	?	?	?	?	0.707	?	?

θ (degrees)	210°	225°	240°	270°	300°	315°	330°	360°
θ (radians)	$\frac{7\pi}{6}$	$\frac{5\pi}{4}$	$\frac{4\pi}{3}$	$\frac{3\pi}{2}$	?	?	?	2π
$\sin\theta$ (exact)	0	$-\frac{\sqrt{2}}{2}$	?	?	?	$\frac{\sqrt{3}}{2}$	?	?
$\sin\theta$ (approx.)	0	?	?	?	-0.866	?	?	?

Resource Masters for Lesson 4-5

Resource Master 81 Lesson 4-6

Resource Master 80 Lesson 4-6

Warm-Up

Graph $y = \sin x$ and $y = \cos x$ on the same axes, for $0 \le x \le 360°$. Then, for five different values of x, take the quotient of the y-values of these functions. Graph these quotients in a different color.

Additional Examples

1. Consider $f(x) = \cos x$.
   a. Give the domain and range of f.
   b. Tell whether f is an odd function, an even function, or neither. Justify your answer.

2. Use the Periodicity Theorem to find $\sin 15780°$.

3. The graph below shows the average travel time from downtown Metropolis to Metropolis International Airport during a typical week (Monday to Friday). For this function, determine each.
   a. the maximum and minimum values
   b. the range
   c. the period

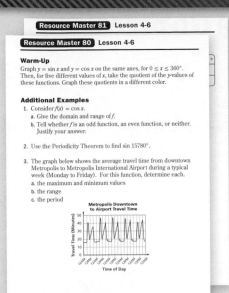

Resource Masters for Lesson 4-6

Resource Master 82 Lesson 4-6

Periodicity Theorem

For any real number x and any integer n,
$$\sin x = \sin(x + n \cdot 2\pi) = \sin(x + n \cdot 360°)$$
$$\cos x = \cos(x + n \cdot 2\pi) = \cos(x + n \cdot 360°)$$
$$\tan x = \tan(x + n \cdot \pi) = \tan(x + n \cdot 180°).$$

Definition of Periodic and Period

A function f is **period** if there is a positive number p such that $f(x + p) = f(x)$ for all x in the domain of f. The smallest such p, if it exists, is called the **period** of f.

Example 3

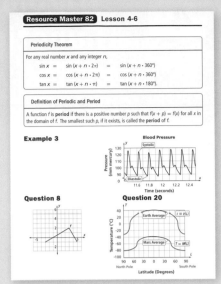

Question 8   Question 20

Resource Master for Lesson 4-6

Resource Master 84 Lesson 4-7

Resource Master 83 Lesson 4-7

Warm-Up

1. Sketch a graph of $y = \sin x$ over the interval $-4\pi \le x \le 4\pi$.
2. How many periods of the sine function are shown in the graph in Warm-Up 1?
3. On the same axes and over the same interval, sketch a graph of $y = \sin 2x$.
4. How many periods of the sine function are shown in the graph in Warm-Up 3?
5. How do the relative maximum and relative minimum values of the graph in Warm-Up 3 compare with the relative maximum and relative minimum values in Warm-Up 1?

Additional Examples

1. Consider the function with equation $y = 3.5 \sin\left(\frac{4x}{5}\right)$.
   a. Explain how this function is related to its parent function $y = \sin x$.
   b. Identify its amplitude and period.

2. The grid below shows a graph of $y = \cos x$ and its image under a scale change. Find an equation for the image.

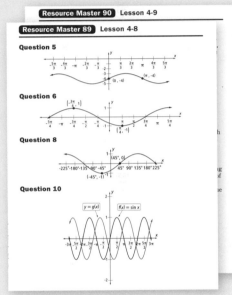

3. A tuning fork vibrates with a frequency of 440 cycles per second. The intensity of the tone is the result of the vibration whose maximum pressure is $15 \frac{N}{m^2}$. Find an equation to model the sound wave produced by the tuning fork.
4. Without using technology, determine how many solutions each equation below has on the interval $0 \le x \le 2\pi$.
   a. $\sin\left(\frac{x}{4}\right) = 0.75$ b. $3 \tan(2x) = -14$

Resource Masters for Lesson 4-7

Resource Master 86 Lesson 4-7

Resource Master 85 Lesson 4-7

Question 4

Question 7

Question 8

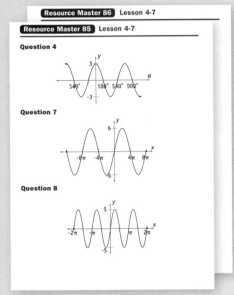

Resource Masters for Lesson 4-7

Resource Master 88 Lesson 4-8

Resource Master 87 Lesson 4-8

Warm-Up

In 1–4, match each equation with the translation that can be applied to the graph of $y = \sin x$ to get its graph.

1. $y = \sin\left(x + \frac{\pi}{3}\right)$ 2. $y = \sin x + \frac{\pi}{3}$
3. $y = \sin x - \frac{\pi}{3}$ 4. $y = \sin\left(x - \frac{\pi}{3}\right)$

A $\frac{\pi}{3}$ units down
B $\frac{\pi}{3}$ units up
C $\frac{\pi}{3}$ units to the right
D $\frac{\pi}{3}$ units to the left

Additional Examples

1. Consider the function g with $g(x) = \cos(x - 38°)$. Identify the phase shift.

2. Compare the graphs of $y = \sin x$, and $y = \sin\left(x + \frac{3\pi}{2}\right)$.

3. Consider the function g, where $g(x) = \sin x$.
   a. Write an equation for its image h under the translation $(x, y) \to \left(x + \frac{\pi}{4}, y + 7\right)$.
   b. Find the amplitude and period of h.

4. Find an equation for the translation image of the graph of the sine function shown below.

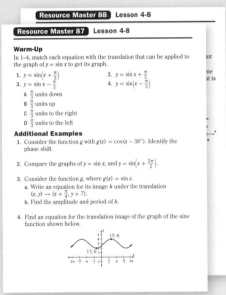

Resource Masters for Lesson 4-8

Resource Master 90 Lesson 4-9

Resource Master 89 Lesson 4-8

Question 5

Question 6

Question 8

Question 10

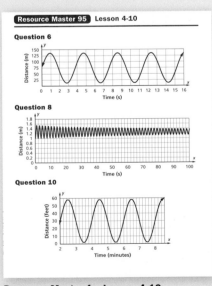

Resource Masters for Lessons 4-8 and 4-9

Resource Master 92 Lesson 4-9

Resource Master 91 Lesson 4-9

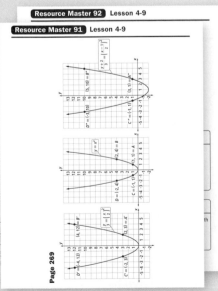

Page 269

Resource Masters for Lesson 4-9

Resource Master 94 Lesson 4-10

Resource Master 93 Lesson 4-10

Warm-Up

Monthly mean temperatures for Memphis, Tennessee are given below.

Month	J	F	M	A	M	J	J	A	S	O	N	D
Temp °F	40	45	54	62	71	79	83	81	75	64	52	43

1. Let $x =$ the number of the month and let $y =$ the mean temperature. Plot the data carefully.
2. By hand, sketch a sine curve to fit the data.

Additional Examples

1. In Houston, New Orleans, and Jacksonville, all of which are at about 30° N latitude, the longest daylight period (June 21) is about 14 hours 5 minutes (845 minutes) long, and the shortest daylight period (December 21) is about 10 hours 13 minutes (613 minutes) long. The vernal equinox (March 21) has about 12 hours 9 minutes (729 minutes) of daylight. Assuming a sine wave model for the length of daylight, find an equation which gives the number of minutes of daylight in these three cities as a function of the day on the year.
2. Assume that when a particular oven is set to 350°F the oven temperature t in degrees Fahrenheit m minutes after the burner first shuts off satisfies $t = 250 + 10 \cos(0.8m)$.
   a. What are the maximum and minimum temperatures of the oven at this setting?
   b. What is the period of this sine wave? What dose the period represent?

Activity

D	1	32	60	91	121	152	182	213	244	274	305	335
N	10.23	10.77	11.55	12.5	13.37	13.98	14.08	13.62	12.77	11.88	10.98	10.35

D	366	397	425	456	486	517	547	578	609	639	670	700
N	10.23	10.77	11.55	12.5	13.37	13.98	14.08	13.62	12.77	11.88	10.98	10.35

Resource Masters for Lesson 4-10

Resource Master 95 Lesson 4-10

Question 6

Question 8

Question 10

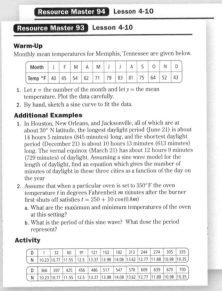

Resource Master for Lesson 4-10

Pacing

Each lesson in this chapter is designed to be covered in 1 day. At the end of the chapter, you should plan to spend 1 day to review the Self-Test, 1 to 2 days for the Chapter Review, and 1 day for a test. You may wish to spend a day on projects, and possibly a day will be needed for quizzes. This chapter should therefore take 14 to 17 days. We strongly advise you not to spend more than 18 days on this chapter, there is ample opportunity to review ideas in Chapter 5 and later chapters. However, it is expected that students have seen examples of the trigonometric functions, even if only with right triangles, in earlier courses. If students have never seen any trigonometry before, then this chapter will take longer due to the extra time needed to discuss the simpler questions.

Students should be expected to do the equivalent of a complete set of Questions from a lesson nearly every day. Two Assignment Options are identified in each lesson. At times you may want to save a few questions to be done by students in class.

Overview

The opener gives the classic application of trigonometric functions to the study of sound. We pick this application (from the many applications possible) because manipulating the sound picked up by the oscilloscope has the effect of translating or stretching the sine wave.

Trigonometric Functions

Contents

4-1 Magnitudes of Rotations and Measures of Arcs

4-2 Sines, Cosines, and Tangents

4-3 Basic Trigonometric Identities

4-4 Exact Values of Sines, Cosines, and Tangents

4-5 The Sine and Cosine Functions

4-6 The Tangent Function and Periodicity

4-7 Scale-Change Images of Trigonometric Functions

4-8 Translation Images of Trigonometric Functions

4-9 The Graph-Standardization Theorem

4-10 Modeling with Trigonometric Functions

Sound is produced by fluctuations in the pressure of the air. Different kinds of fluctuations cause us to hear different kinds of sounds. Variations in air pressure can be picked up by a microphone and can be displayed by an oscilloscope as a graph of air pressure versus time.

Sound Waves Produced by a Violin and a Flute

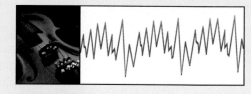

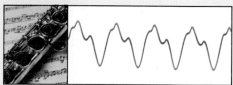

Chapter 4 Overview

This chapter begins the *Functions, Statistics, and Trigonometry* presentation of trigonometry. Those who have taught from earlier editions of FST will notice a reordering of the material so that there are two foci to the chapter: the definitions of the trigonometric functions in terms of the unit circle, and the application of those functions to periodic phenomena. Applications of these functions to right triangles are the subject of Chapter 5.

In Lesson 4-1, properties of angles and rotations are reviewed to prepare for the definitions of the sine, cosine, and tangent in Lesson 4-2 in terms of rotation images of the point (1, 0) around the unit circle. With this definition, in Lessons 4-3 and 4-4, the values of the functions are found and their most common properties derived. The functions themselves are the subject of the last half of the chapter. From the unit circle definition, the periodicity of the functions is evident and displayed by their graphs in

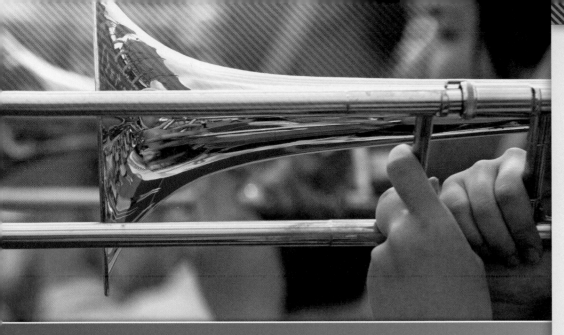

Graphs of different sounds produced by various instruments are on page 220. From such graphs you can see why sound is said to travel in waves.

A pure tone is a tone in which air pressure varies *sinusoidally* with time; that is, as a sine wave, which is the graph of the *sine function*. Pure tones seldom occur in nature, but they can be produced by certain tuning forks and electronic music synthesizers. Mathematically and physiologically, pure tones or sine waves are the foundation of all musical sound.

The sine function, and the related functions called the cosine and tangent functions, are examples of *trigonometric functions*. In this chapter, you will study some of the properties of these functions and study the effects of transformations on the graphs of the parent trigonometric functions. You will also learn how the trigonometric functions are used to model sound, electricity, and other periodic phenomena.

221

Lessons 4-5 and 4-6. With a discussion of the transformations of the graphs in Lessons 4-7 to 4-9, students are prepared for the modeling in Lesson 4-10.

The chapter makes heavy use of the geometry of the unit circle. Yet the important formulas and identities are proved algebraically. This is intended to provide students not only with simply a formula to use, but also a method for reconstructing a formula they may have forgotten. The chapter makes heavy use of

calculators, so there is as much or more emphasis on students being able to approximate values of trigonometric functions as there is on working with exact values.

Teachers familiar with the second edition of this text will notice that the title of this chapter has been changed from "circular functions" to "trigonometric functions." This change recognizes that the phrase "circular functions" has not caught on in the college mathematical world.

This is an appropriate time to assess how much your students know about the content of the chapter. In some physics classes, right triangle trigonometry is discussed quite early and some of your students may have had this content earlier in this school year. You might ask the following:

How many of you know the right triangle definitions for the sine, cosine, and tangent?

If any answer "Yes" to this question, ask:

How many of you have graphed these trigonometric functions?

How many of you have studied the Law of Sines and the Law of Cosines?

The answers will give you some guidance as to the pace you can keep.

Science departments in most high schools have an oscilloscope. Bringing one to class is a good way to start the chapter. Vary the pitch and volume of a tone to produce changes in the period and amplitude of the graph. Point out that Lessons 4-5 to 4-8 deal with the mathematics of these changes in sine waves. Then combine tones to produce more complicated waves.

Chapter 4 Projects

At the end of each chapter, you will find projects related to the chapter. At this time you might want to have students look over the projects on pages 282 and 283. You might want to have students tentatively select a project on which to work. Then, as students read and progress through the chapter, they can finalize their project choices.

Sometimes students might work alone. At other times, you might let them collaborate with classmates for a presentation and discussion. We recommend that you allow for diversity and encourage students to use their imaginations when presenting their projects. As students work on projects throughout the year, they should see many uses of mathematics in the real world.

Lesson
4-1

Lesson 4-1 — Magnitudes of Rotations and Measures of Arcs

GOAL

Relate three different units for measuring angles and rotations: degrees, revolutions, and radians.

SPUR Objective

The SPUR Objectives for all of Chapter 4 are found in the Chapter Review on pages 288–291.

A Convert between degrees, radians, and revolutions.

Materials/Resources

· Lesson Master 4-1
· Resource Masters 69 and 70

HOMEWORK

· **Option 1**
· **Option 2**

- Questions 1–16
- • Questions 17–26
- • Question 27 (extra credit)
- Reading Lesson 4-2
- •Covering the Ideas 4-2 (Questions 1–17)

Local Standards

---

1 — Warm-Up

In 1–5, give the length of the arc of a unit circle whose degree measure is as given.

1. 360°, the full circle 2π
2. 180° π
3. 45° $\frac{\pi}{4}$
4. 120° $\frac{2\pi}{3}$
5. 213° $\frac{71\pi}{60}$

(Each answer is the radian measure equivalent to the degree measure.)

Vocabulary

rotation
center of the rotation
rotation image
magnitude of a rotation
revolution, full turn
half turn
quarter turn
radian

Mental Math

A pie chart is constructed to represent the following ice cream preferences: vanilla, 50%; chocolate, 30%; strawberry, 20%. Find the angle measure of each sector of the pie chart.

vanilla: **180°**;
chocolate: **108°**;
strawberry: **72°**

▶ **BIG IDEA** Magnitudes of rotations are described in revolutions, degrees, and radians.

A **rotation** is a transformation under which each point in the plane turns a fixed magnitude around a fixed point called the **center of the rotation**. In the figure at the right, A and B are on the same circle with center Q. Point A has been rotated counterclockwise about the center Q to the position of B, its **rotation image**.

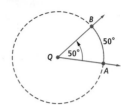

Revolutions and Degrees

There is a way to describe how much A has been rotated to get to B. Use the measure of the central angle, $\angle AQB$. Since m$\angle AQB = 50°$, the **magnitude** of the rotation is 50°. When rotations are measured in this way, the rotation of 360° is called one **revolution**, or a **full turn**. A rotation of 180° or $\frac{1}{2}$ revolution is called a **half turn**, and a rotation of 90° or $\frac{1}{4}$ revolution is called a **quarter turn**.

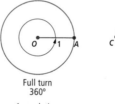

Full turn 360°	Half turn 180°	Quarter turn 90°
1 revolution counterclockwise	$\frac{1}{2}$ revolution counterclockwise	$\frac{1}{4}$ revolution counterclockwise

Above, you could also rotate B 50° clockwise to get to A. The clockwise direction is the negative direction in trigonometry because the four quadrants are numbered in a counterclockwise order. So the rotation that maps B onto A is said to be a -50° rotation, or to have magnitude -50°.

You can multiply both sides of the conversion equation

$$1 \text{ revolution} = 360°$$

to find how many degrees there are in any multiple of a revolution.

222   Trigonometric Functions

Background

After working with degrees for so many years, some students are reluctant to learn another way of measuring angles and rotations. Yet radian measure is used in a large number of real-world applications involving the trigonometric functions, and is almost the exclusive measure used in calculus and its applications. The fundamental reason that radians are used is that mathematical relationships are simpler with this unit. This is analogous to the use of e as a base for logarithms.

The Circle Arc Length Formula shows students how one formula is simpler when written in radians. In calculus, students will study infinite series for the sine and cosine:

$$\sin x = x - \frac{x^3}{3!} + \frac{x^5}{5!} - \frac{x^7}{7!} + \dots + (-1)^{n+1}\frac{x^{2n-1}}{(2n-1)!} + \dots$$

$$\cos x = 1 - \frac{x^2}{2!} + \frac{x^4}{4!} - \frac{x^6}{6!} + \dots + (-1)^{n+1}\frac{x^{2n-2}}{(2n-2)!} + \dots .$$

These formulas require the argument x to be in radians. In degrees, one would have to substitute $\frac{\pi}{180}x$ for x each time it appears.

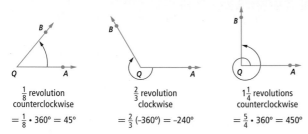

$\frac{1}{8}$ revolution counterclockwise $= \frac{1}{8} \cdot 360° = 45°$

$\frac{2}{3}$ revolution clockwise $= \frac{2}{3}(-360°) = -240°$

$1\frac{1}{4}$ revolutions counterclockwise $= \frac{5}{4} \cdot 360° = 450°$

In skateboarding, snowboarding, and many other sports, you may see rotations called 360s, 540s, 720s, and so on. In gymnastics and figure skating, rotations are measured in revolutions or turns. A 720 means 2 revolutions. In these *physical rotations*, adding 360° or 1 revolution to a turn creates a different movement. But in *mathematical rotations*, all that matters is where you begin and where you end. Physically turning 360° means you turned all the way around, but a mathematical rotation of 360° is the same as a mathematical rotation of –360°, and both are the same as if you did nothing at all!

For this reason, the same rotation can have many different magnitudes. For instance, a rotation of $\frac{1}{8}$ revolution counterclockwise also has magnitude $1\frac{1}{8}$ revolutions counterclockwise or $\frac{7}{8}$ revolution clockwise. In degrees, that rotation has magnitude 45°, 405°, or –315°, respectively. Adding or subtracting 1 revolution (or 360°) to the magnitude of a rotation does not change the rotation.

Let's roll Since 2004, June 21 has been designated "Go Skateboarding Day."

Radian Measure

In a rotation, points that are farther from the center "move" or "turn" a greater distance along the arc of a circle than points that are closer to the center. For example, at the right, *S* moves farther to get to *E* than *G* moves to get to *C*. Measuring a rotation in degrees or revolutions does not tell anything about how far a point has moved. To solve this problem, a unit is needed that is related to the length of the arc. That unit is the *radian*. Radians have been in use for about 125 years and are important in the study of calculus and other advanced mathematics.

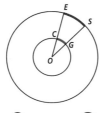

$\widehat{SE}$ is longer than $\widehat{GC}$.

Radian measure is based on arc lengths in the unit circle. As you know, if a circle has radius *r*, its circumference is $2\pi r$. We distinguish between 360° and $2\pi r$ because 360° is *arc measure* and $2\pi r$ is *arc length*.

 QY1

▶ **QY1**

A point moves halfway around a circle of radius 5.

   a. What is the length of the arc traversed by the point?

   b. How many degrees is the rotation?

2 ❘ Teaching

Notes on the Lesson

Radian measure Students should be able to estimate the size of an angle in radian measure. To give meaning to what a radian is and where it comes from, you might draw a large circle on the floor, measure the length of a radius with string, and then put the string on the circle to see how much of the circle it covers. You should find that 1 radian is a little less than 60°. Students can remember this by noting that the entire unit circle covers 360° and has circumference 2π, or about 6.28 radians. Thus 1 unit of its circumference, which is 1 radian, must equal less than 60° of arc.

Radian measure The radian measure of an angle is a real number equal to the length of the corresponding *arc on a unit circle*, and is unit free. At this point we say π *radians* in order to emphasize the origin of the measure, though, later in the text we will drop the word *radians*, and when an angle is measured in degrees the degree sign is always indicated, as in $\sin A = \sin \frac{\pi}{6} = \sin 30°$. The rest of the chapter provides students practice in working with radians.

Many calculators have a key to convert between degrees and radians; on others the user can convert by changing an instruction under Mode. However, except on a CAS, the conversion to radians will not be exact and it is not always easy to determine a particular multiple of π. We think students should be able to do these conversions by hand and also with technology.

4-1

Notes on the Lesson

Converting between radians and degrees To obtain the equivalents for measures of angles often used as the basis for graphing, such as $30° = \frac{\pi}{6}$ radians, stress the need for students to know that π radians = 180° and multiply both sides of that equation by appropriate numbers.

Additional Answers

Activity

Degrees	0°	30°	45°	60°
Radians	0	$\frac{\pi}{6}$	$\frac{\pi}{4}$	$\frac{\pi}{3}$
Revolutions	0	$\frac{1}{12}$	$\frac{1}{8}$	$\frac{1}{6}$

90°	120°	135°	150°	180°	360°
$\frac{\pi}{2}$	$\frac{2\pi}{3}$	$\frac{3\pi}{4}$	$\frac{5\pi}{6}$	π	2π
$\frac{1}{4}$	$\frac{1}{3}$	$\frac{3}{8}$	$\frac{5}{12}$	$\frac{1}{2}$	1

A *unit circle* (radius = 1) has circumference $C = 2\pi \cdot 1 = 2\pi$, which is approximately 6.28. Consider point A on a unit circle O, as pictured at the right. The magnitude in **radians** of the rotation with center O that maps A onto P is defined as the numerical length of $\overset{\frown}{AP}$. In this drawing, $\overset{\frown}{AP}$ is $\frac{3}{8}$ of a circle, so the length of $\overset{\frown}{AP}$ is $\frac{3}{8}$ of the circumference, or $\frac{3}{8} \cdot 2\pi = \frac{3\pi}{4} \approx 2.356$. Notice that $m\angle AOP = 135°$. So 135° corresponds to a rotation of $\frac{3\pi}{4}$ radians.

The radian measure of a full turn is 2π because if point A was physically turned through one complete revolution, it would travel over an arc of length 2π. Similarly, the radian measure of a half-turn is π and of a quarter turn is $\frac{\pi}{2}$.

As when rotations are measured in degrees, a clockwise rotation gives rise to a negative radian magnitude. Also, just as adding or subtracting multiples of 360° to the magnitude of a rotation gives rise to the same rotation, so does adding or subtracting multiples of 2π radians. The three circles below show that a rotation of magnitude $\frac{7\pi}{6}$ radians is the same as a rotation of $\frac{7\pi}{6} - 2\pi = -\frac{5\pi}{6}$ radians, and is the same as a rotation of $2\pi + \frac{7\pi}{6} = \frac{19\pi}{6}$ radians.

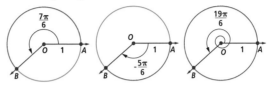

Converting between Radians and Degrees

Some degree measures are easy to convert to radians. For example, 30° is $\frac{1}{12}$ of 360°. Use the conversion formula

$$360° = 1 \text{ revolution} = 2\pi \text{ radians.}$$

Divide by 12 to obtain

$$30° = \frac{1}{12} \text{ revolution} = \frac{\pi}{6} \text{ radians.}$$

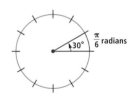

Activity See margin.

The table below lists some of the equivalent measures that result from the basic relationship 2π radians = 360°. Copy and fill in the rest of the table.

Degrees	0°	30°	?	?	90°	120°	?	150°	180°	360°
Radians	0	$\frac{\pi}{6}$	$\frac{\pi}{4}$	$\frac{\pi}{3}$	$\frac{\pi}{2}$	?	$\frac{3\pi}{4}$	?	π	?
Revolutions	?	?	$\frac{1}{8}$	?	?	?	$\frac{3}{8}$	?	$\frac{1}{2}$	1

ENGLISH LEARNERS

Vocabulary Development

The words *revolution* and *rotation* are often used synonymously in everyday language. People will say that Earth "revolves" on its axis or that it "rotates on its axis." In contrast, here we are careful to distinguish the terms. The *turn* is the rotation; the *amount of the turn* can be measured in revolutions.

The values in the Activity are common radian values. You should know them without having to do any paper-and-pencil or calculator work. To convert any rotation measure from one unit to another, use the conversion formula below, since 2π radians $= 360°$.

$$\pi \text{ radians} = 180°$$

Dividing both sides of the conversion formula by the quantity on one side gives rise to two conversion factors, each equal to 1.

$$1 = \frac{180°}{\pi \text{ radians}} \quad \text{or} \quad 1 = \frac{\pi \text{ radians}}{180°}$$

Example 1

a. Convert $1000°$ to radians exactly.

b. Convert $1000°$ to radians approximately.

Solution

a. Multiply by the appropriate conversion factor.

$$1000° = 1000° \cdot \frac{\pi \text{ radians}}{180°} = \frac{1000}{180}\pi = \frac{50}{9}\pi \text{ radians}$$

b. Use a calculator to get a decimal approximation for $\frac{50\pi}{9}$.

$$\frac{50\pi}{9} \approx 17.453, \text{ so } 1000° \text{ is about } 17.5 \text{ radians.}$$

Caution: Computer algebra systems and calculators work in both radians and degrees. Be sure to set the mode to the unit you want.

How large in degrees is an angle or rotation of magnitude 1 radian? Think: If point B on a unit circle is rotated 1 unit around the center to Q, as shown at the right, what is m$\angle BOQ$? The circumference of a unit circle is $2\pi \approx 6.28$. So there are about 6.28 radians in one revolution, and one radian is slightly less than $\frac{1}{6}$ revolution. But $\frac{1}{6}$ revolution is equivalent to $60°$. So one radian should be slightly less than $60°$.

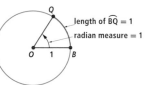

Example 2

Convert 1 radian to degrees.

Solution Use the conversion factor $\frac{180°}{\pi \text{ radians}}$.

So 1 radian $= 1 \text{ radian} \cdot \frac{180°}{\pi \text{ radians}} = \frac{180°}{\pi} \approx 57.3°$.

Why Are Radians Used?

You may have studied angles and rotations for years and never used radians. You may be wondering why radians are used and if they are ever needed. One advantage of radians over degrees is that certain formulas are simpler when written with radians.

Notes on the Lesson

Example 1 Some science classes and earlier UCSMP courses cover the idea of multiplying by a conversion factor to change units. A conversion factor is a fraction whose numerator and denominator are equal quantities but with different units; since the quantities are equal, the value of the factor is 1. In this example, the conversion factor is $\frac{\pi \text{ radians}}{180°}$.

Example 2 Here the conversion factor is the reciprocal of the conversion factor used in Example 1. But because every conversion factor equals 1, there is no change in the value of the quantity from before to after the conversion.

Additional Examples

Example 1

a. Convert $42°$ to radians exactly. $\frac{7\pi}{30}$

b. Convert $42°$ to the nearest hundredth of a radian. ≈ 0.73 radians

Example 2 Convert 28.8 radians to the nearest degree. $\approx 1650°$

Accommodating the Learner ⬇

Some students would benefit from a little extra time spent discussing the use of conversion factors. A conversion factor is a fraction whose numerator and denominator are equal quantities but with different units; since the quantities are equal, the value of the factor is 1. If any students seem unsure about which conversion factor to use in a particular situation, you may wish to show them how to construct the factor themselves using a ratio as follows.

Let $x°$ equal to y radians. Since $180° = \pi$ radians, we can set up the equation: $\frac{x}{180} = \frac{y}{\pi}$ and cross-multiply as needed. To change $x°$ to y radians, we use $y = \frac{x}{180} \cdot \pi$; to change y radians to $x°$, we use $x = \frac{y}{\pi} \cdot 180$.

Additional Examples

Example 3 Find the length of a 200°
arc in a circle of radius 10.5 ft. $\frac{35\pi}{3}$ ft
exactly or about 36.65 ft

Example 4 Refer to Example 4 in
the lesson. The swing height can be
adjusted to accommodate a taller
person by shortening the length of the
ropes to 7 ft. How far would the seat
of the swing travel if it moves through
an angle of 1.5 radians at this shorter
length? **10.5 ft**

3 Assignment

Recommended Assignment

- Questions 1–16
- • Questions 17–26
- • Question 27 (extra credit)
- • Reading Lesson 4-2
- • Covering the Ideas 4-2
  (Questions 1–17)

Example 3

Find the length of an arc of a 50° central angle in a circle of radius 6 feet.

Solution The 50° arc is $\frac{50}{360}$ of the circumference of the circle.
The circumference has length $2\pi r$, or __?__ ft. So, the length of **12π**
the arc is $\frac{50}{360} \cdot$ __?__, which simplifies to __?__ ft exactly, or **12π $\frac{5\pi}{3}$**
__?__ ft, to the nearest hundredth. **5.24**

Example 3 is easily generalized. Notice how much simpler the formula
is if the central angle is measured in radians.

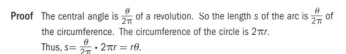
Circle Arc Length Formula

If s is the length of the arc of a central angle of θ radians in a
circle of radius r, then $s = r\theta$.

Proof The central angle is $\frac{\theta}{2\pi}$ of a revolution. So the length s of the arc is $\frac{\theta}{2\pi}$ of
the circumference. The circumference of the circle is $2\pi r$.
Thus, $s = \frac{\theta}{2\pi} \cdot 2\pi r = r\theta$.

STOP QY2

> **QY2**
>
> Find the length of a $\frac{5}{18}\pi$
> radian arc in a circle of
> radius 6 feet.

Example 4

A swing hangs from chains that are 8 ft long. How far does the seat of the
swing travel if it moves through an angle of 1.25 radians?

Solution 1 Since the angle is 1.25 radians,
the length of the intercepted arc on the unit
circle is 1.25. The arc length on the 8-foot
circle is 8 times the length of the arc on the
unit circle. **The distance traveled is
8 · 1.25 = 10 feet.**

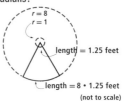

Solution 2 Use the Circle Arc Length Formula.

$S = r\theta$. The swing travels 8 · 1.25, or 10 feet.

Radians are so commonly used in mathematics that when no unit is
given in a problem that could be in degrees or radians, it is understood
that the measure is in radians.

Questions

COVERING THE IDEAS

1. Convert $\frac{9}{10}$ revolution to degrees. **324°**

2. Convert –805° to revolutions, rounding to the nearest tenth. **2.2 revolutions clockwise**

Extension

You might want to remind students (if they
do not already know) that 1 degree = 60
minutes (abbreviated ′), and 1 minute =
60 seconds (abbreviated ″). Thus 1 degree
= 3600 seconds. It is useful to be able to
convert from a measure given in degrees,
minutes, and seconds to one just in
degrees. For instance, 35°43′5″ = 35° + 43′
+ 5″ = $(35 + \frac{43}{60} + \frac{5}{3600})° \approx 35.71806°$.

---

3. At the right is a graph of a circle with radius 1.

   a. Give the length of $\overarc{AC}$. **π**

   b. What is the smallest positive magnitude in radians of the rotation with center O that maps A to C? **π**

In 4 and 5, draw a circle with radius 1. **4–5a. See margin.**

   a. On this circle, heavily shade an arc with the given length.

   b. Give the degree measure of the central angle of this arc.

4. $\frac{2\pi}{3}$ **b.120°**   5. 1 **b.about 57.3°**

In 6 and 7, draw a unit circle and an arc with the given radian measure.

6. $\frac{3\pi}{2}$ **6–7. See margin.**   7. 2

8. Convert the measure to degrees. Round to the nearest thousandth.

   a. –0.2 radians **–11.459°**   b. –0.2π radians **–36°**

9. If a skateboarder does a "540," what is the magnitude of the rotation

   a. in revolutions? *1.5 rev*   b. in radians? **3π**

In 10 and 11, convert to radians exactly without using a calculator.

10. 225° $\frac{5\pi}{4}$ 11. –80° $\frac{-4\pi}{9}$

12. a. Draw an angle representing a rotation with measure $\frac{7\pi}{12}$ radians.

    b. Give two other radian measures of the same rotation.

13. Use the circle at the right. If m∠$ABC = \frac{5\pi}{6}$ radians and the radius of the circle is 33, compute the length of $\overarc{AC}$. $\frac{55\pi}{2}$

In 14 and 15, use a circle with diameter 8 cm.

14. Find the length of the arc intercepted by an angle of $\frac{3\pi}{4}$. **about 9.42 cm**

15. Find the length of the arc intercepted by an angle of 63°. **about 4.398 cm**

16. Suppose the blades of a wind turbine are 16' long. What is the distance traveled by a point on its tip as the blade rotates $\frac{3}{5}$ of a revolution? **about 60.32 ft**

APPLYING THE MATHEMATICS

17. On the clock tower on the Houses of Parliament in London, England, the minute hand is about 14 feet long. How many feet does the end of the minute hand move in 5 minutes? **about 7.3 ft**

18. An angle whose measure is $\frac{\pi}{2}$ is about __?__ times as large as an angle whose measure is $\frac{\pi}{2}°$. **57.3**

19. Musicians use a metronome to produce a steady beat as they practice. Many mechanical metronomes have a swinging arm with a weight to control the tempo. Suppose that a metronome arm is 4 inches long, moves through an angle of $\frac{\pi}{3}$, and beats at a rate of 160 beats per minute. How far does the tip of the arm travel in

    a. 1 beat? **about 4.19 in.**   b. 1 hour? **about 40,212.4 in.**

9a. **1.5 revolutions**

12a.

12b. **Answers vary. Sample:** $-\frac{17\pi}{12}$ **and** $\frac{31\pi}{12}$

(circle with point A at top, point B at left labeled $\frac{5\pi}{6}$, 33 along segment, point C at bottom)

Additional Answers

4a.

5a.

6.

7.

12a.

4-1

Notes on the Questions

Question 21c Have students write the units in each step as they multiply by appropriate conversion factors. Then they can cancel units until mph remains.

Question 22 The actual latitudes and longitudes for the cities in this question are longitude 85°40′ W, latitude 42°58′ N for Grand Rapids and longitude 86°17′ W, latitude 32°22′ N for Montgomery.

Question 26 This question is useful review for later lessons in the chapter.

Question 27 This is another formula that is easier in radians than in degrees. If the measure of the arc is in degrees, then the area of the sector is $\frac{\theta}{360}$ the area of the circle, or $\frac{\theta}{360}\pi r^2$, not as simple as $0.5\pi r^2$.

4 Wrap-Up

Ongoing Assessment

Have students work in groups of three. Ask each student to write two angle measures. One student gives the measures in degreees, one in radians, and one in revolutions. Then have students convert each of the six measures to the other two forms. Have students check each other's work.

---

20. The planet Jupiter rotates on its axis at a rate of approximately 0.6334 radians per hour. What is the approximate length of the Jovian day (the time it takes Jupiter to make a complete revolution)?

21. Suppose you can ride a bike with 22″ wheels (in diameter) so that the wheels rotate 150 revolutions per minute.
    a. Find the number of inches traveled during each revolution.
    b. How many inches are traveled each minute?
    c. Use your answer from Part b to find the speed, in miles per hour, that you are traveling. **about 9.8 mph**

22. Recall that when greater precision is desired, a degree is split into 60 minutes (abbreviated ′). The diagram at the right shows a cross section of Earth. G represents Grand Rapids, MI and M represents Montgomery, AL. Assume that Grand Rapids is directly north of Montgomery. If the radius of Earth is about 3960 miles, estimate the air distance from Grand Rapids to Montgomery. **about 732.62 air miles**

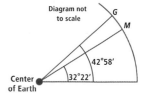

Diagram not to scale

REVIEW

23. Use the Graph-Translation Theorem to find the equation of the image of $y = x^2$ under $T: (x, y) \rightarrow (x + 3, y - 2)$. (**Lesson 3-2**)

24. You discovered a new element, Yournameium, which has a half-life of 15 hours. Suppose the initial amount is A_0. How much will remain after each number of hours? (**Lesson 2-4**)
    a. 45   b. 8   c. 42   d. t

25. The *New York Times* held a contest pitting professionals' stock choices with stocks chosen by throwing darts at a dartboard every six months. The values in the table and box plots below represent the points gained or lost by the stocks. (**Lessons 1-7, 1-6, 1-2**)

Change in Stock Value

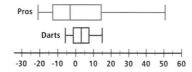

a. Find the mean, median, and standard deviation for each data set.
b. Compare and contrast the distributions using the box plots.

26. Given the point P on the circle with center $(0, 0)$ at the right, fill in the coordinates of the remaining reflection images in the various quadrants. (**Previous Course**)

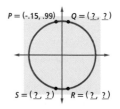

$P = (-.15, .99)$ $Q = (?, ?)$

$S = (?, ?)$ $R = (?, ?)$

EXPLORATION

27. Derive a formula for the area of a sector in terms of the radius r of the circle and the length x of its boundary arc x in radians. $A = \dfrac{xr^2}{2}$

Period #	Pros	Darts
1	51.2	11.7
2	25.2	1.1
3	-3.3	-3.1
4	7.7	-1.4
5	-21.0	7.7
6	-13.0	15.4
7	-2.5	3.6
8	-19.6	5.7
9	6.3	-5.7
10	-5.1	6.9
11	14.1	1.8

20. about 9.92 hr
21a. about 69.1 in.
21b. about 10,367.3 in.

23. $y = (x - 3)^2 - 2$
24.–26. See margin.

QY ANSWERS

1. a. 5π b. $180°$
2. $\frac{5\pi}{3} \approx 5.24$ ft

228 Trigonometric Functions

Additional Answers

24a. $\dfrac{A_0}{8}$

24b. about $0.691A_0$

24c. about $0.144A_0$

24d. $A_0\left(\dfrac{1}{2}\right)^{\frac{t}{15}}$

25a. Pros mean: 3.64; Pros median: –2.5; Pros standard deviation: 21.1; Darts mean: 3.97; Darts median: 3.6; Darts standard deviation: 6.33

25b. The Darts minimum, Q_1, and median are greater than the Pros minimum, Q_1, and median. Nearly all of the Darts data is contained between the Pros median and Q_3. The Pros Q_3 is nearly the same as the Darts maximum. The Pros range is much greater than the Darts range.

26. $Q = (0.15, 0.99)$, $R = (0.15, -0.99)$, $S = (-0.15, -0.99)$

Lesson 4-2

Sines, Cosines, and Tangents

Vocabulary

unit circle

cosine, cos

sine, sin

circular function

trigonometric function

tangent, tan

▶ **BIG IDEA**   The sine and cosine functions relate magnitudes of rotations to coordinates of points on the unit circle.

The Sine, Cosine, and Tangent Functions

The **unit circle** is the circle with center at the origin and radius 1, as shown at the right.

Consider the rotation of magnitude θ with center at the origin. We call this R_θ. Regardless of the value of θ, the image of $(1, 0)$ under R_θ is on the unit circle. Call this point P. We associate two numbers with each value of θ. The **cosine** of θ (abbreviated $\cos \theta$) is the x-coordinate of P; the **sine** of θ (abbreviated $\sin \theta$) is the y-coordinate of P.

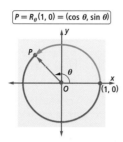

$$P = R_\theta(1, 0) = (\cos \theta, \sin \theta)$$

Definition of cos θ and sin θ

For all real numbers θ, **$(\cos \theta, \sin \theta)$** is the image of the point $(1, 0)$ under a rotation of magnitude θ about the origin. That is, $(\cos \theta, \sin \theta) = R_\theta (1, 0)$.

Because their definitions are based on a circle, the sine and cosine functions are sometimes called **circular functions** of θ. They are also called **trigonometric functions**, from the Greek word meaning "triangle measure," as you will see in the applications for triangles presented in Chapter 5. To find values of trigonometric functions when θ is a multiple of $\frac{\pi}{2}$ or 90°, you can use the above definition and mentally rotate $(1, 0)$.

Example 1

Evaluate $\cos \pi$ and $\sin \pi$.

Solution   Because no degree sign is given, π is measured in radians. Think of $R_\pi(1, 0)$, the image of $(1, 0)$ under a rotation of π. $R_\pi(1, 0) = (-1, 0)$. So, by definition, $(\cos \pi, \sin \pi) = (-1, 0)$. Thus, $\cos \pi = -1$ and $\sin \pi = 0$.

Check   Use a calculator. Make sure it is in radian mode.

$\cos(\pi)$	-1
$\sin(\pi)$	0

Background

In some contexts the sine, cosine, and tangent functions are called *trigonometric* functions only when their arguments θ are such that $0° < \theta < 180°$, that is, when the arguments can be measures of angles in triangles. When the domain extends beyond that interval, these functions are called *circular* functions, reflecting a definition dependent on the unit circle.

We do not adhere to such strict linguistics, because this is not the language used by mathematicians. They are universally called trigonometric functions.

(continued on next page)

Lesson 4-2

GOAL

Enable students to estimate the sine and cosine of any number by referring to their definitions.

SPUR Objectives

C Apply the definitions of the sine, cosine, and tangent functions.

H Use the unit circle to find values of sines, cosines, and tangents.

Materials/Resources

· Lesson Master 4-2
· Resource Masters 71 and 72
· Compass
· Protractor
· Graph paper

HOMEWORK   • Option 1

• Option 2

• Questions 1–17
• • Questions 18–27
• • Questions 28 and 29 (extra credit)
  • Reading Lesson 4-3
  • Covering the Ideas 4-3 (Questions 1–16)

Local Standards

---

1   Warm-Up

Give the exact coordinates of as many points on the unit circle as you can. **Answers may vary but should include the intersections with the axes, (1, 0), (–1, 0), (0, 1), (0, –1), and some other points. Any Pythagorean triple can easily generate 8 points with rational coordinates. For instance, the triple 3-4-5 yields the points $\left(\frac{3}{5}, \frac{4}{5}\right)$ and its reflection images over the x-axis, y-axis, and line $x = y$, and composites of those transformations. More generally, given any number x between 0 and 1, $\left(x, \sqrt{1 - x^2}\right)$ is a point on the unit circle, and so too are its reflection images over the lines mentioned above.**

Mental Math

The following regular polygons are inscribed in a circle. Find the measure of the angle formed by two rays from the center of the circle that contain adjacent vertices of the polygon.

a. triangle   **b.** square

c. pentagon   **d.** octagon

a. $\dfrac{2\pi}{3}$ b. $\dfrac{\pi}{2}$

c. $\dfrac{2\pi}{5}$ d. $\dfrac{\pi}{4}$

Because π radians = 180°, Example 1 shows that cos 180° = –1 and sin 180° = 0. Cosines and sines of other multiples of $\frac{\pi}{2}$ or 90° are shown on the unit circle below.

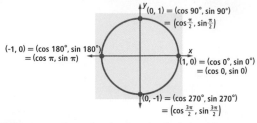

The third most common circular function is defined in terms of the sine and cosine functions. The **tangent** of θ (abbreviated tan θ) equals the ratio of sin θ to cos θ.

> ### Definition of Tangent
> For all real numbers θ, provided cos $\theta \neq 0$, $\tan \theta = \frac{\sin \theta}{\cos \theta}$.

When cos θ *does* equal zero, which occurs at any odd multiple of 90°, tan θ is undefined.

GUIDED

Example 2
a. Evaluate tan π.   b. Evaluate tan (–270°).

Solution

a. From Example 1, cos π = __?__ and sin π = __?__. So tan π = __?__. **–1; 0; 0**
b. cos (–270°) = __?__, sin (–270°) = __?__, so tan (–270°) is __?__. **0; 1; undefined**

For any value of θ, you can approximate sin θ, cos θ, and tan θ to the nearest tenth with a good drawing.

Activity

MATERIALS compass, protractor, graph paper, and calculator

Step 1 Work with a partner. Draw a set of coordinate axes on graph paper. Let each square on your grid have side length 0.1 unit. With the origin as center, draw a circle of radius 1. Label the figure as at the right.

Step 2
a. Use a protractor to mark the image of A = (1, 0) under a rotation of 50°. Label this point P_1, as shown at the right.
b. Use the grid to estimate the x- and y-coordinates of P_1. **(0.65, 0.75)**
c. Estimate the slope of $\overrightarrow{OP}_1$. **$\frac{0.75}{0.65} \approx 1.2$**
d. Use your calculator to find cos 50°, sin 50°, and tan 50°. Make sure your calculator is set to degree mode. **sin 50° ≈ 0.766**
   cos 50° ≈ 0.643   tan 50° ≈ 1.192

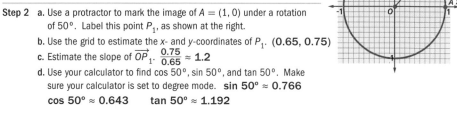

The right triangle definitions of the trigonometric functions do not apply to right or obtuse angles, nor to real numbers, so over the centuries mathematicians have developed a number of ways of extending the ratio idea, each involving a rectangular coordinate system. The traditional way is by means of *reference triangles*; then one still speaks of sines, cosines, and tangents of angles regardless of the measures of such angles. A second way, the *wrapping function* approach, was developed in the 1940s and

first appeared in high school books in the newer mathematics curricula of the late 1950s and early 1960s. In this approach, the trigonometric functions become functions of real numbers; the disadvantage is that the "wrapping" of a real line about a unit circle is a completely new idea that is being used to introduce another new idea.

The method we use is about a century old. It has the advantages of both the other methods; it is related to geometry and it allows the argument θ to be any real

Step 3 **a.** Use a protractor to mark the image of *A* under $R_{155°}$. Label this point P_2. **See margin.**

b. Use the grid to estimate the *x*- and *y*-coordinates of P_2. Estimate the slope of $\overrightarrow{OP_2}$. (–0.9, 0.4); $\frac{0.4}{-0.9} \approx -0.4$

c. With your calculator, find cos 155°, sin 155°, and tan 155°.

Step 4 Repeat Step 3 if the rotation has magnitude –100°. Call the image P_3.

Step 5 How is tan θ related to the slope of the line through the origin and $R_\theta(A)$?

You can find better approximations to other values of sin θ, cos θ, or tan θ using a calculator.

Step 3c.
sin 155° ≈ 0.423
cos 155° ≈ –0.906
tan 155° ≈ –0.466

Step 4. See margin.

Step 5.
tan θ is equal to the slope of the line through the origin and $R_\theta(A)$.

Example 3

Suppose the tips of the arms of a starfish determine the vertices of a regular pentagon. The point *A* = (1, 0) is at the tip of one arm, and so is one vertex of a regular pentagon *ABCDE* inscribed in the unit circle, as shown at the right. Find the coordinates of *B* to the nearest thousandth.

Solution Since the full circle measures 2π around, the measure of arc *AB* is $\frac{2\pi}{5}$. So $B = R_{\frac{2\pi}{5}}(1, 0)$. Consequently, $B = (\cos \frac{2\pi}{5}, \sin \frac{2\pi}{5})$. A calculator shows $B \approx (0.309, 0.951)$.

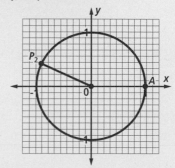

For a given value of θ, you can determine whether sin θ, cos θ, and tan θ are positive or negative without using a calculator by using coordinate geometry and the unit circle. The cosine is positive when $R_\theta(1, 0)$ is in the first or fourth quadrant. The sine is positive when the image is in the first or second quadrant. The tangent is positive when the sine and cosine have the same sign and negative when they have opposite signs. The following table summarizes this information for values of θ between 0 and 360° or 2π.

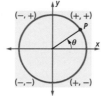

$P = (\cos \theta, \sin \theta) = R_\theta(1, 0)$

θ (radians)	θ (degrees)	quadrant of $R_\theta(1, 0)$	cos θ	sin θ	tan θ
$0 < \theta < \frac{\pi}{2}$	0° < θ < 90°	first	+	+	+
$\frac{\pi}{2} < \theta < \pi$	90° < θ < 180°	second	–	+	–
$\pi < \theta < \frac{3\pi}{2}$	180° < θ < 270°	third	–	–	+
$\frac{3\pi}{2} < \theta < 2\pi$	270° < θ < 360°	fourth	+	–	–

number. In this approach, (cos θ, sin θ) is defined to be the image of (1, 0) under a rotation of magnitude θ around the origin. We choose this definition for its elegance and the ease with which many properties of sine and cosine can be developed. The tangent is defined as the ratio of sine to cosine. All of these approaches result in equivalent mathematics.

Vocabulary Development

Cosine is unrelated to its homonym "co-sign," which means to sign a document along with someone else.

Notes on the Lesson

Activity This activity serves two purposes. The first purpose is to introduce the relationship between the cosine, sine, and tangent and the coordinates of points on the unit circle. The second purpose is to provide an opportunity for students to explore the sine, cosine, and tangent keys on their calculators for negative values of θ and for values outside the interval 0° ≤ θ ≤ 180°. If your students have previously studied the definitions of the cosine and sine using the unit circle, then this activity can be done as a full-class review. Students are often surprised by how well they can approximate sines and cosines using this process.

Additional Example
Example 3

a. Find, to the nearest thousandth, the coordinates of the image of (1, 0) under a rotation of $-\frac{10\pi}{9}$. (–0.940, 0.342)

b. Based on your answer to Part a, tell whether $\tan(-\frac{10\pi}{9})$ is positive or negative. **negative**

Additional Answers

Activity, Step 3a:

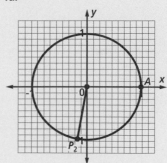

Step 4a:

Step 4b: (–0.15, –0.95); $\frac{-0.95}{-0.15} \approx 6.33$

Step 4c: sin (–100°) ≈ –0.985
cos (–100°) ≈ –0.174
tan (–100°) ≈ 5.671

4-2

Notes on the Lesson

Example 4 This example is a direct application of the definition of the cosine and sine and should be discussed in detail. You might even want to anticipate later work in the chapter by graphing the equation $y = 106 + 106 \sin x$ and showing how the graph indicates the height (in feet) of a seat above ground at time t if the Ferris wheel is turning at a constant rate.

Additional Example

Example 4 A large clock with rotating hour and minute hands is on a building such that its center is 20 meters above the ground. The length of the hour hand is 1.5 meters and the length of the minute hand is 2 meters.

a. Draw a sketch of the clock at time 8:20 and use it to determine the magnitude of rotation from the 3:00 direction of each hand. **minute hand: –30° or 330°; hour hand: –160 or 200°**

b. Use your answer to Part a to give the height off the ground of the tip of each hand at 8:20. **minute hand: $20 + 2 \sin(-30°) = 19$ meters; hour hand: $20 + 1.5 \sin(-160°) \approx 19.487$ meters**

The applications of sines, cosines, and tangents are many and diverse, including the location of points in the plane and the calculation of certain distances.

Example 4

As of 2008, the largest Ferris wheel in North America is the Texas Star at Fair Park in Dallas, Texas. Its seats hang from 44 spokes. This Ferris wheel is 212 feet tall. How high is the seat off the ground as you travel around the wheel?

Solution We need to make some assumptions. Assume that you get on the Ferris wheel when the seat is at the wheel's lowest point and that this is at ground level. Also assume the seat is the same distance directly below the end of the spoke the entire way around.

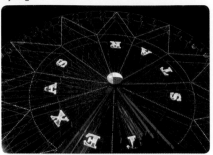

The key to answering the question is to realize that the height of the seat is determined by the magnitude of rotation of the spoke from the horizontal. To see this, imagine the Ferris wheel on a coordinate system whose origin is the center of the wheel. Think of the circle centered at the origin with radius 106 feet. By the definition of the sine, when the spoke has turned θ counterclockwise from the horizontal, the height of the end of the spoke *above the center of the wheel* is given by $106 \sin \theta$.

Add the radius 106 to get the height of the seat *above the ground*. Thus, in general, a seat that has been rotated θ counterclockwise from the horizontal is at a height

$$106 + 106 \sin \theta$$

feet above the ground. Thus, when one seat is at the bottom, going counterclockwise from the right-most seat, the 44 seats on the Ferris wheel are at heights

$$106 + 106 \sin 0 = 106 \text{ feet}$$
$$106 + 106 \sin\left(\frac{2\pi}{44}\right) \approx 121 \text{ feet}$$
$$106 + 106 \sin\left(2 \cdot \frac{2\pi}{44}\right) \approx 136 \text{ feet}$$
$$106 + 106 \sin\left(3 \cdot \frac{2\pi}{44}\right) \approx 150 \text{ feet}$$
$$106 + 106 \sin\left(4 \cdot \frac{2\pi}{44}\right) \approx 163 \text{ feet}$$

and so on.

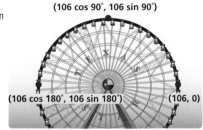

(106 cos 90°, 106 sin 90°)

(106 cos 180°, 106 sin 180°)

(106, 0)

Extension

Ask students to find sin 0.1° and tan 0.1° using their calculators in degree mode. They should notice that the values are identical when rounded to six decimal places. Ask them to describe $\sin \theta$ and $\tan \theta$ for other values of θ between 0° and 1°. **Rounded to four decimal places, $\sin \theta = \tan \theta$ for $0 < \theta < 1$.**

Ask students to explain why sine values and tangent values are nearly identical for very small angles. Since $\tan \theta = \frac{\sin \theta}{\cos \theta}$ for all θ, and for very small angles, $\cos \theta \approx 1$, $\tan \theta \approx \sin \theta$ for those angles.

Questions

COVERING THE IDEAS

1. Suppose the point $A = (1, 0)$ is rotated a magnitude θ around the point $O = (0, 0)$.
   a. $\cos \theta$ is the __?__ of $R_\theta(A)$. **x-coordinate**
   b. $\sin \theta$ is the __?__ of $R_\theta(A)$. **y-coordinate**

In 2–4, use the figure at the right. Which point is $R_\theta(1, 0)$ for the given value of θ?

2. 3π **C**
3. -50π **A**
4. $-450°$ **D**

5. How is $\tan \theta$ related to $\cos \theta$ and $\sin \theta$? $\tan \theta = \dfrac{\sin \theta}{\cos \theta}$

In 6–8, give exact values without a calculator.

6. a. $\sin (-270°)$ **1** b. $\cos (-270°)$ **0** c. $\tan (-270°)$ **undefined**
7. a. $\sin 3\pi$ **0** b. $\cos 3\pi$ **–1** c. $\tan 3\pi$ **0**
8. a. $\sin 0$ **0** b. $\cos 0$ **1** c. $\tan 0$ **0**
9. a. Give two values of θ in degrees for which $\tan \theta$ is undefined.
   b. Give two values of θ in radians for which $\tan \theta$ is undefined.

In 10 and 11, find the coordinates of the indicated image to the nearest thousandth.

10. $R_{67°}$ **(0.391, 0.921)**
11. $R_{1 \text{ (radian)}}$ **(0.540, 0.841)**

12. a. Use a calculator to approximate $\tan 200°$ to three decimal places.
    b. Use a picture to explain how you could have found the sign of $\tan 200°$ without using a calculator.

In 13 and 14, let $P = R_\theta(1, 0)$.

13. If P is in the fourth quadrant, state the sign of the following.
    a. $\cos \theta$ **positive** b. $\sin \theta$ **negative** c. $\tan \theta$ **negative**

14. If $\cos \theta < 0$ and $\sin \theta < 0$, in what quadrant is P? **III**

In 15–17, refer to Example 4.

15. How high is the seat above the ground when it is at the top of the Ferris wheel? **212 ft**

16. How high is the seat above the ground when it has been rotated $\frac{\pi}{3}$ from the horizontal? **about 197.8 ft**

17. Suppose the seat next to you is at ground level. How high are you off the ground? **about 1.1 ft**

APPLYING THE MATHEMATICS

18. a. In the pentagon of Example 3, find the coordinates of C, D, and E to the nearest thousandth.
    b. Why do you only need to use a calculator for one of the points?

19. Find three values of θ for which $\cos \theta = -1$.

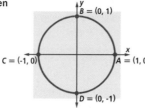

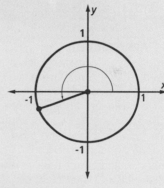

9. a. Answers vary. Sample: 90°, 270°
   b. Answers vary. Sample: $\frac{\pi}{2}$, $\frac{3\pi}{2}$
12. a. 0.364
    b. The image of (1, 0) rotated 200° around (0, 0) is in the third quadrant, so both sin 200° and cos 200° are negative, and therefore tan 200° is positive.

18. a. $C = (-0.809, 0.588)$, $D = (-0.809, -0.588)$, $E = (0.309, -0.951)$
18b. See margin.

19. Answers vary. Sample: 180°, –180°, 540°

---

3 Assignment

Recommended Assignment

- Questions 1–17
- Questions 18–27
- Questions 28 and 29 (extra credit)
- Reading Lesson 4-3
- Covering the Ideas 4-3 (Questions 1–16)

Additional Answers

12b.

18b. *B* and *E* are reflections of each other over the x-axis, as are *C* and *D*. Since *B* is given, only *C* or *D* is needed in order to find all the coordinates.

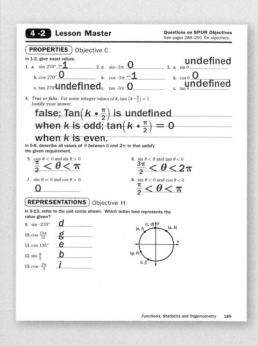

4-2

Notes on the Questions

Question 20 If you speak of the "sign of the sine," you should write what you say so that students know which word you mean when.

Question 27 Images under these transformations are found in Lesson 4-3, so this question should be discussed in anticipation.

Question 28 The simplification of complex fractions is needed to calculate exact values of the tangent function in Lesson 4-4.

4 ▶ Wrap-Up

Ongoing Assessment

Have students work in pairs. Each student should write down five angle measures. Then students should switch papers. Have students convert their partner's angle measures from radians to degrees (or vice versa), and then determine the quadrant each angle lies in. Students should check their partner's work. **Answers vary. Check students' work.**

Project Update

Project 3, *"Noncircular" Functions*, on page 283 relates to the content of this lesson.

Additional Answers

22a. $\tan \theta = \dfrac{QA}{OA} = \dfrac{QA}{1} = QA$

22b. Answers vary. Sample:

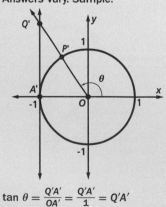

$\tan \theta = \dfrac{Q'A'}{OA'} = \dfrac{Q'A'}{1} = Q'A'$

---

20. For what values of θ between 0 and 2π is $\sin \theta$ positive? $\{\theta \mid 0 < \theta < \pi\}$

21. As θ increases from 0 to 90°, tell whether $\cos \theta$ increases or decreases. **decreases**

22. The name "tangent function" is derived from the use of the word "tangent" in geometry. Here is how. At the right, line ℓ is tangent to the unit circle at $A = (1, 0)$, P is the image of a rotation of A with magnitude θ and center O, and $\overrightarrow{OP}$ intersects ℓ at Q. **See margin.**
    a. When $0 < \theta < \frac{\pi}{2}$, prove that $QA = \tan \theta$.
    b. Draw a diagram similar to the one at the right for the case of $\frac{\pi}{2} < \theta < \pi$. Explain how to find $\tan \theta$ from your diagram.

REVIEW

23. Convert $\frac{5}{6}$ revolution clockwise to degrees. (**Lesson 4-1**) **–300°**

24. Let A' be the image of $A = (1, 0)$ under the rotation of $-\frac{2\pi}{3}$ with center $(0, 0)$. Give two other magnitudes of the rotation with center $(0, 0)$ such that the image of A is A'. (**Lesson 4-1**)

25. In isosceles $\triangle ABC$ at the right, $AB = 1$. What is the length of $\overline{BC}$? (**Previous Course**) $\frac{\sqrt{2}}{2}$

26. $\triangle EQU$ is equilateral, $\overline{UI} \perp \overline{EQ}$, and $EU = k$ as shown at the right.
    a. Find EI in terms of k. $EI = \frac{k}{2}$
    b. Find UI in terms of k. (**Previous Course**) $UI = \frac{k\sqrt{3}}{2}$

27. Suppose (x, y) is a point in the first quadrant. Give the coordinates of its image after each transformation. (**Previous Course**)
    a. reflection over the y-axis $(-x, y)$
    b. reflection over the x-axis $(x, -y)$
    c. rotation of 180° around $(0, 0)$ $(-x, -y)$

28. **Skill Sequence** Simplify in your head. (**Previous Course**)

    a. $\dfrac{\frac{1}{13}}{\frac{7}{13}}$ $\dfrac{1}{7}$
    b. $\dfrac{\frac{\sqrt{5}}{13}}{\frac{7}{13}}$ $\dfrac{\sqrt{5}}{7}$
    c. $\dfrac{\frac{1}{3}}{\frac{\sqrt{5}}{3}} = \dfrac{1}{\sqrt{5}} = \dfrac{\sqrt{5}}{5}$

24. Answers vary.
Sample: $\frac{4\pi}{3}$ and $\frac{10\pi}{3}$

EXPLORATION

29. The first Ferris wheel was designed by George Washington Gale Ferris, Jr., a Pittsburgh bridge builder, for the World's Columbian Exposition in Chicago in 1892–1893. It was also the largest Ferris wheel ever built. It could seat 2160 people at one time. Research this Ferris wheel for the additional information needed to answer Questions 15–17. Then answer the questions.

According to *The Columbia Encyclopedia*, the first Ferris wheel was 250 ft in diameter and had 36 cars. So a seat at the top of the Ferris wheel was 250 ft above the ground. A seat rotated $\frac{\pi}{3}$ from the horizontal was about 233.3 ft above the ground. Finally, if the seat next to a particular car was at ground level, then the particular car was about 1.9 ft above the ground.

The World's Columbian Exposition was a celebration of the 400th anniversary of Columbus arriving in the new world.

Lesson 4-3

Basic Trigonometric Identities

▶ **BIG IDEA** If you know cos θ, you can easily find cos(–θ), cos(90° − θ), cos(180° − θ), and cos(180° + θ) without a calculator, and similarly for sin θ and tan θ.

An **identity** is an equation that is true for all values of the variables for which the expressions on each side are defined. There are five theorems in this lesson; all are identities.

The Pythagorean Identity

$P = (\cos θ, \sin θ)$

The first identity we derive in this lesson comes directly from the equation $x^2 + y^2 = 1$ for the unit circle. Because, for every θ, the point $P = (\cos θ, \sin θ)$ is on the unit circle, the distance from P to (0, 0) must be 1. Using the Distance Formula, $\sqrt{(\cos θ - 0)^2 + (\sin θ - 0)^2} = 1$. Squaring both sides of the equation gives $(\cos θ)^2 + (\sin θ)^2 = 1$. This argument proves a theorem called the *Pythagorean Identity*.

Pythagorean Identity Theorem

For every θ, $\cos^2 θ + \sin^2 θ = 1$.

An abbreviated version of $(\cos θ)^2$ is $\cos^2 θ$, the square of the cosine of θ. Similarly, $(\sin θ)^2$ is written $\sin^2 θ$ and $(\tan θ)^2$ is written $\tan^2 θ$. Notice that we do *not* write $\cos θ^2$ for $(\cos θ)^2$.

🛑 QY1

The name of the above identity comes from the Pythagorean Theorem because in the first quadrant, as shown at the right, cos θ and sin θ are the sides of a right triangle with hypotenuse 1. Among other things, the Pythagorean Identity enables you to obtain either cos θ or sin θ if you know the other.

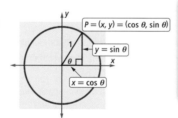

$P = (x, y) = (\cos θ, \sin θ)$
$y = \sin θ$
$x = \cos θ$

Vocabulary

identity

Mental Math

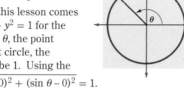

True or False

a. ∠POE and ∠POW are complementary. **false**

b. ∠POE and ∠PON are supplementary. **false**

c. m∠POE = m∠QOW

d. m∠POW = $π − m∠POE$

c. true d. true

▶ **QY1**

Multiple Choice

Which two expressions are equal?

A $\tan^2 θ$

B $\tan θ^2$

C $(\tan θ)^2$

Lesson 4-3

GOAL

Discuss the basic theorems relating values of the sine and cosine functions.

SPUR Objectives

C Apply the definitions of the sine, cosine, and tangent functions.

D Apply theorems about sines, cosines, and tangents.

H Use the unit circle to find values of sines, cosines, and tangents.

Materials/Resources

· Lesson Master 4-3
· Resource Masters 73–75
· Quiz 1
· DGS or graph paper
· Compass
· Protractor

HOMEWORK • Option 1

• • Option 2
• Questions 1–16
• • Questions 17–32
• • Question 33 (extra credit)
• Reading Lesson 4-4
• Covering the Ideas 4-4 (Questions 1–11)

Local Standards

Background

In this lesson, the relationship between the sine and cosine is derived first. Then, for each function, the values of opposite arguments, complements, supplements, and arguments that differ by 360° are derived from the definitions.

The Pythagorean Identity $\cos^2 θ + \sin^2 θ = 1$ follows immediately from the definition of the cosine and sine as coordinates of a particular point on the unit circle. Then,

from the symmetry of the circle, the sines and cosines of -θ, 180° − θ, and 90° − θ can be found in terms of sin θ and cos θ. By division, the tangents of these numbers can be found in terms of tan θ. Later in this chapter, the graphs of these functions will provide verification for the theorems deduced. For now, verification comes from hand calculation of values and from the use of the calculator.

(continued on next page)

---

1 Warm-Up

In 1–5, one coordinate of a point on the unit circle is given. Find all possible values of the other coordinate.

1. (0, a) ±1
2. $\left(\frac{1}{2}, b\right)$ $±\frac{\sqrt{3}}{2}$
3. $\left(c, -\frac{\sqrt{3}}{2}\right)$ $±\frac{1}{2}$
4. (d, 0.28) ±0.96
5. (e, 0.9) ±$\sqrt{0.19}$

2 Teaching

Notes on the Lesson

The word *identity* is defined at the beginning of this lesson. While proving identities is not a major focus of this course, students should be comfortable with the meaning of the term and be able to verify identities for particular instances of the variable.

Given the sine of θ, students should be able to find

the cosine of θ,

the sine of the opposite of θ,

the sine of the complement of θ,

the sine of the supplement of θ, and

the sine of $\theta + 180°$.

They should be able to find the corresponding values given the cosine of θ.

Activity 1 The purpose of this activity is not to find the values, but to see the relationships between the sines and cosines of numbers and their opposites. Be certain students look at the results they found. Encourage your students to use the unit circle and to keep appealing to symmetry when using and verifying the Opposites Theorem and the Supplements Theorem.

Additional Example

Example 1 If $\sin \theta = \frac{8}{17}$, find $\cos \theta$.
$\pm\frac{15}{17}$

Example 1

If $\cos \theta = \frac{3}{5}$, find $\sin \theta$.

Solution Substitute into the Pythagorean Identity.

$$\left(\frac{3}{5}\right)^2 + \sin^2 \theta = 1$$

$$\frac{9}{25} + \sin^2 \theta = 1$$

$$\sin^2 \theta = \frac{16}{25}$$

$$\sin \theta = \pm\frac{4}{5}$$

Thus, $\sin \theta = \frac{4}{5}$ or $\sin \theta = -\frac{4}{5}$.

Check Refer to the unit circle. The vertical line $x = \frac{3}{5}$ intersects the unit circle in two points. One is in the first quadrant, in which case the y-coordinate ($\sin \theta$) is $\frac{4}{5}$. The other is in the fourth quadrant, where $\sin \theta$ is $-\frac{4}{5}$.

STOP QY2

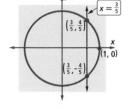

▶ QY2

If $\sin \theta = 0.6$, what is $\cos \theta$?

The Symmetry Identities

Many other properties of sines and cosines follow from their definitions and the symmetry of the unit circle. Recall that a circle is symmetric to any line through its center. This means that the reflection image of any point over one of these lines also lies on the circle.

Activity 1 See margin for screenshots

MATERIALS DGS or graph paper, compass, and protractor

Step 1 Draw a unit circle on a coordinate grid. Plot the point $A = (1, 0)$. Pick a value of θ between 0° and 90°. Let a point P in the first quadrant be the image of A under the rotation R_θ. Find the values of $\cos \theta$ and $\sin \theta$ from the coordinates of P. A sample is shown at the right.

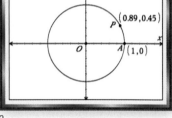

Step 2 Reflect P over the x-axis. Call its image Q. Notice that Q is the image of $(1, 0)$ under a rotation of magnitude $-\theta$. Consequently, $Q = (\cos(-\theta), \sin(-\theta))$.

  a. What are the values of $\cos(-\theta)$ and $\sin(-\theta)$ for your point Q?

  b. How are $\cos \theta$ and $\cos(-\theta)$ related? What about $\sin \theta$ and $\sin(-\theta)$?

Step 3 Rotate your point P 180° around the circle. Call its image H. Notice that H is the image of $(1, 0)$ under a rotation of magnitude $(180° + \theta)$. Consequently, $H = (\cos(180° + \theta), \sin(180° + \theta))$.

  a. What are the values of $\cos(180° + \theta)$ and $\sin(180° + \theta)$ for your point H? **See margin.**

  b. How are $\cos \theta$ and $\cos(180° + \theta)$ related? How are $\sin \theta$ and $\sin(180° + \theta)$ related? **See margin.**

Step 2

  a. $\cos(-\theta) = 0.89$, $\sin(-\theta) = -0.45$

  b. $\cos(-\theta) = \cos \theta$, $\sin(-\theta) = -\sin \theta$

With the exception of the Pythagorean Identity, all the theorems of this lesson are based on the symmetry of the unit circle. The Opposites Theorem is a result of its symmetry to the x-axis. The Supplements Theorem results from its symmetry to the y-axis. The Complements Theorem results from its symmetry to the line $y = x$. And the Half-Turn Theorem results from its point (rotation) symmetry with respect to the origin.

Step 4 Use a calculator to find cos θ and sin θ for your value of θ in Step 1. Then find cos(–θ) and sin(–θ), and also cos(180° + θ) and sin(180° + θ). Explain any differences between the values displayed by the calculator and what you found in Steps 2 and 3.

Step 4

The values displayed are the same as those from Steps 2 and 3.

Save your work for Activity 2.

Activity 1 is based on the following ideas: When a point P on the unit circle is reflected over either axis, or when it is rotated through a half turn, either the coordinates of the three images are equal to the coordinates of P or they are opposites of the coordinates of P. The magnitudes of the rotations that map (1, 0) onto these points are θ (for P at the right), $-\theta$ (for Q), $180° + \theta$ (for H), and $180° - \theta$ (for J). So the sines and cosines of these magnitudes are either equal or opposites.

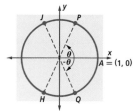

Sines and Cosines of Opposites

Rotations of magnitude θ and $-\theta$ go in opposite directions. The two rotation images are reflection images of each other over the x-axis. Thus they have the same first coordinates (cosines) but opposite second coordinates (sines). It follows that the ratios of the y-coordinates to the x-coordinate are opposites. This argument proves the following theorem.

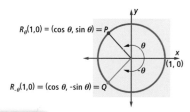

Opposites Theorem

For all θ,

$$\cos(-\theta) = \cos\theta, \quad \sin(-\theta) = -\sin\theta, \quad \text{and} \quad \tan(-\theta) = -\tan\theta.$$

Sines and Cosines of $\theta + 180°$ or $\theta + \pi$

Adding 180° or π to the argument θ of a trigonometric function is equivalent to rotating halfway around the unit circle.

Half-Turn Theorem

For all θ, $\cos(180° + \theta) = -\cos\theta = \cos(\pi + \theta)$
$\sin(180° + \theta) = -\sin\theta = \sin(\pi + \theta)$
and $\tan(180° + \theta) = \tan\theta = \tan(\pi + \theta)$.

Proof Let $A = (1, 0)$ and let $P = R_\theta(A) = R_\theta(1, 0) = (\cos\theta, \sin\theta)$. Now let Q be the image of P under $R_{180°}$. Because $R_{180°}$ maps (a, b) to $(-a, -b)$, Q has coordinates $(-\cos\theta, -\sin\theta)$. But Q is also the image of A under a rotation of magnitude $180° + \theta$. So Q also has coordinates $(\cos(180° + \theta), \sin(180° + \theta))$. Equating the two ordered pairs for Q proves the first two parts of the theorem. The third part follows by dividing the second equation by the first.

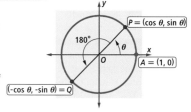

Notes on the Lesson

Half-Turn Theorem This theorem is particularly important for the tangent function because it indicates the periodicity of that function.

Additional Answers

Activity

Step 1: $\theta = 27°$; $\cos\theta \approx 0.89$; $\sin\theta \approx 0.45$

Step 2:

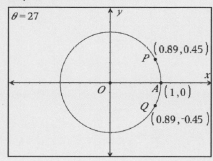

Step 3:

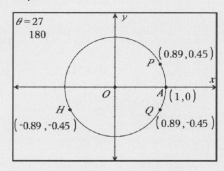

Step 3a. $\cos(180° + \theta) = -0.89$,
$\sin(180° + \theta) = -0.45$

Step 3b. $\cos(180° + \theta) = -\cos\theta$,
$\sin(180° + \theta) = -\sin\theta$

Step 4:

sin(27)	0.4539904997
cos(27)	0.8910065242
sin(−27)	−0.4539904997
cos(−27)	0.8910065242
sin(207)	−0.4539904997
cos(207)	−0.8910065242

4-3

Additional Example

Example 2 Given that sin 172° ≈ 0.1392, find a value of x other than 172° and between 0° and 360° for which sin x = 0.1392. **8°**

Sines and Cosines of Supplements

Recall that if an angle has measure θ, then its supplement has measure $180° - \theta$, that is, $\pi - \theta$. Activity 1 shows that the values of the trigonometric functions of θ and $180° - \theta$ are related, as stated in the following theorem.

Supplements Theorem

For all θ, $\sin(180° - \theta) = \sin\theta = \sin(\pi - \theta)$

$$\cos(180° - \theta) = -\cos\theta = \cos(\pi - \theta)$$

and $\tan(180° - \theta) = -\tan\theta = \tan(\pi - \theta)$.

Proof Let $P = (\cos\theta, \sin\theta)$. Let Q be the reflection image of P over the y-axis, as in the diagram at the right. Because the reflection image of (x, y) over the y-axis is $(-x, y)$,

$$Q = (-\cos\theta, \sin\theta).$$

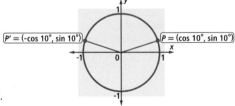

Recall from geometry that reflections preserve angle measure, so

$$m\angle QOB = m\angle POA = \theta.$$

Also, since $\angle AOQ$ and $\angle QOB$ are a linear pair,

$$m\angle AOQ = 180° - \theta.$$

So, by the definitions of cosine and sine,

$$Q = (\cos(180° - \theta), \sin(180° - \theta)).$$

Thus, $(\cos(180° - \theta), \sin(180° - \theta)) = (-\cos\theta, \sin\theta)$.

The x-coordinates are equal, so

$$\cos(180° - \theta) = -\cos\theta.$$

Likewise, the y-coordinates are equal, so

$$\sin(180° - \theta) = \sin\theta.$$

Dividing the latter of these equations by the former gives the third part of the Supplements Theorem,

$$\tan(180° - \theta) = -\tan\theta.$$

🛑 **QY3**

▶ **QY3**

Suppose $\sin\theta = 0.496$ and $\cos\theta = 0.868$. Without using a calculator, find

a. $\sin(\pi - \theta)$.

b. $\cos(180° - \theta)$.

Example 2

Given that sin 10° ≈ 0.1736, find a value of x other than 10° and between 0° and 360° for which sin x = 0.1736.

Solution Think: sin 10° is the second coordinate of the image of (1, 0) under $R_{10°}$. What other rotation will give the same second coordinate? It is the rotation that gives the reflection image of the point P in the diagram at the right. That rotation has magnitude 180° – 10°, or 170°. So sin 170° = sin 10° = 0.1736, and x = 170°.

If the requirement that $0° < x < 360°$ in Example 2 is relaxed, there are other answers. Because you can add or subtract $360°$ to the magnitude of any rotation and get the same rotation, $\sin 10° = \sin 170° = \sin 530° = \sin(-190°)$. Also, in radians, $\sin\left(\frac{\pi}{18}\right) = \sin\left(\frac{17\pi}{18}\right) = \sin\left(\frac{53\pi}{18}\right) = \sin\left(\frac{-19\pi}{18}\right)$.

 QY4

▶ **QY4**

Given that $\cos 10° \approx 0.9848$, find a value of x other than $10°$ for which $\cos x = 0.9848$.

Sines and Cosines of Complements

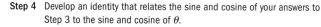 **Activity 2**

MATERIALS DGS or graph paper

Step 1 Begin with the graph from Step 3 of Activity 1. Hide points H and Q. Draw the line $y = x$. Again pick a value of θ between $0°$ and $90°$ and let $P = R_\theta(1, 0)$. Find $\cos \theta$ and $\sin \theta$ for your value of θ.

Step 2 Reflect point P over $y = x$ and call its image K. From your knowledge of reflections, what are the coordinates of K?

Step 3 In terms of θ, what is the magnitude of the rotation that maps $(1, 0)$ onto K? (Hint: K is as far from A along the circle as P is from the point $(0, 1)$.) Answer in both degrees and radians.

Step 4 Develop an identity that relates the sine and cosine of your answers to Step 3 to the sine and cosine of θ.

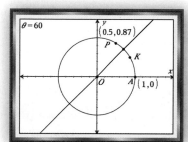

If an angle has measure θ, then its complement has measure $90° - \theta$ or $\frac{\pi}{2} - \theta$. Activity 2 shows that the sines and cosines of θ and $90° - \theta$ are related.

Complements Theorem
For all θ, $\sin(90° - \theta) = \cos \theta = \sin\left(\frac{\pi}{2} - \theta\right)$ and $\cos(90° - \theta) = \sin \theta = \cos\left(\frac{\pi}{2} - \theta\right)$.

These theorems can help extend your knowledge of circular functions.

Example 3

Given that $\sin 30° = \frac{1}{2}$, compute the exact value of each function below.

a. $\cos 60°$ b. $\cos 30°$ c. $\sin 150°$

d. $\cos 210°$ e. $\sin(-30°)$

(continued on next page)

Answers vary. Sample:

Step 1:

$\cos \theta = 0.50$; $\sin \theta = 0.87$

Step 2:

$K = (0.87, 0.50)$

Step 3:

$90° - \theta$; $\frac{\pi}{2} - \theta$

Step 4:

$\sin(90° - \theta) = \cos \theta = \sin\left(\frac{\pi}{2} - \theta\right)$, $\cos(90° - \theta) = \sin \theta = \cos\left(\frac{\pi}{2} - \theta\right)$

Notes on the Lesson

Sines and cosines of complements You can also use symmetry to support the Complements Theorem as follows:

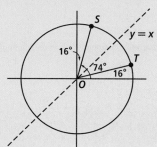

The coordinates of T are related to the coordinates of S. $T = (\cos 16°, \sin 16°)$ and $S = (\cos 74°, \sin 74°)$. But, by reflecting T over $y = x$, we can conclude that $S = (\sin 16°, \cos 16°)$. Thus, $\cos 74° = \sin 16°$ and $\sin 74° = \cos 16°$. You might mention that, before the days of calculators, when everyone used tables to find values of trigonometric functions, the Complements Property made it possible for the table to include only values of θ such that $0 \le \theta \le \frac{\pi}{4}$ or $0 \le \theta \le 45°$, rather than for values for the entire first quadrant.

ENGLISH LEARNERS
Vocabulary Development

Some students may have encountered the word *compliment*, which is very different in meaning than the word *complement*. Complement means something that fills up or completes. Compliment can mean a formal expression of esteem, respect, affection, or admiration, or something given free, as a courtesy.

4-3

Example 3 If sin $x = 0.681$, compute the values of the following.

a. $\cos x \approx 0.732$

b. $\tan x \approx 0.930$

c. $\sin(-x) \approx -0.681$

d. $\sin(\pi - x) \approx 0.681$

e. $\cos(\pi + x) \approx -0.732$

3 Assignment

Recommended Assignment

- Questions 1–16
- • Questions 17–32
- • Question 33 (extra credit)
- • Reading Lesson 4-4
- • Covering the Ideas 4-4
  (Questions 1–11)

Notes on the Questions

Question 2 Students should realize that there are two possible values of cos θ as stated in this question. Later, this will not usually be stated in the question.

Question 10 The explanation is given in one line of the lesson. A student response should be a little more detailed.

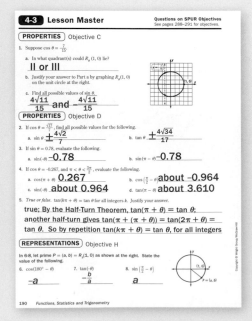

Solution

a. Use the Complements Theorem.
   $\cos 60° = \sin(90° - 60°) = \sin 30°$. So $\cos 60° = \frac{1}{2}$.

b. Use the Pythagorean Identity Theorem. $\sin^2 30° + \cos^2 30° = 1$.
   So $\cos^2 30° = 1 - \left(\frac{1}{2}\right)^2 = \frac{3}{4}$. Thus, $\cos 30° = \pm\sqrt{\frac{3}{4}} = \pm\frac{\sqrt{3}}{2}$.
   However, we know $\cos 30°$ is positive, so $\cos 30° = \frac{\sqrt{3}}{2}$.

c. Use the Supplements Theorem. $\sin 150° = \sin(180° - 150°) = \sin 30°$. So $\sin 150° = \frac{1}{2}$.

d. Use the Half-Turn Theorem. $\cos 210° = \cos(180° + 30°) = -\cos 30° = -\frac{\sqrt{3}}{2}$.

e. Use the Opposites Theorem. $\sin(-30°) = -\sin 30° = -\frac{1}{2}$.

In using these identities, you should also be able to use the unit circle to do a visual check of your answers or to derive a property if you forget one.

Questions

COVERING THE IDEAS

1. **True or False** When $\theta = 180°$, $\cos^2 \theta + \sin^2 \theta = 1$. **true**

2. a. If $\sin \theta = \frac{24}{25}$, what are two possible values of $\cos \theta$? $-\frac{7}{25}$ and $\frac{7}{25}$
   b. Draw a picture to justify your answers to Part a.

3. If $\tan \theta = 3$, what is $\tan(-\theta)$? **-3**

4. a. **True or False** $\cos 14° = \cos(-14°)$ **true**
   b. Justify your answer to Part a with a unit circle diagram.

In 5 and 6, refer to the figure at the right. $P = R_\theta(1, 0)$, $P' = r_{y\text{-axis}}(P)$, $P'' = R_{180°}(P)$, and $P''' = r_{x\text{-axis}}(P)$.

5. Which coordinates equal $\cos(180° - \theta)$? **c, e**

6. Which coordinates equal $\sin(180° + \theta)$? **f, h**

7. **True or False** $\sin(-\theta) = \sin \theta$ **false**

In 8 and 9, $\sin \theta = \frac{1}{3}$. Evaluate without using a calculator.

8. $\sin(-\theta)$ $-\frac{1}{3}$

9. $\sin(180° - \theta)$ $\frac{1}{3}$

10. Using what you know about $\sin(180° - \theta)$ and $\cos(180° - \theta)$, explain why $\tan(180° - \theta) = -\tan \theta$.

11. Use a calculator to verify the three parts of the Supplements Theorem when $\theta = 146.5°$.

In 12 and 13, suppose $\cos x = \frac{5}{13}$. Evaluate without using a calculator.

12. $\cos(180° + x)$ $-\frac{5}{13}$

13. $\sin(90° - x)$ $\frac{5}{13}$

In 14 and 15, $\tan y = k$. Evaluate.

14. $\tan(-y)$ **-k**

15. $\tan(180° - y)$ **-k**

2b.

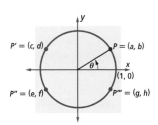

4b.

(0.97, 0.24)

14°

-14°

(0.97, -0.24)

10. $\tan(180° - \theta)$
$= \frac{\sin(180° - \theta)}{\cos(180° - \theta)}$
$= \frac{\sin \theta}{-\cos \theta} = -\tan \theta$

$P' = (c, d)$ $P = (a, b)$

θ

$(1, 0)$

$P'' = (e, f)$ $P''' = (g, h)$

11. $\sin 33.5° \approx 0.552$
$\approx \sin 146.5°$
$\cos 33.5° \approx 0.834$
$\approx -\cos 146.5°$
$\tan 33.5° \approx 0.662$
$\approx -\tan 146.5°$

16. Copy the table below, filling in the blank entries and completing the diagrams, to summarize the theorems in this lesson.

x	180° − θ	−θ	180° + θ	90° − θ
Diagram	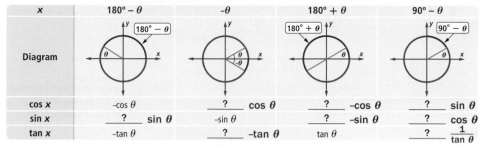			
cos x	−cos θ	___ cos θ	___ −cos θ	___ sin θ
sin x	___ sin θ	−sin θ	___ −sin θ	___ cos θ
tan x	−tan θ	___ −tan θ	tan θ	___ $\frac{1}{\tan θ}$

APPLYING THE MATHEMATICS

In 17–21, the display below shows inputs and outputs of a CAS in degree mode. What theorem justifies each statement?

17. cos(350)   cos(10)   **Half-Turn Theorem and Supplements Theorem**

18. sin(160)   sin(20)   **Supplements Theorem**

19. sin(202)   -sin(22)   **Half-Turn Theorem**

20. cos(84)   sin(6)   **Complements Theorem**

21. tan(187)   tan(7)   **Half-Turn Theorem**

22. Prove that $\sin(\pi - \theta) = \sin \pi - \sin \theta$ is *not* an identity. **22-26 See margin.**

In 23–26, from the fact that $\sin 18° = \frac{\sqrt{5} - 1}{4}$, find each value.

23. $\sin 162°$ 24. $\sin(-18°)$ 25. $\sin \frac{11\pi}{10}$ 26. $\cos \frac{\pi}{5}$

REVIEW

In 27–29, without using a calculator, give exact values. (Lesson 4-2)

27. $\sin 90°$ **1**   28. $\cos 810°$ **0**   29. $\tan(90° + 90°)$ **0**

30. Convert $\frac{11}{6}$ clockwise revolutions to degrees. (Lesson 4-1) **−660°**

31. a. What is the magnitude of the rotation of the minute hand of a clock in 6 minutes? **36°**

   b. What is the measure of the angle between the minute hand and the second hand of a clock at exactly 12:06 A.M.? (Lesson 4-1) **36°**

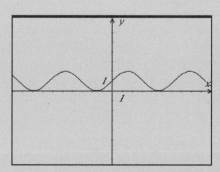

32. Find an equation for the image of the graph of $y = x^2$ under the scale change $(x, y) \rightarrow \left(\frac{1}{2}x, 5y\right)$. (Lesson 3-5) $y = 20x^2$

EXPLORATION

33. Use a calculator to investigate whether $\frac{\cos^2 \theta}{1 - \sin \theta} = 1 + \sin \theta$ is an identity. Try to prove your conclusion, either by providing a counterexample or by using definitions and properties. **See margin.**

Notes on the Questions

Questions 23–26 We do not ask for cos 18°, but an expression could be found for that using the Pythagorean Identity. You might challenge students to show that $\cos 18° = \sqrt{\frac{5 + \sqrt{5}}{8}}$.

Question 33 The given equation is true except when sin θ = 1. Do your students see why there is an exception? (The denominator of the left side is 0 when sin θ = 1.) Otherwise, multiplying both sides by 1 − sin θ, the Pythagorean Identity occurs. You might want to have your students graph $y - 1 + \sin \theta$ and $y = \frac{\cos \theta}{1 - \sin \theta}$ to show that the graphs look identical. Some calculators will give a warning about the domain of θ.

4 Wrap-Up

Ongoing Assessment
Give students the following information: θ is in the second quadrant and sin θ = 0.3. Have students find the cosine of θ, the sine of the opposite of θ, the sine of the supplement of θ, and the sine of the complement of θ. **Students apply the Pythagorean Identity, the Opposites Theorem, the Supplements Theorem, and the Complements Theorem.**

Administer Quiz 1 (or a quiz of your own) after students complete this lesson.

Lesson 4-4

Exact Values of Sines, Cosines, and Tangents

GOAL

Apply the definition of sine and cosine to obtain values for the sine, cosine, and tangent of multiples of $\frac{\pi}{6}$ (30°) or $\frac{\pi}{4}$ (45°).

SPUR Objectives

B Find values of sines, cosines, and tangents.

Materials/Resources

· Lesson Master 4-4
· Resource Masters 76 and 77

HOMEWORK
• Option 1
• Option 2

• Questions 1–11
•• Questions 12–24
•• Question 25 (extra credit)
• Reading Lesson 4-5
• Covering the Ideas 4-5
  (Questions 1–5)

Local Standards

1 Warm-Up

In 1–4, give the coordinates of the indicated image to the nearest thousandth.

1. $R_{30}(1, 0)$ (0.866, 0.5)
2. $R_{45}(1, 0)$ (0.707, 0.707)
3. $R_{60}(1, 0)$ (0.5, 0.866)
4. $R_{135}(1, 0)$ (−0.707, 0.707)

▶ **BIG IDEA** Exact trigonometric values for multiples of 30°, 45°, and 60° can be found without a calculator from properties of special right triangles.

For most values of θ, the values of $\sin \theta$, $\cos \theta$, and $\tan \theta$ cannot be found exactly and must be approximated. For this reason, you used approximate values found with a calculator in previous lessons.

In this lesson, you will apply what you know about 45°-45°-90° and 30°-60°-90° triangles to obtain exact values of $\cos \theta$, $\sin \theta$, and $\tan \theta$ when θ is a multiple of 30°, 45°, or 60°.

Exact Values of Trigonometric Functions for $\theta = 45°$

You can use the properties of isosceles right triangles to find $\cos 45°$ and $\sin 45°$.

> **GUIDED**

Example 1
Use △OPF at the right to compute the exact values of $\cos 45°$ and $\sin 45°$. Justify your answer.

Solution Because m∠FOP = 45°, m∠P = 45°. So △OPF is isosceles with legs $\overline{OF}$ and __?__. a and b are the $\overline{PF}$ lengths of the legs, so a = b. By the Pythagorean Theorem, $a^2 + b^2 = 1$, so $2a^2 = 1$, and $a^2 = $ __?__. $\frac{1}{2}$
Therefore, $a = b = \pm\frac{1}{\sqrt{2}}$. Because a and b are lengths,
$a = b = \frac{1}{\sqrt{2}}$.
But $\cos 45° = a$ and $\sin 45° = $ __?__. b
Thus, $\cos 45° = \sin 45° = \frac{1}{\sqrt{2}} = \frac{\sqrt{2}}{2}$.

STOP QY1

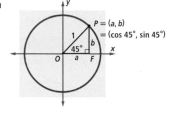

▶ **QY1**
Explain why $\tan 45° = 1$.

A side of square *SQUA*, below, has length 5.

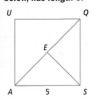

a. What is the length of $\overline{AQ}$? **5√2**

b. If *E* is the midpoint of $\overline{AQ}$, what is the length of $\overline{SE}$? **$\frac{5\sqrt{2}}{2}$**

Exact Values of Trigonometric Functions for $\theta = 30°$ and $\theta = 60°$

In Example 3 of Lesson 4-3, you were told that $\sin 30° = \frac{1}{2}$. You can verify this by using properties of equilateral triangles.

242   Trigonometric Functions

Background

There was a long discussion among the authors of this book when this lesson was first being considered. Some felt that, with calculators being able to approximate values of the trigonometric functions with such accuracy, knowing exact values was not necessary. They pointed out the danger of thinking of these as the only exact values. They thought, as a single number, $\sin x$ is an exact value.

Other authors (the ones whose views won out) pointed out that exact values provide (1) key points in the behavior of these functions, (2) a basis from which to graph them, and (3) the means to check some of the identities that relate the functions. The "exactness" of exact values also emphasizes for students the approximate nature of other trigonometric values, reminding them that calculator values are generally not exact. They also provide a review of some of the properties of equilateral triangles, isosceles right triangles, and regular hexagons from geometry.

GUIDED

Example 2

Derive the exact values of cos 30° and sin 30°.

Solution In equilateral △OPQ at the right, since $OP = 1$,
$PQ = \underline{\quad?\quad}$. Consequently, $PR = d = \underline{\quad?\quad}$. **1; $\frac{1}{2}$**

By the Pythagorean Theorem, $c^2 + d^2 = 1$.

$$\text{So } c^2 + \underline{\quad?\quad} = 1. \quad \frac{1}{4}$$

$$c^2 = \underline{\quad?\quad} \quad \frac{3}{4}$$

$$c = \underline{\quad?\quad} \quad \frac{\sqrt{3}}{2}$$

Thus, $(\cos 30°, \sin 30°) = (c, d) = (\underline{\quad?\quad}, \underline{\quad?\quad}). \quad \left(\frac{\sqrt{3}}{2}, \frac{1}{2}\right)$

So, $\cos 30° = \underline{\quad?\quad}$ and $\sin 30° = \underline{\quad?\quad}$. $\quad \frac{\sqrt{3}}{2}; \frac{1}{2}$

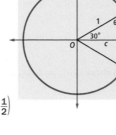

$P = (c, d)$
$= (\cos 30°, \sin 30°)$

To obtain the exact values of cos 60° and sin 60°, use the Complements Theorem: $\cos 60° = \sin 30° = \frac{1}{2}$ and $\sin 60° = \cos 30° = \frac{\sqrt{3}}{2}$.

Example 3

Find the exact value of tan 30°.

Solution Use $\tan \theta = \frac{\sin\theta}{\cos\theta}$.

$$\tan 30° = \frac{\sin 30°}{\cos 30°} = \frac{\frac{1}{2}}{\frac{\sqrt{3}}{2}} = \frac{1}{2} \cdot \frac{2}{\sqrt{3}} = \frac{1}{\sqrt{3}} = \frac{\sqrt{3}}{3}.$$

STOP QY2

You should memorize the exact values of cos θ, sin θ, and tan θ for θ = 30°, 45°, and 60°. They are important tools in mathematics and science because they are exact. To help you learn them, they are summarized below.

$\sin 45° = \frac{\sqrt{2}}{2} = \sin\frac{\pi}{4} \quad \sin 30° = \frac{1}{2} = \sin\frac{\pi}{6} \quad \sin 60° = \frac{\sqrt{3}}{2} = \sin\frac{\pi}{3}$

$\cos 45° = \frac{\sqrt{2}}{2} = \cos\frac{\pi}{4} \quad \cos 30° = \frac{\sqrt{3}}{2} = \cos\frac{\pi}{6} \quad \cos 60° = \frac{1}{2} = \cos\frac{\pi}{3}$

$\tan 45° = 1 = \tan\frac{\pi}{4} \quad \tan 30° = \frac{\sqrt{3}}{3} = \tan\frac{\pi}{6} \quad \tan 60° = \sqrt{3} = \tan\frac{\pi}{3}$

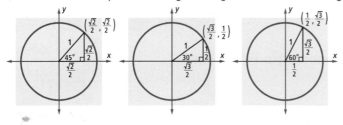

STOP QY3

▶ **QY2**

Find the exact value of tan 60°.

▶ **QY3**

Which theorem verifies that sin 30° = cos 60°?

---

2 Teaching

Notes on the Lesson

Students should either memorize or be able to derive the exact values of these trigonometric functions (in terms of rational numbers and radicals) in the first quadrant in this lesson, and be able to derive the exact values for other quadrants.

Throughout this lesson we adhere to the common convention of rationalizing the denominator of expressions such as $\frac{1}{\sqrt{3}}$, but this is not to be taken as a recommendation that students be required to do so. Historically, denominators were rationalized because it was easier and more accurate to find a decimal approximation for $\frac{\sqrt{3}}{3}$ than for $\frac{1}{\sqrt{3}}$. Students should know the two expressions are equivalent, but in today's world of hand-held calculators, the ease and greater accuracy arguments are no longer as valid.

Additional Examples

Example 1 Using a sketch like the one in Example 1, compute the exact values of cos –45° and sin –45°. $\frac{\sqrt{2}}{2}, -\frac{\sqrt{2}}{2}$

Example 2 Derive the exact values of cos –60° and sin –60°. $\frac{1}{2}, -\frac{\sqrt{3}}{2}$

Example 3 Find the exact value of tan –60°. $-\sqrt{3}$

Students might ask if there are other values of π for which sin θ, cos θ, and tan θ can be found exactly. Under the conditions that θ be a rational multiple of 180°, and that the trigonometric values of θ are rational numbers or rational multiples of simple radicals, only the values given and found in Activity 2 qualify. However, if the conditions are that θ be a whole number multiple of 1° and that the trigonometric values of θ be in terms of rational numbers and simple radicals, then the trigonometric values of

any multiple of 3° can be found using identities students encounter in high school. The values in Questions 23–26 in Lesson 4-3 are instances.)

4-4

Exact Values for Sines and Cosines of Multiples of 30°, 45°, and 60°

Using the definitions of sine and cosine and the Symmetry Identities, you can find exact values of the trigonometric functions for all integer multiples of 30°, 45°, and 60°.

GUIDED

Example 4

Find exact values of cos 120°, sin 120°, and tan 120°.

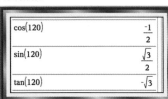

Solution By the Supplements Theorem,

$$\cos 120° = \underline{\ ?\ } = -\frac{1}{2} \text{ and } \sin 120° = \underline{\ ?\ } = \frac{\sqrt{3}}{2}. \quad -\cos 60°; \sin 60°$$

$$\tan 120° = \frac{\sin 120°}{\cos 120°} = \frac{\frac{\sqrt{3}}{2}}{-\frac{1}{2}} = -\sqrt{3}.$$

Check Use a calculator.

cos(120)	$\frac{-1}{2}$
sin(120)	$\frac{\sqrt{3}}{2}$
tan(120)	$-\sqrt{3}$

On the unit circle below are the images of (1, 0) under rotations of integer multiples of 30° or 45° between 0° and 360°. You should be able to calculate exact values of the sine, cosine, and tangent functions for all pictured values of θ by relating them to one of the points in the first quadrant or on the axes.

Activity

Copy the unit circle and the exact values of (cos θ, sin θ) given at the right. Use your knowledge of reflections and symmetries to add the exact values of trigonometric functions for multiples of 30°, 45° and 60° in Quadrants II, III, and IV.

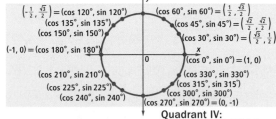

Exact Values for Trigonometric Functions of Radians

It is important to know the exact values of trigonometric functions for certain radians. You can compute those values by converting to degrees, but in the long run, it is helpful to learn to "think radian."

Activity Quadrant II:

$(\cos 135°, \sin 135°) = \left(-\frac{\sqrt{2}}{2}, \frac{\sqrt{2}}{2}\right)$

$(\cos 150°, \sin 150°) = \left(-\frac{\sqrt{3}}{2}, \frac{1}{2}\right)$

Quadrant III:

$(\cos 210°, \sin 210°) = \left(-\frac{\sqrt{3}}{2}, -\frac{1}{2}\right)$

$(\cos 225°, \sin 225°) = \left(-\frac{\sqrt{2}}{2}, -\frac{\sqrt{2}}{2}\right)$

$(\cos 240°, \sin 240°) = \left(-\frac{1}{2}, -\frac{\sqrt{3}}{2}\right)$

Quadrant IV:

$(\cos 300°, \sin 300°) = \left(\frac{1}{2}, -\frac{\sqrt{3}}{2}\right)$

$(\cos 315°, \sin 315°) = \left(\frac{\sqrt{2}}{2}, -\frac{\sqrt{2}}{2}\right)$

$(\cos 330°, \sin 330°) = \left(\frac{\sqrt{3}}{2}, -\frac{1}{2}\right)$

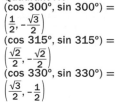
Accommodating the Learner ⬆

Let θ be an angle formed by the longest diagonal of a cube and a diagonal of a face of the cube. Find sin θ exactly. $\frac{1}{\sqrt{3}}$, or $\frac{\sqrt{3}}{3}$

Extension

Ask students to use the formula $A = \frac{1}{2}ab \sin θ$ for the area of a triangle with sides a and b and included angle θ, to find the following.

1. The area of a regular octagon inscribed in a circle of radius 10. $200\sqrt{2}$

2. A formula for the area of an equilateral triangle with sides of length s. $A = \frac{s^2\sqrt{3}}{4}$

3. A formula for the area of a regular hexagon with sides of length s. $A = \frac{3s^2\sqrt{3}}{2}$

GUIDED

Example 5

Without using technology, compute the exact value of each trigonometric function below.

a. $\sin \frac{\pi}{4}$ b. $\cos \frac{5\pi}{6}$ c. $\tan \pi$

Solution

a. Convert to degrees: $\frac{\pi}{4} \cdot \frac{180°}{\pi} = 45°$. $\sin 45° = \frac{\sqrt{2}}{2} = \sin \frac{\pi}{4}$

b. $\frac{5\pi}{6} = \underline{\ ?\ }°$, so $\cos \frac{5\pi}{6} = \underline{\ ?\ }$.   150; $-\frac{\sqrt{3}}{2}$

c. $\tan \pi = \frac{\sin \pi}{\cos \pi} = \frac{?}{?} = \underline{\ ?\ }$ $\frac{0}{-1}$; 0

Questions

COVERING THE IDEAS

In 1–3, refer to the unit circle at the right in which m∠POA = 30°, m∠QOA = 45°, and m∠ROA = 60°. Name a segment whose length equals the following.

1. $\cos 30°$ **OF**   2. $\sin 45°$ **QG**   3. $\sin 60°$ **RH**

4. Evaluate.
   a. $\cos \frac{\pi}{3}$ $\frac{1}{2}$ b. $\tan \frac{\pi}{4}$ **1**   c. $\sin \frac{\pi}{6}$ $\frac{1}{2}$

In 5–10, find the exact value.

5. a. $\sin 240°$ $-\frac{\sqrt{3}}{2}$ b. $\cos 240°$ $-\frac{1}{2}$ c. $\tan \frac{4\pi}{3}$ $\sqrt{3}$

6. a. $\sin \frac{3\pi}{4}$ $\frac{\sqrt{2}}{2}$ b. $\cos \frac{3\pi}{4}$ $-\frac{\sqrt{2}}{2}$ c. $\tan 135°$ -1

7. a. $\sin \frac{11\pi}{6}$ $-\frac{1}{2}$ b. $\cos(-30°)$ $\frac{\sqrt{3}}{2}$ c. $\tan \frac{11\pi}{6}$ $-\frac{\sqrt{3}}{3}$

8. $\sin 210°$ $-\frac{1}{2}$ 9. $\cos \frac{5\pi}{3}$ $\frac{1}{2}$ 10. $\tan(-405°)$ -1

11. Draw a unit circle as in the Activity, labeling the angles in *radians* and filling in all the values of the trigonometric functions.

APPLYING THE MATHEMATICS

12. a. Find two values of θ between –90° and 90° for which $\cos \theta = \frac{1}{2}$.
    b. Find two values of θ between 270° and 450° for which $\cos \theta = \frac{1}{2}$.
    c. What is the relation between the two pairs of angles formed in Parts a and b?

13. Consider the equation $\sin \theta = -\frac{1}{2}$.
    a. Draw a unit circle and mark the two points for which $\sin \theta = -\frac{1}{2}$.
    b. Give two values of θ between 0° and 360° that satisfy the equation. **210° and 330°**
    c. Give two values of θ between 0 and 2π radians that satisfy the equation. $\frac{7\pi}{6}$ **and** $\frac{11\pi}{6}$

14. a. Find two values of θ between 0 and 2π such that $\cos \theta = \sin \theta$.
    b. What is the value of $\tan \theta$ for each value of θ in Part a? **1**

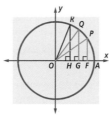

11. See margin.

12. a. –60° and 60°
    b. 300° and 420°
    c. Angles with magnitudes –90° and 90° are the same as angles with magnitudes 270° and 450°, respectively.

13. a.

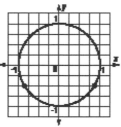

14. a. $\frac{\pi}{4}$ and $\frac{5\pi}{4}$

3 Assignment

Recommended Assignment
- Questions 1–11
- Questions 12–24
- Question 25 (extra credit)
  - Reading Lesson 4-5
  - Covering the Ideas 4-5 (Questions 1–5)

Notes on the Questions
Question 12 If students are not able to do these based on the exact values discussed in this lesson, you might suggesting looking where the line with equation $x = \frac{1}{2}$ intersects the unit circle.

Question 13 Here one might begin by asking where the line with equation $y = -\frac{1}{2}$ intersects the unit circle.

Additional Answers

11.

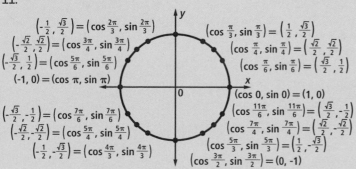

$\left(-\frac{1}{2}, \frac{\sqrt{3}}{2}\right) = \left(\cos \frac{2\pi}{3}, \sin \frac{2\pi}{3}\right)$ $\left(\cos \frac{\pi}{3}, \sin \frac{\pi}{3}\right) = \left(\frac{1}{2}, \frac{\sqrt{3}}{2}\right)$

$\left(-\frac{\sqrt{2}}{2}, \frac{\sqrt{2}}{2}\right) = \left(\cos \frac{3\pi}{4}, \sin \frac{3\pi}{4}\right)$ $\left(\cos \frac{\pi}{4}, \sin \frac{\pi}{4}\right) = \left(\frac{\sqrt{2}}{2}, \frac{\sqrt{2}}{2}\right)$

$\left(-\frac{\sqrt{3}}{2}, \frac{1}{2}\right) = \left(\cos \frac{5\pi}{6}, \sin \frac{5\pi}{6}\right)$ $\left(\cos \frac{\pi}{6}, \sin \frac{\pi}{6}\right) = \left(\frac{\sqrt{3}}{2}, \frac{1}{2}\right)$

$(-1, 0) = (\cos \pi, \sin \pi)$ $(\cos 0, \sin 0) = (1, 0)$

$\left(-\frac{\sqrt{3}}{2}, -\frac{1}{2}\right) = \left(\cos \frac{7\pi}{6}, \sin \frac{7\pi}{6}\right)$ $\left(\cos \frac{11\pi}{6}, \sin \frac{11\pi}{6}\right) = \left(\frac{\sqrt{3}}{2}, -\frac{1}{2}\right)$

$\left(-\frac{\sqrt{2}}{2}, -\frac{\sqrt{2}}{2}\right) = \left(\cos \frac{5\pi}{4}, \sin \frac{5\pi}{4}\right)$ $\left(\cos \frac{7\pi}{4}, \sin \frac{7\pi}{4}\right) = \left(\frac{\sqrt{2}}{2}, -\frac{\sqrt{2}}{2}\right)$

$\left(-\frac{1}{2}, -\frac{\sqrt{3}}{2}\right) = \left(\cos \frac{4\pi}{3}, \sin \frac{4\pi}{3}\right)$ $\left(\cos \frac{5\pi}{3}, \sin \frac{5\pi}{3}\right) = \left(\frac{1}{2}, -\frac{\sqrt{3}}{2}\right)$

$\left(\cos \frac{3\pi}{2}, \sin \frac{3\pi}{2}\right) = (0, -1)$

4-4

Notes on the Questions

Question 16c This question anticipates a calculation done in the derivation of the Law of Cosines and in the derivation of the formula for $\cos(x + y)$.

Question 25 It should be clear to students that the perimeter of a regular n-gon inscribed in a unit circle approaches 2π as $n \to \infty$. It is not difficult, using right triangle trigonometry, to prove that the perimeter of an n-gon inscribed in a unit circle is $2n \cdot \sin\left(\frac{180°}{n}\right)$. You might have students use this formula to find the exact perimeter of a regular 24-gon, 48-gon, etc., to show how close the perimeter is to 2π.

4 Wrap-Up

Ongoing Assessment

Have students choose $\theta = \frac{\pi}{6}$, $\theta = \frac{\pi}{4}$, or $\theta = \frac{\pi}{3}$. Using right triangle geometry, ask students to show how to determine the exact values of the sine, cosine, and tangent of θ. Then have them use a unit circle to determine the sine, cosine, and tangent of $\pi - \theta$, $\pi + \theta$, and $2\pi - \theta$. **Answers vary. Check students' work.**

---

15. **True or False** If $\tan \theta = \pm 1$, then $\theta = (45n)°$ and n is an odd integer. Justify your answer. **See margin.**

16. The regular nonagon $ABCDEFGHI$ pictured here is inscribed in the unit circle.
    a. Give the exact coordinates of point B in terms of θ. **($\cos \theta$, $\sin \theta$)**
    b. Give the value of θ in radians. $\frac{2\pi}{9}$
    c. Estimate AB to the nearest thousandth. **0.684**

REVIEW

17. Without using a calculator, given that $\sin 52° \approx 0.788$, estimate each value. **(Lesson 4-3)**
    a. $\sin(-52°)$ b. $\sin 128°$ c. $\sin 232°$ d. $\cos 38°$

18. **True or False** For all θ, $\cos(\theta + 90°) = \sin \theta$. **(Lesson 4-3) false**

19. Without using a calculator, give the exact value for $\sin\left(-\frac{\pi}{2}\right)$. **(Lesson 4-2) –1**

20. a. Prove that $\cos \theta \cdot \tan \theta = \sin \theta$ for all $\cos \theta \neq 0$.
    b. Why is it impossible to have $\cos \theta = 0$ in Part a? **(Lesson 4-2)**

21. Convert the following measures to radians. **(Lesson 4-1)**
    a. $135°$ $\frac{3\pi}{4}$ b. $390°$ $\frac{13\pi}{6}$ c. $-215°$ $-\frac{43\pi}{36}$ d. $-270°$ $-\frac{3\pi}{2}$

In 22 and 23, consider $g(t) = t^2 + 1$ and $f(t) = 3t - 1$. **(Lesson 3-7)**
22. Evaluate $g(f(-80))$. **58,082**
23. Find a formula for $(f \circ g)(t)$. $(f \circ g)(t) = 3(t^2 + 1) - 1$

24. When a certain drug enters the blood stream, its potency decreases exponentially with a half-life of 8 hours. Suppose the initial amount of drug present is A. How much of the drug will be present after each number of hours? **(Lesson 2-5)**
    a. 8 $\frac{1}{2}$ b. 24 $\frac{1}{8}$ c. t $\left(\frac{1}{2}\right)^{\frac{t}{8}}$

EXPLORATION

25. A regular triangle, hexagon, and dodecagon have been inscribed in the unit circle. Find the exact perimeter of each polygon. You may find a CAS useful. $3\sqrt{3}$; 6; $6\sqrt{2}(\sqrt{3} - 1)$

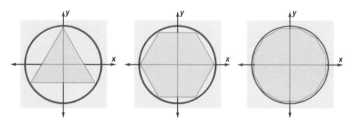

17. a. –0.788
    b. 0.788
    c. –0.788
    d. 0.788

20. a. Let $\cos \theta \neq 0$. By definition, $\tan \theta = \frac{\sin \theta}{\cos \theta}$, so $\cos \theta \cdot \tan \theta = \sin \theta$.
    b. If $\cos \theta = 0$, then $\tan \theta$ is undefined because division by 0 is not defined.

QY ANSWERS

1. $\tan 45° = \frac{\sin 45°}{\cos 45°}$
   $= \frac{\frac{\sqrt{2}}{2}}{\frac{\sqrt{2}}{2}} = 1$

2. $\tan 60° = \frac{\sin 60°}{\cos 60°} = \frac{\frac{\sqrt{3}}{2}}{\frac{1}{2}}$
   $= \sqrt{3}$

3. Complements Theorem

Additional Answers

15. True; when $\theta = 45n$ for same odd n then the triangle made from an extension to the unit circle and a line directly up or down to the x-axis is isosceles. This means that the leg representing $\sin \theta$ is the same length as the leg representing $\cos \theta$. Because $\tan \theta = \frac{\sin \theta}{\cos \theta}$, this makes $|\tan \theta| = 1$, or $\tan \theta = \pm 1$.

The Sine and Cosine Functions

Vocabulary

sine function

cosine function

▶ **BIG IDEA** The values of cos θ and sin θ determine functions with equations $y = \sin x$ and $y = \cos x$ whose domain is the set of all real numbers.

From the exact values of sines, cosines, and tangents you calculated in Lesson 4-4, you can see the shape of a function called the *sine function*.

Mental Math

If gasoline costs $4.00 a gallon and a car gets 25 miles to the gallon, what does it cost for gas per mile?

$0.16 per mile

Activity 1 See margin.

Step 1 The table below contains some exact values of sin θ. It also shows decimal approximations to those values. Complete the table, using a unit circle to help you.

θ (degrees)	0°	30°	45°	60°	90°	120°	135°	150°	180°
θ (radians)	0	$\frac{\pi}{6}$	$\frac{\pi}{4}$	$\frac{\pi}{3}$	$\frac{\pi}{2}$	$\frac{2\pi}{3}$	$\frac{3\pi}{4}$	$\frac{5\pi}{6}$	π
sin θ (exact)	0	$\frac{1}{2}$	?	?	?	$\frac{\sqrt{3}}{2}$	?	?	?
sin θ (approx.)	0	0.5	?	?	?	?	0.707	?	?

θ (degrees)	210°	225°	240°	270°	300°	315°	330°	360°
θ (radians)	$\frac{7\pi}{6}$	$\frac{5\pi}{4}$	$\frac{4\pi}{3}$	$\frac{3\pi}{2}$	?	?	?	2π
sin θ (exact)	?	$-\frac{\sqrt{2}}{2}$	?	?	?	?	?	?
sin θ (approx.)	?	?	?	?	-0.866	?	?	?

Step 2 Here is a graph of the first five points in the first part of the table. Copy this graph, and on it plot the points you found in Step 1. Then draw a smooth curve through the points.

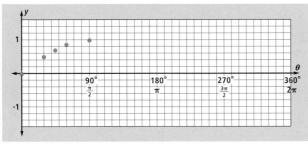

(continued on next page)

Background

The congruence of the graphs of the sine and cosine functions can be derived from the definition of sine and cosine. If the coordinate plane is reflected over the line with equation $y = x$, then the x-axis and y-axis are switched. This line intersects the unit circle when $\theta = 45°$. Thus when the graph of $y = \cos x$ is reflected over the line $x = 45°$, the graph of $y = \sin x$ results.

Another reason for the congruence of the graphs is that for all θ, $\cos(\theta - 90°) = \cos\left(\frac{\pi}{2} - \theta\right) = \sin \theta$. This implies that the image of the graph of $y = \cos \theta$ under a horizontal translation of $\frac{\pi}{2}$ units coincides with the graph of $y = \sin \theta$.

GOAL

Graph and analyze the functions
sine: $\theta \rightarrow \sin \theta$ and cosine: $\theta \rightarrow \cos \theta$.

SPUR Objectives

B Find values of sines and cosines.

C Apply the definitions of the sine and cosine functions.

I Draw or interpret graphs of the parent sine and cosine functions in degrees or radians.

Materials/Resources

· Lesson Master 4-5
· Resource Masters 78 and 79

HOMEWORK • Option 1

• Questions 1–5   • Option 2
• • Questions 6–16
• • Question 17 (extra credit)
  • Reading Lesson 4-6
  • Covering the Ideas 4-6
  (Questions 1–7)

Local Standards

1 Warm-Up

Without using a calculator, given that $\sqrt{2} \approx 1.414$ and $\sqrt{3} \approx 1.732$, approximate to the nearest hundredth:

1. $\frac{\sqrt{2}}{2}$ 0.71

2. $\frac{\sqrt{3}}{2}$ 0.87

3. $\frac{\sqrt{3}}{3}$ 0.58

4. $(\sqrt{2})^2$ 2

Additional Answers

Activity 1

Step 1: See the Additional Answers section at the back of the book.

(continued on next page)

4-5

2 Teaching

Notes on the Lesson

Activity 1 This activity can be skipped if your students have previously graphed the sine and cosine functions. Otherwise it is an important activity, because it relates the values of a trigonometric function with the familiar graph.

In this activity, the scales on the two axes are of different units, with the unit on the y-axis being larger than the unit on the x-axis (θ-axis). In the table, sin θ is given in terms of both decimal approximations and exact values. Students should be comfortable with both expressions.

The graph of the sine function Point out that the part of the graph that is above the x-axis is congruent to the part below the x-axis. It is *not* a semicircle. Finally, note that if one can carefully plot the part of the graph from θ = 0° to θ = 90°, then the rest of the graph follows because all parts are congruent to this part. This is a consequence of the property that if the sine values are on the unit circle for the first quadrant, then all other values can be found.

Additional Answers

Activity 1

Step 2:

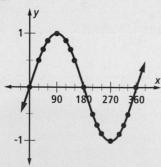

Step 3:

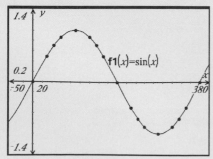

Step 3 Check Step 2 by using a graphing utility to plot $y = \sin \theta$ for $0° \leq \theta \leq 360°$ and for $0 \leq \theta \leq 2\pi$.

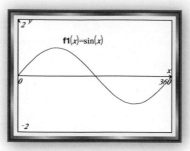

The Graph of the Sine Function

The function that maps each real number θ to the y-coordinate of the image of (1, 0) under a rotation of θ is called the **sine function**. From the unit circle, you can tell that sin θ is positive when 0° < θ < 180° and negative when 180° < θ < 360°. The maximum value is 1, when θ = 90°, and the minimum value is –1, when θ = 270°.

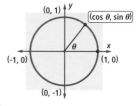

STOP QY

Restate the preceding paragraph for θ in radians.

A graph of the sine function, for 0° ≤ θ ≤ 360°, is shown at the right. To make it easier to locate zeros, maxima, and minima, the scale on the horizontal axis is in multiples of $\frac{\pi}{2}$ and 90°.

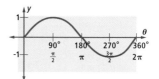

This is one *cycle* of the graph of the sine function. Because the image of (1, 0) under a rotation of θ repeats itself every 2π radians, the y-coordinates in the ordered pairs of the function *f* with equation $f(\theta) = \sin \theta$ repeat every 2π. Thus, the graph above can be easily extended both to the right and left without calculating any new sine values. The graph of the entire sine function has infinitely many cycles. A graph showing three complete cycles of the sine function appears below.

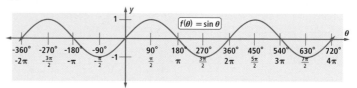

Notice from the graph that the y-intercept of the sine function is 0. The sine function's x-intercepts (zeros) are ..., –2π, –π, 0, π, 2π, 3π, 4π, ..., that is, the integer multiples of π.

Accommodating the Learner ⬇

The graphs of the sine and cosine functions are similar in shape, but have different x- and y-intercepts. For students who may confuse one with the other, it may be helpful to remind them that the point (1, 0) on the unit circle corresponds to (cos 0, sin 0). This means that when θ = 0, the y-intercepts for each graph are 1 and 0, respectively. That is, the y-intercept of the graph of sin θ is 0, and the y-intercept of the graph of cos θ is 1.

If students can remember the y-intercept of each graph, they have a good starting point to complete the sketch of a graph without using technology.

As the graph on the previous page makes clear, the domain of the sine function is the set of real numbers. Because the maximum and minimum values of the sine function are 1 and –1 (the *y*-intercepts of the unit circle) the range is the interval $-1 \leq y \leq 1$. Also notice that the graph of the sine function is point-symmetric about the origin. Thus, the sine function is an odd function. This is because of the Opposites Theorem that states for all θ, $\sin(-\theta) = -\sin\theta$.

The Graph of the Cosine Function

Remember that the image of (1, 0) under a rotation of magnitude θ is $(\cos\theta, \sin\theta)$. The function that maps each real number θ to the *first* coordinate of the image of (1, 0) under a rotation of θ is called the **cosine function**. The cosine function has many characteristics like those of the sine function. A graph of the cosine function is shown below.

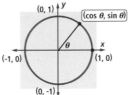

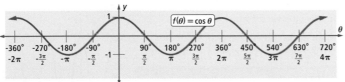

Activity 2   See margin.

Use the definitions and graphs of the sine and cosine functions to fill in the table.

	sine function (degrees)	sine function (radians)	cosine function (degrees)	cosine function (radians)
Domain	?	?	?	?
Range	?	?	?	?
Zeros	?	?	?	?
Maxima	$\sin\theta = 1$ when $\theta = 90°, 450°, 810°, \ldots$	?	?	?
Minima	?	?	?	?

Questions

COVERING THE IDEAS

1. a. Identify the domain and the range of the sine function.
    b. Find five values of x such that $\sin x = 0$.

2. a. Sketch a graph of $y = \sin x$ for $0 \leq x \leq 2\pi$. **See margin.**
    b. Find all values of x on this interval such that $\sin x = 1$. $\dfrac{\pi}{2}$
    c. Find all values of x on this interval for which $\sin x = 0.5$. $\dfrac{\pi}{6}, \dfrac{5\pi}{6}$

1a. domain: $\{x \mid x \in \mathbb{R}\}$; range: $\{y \mid -1 \leq y \leq 1\}$

1b. Answers vary. Sample: $-\pi, 0, \pi, 2\pi, 3\pi$

The Sine and Cosine Functions   **249**

Notes on the Lesson
Throughout the lesson, we represent the independent variable in the three trigonometric functions $f(\theta) = \sin\theta$ and $g(\theta) = \cos\theta$ with θ rather than x. This is because the values of the cosine function are the *first* coordinates of the image of the point (1, 0) under a rotation of magnitude Q about the origin, and to use x and y for the cosine function would at this point confuse the issue. However, students should realize that $f(x) = \cos x$ defines the same function as $g(\theta) = \cos\theta$. Many graphing utilities use x for the independent variable, so students need to be comfortable using either θ or x.

Activity 2 This activity is useful in summarizing the properties of both the sine and cosine functions.

3   Assignment

Recommended Assignment
* Questions 1–5
* • Questions 6–16
* • Question 17 (extra credit)
* Reading Lesson 4-6
* Covering the Ideas 4-6 (Questions 1–7)

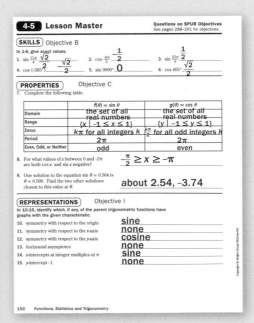

Additional Answers

Activity 2: See the Additional Answers section at the back of the book

2a.

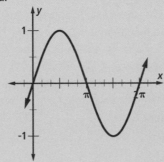

4-5

Notes on the Questions

Question 4 This is an important question that should be discussed in detail.

Questions 6 and 7 These questions are important to discuss in preparation for Lesson 4-7.

Question 8 Many periodic functions arise from natural phenomena, of which predator-prey relationships are one of the less obvious.

Additional Answers

3a.

x	$\frac{2\pi}{3}$	$\frac{3\pi}{4}$
cos x exact	$-\frac{1}{2}$	$-\frac{\sqrt{2}}{2}$
cos x approx	−0.5	−0.707

$\frac{7\pi}{6}$	$\frac{5\pi}{4}$	$\frac{4\pi}{3}$	$\frac{3\pi}{2}$
$-\frac{\sqrt{3}}{2}$	$-\frac{\sqrt{2}}{2}$	$-\frac{1}{2}$	0
−0.866	−0.707	−0.5	0

$\frac{5\pi}{3}$	$\frac{7\pi}{4}$	$\frac{11\pi}{6}$	2π
$\frac{1}{2}$	$\frac{\sqrt{2}}{2}$	$\frac{\sqrt{3}}{2}$	1
0.5	0.707	0.866	1

3b.

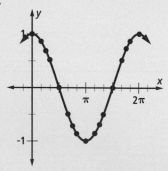

3. a. Copy the table below. Fill in exact and approximate values (rounded to three decimal places) for some of the coordinates of points on the graph of the cosine function.

3. See margin.

x	0	$\frac{\pi}{6}$	$\frac{\pi}{4}$	$\frac{\pi}{3}$	$\frac{\pi}{2}$	$\frac{2\pi}{3}$	$\frac{3\pi}{4}$	$\frac{5\pi}{4}$
cos x (exact)	1	$\frac{\sqrt{3}}{2}$	$\frac{\sqrt{2}}{2}$	$\frac{1}{2}$	0	?	?	$-\frac{\sqrt{3}}{2}$
cos x (approx.)	1	0.866	0.707	0.5	0	?	?	−0.866

x	π	$\frac{7\pi}{6}$	$\frac{5\pi}{4}$	$\frac{4\pi}{3}$	$\frac{3\pi}{2}$	$\frac{5\pi}{3}$	$\frac{7\pi}{4}$	$\frac{11\pi}{6}$	2π
cos x (exact)	−1	?	?	?	?	?	?	?	?
cos x (approx.)	−1	?	?	?	?	?	?	?	?

b. Use the points from the table to graph $y = \cos x$.

4. a. Sketch a graph of $y = \cos \theta$ for $-360° \leq \theta \leq 720°$.
   b. Find five values of θ on this interval for which $\cos \theta = 0$.

5. Describe three ways in which the graph of $y = \cos \theta$ is like the graph of $y = \sin \theta$ and two ways in which the graphs are different.

APPLYING THE MATHEMATICS

6. Describe the translation with the smallest positive magnitude that maps the graph of $g(x) = \cos x$ onto that of $y = \sin x$. $T : x \rightarrow x + \frac{\pi}{2}$

7. The graph of the sine function is reflection-symmetric to the line with equation $x = \frac{\pi}{2}$.
   a. What property of sines is a result of this symmetry?
   b. Name two other lines of symmetry for the graph.

8. In a stable environment, predator-prey populations can be modeled by sine waves. Refer to the graph below. **See margin.**

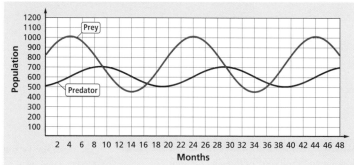

a. Describe what is happening with the prey population when the predator population is at its peak.
b. Describe what is happening with the prey population when the predators are the fewest.

3. See margin.

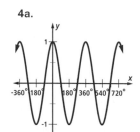

4a.

4b. −270°, −90°, 90°, 270°, 450°

5. See margin.

7a. $\sin\left(\theta + \frac{\pi}{2}\right) = \sin\left(\frac{\pi}{2} - \theta\right)$
7b. Answers vary. Sample: $x = \frac{3\pi}{2}$ and $x = -\frac{3\pi}{2}$

Additional Answers

5. Answers vary. Sample: The graphs of both sin x and cos x have a cycle of length 2π (or 360°), a maximum value of 1, and a minimum value of −1. The graph of cos x crosses the y-axis at (0, 1) and the graph of sin x crosses the y-axis at (0, 0). The graph of cos x is symmetric about the y-axis and the graph of sin x is not.

8a. Answers vary. Sample: When the predator population is at its peak, the prey population is decreasing at its fastest rate.

8b. Answers vary. Sample: When the predator population is at its lowest level, the prey population is growing at its fastest rate.

9. Use the graph of $y = f(x)$ at the right. Suppose f is known to be either the cosine function or the sine function.

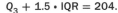

a. Evaluate $f\left(\frac{23\pi}{2}\right)$. **–1**

b. For what value of x, in the interval from 10π to 12π, does $f(x) = 1$? **$\frac{21\pi}{2}$**

c. Tell whether f is the cosine function or sine function. Justify your answer.

REVIEW

10. The graph of the cosine function is reflection-symmetric to the y-axis. What property of cosines is a result of this symmetry? (**Lesson 4-4**) $\cos \theta = \cos (-\theta)$

In 11 and 12, A is a point on a circle with center at the origin. Find the coordinates of A for the given value of θ. (**Lesson 4-4**)

11. $\left(-\frac{1}{2}, \frac{\sqrt{3}}{2}\right)$ 12. $\left(\frac{\sqrt{2}}{2}, -\frac{\sqrt{2}}{2}\right)$

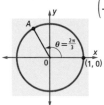 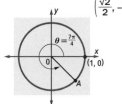

13. In radians, what is the sum of the measures of the angles of a pentagon? (**Lesson 4-4**) 3π

14. An old 78 RPM record revolves through 78 revolutions in a minute. How many radians is this per second? (**Lesson 4-1**) $\frac{13\pi}{5}$

15. The measure of an angle is k radians. Convert this measure to degrees. (**Lesson 4-1**) $\frac{k180°}{\pi}$

16. The students in Ms. T. Chare's 1st period geometry class measured their heights h in centimeters and recorded the following five-number summary of their data: $\bar{h} = 165$; min $= 137$; $Q_1 = 154$; median $= 168$; $Q_3 = 174$; max $= 188$. Are there any outliers in the data set? Explain your answer. (**Lesson 1-4**)

EXPLORATION

17. At what angle to the x-axis does the graph of $y = \sin x$ pass through $(0, 0)$? Give numerical and visual evidence supporting your answer.

Answers vary. Sample: Note that (0, 0) and (0.001, 0.001) lie on, or nearly on, the line $y = \sin x$, and the slope of the line through those points is 1. Small positive values of x and the graph of $y = \sin x$ support this contention. See margin for graph.

9c. f is the sine function, because $\sin(10\pi) = 0$ whereas $\cos(10\pi) = 1$.

16. No, the minimum is greater than $Q_1 - 1.5 \cdot \text{IQR} = 124$, and the maximum is less than $Q_3 + 1.5 \cdot \text{IQR} = 204$.

QY ANSWER

From the unit circle, you can tell that $\sin \theta$ is positive when $0 < \theta < \pi$ and negative when $\pi < \theta < 2\pi$. The maximum value is 1, when $\theta = \frac{\pi}{2}$, and the minimum value is –1, when $\theta = \frac{3\pi}{2}$.

Notes on the Questions

Question 13 You might extend this question by asking for the sum of the measures of the angles of an n-gon in radians. $\pi(n - 2)$; again the formula in radians is easier than the corresponding formula in degrees.

Question 14 The question requires only arithmetic, but is difficult for many students.

4   **Wrap-Up**

Ongoing Assessment

Expand on Question 5 by having students take a few minutes to write down a list of as many similarities and differences between the graphs of the sine and cosine functions as they can. When time is up, have students write a collective list on the board. **Answers vary. Check that students' descriptions are as accurate, concise, and mathematical as possible.**

Project Update

Project 1, *Sums of Sine Waves with the Same Period* and Project 2, *Beat Matching and DJing* 101, on page 282, and Project 4, *Square Waves*, on page 283 relate to the content of this lesson.

Additional Answers

17.

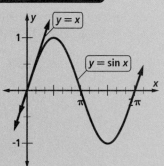

Lesson 4-6

Lesson 4-6

The Tangent Function and Periodicity

GOAL

Graph and analyze the function tangent: $\theta \rightarrow \tan \theta$. Discuss the periodicity of the three basic trigonometric functions.

SPUR Objectives

C Apply the definition of the tangent function.

D Apply theorems about sines, cosines, and tangents.

I Draw or interpret graphs of the parent tangent function in degrees or radians.

Materials/Resources

· Lesson Master 4-6
· Resource Masters 80, 81 and 82
· Quiz 2

HOMEWORK
• Option 1
• Option 2

- Questions 1–7
- • Questions 8–20
- • Question 21 (extra credit)
  - Reading Lesson 4-7
  - Covering the Ideas 4-7 (Questions 1–13)

Local Standards

---

1 Warm-Up

Graph $y = \sin x$ and $y = \cos x$ on the same axes, for $0 \leq x \leq 360°$. Then, for five different values of x, take the quotient of the y-values of these functions. Graph these quotients in a different color. **The points lie on the graph of the tangent function.**

> ▶ **BIG IDEA** The sine and cosine functions are periodic, repeating every 2π or 360°. The tangent function is periodic, repeating every π or 180°.

A frieze pattern is a visual design that repeats over and over along a line. The frieze pattern at the right appears on the Chan Chan ruins in Trujillo, Peru.

In Lesson 4-5, you used values of sine and cosine to graph trigonometric functions. You also observed that, like frieze patterns, their graphs repeat as you move horizontally. This lesson extends those ideas to the tangent function.

Mental Math

How many times does the minute hand of a clock pass the number 6 between 10 A.M. and 6 P.M.?
8 times

The Tangent Function

The correspondence $\theta \rightarrow \tan \theta$, when θ is a real number, defines the **tangent function**. From the definition $\tan \theta = \frac{\sin \theta}{\cos \theta}$, values for the tangent function can be generated.

Activity See margin.

Step 1 The table below contains some exact values of $\tan \theta$. It also shows decimal equivalents of those values. Fill in the missing values.

θ	0	$30° = \frac{\pi}{6}$	$45° = \frac{\pi}{4}$	$60° = \frac{\pi}{3}$	$90° = \frac{\pi}{2}$	$120° = \frac{2\pi}{3}$	$135° = \frac{3\pi}{4}$	$150° = \frac{5\pi}{6}$	$180° = \pi$
$\tan \theta$ (exact)	0	$\frac{\sqrt{3}}{3}$	1	$\sqrt{3}$	undefined	?	?	?	0
$\tan \theta$ (approx.)	0	0.577	1	1.732	undefined	?	?	?	0

θ	$210° = \frac{7\pi}{6}$	$225° = \frac{5\pi}{4}$	$240° = \frac{4\pi}{3}$	$270° = \frac{3\pi}{2}$	$300° = \frac{5\pi}{3}$	$315° = \frac{7\pi}{4}$	$330° = \frac{11\pi}{6}$	$360° = 2\pi$
$\tan \theta$ (exact)	?	?	?	?	?	?	?	?
$\tan \theta$ (approx.)	?	?	?	?	?	?	?	?

Background

Students may think it unusual that the graph of $y = \tan \theta$ is so different from the graph of the sine and cosine functions, but point out that graphs of quotients of functions are often quite different from the graphs of either individual function. For instance, $x = \frac{x^3}{x^2}$, and the graph of $y = x$ is certainly quite different from the graphs of either $y = x^3$ or $y = x^2$. Similarly, $\tan \theta = \frac{\sin \theta}{\cos \theta}$, and the graph of the tangent function is quite different from the graphs of the sine and cosine function.

Example 3 As strange as the graph of blood pressure may seem, it can be closely described as the sum of sine and cosine functions.

Step 2 At the right, a graph of the values of the tangent function given in the first part of the table from Step 1 is shown. Copy this graph, and add the points you found in Step 1 to the graph.

Step 3 Draw a smooth curve through these points, to show the graph of $y = \tan \theta$ for all θ, $0° \le \theta \le 360°$, $0 \le \theta \le 2\pi$ where $\tan \theta$ is defined.

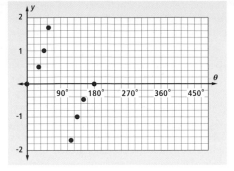

The Graph of the Tangent Function

At the right is a graph of $y = \tan x$ for $-\frac{3\pi}{2} \le x \le \frac{5\pi}{2}$. Notice that this graph looks strikingly different from the graphs of both the sine and cosine functions. The tangent function has asymptotes and does not have a maximum or minimum value.

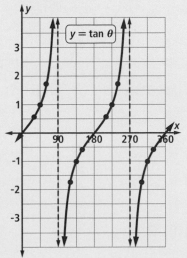

$h(x) = \tan x$

Example 1

Consider $f(x) = \tan x$.

a. Give the domain and range of the function f.

b. Is f an odd function, an even function, or neither? Justify your answer.

Solution

a. Because the tangent function has multiple vertical asymptotes, the domain of the tangent function is the set of all real numbers except odd multiples of 90° or $\frac{\pi}{2}$. Notice that the tangent function has no minimum or maximum values. Therefore, its range is the set of all real numbers.

b. From the Opposites Theorem, $\tan(-x) = -\tan x$ for all x. Thus, the tangent function is an odd function.

Periodicity and the Trigonometric Functions

The periodic nature displayed by sine, cosine, and tangent is summarized in the following theorem.

> **Periodicity Theorem**
>
> For any real number x and any integer n,
> $$\sin x = \sin (x + n \cdot 2\pi) = \sin (x + n \cdot 360°)$$
> $$\cos x = \cos (x + n \cdot 2\pi) = \cos (x + n \cdot 360°)$$
> $$\tan x = \tan (x + n \cdot \pi) = \tan (x + n \cdot 180°).$$

The Tangent Function and Periodicity **253**

---

2 Teaching

Notes on the Lesson

Activity 1 Students should complete this activity carefully. In Steps 2 and 3, encourage students to mark both the θ-axis and the tan θ-axis with exact values and decimal approximations.

In the table, tan θ is given in terms of both decimal approximations and exact values.

Example 1 This example indicates some of the properties of the cosine function that students should know at this time. Others are its domain and range, maximum and minimum values, its period, and the graph.

> **Additional Example**
>
> **Example 1** Consider $f(x) = \cos x$.
>
> a. Give the domain and range of f. **The domain of the cosine function is the set of all real numbers, $\mathbb{R}$; the range of f is $-1 \le f(x) \le 1$.**
>
> b. Tell whether f is an odd function, an even function or neither. Justify your answer. **From the Opposites Theorem, $\cos(-x) = \cos x$ for all x. Thus the cosine function is an even function.**

Additional Answers

Activity

Steps 2 and 3:

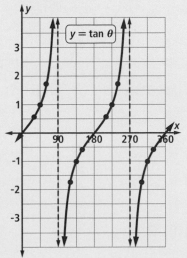

$y = \tan \theta$

Additional Answers

Activity

Step 1:

θ	$120° = \frac{2\pi}{3}$	$135° = \frac{3\pi}{4}$	$150° = \frac{5\pi}{6}$
tan θ (exact)	$-\sqrt{3}$	-1	$-\frac{\sqrt{3}}{3}$
tan θ (approx.)	-1.732	-1	-0.577

210°	225°	240°	270°	300°	315°	330°	360°
$\frac{\sqrt{3}}{3}$	1	$\sqrt{3}$	undefined	$-\sqrt{3}$	-1	$-\frac{\sqrt{3}}{3}$	0
0.577	1	1.732	undefined	-1.732	-1	-0.577	0

4-6

Notes on the Lesson

Example 3 This example anticipates some of the analysis students will be doing in the next few lessons in order to graph trigonometric functions.

Additional Example

Example 2 Use the Periodicity Theorem to find sin 15780°. $-\frac{\sqrt{3}}{2}$

Example 3 The graph below shows the average travel time from downtown Metropolis to Metropolis International Airport during a typical week (Monday to Friday). For this function, determine each.

a. the maximum and minimum values
about 47 minutes; about 16 minutes

b. the range about 31 minutes

c. the period about 24 hours

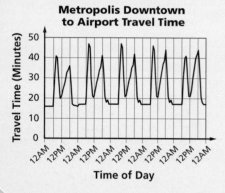

Metropolis Downtown to Airport Travel Time

The theorem states that the sine and cosine functions are *periodic functions* with *period* 360° or 2π radians, while the tangent function is a periodic function with period 180° or π radians.

Definitions of Periodic and Period

A function f is **periodic** if there is a positive number p such that $f(x + p) = f(x)$ for all x in the domain of f. The smallest such p, if it exists, is called the **period** of f.

A part of the function from any particular x to $x + p$, where p is the period of the function, is called a *cycle* of the function. For instance, one cycle of the tangent function is from 0 to π; another is from $-\frac{\pi}{2}$ to $\frac{\pi}{2}$.

Example 2

Use the Periodicity Theorem to find cos 2670°.

Solution $\frac{2670°}{360°} \approx 7.4$, so $2670° - 7 \cdot 360°$ will be less than 360°. $2670° - 7 \cdot 360° = 150°$, so $R_{2670°} = R_{150°}$. Therefore,
$\cos 2670° = \cos 150° = -\frac{\sqrt{3}}{2}$.

Many phenomena are periodic, including tides, calendars, heart beats, actions of circular gears, phases of the moon, and seasons of the year.

GUIDED

Example 3

The graph at the right shows normal human blood pressure as a function of time. Blood pressure is *systolic* when the heart is contracting and *diastolic* when the heart is expanding. The changes from systolic to diastolic blood pressure create the pulse. For this function, determine each.

Blood Pressure

a. the maximum and minimum values

b. the range

c. the period

Solution

about 128; about 87

a. The maximum and minimum values of the graph are those values in which the graph obtains a highest and lowest point, respectively. The maximum value on this graph is __?__, the minimum value is __?__.

b. The range is the maximum value minus the minimum value. From Part a, the range shown on this graph is __?__. about 41

c. The period is the range of x-values for the smallest section of the graph that can be translated horizontally onto itself. The period shown on this graph is __?__ seconds. about 0.167 seconds

Accommodating the Learner ⬆

Students might be confused by the fact that the tangent function does not have the same period as the sine and cosine functions. You might want to point out to students that the period of π for the tangent function agrees with the Half-Turn Theorem which states that tan (π + θ) = tan θ. Furthermore, the period of the sine and cosine functions cannot be π because sin (π + θ) ≠ sin θ and cos (π + θ) ≠ cos θ.

Additional Answers

1c. The graph of the tangent function has a vertical asymptote at values where cos θ = 0.

Questions

COVERING THE IDEAS

1. a. List all values of θ between $0°$ and $360°$ such that $\cos\theta = 0$.
   b. What is $f(\theta) = \tan\theta$ for these θ-values? **undefined**
   c. What do these values of θ mean for the graph of the tangent function? **See margin.**

2. List all of the values of x from 0 to 2π for which $\sin x = 0$. What do these x-values indicate for the graph of the tangent function?

In 3–5, use the Periodicity Theorem to evaluate.

3. $\sin 495°$ 4. $\cos 810°$ 5. $\tan 3570°$

6. Given that $\tan\frac{4\pi}{9} \approx 5.671$, use the Periodicity Theorem to evaluate.
   a. $\tan\frac{13\pi}{9}$ b. $\tan -\frac{5\pi}{9}$ c. $\tan\frac{22\pi}{9}$

7. What is the period of the function with the given equation?
   a. $y = \sin x$ **2π**   b. $y = \cos x$ **2π**   c. $y = \tan x$ **π**

APPLYING THE MATHEMATICS

8. Suppose that f is a periodic function whose domain is the real numbers. One cycle of f is graphed at the right.
   a. What is the period of f? **8**
   b. Graph f on the interval $-15 \leq x \leq 15$. **See margin.**
   c. Find $f(51)$. **$f(51) = f(3) = 2$**
   d. Find four integer values of x such that $f(x) = 0$.

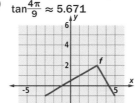

9. If one endpoint of a cycle of the cosine function is $90°$, where is the other endpoint? **450°**

10. If one endpoint of a cycle of the tangent function is $\frac{\pi}{2}$, where is the other endpoint? **$\frac{3\pi}{2}$**

11. State equations for two of the asymptotes of the tangent function
    a. in radians. **$x = \frac{\pi}{2}, x = -\frac{\pi}{2}$**   b. in degrees. **$x = 90°, x = -90°$**

12. Let $f(n)$ be the number in the nth decimal place of $\frac{1}{7}$.
    a. Give the values of $f(1), f(2), f(3),$ and $f(4)$. **1, 4, 2, 8**
    b. f is a periodic function. What is its period? **6**

REVIEW

13. The table at the right contains hourly data for the height of tide relative to the mean low water level in Pago Pago, American Samoa on October 5, 2008. (**Lesson 4-5**) **See margin.**
    a. Create a scatterplot of the data.
    b. Determine the range of the data.
    c. From the scatterplot, estimate the period of the data.

1a. **90°, 270°**

2. **0, π, 2π; The graph of the tangent function intercepts the x-axis at values where $\sin x = 0$.**

3. $\sin 495° = \sin(135° + 1 \cdot 360°) = \sin 135° = \frac{\sqrt{2}}{2}$

4. $\cos 810° = \cos(90° + 2 \cdot 360°) = \cos 90° = 0$

5. $\tan 3750° = \tan(330° + 9 \cdot 360°) = \tan 330° = -\frac{\sqrt{3}}{3}$

6a. $\tan\left(\frac{4\pi}{9} + 1 \cdot \pi\right) = \tan\frac{4\pi}{9} \approx 5.671$

6b. $\tan\left(\frac{4\pi}{9} - 1 \cdot \pi\right) = \tan\frac{4\pi}{9} \approx 5.671$

6c. $\tan\left(\frac{4\pi}{9} + 2 \cdot \pi\right) = \tan\frac{4\pi}{9} \approx 5.671$

8d. **Answers vary. Sample: $x = -1, 63, 7, 119$**

Hour	Height	Hour	Height
0	1.59	12	2.03
1	1.29	13	1.65
2	0.91	14	1.14
3	0.61	15	0.83
4	0.65	16	0.62
5	0.79	17	0.49
6	1.04	18	0.53
7	1.32	19	0.87
8	1.75	20	1.15
9	2.01	21	1.49
10	2.20	22	1.77
11	2.21	23	1.87

Source: National Oceanographic and Atmospheric Administration

The Tangent Function and Periodicity   **255**

---

3 Assignment

Recommended Assignment
- Questions 1–7
- • Questions 8–20
- • Question 21 (extra credit)
- Reading Lesson 4-7
- Covering the Ideas 4-7 (Questions 1–13)

Notes on the Questions

Question 6 You might pose the following question: Find all solutions to $\sin x = 5.671$. **There are none.** Why? **5.671 is not in the range of the sine function; 5.671 is not a second coordinate of a point on the unit circle.**

Question 8 The full graph of the function f resembles a frieze pattern.

Question 12 In this regard, every infinite repeating decimal generates a periodic function.

Question 13 The periodicity of the tides is caused by the rotation of Earth about its axes and the rotation of the Moon around Earth.

Additional Answers

8b.

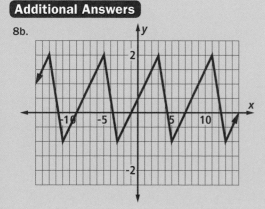

13a.

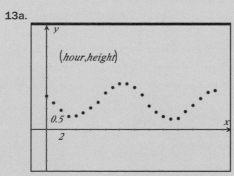

13b. $\{h \mid 0.5 \leq h \leq 2.25\}$ where h is the height after t hours

13c. **about 14 hours**

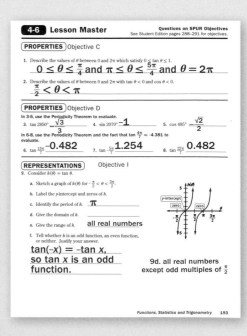

4-6 Lesson Master   Questions on SPUR Objectives
See Student Edition pages 288–291 for objectives.

PROPERTIES Objective C

1. Describe the values of θ between 0 and 2π which satisfy $0 \leq \tan\theta \leq 1$.
   $0 \leq \theta \leq \frac{\pi}{4}$ and $\pi \leq \theta \leq \frac{5\pi}{4}$ and $\theta = 2\pi$

2. Describe the values of θ between 0 and 2π with $\tan\theta < 0$ and $\cos\theta < 0$.
   $\frac{\pi}{2} < \theta < \pi$

PROPERTIES Objective D

In 3–5, use the Periodicity Theorem to evaluate.
3. $\tan 2850°$ $\frac{\sqrt{3}}{3}$ 4. $\sin 2070°$ -1 5. $\cos 495°$ $-\frac{\sqrt{2}}{2}$

In 6–8, use the Periodicity Theorem and the fact that $\tan\frac{4\pi}{7} \approx -4.381$ to evaluate.
6. $\tan\frac{13\pi}{7}$ -0.482 7. $\tan -\frac{5\pi}{7}$ 1.254 8. $\tan\frac{22\pi}{7}$ 0.482

REPRESENTATIONS Objective I
9. Consider $h(\theta) = \tan\theta$.
   a. Sketch a graph of $h(\theta)$ for $-\frac{\pi}{2} < \theta < \frac{3\pi}{2}$.
   b. Label the y-intercept and zeros of h.
   c. Identify the period of h. π
   d. Give the domain of h.
   e. Give the range of h. all real numbers
   f. Tell whether h is an odd function, an even function, or neither. Justify your answer.
   $\tan(-x) = -\tan x$, so $\tan x$ is an odd function.

9d. all real numbers except odd multiples of $\frac{\pi}{2}$

Functions, Statistics and Trigonometry   **193**

4 Wrap-Up

Ongoing Assessment

Have students take a few minutes to write down a list of as many similarities and differences between the graph of the tangent function and those of the and sine and cosine functions as they can. When time is up, have students write a collective list on the board. **Answers vary.** Check that students' descriptions are as accurate, concise, and mathematical as possible.

Administer Quiz 2 (or a quiz of your own) after students complete this lesson.

Project Update

Project 2, *Beat Matching and DJing 101*, on page 282 relates to the content of this lesson.

14. Fill in the blanks for the graph of the sine function at the right. (**Lesson 4-5**) 2π; $\frac{7\pi}{2}$; -1; 4π

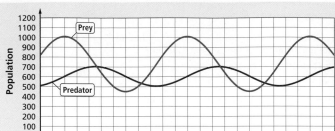

15. Refer to the predator-prey graph below. (**Lesson 4-5**)
    For both the predator and the prey functions, determine the
    a. domain.   **b.** maximum and minimum.   **c.** period.

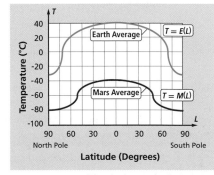

Months

15a. predator: $\{t \mid t > 0\}$; prey: $\{t \mid t > 0\}$ where t is months after the first measurement

15b. predator: maximum $\approx$ 710, minimum $\approx$ 500; prey: maximum $\approx$ 1,025, minimum $\approx$ 450

15c. predator: 20 months; prey: 20 months

16. Find x such that $0 \le x \le 2\pi$, if $\cos x = \frac{1}{2}$ and $\sin x = -\frac{\sqrt{3}}{2}$.
    (**Lesson 4-4**) $\frac{5\pi}{3}$

17. Is the cosine function odd, even, or neither? Justify your conclusion. (**Lessons 4-3, 3-4**) **even; $\cos(-x) = \cos x$**

18. Suppose $R_\theta(1, 0) = (0.75, y)$ and is a point in Quadrant II. Find y.
    (**Lesson 4-3**) **about 0.661**

19. Under some translation T, the point $(-6, 2)$ is mapped to $(0, 7)$.
    a. State the rule for T.   **b.** Find $T(9, 9)$. (**Lesson 3-2**)

19a. $T(x, y) \rightarrow (x + 6, y + 5)$

19b. (15, 14)

20. The graph at the right is from *Weather on the Planets*, by George Ohring. It shows how temperature is a function of latitude on Earth and Mars when it is spring in one hemisphere on each planet. Let L be the latitude on each planet, $E(L)$ be the average temperature at latitude L on Earth, and $M(L)$ be the average temperature at latitude L on Mars.
    a. Is L the dependent or independent variable?
    b. Estimate $E(60)$. **20°C**
    c. Estimate $E(0) - M(0)$, and state what quantity this expression represents.
    d. What is the range of M? (**Lesson 2-1**)

20a. independent variable

20c. 80°C; At the equator, the Earth is on average 80°C warmer than Mars at the equator.

20d. $\{T \mid -80 \le T \le -40\}$

EXPLORATION

21. The word *tangent* has another meaning in geometry. It also has another meaning in English. What are these meanings?
    See margin.

Additional Answers

21. In English, a tangent is a remark that is not really relevant to the current topic at hand. Two geometric objects are considered to be tangents if they meet at a single point and do not cross.

Lesson 4-7

Scale-Change Images of Trigonometric Functions

Vocabulary

sine wave

amplitude

frequency

▶ **BIG IDEA** The Graph Scale-Change Theorem can be applied to obtain the equation, amplitude, and period of scale-change images of the graph of a parent trigonometric function.

Sine Waves

A pure tone, such as that produced by a tuning fork, travels in a *sine wave*. A **sine wave** is the image of the graph of the sine or cosine function under a composite of translations and scale changes. The pitch of the tone is related to the period of the wave; the longer the period, the lower the pitch. The intensity of the tone is related to the *amplitude* of the wave. The **amplitude** of a sine wave is half the distance between its maximum and minimum values.

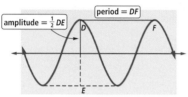

amplitude $= \frac{1}{2} DE$

period $= DF$

STOP QY1

Stretching a sound sine wave vertically changes the intensity of the tone. Stretching a sound wave horizontally changes its pitch. Recall from Lesson 3-5 that a scale change is a mapping $S: (x, y) \rightarrow (ax, by)$ centered at the origin with $a \neq 0$ and $b \neq 0$. Under this scale change, an equation for the image of $y = f(x)$ is $\frac{y}{b} = f\left(\frac{x}{a}\right)$.

Example 1 shows how a scale change affects both the amplitude and period of a sine wave.

Example 1

Consider the function with equation $y = 6 \cos\left(\frac{x}{3}\right)$.

a. Explain how this function is related to its parent function, the cosine function.

b. Identify its amplitude and its period.

(continued on next page)

Mental Math

The expression $3r - 8$ is in the form $ax - h$. Rewrite it in the form $\frac{x - \frac{h}{a}}{\frac{1}{a}}$.

$$\frac{r - \frac{8}{3}}{\frac{1}{3}}$$

An oscilloscope is used to record changes in the voltage of an electric current.

▶ **QY1**

The range of the sine function is $\{y \mid -1 \leq y \leq 1\}$, so the amplitude of the graph of $y = \sin x$ is __?__.

Background

This lesson displays one of the obvious benefits of the Graph Scale-Change Theorem. All of the sine waves in this lesson have shapes that are predictable as scale change images of the parent functions $y = \sin x$ and $y = \cos x$. By comparing them with the parent functions, the amplitude, period, and frequency of these sine waves can rather easily be found. Students are expected to check their work using a graphing utility.

The terms *amplitude* and *period* both derive from the fact that sound travels in sine waves. By this we mean that sound is formed when an object hits an elastic membrane. A point on that membrane vibrates like the weight on a spring. The faster it vibrates (the shorter the period), the higher the pitch of the sound. The greater the distance it vibrates (the greater the amplitude), the louder the sound.

(continued on next page)

Lesson 4-7

GOAL

Apply the scale changes that can be done with the graph of any relation to the graphs of the sine, cosine, and tangent functions, where they have special meaning.

SPUR Objectives

E Identify the amplitude, period, frequency, phase shift, and other properties of trigonometric functions.

F Write and solve equations for phenomena described by trigonometric functions.

J Graph and describe transformation images of graphs of trigonometric functions.

Materials/Resources

· Lesson Master 4-7
· Resource Masters 83–86

HOMEWORK   • Option 1

• Questions 1–13   • Option 2
• • Questions 14–23
• • Question 24 (extra credit)
  • Reading Lesson 4-8
  • Covering the Ideas 4-8
    (Questions 1–9)

Local Standards

---

1 ### Warm-Up

1. Sketch a graph of $y = \sin x$ over the interval $-4\pi \leq x \leq 4\pi$.

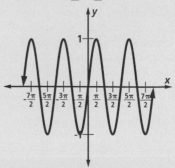

(continued on next page)

4-7

2. How many periods of the sine function are shown in the graph in Warm-Up 1? **4**

3. On the same axes and over the same interval, sketch a graph of $y = \sin 2x$.

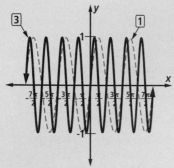

4. How many periods of the sine function are shown in the graph in Warm-Up 3? **8**

5. How do the relative maximum and relative minimum values of the graph in Warm-Up 3 compare with the relative maximum and relative minimum values in Warm-Up 1? **They are the same.**

2 ❙ Teaching

Notes on the Lesson

Sine waves The actual process of graphing sine waves can be quite tedious. Some sketching of sine waves by hand is useful but time-consuming. Capitalize on the speed and accuracy of graphing utilities. Especially valuable for students is seeing an image graphed with its preimage, as in Example 1. If your graphing utility has color capabilities, the graphics can be impressive. It is worthwhile to verify some answers as part of the class discussion.

Additional Example

Example 1 Consider the function with equation $y = 3.5 \sin\left(\frac{4x}{5}\right)$.

a. Explain how this function is related to its parent function $y = \sin x$.
   The graph of the parent function is stretched by a factor of 3.5 vertically and by a factor of $\frac{5}{4}$ horizontally.

b. Identify its amplitude and period.
   The given function has amplitude 3.5 and period $\frac{5\pi}{2}$.

Solution

a. Divide each side of the given equation by 6. This rewrites the function rule in a form that can be analyzed using the Graph Scale-Change Theorem.
$$\frac{y}{6} = \cos\left(\frac{x}{3}\right)$$
In the equation $y = \cos x$, y has been replaced by $\frac{y}{6}$ and x by $\frac{x}{3}$. The graph of the parent function is stretched vertically by a factor of 6 and horizontally by a factor of 3.

b. The vertical stretch means that the maximum and minimum values of the parent function are multiplied by 6. Hence, the given function has amplitude $\frac{1}{2}(6 - -6) = 6$. The horizontal stretch means that the period 2π of the parent function is also stretched by a factor of 3. So the given function has a period of $3(2\pi) = 6\pi$.

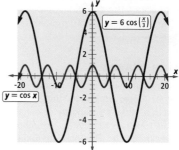

Check Graphs of parts of $y = \cos x$ and $y = 6\cos\left(\frac{x}{3}\right)$ are shown at the right. Only a little more than two cycles of $y = 6\cos\left(\frac{x}{3}\right)$ are shown, but from this you can see that the amplitude and period found above were correct.

If the graphs of $y = \cos x$ and $y = 6\cos\left(\frac{x}{3}\right)$ in Example 1 represented sound waves, the sound of $y = 6\cos\left(\frac{x}{3}\right)$ would be 6 times as loud and have a lower pitch than that of $y = \cos x$.

In general, the functions defined by $\frac{y}{b} = \sin\left(\frac{x}{a}\right)$ and $\frac{y}{b} = \cos\left(\frac{x}{a}\right)$ are equivalent to the functions defined by
$$y = b\sin\left(\frac{x}{a}\right) \quad \text{and} \quad y = b\cos\left(\frac{x}{a}\right),$$
where $a \neq 0$ and $b \neq 0$, and their graphs are images of the graphs of the parent functions
$$y = \sin x \quad \text{and} \quad y = \cos x$$
under the scale change that maps (x, y) to (ax, by). The theorem below indicates the relationship of the constants a and b to the properties of the sine waves.

Theorem (Properties of Sine Waves)

The graphs of the functions defined by $y = b\sin\left(\frac{x}{a}\right)$ and $y = b\cos\left(\frac{x}{a}\right)$ have amplitude $= |b|$ and period $= 2\pi|a|$.

STOP **QY2**

There is a corresponding theorem for the graph of the function with equation $\frac{y}{b} = \tan\left(\frac{x}{a}\right)$. However, the parent tangent function does not have an amplitude and the period of the parent tangent function is π, so the period of $\frac{y}{b} = \tan\left(\frac{x}{a}\right)$ is $\pi|a|$.

▶ **QY2**

In the theorem, why is absolute value used in the calculation of both amplitude and period?

An obvious example of this is when a stick hits a drum in a band, but our ears also have membranes and they too vibrate when sound hits them.

Accommodating the Learner ⬆

The coefficients in the equations in this lesson are rational numbers written as fractions. Have students give the amplitude and period of the following.

1. $y = -\sqrt{2}\cos(0.45x)$ **amplitude: $\sqrt{2}$; period: $\frac{40\pi}{9}$**

2. $3y = 5\sin(2\pi x)$ **amplitude: $\frac{5}{3}$; period: 1**

Example 2

The graph at the right shows an image of the graph of $y = \sin x$ under a scale change. Find an equation for the image.

Solution An equation for the image is of the form $y = b \sin\left(\frac{x}{a}\right)$. From the graph, there is a minimum at (45°, –4) and a maximum at (135°, 4). The difference between the maximum and minimum values of y is 8, so the amplitude is 4. The graph shows a cycle from 0° to 180°, so the period is 180°. Therefore, $|b| = 4$ and $360°|a| = 180°$. Thus, $b = 4$ or -4 and $a = \frac{1}{2}$ or $-\frac{1}{2}$. Consider the four possibilities.

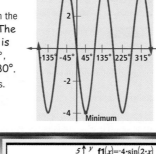

$$y = 4 \sin(2x)$$
$$y = -4 \sin(2x)$$
$$y = 4 \sin(-2x)$$
$$y = -4 \sin(-2x)$$

Notice that the graph pictured must be a reflection image of the graph of the parent sine function since, for example, starting at zero, the graph decreases as you move towards 45°. **One equation that will produce the graph is $y = -4 \sin(2x)$.**

Check Use a graphing utility to check that your equation produces the given graph.

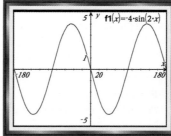

STOP QY3

▶ **QY3**

Which of the other choices in the solution will produce the graph?

The Frequency of a Sine Wave

Notice that the graph of $y = \cos x$ in Example 1 completes 3 cycles for every one completed by the graph of $y = 6 \cos\left(\frac{x}{3}\right)$. We say that $y = \cos x$ has three times the *frequency* of $y = 6 \cos\left(\frac{x}{3}\right)$. In general, the **frequency** of a periodic function is the reciprocal of the period, and represents the number of cycles the curve completes per unit of the independent variable. Thus, the frequency of the cosine function is $\frac{1}{2\pi}$, and the frequency of the function $y = 6 \cos\left(\frac{x}{3}\right)$ is $\frac{1}{6\pi}$.

When a sine wave represents sound, doubling the frequency results in a pitch one octave higher. So the graph of $y = 6 \cos\left(\frac{x}{3}\right)$ represents a sound with pitch between one and two octaves lower than the pitch represented by $y = \cos x$ and with 6 times the intensity. It is common in these situations to view the x-axis as representing time. In sound waves, the y-axis represents pressure, typically measured in newtons (abbreviated N) per square meter, $\frac{N}{m^2}$.

Accommodating the Learner ⬇

In situations where students must work with a trigonometric function whose graph is scaled both horizontally and vertically, it may be very helpful to have them visualize the transformation in only one dimension at a time. In Example 1, you might wish to graph the intermediate equation $y = \cos\left(\frac{x}{3}\right)$, in which only the horizontal scale change has been applied.

If the vertical scale change is then applied to this graph, it would be like grabbing all the maximum and minimum points and pulling them up to 6 and down to –6 respectively (the roots, or x-intercepts, remain in place like anchors since they are fixed under the scale change).

Notes on the Lesson

Theorem You may be accustomed to considering functions of the form $y = A \sin bx$ and $y = A \cos bx$. We use the forms $y = b \sin \frac{x}{a}$ and $y = b \cos \frac{x}{a}$ so that students can easily see the application of the Graph Scale-Change Theorem. That is, the forms we use are equivalent to $\frac{y}{b} = \sin \frac{x}{a}$ and $\frac{y}{b} = \cos \frac{x}{a}$. Because these are only special cases of something students already know, this lesson is easy for most students.

A difficult part of the algebra in this lesson is realizing that $\sin (kx)$ is equal to $\sin\left(\frac{x}{\frac{1}{k}}\right)$, so replacing x by kx means a horizontal scale change of magnitude $\frac{1}{k}$, not k. Although this idea has been discussed earlier, in Chapter 3, some students may still get confused. Such confusion is natural and should be expected.

The frequency of a sine wave You might bring an oscilloscope to class (or use the oscilloscope you brought at the start of this chapter). Use it to show that doubling the frequency produces a tone an octave higher and period $\frac{1}{2}$ that of the given tone. Show a sound and give its frequency, and have students indicate the scale on the x-axis that would be appropriate for that sound.

Students also sometimes confuse frequency and period. As the word "frequency" is used in statistics, the frequency of a sound or of a function is the number of times the wave function repeats in a given time interval. The more times the function repeats in an interval, the smaller the period; they are inversely proportional since their product is a constant.

Additional Example

Example 2 The grid below shows a graph of $y = \cos x$ and its image under a scale change. Find an equation for the image. $y = 3 \cos \frac{x}{3}$

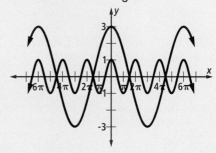

4-7

Example 3

A tuning fork vibrates with a frequency of 512 cycles per second. The intensity of the tone is the result of a vibration whose maximum pressure is $22 \frac{N}{m^2}$. Find an equation to model the sound wave produced by the tuning fork.

Solution The equation has the form $y = b \sin\left(\frac{x}{a}\right)$ where x is the time in seconds after the tuning fork is struck. The frequency is the reciprocal of the period, so

$$512 = \frac{1}{2\pi|a|}.$$

Solve for a to get $\qquad a = \pm\frac{1}{1024\pi}.$

The maximum pressure of the air gives the amplitude $b = 22$. Choosing the positive value of a, the equation is $y = 22 \sin(1024\pi x)$.

Knowing the number of cycles per unit of independent variable can help you solve trigonometric equations.

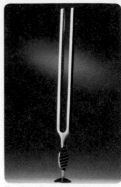

Tuning In Tuning forks are most commonly used to tune musical instruments to the note "A."

Example 4

Without using technology, determine how many solutions each equation below has on the interval $0 \leq x \leq 2\pi$. Confirm your answer with a graph.

a. $\cos(3x) = 0.8$ **b.** $5 \tan\left(\frac{x}{2}\right) = 3$

Solution

a. The parent cosine function has two solutions in the interval $0 \leq x \leq 2\pi$ because this domain represents one cycle. $y = \cos(3x)$ is the image of $y = \cos x$ under a horizontal shrink of magnitude $\frac{1}{3}$. That means that each cycle of $y = \cos(3x)$ is one-third as long as a cycle of $y = \cos x$, so there will be three cycles on the interval $0 \leq x \leq 2\pi$ and six solutions. A graph confirms that there are six points of intersection of $y = \cos(3x)$ and $y = 0.8$ on $0 \leq x \leq 2\pi$.

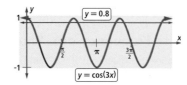

b. The graph of $y = 5 \tan\left(\frac{x}{2}\right)$ is the image of the graph of $y = \tan x$ under a horizontal stretch by a factor of 2. So each cycle is twice as long, and there are half as many points of intersection on the interval $0 \leq x \leq 2\pi$. Therefore, there is only one solution. The graph at the right confirms a single solution.

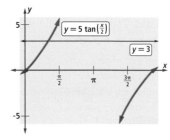

ENGLISH LEARNERS

Vocabulary Development

You might find it useful to speak of the etymology of some of the terms in this lesson. The word "amplitude" is related to the word "ample," indicating how ample (loud) a sound is. A "period" to a sentence indicates its completion. Similarly, a "period" of a sine wave indicates the completion of one cycle of that wave. This is not a contrived connection; periods were originally punctuation marks that indicated periods of time, such as at the end of lines of verse.

When the verse was regular, the end of the line was also the end of a time interval of fixed length.

Questions

COVERING THE IDEAS

1. Consider the function with equation $y = \frac{1}{5}\sin x$.
   a. **True or False** The graph of this function is a sine wave. **true**
   b. What is its period? **2π**
   c. What is its amplitude? **$\frac{1}{5}$**
   d. Sketch graphs of $y = \frac{1}{5}\sin x$ and $y = \sin x$ on the same set of axes for $-\pi \le x \le 2\pi$. **See margin.**
   e. Describe how the two graphs in Part d are related.

In 2 and 3, an equation for a sine wave is given.
   a. Find its amplitude.   b. Find its period.

2. $y = 3\cos x$ **a. 3   b. 2π**   3. $\frac{y}{4} = \cos\left(\frac{x}{3}\right)$ **a. 4   b. 6π**

4. **Multiple Choice** Which equation could yield the graph at the right? **C**

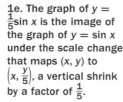

   A $y = 3\sin(2\theta)$ B $y = 3\cos(2\theta)$
   C $y = 3\cos\left(\frac{\theta}{2}\right)$ D $y = 3\sin\left(\frac{\theta}{2}\right)$

5. a. Find an equation of the image of the graph of $y = \sin x$ under the transformation $(x, y) \to (5x, y)$. **$y = \sin\left(\frac{x}{5}\right)$**
   b. Find the amplitude and period of the image. **1; 10π**

6. a. Give the period and amplitude of $y = \frac{1}{5}\sin(3\theta)$.
   b. Check using a graphing utility. **See margin.**

7. The graph at the right is an image of the graph of $y = \sin x$ under a scale change. Find an equation for this curve. **$y = 6\sin\left(\frac{x}{4}\right)$**

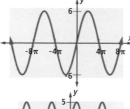

8. Refer to the graph sketched at the right.
   a. Identify the amplitude, period, and frequency.
   b. **Fill in the Blanks** If this graph represents a sound wave, then that sound is __?__ times as loud and has __?__ times the frequency of the parent sound wave with equation $y = \sin x$.

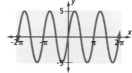

9. Suppose one tone has a frequency of 330 cycles per second, and a second has a frequency of 660 cycles per second.
   a. Which has the higher pitch? **the tone with frequency of 660 cycles per second**
   b. How many octaves higher is that pitch? **It is one octave higher.**

10. How many solutions does $\sin(5x) = 0.65$ have for $0 \le x \le 2\pi$? **10**

11. Sketch one cycle of $6y = \cos\left(\frac{x}{4}\right)$, and label the zeros of the function. **See margin.**

12. **Multiple Choice** A sound wave whose parent is the graph of $y = \sin x$ has 3 times the frequency and 7 times the amplitude of the parent. What is a possible equation for this sound wave? **A**

   A $y = 7\sin(3x)$ B $y = 7\sin\left(\frac{1}{3}x\right)$
   C $y = 3\sin\left(\frac{1}{7}x\right)$ D $y = \frac{1}{3}\sin\left(\frac{1}{7}x\right)$

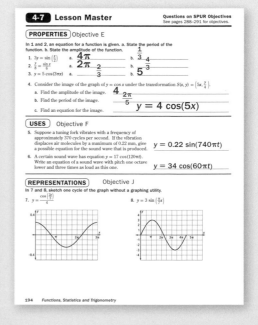

Most modern full-size pianos have 88 keys spanning $7\frac{1}{4}$ octaves.

Scale-Change Images of Trigonometric Functions   **261**

1e. The graph of $y = \frac{1}{5}\sin x$ is the image of the graph of $y = \sin x$ under the scale change that maps (x, y) to $\left(x, \frac{y}{5}\right)$, a vertical shrink by a factor of $\frac{1}{5}$.

8a. amplitude: 5; period: π, frequency: $\frac{1}{\pi}$

8b. 5; 2

---

③ Assignment

Recommended Assignment
- Questions 1–13
- • Questions 14–23
- • Question 24 (extra credit)
- Reading Lesson 4-8
- Covering the Ideas 4-8 (Questions 1–9)

Notes on the Questions
Questions 5, 9, and 12 It is a good idea to display the graphs of the parent and the offspring so students can see and discuss them. Either a hard copy printout or a tracing of the computer or calculator screen can be used as sketches for these graphs.

Additional Answers

11. Answers vary. Sample:

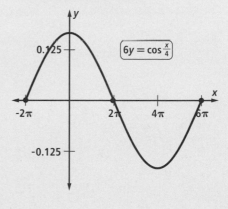

$6y = \cos\frac{x}{4}$

Questions on SPUR Objectives
See pages 288-291 for objectives.

PROPERTIES Objective E

In 1 and 2, an equation for a function is given. a. State the period of the function. b. State the amplitude of the function.

1. $3y = \sin\left(\frac{x}{2}\right)$ a. **4π**   b. **$\frac{1}{3}$**
2. $\frac{y}{8} = \frac{\sin x}{6}$ a. **2π**   b. **$\frac{4}{3}$**
3. $y = 5\cos(3\pi x)$ a. **$\frac{2}{3}$**   b. **5**

4. Consider the image of the graph of $y = \cos x$ under the transformation $S(x, y) = \left(5x, \frac{7}{4}\right)$.
   a. Find the amplitude of the image. **4**
   b. Find the period of the image. **$\frac{2\pi}{5}$**
   c. Find an equation for the image. **$y = 4\cos(5x)$**

USES Objective F

5. Suppose a tuning fork vibrates with a frequency of approximately 370 cycles per second. If the vibration displaces air molecules by a maximum of 0.22 mm, give a possible equation for the sound wave that is produced. **$y = 0.22\sin(740\pi t)$**
6. A certain sound wave has equation $y = 17\cos(120\pi t)$. Write an equation of a sound wave with pitch one octave lower and three times as loud as this one. **$y = 34\cos(60\pi t)$**

REPRESENTATIONS Objective J

In 7 and 8, sketch one cycle of the graph without a graphing utility.
7. $y = \frac{\cos\left(\frac{2x}{3}\right)}{4}$ 8. $y = 3\sin\left(\frac{\pi}{2}x\right)$

194   *Functions, Statistics and Trigonometry*

Additional Answers

1d.

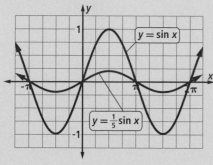

$y = \sin x$

$y = \frac{1}{5}\sin x$

6a. period: $\frac{2\pi}{3}$, amplitude $\frac{1}{5}$
6b.

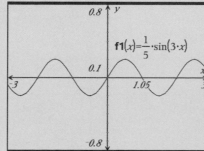

$f1(x) = \frac{1}{5} \cdot \sin(3 \cdot x)$

4-7

13. Consider a tuning fork vibrating at 440 cycles per second and displacing air molecules by a maximum of $32 \frac{N}{m^2}$. Give a possible equation for the sound wave that is produced. $y = 32 \sin(880\pi x)$

4 Wrap-Up

Ongoing Assessment
Have students write down an equation of a scale-change image of a sine or cosine function, like those in Examples 1 and 2. Have students give their paper to a partner, who should then graph the function, identify its amplitude and period, and explain how the function is related to its parent function. **Answers vary. Check students' work.**

Project Update
Project 1, *Sums of Sine Waves with the Same Period*, Project 2, *Beat Matching and DJing 101*, and Project 4, *Square Waves*, on pages 282 and 283 relate to the content of this lesson.

APPLYING THE MATHEMATICS

14. Residential electricity is called AC for "alternating current," because the direction of current flow alternates through a circuit. The current (measured in amperes) is a sine function of time. The graph at the right models an AC situation.

    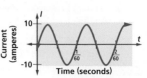

    a. Write an equation for current I as a function of time t.
    b. Find the current produced at 0.04 seconds. **5.88 amperes**

15. Which of the functions f, g, and h, defined by $f(x) = \tan x$, $g(x) = \tan(3x)$, and $h(x) = 3 \sin\left(\frac{x}{2}\right)$, have the same period? **f and h**

In 16–18, match each equation with its graph below.

16. $\frac{y}{2} = \sin\left(\frac{x}{2}\right)$ **C**   17. $2y = \sin\left(\frac{x}{2}\right)$ **A**   18. $\frac{y}{2} = \sin(2x)$ **B**

A 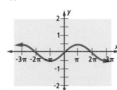   B 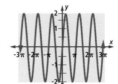   C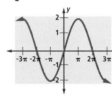

REVIEW

19. Given that $\tan 0.675 \approx 0.8$, find three other values of θ with $\tan \theta \approx 0.8$. (**Lesson 4-6**) **Answers vary. Sample: –2.467; 3.817; 6.958**

20. Find the exact value of $\tan(-120°)$. (**Lesson 4-4**) $\sqrt{3}$

21. Give the radian equivalent to each. (**Lesson 4-1**)
    a. $-720°$ **-4π**   b. $225°$ **$\frac{5\pi}{4}$**   c. $315°$ **$\frac{7\pi}{4}$**

22. State the Graph-Translation Theorem. (**Lesson 3-2**)

23. a. Graph $f(x) = x^3$ and its image under the translation $T: (x, y) \rightarrow (x + 3, y - 1)$. **See margin.**
    b. Find an equation for the image. (**Lesson 3-2**) $y + 1 = (x - 3)^3$

EXPLORATION

24. Pitch and loudness are common words for the frequency and amplitude of sound. Light waves are also modeled with trigonometric functions.
    a. What properties of light do the frequency and amplitude of light waves represent?
    b. Name some other characteristics that sound waves and light waves share.

22. Given a preimage graph described by a sentence in x and y, the following two processes yield the same image: (1) replacing x by $x - h$ and y by $h - k$ in the sentence; (2) applying the translation $(x, y) \rightarrow (x + h, y + k)$ to the preimage graph.

24a. Frequency: the frequency of light determines its classification as infrared, visible, or ultraviolet; amplitude: the amplitude of the wave determines the intensity of light.

24b. Answers vary. Sample: Both light waves and sound waves exhibit the properties of reflection, refraction, diffraction, and dispersion.

QY ANSWERS

1. 1

2. Both are distances and cannot be negative.

3. $y = 4 \sin(-2x)$

Additional Answers

23a.

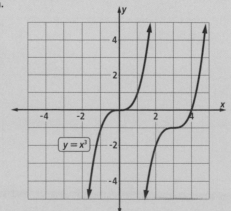

Lesson 4-8

Translation Images of Trigonometric Functions

Vocabulary

phase shift

▶ **BIG IDEA** Translations do not affect the period or amplitude of parent trigonometric functions.

Phase Shifts

The graph of $y = \cos x$ is shown in blue along with a graph of a translation image.

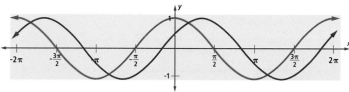

Recall from Lesson 3-2 how to translate graphs of functions horizontally and vertically. Horizontal translations of trigonometric functions have a special name: *phase shifts*. This name comes from the study of sound and electricity, where trigonometric functions are often applied. In general, the **phase shift** of a sine wave is the least positive or the greatest negative magnitude of a horizontal translation that maps the graph of $\left(\frac{y}{b}\right) = \cos\left(\frac{x}{a}\right)$ or $\left(\frac{y}{b}\right) = \sin\left(\frac{x}{a}\right)$ onto the wave.

GUIDED

Example 1

Consider the function h with $h(x) = \sin(x + 60°)$. Identify the phase shift.

Solution The expression $x + 60°$ is equivalent to $x -$ __?__.
Rewrite the equation as $h(x) = \sin(x - -60°)$. The graph of h is the image of the graph $y = \sin x$ under a horizontal translation of __?__ (left/right). Thus the phase shift is __?__.

People who work with electricity, such as electrical engineers and electricians, use phase shifts. In an alternating current circuit, for example, two waves—the voltage and the current flow—are involved. If these waves coincide, then they are said to be *in phase*. If the current flow lags behind the voltage, then the circuit is *out of phase* and an *inductance* is created. Inductance helps to keep the current flow stable.

Translation Images of Trigonometric Functions **263**

Mental Math

Give the vertex of the parabola described by each equation.

a. $y = -x^2$ **(0, 0)**

b. $y = (x - 5)^2 + 2$

c. $y = 4(x + 50)^2$

d. $y = ax^2 - c$

b. **(5, 2)**

c. **(–50, 0)**

d. **(0, –c)**

–60°; 60° left; –60°

Lesson 4-8

GOAL
Extend the transformations of graphs of trigonometric functions to include horizontal and vertical translations.

SPUR Objectives

E Identify the amplitude, period, frequency, phase shift, and other properties of trigonometric functions.

F Write and solve equations for phenomena described by trigonometric functions.

J Graph and describe transformation images of graphs of trigonometric functions.

Materials/Resources
· Lesson Master 4-8
· Resource Masters 87–89

HOMEWORK
• **Option 1**
• **Option 2**
•   Questions 1–12
• • Questions 13–20
• • Question 21 (extra credit)
   • Reading Lesson 4-9
   • Covering the Ideas 4-9
   (Questions 1–9)

Local Standards

Background

Phase shifts There are two basic reasons for the idea in this lesson. First, in order to model the sine waves that occur in real situations, it is necessary to be able to position the wave anywhere in the coordinate plane. As the name *phase shift* indicates, the particular application of sine waves to alternating current is quite important.

Second, translations illustrate and confirm certain properties of trigonometric functions. For instance, that $\cos\left(x - \frac{\pi}{2}\right) = \sin x$ for all x is confirmed by noting that a shift of the graph of $y = \cos x$ to the right $\frac{\pi}{2}$ units yields the graph of $y = \sin x$. This is easy for most students.

① Warm-Up

Matching In 1–4, match each equation with the translation that can be applied to the graph of $y = \sin x$ to get its graph.

1. $y = \sin\left(x + \frac{\pi}{3}\right)$ **D**

2. $y = \sin x + \frac{\pi}{3}$ **B**

3. $y = \sin x - \frac{\pi}{3}$ **A**

4. $y = \sin\left(x - \frac{\pi}{3}\right)$ **C**

A $\frac{\pi}{3}$ units down

B $\frac{\pi}{3}$ units up

C $\frac{\pi}{3}$ units to the right

D $\frac{\pi}{3}$ units to the left

2 Teaching

Students should be able to predict the effect of substitutions for x and y on the position of sine waves in the coordinate plane, and to check their work using a graphing utility.

The general formulas for $\cos(a - b)$ and $\sin(a - b)$ also could be used to confirm properties of phase shifts; these formulas are discussed in Chapter 12.

As in the previous lesson, it is valuable for your students to verify the graphs in the examples during class discussion. Seeing the graphs drawn in color on a graphing utility helps emphasize which graph is the image and which is the preimage.

Example 2 Because the graphs of $y = \sin x$ and $y = \cos x$ are translation images of each other, any sine wave can be described either as an image of $y = \sin x$ or as an image of $y = \cos x$. Thus in this example, to obtain a single answer, we are obliged to state that the voltage is modeled by an image of a cosine function rather than by a trigonometric function. Also, since many translations map a given sine wave onto its image, many different equations, differing in phase shifts by integer multiples of 2π, could be used.

Additional Examples

Example 1 Consider the function g with $g(x) = \cos(x - 38°)$. Identify the phase shift. **The phase shift is 38°.**

Example 2 Compare the graphs of $y = \sin x$, and $y = \sin\left(x + \frac{3\pi}{2}\right)$.

The second graph is $\frac{3\pi}{2}$ units to the left of the first graph.

Example 3 Consider the function g, where $g(x) = \sin x$.

a. Write an equation for its image h under the translation
$(x, y) \longrightarrow \left(x + \frac{\pi}{4}, y + 7\right)$.

$h(x) = 7 + \sin\left(x - \frac{\pi}{4}\right)$.

b. Find the amplitude and period of h.
amplitude: 1; period: 2π

Example 2

Maximum inductance in an alternating current occurs when the current flow lags behind the voltage by $\frac{\pi}{2}$. In a situation of maximum inductance, find an equation for the current, and sketch the two waves. Assume that the two waves have the same amplitude and period, and that the voltage is modeled by the equation $y = \cos x$.

> **Solution** Maximum inductance occurs when the current has a phase shift of $\frac{\pi}{2}$. There is no vertical shift. If the equation for the current is of the form $y - k = \cos(x - h)$, then $k = 0$ and $h = \frac{\pi}{2}$. **An equation for the current is** $y = \cos\left(x - \frac{\pi}{2}\right)$. The waves are graphed at the right.

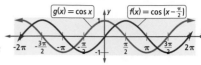

Examine the graphs carefully. Notice that the graph of $y = \cos\left(x - \frac{\pi}{2}\right)$ seems to coincide with the graph of $y = \sin x$. This relationship gives rise to an identity that is similar to the Complements Theorem.

> **Theorem (Phase Shift Identity)**
>
> For all real numbers x, $\cos\left(x - \frac{\pi}{2}\right) = \sin x$ and $\sin\left(x + \frac{\pi}{2}\right) = \cos x$.

Because the graph of the cosine function is a translation image of the graph of the sine function, these graphs are congruent.

Translation Images of Sine Waves

Example 3

Consider the graph of the function f, where $f(x) = \cos x$.

a. Find an equation for its image g under the translation $(x, y) \rightarrow (x, y - 2)$, and sketch a graph of $y = g(x)$.

b. Find the amplitude and period of the function g.

> **Solution**
>
> a. By the Graph-Translation Theorem, **an equation for the image is $y = \cos x - 2$.** This results in a vertical shift two units down from the parent function. Graphs of f and g are on the right.
>
>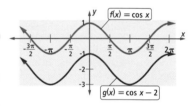
>
> b. The maximum and minimum values of the cosine function are 1 and –1, respectively. So the maximum and minimum values of g are –1 and –3, respectively. Thus, **the amplitude of g is $\frac{1}{2}\left|(-1 - -3)\right| = \frac{1}{2} \cdot 2 = 1$,** the same as the amplitude of the cosine function. Similarly, **the period of g is 2π,** the same as the period of the parent function.

> ### Accommodating the Learner ⬆
>
> Have students answer the following questions.
>
> 1. A buoy oscillates as waves move past. The bottom of the buoy moves 4 feet from low to high point and returns to its lowest point every 10 seconds. Write a function describing this motion.
>   **Answers vary. Sample: $d = 2 \sin \frac{\pi t}{5}$**
>
> 2. Correct answers to Question 1 above can vary considerably. Some may even use different trigonometric functions.

Explain why that is possible. **Images of both the sine and cosine functions can be constructed with the same given period and amplitude.**

In general, if two curves are translation images of each other, then they are congruent. Thus, a translation of a sine or cosine wave preserves both its amplitude and its period.

From an analysis of a graph showing a translation image of any of the parent trigonometric functions, you can determine an equation for a translation image.

Example 4

Find an equation for the translation image of the graph of the cosine function shown below.

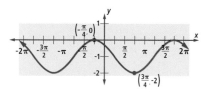

Solution There is both a phase shift and a vertical shift. Since the coordinates of a relative maximum are given, it is convenient to consider $\left(-\frac{\pi}{4}, 0\right)$ as the image of the maximum point $(0, 1)$ of the cosine function. You can consider the point $(0, 1)$ as having been translated $\frac{\pi}{4}$ units to the left and 1 unit down. So the phase shift is $= -\frac{\pi}{4}$.

The vertical shift is 1 unit down. Thus, an equation for this graph is
$y = \cos\left(x + \frac{\pi}{4}\right) - 1$.

The two graphs are congruent, so the amplitude and period remain the same.

Check A graph of $y = \cos\left(x + \frac{\pi}{4}\right) - 1$ shows that the graph corresponds to the given graph.

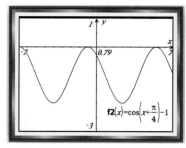

 QY

In Example 4, you could have thought of the graph as a translation image of the sine function. (See Question 7.) In general, when using a sine or cosine function as a model (as you will in Lesson 4-10), the choice of which function is a matter of convenience. Sines and cosines can be used interchangeably if you pay attention to the phase shift.

> ▶ **QY**
>
> Identify the phase shift and vertical translation of the graph of $y = \sin x$ so that its image is the graph of $y = \sin\left(x - \frac{\pi}{3}\right) + 4$.

Additional Example

Example 4 Find an equation for the translation image of the graph of the sine function shown below. **Answers vary. Sample:** $y = \sin\left(x - \frac{\pi}{6}\right) + 3$

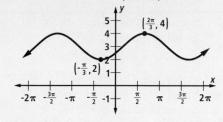

---

3 Assignment

Recommended Assignment

- Questions 1–12
- • Questions 13–20
- • • Question 21 (extra credit)
- • Reading Lesson 4-9
- • Covering the Ideas 4-9
  (Questions 1–9)

Notes on the Questions

Question 2 This question provides concrete evidence of the Graph-Translation Theorem and should be discussed in detail.

Questions 5 and 6 For each question, you might ask how many students considered the sine function as the parent and how many considered the cosine function as the parent.

Question 8 The purpose of this question is to show that the Graph-Translation Theorem can picture some trigonometric identities, in this case, that $\sin\left(x + \frac{\pi}{2}\right) = \cos x$, or, equivalently, that $\cos\left(x - \frac{\pi}{2}\right) = \sin x$.

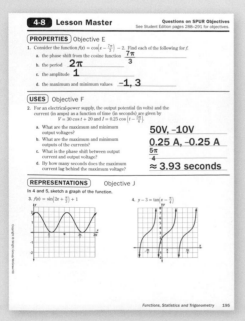

Questions

COVERING THE IDEAS

1. **True or False** The graph of any function and its image under a translation are congruent. **true**

2. Consider the function with equation $y = \cos\left(x + \frac{\pi}{3}\right)$.
   a. Identify the phase shift from $y = \cos x$. $-\frac{\pi}{3}$
   b. Copy and complete the table at the right, which shows the translation images of the points $(0, 1)$, $\left(\frac{\pi}{2}, 0\right)$, $(\pi, -1)$, $\left(\frac{3\pi}{2}, 0\right)$, and $(2\pi, 1)$.
   c. Use the points found in Part b to help you sketch two cycles of the graph of $y = \cos\left(x + \frac{\pi}{3}\right)$. **See margin.**

Preimage on $y = \cos x$	Image on $y = \cos\left(x + \frac{\pi}{3}\right)$
$(0, 1)$	? $\left(-\frac{\pi}{3}, 1\right)$
$\left(\frac{\pi}{2}, 0\right)$	? $\left(\frac{\pi}{6}, 0\right)$
$(\pi, -1)$	? $\left(\frac{2\pi}{3}, -1\right)$
$\left(\frac{3\pi}{2}, 0\right)$	? $\left(\frac{7\pi}{6}, 0\right)$
$(2\pi, 1)$	? $\left(\frac{5\pi}{3}, 1\right)$

3. Consider the function with equation $y = \sin\left(x + \frac{3\pi}{4}\right) + 5$
   a. Identify the phase shift from $y = \sin x$. $-\frac{3\pi}{4}$
   b. Identify the vertical shift. **5**

4. Consider the translation $T: (x, y) \rightarrow \left(x + \frac{\pi}{6}, y + 0.5\right)$.
   a. Find an equation for the image of the graph of the sine function under T. $y = \sin\left(x - \frac{\pi}{6}\right) + 0.5$
   b. Find the amplitude, the period, and the phase shift of the image.

4b. amplitude: 1; period: 2π; phase shift: $\frac{\pi}{6}$

In 5 and 6, write an equation for the function that is graphed.

5.

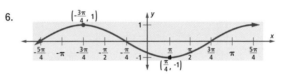

6.

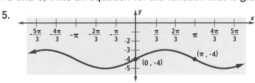

5. Answers vary. Sample: $y = \sin x - 4$

6. Answers vary. Sample: $y = \cos\left(x + \frac{3\pi}{4}\right)$

7. $y = \sin\left(x + \frac{3\pi}{4}\right) - 1$

7. Refer to Example 4. Find an equation for the graph, thinking of it as a translation image of the graph of the sine function.

8. Consider the graph at the right. **Answers vary. Sample:**
   a. Write an equation using the sine function to describe the graph. $y = \sin(x - 45°)$
   b. Write an equation using the cosine function to describe the graph. $y = \cos(x - 135°)$

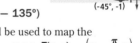

9. a. Give an equation for a translation that could be used to map the graph of $f(x) = \sin x$ onto the graph of $g(x) = \cos x$. $T(x, y) = \left(x - \frac{\pi}{2}, y\right)$
   b. Use your answer to Part a to write an expression for $\cos x$ in terms of $\sin x$. $\cos x = \sin\left(x + \frac{\pi}{2}\right)$

Additional Answers

2c.

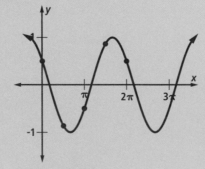

APPLYING THE MATHEMATICS

10. When two waves from the same source travel different distances to reach an object—for example, when radio waves are reflected off of buildings in a city—they may arrive out of phase. Suppose that two such waves are shown in the graph at the right.

    a. Find a formula for $g(x)$. $g(x) = \sin\left(x - \frac{3\pi}{4}\right)$

    b. The signal you would receive is represented by the sum $f + g$. Graph that function. **See margin.**

    c. Find the period, amplitude, and phase shift from the sine function of the function you graphed in Part b.

    d. Identify a value of x for which $f(x) + g(x) = 0$. How can that value be found using just the graphs of f and g?

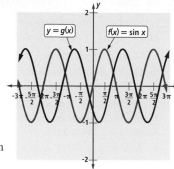

11. Consider the functions f and g defined by $f(x) = \tan x$ and $g(x) = \tan\left(x - \frac{\pi}{4}\right)$.

    a. Give the period for both f and g. **π**

    b. Describe the transformation that maps the graph of f onto the graph of g. **phase shift to the right by $\frac{\pi}{4}$**

    c. What is the image of the point $\left(\frac{\pi}{4}, 1\right)$ under this transformation?

    d. Write the equations of the asymptotes of the graph of g on the interval $\frac{\pi}{4} \le x \le \frac{9\pi}{4}$. $x = \frac{3\pi}{4}, x = \frac{7\pi}{4}$

    e. Sketch two cycles of the graph of g on the interval $\frac{\pi}{4} \le x \le \frac{9\pi}{4}$. **See margin.**

12. The height h in meters of the tide in a harbor is given by $h = 0.8 \cos\left(\frac{\pi}{6}t\right) + 6.5$, where t is the time in hours after high tide.

    $h(0) = 7.3$; $h(1) \approx 7.19$; $h(2) = 6.9$

    a. Calculate h at $t = 0$, $t = 1$, and $t = 2$.

    b. Sketch a graph of this function for $0 \le t \le 24$. **See margin.**

    c. What is the minimum height of the tide during this 24-hour time period? **5.7**

    d. At what times during the 24 hours after high tide does the minimum height occur? **$t = 6$ and $t = 18$**

    e. What is the period of this sine wave and what does the period mean in terms of the tide?

10c. period: 2π; amplitude $\sqrt{2 - \sqrt{2}}$; phase shift: $\frac{3\pi}{8}$

10d. Answers vary. Sample: $\frac{3\pi}{8}$; it is the value of x where f and g are equal but opposite distances away from the x-axis.

11c. $\left(\frac{\pi}{2}, 1\right)$

Tides describe the rise and fall in sea level relative to the land due to gravitational pull of the moon and Sun.

12e. The period is 12 hours. This means that the tide level repeats every 12 hours.

REVIEW

In 13 and 14, an equation for a function is given.

   a. Find its amplitude.   b. Find its period. (Lesson 4-7)

13. $y = 4 \sin x$ **a. 4   b. 2π**   14. $y = 5 \cos\left(\frac{x}{2}\right)$ **a. 5   b. 4π**

15. Sketch one complete cycle of the graph of $3y = \sin\left(\frac{x}{2}\right)$, and label the zeros of the function shown on the graph. (Lesson 4-7) **See margin.**

Additional Answers

12b.

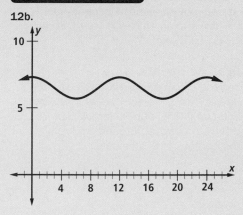

15.

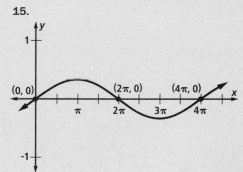

Additional Answers

10b.

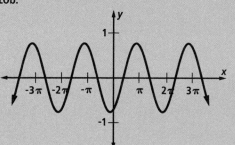

11e.

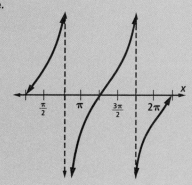

4-8

4 Wrap-Up

Ongoing Assessment

Define a translation like the one given in Question 4. Have students give the equation of the images of the sine, cosine, and tangent functions under the translation. **Answers vary. Check students' work.**

Project Update

Project 1, *Sums of Sine Waves with the Same Period,* Project 2, *Beat Matching and DJing* 101, and Project 4, *Square Waves,* on pages 282 and 283 relate to the content of this lesson.

In 16 and 17, give the degree equivalent. (Lesson 4-1)

16. 7π **1260°**

17. $\frac{5\pi}{4}$ **225°**

18. Let f and g be functions whose equations are $f(x) = x^2 - 3$ and $g(x) = 2x + 1$. Find a formula for $f(g(x))$. (Lesson 3-7)

19. a. Draw $\triangle NOW$, where $N = (2, 6)$, $O = (-1, 4)$, and $W = (1, -4)$.
    b. Draw $\triangle N'O'W'$, the reflection image of $\triangle NOW$ over the y-axis.
    c. If r_y represents reflection over the y-axis, then $r_y : (x, y) \rightarrow \underline{\quad?\quad}$. (Lesson 3-4) **(-x, y)**

20. Match each transformation with the *best* description. (Lessons 3-5, 3-4, 3-2)
    a. $M(x, y) = (x - 7, y + 5)$ **v**   (i) reflection over the x-axis
    b. $N(x, y) = (y, x)$ **ii**   (ii) reflection over the line $y = x$
    c. $P(x, y) = (x, -y)$ **i**   (iii) scale change
    d. $Q(x, y) = (0.2x, 20y)$ **iii**   (iv) size change
    e. $V(x, y) = \left(\frac{x}{2}, \frac{y}{2}\right)$ **iv**   (v) translation

EXPLORATION

21. Noise canceling headphones were developed using the concept of "antiphase."
    a. Find out what antiphase means and how it is used in noise canceling headphones.
    b. If a sound wave is modeled by the equation $y = 12 \cos\left(\frac{x}{4}\right)$, write an equation for the antiphase that would cancel the sound.
    c. Find other applications where antiphasing is used.

21a. Answers vary. Sample: If two waves have a period of x radians, then the two waves are said to be in antiphase when the phase difference between the two waves is $\frac{x}{2}$ radians. For example, sin x and sin$(x + \pi)$ are in antiphase, as are sin x and –sin x. When two waves are in antiphase the peaks of one wave will align with the troughs of the other wave, so the sum of the two waves will be a reduced wave, the result of destructive interference. If the amplitudes of the original two waves are equal, they completely cancel. In noise canceling headphones, sound waves are produced by the headphones to destructively interfere with the sound waves of background noise.

21b. Answers vary. Sample: $y = -12 \cos \frac{x}{4}$

21c. Answers vary. Sample: Antiphasing is also used in some work with lasers.

18. $f(g(x)) = (2x + 1)^2 - 3$

19a–b.

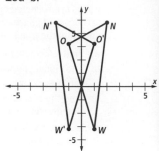

QY ANSWER

phase shift: $\frac{\pi}{3}$;

vertical translation: 4

Lesson 4-9
The Graph-Standardization Theorem

▶ **BIG IDEA** The image of the graph of a parent trigonometric function under the composite of a scale change followed by a translation has a predictable equation, amplitude, phase shift, and period.

Recall that a sine wave is the image of the graph of $y = \sin x$ under a composite of translations and scale changes.

In Lessons 4-7 and 4-8, you saw how scale changes affect the amplitude and frequency of sine waves and how translations introduce phase shifts and vertical shifts. In this lesson, you will see how composites of scale changes and translations affect sine waves.

A Specific Example

We first apply a composite to a graph that is not a sine wave. Consider the parabola with equation $y = x^2$. Apply the scale change $S: (x, y) = (2x, 3y)$. This stretches the parent graph by a factor of 2 in the x-direction and by a factor of 3 in the y-direction. To this image apply the translation $T: (x, y) \rightarrow (x + 1, y - 2)$. This translates the image 1 unit to the right and 2 units down. The graphs below show the order of transformations.

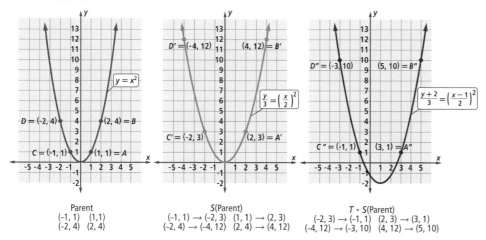

Parent
(–1, 1) (1,1)
(–2, 4) (2, 4)

S(Parent)
(–1, 1) → (–2, 3) (1, 1) → (2, 3)
(–2, 4) → (–4, 12) (2, 4) → (4, 12)

$T \circ S$(Parent)
(–2, 3) → (–1, 1) (2, 3) → (3, 1)
(–4, 12) → (–3, 10) (4, 12) → (5, 10)

Mental Math

(23, 40)
(5, 17)   (25, 17)

The graph above shows $2\frac{1}{2}$ cycles of a sine wave. What are the period and amplitude of this wave?

period: 8; amplitude: 23

The Graph-Standardization Theorem   **269**

Background

The equations for the functions studied in this lesson are often seen in the form $y = A \sin(Bx + C) + D$ or $y = A \sin B(x - C) + D$. We have chosen the form $\frac{y - k}{b} = \sin \frac{x - h}{a}$ for two reasons. First, this form is a natural extension of the work we have done with graphs of all functions (and relations). The parabola with which the lesson begins points this out.

Second, the expressions $\frac{y - k}{b}$ and $\frac{x - h}{a}$ are of the same form as the expression $\frac{x - m}{s}$ used in statistics (and studied in Chapter 3) to standardize data so that the mean is 0 and standard deviation is 1. This idea indicates why we called the theorem of this lesson the Graph-Standardization Theorem.

(continued on next page)

GOAL

Consider situations where a composite of translations and scale changes have been applied to a graph.

SPUR Objectives

E Identify the amplitude, period, frequency, phase shift, and other properties of trigonometric functions.

F Write and solve equations for phenomena described by trigonometric functions.

J Graph and describe transformation images of graphs of trigonometric functions.

Materials/Resources

· Lesson Master 4-9
· Resource Masters 90–92
· Sinusoidal graph applet

HOMEWORK
• Option 1
• Option 2

• Questions 1–9
•• Questions 10–21
•• Question 22 (extra credit)
• Reading Lesson 4-10
• Covering the Ideas 4-10
  (Questions 1–7)

Local Standards

---

1 Warm-Up

Let $S(x, y) = (2x, 3y)$ and $T(x, y) = (x + 1, y - 2)$, the transformations at the beginning of this lesson. Instead of applying $T \circ S$ to the graph, as is done there, apply $S \circ T$. What is the equation of the image of the graph of $y = x^2$ under $S \circ T$?

$\frac{y}{3} + 2 = \left(\frac{x}{2} - 1\right)^2$; **Note that this provides a justification for the answer to Question 22.**

2 Teaching

Notes on the Lesson

Example 1 In order to use the valuable notion of a phase shift, under which all points on a graph are translated a fixed amount horizontally, the shape of the graph must be transformed first. Thus, in this example, the scale change S of the parent function comes *before* the translation T (just as s precedes t in the alphabet). You might note that a generation ago, students would spend quite a bit of time graphing these equations by hand. Today, few people would graph the function of Example 1 (or even the simpler Example 2) by hand. The goal of the lesson is for students to be able to explain what is drawn with a graphing utility.

By the Graph Scale-Change Theorem, the image of the graph of $y = x^2$ under the scale change $S: (x, y) \rightarrow (2x, 3y)$ has equation

$$\frac{y}{3} = \left(\frac{x}{2}\right)^2.$$

By the Graph-Translation Theorem, the image of the graph of this new equation under $T: (x, y) \rightarrow (x + 1, y - 2)$ is

$$\frac{y + 2}{3} = \left(\frac{x - 1}{2}\right)^2.$$

This is an equation for the image of the graph of $y = x^2$ under the composite $T \circ S$. For instance, the point $D'' = (-3, 10)$ is the image of $D = (2, -4)$ under $T \circ S$. When $(-3, 10)$ is substituted into the equation $\frac{y + 2}{3} = \left(\frac{x - 1}{2}\right)^2$, we get $\frac{10 + 2}{3} = \left(\frac{-3 - 1}{2}\right)^2$. It checks.

 QY

▶ QY

Find the coordinates of the vertex of each parabola on the previous page.

The General Idea

Suppose S is a scale change and T a translation with

$$S(x, y) = (ax, by), \text{ where } a \neq 0 \text{ and } b \neq 0,$$
$$\text{and } T(x, y) = (x + h, y + k).$$

Then the translation image of the scale-change image of (x, y) is

$$\begin{aligned}
T \circ S(x, y) &= T(S(x, y)) \\
&= T(ax, by) \\
&= (ax + h, by + k).
\end{aligned}$$

Thus, $T \circ S$ maps (x, y) to $(ax + h, by + k)$. That is, if (x', y') is the image of (x, y) under $T \circ S$, then

$$T \circ S(x, y) = (x', y') = (ax + h, by + k).$$

This equation for $T \circ S$ helps to determine how this transformation affects equations. Since

$$x' = ax + h \text{ and } y' = by + k,$$

it follows that $\quad \frac{x' - h}{a} = x \quad$ and $\quad \frac{y' - k}{b} = y.$

This argument proves the following theorem.

Graph-Standardization Theorem

Given a preimage graph described by a sentence in x and y, the following processes yield the same graph:

(1) replacing x by $\frac{x - h}{a}$ and y by $\frac{y - k}{b}$ in the sentence;

(2) applying the scale change $(x, y) \rightarrow (ax, by)$ followed by the translation $(x, y) \rightarrow (x + h, y + k)$ to the preimage graph.

The Graph-Standardization Theorem applies to all relations graphed on a rectangular coordinate grid.

When a scale change $(x, y) \rightarrow (ax, by)$ and a translation $(x, y) \rightarrow (x + h, y + k)$ are applied to a graph in that order, the effect is to apply the transformation $(x, y) \rightarrow (ax + h, by + k)$ to the graph. This transformation can be effected by substituting $\frac{x - a}{h}$ for x and $\frac{y - b}{k}$ for y. The effects of these substitutions on the amplitude, phase shift, and period of sine functions are all easily obtained from properties of the translation and scale change to the graph. They are the focus of this lesson.

In the first edition, we used the term *linear change* for the transformation $(x, y) \rightarrow (ax + h, by + k)$. That name comes from the algebraic description of the transformation. In the second edition, we used the term *rubberband transformation*. The word "rubberband" supplies the visual picture we wish students to have: a rubberband is usually stretched in its long direction but can be stretched in the perpendicular short direction. It can be translated to begin at any point.

The Graph-Standardization Theorem and Trigonometric Functions

The scale change $(x, y) \rightarrow (ax, by)$ multiplies the period of a sine wave by $|a|$ and its amplitude by $|b|$. The translation $(x, y) \rightarrow (x + h, y + k)$ shifts the image h units horizontally and k units vertically. Combining these two transformations produces the following theorem.

> **Theorem (Characteristics of a Sine Wave)**
>
> The graphs of the functions with equations $\frac{y - k}{b} = \sin\left(\frac{x - h}{a}\right)$ and $\frac{y - k}{b} = \cos\left(\frac{x - h}{a}\right)$, with $a \neq 0$ and $b \neq 0$, have
>
> amplitude $= |b|$,   period $= 2\pi|a|$,
>
> phase shift $= h$,   and vertical shift $= k$.

Forms of Equations

We call $\frac{y - k}{b} = \sin\left(\frac{x - h}{a}\right)$ or $\frac{y - k}{b} = \cos\left(\frac{x - h}{a}\right)$ the *graph-standardized form* of the equation for a sine or cosine function. When an equation is in this form, you can use the above theorem to determine characteristics of the sine wave.

Example 1

a. Explain how the graph of $\frac{y - 1}{2} = \cos\left(\frac{x + \pi}{3}\right)$ is related to the graph of $y = \cos x$.

b. Identify the amplitude, period, vertical shift, and phase shift of this function.

Solution

a. The given equation results from the equation $y = \cos x$ by replacing x by $\frac{x - (-\pi)}{3}$ and y by $\frac{y - 1}{2}$. Thus the graph of $\frac{y - 1}{2} = \cos\left(\frac{x + \pi}{3}\right)$ is the image of the graph of $y = \cos x$ under the scale change $(x, y) \rightarrow (3x, 2y)$ followed by the translation $(x, y) \rightarrow (x - \pi, y + 1)$.

b. From the Characteristics Theorem above, you can determine that the amplitude of $\frac{y - 1}{2} = \cos\left(\frac{x + \pi}{3}\right)$ is 2; its period is 6π, the vertical shift is up 1 and the phase shift is $-\pi$.

Check Graph $y = \cos x$, as shown in blue. Next, graph its image under the scale change as shown by the curve drawn in red. Then graph the translation image of the red curve to get the green curve.

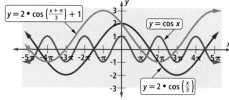

In this third edition, we use no specific name for the transformation and you might give it whatever name you want. A sine wave can be efficiently defined as the image of the graph of $y = \sin x$ under this kind of (linear change, rubberband, etc.) transformation.

The transformation $(x, y) \rightarrow (ax + h, by + k)$ is a type of affine transformation. In general, an *affine transformation* in two dimensions is a mapping of the form $(x, y) \rightarrow (ax + by + c, dx + ey + f)$, where

$ab \neq 0$ and $cd \neq 0$. If $c = f = 0$, then the affine transformation is called a *linear transformation*. That is, a linear transformation has the form $(x, y) \rightarrow (ax + by, cx + dy)$. Linear transformations in dimension n can be represented by $n \times n$ matrices. In fact, we decided not to use the term "linear change" because of its confusion with "linear transformation."

Notes on the Lesson

Activity If they are using the UCSMP applet, students can print their work after Step 5 by entering their name at the bottom of the screen and clicking the Print button.

Activity

MATERIALS sinusoidal graph application provided by your teacher

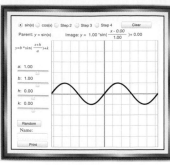

Step 1 Open the sinusoidal graph application. The x-axis of the graph is measured in radians. The display shows the parent graph of $y = \sin x$ in black along with another sinusoidal image in red. Move the sliders one at a time to see how each variable affects the image. Change the parent function to the cosine function by clicking the cos(x) button at the top of the screen. Experiment with the sliders again. Record what property of the parent function is affected by each of a, b, h, and k.

Step 2 Click the Step 2 check box button at the top of the screen to create a new sinusoidal image in blue. Note that the parent function is the sine function. Move one slider to scale the red graph to have the same amplitude as the blue graph. Then move another slider to have the red graph coincide with the blue graph. Write the equation of the red graph in $\frac{y - k}{b} = \sin\left(\frac{x - h}{a}\right)$ form, and then simplify $\frac{y - k}{b}$ and $\frac{x - h}{a}$ if possible.

Step 3 Click the Step 3 check box. Note that the parent function has changed to the cosine function. Move a slider to make the red graph have the same period as the blue graph. Then move a slider to translate the red graph to match the blue graph. Write the equation of the red graph in $\frac{y - k}{b} = \cos\left(\frac{x - h}{a}\right)$ form, and then simplify.

Step 4 Click the Step 4 check box. What is the parent function? Move the sliders to make the red graph completely match the blue graph. Write an equation for the red graph in graph-standardized form.

Step 5 Choose a parent function by clicking the sin(x) or cos(x) button at the top of the screen. Press the Random button to generate the graph of a random sinusoidal function. Adjust the sliders for a and b to transform the red graph to have the same shape as the generated graph, then adjust the sliders for k and h to translate your graph to coincide with the generated graph. Record your values of a, b, h, and k, and write the equation in graph-standardized form.

The form $y = A \sin(Bx + C) + D$ or $y = A \cos(Bx + C) + D$ is used in many applications. To convert $\left(\frac{y - 1}{2}\right) = \cos\left(\frac{x - \pi}{3}\right)$ to this form, multiply the equation by 2 and add 1 to both sides to get

$$y = 2 \cos\left(\frac{x - \pi}{3}\right) + 1.$$

Then, note that this can be rewritten as

$$y = 2 \cos\left(\frac{x}{3} - \frac{\pi}{3}\right) + 1,$$

or equivalently,

$$y = 2 \cos\left(\frac{1}{3}x - \frac{\pi}{3}\right) + 1.$$

In this form, $A = 2$, $B = \frac{1}{3}$, $C = -\frac{\pi}{3}$, and $D = 1$.

272 Trigonometric Functions

Step 1: a changes the period of the function. b changes the amplitude of the function. h changes the horizontal orientation of the function. k changes the vertical orientation of the function.

Step 2: Answers vary. Sample: $\frac{y}{4} = \sin\left(\frac{x + 3.00}{1.00}\right)$; $y = 4 \sin(x + 3)$

Step 3: Answers vary. Sample: $\frac{y + 3}{1} = \cos\left(\frac{x}{0.5}\right)$; $y = \cos(2x) - 3$

Step 4: Answers vary. Sample: The parent function is sin x. $y = \sin\left(\frac{x - 0.25}{0.25}\right)$; $y = \sin(4x - 1)$

Step 5: Answers vary. Sample: $a = 0.5$, $b = 1$, $h = -0.25$, $k = 0$; $y = \sin\left(\frac{x + 0.25}{0.50}\right)$; $y = \sin(2x + 0.5)$

Accommodating the Learner ⬇

If students become confused as to which comes first, the scale change or the translation, point out that the order in this chapter is the order in which the transformations should be done.

It is useful to be able to convert between forms. To find the characteristics of the sine wave, it helps to rewrite an equation in graph-standardized form.

Example 2

Consider the graph of $y = 2\sin(3x + \pi)$.

a. Describe this graph as the image of the graph of $y = \sin x$ under a composite of transformations.

b. Without graphing, determine the amplitude, period, vertical shift, and phase shift of the sine wave.

Solution

a. Convert the equation into graph-standardized form.

$$\frac{y}{2} = \sin(3x + \pi) = \sin\left(3\left(x + \frac{\pi}{3}\right)\right) = \sin\left(\frac{x - \left(\frac{-\pi}{3}\right)}{\frac{1}{3}}\right)$$

Thus the graph of $y = 2\sin(3x + \pi)$ is the image of the graph of $y = \sin x$ under the scale change $(x, y) \to (\frac{1}{3}x, 2y)$ followed by the translation $(x, y) \to (x - \frac{\pi}{3}, y)$.

b. The amplitude of the sine wave is $|2| = 2$. The period is $2\pi\left(\frac{1}{3}\right) = \frac{2\pi}{3}$. There is no vertical shift. The phase shift is $\frac{-\pi}{3}$.

Circular Motion

Trigonometric functions of the forms studied in this lesson arise naturally from situations of circular motion.

Example 3

The first Ferris wheel was built in 1893 for the Columbian Exposition. The radius of the wheel was about 131 feet and its center was about 140 feet above the ground. Find an equation that models the height above ground level of a car at time x (in minutes) assuming the wheel is continually rotating at 9 minutes per revolution, and that the car is initially at the maximum height.

Solution Let y be the height of the car that starts at the top. Since the car is initially at maximum height, there is no horizontal translation (phase shift) if the cosine function is used as the parent. So model this situation with the equation $\frac{y - k}{b} = \cos\left(\frac{x - h}{a}\right)$.

Because there is no translation, $h = 0$.

Reinventing the wheel
The original Ferris wheel had 36 cars that could hold 60 passengers each.

(continued on next page)

Notes on the Lesson

Example 3 If your students answered the Exploration question in Lesson 4-2, they will already know something about this Ferris wheel. You might center class discussion around this example. Here the origin of the coordinate system is ground level under the center of the wheel. At this point, concentrate on students' understanding the relationships between the equation and the graph, not on the origin of the equation. The equation of the function is a natural extension of the definition of $(\cos\theta, \sin\theta)$ as the rotation image of $(1, 0)$ about the origin. Now the circle has radius 131 and is not centered at the origin (the vertical shift), the amount of revolution is a function of time (the scale change), and the boarding is not at a point on the same horizontal line as the center of the wheel (the horizontal shift).

Additional Examples

Example 2 Consider the graph of $y = 5\cos\left(2x - \frac{\pi}{2}\right) - 7$.

a. Describe the composite of transformations that maps the graph of $y = \cos x$ onto this graph. The equation can be rewritten as $\frac{y + 7}{5} = \cos\left(\frac{x - \frac{\pi}{4}}{\frac{1}{2}}\right)$. Thus the graph is the image of $y = \cos x$ under the composite of the scale change $(x, y) \to \left(\frac{1}{2}x, 5y\right)$ followed by the translation $(x, y) \to \left(x + \frac{\pi}{4}, y - 7\right)$.

b. Without graphing, determine the amplitude, period, vertical shift, and phase shift of the function that is graphed. amplitude: 5; period: π; vertical shift: down 7; phase shift: $\frac{\pi}{4}$

Example 3 A large clock with rotating hour and minute hands is on a building such that its center is 20 meters above the ground. The length of the hour hand is 1.5 meters and the length of the minute hand is 2 meters. Find an equation that models the height of the tip of the minute hand at time t (in minutes). $y = 20 + 2\cos\left(\frac{\pi}{30}t\right)$

3 Assignment

Recommended Assignment

- Questions 1–9
- • Questions 10–21
- • Question 22 (extra credit)
- Reading Lesson 4-10
- Covering the Ideas 4-10 (Questions 1–7)

Notes on the Questions

Questions 3 and 4 One way to graph these functions is to begin by drawing an accurate sine wave without regard for the location of the x- and y-axes or their scales. Then place the axes and adapt the scales on them to fit the amplitude, period, and phase shift. However, this way does not yield the relationship between the function and its parent. Expect students to use a graphing utility as an aid.

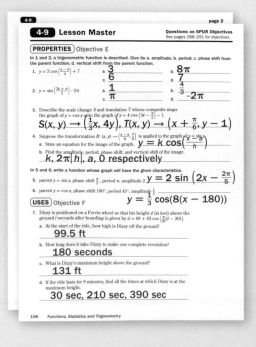

The amplitude is the radius of the wheel, so **the amplitude b is 131.** Since the center was 140 feet above ground, there is **a vertical translation of** k = 140. The period (one complete revolution or 2π) takes 9 minutes, so if we want time in minutes, we need to shrink the period from 2π to 9. A horizontal shrink with magnitude $\frac{9}{2\pi}$ will do this. Thus $a = \frac{9}{2\pi}$.

Substituting $a = \frac{9}{2\pi}$, $b = 131$, $h = 0$, and $k = 140$ into the equation, we obtain $\frac{y - 140}{131} = \cos\left(\frac{x - 0}{\frac{9}{2\pi}}\right)$, or $y = 131 \cos\left(\frac{2\pi}{9}x\right) + 140$.

Check After $2\frac{1}{4}$ minutes, the car should be at the level of the center of the wheel. Is this predicted by the equation? Substitute $2\frac{1}{4}$ for x.

$y = 131 \cdot \cos\left(\frac{2\pi}{9} \cdot 2\frac{1}{4}\right) + 140 = 140.$ It checks.

Questions

COVERING THE IDEAS

1. On page 269, the graph of $\frac{y + 2}{3} = \left(\frac{x - 1}{2}\right)^2$ is shown to be the image of the graph of $y = x^2$ under the composite of a translation and a scale change. Find the image of each point under that composite.
   a. $(0, 0)$ **(1, -2)**   b. $(10, 100)$ **(21, 298)** c. $(-10, 100)$ **(-19, 298)**

2. What transformations and in what order can be applied to the graph of $y = x^2$ to obtain the graph of $\frac{y - 7}{4} = \left(\frac{x + 8}{3}\right)^2$?

3. Consider the graph of the function with equation $y = \sin\left(\frac{x - \pi}{3}\right)$.
   a. Give the amplitude, period, and phase shift of the graph.
   b. The graph is the image of the graph of $y = \sin x$ under the composite of what two transformations?

4. Consider the graph of $y = \frac{1}{5}\cos\left(\frac{x + \pi}{6}\right)$.
   a. Give the amplitude, period, and phase shift of the graph.
   b. The graph is the image of the graph of $y = \cos x$ under the composite of what two transformations?

In 5 and 6, an equation of a sine wave is given.
   a. Write the equation in graph-standardization form.
   b. Find its amplitude, period, phase shift, and vertical shift from the graph of the parent function.

5. $y = 7 \sin(\pi x) - 5$ 6. $s = 6 + 2 \cos(3t + 4)$

In 7–9, refer to Example 3.

7. What are the minimum and maximum heights of the cars?

8. Check that after $4\frac{1}{2}$ minutes you are at the minimum height.

9. Model the height y of the wheel at time x by an equation in the form $\frac{y - k}{b} = \sin\left(\frac{x - h}{a}\right)$, using the sine function as the parent.

274   Trigonometric Functions

---

2. A scale change of $(x, y) \rightarrow (3x, 4y)$ followed by a translation of $(x, y) \rightarrow (x - 8, y + 7)$.

3a. amplitude: 1; period: 6π; phase shift: π units to the right

3b. A scale change of $(x, y) \rightarrow (3x, y)$, followed by a translation of $(x, y) \rightarrow (x + \pi, y)$.

4a. amplitude: $\frac{1}{5}$; period: 12π; phase shift: π units to the left

4b. A scale change of $(x, y) \rightarrow \left(6x, \frac{1}{5}y\right)$, followed by a translation of $(x, y) \rightarrow (x - \pi, y)$.

5a. $\frac{y + 5}{7} = \sin\left(\frac{x}{\frac{1}{\pi}}\right)$

5b. amplitude: 7; period: 2; phase shift: none; vertical shift: 5 units down

6a. $\frac{s - 6}{2} = \cos\left(\frac{t + \frac{4}{3}}{\frac{1}{3}}\right)$

6b. amplitude: 2; period: $\frac{2\pi}{3}$; phase shift: $\frac{4}{3}$ units to the left; vertical shift: 6 units up

7. minimum: 9 ft; maximum: 271 ft

8. $131 \cos\left(\frac{2\pi}{9} \cdot \frac{9}{2}\right) + 140 = 131 \cos(\pi) + 140 = -131 + 140 = 9$

9. $\frac{y - 140}{131} = \sin\left(\frac{x + \frac{9}{4}}{\frac{9}{2\pi}}\right)$

APPLYING THE MATHEMATICS

10. Suppose $f(x) = \tan\left(\frac{x+\pi}{4}\right)$.
    a. Describe a scale change and translation whose composite maps the graph of $y = \tan x$ onto the graph of $y = f(x)$.
    b. Draw a graph of $y = f(x)$ and state its period and phase shift. **See margin.**

11. Create a version of the Graph-Standardization Theorem for the tangent function. **See margin.**

In 12–14, write an equation for the function whose graph has the given characteristics.

12. Parent $y = \cos x$, phase shift $-\frac{\pi}{3}$, period $\frac{\pi}{2}$, and amplitude 9.

13. Parent $y = \sin x$, amplitude 5, period 6π, phase shift $\frac{\pi}{4}$, and vertical shift –1.

14. Parent $y = x^3$, scaled by S: $(x, y) \rightarrow (2x, 3y)$, then translated by T: $(x, y) \rightarrow (x - 1, y + 5)$.

15. The function graphed at the right has maximum value 15, minimum value –5, and period 2π. Write an equation for it.

16. For the sine wave modeled by $y = A \sin (Bx + C) + D$, give formulas in terms of A, B, C, and D for the
    a. amplitude. **A** b. period. $\frac{2\pi}{B}$ c. phase shift. $-\frac{C}{B}$

REVIEW

17. Consider the translation T: $(x, y) \rightarrow \left(x + \frac{\pi}{3}, y + 2\right)$. Find an equation for the image of the graph of $y = |x|$ under T. (**Lesson 4-8**)

18. Identify the following characteristics for the function g defined by $g(x) = A \sin(Bx)$. (**Lesson 4-7**)
    a. period $\frac{2\pi}{B}$ b. amplitude **A** c. domain d. range

19. Solve $\sin c = 0$ for $0 \le c \le 6\pi$. (**Lesson 4-5**)

20. A teacher made two forms of a test. The test scores are below.

Form A	93	62	89	77	68	94	73	82	85	76	83	79
Form B	65	87	71	76	67	87	76	81	77	82	62	78

Compared to the other students who took the same test, who performed better, the student with an 85 on Form A or the student with an 82 on Form B? (**Lesson 3-9**)

21. Simplify. (**Previous Course**)
    a. $\frac{10^8}{10^3}$ **10^5** b. $\frac{6 \cdot 10^5}{2 \cdot 10^{-3}}$ c. $\frac{2.8 \cdot 10^{-2}}{1.4 \cdot 10^3}$ d. $\frac{a \cdot 10^m}{b \cdot 10^n}$

EXPLORATION

22. Does it make a difference whether you translate a graph first and then scale the image, or scale the graph first and then translate the image? Defend your answer with at least two examples. **See margin.**

10a. A scale change of $(x, y) \rightarrow (4x, y)$ followed by a translation of $(x, y) \rightarrow (x - \pi, y)$.

12. $y = 9 \cos\left(\dfrac{x + \frac{\pi}{3}}{\frac{1}{4}}\right)$

13. $\dfrac{y + 1}{5} = \sin\left(\dfrac{x - \frac{\pi}{4}}{3}\right)$

14. $\dfrac{y - 5}{3} = \left(\dfrac{x + 1}{2}\right)^3$

15. Answers vary.
Sample: $y - 5 = 10 \sin\left(x - \frac{\pi}{2}\right)$

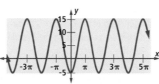

17. $y - 2 = \left|x - \frac{\pi}{3}\right|$

18c. all real numbers

18d. $\{y | -A \le y \le A\}$

19. $c = 0, \pi, 2\pi, 3\pi, 4\pi, 5\pi, 6\pi$

20. The student with an 82 on Form B.

21b. $3 \cdot 10^8$

21c. $2 \cdot 10^{-5}$

21d. $\left(\frac{a}{b}\right) \cdot 10^{m - n}$

QY ANSWER

$(0, 0), (0, 0), (1, -2)$

The Graph-Standardization Theorem **275**

Notes on the Questions

Question 10 Expect students to use a graphing utility to graph the function.

4) Wrap-Up

Ongoing Assessment

Have students work in pairs. Ask each student to make up a problem like the one given in Example 2 for his or her partner to solve. Partners should check each other's work on a graphing utility. Answers vary. Check students' work.

Additional Answers

22. By the rules of the Graph-Standardization Theorem, we can see that the order of operations may matter. Consider the scale change $S(x, y) = (ax, by)$ and the translation $T(x, y) = (x + h, b + k)$. Then, $T \circ S(x, y) = T(S(x, y)) = T(ax, by) = (ax + h, by + k)$, and $S \circ T(x, y) = S(x + h, y + k) = (ax + ah, by + bk)$. Consider two examples: in the first, $a = 2, b = 3, h = 4, k = 5$, and in the second, $a = 2, b = 1, h = 0, k = 3$. In the first case the order of operations matters, because $T \circ S(x, y) = (2x + 4, 3y + 5) \neq (2x + 8, 3y + 15) = S \circ T(x, y)$. In the second case the order of operators does not matter, because $T \circ S(x, y) = (2x, y + 3) = (2x, y + 3) = S \circ T(x, y)$.

Additional Answers

10b.

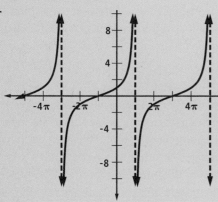

period: 4π; phase shift: π units to the left

11. The graphs of functions with equations $\dfrac{y - k}{b} = \tan\left(\dfrac{x - h}{a}\right)$, with $a \neq 0$ and $b \neq 0$, have vertical scale change = b, period = $\pi|a|$, phase shift = h, and vertical shift = k.

Lesson
4-10

GOAL

Show how sine waves model a variety of situations.

SPUR Objective

G Find equations of trigonometric functions to model periodic phenomena.

Materials/Resources

· Lesson Master 4-10
· Resource Masters 93–95

HOMEWORK

· Option 1
· Option 2

· Questions 1–7
· · Questions 8–18
· · Question 19 (extra credit)
· · Self-Test

Local Standards

1 Warm-Up

Monthly mean temperatures for Memphis, Tennessee are given below.

Month	Temp °F
Jan	40
Feb	45
Mar	54
Apr	62
May	71
Jun	79
Jul	83
Aug	81
Sep	75
Oct	64
Nov	52
Dec	43

1. Let x = the number of the month and let y = the mean temperature. Plot the data carefully.
2. By hand, sketch a sine curve to fit the data.

Lesson
4-10

Modeling with Trigonometric Functions

Vocabulary

simple harmonic motion

> ▶ **BIG IDEA** The Graph-Standardization Theorem can be used to build an equation that models real-world periodic data.

Many natural phenomena involving periodic behavior can be modeled by a single sine or cosine function.

Activity See margin.

The tables below show the number N of hours of daylight in Jacksonville, FL as a function of the number D of days after December 31st of a certain year. The data were collected on the first day of each month over a two-year period. Neither year was a leap year.

D	1	32	60	91	121	152	182	213	244	274	305	335
N	10.23	10.77	11.55	12.5	13.37	13.98	14.08	13.62	12.77	11.88	10.98	10.35
D	366	397	425	456	486	517	547	578	609	639	670	700
N	10.23	10.77	11.53	12.48	13.35	13.98	14.08	13.62	12.78	11.88	10.98	10.35

Source: The Old Farmer's Almanac, 2009

Step 1 Work with a partner and use a statistics utility to create a scatterplot of the data. The data should appear periodic.

Step 2 Assuming the data fit a sine function, estimate the following from the graph and interpret its meaning in this situation.

a. amplitude   b. period   c. vertical translation   d. phase shift

Step 3 Use the information from Step 2 to create a model of the form $\frac{y - k}{b} = \sin\left(\frac{x - h}{a}\right)$. Graph your model on the same grid as the scatterplot. You may need to convert your equation to a form that your technology can graph. How well does your model seem to fit the data?

Step 4 Check your model by using the sine regression function on your calculator.

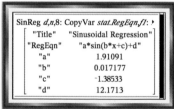

U.S. Census for 2007 ranked Jacksonville, FL, as the 12th largest city in the United States with a population of 805,605.

Mental Math

Find an equation for $f \circ g$ if f and g have the given equations.

a. $f(x) = x^2$ and $g(x) = x^5$

b. $f(x) = x^5$ and $g(x) = x^2$

c. $f(x) = \sqrt{x}$ and $g(x) = 4x - 17$

d. $f(x) = 4x - 17$ and $g(x) = \sqrt{x}$

Mental Math

a. x^{10}

b. x^{10}

c. $\sqrt{4x - 17}$

d. $4\sqrt{x} - 17$

Background

In 1960, three years before he received the Nobel Prize for physics for his work in quantum mechanics, Eugene Wigner, a professor at Princeton, wrote an essay titled, "The Unreasonable Effectiveness of Mathematics in the Natural Sciences." (You may be able to find this lesson online.) In 1980, Richard Hamming, then a professor at the Naval Postgraduate School, wrote more generally about the unreasonable effectiveness of mathematics. Both writers were reflecting the awe that many people

have when they realize that something they have learned has so many and such diverse applications.

Such is certainly the case with the trigonometric functions. Their definitions enable them to describe circular motion and cause them to be periodic. But many phenomena are periodic and do not have features resembling sine waves. In this lesson, the number of hours of daylight, the motion of a pendulum, the temperature of an oven, the motion of a spring, and a

Simple Harmonic Motion

The motion of a pendulum swinging back and forth in a vacuum and the motion of a weight bobbing on a spring are examples of *harmonic motion*. The graphs of these motions appear to be sine waves. Motion that can be described using a sine or cosine function is called **simple harmonic motion**. Each point on the graph corresponds to a location of the pendulum or weight at a particular time.

Example 1

A pendulum swings back and forth in a vacuum. Its distance from an object is captured using a motion detector for the object. The setup is pictured below at the left; at the right is a graph of the pendulum's distance from the motion detector. Write an equation for the distance from the pendulum to the object as a function of time.

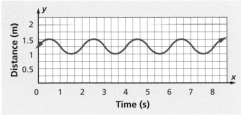

Solution We want to find the values of a, b, h, and k in the equation $\frac{y - k}{b} = \sin\left(\frac{x - h}{a}\right)$. First, identify the period P, because $a = \frac{P}{2\pi}$. The pendulum makes a round-trip every 2 seconds, so **the period is 2 seconds. Thus** $a = \frac{2}{2\pi} \approx 0.3183$. Next, calculate the amplitude b. The amplitude is half of the difference between the maximum and minimum y-values. So $b = \frac{1.5 - 1.0}{2} = 0.25$. Then find the vertical shift k, the distance from the x-axis to the center line of the graph. This distance is 1.25, so $k = 1.25$. Finally, compare the graph to a graph of the sine or cosine function. We pick the sine function. **The phase shift is 0 with respect to $y = \sin x$, so $h = 0$.**

Now substitute in the equation to write a formula for the function.
$\frac{y - 1.25}{0.25} = \sin\left(\frac{x}{0.3183}\right)$ or $y = 0.25 \sin\left(\frac{x}{0.3183}\right) + 1.25$, where y is the distance (in meters) of the pendulum from the object and x is time (in seconds).

Interpreting a Given Model

When you are given the equation of a sine wave model, you can interpret the coefficients to describe the situation.

lung volume when breathing give rise to situations that can be modeled by sine waves. Discussion of these applications can take a lot of time but also can be very motivating.

Additional Answers

Activity

See the Additional Answers section at the back of the book.

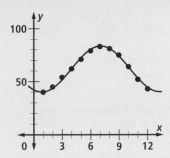

3. Estimate the amplitude of your sine curve. **21.5**

4. Using a period of 1 year, give an approximate equation for your curve. **A rather precise equation is** $y = 21.53 \sin (0.495x - 1.92) + 61.23$.

2 Teaching

Notes on the Lesson

One general algorithm for modeling with a sine wave is first to determine the period of the situation and use that for the period of the wave. Then find the maximum and minimum values of the situation and use that for the amplitude of the wave and for the horizontal line between the maximum and minimum values. Finally, determine the phase shift.

Activity You can use either the Activity or the Warm-Up to introduce students to the idea of modeling data using a sine wave. The Activity shows how the model can be quite close to the data.

Example 1 A graph is easily made from the data and students are asked to find an equation that fits it. This is something that was done in Lesson 4-9. Questions 3 and 4 relate to this example.

Additional Example

Example 1 In Houston, New Orleans and Jacksonville, all of which are at about 30° N latitude, the longest daylight period (June 21) is about 14 hours 5 minutes (845 minutes) long, and the shortest daylight period (December 21) is about 10 hours 13 minutes (613 minutes) long. The vernal equinox (March 21) has about 12 hours 9 minutes (729 minutes) of daylight. Assuming a sine wave model for the length of daylight, find an equation which gives the number of minutes of daylight in these three cities as a function of the day on the year.

$$\frac{y - 729}{116} = \sin\left(\frac{x - 80}{\frac{365}{2\pi}}\right)$$

4-10

Notes on the Lesson

Example 2 An equation is given from which students are asked to obtain characteristics of the situation. This is the reverse of Example 1.

Additional Example

Example 2 Assume that when a particular oven is set to 350°F, the oven temperature t in degrees Fahrenheit m minutes after the burner first shuts off satisfies $t = 350 + 10 \cos(0.8m)$.

a. What are the maximum and minimum temperatures of the oven at this setting? **maximum: 360°F; minimum: 340°F**

b. What is the period of this sine wave? What does the period represent? $\frac{5\pi}{2} \approx 7.9$ **minutes; It takes the oven about 7.9 minutes to go from one maximum (or minimum) temperature to the next maximum (or minimum) temperature.**

---

3 Assignment

Recommended Assignment

- Questions 1–7
- • Questions 8–18
- • Question 19 (extra credit)
- • Self-Test

Example 2

When an oven is set to a particular temperature, the heat level rises and falls, actually fluctuating slightly above and below that level as time passes. Assume that when a particular oven is set to 425°F, the oven temperature t in degrees Fahrenheit m minutes after the burner first shuts off satisfies $t = 425 + 6 \cos(0.9m)$.

a. What are the maximum and minimum temperatures of the oven at this setting?

b. What is the period of this sine wave? What does the period represent?

Solution First, transform the equation into the form $\frac{t - k}{b} = \cos\left(\frac{m - h}{a}\right)$ to identify the coefficients of the model.

$$\frac{t - 425}{?} = \cos\left(\frac{m}{?}\right)$$

a. The sum and difference of the amplitude and vertical translation of the sine wave tell us the maximum and minimum values of the model. This function has an amplitude of __?__ and a vertical translation of 6 __?__. Using these values, the maximum temperature of the oven **425°F** is __?__ while the minimum temperature is __?__. **431°F; 419°F**

b. The period $= 2\pi|a| = $ __?__. For this sine wave, the period $\frac{20\pi}{9} \approx 7$ **minutes** represents how long it takes the oven to go from one maximum (or minimum) temperature to the next maximum (or minimum) temperature.

Modeling an arbitrary sine wave, especially one with a nonzero phase shift, can be an involved process. It is easier if you focus your attention on one graph characteristic at a time. By asking a question like "What's the period?" or "What's the amplitude?" you can deal with one piece of the model at a time instead of trying to figure out everything at once.

Questions

COVERING THE IDEAS

In 1 and 2, use the sine regression model from Step 4 of the Activity. **the 174th day, or June 23rd; 14.086 hours**

1. What is the calendar day on which the number of hours of daylight is the greatest (the summer solstice) for the first year? How many hours of daylight are there on that day?

2. How many hours of daylight does your model predict for January 1st for the next year after the data shown? **10.27 hours**

3. Bernie has just purchased an oven. The manufacturer claims that less heat escapes from this oven than from the oven in Example 2. Assume that Bernie's oven takes twice as long to cool from the maximum to the minimum temperature. Write an equation to model Bernie's oven temperature as he cooks a roast at 425°. $t = 425 + 6 \cos 0.45m$

In 4 and 5, a pendulum's motion is captured and graphed below.

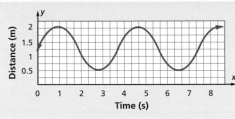

4. a. To the nearest 0.1 second, identify the time(s) at which the pendulum is furthest from the motion detector.

   b. To the nearest 0.1 second, identify the time(s) at which the pendulum is closest to the motion detector.

5. a. For each attribute below, describe its meaning in this situation, and find its value.

       i. amplitude   ii. period   iii. vertical shift

   b. Write a formula for the pendulum's motion in terms of time.

6. Write a formula describing the graph below.

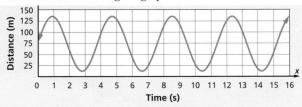

7. A model for an earthquake tremor is $f(t) = 1.6 \sin(188.5t)$. Find the period and amplitude of the tremor.

APPLYING THE MATHEMATICS

8. A pendulum swings for 100 seconds; its motion is captured and graphed below. Considering only period, vertical shift, and amplitude, which properties seem to be changing over time? Which seem to be constant? Why might this be so?

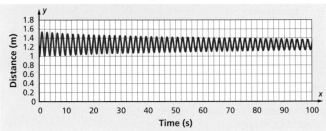

4a. 0.9 s, 4.7 s, 8.5 s

4b. 2.8 s, 6.6 s

5a.i. half of the range of the pendulum's distance from the motion detector; 0.75 m

5a.ii. the time the pendulum takes to complete full swing; 3.8 sec

5a.iii. the distance of the midpoint of the pendulum's swing from the motion detector; 1.3 m

5b. $\dfrac{d-1.3}{0.75} = \sin\left(\dfrac{\pi t}{1.9}\right)$

6. $\dfrac{d-75}{60} = \sin\left(\dfrac{\pi t}{2}\right)$

7. period: about 0.033 s, amplitude: 1.6

8. Amplitude seems to be changing over time, period and vertical shift do not. The pendulum is traveling a shorter distance in the same amount of time.

Notes on the Questions

Question 8 The graph shows a damped vibration, that is, one whose amplitude is decreasing over time. This is not a sine wave.

4-10

10a.

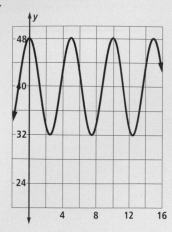

10b. $\dfrac{y-40}{8} = \sin\left(\dfrac{x+1.25}{\frac{5}{2\pi}}\right)$

11a–b.

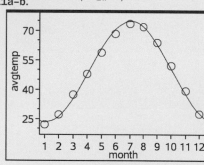

Answers vary. Sample: about **25.63**

11e. Answers vary. Sample:

$\dfrac{y-49}{-25.63} = \sin\left(\dfrac{\pi x - 3.5 + 3\pi}{6}\right)$

9. Rose Tate's height above ground level was tracked as she traveled on a Ferris wheel. The graph is shown below.

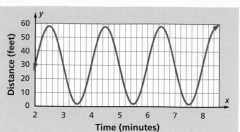

9e. $\dfrac{y-30}{28} = \sin\left(\dfrac{x}{\frac{1}{\pi}}\right)$

10b. $\dfrac{y-40}{8} = \sin\left(\dfrac{x+2.5}{\frac{5}{2\pi}}\right)$

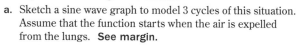

a. What is the radius of the Ferris wheel? **28 ft**

b. How high was Rose above the ground at her lowest point? **2 ft**

c. How high was she when she boarded the Ferris wheel? **30 ft**

d. How long does it take the Ferris wheel to make one revolution? **2 minutes**

e. Write an equation that approximates the graph.

10. The average adult normally breathes in and out every 5 seconds. The amount taken in and expelled from the lungs in a single breath is called the person's *tidal volume*. In adults, the tidal volume is about 16 fluid ounces. The maximum amount usually held in the lungs is 48 ounces.

a. Sketch a sine wave graph to model 3 cycles of this situation. Assume that the function starts when the air is expelled from the lungs. **See margin.**

b. Find a sine equation to model this situation.

11. Average monthly temperatures in degrees Fahrenheit for Chicago for the years 1971–2000 are given below.

month	Jan	Feb	Mar	Apr	May	Jun	Jul	Aug	Sep	Oct	Nov	Dec
avg. temp (°F)	22.0	27.0	37.3	47.8	58.7	68.2	73.3	71.7	63.8	52.1	39.3	27.4

Source: Statistical Abstract of the United States, 2009

a. Draw a scatterplot of these data. Plot $x =$ the number of the month on the horizontal axis, and $y =$ the temperature on the vertical axis. **a–b. See margin.**

b. Carefully sketch a sine curve to fit the data and estimate its amplitude to the nearest hundredth.

c. What is the period of this function? **12**

d. **Multiple Choice** Which of these four models is best for these data? **B**

A $\dfrac{y}{a} = \cos\left(\dfrac{\pi x - 3.5}{6}\right)$ B $\dfrac{y-49}{-a} = \cos\left(\dfrac{\pi x - 3.5}{6}\right)$

C $\dfrac{y-49}{a} = \cos\left(\dfrac{\pi x - 3.5}{6}\right)$ D $\dfrac{y-49}{a} = \cos\left(\dfrac{\pi x - 3.5}{6}\right)$

e. Find another equation equivalent to your answer in Part d that also describes these data. **See margin.**

12. Listed below are the hours of daylight in International Falls, Minnesota, for ten days of the year. **a–b. See margin.**

Date	1/1	2/28	3/21	4/27	5/6	6/21	8/14	9/23	10/25	12/21
Hours	8.38	10.95	12.27	14.40	14.87	16.15	14.40	12.12	10.27	8.30

Source: The Old Farmer's Almanac 2009

a. Draw a scatterplot of the data indicating dates as days of the year. (1/1 would be 1, 2/28 would be 59, and so on.) Assume this year was not a leap year.

b. Using paper and pencil, fit a sine wave to the scatterplot.

c. Determine an equation of a cosine function that models the data.

d. Using the model in Part c, estimate the hours of daylight on July 3.

e. Estimate what days International Falls had at least 10 hours of daylight.

REVIEW

13. Consider the function with equation $y = \cos\left(\frac{x + \pi}{4}\right)$.

a. Sketch a graph of the function. **See margin.**

b. Give the amplitude, period, and phase shift of its graph.

c. The graph is the image of the graph of $y = \cos x$ under the composite of which two transformations? **(Lesson 4-9)**

14. Given $\cos \theta = m$, find each value. **(Lesson 4-3)**

a. $\cos(-\theta)$ m b. $\cos(\pi - \theta)$ $-m$ c. $\sin(\theta - \pi)$ $\pm\sqrt{1 - m^2}$

In 15 and 16, refer to the unit circle at the right. **(Lesson 4-3)**

15. a. If $c = d$, find the exact value of c. $c = \frac{\sqrt{2}}{2}$

b. What is the value of θ_1? $\frac{\pi}{4}$

16. If $\theta_2 = \frac{-2\pi}{3}$, find e and f. $e = -\frac{1}{2}, f = -\frac{\sqrt{3}}{2}$

In 17 and 18, let $f(x) = x^2 - 2$ and $g(x) = \frac{1}{3x - 1}$. **(Lesson 3-7)**

17. a. Calculate $g \circ f \circ g(-2)$. $-\frac{49}{340}$

b. Calculate $f \circ g \circ f(-2)$. $-\frac{49}{25}$

18. a. Give the domain of $f \circ g \circ f$. $\{x \mid x \neq \pm\sqrt{\frac{7}{3}}\}$

b. Give the domain of $g \circ f \circ g$. $\{x \mid x \neq \frac{1}{3}, \frac{7 \pm \sqrt{21}}{21}\}$

EXPLORATION

19. The French physicist Léon Foucault used a large pendulum to demonstrate the fact that Earth rotates on its axis. The original Foucault Pendulum hangs in the Panthéon in Paris, France; copies are exhibited in science museums around the world. How does the pendulum's motion show Earth's rotation? Research Foucault to find the answer and to find out about his other inventions. **See margin.**

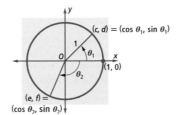

12c. Answers vary.
Sample: $y = -3.86 \cos\left(0.017x - 1.3 + \frac{\pi}{2}\right) + 12.13$

12d. Answers vary.
Sample: about 15.9

12e. days 43 through 301 (Feb. 12 through Oct. 28)

13b. amplitude: 1, period: 8π, phase shift: π units to the left

13c. a scale change of $(x, y) \rightarrow (4x, y)$ followed by a translation of $(x, y) \rightarrow (x - \pi, y)$

Modeling with Trigonometric Functions   **281**

Notes on the Questions
Question 19 Information about the Foucault pendulum can be found on the website http://www.calacademy.org/products/pendulum/sitemap.htm.

4   Wrap-Up

Ongoing Assessment
Have students write a paragraph describing how the same data can be modeled either by a sine function or a cosine function. **Students should demonstrate that they understand that in general, x can be replaced by $x + \frac{\pi}{2}$ to change from cosine to sine, or x can be replaced by $x - \frac{\pi}{2}$ to change from sine to cosine.**

Project Update
Project 5, *Sunrise and Sunset Times*, on page 283 relates to the content of this lesson.

Additional Answers
19. Answers vary. Sample: A Foucault Pendulum is a tall pendulum that oscillates in an open space. Because Earth rotates, the direction of the pendulum's oscillation changes with time. If the pendulum were at the North Pole or the South Pole, the direction of oscillation would remain fixed. He also created a device called the Foucault Disk, which shows how eddy currents work.

Additional Answers

12a–b.

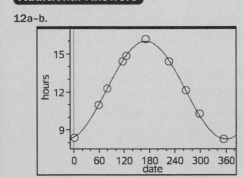

13a.

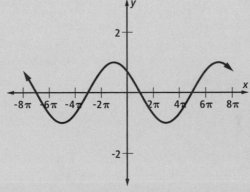

Chapter 4

Chapter 4 Projects

The projects relate to the content of the lessons of this chapter as follows:

Project	Lesson(s)
1	4-5, 4-7, 4-8
2	4-5, 4-6, 4-7, 4-8
3	4-2
4	4-5, 4-7, 4-8
5	4-10

1 Sums of Sine Waves with the Same Period

Students may be surprised that all the graphs are single sine waves. At this time in the course, students have not learned enough mathematics to prove this. Chapter 12, with formulas for $\sin(x + y)$ and $\cos(x + y)$, affords the opportunity.

1 Sums of Sine Waves with the Same Period

Consider functions with equations of the form $f(x) = a \sin x + b \cos x$. Here are some examples:

$$a = 1, b = 1: f(x) = \sin x + \cos x$$
$$a = \sqrt{3}, b = 1: f(x) = \sqrt{3} \sin x + \cos x$$
$$a = 1, b = -1: f(x) = \sin x - \cos x$$
$$a = 5, b = 12: f(x) = 5 \sin x + 12 \cos x$$

a. Can you predict the shapes of the graphs of such functions from the values of a and b? Graph the four examples above. Then choose some other values for a and b. What shapes are the graphs?

b. Can you predict the amplitude of a graph before you draw it? For example, what is the amplitude of $f(x) = 3 \sin x + 4 \cos x$? Check your prediction using a graphing utility. What is the period of the graph of $f(x) = a \sin x + b \cos x$?

c. What is the phase shift of the graph of $f(x) = a \sin x + b \cos x$? Predict the phase shift of $g(x) = \sin x + \sqrt{3} \cos x$. Check your prediction using a graphing utility.

d. For $a > 0$ and $b > 0$, the amplitude and the phase shift are related to a right triangle with legs of lengths a and b. Find out what the relationship is.

e. How are the graphs of $y = a \sin x - b \cos x$ and $y = a \sin x + b \cos x$ related if a and b are positive? How does your response to this question change if a and b are not both positive?

2 Beat Matching and DJing 101

Beat matching, once an art mastered only by DJs (disc jockeys) with vinyl records and turntables, can now be mastered by anyone using digital mp3 files, software, and special equipment such as Scratch Live. Some software allows you to see the graphs of files in order to match songs with similar frequencies, or beats, in order to mix different songs together as DJs do. Pick two songs, parts of which share a beat or rhythm which you can identify by ear using the mp3s and audio software.

a. Compare the period of the beat you hear in both songs. Are they similar?

b. What about the amplitude?

c. If you were to translate one of the songs at the cusp of the beat you are looking at and start it at the same time as the associated cusp in the second song, what would happen if you let both songs play at the same time?

d. Beat juggling can be performed when a new rhythmical composition is created using two songs and manipulating the arrangement and order of what is being played. A simple beat juggle might play one or more bars of the beat in song A, and then cross over to the beatmatched song B for several bars before going back to song A, and so on. Using audio software, copy and paste portions of the beat you analyzed in Parts a–c from both songs and compose a beat juggling session by putting them next to each other and letting them play. If your teacher allows, play the remix for your class.

Project Rubric

Advanced	Student correctly provides all of the details asked for in the project as well as additional correct independent conclusions.
Proficient	Student correctly provides all of the details asked for in the project.
Partially proficient	Student correctly provides some of the details asked for in the project or provides all details with some inaccuracies.
Not proficient	Student correctly provides few of the details asked for in the project or provides all details with many inaccuracies.
No attempt	Student makes little or no attempt to complete the project.

3 "Noncircular" Functions

The trigonometric functions are defined in terms of a unit circle. Imagine using a different shape centered at the origin O and passing through $A = (1, 0)$. Below are three possible alternatives: two squares (Figures A and B) and a regular octagon (Figure C).

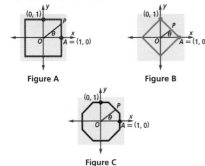

Figure A   Figure B

Figure C

In each case, define the functions side, coside, and tide (to distinguish them from sine, cosine, and tangent) as follows. For any rotation θ in radians, let P be the point on the figure such that $m\angle POA = \theta$. Then define

$$P = (\text{coside } \theta, \text{side } \theta)$$
$$\text{and tide } \theta = \frac{\text{side } \theta}{\text{coside } \theta}, \text{ if coside } \theta \neq 0.$$

a. Choose either Figure A or Figure B. Draw (separate) graphs of $s(x) = \text{side } x$, $c(x) = \text{coside } x$, and $t(x) = \text{tide } x$. Compare and contrast these with the graphs of the trigonometric functions.

b. Suggest theorems about the side, coside, and tide functions analogous to those studied in this chapter, such as the Pythagorean Identity, the Opposites Theorem, or the Supplements Theorem. Prove your results.

c. Choose one of the two other figures and repeat Parts a and b.

4 Square Waves

a. Graph the functions
$$F_1(x) = \sin x,$$
$$F_2(x) = \sin x + \tfrac{1}{3}\sin(3x),$$
$$F_3(x) = \sin x + \tfrac{1}{3}\sin(3x) + \tfrac{1}{5}\sin(5x), \text{ and}$$
$$F_{10}(x) = \sin x + \tfrac{1}{3}\sin(3x) + \tfrac{1}{5}\sin(5x) + \cdots$$
$$\qquad\qquad + \tfrac{1}{19}\sin(19x).$$

Describe the patterns you observe in the general shape, amplitude, and period. Predict the behavior of the function
$$F_n(x) = \sum_{i=1}^{n} \frac{\sin(2i-1)}{2i-1} \text{ for large } n.$$

b. These kinds of waves are important in understanding alternating current in electricity. Find out how and why.

5 Sunrise and Sunset Times

From an almanac or other reference, find the times of sunrise and sunset for various dates in a particular city in a particular year.

a. Make scatterplots of date versus time of sunrise and date versus time of sunset. Sketch curves of good fit through the data. Find an equation to model each set of data.

b. How does Daylight Saving Time affect a graph of time of sunset or sunrise?

c. From the equations of sunset and sunrise in relation to date, how could you determine an equation for the number of hours of daylight in relation to the date?

d. How does the latitude or longitude of a city affect the time of sunset or sunrise? Collect other data and supply theoretical evidence to support your answer.

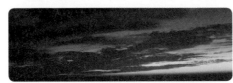

3 "Noncircular" Functions

This project requires some mathematical sophistication. Figures A and B are easier than Figure C.

4 Square Waves

This project was the subject of the entire Lesson 6-8 in the first edition of *Functions, Statistics, and Trigonometry*. If you have that book, you can use it for reference.

5 Sunrise and Sunset Times

The data for this project are relatively easy to find. Students might also wish to plot the length of daylight for the same location.

Sample answers for projects are in the Solution Manual in the Electronic Teacher's Edition.

Chapter 4

Chapter 4

Summary and Vocabulary

Summary and Vocabulary

The Summary gives an overview of the entire chapter and provides an opportunity for students to consider the material as a whole. Thus, the Summary can be used to help students relate and unify the concepts presented in the chapter.

Vocabulary words and symbols are listed by lesson to provide a checklist of concepts that students must know. Emphasize to students that they should read the vocabulary list carefully before starting the Self-Test on page 286. If students do not understand the meaning of a vocabulary word, they should refer back to the indicated lesson.

Theorems and Properties covered in the chapter are listed below the Summary with page references included to lead students back to the location in the chapter where the theorem or property is stated.

○ Degrees, **radians**, and **revolutions** measure **magnitudes** of rotations. Radians are often preferred for their convenience. By convention, counterclockwise rotations have positive measure and clockwise rotations have negative measure. The formula $360° = 1$ revolution $= 2\pi$ radians can be used to convert from one unit to another. In a circle with radius r, the length of an arc determined by a central angle of measure θ radians is $r\theta$.

○ The image of $(1, 0)$ under the rotation R_θ, with center $(0, 0)$ and magnitude θ, is defined to be (**cos θ, sin θ**). For all θ, since $R_{\theta+2\pi} = R_\theta$, $\cos(\theta + 2\pi) = \cos\theta$ and $\sin(\theta + 2\pi) = \sin\theta$. The **sine function** $\theta \to \sin\theta$ and **cosine function** $\theta \to \cos\theta$ each have domain the set of real numbers and range $\{y | -1 \le y \le 1\}$. For all θ except odd integer multiples of $\frac{\pi}{2}$, **tan $\theta = \frac{\sin\theta}{\cos\theta}$**. The range of the **tangent function** $\theta \to \tan\theta$ is the set of all real numbers. Graphs of these **trigonometric functions** are found on pages 248, 249, and 253.

○ **Sine waves** are images of graphs of the parent **circular functions** under composites of translations and scale changes. The sine wave with equation $\frac{y-k}{b} = \sin\left(\frac{x-h}{a}\right)$ or $\frac{y-k}{b} = \cos\left(\frac{x-h}{a}\right)$ has **amplitude** $|b|$, **period** $2\pi|a|$, **phase shift** h, and vertical shift k from its parent. Periodic phenomena and heights of objects that travel in circles on a vertical plane can be described by these equations.

○ The Pythagorean Identity, $\sin^2\theta + \cos^2\theta = 1$, comes from the definition of sine and cosine and the equation of a **unit circle**. Symmetries of the unit circle give rise to properties of the sine, cosine, and tangent of all x for which they are defined. These properties are described in the table at the top of the next page.

Vocabulary

4-1
*rotation, rotation image
center of the rotation
magnitude of a rotation
revolution
full turn
half turn
quarter turn
*radian

4-2
*unit circle
*cosine, cos
*sine, sin
circular function
trigonometric function
*tangent, tan

4-3
*identity

4-5
*sine function
*cosine function

4-6
tangent function
*periodic function
period of a function

4-7
*sine wave
*amplitude
*frequency

4-8
*phase shift

4-10
simple harmonic motion

Theorem	Symmetry of circle	Properties
Opposites Theorem	to x-axis	$\cos(-\theta) = \cos\theta$ $\sin(-\theta) = -\sin\theta$ $\tan(-\theta) = -\tan\theta$
Supplements Theorem	to y-axis	$\cos(\pi - \theta) = -\cos\theta$ $\sin(\pi - \theta) = \sin\theta$ $\tan(\pi - \theta) = -\tan\theta$
Complements Theorem	to the line $y = x$	$\cos\left(\frac{\pi}{2} - \theta\right) = \sin\theta$ $\sin\left(\frac{\pi}{2} - \theta\right) = \cos\theta$
Half-Turn Theorem	about the origin	$\cos(\pi + \theta) = -\cos\theta$ $\sin(\pi + \theta) = -\sin\theta$ $\tan(\pi + \theta) = \tan\theta$

● From the properties above and plane geometry, you can determine exact values of the sine, cosine, and tangent functions for arguments that are multiples of $\frac{\pi}{4}$ or $\frac{\pi}{6}$.

Theorems and Properties

Circle Arc Length Formula (p. 226)

Pythagorean Identity Theorem (p. 235)

Opposites Theorem (p. 237)

Half-Turn Theorem (p. 237)

Supplements Theorem (p. 238)

Complements Theorem (p. 239)

Periodicity Theorem (p. 253)

Theorem (Properties of Sine Waves) (p. 258)

Theorem (Phase Shift Identity) (p. 264)

Graph-Standardization Theorem (p. 270)

Theorem (Characteristics of a
   Sine Wave (p. 271)

Self-Test

For the development of mathematical competence, feedback and correction, along with the opportunity for practice, are necessary. The Self-Test provides the opportunity for feedback and correction; the Chapter Review provides additional opportunities for practice. We cannot overemphasize the importance of these end-of-chapter materials. It is at this point that the material gels for many students, allowing them to solidify skills and understanding. In general, student performance should improve after these pages.

Assign the Self-Test as a one-night assignment. Worked-out solutions for all questions are in the Selected Answers section of the student book. Encourage students to take the Self-Test honestly, grade themselves, and then be prepared to discuss the test in class.

Advise students to pay special attention to those Chapter Review questions (pages 288–291) that correspond to the questions they missed on the Self-Test. These are identified in the Self-Test Correlation Chart located in the Selected Answers section at the back of the book.

Chapter 4 Self-Test

Take this test as you would take a test in class. You will need a calculator. Then use the Selected Answers section in the back of the book to check your work.

In 1–5, give exact values.

1. Convert $\frac{7}{9}$ of a revolution to radians.
2. How many degrees equal $-\frac{5\pi}{2}$ radians?
3. Convert 120° to radians. Give your answer in terms of π. **120° · $\frac{\pi \text{ radians}}{180°} = \frac{2\pi}{3}$ radians**
4. Find $\sin\left(\frac{3\pi}{4}\right)$. $\frac{\sqrt{2}}{2}$
5. What is $\tan 60°$? $\sqrt{3}$
6. Approximate $\cos\left(\frac{7\pi}{5}\right)$ to four decimal places. **–0.3090**
7. Identify each of the following for the function with equation $y = \sin(x - \pi) + 3$.
   a. domain   b. range
   c. amplitude **1**   d. period **2π**
   e. phase shift **π**   f. vertical shift **3**
8. a. For what values of θ from 0 to 2π are $\cos \theta$ and $\tan \theta$ both positive? $\{\theta | 0 < \theta < \frac{\pi}{2}\}$
   b. For what values in the same range are they both negative? $\{\theta | \frac{\pi}{2} < \theta < \pi\}$

In 9 and 10, consider the unit circle below.

9. Find $\sin \theta$. **–0.988**
10. Find $\cos(\theta + \pi)$.

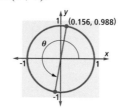

11. **True or False** Justify your answer. For all θ, $\cos(\theta + 3\pi) = \cos \theta$.

1. $\frac{7}{9}$ revolution · $\frac{2\pi \text{ radians}}{1 \text{ revolution}} = \frac{14\pi}{9}$ radians
2. $-\frac{5\pi}{2}$ radians · $\frac{180°}{\pi \text{ radians}} = -450°$
7. a. $\{x | x \in \mathbb{R}\}$
   b. $\{y | 2 \leq y \leq 4\}$
10. By the Half-Turn Theorem, $\cos(\theta + \pi) = -\cos \theta$, so $-\cos \theta = 0.156$.

286   Trigonometric Functions

12. Below is part of the graph of a function f. Which could be an equation for f: $f(x) = \sin x$ or $f(x) = \cos x$? Justify your answer.

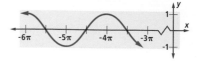

13. Below is a graph of a sine wave together with a general form of an equation for it. Find the values of a, b, h, and k in the equation. $b = 2, k = -3, a = 1, h = \frac{\pi}{2}$

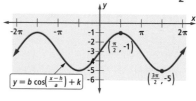

14. Give an exact value of $\cos(-\theta)$ if $\sin \theta = \frac{5}{13}$ and $\frac{\pi}{2} < \theta < \pi$.

15. Suppose the transformation $(x, y) \rightarrow \left(\frac{x}{3} + \pi, y\right)$ is applied to the graph of $y = \tan x$. Write an equation for the image.

16. **Multiple Choice** Which property of a circular function changes under a vertical scale change of its graph? **B**
    A phase shift   B amplitude
    C frequency   D period

11. False. The cosine function repeats every 2π so $\cos(\theta + 3\pi) = \cos(\theta + \pi) = -\cos \theta$
12. $f(x) = \cos x$ because $\sin(\pi n) = 0$, for $n \in \mathbb{N}$
14. $\sin \theta = \frac{5}{13}$ and $\frac{\pi}{2} < \theta < \pi$, so $\cos \theta = -\sqrt{1 - \left(\frac{5}{13}\right)^2} = -\frac{12}{13}$. Thus, $\cos(-\theta) = -\frac{12}{13}$.
15. $y = \tan(3(x - \pi))$

17. A sine wave model for the average temperature T for Grand Rapids, Michigan, during month n is shown in the graph below.

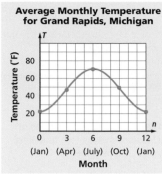

Average Monthly Temperature for Grand Rapids, Michigan

a. What is the amplitude of the wave?

b. What is the period of the wave?

c. Write an equation to model these data.

d. Use the model to estimate the average temperature for Grand Rapids in February.

18. The voltage E in volts in a circuit after t seconds ($t > 0$) is given by $E = 12 \cos(14\pi t)$.

a. What is the maximum voltage achieved in the circuit?

b. Find three times at which the voltage achieves its maximum value.

19. **Multiple Choice** Which equation could yield the graph below?

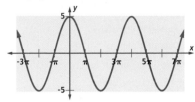

A $y = 5 \sin(2x)$ **B** $y = 5 \cos(2x)$

C $y = 5 \sin\left(\frac{x}{2}\right)$ **D** $y = 5 \cos\left(\frac{x}{2}\right)$

20. The hum you hear on a radio when it is not functioning properly is a sinusoidal sound wave with a frequency of 60 vibrations per second. If the amplitude of this wave is 0.1, write an equation for the displacement y as a function of time t.

17. a. The maximum is 70 and the minimum is 22 so the amplitude is $\frac{70 - 22}{2} = 24°$.

b. The period is from minimum (January) to minimum (January), or 12 months.

c. Answers vary. Sample: The vertical shift is about $22 + 24 = 46$ and the phase shift from the sine function is about 3 months. The equation, using the Characteristics of Sine Waves Theorem, is $\frac{T - 46}{24} = \sin\left(\frac{n - 3}{\frac{12}{2\pi}}\right)$ or $T = 24 \sin\frac{\pi}{6}(n - 3) + 46$.

d. Substitute 1 into the equation. $T = 25.2°$

18. a. The maximum of $\cos\theta$ is 1 so the maximum of $12\cos(14\pi t)$ is 12 volts.

b. The maximum of $\cos\theta$ is achieved when $\theta = 2\pi n$ for any integer n, so $\cos(14\pi t)$ is at a maximum when $14\pi t = 2\pi n$ for some integer n, or when $t = \frac{n}{7}$. Answers vary. Sample: $t = \frac{1}{7}, \frac{2}{7}, \frac{3}{7}$

19. D; The graph shows no phase shift from a cosine function with its maximum when $x = 0$. The amplitude is 5 and period is 4π, so the equation must be D.

20. Answers vary. Sample: The frequency is the reciprocal of the period, so the period is $\frac{1}{60}$. Because no starting point is specified, either a sine or a cosine wave will work. Using the Characteristics of Sine Waves Theorem, an equation is $y = 0.1\sin(120\pi x)$ or $y = 0.1\cos(120\pi x)$.

Chapter Review

The main objectives for the chapter are organized in the Chapter Review under the four types of understanding this book promotes: Skills, Properties, Uses, and Representations.

Whereas end-of-chapter material may be considered optional in some texts, in UCSMP *Functions, Statistics, and Trigonometry* we have selected these objectives and questions with the expectation that they will be covered. Students should be able to answer these questions with about 85% accuracy after studying the chapter.

You may assign these questions over a single night to help students prepare for a test the next day or you may assign the questions over a two-day period. If you work the questions over two days, we recommend assigning the evens for homework the first night so that students get feedback in class the next day, and then assigning the odds the night before the test because the answers are provided to the odd-numbered questions in the Selected Answers section at the back of the book.

It is effective to ask students which questions they still do not understand and use the day as a total class discussion of the material that the class finds most difficult.

Resources

- Assessment Resources: Chapter 4 Test

Technology Resources

Teacher's Assessment Assistant, Ch. 4
Electronic Teacher's Edition, Ch. 4

1, 2, 12–17, 26–30, 32, 33. See margin.
SKILLS Procedures used to get answers

OBJECTIVE A Convert between degrees, radians, and revolutions. (Lesson 4-1)

In 1 and 2, a rotation is given.
  a. Convert to degrees.
  b. Convert to radians.
1. $\frac{2}{5}$ revolution counterclockwise
2. $\frac{1}{3}$ revolution clockwise

In 3 and 4, convert to degrees without using a calculator.
3. $-\frac{5\pi}{6}$ radians **–150°**   4. $\frac{\pi}{12}$ radians **15°**

In 5 and 6, convert to radians without using a calculator.
5. 225° $\frac{5\pi}{4}$ 6. 330° $\frac{11\pi}{6}$

In 7 and 8, tell how many revolutions are represented by a rotation of the given magnitude.
7. $\frac{2\pi}{3}$ $\frac{1}{3}$ of a revolution   8. 630° $\frac{7}{4}$ revolutions

OBJECTIVE B Find values of sines, cosines, and tangents. (Lessons 4-4, 4-5)

In 9–11, give exact values without using a calculator.
9. $\sin\left(\frac{\pi}{4}\right)$ $\frac{\sqrt{2}}{2}$ 10. $\cos\left(\frac{\pi}{3}\right)$ $\frac{1}{2}$ 11. $\tan\left(\frac{\pi}{6}\right)$ $\frac{\sqrt{3}}{3}$

In 12–14, approximate to the nearest thousandth.
12. $\tan 1.3$ 13. $\cos 0.0926$ 14. $\sin 0.4563$

In 15–17, evaluate to the nearest hundredth.
15. $\cos 3$ 16. $\sin(-4.2)$ 17. $\tan 251°$

In 18–21, give exact values without using a calculator.
18. $\sin\left(\frac{5\pi}{4}\right)$ $-\frac{\sqrt{2}}{2}$ 19. $\cos 210°$ $-\frac{\sqrt{3}}{2}$
20. $\tan\left(-\frac{\pi}{4}\right)$ **–1**   21. $\cos\left(\frac{9\pi}{2}\right)$ **0**

22. Give two values of θ between -2π and 2π such that $\sin\theta = 1$. $-\frac{3\pi}{2}, \frac{\pi}{2}$

In 23 and 24, let $P = R_\theta(1, 0)$. Find the coordinates of P when θ is the following.
23. 5π **(–1, 0)**   24. $\frac{2}{5}$ of a revolution clockwise
    $(\cos(-144°), \sin(-144°)) \approx (-0.809, -0.588)$

288   Trigonometric Functions

---

25. Solve $\cos x = -\frac{1}{2}$ exactly for x in the interval $-\frac{\pi}{2} \le x \le \frac{5\pi}{2}$. $x = \frac{2\pi}{3}, \frac{4\pi}{3}$

PROPERTIES Principles behind the mathematics

OBJECTIVE C Apply the definitions of the sine, cosine, and tangent functions. (Lessons 4-2, 4-3, 4-5, 4-6)

26. Describe the domain and range of the cosine function.

27. For what values of θ is $\tan\theta$ undefined?

In 28 and 29, let $f(x) = \sin x$. **True or False** Explain your answer.
28. f is an even function.
29. The maximum value of f is 1.
30. In what domain interval(s) between 0 and 2π are the values of both the sine and tangent functions negative?

31. **Multiple Choice** For which values of θ is $\sin\theta < 0$ and $\cos\theta > 0$? **D**

  A $0 < \theta < \frac{\pi}{2}$ **B** $\frac{\pi}{2} < \theta < \pi$
  C $\pi < \theta < \frac{3\pi}{2}$ **D** $\frac{3\pi}{2} < \theta < 2\pi$

OBJECTIVE D Apply theorems about sines, cosines, and tangents. (Lessons 4-3, 4-6)

32. Why is the statement that for all θ, $\sin(\pi - \theta) = \sin\theta$ called the Supplements Theorem?

33. Use theorems about sines and cosines to prove that $-\sin\left(\frac{\pi}{2} - \theta\right) = \cos(\pi - \theta)$.

In 34–37, given $\sin\theta = k$ for $0 < \theta < \frac{\pi}{2}$, without using a calculator, find each.
34. $\sin\left(\frac{\pi}{2} - \theta\right)$ $\sqrt{1 - k^2}$ 35. $\cos(\pi - \theta)$ $-\sqrt{1 - k^2}$
36. $\sin(\theta - \pi)$ **–k**   37. $\cos(\pi + \theta)$ $-\sqrt{1 - k^2}$

Additional Answers

1a. 144°
1b. $\frac{4\pi}{5}$
2a. –120°
2b. $-\frac{2\pi}{3}$
12. 3.602
13. 0.996
14. 0.441
15. –0.99
16. 0.87
17. 2.90
26. domain: $\{x \mid x \in \mathbb{R}\}$; range: $\{y \mid -1 \le y \le 1\}$
27. $\frac{\pi}{2} + \pi n$, for $n \in \mathbb{Z}$

28. false; for example, $\sin\left(-\frac{\pi}{4}\right) = -\frac{\sqrt{2}}{2} \ne \frac{\sqrt{2}}{2} = \sin\left(\frac{\pi}{4}\right)$
29. true; the range of the sine function is $\{y \mid -1 \le y \le 1\}$ as determined by the unit circle
30. $\{x \mid \frac{3\pi}{2} < x < 2\pi\}$
32. It is called the Supplements Theorem because the angles θ and $\pi - \theta$ are supplements.
33. By the Complements Theorem, $-\sin\left(\frac{\pi}{2} - \theta\right) = -\cos\theta$. By the Supplements Theorem, $-\cos\theta = \cos(\pi - \theta)$.

42–54. See Margin.

In 38–40, **True or False** Justify your answer.

38. For all θ, $\cos(\theta + 5\pi) = \cos \theta$.

39. For all θ, $\sin(\theta + 4\pi) = \sin \theta$.

40. For all θ, $\cos^2\theta + \sin^2\theta = \tan^2\theta$.

41. If $\cos \theta = -\frac{1}{4}$, without using a calculator, find all possible values of

   a. $\sin \theta$.   **b.** $\tan \theta$.

| **OBJECTIVE E** Identify the amplitude, period, frequency, phase shift, and other properties of trigonometric functions. (Lessons 4-7, 4-8, 4-9)

In 42-45, an equation is given. If they exist, find the following features of the graph of the equation.

  a. the period   **b.** the amplitude   **c.** the phase shift

42. $\frac{y}{5} = \cos\left(\frac{x}{2}\right)$ 43. $y = 2\sin(3\pi x)$

44. $y = 2\sin\left(x - \frac{\pi}{3}\right)$ 45. $h(\theta) = \frac{1}{2}\tan(3\theta)$

46. Identify each of the following for the function defined by the equation $y = -4\sin\left(\frac{x}{3}\right)$.

  a. amplitude   **b.** period   **c.** frequency

47. State the maximum and minimum values of the function f with $f(t) = 10 + 5\cos(2t)$.

48. Suppose the transformation $(x, y) \rightarrow (3x, y - 1)$ is applied to the graph of $y = \sin x$.

  a. State an equation for the image.

  b. Find the amplitude, period, phase shift, and vertical shift of the image.

49. Let $S(x, y) = \left(\frac{x}{4}, -3y\right)$ and $T(x, y) = (x + 7, y)$.

  a. Find the image of the graph of $y = \cos x$ under the composite $T \circ S$.

  b. Find a single transformation that maps $y = \cos x$ to the graph in Part a.

38. false; by the Half-Turn Theorem, $\cos(\theta + 5\pi) = -\cos(\theta + 4\pi)$, and by the Periodicity Theorem, $-\cos(\theta + 4\pi) = -\cos \theta$

39. true; by the Periodicity Theorem, $\sin(\theta + 4\pi) = \sin \theta$

40. false; by the Pythagorean Identity, $\cos^2 \theta + \sin^2 \theta = 1$, but for $\theta = \frac{\pi}{3}$, $\tan^2 \theta = 3$

41a. $\frac{\sqrt{15}}{4}$ and $-\frac{\sqrt{15}}{4}$ 41b. $\sqrt{15}$ and $-\sqrt{15}$

USES Applications of mathematics in real-world situations

| **OBJECTIVE F** Write and solve equations for phenomena described by trigonometric functions. (Lessons 4-7, 4-8, 4-9)

50. An alternating current I in amps of a circuit at time t in seconds is given by the formula $I = 35\cos(72\pi t)$.

  a. Find the maximum and minimum values of the current.

  b. How many times per second does the current reach its maximum value?

51. The voltage V in volts in a circuit after t seconds is given by $V = 110\cos(50\pi t)$.

  a. Find the first time the voltage is 55 volts.

  b. Find three times at which the voltage is maximized.

52. A certain sound wave has equation $y = 34\cos(15\pi t)$. Give an equation of a sound wave with twice the frequency and half the intensity of this one.

53. A pendulum is shown at the right. The angular displacement from vertical (in radians) as a function of time t in seconds is given by $f(t) = \frac{1}{2}\sin\left(3t + \frac{\pi}{2}\right)$.

  a. What is the initial angular displacement from the pendulum's rest position?

  b. What is the frequency of f?

  c. How long will it take for the pendulum to make 5 complete swings?

| **OBJECTIVE G** Find equations of trigonometric functions to model periodic phenomena. (Lesson 4-10)

54. Suppose the height h in meters of a tide at time t is given in the table below.

t	0	5.1	6.2	11.9	18.2	23.7
h	3.7	0.2	0.8	3.5	0.5	3.7

  a. Fit a sine wave to these data.

  b. What is the period of the sine wave?

  c. What is the amplitude of the sine wave?

Assessment

Evaluation The *Assessment Resources* provide a form of the Chapter 4 Test. Here are our recommendations for assigning a letter grade: 85–100 = A; 72–84 = B; 60–71 = C; 50–59 = D.

Feedback After students have taken the test for Chapter 4 and you have scored the results, return the tests to students for discussion. Class discussion on the questions that caused trouble for most students can be very effective in identifying and clarifying misunderstandings. You might want to have them note the items they missed and work either in groups or at home to correct them. It is important for students to receive feedback on every chapter test, and we recommend that students see and correct their mistakes before proceeding too far into the next chapter.

Suggestions for Assignment Assign Reading Lesson 5-1 and Covering the Ideas 5-1 for homework the evening of the test. It gives students work to do after they have completed the test and keeps the class moving. If you do not do this, you may cover one less chapter over the course of the year.

Additional Answers

50a. maximum: 35; minimum –35

50b. 36 times per second

51a. $\frac{1}{150}$ seconds ≈ 0.00667 seconds

51b. Answers vary. Sample: $t = \frac{1}{25}, \frac{2}{25}, \frac{3}{25}$

52. $y = 17\cos(30\pi t)$

53a. $\frac{1}{2}$ radians

53b. $\frac{3}{2\pi} \approx 0.477$

53c. $\frac{10\pi}{3} \approx 10.472$ seconds

54a. $y = 1.85\sin(0.52x + 2.18) + 2.05$

54b. about 12.083

54c. about 1.85

Additional Answers

42a. 4π

42b. 5

42c. 0

43a. $\frac{2}{3}$

43b. 2

43c. 0

44a. 2π

44b. 2

44c. $\frac{\pi}{3}$

45a. $\frac{\pi}{3}$

45b. does not exist

45c. 0

46a. 4

46b. 6π

46c. $\frac{1}{6\pi}$

47. maximum: 15; minimum: 5

48a. $y = \sin\left(\frac{x}{3}\right) - 1$

48b. amplitude: 1; period: 6π; phase shift: 0; vertical shift: –1

49a. $y = -3\cos(4(x - 7))$

49b. $(x, y) \rightarrow \left(\frac{x}{4} + 7, -3y\right)$

Chapter 4 Review

55a. $y = 2.233 \sin (0.017x - 1.317) + 12.133$

55b. about 372.9

55c. about 9.90 hours

56a. 12

56b. 12

56c. $d = 12\sin \frac{\pi t}{6} + 8$

56d. 3 seconds

57a. $y = 3 \sin(5\pi t)$

57b. 0 cm

57c. $h = 3 \cos (5\pi t) + 3 \sin (5\pi t)$

58a. b

58b. 0.342

59a. g

59b. -0.940

60a. e

60b. -0.940

61a. f

61b. 0.342

55–61. See margin.

55. The length of the day from sunrise to sunset in a city at 34° N latitude (such as Los Angeles, California) is given in the table below.

Date	Days after Jan 1	Length (hours)
1/1	0	9.93
2/1	31	10.55
3/1	59	11.45
4/1	90	12.55
5/1	120	13.55
6/1	151	14.27
7/1	181	14.38
8/1	212	13.83
9/1	243	12.88
10/1	273	11.83
11/1	304	10.8
12/1	334	10.07
1/1	365	9.93

Source: National Oceanic and Atmospheric Administration

a. Find an equation using the sine function to model these data.

b. What is the period of any function used to model these data?

c. Use your model from Part a to predict the length of the day on December 21, the winter solstice, at 34° N latitude.

56. The figure below shows a water wheel rotating at 5 revolutions per minute. The distance d of point P from the surface of the water as a function of time t in seconds can be modeled by a sine wave with an equation of the form $\frac{d - k}{b} = \sin\left(\frac{t - h}{a}\right)$.

a. What is the amplitude of the sine wave?

b. What is the period of the sine wave?

c. After point P emerges from the water, you start a stopwatch when $d = 8$. Write an equation for the sine wave.

d. Approximately when does point P first reach its highest point?

---

57. A gear with a 3-cm radius rotates counterclockwise at a rate of 150 revolutions per minute. The gear starts with the tooth labeled A level with the center of the wheel as shown below.

a. Write an equation to give the vertical distance y that point A is above or below its starting position at time t in seconds.

b. How far above or below the starting position will point A be after 4 minutes?

c. Write an equation for the vertical distance h that point A is above point B at time t.

REPRESENTATIONS Pictures, graphs, or objects that illustrate concepts

OBJECTIVE H Use the unit circle to find values of sines, cosines, and tangents. (Lessons 4-2, 4-3)

In 58–61, refer to the unit circle below.

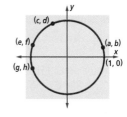

a. Identify the letter that best represents the value given.

b. Estimate the value to the nearest thousandth.

58. $\sin 20°$

59. $\cos(520°)$

60. $\cos\left(\frac{8\pi}{9}\right)$

61. $\sin\left(-\frac{28\pi}{9}\right)$

62.

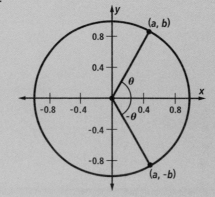

62, 66, 69, 70, 74, 75, 78. See margin.

62. Use a unit circle to show why the cosine function is an even function.

In 63–65, let P' be the reflection image of P over the y-axis, as shown in the unit circle below. State the value of the following.

63. $\sin(180° - \theta)$ **–b**

64. $\tan(-\theta)$ **$\frac{b}{a}$**

65. $\cos\left(\frac{\pi}{2} - \theta\right)$ **–b**

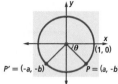

$P' = (-a, -b)$ $P = (a, -b)$

OBJECTIVE I Draw or interpret graphs of the parent sine, cosine, and tangent functions in degrees or radians. **(Lessons 4-5, 4-6)**

66. Sketch a graph of the cosine function without using technology, indicating key points and the period.

67. Below is part of the graph of a function f. Which of the following could be an equation for f: $f(x) = -\cos x$ or $f(x) = -\sin x$? Justify your answer.

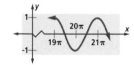

68. Consider the graphs of $f(x) = 4 \sin x$ and $g(x) = 4 \cos x + 8$. What translation maps the graph of f onto the graph of g?

69. a. Use a graphing utility to graph $y = \sin x$ and $y = \sin(\pi - x)$ on the same set of axes.

    b. Describe the relationship between the graphs.

    c. What theorem does the relationship between these two graphs represent?

70. a. Sketch a graph of the tangent function.

    b. Write equations for two of the asymptotes of the graph of the tangent function.

67. $f(x)$ must be $-\cos(x)$ because $-\sin(20\pi) = 0$

68. $T: (x, y) \rightarrow \left(x - \frac{\pi}{2}, y + 8\right)$

OBJECTIVE J Graph and describe transformation images of graphs of trigonometric functions. **(Lessons 4-7, 4-8, 4-9)**

In 71–73, match each graph with its equation.

A

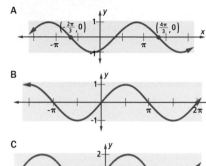

B

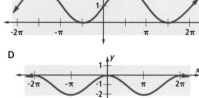

C

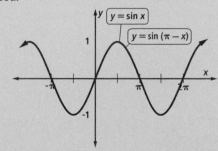

D

71. $y = 1 + \sin x$ **C**

72. $y = \cos\left(x - \frac{\pi}{2}\right)$ **B**

73. $y = \sin\left(x - \frac{\pi}{3}\right)$ **A**

In 74 and 75, sketch one cycle of the graph without using a graphing utility.

74. $y = \frac{1}{3} \sin(2x)$ 75. $y = 7 \cos\left(\frac{\pi}{2}x\right)$

76. Write an equation for the image of the graph of $y = \sin x$ under a phase shift of $\frac{3\pi}{4}$.

77. Write an equation for the image of the graph of $y = \cos x$ under a phase shift of $-\frac{\pi}{3}$ and with a period of 4π.

78. Consider the equation $y = 4 - 7 \sin(2x + 1)$.

    a. Sketch a graph of the equation.

    b. State the period and maximum value of the function with this equation, if they exist.

76. $y = \sin\left(x - \frac{3\pi}{4}\right)$ **77.** $y = \cos\left(\dfrac{x + \frac{\pi}{3}}{2}\right)$

Additional Answers

70a.

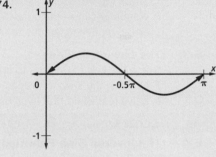

70b. Answers vary. Sample: $x = -\frac{\pi}{2}$ and $x = \frac{\pi}{2}$

74.

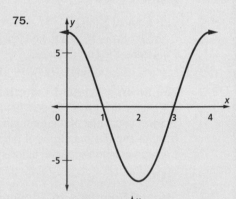

75.

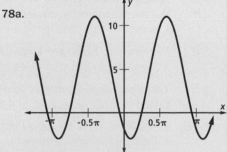

78a.

78b. period: π; **maximum: 11**

Additional Answers

66. The period is 2π.

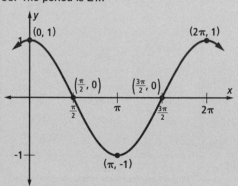

69a.

$y = \sin x$

$y = \sin(\pi - x)$

69b. the graphs are identical

69c. Supplements Theorem

Chapter

5 Trigonometry

Chapter Overview

		Local Standards	Pacing (in days)		
			Average	Advanced	Block
5-1	**Trigonometric Ratios in Right Triangles** **A** Find sines, cosines, and tangents of angles. **C** Use trigonometry to find lengths in triangles. **H** Use trigonometry to solve problems involving right triangles.		1	1	0.5
5-2	**The Inverse Cosine Function** **B** Evaluate the inverse trigonometric functions. **D** Solve trigonometric equations. **G** State and use properties of the inverse trigonometric functions. **J** Write and solve equations for phenomena described by trigonometric functions. **L** Graph or identify graphs of the inverse trigonometric functions.		1	1	0.5
5-3	**The Law of Cosines** **C** Use the Law of Cosines to find lengths and angle measures in triangles. **F** Interpret the Law of Cosines. **I** Solve real-world problems using the Law of Cosines.		1	1	0.5
	QUIZ 1		0.5	0.25	0.25
5-4	**The Inverse Sine Function** **B, D, G, J, L** See 5-2.		1	1	0.5
5-5	**The Law of Sines** **C** Use the Law of Sines to find lengths and angle measures in triangles. **F** Interpret the Law of Sines. **I** Solve real-world problems using the Law of Sines.		1	1	0.5
5-6	**The Inverse Tangent Function** **B** Evaluate the inverse tangent function. **D** Solve equations of the form $\tan \theta = k$. **G** State and use properties of the inverse tangent function. **L** Graph or identify graphs of inverse tangent function.		1	1	0.5
	QUIZ 2		0.5	0.25	0.25
5-7	**General Solutions to Trigonometric Equations** **D** Solve trigonometric equations. **J** Write and solve equations for phenomena described by trigonometric functions.		1	1	0.5
5-8	**Parametric Equations for Circles and Ellipses** **M** Graph parametric equations of circles and ellipses.		1	1	0.5
5-9	**The Secant, Cosecant, and Cotangent Functions** **E** Find secants, cosecants, and cotangents.		1	1	0.5
5-10	**From New York to New Delhi** **K** Find the shortest distance between two points on Earth given their longitude and latitude.		1	1	0.5
	Self-Test		1	0.5	0.5
	Chapter Review		2	1	0.5
	Test		1	1	0.5
	TOTAL		**15**	**13**	**7**

Technology Resources

Teacher's Assessment Assistant, Ch. 5

Electronic Teacher's Edition, Ch. 5

Differentiated Options Universal Access

	Accommodating the Learner	Vocabulary Development	Ongoing Assessment	Materials
5-1	pp. 296, 297		p. 298	
5-2	pp. 301, 302	p. 300	p. 303	
5-3	p. 305		p. 308	
5-4	pp. 310, 311		p. 313	
5-5	p. 316		p. 319	
5-6	p. 321		p. 324	
5-7	pp. 326, 327		p. 330	graphing utility
5-8			p. 335	graphing utility
5-9	p. 338		p. 340	graph paper
5-10	p. 344		p. 348	Internet access

Objectives

Ⓢkills		Lessons	Self-Test Questions	Chapter Review Questions
A	Find sines, cosines, and tangents of angles.	5-1	1, 2	1–7
B	Evaluate the inverse trigonometric functions.	5-2, 5-4, 5-6	3, 4, 5	8–13
C	Use trigonometry to find lengths and angle measures in triangles.	5-1, 5-3, 5-5	11	14–21
D	Solve trigonometric equations.	5-2, 5-4, 5-6, 5-7	9, 10, 13	22–37
E	Find secants, cosecants, and cotangents.	5-9	6, 18	38–43
Ⓟroperties				
F	Interpret the Law of Sines, Law of Cosines, and related theorems.	5-3, 5-5	12	44–47
G	State and use properties of the inverse trigonometric functions.	5-2, 5-4, 5-6	7	48–55
Ⓤses				
H	Use trigonometry to solve problems involving right triangles.	5-1	14	56–59
I	Solve real-world problems using the Law of Sines and the Law of Cosines.	5-3, 5-5	16	60–63
J	Write and solve equations for phenomena described by trigonometric functions.	5-2, 5-4, 5-7	15	64–68
K	Find the shortest distance between two points on Earth given their longitude and latitude.	5-10	19	69–71
Ⓡepresentations				
L	Graph or identify graphs of inverse trigonometric functions.	5-2, 5-4, 5-6	8	72–74
M	Graph parametric equations of circles and ellipses.	5-8	17	75–78

Resource Masters Chapter 5

Resource Master 152, Four Quadrant Graph Paper, (page 152) can be used with Lesson 5-8.

Resource Master 97 Lesson 5-1
Resource Master 96 Lesson 5-1

Warm-up
1. State and give an instance of the SAS Triangle Similarity Theorem.
2. State and give an instance of the AA Triangle Similarity Theorem.
3. There is one other basic similarity theorem. State it and give an instance.

Additional Examples
1. In $\triangle DEF$, $\angle D$ is a right angle. If $DF = 40$ and $EF = 41$, find:
   a. sin E.
   b. cos E.
   c. tan E.
2. The 60-meter-long string of a kite you are flying is being pulled taut by the wind and makes an angle of 68° with the ground. How far from you would a person be if that person is directly underneath the kite?
3. From a height of 5'6" off the ground, a person looks up 30° to see the top of a flagpole. The person then walks 85 feet to the base of the flagpole. How tall is the flagpole?
4. A roof of a house is slanted at an angle of 28° to the horizontal. If the roof ends at a side of the house 22 feet above the ground, how long would the extension of the roof be if the roof were to extend to the ground?

Page 294

Theorem (Right Triangle Ratios for Sine, Cosine, and Tangent)

If θ is the measure of an acute angle in a right triangle, then
$$\frac{\text{leg opposite } \theta}{\text{hypotenuse}} = \sin \theta.$$
$$\frac{\text{leg adjacent to } \theta}{\text{hypotenuse}} = \cos \theta. \text{ and}$$
$$\frac{\text{leg opposite } \theta}{\text{leg adjacent to } \theta} = \tan \theta.$$

Resource Masters for Lesson 5-1

Resource Master 99 Lesson 5-2
Resource Master 98 Lesson 5-2

Warm-up
1. Give the measure of an angle whose sine equals 0.5.

2. Give the measure of an angle whose cosine equals 0.5.

3. Give the measure of an angle whose cosine equals 0.

Additional Examples
1. Evaluate $\cos^{-1}(-0.5)$ in radians without a calculator.

2. Evaluate $\cos^{-1}(0.99426)$ to the nearest hundredth of a degree.

3. To prop up a proscenium on the back of a stage, you have a 9'6" board whose foot is 5'3" from the back of the proscenium. What is the measure of the acute angle made by the board with the floor?

Resource Masters for Lesson 5-2

Resource Master 101 Lesson 5-3
Resource Master 100 Lesson 5-2

Question 1

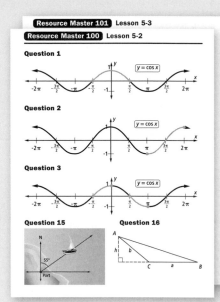

Question 2

Question 3

Question 15   **Question 16**

Resource Masters for Lesson 5-2 and 5-3

Resource Master 103 Lesson 5-3
Resource Master 102 Lesson 5-3

Theorem (Law of Cosines)

In any $\triangle ABC$, $c^2 = a^2 + b^2 - 2ab \cos C$.

Proof of Law of Cosines

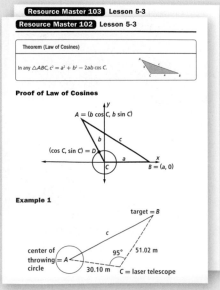

$A = (b \cos C, b \sin C)$

$(\cos C, \sin C) = D$

$B = (a, 0)$

Example 1

target $= B$

center of throwing $= A$

circle

95°   51.02 m

30.10 m C = laser telescope

Resource Masters for Lesson 5-3

Resource Master 105 Lesson 5-4
Resource Master 104 Lesson 5-4

Warm-up
1. Give the measure of an acute angle whose sine equals $\frac{\sqrt{3}}{2}$.

2. Give the measure of an obtuse angle whose sine equals $\frac{\sqrt{3}}{2}$.

3. Give the measure of an angle whose sine equals 1.

Additional Examples
1. Evaluate $\sin^{-1}(-0.5)$ in radians without a calculator.

2. Suppose ϕ is an angle in a triangle and $\sin \phi = 0.2616$. Find ϕ to the nearest hundredth of a degree.

3. For what θ with $0 < \theta < 180°$ is it the case that $\sin^{-1}(\sin \theta) \neq \theta$?

Resource Masters for Lesson 5-4

Resource Master 107 Lesson 5-5
Resource Master 106 Lesson 5-4

Question 3a

point on $y = \sin x$	$\left(-\frac{\pi}{2}, -1\right)$	$\left(-\frac{\pi}{3}, ?\right)$	$\left(-\frac{\pi}{4}, ?\right)$	$\left(-\frac{\pi}{6}, ?\right)$	$(0, ?)$	$\left(\frac{\pi}{6}, ?\right)$	$\left(\frac{\pi}{4}, ?\right)$	$\left(\frac{\pi}{3}, ?\right)$	$\left(\frac{\pi}{2}, ?\right)$
corresponding point on $y = \sin^{-1} x$	$\left(-1, -\frac{\pi}{2}\right)$	$(?, ?)$	$(?, ?)$	$(?, ?)$	$(?, ?)$	$(?, ?)$	$(?, ?)$	$(?, ?)$	$(?, ?)$

Question 7

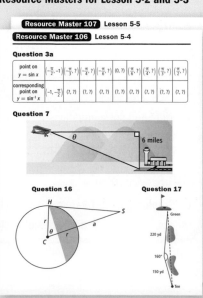

θ

6 miles

Question 16   **Question 17**

Resource Masters for Lesson 5-4 and 5-5

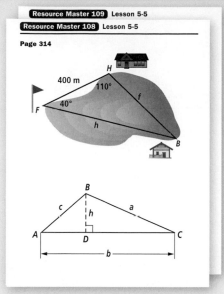

Resource Master 109 Lesson 5-5
Resource Master 108 Lesson 5-5

Page 314

Resource Masters for Lesson 5-5

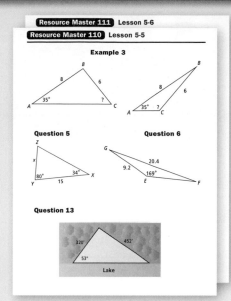

Resource Master 111 Lesson 5-6
Resource Master 110 Lesson 5-5

Example 3

Question 5   Question 6

Question 13

Lake

Resource Masters for Lesson 5-5 and 5-6

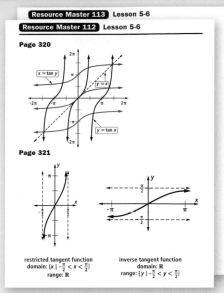

Resource Master 113 Lesson 5-6
Resource Master 112 Lesson 5-6

Page 320

Page 321

restricted tangent function
domain: $\{x \mid -\frac{\pi}{2} < x < \frac{\pi}{2}\}$
range: $\mathbb{R}$

inverse tangent function
domain: $\mathbb{R}$
range: $\{y \mid -\frac{\pi}{2} < y < \frac{\pi}{2}\}$

Resource Masters for Lesson 5-6

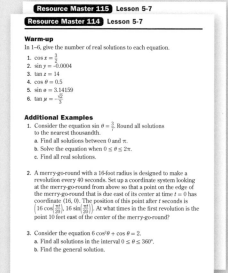

Resource Master 115 Lesson 5-7
Resource Master 114 Lesson 5-7

Warm-up
In 1–6, give the number of real solutions to each equation.
1. $\cos x = \frac{3}{2}$
2. $\sin y = -0.0004$
3. $\tan z = 14$
4. $\cos \theta = 0.5$
5. $\sin \theta = 3.14159$
6. $\tan \mu = -\frac{\sqrt{2}}{3}$

Additional Examples
1. Consider the equation $\sin \theta = \frac{3}{7}$. Round all solutions to the nearest thousandth.
   a. Find all solutions between 0 and π.
   b. Solve the equation when $0 \le \theta \le 2\pi$.
   c. Find all real solutions.

2. A merry-go-round with a 16-foot radius is designed to make a revolution every 40 seconds. Set up a coordinate system looking at the merry-go-round from above so that a point on the edge of the merry-go-round that is due east of its center at time $t = 0$ has coordinate (16, 0). The position of this point after t seconds is $\left(16 \cos\left(\frac{\pi t}{20}\right), 16 \sin\left(\frac{\pi t}{20}\right)\right)$. At what times in the first revolution is the point 10 feet east of the center of the merry-go-round?

3. Consider the equation $6 \cos^2\theta + \cos \theta = 2$.
   a. Find all solutions in the interval $0 \le \theta \le 360°$.
   b. Find the general solution.

Resource Masters for Lesson 5-7

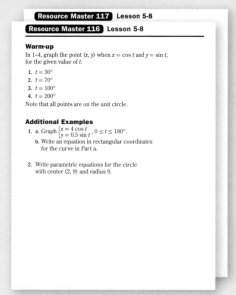

Resource Master 117 Lesson 5-8
Resource Master 116 Lesson 5-8

Warm-up
In 1–4, graph the point (x, y) when $x = \cos t$ and $y = \sin t$, for the given value of t.
1. $t = 30°$
2. $t = 70°$
3. $t = 100°$
4. $t = 200°$
Note that all points are on the unit circle.

Additional Examples
1. a. Graph $\begin{cases} x = 4 \cos t \\ y = 0.5 \sin t \end{cases}$, $0 \le t \le 180°$.
   b. Write an equation in rectangular coordinates for the curve in Part a.

2. Write parametric equations for the circle with center (2, 9) and radius 9.

Resource Masters for Lesson 5-8

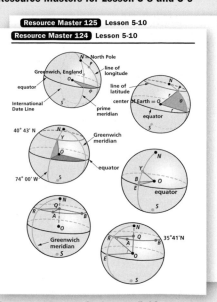

Resource Master 119 Lesson 5-9
Resource Master 118 Lesson 5-8

Question 18

Question 22

Resource Masters for Lesson 5-8 and 5-9

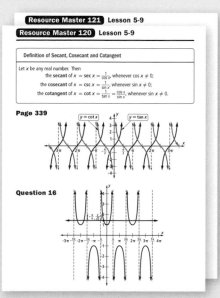

Resource Master 121 Lesson 5-9
Resource Master 120 Lesson 5-9

Definition of Secant, Cosecant and Cotangent

Let x be any real number. Then
the **secant** of $x = \sec x = \frac{1}{\cos x}$, whenever $\cos x \ne 0$;
the **cosecant** of $x = \csc x = \frac{1}{\sin x}$, whenever $\sin x \ne 0$;
the **cotangent** of $x = \cot x = \frac{1}{\tan x} = \frac{\cos x}{\sin x}$, whenever $\sin x \ne 0$.

Page 339

Question 16

Resource Masters for Lesson 5-9

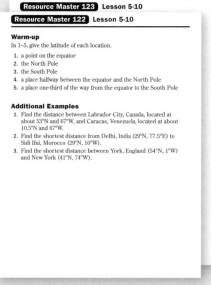

Resource Master 123 Lesson 5-10
Resource Master 122 Lesson 5-10

Warm-up
In 1–5, give the latitude of each location.
1. a point on the equator
2. the North Pole
3. the South Pole
4. a place halfway between the equator and the North Pole
5. a place one-third of the way from the equator to the South Pole

Additional Examples
1. Find the distance between Labrador City, Canada, located at about 53°N and 67°W, and Caracas, Venezuela, located at about 10.5°N and 67°W.
2. Find the shortest distance from Delhi, India (29°N, 77.5°E) to Sidi Ifni, Morocco (29°N, 10°W).
3. Find the shortest distance between York, England (54°N, 1°W) and New York (41°N, 74°W).

Resource Masters for Lesson 5-10

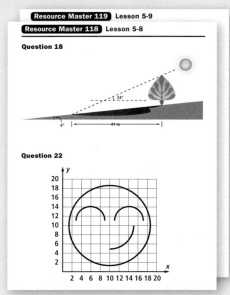

Resource Master 125 Lesson 5-10
Resource Master 124 Lesson 5-10

North Pole
line of longitude
Greenwich, England
equator
line of latitude
International Date Line
prime meridian
center of Earth
equator

40° 43' N
Greenwich meridian
74° 00' W
equator

Greenwich meridian

35°41'N

Resource Masters for Lesson 5-10

Pacing

Each lesson in this chapter is designed to be covered in 1 day. At the end of the chapter, you should plan to spend 1 day to review the Self-Test, 1 to 2 days for the Chapter Review, and 1 day for a test. You may wish to spend a day on projects, and possibly a day will be needed for quizzes. This chapter should therefore take 14 to 17 days. We strongly advise you not to spend more than 18 days on this chapter; there is ample opportunity to review ideas in later chapters. However, it is expected that students have seen examples of the trigonometric functions, even if only with right triangles, in earlier courses.

Students should be expected to do the equivalent of a complete set of Questions from a lesson nearly every day. Two Assignment Options are identified in each lesson. At times you may want to save a few questions to be done by students in class.

Overview

The opener gives a variety of applications of the trigonometric functions in relation to right triangles. These applications were discovered earlier in history than the applications to periodic motion and waves that students encountered in Chapter 4.

The three questions on the page all involve the use of trigonometry to ascertain distances between points without having to measure the distances directly. Of course, a throw from 10 feet behind second base to first base can be measured directly, with a tape measure. But the distance to the Moon, or the distance between two cities on Earth, is an entirely different matter. One aspect of the power of mathematics is that the same ideas that can be applied to small numbers and short distances can be also applied to very large numbers and long distances.

▷ **Contents**

5-1   Trigonometric Ratios in Right Triangles

5-2   The Inverse Cosine Function

5-3   The Law of Cosines

5-4   The Inverse Sine Function

5-5   The Law of Sines

5-6   The Inverse Tangent Function

5-7   General Solutions to Trigonometric Equations

5-8   Parametric Equations for Circles and Ellipses

5-9   The Secant, Cosecant, and Cotangent Functions

5-10   From New York to New Delhi

In Chapter 4, you studied the use of the sine, cosine, and tangent functions in describing circular motion and other periodic phenomena. The first known uses of these functions arose from the need to solve practical, everyday problems in which lengths or angles in triangles had to be found. This is why the study of the sine, cosine, and tangent functions is called *trigonometry*, a word derived from Greek words meaning "triangle measurement."

The origins of trigonometry have been traced back to the Egyptians of the 13th century B.C.E., whose tables of shadow lengths correspond to today's tangent and cotangent functions. The Babylonians and Greeks used trigonometry to study the heavens, and more recent travelers used it to navigate.

Chapter 5 Overview

This chapter discusses the aspects from which "trigonometry" receives its name, namely "triangle measurement," the measuring of sides and angles in triangles. In Lesson 5-1, students review the trigonometric ratios in right triangles, which we hope they have seen once or twice before. Then the material moves to the first of two important theorems that apply in all triangles, the Law of Cosines. The solving of the equation $\cos x = k$ is needed in some problems, so a discussion

of the inverse cosine function is done in Lesson 5-2 with the Law of Cosines in Lesson 5-3. Lessons 5-4 and 5-5 are analogous, with discussion of the inverse sine function and the Law of Sines. With a discussion of the inverse tangent function in Lesson 5-6, students are prepared for the general solution to any trigonometric equation of the form $\sin x = k$, $\cos x = k$, or $\tan x = k$, which is covered in Lesson 5-7. Two nice applications of sines and cosines, to the parametric equations for circles and

In this chapter, you will study additional properties of these functions and you will use trigonometry to solve problems, such as the following, that are based on triangle measurement.

In baseball, how long is a throw from 10 feet behind second base to first base?

What is the diameter of the Moon?

How far is it from New York to New Delhi, India?

North Pole

New York

New Delhi

South Pole

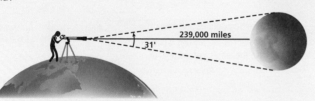

239,000 miles

31'

293

ellipses (in Lesson 5-8) and the Spherical Law of Cosines and the approximation of the great circle distances between any two locations on Earth, are found in Lesson 5-10. In between, we introduce the other three ratios of sides in a right triangle, to complete the study of triangle trigonometry.

Because students will be using calculators to solve problems, there is as much or more emphasis on students being able to approximate angle measures or values of trigonometric functions as there is on

working with exact values. Yet, whenever possible, formulas and identities are proved as theorems. This is intended to provide students not with simply a formula to use, but a method for reconstructing a formula they may have forgotten.

Using Pages 292–293

This is an appropriate time to assess how much your students know about the content of the chapter. In some physics classes, right triangle trigonometry is discussed quite early and some of your students may have had this content earlier in this school year. You might ask the following:

How many of you know the right triangle definitions for the sine, cosine, and tangent? (These definitions are found and applied in UCSMP *Geometry*.)

If any answer "Yes" to this question, ask:

How many of you have graphed these trigonometric functions?

How many of you have studied the Law of Sines and the Law of Cosines?

(These graphs and these theorems are found in UCSMP *Advanced Algebra*, including a lesson on the famous historical uses of trigonometry in calculating the circumference of Earth and the distance to the Moon.)

The answers will give you some guidance as to the pace you can keep.

Chapter 5 Projects

At the end of each chapter, you will find projects related to the chapter. At this time you might want to have students look over the projects on pages 349 and 350. You might want to have students tentatively select a project on which to work. Then, as students read and progress through the chapter, they can finalize their project choices.

Sometimes students might work alone. At other times, you might let them collaborate with classmates for a presentation and discussion. We recommend that you allow for diversity and encourage students to use their imaginations when presenting their projects. As students work on projects throughout the year, they should see many uses of mathematics in the real world.

Lesson 5-1

GOAL

Present the definitions of sine, cosine, and tangent as ratios of sides of a right triangle, apply the ratios and use calculators appropriately.

SPUR Objectives

The SPUR objectives for all of Chapter 5 are found in the Chapter Review on pages 354–357.

A Find sines, cosines, and tangents of angles.

C Use trigonometry to find lengths in triangles.

H Use trigonometry to solve problems involving right triangles.

Materials/Resources

· Lesson Master 5-1
· Resource Masters 96 and 97

HOMEWORK • Option 1

• Questions 1–7 • Option 2
• • Questions 8–16
• • Question 17 (extra credit)
• Reading Lesson 5-2
• Covering the Ideas 5-2
(Questions 1–9)

Local Standards

---

1 Warm-Up

1. State and give an instance of the SAS Triangle Similarity Theorem. **If two sides of one triangle are proportional to two sides of another, and the included angles are congruent, then the triangles are similar. Answers vary. Sample: Two right triangles, one with legs of length 2 and 3, and the other with legs of length 20 and 30, are similar.**

2. State and give an instance of the AA Triangle Similarity Theorem. **If two angles of one triangle are congruent to two angles of another,**

Lesson 5-1 Trigonometric Ratios in Right Triangles

Vocabulary

angle of depression
angle of elevation

▶ **BIG IDEA** The sine, cosine, and tangent of magnitudes between 0° and 90° each equal a ratio of sides of a right triangle.

The picture below reviews some terminology about right triangles. Examine it closely. Each leg is opposite one acute angle and adjacent to the other. Recall that the side opposite a vertex is named by the small letter of that vertex. For example, opposite vertex B is side b.

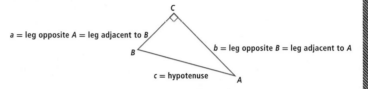

a = leg opposite A = leg adjacent to B
b = leg opposite B = leg adjacent to A
c = hypotenuse

Mental Math

Consider the four numbers 0.5, 0.7, 0.8 and 0.9.

a. Which is the best approximation to $\frac{\sqrt{2}}{2}$?

b. Which is the best approximation to $\frac{\sqrt{3}}{3}$?

c. Which is the best approximation to $\frac{\sqrt{4}}{4}$?

a. 0.7
b. 0.5
c. 0.5

Relating Sines, Cosines, and Tangents to Sides in Right Triangles

In an earlier course, you may have seen sines, cosines, and tangents defined in terms of the lengths of sides in right triangles. These relationships can be *proved* from the definitions of sine, cosine, and tangent that were given in Lesson 4-2.

> **Theorem (Right Triangle Ratios for Sine, Cosine, and Tangent)**
>
> If θ is the measure of an acute angle in a right triangle, then
>
> $\dfrac{\text{leg opposite }\theta}{\text{hypotenuse}} = \sin\theta,$
>
> $\dfrac{\text{leg adjacent to }\theta}{\text{hypotenuse}} = \cos\theta,$ and
>
> $\dfrac{\text{leg opposite }\theta}{\text{leg adjacent to }\theta} = \tan\theta.$
>
>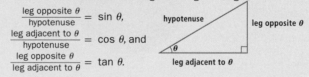

Proof Here we prove that $\dfrac{\text{leg opposite }\theta}{\text{hypotenuse}} = \sin\theta$. The other proofs are similar. A right triangle with hypotenuse 1 can be positioned on the unit circle as shown at the right. The coordinates of P give the lengths of the legs of $\triangle PAE$, so $PE = \sin\theta$. Thus,
$\dfrac{\text{leg opposite }\theta}{\text{hypotenuse}} = \dfrac{\sin\theta}{1} = \sin\theta.$

$P = (\cos\theta, \sin\theta)$

Background

We assume that students have encountered trigonometric ratios in a previous course. They are found in UCSMP *Geometry* and *Advanced Algebra*. If not, this may be a two-day lesson. Then we suggest covering through Example 2 and assigning Questions 1–5, 8, 10, 13, and 15 on the first day and the rest of the problems on the second day along with the reading of Lesson 5-2.

Whether or not students have had this material before, these ideas are important enough to warrant review. Emphasize that the reason one can have trigonometric ratios at all is because of properties of similarity. Specifically, all right triangles with acute angles of the same measure are similar, so the ratios of any corresponding sides are equal.

If the hypotenuse of $\triangle ABC$ is not 1, place the triangle as in the diagram at the right, where both $\triangle PAE$ and $\triangle BAC$ contain $\angle A$ and a right angle. The triangles are similar, so
$$\frac{BC}{BA} = \frac{PE}{PA}.$$
$PE = \sin \theta$ and $PA = 1$, so substitute.
$$\frac{BC}{BA} = \frac{\sin \theta}{1} = \sin \theta.$$

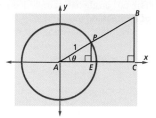

In $\triangle BAC$, $\overline{BC}$ is opposite θ and $\overline{BA}$ is the hypotenuse. So
$$\frac{\text{leg opposite } \theta}{\text{hypotenuse}} = \sin \theta.$$
In the above proof, $\theta = m\angle A$, so you could write
$\sin(m\angle A) = \dfrac{\text{leg opposite } A}{\text{hypotenuse}}$. However, it is customary to write $\sin A$, $\cos A$, and $\tan A$ rather than $\sin(m\angle A)$, $\cos(m\angle A)$, and $\tan(m\angle A)$.

GUIDED

Example 1

In $\triangle ABC$, the leg opposite A has length 20, the leg adjacent to A has length 21, and the hypotenuse has length 29. Calculate $\sin A$, $\cos A$, and $\tan A$.

Solution

$\sin A = \dfrac{\text{leg opposite } A}{?} = \underline{\ ?\ }$ hypotenuse; $\dfrac{20}{29}$

$\cos A = \dfrac{?}{\text{hypotenuse}} = \underline{\ ?\ }$ leg adjacent to A; $\dfrac{21}{29}$

$\tan A = \dfrac{?}{?} = \underline{\ ?\ }$ leg opposite A;
leg adjacent to A; $\dfrac{20}{21}$

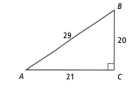

Finding Sides in Right Triangles

In many situations, you know only the length of one side and the measure of one acute angle in a right triangle. Using the appropriate trigonometric ratio, you can determine the lengths of the other sides.

Example 2

Sonar on a salvage boat locates an object at a downward angle of 50° and a distance of 510 meters, as shown in the drawing. How far below the level of the water is the object?

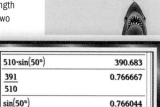

Solution In this situation, the measure of an acute angle and the length of the hypotenuse in a right triangle are known. The problem asks for the length of the leg opposite the known acute angle. The sine ratio involves these two lengths, so it is the appropriate ratio to use.

Let d be the depth of the object. Then
$$\sin 50° = \frac{d}{510},$$
so $510 \sin 50° = d$.

A calculator shows that $d = 390.68\ldots \approx 391$ meters.

510·sin(50°)	390.683
$\frac{391}{510}$	0.766667
sin(50°)	0.766044

Check Compare $\frac{391}{510}$ with $\sin 50°$. They should be very close.

Trigonometric Ratios in Right Triangles   **295**

Relating sines, cosines, and tangents to sides in right triangles You may be surprised to see the right triangle ratios for sine, cosine, and tangents proved in a theorem. This is because we have defined these functions in terms of the unit circle. In order to use the properties deduced from that definition, such as the Supplements Theorem $\sin(\pi - \theta) = \sin \theta$ for all θ, we need to show that the two characterizations of the trigonometric functions – via unit circles and via right triangles – are consistent with each other. Thus this theorem, which seems trivial, is actually critical for applying the mathematics students have already learned.

None of the problems in this lesson involve finding angle measures using trigonometry. That requires the inverse trigonometric functions that are discussed beginning in Lesson 5-2.

---

then the triangles are similar. Answers vary. Sample: Two triangles, each with a 70° angle and a 43° angle, are similar.

3. There is one other basic similarity theorem. State it and give an instance. **The SSS Triangle Similarity Theorem: If three sides of one triangle are proportional to three sides of another, then the triangles are similar.** Answers vary. Sample: Two triangles, one with sides of 72, 82, and 98, and the other with sides of 108, 123, and 147, are similar (with ratio of similitude 1.5 or $\frac{2}{3}$).

2 Teaching

Notes on the Lesson

The AA Triangle Similarity Theorem in the Warm-Up can be applied to show that all right triangles with an acute angle of specified measure θ are similar triangles, so the ratios of any two corresponding sides are equal. This means that $\sin \theta$ depends only on θ; it has the same value in a large right triangle as it has in a small one.

Relating sines, cosines, and tangents to sides in right triangles For students who have never studied these ratios, you may want to do Example 1 before discussing the proof of the theorem on pages 294–295. Students should go through the proof of the theorem in this lesson in detail.

Example 1 You might want to note that if $\triangle ABC$ in Example 1 were the triangle superimposed on the unit circle in the proof, the coordinates of point P would be $\left(\frac{20}{29}, \frac{21}{29}\right)$.

Example 2 Remind students to check the mode (degree, radian, or gradian) to which their calculator is set. Even experienced users have made the mistake of using the wrong key on many occasions. The frequency of this error is a strong argument for checking to see if answers make sense.

Additional Example

Example 1 In $\triangle DEF$, $\angle D$ is a right angle. If $DF = 40$ and $EF = 41$, find:
a. $\sin E$. $\frac{40}{41}$
b. $\cos E$. $\frac{9}{41}$
c. $\tan E$. $\frac{40}{9}$

Notes on the Lesson

Example 3 It is important that students realize that an angle of elevation as seen from *E* has the same measure as an angle of depression as seen from *T*. You might ask students why. **These are alternate interior angles created by parallel horizontal lines and the transversal $\overline{ET}$.**

Example 4 With the Pythagorean Theorem, you can tell how high up the wall the ladder is, but you can also find that height using the sine function. (The ladder is 12 sin 75° or about 11.6 feet up the wall. Students may be surprised that a 12-foot ladder goes so far up the wall.) You also might ask: How many inches is 3.11 feet? **0.11 feet is 0.11 • 12 inches or 1.32 inches, so 3.11 feet is 37.32 inches.**

Additional Examples

Example 2 The 60-meter-long string of a kite you are flying is being pulled taut by the wind and makes an angle of 68° with the ground. How far from you would a person be if that person is directly underneath the kite?
Let the distance be *d*. $d = 60 \cos 68° \approx$ 22.48 meters.

Example 3 From a height of 5'6" off the ground, a person looks up 30° to see the top of a flagpole. The person then walks 85 feet to the base of the flagpole. How tall is the flagpole?
Draw a diagram as shown here.

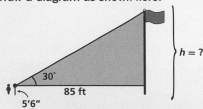

$h - 5.5 = 85 \cdot \tan 30°$, $h \approx 54.6$ **feet**

Example 4 A roof of a house is slanted at an angle of 28° to the horizontal. If the roof ends at a side of the house 22 feet above the ground, how long would the extension of the roof be if the roof were to extend to the ground?
Draw a diagram as shown here.

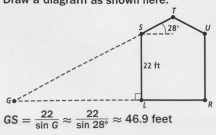

$GS = \dfrac{22}{\sin G} \approx \dfrac{22}{\sin 28°} \approx 46.9$ **feet**

The 50° angle in Example 1 is called an *angle of depression*. The **angle of depression** to an object is the angle formed by a horizontal ray and a ray with the same endpoint that contains the object if the object is below the horizontal. If the object is above the horizontal ray, then the angle is an **angle of elevation**.

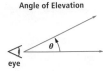

Angle of Depression   Angle of Elevation

GUIDED

Example 3

You wonder how tall a grain silo is. You walk 60′ from the silo and find that you have to look up at a 38° angle to see the top. If your eyes are 5′3″ off the ground, how tall is the silo without the roof?

Solution Draw a diagram showing the right triangle formed by the top *T* of the silo, your eye *E*, and the point *P* below *T* at your eye level. Angle *TEP* is an angle of elevation. Given are m∠*TEP* and *EP*, the length of the leg adjacent to it. You must find *TP*, the length of the leg opposite ∠*E*. Use the tangent ratio and solve for *TP*.

$$\tan 38° = \frac{TP}{?} \quad EP$$
$$TP = \underline{\;?\;} \tan 38° \quad 60$$
So $\quad TP \approx \underline{\;?\;}$ feet. **46.9**

Add 5.25 feet to *TP* to obtain the height of the silo.

The silo is about $\underline{\;?\;}$ feet tall. **52.1**

Check Divide your value of *TP* by 60. The quotient should be very close to tan 38°.

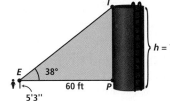

Example 4

For safety, in climbing a ladder against a wall, the ladder should ideally make an angle of 75° with the ground. If a ladder is 12′ long, how far from the wall should you put the base of the ladder?

Solution Draw a picture, as shown at the right, including the known information. Since the hypotenuse is known and the leg adjacent to a known angle is desired, use the cosine function.

$$\cos 75° = \frac{\ell}{12}$$
$$\ell = 12 \cos 75° \approx 3.11 \text{ feet}$$

You should put the ladder about 3.1 feet from the wall.

Accommodating the Learner ⬆

Have students prove the following.
In any triangle *ABC* with a right angle at *C*,
$\tan A \cdot \tan B \cdot \sin A \cdot \cos B + \tan A \cdot \tan B \cdot \cos A \cdot \sin B = 1$. **Let *a* = length of side opposite angle *A*, *b* = length of side opposite angle *B*, and *c* = length of side opposite angle *C*. Then**
$$\frac{a}{b} \cdot \frac{b}{a} \cdot \frac{a}{c} \cdot \frac{a}{c} + \frac{a}{b} \cdot \frac{b}{a} \cdot \frac{b}{c} \cdot \frac{b}{c} =$$
$$1 \cdot \frac{a^2}{c^2} + 1 \cdot \frac{b^2}{c^2} = \frac{a^2}{c^2} + \frac{b^2}{c^2} =$$
$$\frac{a^2 + b^2}{c^2} = \frac{c^2}{c^2} = 1.$$

Questions

COVERING THE IDEAS

1. Prove the theorem in this lesson for tan θ.

2. Consider $\triangle ART$ as shown at the right. Give the exact value of
   a. sin A. $\frac{12}{13}$ b. cos A. $\frac{5}{13}$ c. tan A. $\frac{12}{5}$

In 3 and 4, find the unknown length to the nearest tenth.

3.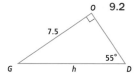

4.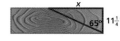

5. Refer to Example 2. Suppose sonar on the surface of the sea locates an object at an angle of depression of 65° and a distance of 320 feet. How deep is the object? **about 290 ft**

6. Refer to Example 3. To determine the height of a flagpole, you walk 30′ away from it and measure the angle of elevation to its top to be about 50°. How high is the flagpole? **about 41.0 ft**

7. Consider $\triangle BED$ with a right angle at E. $BE = 3$ and $DE = 4$.
   a. Find exact values for sin D and cos B. $\frac{3}{5}, \frac{3}{5}$
   b. Explain why these two values are equal.

APPLYING THE MATHEMATICS

8. Suppose you are looking at Taipei 101, a building in Taipei, Taiwan, which has a height of about 509 meters. From where you are, you estimate the angle of elevation to the top of this building to be about 10°. **about 2890 m**
   a. How far are you from the building, to the nearest ten meters?
   b. If the angle of elevation is only correct to the nearest three degrees, give the maximum and minimum values for your distance from Taipei 101. **maximum ≈ 4,150 m; minimum ≈ 2,200 m**

9. Lumber sold in the U.S. as 12″ is actually only $11\frac{1}{4}$″ wide. Suppose you need to cut a 65° angle for a woodwork project, but you don't have a protractor. To the nearest $\frac{1}{8}$ inch, how many inches should you mark off on the other side of a 12″ board? $24\frac{1}{8}$ **in.**

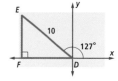

10. A triangle is drawn in the coordinate plane as shown at the right.
    a. What is m∠EDF? **53°**
    b. Find the coordinates of E to the nearest tenth. **(–6.0, 8.0)**

1. tan $\theta = \dfrac{\sin\theta}{\cos\theta}$
$$= \dfrac{\dfrac{\text{leg opposite } \theta}{\text{hypotenuse}}}{\dfrac{\text{leg adjacent to } \theta}{\text{hypotenuse}}}$$
$$= \dfrac{\text{leg opposite } \theta}{\text{leg adjacent to } \theta}$$

7b. The two values are equal because the leg opposite D is the same as the leg adjacent to B.

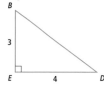

---

3 Assignment

Recommended Assignment

- Questions 1–7
- • Questions 8–16
- • • Question 17 (extra credit)
- • • Reading Lesson 5-2
- • Covering the Ideas 5-2 (Questions 1–9)

Notes on the Questions

Question 8 This question can be used to introduce a discussion on accuracy of measurement and its consequences. If possible, it would be valuable for groups of students to inspect some surveying equipment to see how difficult it is to measure small angles accurately, and to repeat calculations with slightly different angle measures to obtain a feel for the errors introduced by inaccurate measurements.

Questions 10 and 11 These questions are useful preparation for the later study of polar coordinates and vectors and also for the use of trigonometry in physics. You might want to generalize the results. (In Question 11, $B = (AB \cos \theta, AB \sin \theta)$, where θ is the magnitude of the rotation that maps the nonnegative x-axis onto $\overrightarrow{AB}$.)

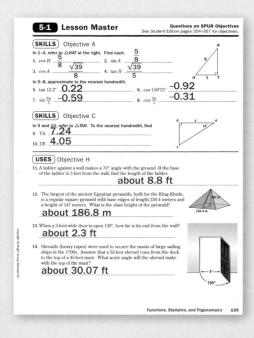

Accommodating the Learner

Some students may need more explanation about the similar triangles in the proof of the Right Triangle Ratios Theorem. You might want to take the time to establish $\triangle PAE \sim \triangle BAC$ by the Angle-Angle Similarity Theorem. Then $\frac{PE}{AP} = \frac{BC}{AB}$ because corresponding sides of similar figures are proportional.

5-1

Notes on the Questions

Question 12 Navigators and mathematicians differ with regard to their reference direction (the direction from which other directions are measured). Whereas navigators in the northern hemisphere use north as a reference direction because of the North Star, mathematicians measure from the ray with endpoint (0, 0) and passing through (1, 0), which on maps usually represents east.

Question 17 The sun also covers an angle of about 30′ in the sky. This is why it is possible for the Moon to eclipse the sun. (When there is a light cloud cover so that a person can look more or less in the direction of the sun, the size of the sun as seen from Earth can be seen to be about that of the Moon.)

4 Wrap-Up

Ongoing Assessment

Draw right triangle *ABC* on the board, with sides *a*, *b*, and *c*. Have students find the sine, cosine, and tangent of each acute angle in the triangle and list any relationships between them that they notice. **Check students' work.**

Project Update

Project 1, *Determining Maximum Altitude*, on page 349 and Project 4, *The Noon Day Project*, on page 350 relate to the content of this lesson.

---

11. A right triangle *ABC* is drawn in the coordinate plane as shown at the right. Use the given information to find the coordinates of point *B*. Round lengths to the nearest tenth. **(11.3, 22.3)**

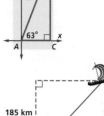

12. A ship is on a bearing of 47° east of north as shown at the right.
    a. How far has the ship sailed if it is 185 km north of its original position? **about 271.3 km**
    b. How far east of its original position is the ship? **about 198.4 km**
    c. If the ship's average speed is 12 km per hour, for how long has it been sailing? **about 22.6 hours**

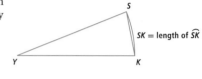

REVIEW

In 13 and 14, use identities to simplify. (Lesson 4-3)

13. $\sin(90° - \theta)$ **$\cos \theta$**   14. $\tan(180° - \theta)$ **$-\tan \theta$**

15. If $\sin \theta = 0.28$ and $90° < \theta < 180°$, compute. **(Lesson 4-2)**
    a. $\sin(180° - \theta)$ **0.28**   b. $\tan \theta$ **−0.292**   c. $\cos(180° + \theta)$ **0.96**

16. Find the distance between the points. **(Previous Course)**
    a. (x_1, y_1) and (x_2, y_2) $\sqrt{(x_2 - x_1)^2 + (y_2 - y_1)^2}$
    b. $(0, 0)$ and $(\cos \theta, \sin \theta)$ **1**
    c. $(6, -7)$ and $(7, -6)$ $\sqrt{2}$

EXPLORATION

17. For small angles, the length of an arc and the length of the associated chord of a circle are approximately equal. Astronomical measurements are commonly made by measuring the small angle formed by the extremities of a distant object. The Moon covers an angle of 31 minutes (31′) when it is about 239,000 miles away.

    SK = length of $\overset{\frown}{SK}$

    a. From this information, estimate the diameter of the Moon by finding the length of $\overset{\frown}{SK}$. **≈ 2155.2 miles**
    b. Estimate the diameter of the Moon by finding the length of $\overline{SK}$ using a trigonometric function. **≈ 2155.2 miles**

    c. Compare your estimates to the value found in an almanac or other reference book. What do you think accounts for the differences? **Answers vary. Sample: The diameter of the Moon is about 2160 miles. The differences may be due to rounding.**

Lesson 5-2
The Inverse Cosine Function

Vocabulary

inverse cosine function,
$\cos^{-1}$, Arccos

▶ **BIG IDEA** If you know $\cos \theta$ and that $0 \leq \theta \leq 180°$, then θ is uniquely determined.

In Lesson 5-1, you used trigonometric functions to find the length of a side in a right triangle. By using inverse trigonometric functions, you can find measures of angles of triangles. In this lesson, properties of the inverse cosine function, $\cos^{-1}$, are examined.

Recall the ladder problem in Example 4 of Lesson 5-1. The ladder is unsafe to climb if the angle it makes with the ground is less than 75°. Suppose you place a 16′ ladder so that its base is 5′ from a wall. Is this safe? In this case,

$$\cos \theta = \frac{5}{16} = 0.3125.$$

A problem in solving this equation for θ is that there are infinitely many values of θ that satisfy the equation. We need to restrict the domain of the cosine function to obtain a solution between 0° and 90°.

Mental Math

Find the exact value.

a. $\cos 60°$ $\frac{1}{2}$

b. $\cos \frac{\pi}{4}$ $\frac{\sqrt{2}}{2}$

c. $\cos -225°$ $-\frac{\sqrt{2}}{2}$

16′

θ

3′

The Domain of the Restricted Cosine Function

Recall the graph of $y = \cos x$.

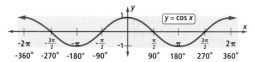

Many values of x yield the same value of y. For this reason, in order for the inverse of the cosine function to be a function, the domain must be restricted. There are many possible restricted domains. Here are three criteria for an appropriate domain:

1. The domain should include the angles between 0 and $\frac{\pi}{2}$ (or 0° and 90°), because they are the measures of the acute angles of a right triangle.

2. On the restricted domain, the function should take on all the values of the range, that is, all real numbers between –1 and 1.

3. The function should be continuous on the restricted domain.

The Inverse Cosine Function   **299**

GOAL

Formalize the inverse cosine function that students have already seen and used on their calculators.

SPUR Objectives

B Evaluate the inverse cosine function.

D Solve equations of the form $\cos \theta = k$.

G State and use properties of the inverse cosine function.

J Write and solve equations for phenomena described by the cosine and inverse cosine functions.

L Graph and identify the graph of the inverse cosine function.

Materials/Resources

· Lesson Master 5-2
· Resource Masters 98–100

HOMEWORK   • **Option 1**

- Questions 1–9   • Option 2
- • Questions 10–18
- • Question 19 (extra credit)
- Reading Lesson 5-3
- Covering the Ideas 5-3 (Questions 1–11)

Local Standards

Background

With the definition of "inverse of a function" used in this book, every function has an inverse. In some places the inverses of sin, cos, etc., are called *arcsin, arccos*, etc., with a small a. Then the restrictions are called *Arcsin, Arccos*, etc., with capital A. But even this use is not consistent, and definitions vary among mathematical dictionaries.

Caution: Because $\sin^2 x$ means $(\sin x)^2$ and $\sin^3 x$ means $(\sin x)^3$, the names Arcsin, Arccos, and Arctan remain in use in some places because it is very possible that a person could misinterpret $\sin^{-1} x$ to mean $(\sin x)^{-1}$.

(continued on next page)

---

1   Warm-Up

1. Give the measure of an angle whose sine equals 0.5. **30°**
2. Give the measure of an angle whose cosine equals 0.5. **60°**
3. Give the measure of an angle whose cosine equals 0. **90°**

(These are all sample answers. These particular answers can also be written as $\sin^{-1}(0.5)$, $\cos^{-1}(0.5)$, and $\cos^{-1}(0)$.)

5-2

2 Teaching

Notes on the Lesson

The inverse circular functions $\sin^{-1}$, $\cos^{-1}$, and $\tan^{-1}$ are defined by restricting the domains of sine, cosine, and tangent. The rules for restriction at the bottom of page 299 are the same for all three trigonometric functions. They force the domain of the cosine function to be $0° \leq x \leq 180°$ or, equivalently, $0 \leq x \leq \pi$. The restricted domain becomes the range of the inverse cosine function.

All calculators in our possession use the ranges for the inverse functions that we use. For instance, when $[\cos^{-1}]$ is pressed, the calculator will give a positive value even though there are negative numbers x for which $\cos x = -0.1$.

The most difficult part of dealing with inverses is reversing one's thinking. Emphasize that $\cos^{-1} x$ is a real number representing the measure of an angle or arc or the magnitude of a rotation. Suggest that students use the definition to rewrite an expression. For example, if $x = \cos^{-1}\frac{1}{2}$ then say "x is the angle (or number) whose cosine is $\frac{1}{2}$," and write $\cos x = \frac{1}{2}$; that is, go back to the original function if students have difficulty.

Additional Example

Example 1 Evaluate $\cos^{-1}(-0.5)$ in radians without a calculator. $\frac{2\pi}{3}$

Only one domain fits all three criteria. It is $\{x \mid 0 \leq x \leq \pi\}$ or $\{x \mid 0° \leq x \leq 180°\}$. The function that is the inverse of this restricted cosine function is denoted **cos⁻¹** and called the **inverse cosine** function. You can read $\cos^{-1} x$ as "the number whose cosine is x."

Definition of Inverse Cosine Function

$y = \cos^{-1} x$ if and only if $x = \cos y$ and $0 \leq y \leq \pi$.

Calculators are programmed to give approximations to values of the $\cos^{-1}$ function. To solve $\cos \theta = 0.3125$ from the ladder problem (on the previous page), note that

$$\theta = \cos^{-1}(0.3125) \approx 71.8°.$$

So the angle is a little smaller than what would be considered safe.

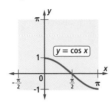

restricted cosine function
domain: $\{x \mid 0 \leq x \leq \pi\}$
range: $\{y \mid -1 \leq y \leq 1\}$

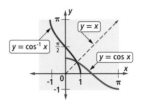

inverse cosine function
domain: $\{x \mid -1 \leq x \leq -1\}$
range: $\{y \mid 0 \leq y \leq \pi\}$

Recall that the graph of the inverse of any function is the reflection image of the graph of that function over the line with equation $y = x$. Also notice that, as with all inverse functions, the domain of $y = \cos^{-1} x$ is the range of $y = \cos x$ and the range of $y = \cos^{-1} x$ is the domain of $y = \cos x$. The notation **Arccos** is sometimes used in place of $\cos^{-1}$.

Evaluating Inverse Cosines

The values of the inverse cosine function must lie in the range of $y = \cos^{-1} x$, that is, from 0 to π or from 0° to 180°.

Example 1

Evaluate $\cos^{-1}\left(\frac{\sqrt{3}}{2}\right)$ without a calculator. Give an exact answer in radians.

Solution Recall the unit circle. If $y = \cos^{-1}\left(\frac{\sqrt{3}}{2}\right)$, then, by definition of $\cos^{-1}$, y is the unique number on the interval $0 \leq y \leq \pi$ whose cosine is $\frac{\sqrt{3}}{2}$. Because $\cos \frac{\pi}{6} = \frac{\sqrt{3}}{2}$ and $0 \leq \frac{\pi}{6} \leq \pi$, $\cos^{-1}\left(\frac{\sqrt{3}}{2}\right) = \frac{\pi}{6}$.

Check Enter $\cos^{-1}\left(\frac{\sqrt{3}}{2}\right)$ on a calculator set to radian mode. Multiply this value by 6 and compare it to π.

When the criteria for the domain of the restricted cosine function are followed, the domain that results has the property that it covers all of the measures of angles in triangles. Consequently, each possible cosine value from a triangle situation corresponds to only one possible angle measure. This makes the inverse cosine function a better function to consider first than the inverse sine function, where the same sine value can come from two different (supplementary) angles.

ENGLISH LEARNERS
Vocabulary Development

Do not take it for granted that all students are familiar with the word *restrict*. You might want to ask for uses of this word outside of mathematics (restrictions on who can drive, restrictions on weights or ages of high-school athletes, etc.).

Example 2

Evaluate $\cos^{-1}(-0.33333)$. Give your answer in degrees.

Solution According to the definition, $y = \cos^{-1}(-0.33333)$
if and only if $\cos y = -0.33333$ and $0° \le y \le 180°$. Use a
calculator. **The answer is approximately 109.47°.**

Check Is $0° \le 109.47° \le 180°$? Yes, so the answer
from the calculator is in the correct range. Now evaluate
$\cos(109.47°)$. Our calculator gives the answer as -0.333313,
which is about -0.33333.

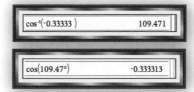

| $\cos^{-1}(-0.33333)$ | 109.471 |
| $\cos(109.47°)$ | -0.333313 |

Applications of the Inverse Cosine

Wherever there are applications of the cosine function, applications of
the inverse cosine function may appear.

Example 3

The Landsat 7 satellite orbits Earth at an altitude of 705 km (438 miles) above
the equator. It can only see a portion of Earth's surface (bounded by a horizon
circle as shown below at the left) at any given time. Imagine looking at a cross
section of the satellite and Earth, as shown below at the right. Point C is the
center of Earth, H is a point on the horizon circle, and S is the location of the
satellite. Let $\theta = m\angle HCS$. The altitude a of the satellite is the distance in
kilometers of the satellite above Earth. Notice that $\angle CHS$ is a right angle,
because the tangent to a circle is perpendicular to the point of tangency.

a. Write a formula for θ in terms of r and a.

b. The radius of Earth is about 6378 km. To the nearest degree, what is θ?

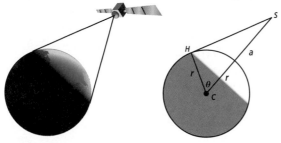

Solution

a. Since the hypotenuse of $\triangle CHS$ and the side adjacent to θ involve r and a,
use the cosine of θ.

$$\cos \theta = \frac{r}{r + a}$$

Solve for θ. $\theta = \cos^{-1}\left(\frac{r}{r + a}\right)$

b. For $r = 6378$ and $a = 705$,

$$\theta = \cos^{-1}\left(\frac{6378}{6378 + 705}\right) \approx \cos^{-1}(0.900466) \approx 26°.$$

Accommodating the Learner ⬍

Some students may not truly understand
the need to restrict the domain of $y = \cos x$
in order for its inverse to be a function.
It may be illuminating for them if you
draw a horizontal line across the graph of
$y = \cos x$ and show that the horizontal line
cuts the curve in more than one place. If
you then draw dotted lines to the x- and
y-values that correspond with these points
of intersection, this will provide a visual to
match the concept that many values of x
yield the same value of y.

The informal idea is that if the graph of a
function fails the "horizontal line test" over
a domain, then the graph of its inverse
will fails the "vertical line test" over that
corresponding range.

5-2

3 Assignment

Recommended Assignment

- Questions 1–9
- • Questions 10–18
- • Question 19 (extra credit)
- • Reading Lesson 5-3
- • Covering the Ideas 5-3
- • (Questions 1–11)

Notes on the Questions

Question 1–3 After completing these questions, show the graph of the cosine function with the part from 0 to π highlighted to emphasize that this restriction does meet the criteria for an appropriate domain.

Questions 10 and 11 For all x, $\cos(\cos^{-1} x) = x$, but it is only for $0° \leq x \leq 180°$ that $\cos^{-1}(\cos x) = x$, because in the latter case the first x could be a number outside the range of the inverse cosine function. You might have students try these on their calculators to see what values are shown. You also might have students try $\cos(\cos^{-1} 2)$. What does the calculator return, and why? **The calculator will show some sort of error message because 2 is not in the range of the cosine function, so cannot be in the domain of the inverse cosine function.**

Questions

COVERING THE IDEAS

In 1–3, the graphs below show several ways to restrict the domain of $y = \cos x$. Each graph fails to meet the criteria for appropriate domain in some way. How does it fail?

1.

domain: $\{x \mid -\frac{\pi}{2} \leq x \leq \frac{\pi}{2}\}$

2.

domain: $\{x \mid \pi \leq x \leq 2\pi\}$

3.

domain: $\{x \mid -\frac{\pi}{2} < x \leq 0 \text{ or } \frac{\pi}{2} \leq x \leq \pi\}$

4. a. What transformation maps the graph of the restricted cosine function onto the graph of the inverse cosine function?
   b. State the domain and range of the inverse cosine function.

In 5–7, find the exact value of the expression in radians and degrees without a calculator.

5. $\cos^{-1}\left(\frac{\sqrt{2}}{2}\right)$ $\frac{\pi}{4}$; **45°**

6. Arccos 0 $\frac{\pi}{2}$; **90°**

7. $\cos^{-1}\left(-\frac{\sqrt{3}}{2}\right)$ $\frac{5\pi}{6}$; **150°**

8. Refer to the diagram at the right. For safety, many people recommend no more than a 1:4 ratio between distance from a wall and the length of a ladder. What is the measure of the angle the ladder makes with the ground when this ratio is used? **about 75.5°**

9. Refer to Example 3. Give the measure of θ when the height of a satellite above Earth is about 402 km (250 miles), as is the case with the International Space Station. **about 19.8°**

APPLYING THE MATHEMATICS

In 10 and 11, compute without using your calculator.

10. $\cos\left(\cos^{-1}\left(\frac{\sqrt{2}}{2}\right)\right)$ $\frac{\sqrt{2}}{2}$

11. $\cos^{-1}(\cos 410°)$ **50°**

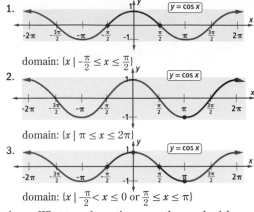

1. Answers vary. Sample: The function does not take every value in the range of cosine.

2. Answers vary. Sample: The domain does not include angles between 0 and $\frac{\pi}{2}$.

3. Answers vary. Sample: The function is not continuous on the restricted domain.

4a. reflection over the line with equation $y = x$; $T(x, y) = (y, x)$

4b. domain: $\{x: -1 \leq x \leq 1\}$; range: $\{y: 0 \leq y \leq \pi\}$

Accommodating the Learner ↑

Ask students to describe all solutions to $\cos \theta = \frac{2}{3}$.

$\theta \approx (48.2 + 360n)°$ or $\theta \approx (311.8 + 360n)°$, where n is any integer.

In **12** and **13**, find five solutions to each equation to the nearest degree.

12. $\cos x = \frac{1}{2}$

13. $\cos y = 0.9263$

14. A 26″ bicycle tire has a chalk mark at its top. As the bike moves forward, the height h of the chalk mark in terms of distance d traveled can be modeled by $h = f(d) = 13 + 13 \cos\left(\frac{d}{13}\right)$, with d measured in inches.

Chalk mark

  a. What is the period of the function f? How do you know?

  b. Graph one period of f.

  c. How far has the bike traveled the first time the chalk mark is 20″ above ground? The second time?

12–14. See margin.

REVIEW

15. A fishing boat sails at a steady speed of 10 mph on a bearing of 55° (from north). If the boat set sail at 2:20 A.M., describe its location east and north of its port at 6:20 A.M. (**Lesson 5-1**)   **about 22.9 miles north, about 32.8 miles east**

16. Consider $\triangle ABC$ below.

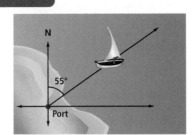

N
55°
Port

  a. Find h, the altitude to side $\overline{BC}$, in terms of b and m$\angle ACB$.

  b. Derive a formula for the area of $\triangle ABC$ in terms of a, b, and m$\angle ACB$. (**Lessons 5-1, 4-3**)

16a. $h = b \sin(180 - $ m$\angle ABC)$

16b. Area $= \frac{1}{2} ab$ $\sin(180 - $ m$\angle ACB)$

17. Find images of each of the following under a scale change $S: (x, y) \rightarrow \left(80x, \frac{y}{8}\right)$.

  a. $(5, -4)$ **a.** $\left(400, -\frac{1}{2}\right)$ **c.** $\left(60, \frac{1}{16}\right)$

  b. $(0, 1)$ $\left(0, \frac{1}{8}\right)$ **c.** $\left(\frac{3}{4}, \frac{1}{2}\right)$ (**Lesson 3-5**)

18. A data set consists of exactly four numbers. The mode of the data set is 5, the mean and median are 10 and 15. Which number is the mean? Explain how you can tell. (**Lesson 1-2**)

EXPLORATION

19. **a.** Find $\sin(\cos^{-1} 0.8)$. **0.6**

  b. Find $\sin\left(\cos^{-1}\left(\frac{21}{29}\right)\right)$. $\frac{20}{29}$

  c. Generalize the results above. That is, find $\sin(\cos^{-1} a)$ when $0° \le \cos^{-1} a \le 90°$. $\sin(\cos^{-1} a) = \sqrt{1 - a^2}$

18. The mean must be 15. If the median were 15, a number of restrictions would be in effect. First, the mode of 5 could be no more than the first two numbers chronologically. Second, the third number would then have to be 25 making the sum greater than 40, which would make the mean greater than 10.

Notes on the Questions
Question 14 The path of a point on a circle as it rolls along a plane is called a *cycloid* and has a shape different from that of a sine wave, circular arc, or elliptical arc.

4 Wrap-Up

Ongoing Assessment
Have students write five equations like those in Questions 10–13, switch papers with a partner, and solve their partner's equations. Students should then check their partner's work. **Answers vary. Check students' work.**

Project Update
Project 1, *Determining Maximum Altitude*, on page 349 relates to the content of this lesson.

Additional Answers

12. Answers vary. Sample: –300°, –60°, 60°, 300°, 420°

13. Answers vary. Sample: –338°, –22°, 22°, 338°, 382°

14a. 26π; The chalk returns to the same place after it has moved around the tire's circumference.

14b.

14c. about 13.0 inches; about 68.7 inches

Lesson 5-3

Lesson 5-3

The Law of Cosines

GOAL

Derive, apply, and prove the Law of Cosines using the definitions of cosine and sine and the formula for the distance between two points on the coordinate plane.

SPUR Objectives

C Use the Law of Cosines to find lengths and angle measures in triangles.

F Interpret the Law of Cosines.

I Solve real-world problems using the Law of Cosines.

Materials/Resources

· Lesson Master 5-3
· Resource Masters 101–103
· Quiz 1

HOMEWORK
· **Option 1**
· **Option 2**

· Questions 1–11
· · Questions 12–22
· · Question 23 (extra credit)
· Reading Lesson 5-4
· Covering the Ideas 5-4
  (Questions 1–8)

Local Standards

---

1 ▶ Warm-Up

1. Give an expression for the distance between two points (x_1, y_1) and (x_2, y_2). $\sqrt{(x_2 - x_1)^2 + (y_2 - y_1)^2}$
2. Apply your answer to Warm-Up 1 to find the exact distance between $(\sqrt{3}, 1)$ and $(2, 0)$. $2\sqrt{2 - \sqrt{3}}$
3. Estimate your answer to Warm-Up 2 to the nearest thousandth. **1.035**
(The calculations in Warm-Up 2 are similar to those found in the proof of the Law of Cosines, but without the cosines.)

> ▶ **BIG IDEA** Given SAS or SSS in a triangle, the Law of Cosines enables you to find the remaining sides or measures of angles of the triangle.

Trigonometry enables lengths of sides and angle measures to be found in *any* triangle, not just right triangles. One important application is in finding distances that are difficult to measure directly. Here is an example.

A discus is thrown by means of a whirling movement made by the athlete within a circle 2.5 m in diameter. The winner is the one who makes the longest throw without stepping outside of the throwing circle before the discus touches the ground.

The length of a throw is the distance from the edge of the circle to where the discus lands. But how is the length measured? In the past a referee rolled out a long measuring tape, but now lasers and the *Law of Cosines* are used.

Jim Thorpe (1887-1953)
Named by one group the greatest athlete of the 20th century

This desired length is w in the diagram at the right. Because $\triangle MZL$ is not a right triangle, the methods of Lesson 4-4 cannot be used directly. However, the problem can be solved using a powerful theorem called the *Law of Cosines*.

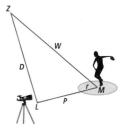

The Law of Cosines is proved using the definitions of cosine and sine and the formula for the distance between two points in the coordinate plane. Also, remember that for any θ, $\cos^2 \theta + \sin^2 \theta = 1$.

Theorem (Law of Cosines)

In any $\triangle ABC$, $c^2 = a^2 + b^2 - 2ab \cos C$.

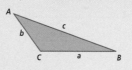

Mental Math

Simplify
a. $\cos(-t)$ $\cos t$
b. $\cos(180° - t)$ $-\cos t$
c. $\cos(90° - t)$ $\sin t$

Background

In geometry, students learn that two triangles are congruent if certain sets of corresponding parts are congruent: SAS (two sides and the included angle); SSS (three sides); ASA (two angles and the included side); AAS (two angles and a non-included side); and, if they have studied from UCSMP *Geometry*, SsA (two sides and the angle opposite the longer side). Another way of interpreting these theorems is that they tell when the measures of all unknown parts of the triangle are uniquely

determined. It is natural to want to determine these parts, and the Law of Cosines enables this to be done for the SAS and SSS conditions.

In particular, given the SAS condition AC, BC, and m$\angle C$, the Law of Cosines can be used in the form $c^2 = a^2 + b^2 - 2ab \cos C$ to find AB directly. If three sides a, b, and c are given, then one first finds $\cos C$ and then uses the inverse cosine function to find m$\angle C$.

Proof Impose a coordinate plane on $\triangle ABC$ so that $C = (0, 0)$ and $\overline{BC}$ lies on the x-axis. Since $BC = a$, the coordinates of B are $(a, 0)$.

To find the coordinates of A, draw a unit circle that intersects $\overrightarrow{CA}$ at D. By the definition of the cosine and sine, $D = (\cos C, \sin C)$. Since $AC = b$, A can be considered the image of D under the size change $(x, y) \rightarrow (bx, by)$.

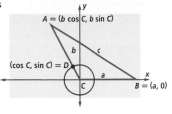

So,

By the Pythagorean distance formula,

$$A = (b \cos C, b \sin C).$$
$$c = \sqrt{(b \cos C - a)^2 + (b \sin C - 0)^2}.$$

Now we rewrite the equation into the form in which it appears in the statement of the theorem.

Square both sides. $\quad c^2 = (b \cos C - a)^2 + (b \sin C - 0)^2$

Expand the binomials. $\quad c^2 = b^2\cos^2 C - 2ab \cos C + a^2 + b^2\sin^2 C$

Apply the Commutative Property of Addition. $\quad c^2 = a^2 + b^2\sin^2 C + b^2\cos^2 C - 2ab \cos C$

Factor. $\quad c^2 = a^2 + b^2 (\sin^2 C + \cos^2 C) - 2ab \cos C$

Use the Pythagorean Identity. $\quad c^2 = a^2 + b^2 - 2ab \cos C$

 QY

> **QY**
>
> Suppose $a = 12$, $b = 5$, and $\cos C = \frac{1}{2}$.
> What is c?

Using the Law of Cosines to Find a Side

Note the power of the Law of Cosines. Given two sides and the included angle of *any* triangle (the SAS condition), you can find the third side.

Example 1

Suppose that the distance of a laser telescope to the center of the throwing circle in a discus competition is 30.10 meters, from the telescope to the target is 51.02 meters, and the angle between the telescope's paths to the target and to the center of the throwing circle is 95°. Find the length of a throw from the circle to the target.

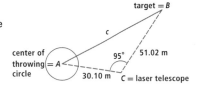

Solution 1 Use the Law of Cosines since two sides and the included angle are given. For this situation, $a = 51.02$ m, $b = 30.10$ m, and $C = 95°$.

$$c^2 = a^2 + b^2 - 2ab \cos C$$
$$= 51.02^2 + 30.10^2 - 2(51.02)(30.10)\cos 95° \approx 3776.7409$$

So, $c \approx \sqrt{3776.7409} \approx 61.46$ meters

The length c is measured from the center of the throwing circle, but discus throws are measured from the edge of the circle. So the radius of the 2.5-m diameter throwing circle must be subtracted.

$$\text{length of throw} = c - \text{radius of throwing circle}$$
$$= 61.46 - 1.25 = 60.21 \text{ m}$$

(continued on next page)

Accommodating the Learner

Have students explain how, from the Law of Cosines, if two sides of a triangle have the same length, then the angles opposite to those sides have the same measure.

In $\triangle ABC$, suppose $a = b$. By the Law of Cosines, $b^2 = a^2 + c^2 - 2ac \cos B$ and $a^2 = b^2 + c^2 - 2bc \cos A$, but since $a = b$, we have $a^2 + c^2 - 2ac \cos B = b^2 + c^2 - 2bc \cos A$, from which $\cos B = \cos A$, and, applying the inverse cosine to both sides, $m\angle B = m\angle A$.

---

2 Teaching

Notes on the Lesson

This lesson and Lesson 5-5 on the Law of Sines round out the applications of trigonometric functions to solving triangle problems in the plane. Most students find both lessons relatively easy, perhaps because the applications of these theorems are rather straightforward.

The proof of the Law of Cosines is an elegant one in its use of transformations to justify the coordinates of A. Many books require the construction of a perpendicular from A to the x-axis and the use of right-triangle definitions of sine and cosine to find the coordinates. Students in this course should be able to accept the scale change (more precisely a *size* change) that maps point D to point A. In this proof, we have derived rectangular coordinates for a point given its polar coordinates, but students will not see the formal derivation until a later chapter.

Emphasize that the Law of Cosines is applicable to *any* triangle whereas the Pythagorean Theorem is a theorem about right triangles only.

Students who have studied from UCSMP *Geometry* will be familiar with phrases like "SAS condition." In that course, it is used in two ways: to signal the given information that enables two triangles to be proved congruent; and to indicate the information sufficient to construct a unique triangle ("unique" in the sense that all such triangles are congruent). The latter of these is closer to the idea here.

Using the Law of Cosines to find a side

The most common error in applying the Law of Cosines is to add instead of subtract (or vice versa), particularly when cos C is negative. Also watch for an order of operations error, subtracting $2ab$ before multiplying by cos C.

5-3

Solution 2 Use a CAS to substitute values into the Law of Cosines using the "such that" feature. Since most technology will not distinguish between C and c, we renamed C as cc.

Check Since $\angle C$ is obtuse, c is the longest side of $\triangle ABC$ and 61.46 is larger than the lengths of the other two sides. Also, by the Triangle Inequality, c must be less than $30.10 + 51.02$, and it is. So the answer is reasonable.

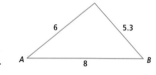

The first known appearance of the Law of Cosines is in Book II of Euclid's *Elements,* written around 300 B.C.E. The Law of Cosines is a generalization of the Pythagorean Theorem, since if $m\angle C = 90°$, then

$$
\begin{aligned}
c^2 &= a^2 + b^2 - 2ab \cos 90° \\
&= a^2 + b^2 - 2ab \cdot 0,
\end{aligned}
$$

so $c^2 = a^2 + b^2$.

Using the Law of Cosines to Find an Angle

Example 1 shows how the Law of Cosines can be used given SAS. Because each angle between 0° and 180° has a unique cosine, the Law of Cosines can also be used to find the measure of any angle of a triangle if the lengths of all three sides are known (the SSS condition). The Law of Cosines can be rewritten to give a formula for the measure of the angle.

Example 2

$\triangle ABC$ has side lengths of 5.3, 6, and 8 as shown at the right. Find the measure of its largest angle.

Solution 1 In any triangle, the largest angle is opposite the longest side. The longest side is $\overline{AB}$ and so angle C has the largest measure. Rewrite the Law of Cosines in terms of a, b, and c.

$$
\begin{aligned}
c^2 &= a^2 + b^2 - 2ab \cdot \cos C \\
c^2 - a^2 - b^2 &= -2ab \cdot \cos C \\
\cos C &= \frac{c^2 - a^2 - b^2}{-2ab}
\end{aligned}
$$

Making appropriate substitutions,

$$\cos C = \frac{8^2 - 5.3^2 - 6^2}{-2 \cdot 5.3 \cdot 6} = 0.00141....$$

Use a calculator and the inverse cosine function to calculate C.

$$\cos^{-1}(0.00141...) \approx 89.9°.$$

Solution 2 Use a CAS to substitute values into the Law of Cosines and solve the equation step-by-step as shown at the right. Note that the CAS does not simplify $\cos^{-1}(\cos(cc))$ due to domain restrictions.

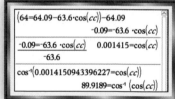

Using the Law of Cosines for finding the included angle is straightforward, but the algebra can be tricky. Fortunately, with a CAS you can substitute directly into the Law of Cosines formula for a, b, and c and solve for C.

Questions

COVERING THE IDEAS

1. Refer to triangle TAB at the right. a. $t = \sqrt{a^2 + b^2 - 2ab \cos T}$
   a. Write a formula for t in terms of $m\angle T$, a, and b.
   b. Suppose $a = 4$ cm, $b = 7$ cm, and $m\angle T = 135°$. Find the exact length t. $t = \sqrt{65 + 28\sqrt{2}}$

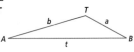

2. The sides of a triangle are of lengths 7.1 m, 3.9 m, and 7.1 m. Find the measure of the smallest angle. **31.88°**

Multiple Choice In 3 and 4, which formula can be used to find the required measure directly?

A $a^2 = b^2 + c^2 - 2bc \cos A$ B $b^2 = a^2 + c^2 - 2ac \cos B$

C $c^2 = a^2 + b^2 - 2ab \cos C$ D none of the above

3. Given: a, b, $m\angle A$. Find c. **A**   4. Given: a, b, c. Find $m\angle B$. **B**

In 5 and 6, refer to the proof of the Law of Cosines.

5. a. Find the slopes of $\overline{CD}$ and $\overline{CA}$.
   b. Use the results of Part a to show that A, D, and C are collinear.

6. Use the distance formula to verify that $AC = b$.

7. $\triangle ABC$ is isosceles, with $AB = AC = 15$ cm, and $m\angle A = 150°$. Use the Law of Cosines to find the exact length of $\overline{BC}$.

8. It is 1.9 miles from a house to a restaurant and 1.2 miles to a pier, as shown at the right. The angle between the two lines of sight is 87°. How far is it from the pier across the water to the restaurant? **about 2.2 mi**

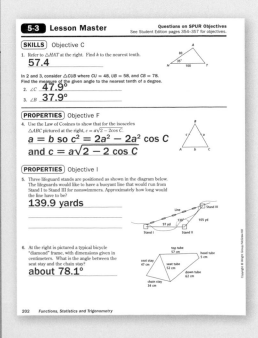

9. At one corner of a triangular piece of property, the angle measures 51.7°. The sides that meet at this corner are 105 and 140 feet long. How long is the third side?

10. In $\triangle XYZ$, $x = 12''$, $y = 14''$, and $z = 16''$. Find $m\angle Z$ and $m\angle X$.

11. Refer to the diagram on page 304. An opto-electronic telescope can be used to measure the length of a throw in a shot-put competition. If the distance from the telescope to the center of the throwing circle is 19.2 m, and the distance from the telescope to the target is 22.1 m, and the angle between the telescope's paths to the throwing circle and to the target is 55.9°, find the length of the throw. The diameter of the throwing circle in the shot-put is 2.135 m. **about 18.459 m**

5a. slope of $\overline{CD}$ = tan C; slope of $\overline{CA}$ = tan C

5b. The lines through both $\overline{CA}$ and $\overline{CD}$ have the same slope (tan C) and y-intercept (0, 0) so the points are collinear.

6. See margin.

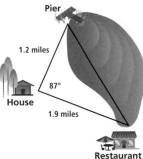

7. $(BC)^2 = 2(15)^2 - 2(15)^2\cos 150° = 225(\sqrt{3} + 2)$, $BC = 15\sqrt{2 + \sqrt{3}}$

9. about 111.4 ft

10. $m\angle Z \approx 75.5°$ or 1.32 radians;

$m\angle X \approx 46.6°$ or 0.81 radians

The Law of Cosines   **307**

Additional Answers

6. $\sqrt{(b \cos C - 0)^2 + (b \sin C - 0)^2}$
$= \sqrt{b^2(\cos^2 C + \sin^2 C)} = \sqrt{b^2} = b$

---

3 Assignment

Recommended Assignment

- Questions 1–11
- • Questions 12–22
- • Question 23 (extra credit)
- Reading Lesson 5-4
- Covering the Ideas 5-4 (Questions 1–8)

Notes on the Questions

Question 5 The fact that the slopes of $\overline{CD}$ and $\overline{CA}$ are equal means that A is on the ray with endpoint C going through D. That is critical for finding the coordinates of A in the proof.

Question 6 Since $AC = b$, we know that A is indeed the image of D under a size transformation of magnitude b, which means that its coordinates are those of D multiplied by b.

Notes on the Questions

Questions 12 and 17 These questions involve polygons with more sides than triangles and show the power of the Law of Cosines. Since any polygon can be split into triangles, there is no need for any theorems other than those for triangles in obtaining the lengths of sides or measures of angles of polygons as long as enough information is given to determine the polygon.

Question 13 Regardless of which angle θ of this triangle students try to find, calculation shows that $|\cos \theta| > 1$. When a calculator is used to determine θ, an error message will appear. Students may not realize that there is no possible value of θ that works. You might ask students what happens when three lengths a, b, and c are such that $a + b = c$, such as when $a = 1$, $b = 2$, and $c = 3$.

Question 23 Students are expected to use properties of 30-60-90 triangles.

4 Wrap-Up

Ongoing Assessment

Have students work in pairs. Ask each student to draw a triangle. One student should measure and label the length of the three sides of their triangle and the other student should measure and label the lengths of two sides and the measure of the included angle. Have students exchange papers and solve for all the missing parts in their partner's triangle. Have students include a summary explaining how they solved for the missing parts. **Answers vary. Check students' work.**

Administer Quiz 1 (or a quiz or your own) after students complete this lesson.

Project Update

Project 3, *Bond Angles in Molecules*, on page 349 relates to the content of this lesson.

APPLYING THE MATHEMATICS

12. Find the exact length of $\overline{AD}$ of the regular hexagon shown. **$12\sqrt{3}$**

13. Using the Law of Cosines, show that there can be no triangle with sides 3 cm, 2 cm, and 7 cm long. **See margin.**

14. A gannet (a sea bird) has a nest on an island and flies in a horizontal line for 160 m over the sea looking for fish, then flies 150 m downward, diving to catch a fish. The direct flight back to the nest is 250 m. At what angle did the bird turn to dive into the water?

15. A baseball player is 20 feet behind 2nd base. Use the figure at the right to determine how far it is to throw from there to 1st base. **about 105 feet**

16. Refer to Question 8. A canoe located at the restaurant and a runner decide to race. The runner takes the path from the restaurant to the house to the pier. If the runner averages 9.3 mph and the boat averages 5.9 mph, who wins and by how much time? **See margin.**

17. Suppose a parallelogram is made with bars of 8″ and 15″ that are hinged so the included angle θ between its sides can be changed as shown at the right.
    a. Write an equation for d in terms of θ. **$d = \sqrt{289 - 240\cos\theta}$**
    b. Solve the equation for θ. **$\theta = \cos^{-1}\left(d^2 \dfrac{-289}{-240}\right)$**

REVIEW

18. a. State the domain and range of the inverse cosine function.
    b. How are its domain and range related to the domain and range of the restricted cosine function? **(Lesson 5-2)**

19. Compute without using your calculator. **(Lesson 5-2)**
    a. $\cos^{-1} 1$ **0° or 0 radians**
    b. $\cos^{-1}\left(-\dfrac{\sqrt{3}}{2}\right)$ **150° or $\dfrac{5\pi}{6}$**

20. To estimate the height of a 2-story building, Howard walks 40 steps away from the building. The angle of elevation at this point to the top edge of the building is about 60°. About how tall is the building if Howard's steps are about 9 inches long? **(Lesson 5-1)** **≈ 52 ft**

21. Consider the equation $\cos \theta = -\dfrac{1}{2}$. **(Lesson 4-4)**
    a. Draw a unit circle and mark the two points for which $\cos \theta = -\dfrac{1}{2}$.
    b. Give two values of θ between 530° and 890° that make the equation true.
    c. Give a negative value of θ that makes the equation true.

22. **Multiple Choice** A parabola has its vertex at (-5, 6). Which of the following might be an equation for the parabola? **(Lesson 3-2) C**
    A $f(x) = (x - 5)^2 - 6$ B $f(x) = (x - 5)^2 + 6$
    C $f(x) = (x + 5)^2 + 6$ D $f(x) = (x + 5)^2 - 6$

EXPLORATION

23. Find BC in Question 7 without using trigonometry.
    See margin.

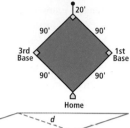
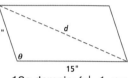

2nd Base

3rd Base — 1st Base

Home

8″ 15″

8″ 15″

18a. domain: $\{x|\,-1 \le x \le 1\}$ range: $\{y|\,0 \le y \le \pi\}$

18b. The domain and range have switched.

21a. See margin.

21b. Two known values that satisfy the equation are 120° and –120°. By the periodicity theorem, adding 360° to each will result in the same cosine. Doing this twice gives us solutions 600°, 840°, which are both in the range. In radians these are $\dfrac{10\pi}{3}$, and $\dfrac{14\pi}{3}$.

21c. –120° or $-\dfrac{2\pi}{3}$

QY ANSWER

$c = \sqrt{109}$

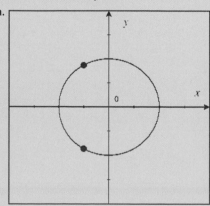

Lesson 5-4

The Inverse Sine Function

Vocabulary

inverse sine function,
$\sin^{-1}$, Arcsin

▶ **BIG IDEA** If you know $\sin \theta$ and that $0° \leq \theta \leq 180°$, two values of θ are possible unless $\theta = 90°$.

In Lesson 5-2, you studied the inverse cosine function. This lesson is about the *inverse sine function.*

In Lesson 4-3, you saw that for all x, $\sin x = \sin(\pi - x)$, so an angle and its supplement have the same sine. Thus, if you know the sine of an angle, the angle is usually not uniquely determined. For instance, in $\triangle ABC$, if $\sin C \approx 0.84787$, the measure of $\angle C$ could be about $58°$ or about $122°$, as shown below.

Mental Math

Find θ if θ is an acute angle and

a. $\sin \theta = \frac{\sqrt{2}}{2}$. **45°**

b. $\sin \theta = \frac{1}{2}$. **30°**

c. $\sin \theta = \frac{\sqrt{3}}{2}$. **60°**

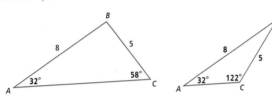

If you evaluate $\sin^{-1}(0.84787)$ on a calculator, it will return the degree or equivalent radian measure shown at the right. The calculator ignores the value between $90°$ and $180°$. Here is why.

| $\sin^{-1}(0.84787)$ | 57.980749 |
| $\sin^{-1}(0.84787)$ | 1.011955 |

The Domain of the Restricted Sine Function

At the right is a graph of the sine function $y = \sin x$ (in blue), and its reflection image $x = \sin y$ (in red) over the line with equation $y = x$. Notice that the inverse of the sine function is not a function.

However, as with the cosine function, it is possible to restrict the domain of the sine function so that its inverse is a function. The following three criteria stated in Lesson 5-2 can again be met.

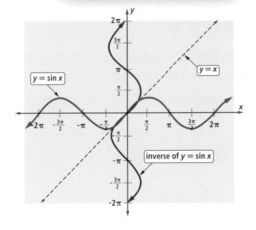

$y = \sin x$

$y = x$

inverse of $y = \sin x$

The Inverse Sine Function **309**

Background

When the criteria for the domain of the restricted cosine function are followed, the domain that results has the property that it covers all of the measures of angles in triangles. Consequently, each value of $\cos \theta$ from a triangle situation corresponds to only one possible angle measure θ. However, when these criteria are followed for the sine function, because $\sin \theta = \sin(\pi - \theta)$, to obtain a unique value for $\sin^{-1} \theta$, obtuse angle measures are not allowed. For this reason, the inverse sine

function does not give the measures of obtuse angles, and they need to be checked when solving $\sin \theta = k$ for an angle measure θ.

Lesson 5-4

GOAL

Formalize the inverse sine function that students have already seen and used on their calculators.

SPUR Objectives

B Evaluate the inverse sine function.

D Solve equations of the form $\sin \theta = k$.

G State and use properties of the inverse sine function.

J Write and solve equations for phenomena described by the sine and inverse sine functions.

L Graph and identify the graph of the inverse sine function.

Materials/Resources

· Lesson Master 5-4
· Resource Masters 104–106

HOMEWORK   • **Option 1**
                  • **Option 2**

• Questions 1–8
• • Questions 9–21
• • Question 22 (extra credit)
  • Reading Lesson 5-5
  • Covering the Ideas 5-5
    (Questions 1–11)

Local Standards

① Warm-Up

1. Give the measure of an acute angle whose sine equals $\frac{\sqrt{3}}{2}$. **60°**
2. Give the measure of an obtuse angle whose sine equals $\frac{\sqrt{3}}{2}$. **120°**
3. Give the measure of an angle whose sine equals 1. **90°**

(The answers can also be written as $\sin^{-1}\left(\frac{\sqrt{3}}{2}\right)$; $180 - \sin^{-1}\left(\frac{\sqrt{3}}{2}\right)$; $\sin^{-1}(1)$.)

5-4

2 Teaching

Notes on the Lesson

Continue to emphasize that $\sin^{-1} x$ and $\cos^{-1} x$ (and, in Lesson 5-6, $\tan^{-1} x$) are real numbers often representing measures of angles or arcs or magnitudes of rotation. Read the expression and use the definition to rewrite an expression. For example, if $x = \sin^{-1} \frac{1}{2}$, then say "$x$ is the angle (or number) whose sine is $\frac{1}{2}$," and write $\sin x = \frac{1}{2}$; that is, go back to the original function if students have difficulty.

Since the domain and range of the sine and cosine functions are the same, some students may think that the domain and range of the inverse functions are the same. (The domain is, but the range is not.) Remind students that restrictions were placed on the domains of the original functions so that the corresponding inverse is also a function.

Example 1 Unlike the inverse cosine function, values of the inverse sine function can be negative, and these numbers cannot be measures of angles in triangles.

Additional Example

Example 1 Evaluate $\sin^{-1}(-0.5)$ in radians without a calculator. $-\frac{\pi}{6}$

---

1. The domain should include the angles between 0 and $\frac{\pi}{2}$ (or 0° and 90°), because they are the measures of the acute angles of a right triangle.

2. On the restricted domain, the function should take on all the values of the range, that is, all real numbers between –1 and 1.

3. The function should be continuous on the restricted domain.

These criteria force the restriction of the domain of $y = \sin x$ to $\{x \mid -\frac{\pi}{2} \leq x \leq \frac{\pi}{2}\}$ or $\{x \mid -90° \leq x \leq 90°\}$. The **inverse sine function**, denoted **sin⁻¹**, is the inverse of this restricted sine function. You can read $\sin^{-1} x$ as "the number (or angle) whose sine is x", just as you did with $\cos^{-1} x$.

> **Definition of Inverse Sine Function**
>
> $y = \sin^{-1} x$ if and only if $x = \sin y$ and $-\frac{\pi}{2} \leq y \leq \frac{\pi}{2}$.

restricted sine function
domain: $\{x \mid -\frac{\pi}{2} \leq x \leq \frac{\pi}{2}\}$
range: $\{y \mid -1 \leq y \leq 1\}$

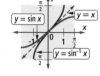

inverse sine function
domain: $\{x \mid -1 \leq x \leq 1\}$
range: $\{y \mid -\frac{\pi}{2} \leq y \leq \frac{\pi}{2}\}$

As always, the domain and range of a function and its inverse are switched. Thus, the domain of $y = \sin^{-1} x$ is $-1 \leq x \leq 1$, and the range is $-\frac{\pi}{2} \leq y \leq \frac{\pi}{2}$ (or $-90° \leq y \leq 90°$). That is, when $y = \sin^{-1} x$, y is the number from $-\frac{\pi}{2}$ to $\frac{\pi}{2}$ whose sine is x. The notation **Arcsin** is sometimes used in place of $\sin^{-1}$.

 QY

Finding Values of Inverse Sines

Some inverse sine values can be found exactly without a calculator.

> **Example 1**
>
> Evaluate $\sin^{-1}$ in radians $\left(-\frac{\sqrt{3}}{2}\right)$ in radians.
>
> **Solution** If $y = \sin^{-1}\left(-\frac{\sqrt{3}}{2}\right)$, then y is the unique number in the interval $-\frac{\pi}{2} \leq y \leq \frac{\pi}{2}$ whose sine is $-\frac{\sqrt{3}}{2}$. From your knowledge of exact values, $\sin\left(-\frac{\pi}{3}\right) = -\frac{\sqrt{3}}{2}$. Because $-\frac{\pi}{2} \leq -\frac{\pi}{3} \leq \frac{\pi}{2}$, $y = -\frac{\pi}{3}$. Thus, $\sin^{-1}\left(-\frac{\sqrt{3}}{2}\right) = -\frac{\pi}{3}$.

> **▶ QY**
>
> What is Arcsin 1?

Accommodating the Learner ⬇

If students have difficulty with the notion of inverse trigonometric functions, refer them to the Check in Example 1. A check will serve as a reminder that they have determined the angle whose sine (or cosine) has the given value.

All values of the inverse sine function can be estimated using a calculator.

GUIDED

Example 2

Suppose θ is an angle in a triangle and $\sin \theta = 0.7214$. Find θ in degrees.

Solution One solution is $\sin^{-1}(0.7214) \approx$ __?__. The second **46.17°** solution is the measure of a supplement of this angle, __?__. **133.83°**

Check Evaluate $\sin$ __?__ with a calculator. The display shows 0.7213977... It checks. **46.17°**

Recall that if f and f^{-1} are inverse functions, then $f \circ f^{-1}(x) = x$ for all x in the domain of f^{-1}, and $f^{-1} \circ f(x) = x$ for all x in the domain of f. Thus, $\sin(\sin^{-1} x) = x$ for all x in the domain of $\sin^{-1}$, and $\sin^{-1}(\sin x) = x$ for all x in the restricted domain of the sine function.

Example 3

Explain why $\sin^{-1}\left(\sin \frac{5\pi}{4}\right) \neq \frac{5\pi}{4}$.

Solution 1 Evaluate directly.
$$\sin \frac{5\pi}{4} = -\frac{\sqrt{2}}{2}$$
$$\sin^{-1}\left(\sin \frac{5\pi}{4}\right) = \sin^{-1}\left(-\frac{\sqrt{2}}{2}\right) = -\frac{\pi}{4}$$
Thus, $\sin^{-1}\left(\sin \frac{5\pi}{4}\right) \neq \frac{5\pi}{4}$.

Solution 2 Since $\frac{5\pi}{4}$ is not in the restricted domain of the sine function necessary for the inverse to be a function, it is not in the range of the inverse sine function. So it is impossible for $\frac{5\pi}{4}$ to be a value of the inverse sine function.

Applying the Inverse Sine Function

The inverse sine function has applications in all situations involving the sine function.

Activity

An 18-ft ladder leans against a building as shown at the right.

Step 1 Express θ, the measure of the angle the ladder makes with the ground, as a function of h, the height of the top of the ladder. $\theta = \sin^{-1}\left(\frac{h}{18}\right)$

Step 2 Pick three possible values of h and find the three corresponding values of θ.

Step 3 a. Describe the set of all possible values of h. $\{h: 0 \leq h \leq 18\}$

b. Describe the set of all possible values of θ. $\{\theta: 0° \leq \theta \leq 90°\}$

(continued on next page)

Step 2: Answers vary.
Sample: (16, 62.7°),
(15, 56.4°), (13, 46.2°)

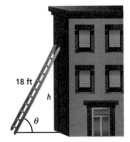

18 ft

h

θ

Notes on the Lesson

Activity This Activity generalizes a ladder situation like the one students encountered in Lesson 5-1. Here we see that, when we think of θ as a function of h and try to write a formula for that, then we are forced into the inverse sine function.

Additional Examples

Example 2 Suppose ϕ is an angle in a triangle and $\sin \phi = 0.2616$. Find ϕ to the nearest hundredth of a degree. **15.17°**

Example 3 For what θ with $0 < \theta < 180°$ is it the case that $\sin^{-1}(\sin \theta) \neq \theta$? **90° < θ < 180°.**

Accommodating the Learner ⬆

Ask students to describe all solutions to $\sin \theta = -\frac{2}{3}$. $\theta \approx (-41.8 + 360n)°$ or $\theta \approx (-138.2 + 360n)°$, where n is any integer.

5-4

3 Assignment

Recommended Assignment
- Questions 1–8
- • Questions 9–21
- • Question 22 (extra credit)
- • Reading Lesson 5-5
- • Covering the Ideas 5-5
  (Questions 1–11)

Notes on the Questions

Question 7 In Example 3 of Lesson 5-6, this same situation is given but students are asked to find θ as a function of the adjacent side rather than as a function of the hypotenuse.

Question 11 For all x, $\sin(\sin^{-1} x) = x$, but it is not case that for all x, $\sin^{-1}(\sin x) = x$, because in the latter case the first x could be a number outside the interval $-90° \le x \le 90°$, yet applying the inverse sine function returns a value of x between $-90°$ and $90°$. Question 22 is related.

Additional Answers

Activity

Step 4a–b:

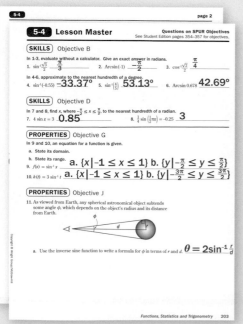

Step 4 a. Graph the function in Step 1 over the domain in Step 3a, so that the entire range in Step 3b shows.

   b. On your graph, identify the 3 points corresponding to your answers to Step 2. **See margin.**

Questions

COVERING THE IDEAS

1. Explain why the inverse of the sine function is not a function.
2. How is the expression $\theta = \sin^{-1} k$ read?
3. a. Complete the table of values below. **a–b. See margin.**

point on $y = \sin x$	$\left(-\frac{\pi}{2}, -1\right)$	$\left(-\frac{\pi}{3}, ?\right)$	$\left(-\frac{\pi}{4}, ?\right)$	$\left(-\frac{\pi}{6}, ?\right)$	$(0, ?)$	$\left(\frac{\pi}{6}, ?\right)$	$\left(\frac{\pi}{4}, ?\right)$	$\left(\frac{\pi}{3}, ?\right)$	$\left(\frac{\pi}{2}, ?\right)$
corresponding point on $y = \sin^{-1} x$	$\left(-1, -\frac{\pi}{2}\right),$	$(?, ?)$	$(?, ?)$	$(?, ?)$	$(?, ?)$	$(?, ?)$	$(?, ?)$	$(?, ?)$	$(?, ?)$

   b. Graph $y = \sin x$ and $y = \sin^{-1} x$ on the same set of axes.
   c. State the domain and range of the inverse sine function.
   d. What transformation maps the graph of $y = \sin x$ to the graph of $y = \sin^{-1} x$? **reflection over the line $y = x$; $T(x, y) = (y, x)$**

In 4–6, find an exact value in radians and degrees without a calculator.

4. $\sin^{-1}\left(\frac{1}{2}\right)$ $\frac{\pi}{6}$; 30°
5. Arcsin 1 $\frac{\pi}{2}$; 90°
6. $\sin^{-1}\left(-\frac{\sqrt{2}}{2}\right)$ $-\frac{\pi}{4}$; −45°

7. A plane flying at an altitude of 32,000 feet (about 6 miles) descends to an airport at a constant angle θ in radians on a path m miles long.
   a. Write an equation for θ as a function of m. $\theta = \sin^{-1}\left(\frac{6}{m}\right)$
   b. Graph your function from Part a using $0 \le m \le 100$.
   c. If $m = 30$, find θ to the nearest tenth. Explain the meaning of your answer in the context of the problem.

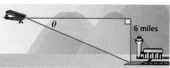

8. Suppose $0° < x < 180°$ and $\sin x = 0.1$. Find all possible values of x to the nearest tenth of a degree. **5.7° and 174.3°**

APPLYING THE MATHEMATICS

9. One statement below is true; the other is false. Which one is false, and why?
   A If $\theta = \sin^{-1} n$, then $n = \sin \theta$.   **B** If $n = \sin \theta$, then $\theta = \sin^{-1} n$.
10. Explain why $\{x \mid 0 \le x \le \pi\}$ is not used as the domain of the restricted sine function.
11. Explain why $\sin(\sin^{-1} x) = x$ for all x such that $-1 \le x \le 1$. **See margin.**
12. a. Evaluate $\cos(\sin^{-1} 0.8)$ using a calculator. **See margin.**
    b. Draw an appropriate triangle to show how the answer to Part a could have been found without a calculator.
    c. Evaluate $\cos\left(\sin^{-1}\left(\frac{b}{c}\right)\right)$, where $b \neq 0$ and $c \neq 0$. $\dfrac{\sqrt{c^2 - b^2}}{c}$

312   Trigonometry

Right margin answers

1. Answers vary. Sample: A value in the domain of the inverse sine function could have more than one value in the range, so it cannot be a function.

2. θ is the number whose sine is k.

3c. domain: $\{x \mid -1 \le x \le 1\}$
     range: $\left\{y \mid -\frac{\pi}{2} \le y \le \frac{\pi}{2}\right\}$

7b. See margin.

7c. 0.2; This is the angle in radians at which the plane is descending.

9. B is false because, since the domain is restricted for the inverse sine function, there are values of θ that are not in the inverse sine function's domain.

10. Answers vary. Sample: This domain would not take on all values in the desired range.

Additional Answers

3a.

Point on $y = \sin x$	$\left(-\frac{\pi}{2}, -1\right)$	$\left(-\frac{\pi}{3}, \frac{\sqrt{3}}{2}\right)$	$\left(-\frac{\pi}{4}, -\frac{\sqrt{2}}{2}\right)$	$\left(-\frac{\pi}{6}, -\frac{1}{2}\right)$	$(0, 0)$	$\left(\frac{\pi}{6}, \frac{1}{2}\right)$	$\left(\frac{\pi}{4}, \frac{\sqrt{2}}{2}\right)$	$\left(\frac{\pi}{3}, \frac{\sqrt{3}}{2}\right)$	$\left(\frac{\pi}{2}, \frac{1}{2}\right)$
Corresponding point on $y = \sin^{-1} x$	$\left(-1, -\frac{\pi}{2}\right)$	$\left(\frac{\sqrt{3}}{2}, -\frac{\pi}{3}\right)$	$\left(-\frac{\sqrt{2}}{2}, -\frac{\pi}{4}\right)$	$\left(-\frac{1}{2}, -\frac{\pi}{6}\right)$	$(0, 0)$	$\left(\frac{1}{2}, \frac{\pi}{6}\right)$	$\left(\frac{\sqrt{2}}{2}, \frac{\pi}{4}\right)$	$\left(\frac{\sqrt{3}}{2}, \frac{\pi}{3}\right)$	$\left(\frac{1}{2}, \frac{\pi}{2}\right)$

3b.

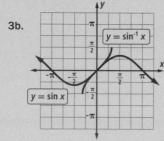

7b.

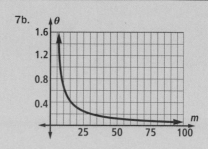

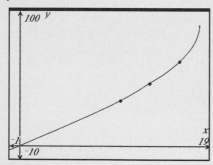

13. The equation $E = 4\sin(60\pi t)$ describes the electrical voltage E in a circuit at a time t.
    a. Solve for t in terms of E. $t = \frac{1}{60\pi}\sin^{-1}\left(\frac{E}{4}\right)$
    b. How is the graph of t as a function of E related to the graph of $E = 4\sin(60\pi t)$?

14. A satellite orbits Earth. At time $t = 0$ hours it is at its farthest distance of 600 miles above Earth. At $t = 1$ hour, it is at its closest distance of 450 miles above Earth.
    a. Assume that the distance d varies sinusoidally with time. Write an equation using the sine function to model this situation.
    b. Solve this equation for t in terms of d.
    c. What are the first four times the satellite is 500 miles above Earth? ≈ 0.61, ≈ 1.39, ≈ 2.61, and ≈ 3.39 hours

15. Find the smallest positive value of x in radians with $2\sin x + 6 = 5$. $\frac{7\pi}{6}$

16. Example 3 in Lesson 5-2 shows the diagram at the right representing Earth and the Landsat 7 satellite.
    a. Give a formula for $m\angle HSC$ in terms of r and a. ($\angle HSC$ is called the *angular separation* of the horizon.)
    b. Give a relationship between $\cos\theta$ and $\sin(m\angle HSC)$.

13b. The graph of t is the image of the graph of the inverse sine function under S: $(x, y) \rightarrow \left(4x, \frac{y}{60\pi}\right)$.

14a. $d = 525 + 75\sin\left(\pi t + \frac{\pi}{2}\right)$

14b. $t = \frac{1}{\pi}\left(\sin^{-1}\left(\frac{d - 525}{75}\right) - \frac{\pi}{2}\right)$

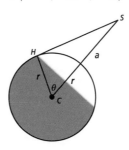

17. The figure at the right represents the way a golfer played a hole to avoid two water hazards. To the nearest yard, how far is it from the tee to the green directly over the water? (**Lesson 5-3**)

18. In $\triangle PQR$, $p = 19$, $q = 5$, and $r = 17$. Find $m\angle P$. (**Lesson 5-3**) $\approx 106.0°$

In 19 and 20, use a calculator only to check answers. (Lessons 4-6, 4-5, 4-3)

19. Given $\sin 144° \approx 0.588$, a. Answers vary. Sample: 504°
    a. find θ such that $\theta > 360°$ and $\sin\theta \approx 0.588$. b. Answers vary.
    b. find θ such that $\theta < 0°$ and $\sin\theta \approx 0.588$. Sample: –216°
    c. find θ such that $\theta \neq 144°$, $0° \leq \theta < 360°$, and $\sin\theta \approx 0.588$. 36°

20. Given $\cos 80° \approx 0.174$, find each value.
    a. $\cos 440°$ **0.174**   b. $\cos -440°$ **0.174**   c. $\cos 460°$ **–0.174**

21. Consider the graph of the function f with $f(x) = 2x^2 + x - 15$.
    a. Find its y-intercept and x-intercepts.
    b. Tell whether the graph has a maximum or minimum point and find its coordinates. (**Lesson 2-6**) It has a minimum at $\left(-\frac{1}{4}, -\frac{121}{8}\right)$.

22. Graph the function with equation $y = \sin^{-1}(\sin x)$ on a calculator on the domain $-720° \leq x \leq 720°$. Describe and explain the result.

    See margin.

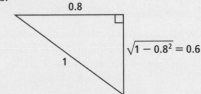

Green

220 yd

160°

150 yd

Tee

16. a. $m\angle HSC = \sin^{-1}\left(\frac{r}{r+a}\right)$
    b. $\cos\theta = \sin(m\angle HSC)$

17. about 365 yards

21a. y-intercept: –15; x-intercepts: –3 and 2.5

QY ANSWER

$\frac{\pi}{2}$ or 90°

The Inverse Sine Function   313

4 **Wrap-Up**

Ongoing Assessment
Have students give an oral explanation of Question 10. Answers vary. Students' presentations should indicate an understanding of the restriction on the sine function used to define the inverse sine function.

11. For $-1 \leq x \leq 1$, let $y = \sin^{-1} x$. By the definition of $\sin^{-1} x$, $\sin y = x$. Therefore, $\sin(\sin^{-1} x) = x$ for all x such that $-1 \leq x \leq 1$.

12a.

$\cos\left(\sin^{-1}(0.8)\right)$	0.6

12b.

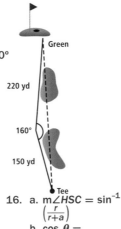

$\sqrt{1 - 0.8^2} = 0.6$

22. Since $f(x) = \sin x$ and $g(x) = \sin^{-1} x$ are inverses of each other, on the restricted domain of $g(x)$, $\{x \mid -90° \leq x \leq 90°\}$, $g(f(x)) = x$. From the graph we can see that this is true. Since these are cyclical functions for $\{x \mid -90 + 360n° \leq x \leq 90 + 360n°\}$ where n is an integer, $g(f(x)) = x - 360n$. From the graph, it appears that $g(f(x)) = -x + 180 + 360n$ for $\{x \mid 90 + 360n° \leq x \leq 270 + 360n°\}$ where n is an integer. This is because $\sin(180° + x) = -\sin x$.

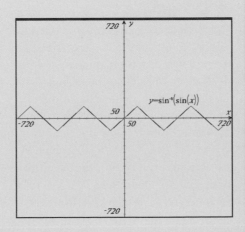

Lesson 5-5

Lesson 5-5 **The Law of Sines**

GOAL

Cover two formulas involving triangles and sines: the SAS Area Formula and the Law of Sines.

SPUR Objectives

C Use the Law of Sines to find lengths and angle measures in triangles.

F Interpret the Law of Sines.

I Solve real-world problems using the Law of Sines.

Materials/Resources

· Lesson Master 5-5
· Resource Masters 107–110

HOMEWORK • **Option 1**
• Option 2

• Questions 1–11
• • Questions 12–25
• • Question 26 (extra credit)
• Reading Lesson 5-6
• Covering the Ideas 5-6
(Questions 1–8)

Local Standards

---

1 Warm-Up

Draw an accurate picture to show that two noncongruent triangles *ABC* can have *AC* = 50, *BC* = 30, and m∠*A* = 27°.

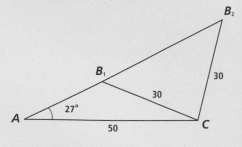

▶ **BIG IDEA** The Law of Sines allows you to find unknown lengths in a triangle given the ASA, AAS, or SSA conditions.

The Law of Cosines is not always helpful in finding sides and angles in triangles. Consider this situation. Some campers want to find the distance f across a lake. They measure the distance from the flagpole to the headquarters and measure the angles as indicated. This provides them with the measures of two angles and the included side of $\triangle FBH$. The ASA condition is met, so this is enough information to find f.

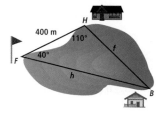

However, when the campers apply the Law of Cosines to find f, they get
$$f^2 = b^2 + h^2 - 2bh \cos F$$
$$f^2 = 400^2 + h^2 - 2 \cdot 400 \cdot h \cos 40°$$
$$f^2 = 160{,}000 + h^2 - 800h \cos 40°.$$
The result is a single equation with two unknowns, so the campers are unable to proceed any further with this solution.

Fortunately, there is another way to find f, using a theorem known as the *Law of Sines*. The proof of the Law of Sines involves the area of a triangle, so we first review area.

The SAS Area Formula for a Triangle

The area K of triangle ABC as shown at the right is given by the familiar formula $K = \frac{1}{2}bh$.

If h is not known, you can find h using right triangle BCD.

$$\sin C = \frac{h}{a}, \text{ so } h = a \sin C.$$

Substituting this value in the area formula gives

$$K = \frac{1}{2} ab \sin C.$$

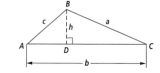

1. Which of these sets of numbers cannot be lengths of sides of a right triangle? **A, C, D**

2. Which of these sets of numbers cannot be lengths of sides of any triangle? **A, D**

A 30, 10, 40
B 30, 50, 40
C 30, 60, 40
D 30, 80, 40

Background

The SAS area formula for a triangle
Just as values that satisfy any triangle congruence condition uniquely determine all angles and sides in the triangle, so too do they determine area. In their study of geometry, students may have encountered Hero's (or Heron's) formula $A = \sqrt{s(s-a)(s-b)(s-c)}$, which gives the area in terms of the lengths of three sides, the SSS condition. The SAS Area Formula in this lesson gives the area from the SAS condition, that is, in terms of two sides and an included angle.

It is then reasonable to ask whether there is an area formula using the ASA or AAS condition. The answer is Yes: Write down the three SAS area formulas for a triangle. Multiply two of the expressions for the area and divide the product by the third expression for the area. For instance,

let the area of the triangle be K. Then K
$$= \frac{K^2}{K} = \frac{\frac{1}{2}ab \sin C \cdot \frac{1}{2}ac \sin B}{\frac{1}{2}bc \sin A} = \frac{1}{2}a^2 \frac{\sin B \sin C}{\sin A}.$$

Similarly, $\sin A = \frac{h}{c}$. So $h = c \sin A$, and so another formula is

$$K = \tfrac{1}{2} bc \sin A.$$

Activity

For $\triangle ABC$ at the right, use $\overline{AB}$ as the base and h as the altitude. Derive yet a third formula for the area of $\triangle ABC$.

This argument proves the following theorem.

> **Theorem (SAS Area Formula for a Triangle)**
>
> In any triangle, the area is one-half the product of the lengths of any two sides and the sine of their included angle.

A Proof of the Law of Sines

The Law of Sines is one of the most beautiful results in all of mathematics—simple and elegant.

> **Theorem (Law of Sines)**
>
> In any triangle ABC, $\frac{\sin A}{a} = \frac{\sin B}{b} = \frac{\sin C}{c}$.
>
>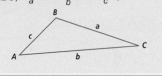

Proof Let $\triangle ABC$ be any triangle. To find the area of $\triangle ABC$ with the SAS Formula, any two sides and their included angle may be used. Because the area of a given triangle is constant,

$$\tfrac{1}{2} bc \sin A = \tfrac{1}{2} ac \sin B = \tfrac{1}{2} ab \sin C.$$

Multiply by 2. $bc \sin A = ac \sin B = ab \sin C$

Divide by abc. $\dfrac{bc \sin A}{abc} = \dfrac{ac \sin B}{abc} = \dfrac{ab \sin C}{abc}$

Rewrite the fractions in lowest terms. $\dfrac{\sin A}{a} = \dfrac{\sin B}{b} = \dfrac{\sin C}{c}$

Using the Law of Sines with the ASA Condition

You can use the Law of Sines to find the length of a second side of a triangle given the measures of two angles and one side (the ASA or AAS conditions).

Activity

$K = \frac{1}{2}ch$; $\sin B = \sin(180 - m\angle B) = \frac{h}{a}$
so
$h = a \sin B$; $K = \frac{1}{2}ac \sin B$

---

2 Teaching

Notes on the Lesson

Students who have studied from UCSMP *Geometry* should be familiar with the SsA Theorem (capital S, lower case s, capital A). The capital and lower cases indicate that the non-included angle is opposite the larger side. When two triangles have two sides and the corresponding non-included angle opposite the larger side congruent, then they are congruent.

There are three other SSA possibilities that can occur:

1. The side opposite the given angle can be too short to even create a triangle. For example, if $m\angle A = 30°$, $b = 8$ and $a = 3$. Students will get an error message on their calculators because $\sin B > 1$.

2. The side opposite the given angle can be exactly long enough to create a right triangle. For example, $m\angle A = 30°$, $b = 8$, and $a = 4$. There is a unique triangle in this case.

3. The two given sides can be equal. Again, there is a unique triangle.

We want students to realize that in an SSA case, if the side opposite the given angle is longer than the other given side, there is one possible triangle; otherwise there may be more than one possible triangle. The fact that there can be 0, 1, or 2 solutions should not be treated as any more unusual than the fact that a quadratic equation can have 0, 1, or 2 real solutions.

This formula gives the area in terms of one side and the sines of the three angles, but if measures of two angles are given, the measure of the third can easily be determined. Specifically, since $m\angle A + m\angle B + m\angle C = 180°$, $\sin A = \sin(180° - A) = \sin(B + C)$, so $K = \frac{1}{2} a^2 \frac{\sin B \sin C}{\sin(B + C)}$.

When the AAS or ASA conditions are satisfied, the Law of Sines enables the determination of the unique measures of the other two sides. When the SSA condition is given, the Law of Sines enables

determination of a second angle, which with the Law of Cosines allows the third side to be determined. When the SSA condition is satisfied but the given angle is not opposite the larger side, there may be no value or two values possible for the third side.

5-5

Notes on the Lesson

Using the Law of Sines with the SSA condition Because of the potential for ambiguity, many geometry courses dismiss SSA triangle congruence as a theorem, so your students may not accept the possible unique solutions to a SSA problem using the Law of Sines. This will be reinforced by Example 3, which shows two different solutions to such a problem. However, note that in Example 2, when the side opposite the given angle is longer than the other given side, there is a unique triangle and no ambiguity is possible. This is the SsA condition.

Additional Examples

Example 1 From Bud's house, a tower is 17° south of east. From Pal's house, which is 4 km due north of Bud's house, the tower is 40° south of east. How far is it from Bud's house to the tower? **about 7.8 km**

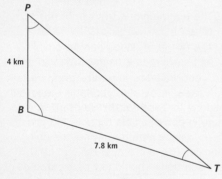

Example 2 In △PQR, PQ = 7, QR = 8 and m∠P = 20°. Find m∠QRP and draw a picture of △QRP. **m∠QRP ≈ 17.4°**

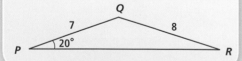

Example 1

Refer to the camp situation on page 314. Find the distance *f* across the lake.

Solution Since the sum of the measures of the angles of a triangle is 180°,

$$m\angle B = 180° - 40° - 110° = 30°.$$

Use the Law of Sines to find *f*. First write the Law of Sines for this triangle.

$$\frac{\sin F}{f} = \frac{\sin B}{b} = \frac{\sin H}{h}$$

$$\frac{\sin 40°}{f} = \frac{\sin 30°}{400} = \frac{\sin 110°}{h}$$

Use the left and middle fractions to solve for *f*.

$$f \sin 30° = 400 \sin 40°$$

$$f = \frac{400 \sin 40°}{\sin 30°} \approx 514$$

It is about 514 meters across the lake from the beach house to headquarters.

Check Recall that in a triangle the longer sides are opposite the larger angles. The 514-meter side is opposite the 40° angle, and the shorter 400-meter side is opposite the (smaller) 30° angle, as it should be.

🛑 **QY**

Using the Law of Sines with the SSA Condition

The Law of Sines can also be used to determine the measure of a second angle of a triangle when two sides and a nonincluded angle are known. This is the SSA condition. However, as you studied in geometry, SSA is not a condition that, in general, guarantees congruence. Thus, when the Law of Sines is used in an SSA situation, it is possible to get no solution, one solution, or two solutions.

When the side opposite the given angle is larger than the other given side, the SSA condition leads to a unique triangle. We then call it the *SsA condition*.

▶ **QY**

Find the value of *h* in Example 1.

Example 2

In △XYZ, y = 5, z = 3, and m∠Y = 60°. Find m∠Z.

Solution Make a rough sketch. Use the Law of Sines to get

$$\frac{\sin 60°}{5} = \frac{\sin Z}{3}.$$

$$\sin Z = \frac{3}{5} \sin 60° = \frac{3\sqrt{3}}{10} \approx 0.52$$

$$m\angle Z = \sin^{-1}(0.52) \approx 31.3°$$

Test whether there is a second solution. From the Supplements Theorem,

$\sin(180° - 31.3°) = \sin 148.7° \approx 0.52$ also. But if 148.7° were a solution to this problem, then the sum of the angles of △XYZ would be more than 180°. So m∠Z = 31.3° is the only solution.

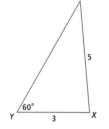

316 Trigonometry

Accommodating the Learner ⬆

Have students work in groups to find the perimeter of a regular pentagon inscribed in a circle with radius 12. **120 sin 36° ≈ 70.53**

Example 3 illustrates when two solutions are possible.

GUIDED

Example 3
In △*ABC*, m∠*A* = 35°, *AB* = 8, and *BC* = 6. Find all possible values of m∠*C* to the nearest degree.

Solution Make a rough sketch. Use the Law of Sines.

By the Law of Sines, $\frac{?}{6} = \frac{\sin C}{?}$. **sin 35°; 8**

Solve for m∠*C*. $\sin C = \frac{?}{6} \approx \underline{\ ?\ }$ **8 sin 35°; 0.7648**

$m\angle C = \sin^{-1}(\underline{\ ?\ }) \approx \underline{\ ?\ }$ **0.7648; 49.89°**

A triangle determined by this value is pictured at the right.

However, from the Supplements Theorem, a second angle *C* has sin *C* = 0.7647. The measure of this angle is 180° − $\underline{\ ?\ } \approx \underline{\ ?\ }$°. **49.89°; 130.11**

A triangle determined by this value is shown below.

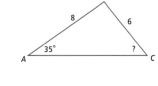

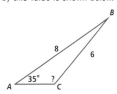

So there are two possible values of m∠*C*, $\underline{\ ?\ }$ and $\underline{\ ?\ }$, and the two triangles are not congruent. **49.89°, 130.11°**

As you will see in the Questions, there are also SSA cases when no triangle is possible.

In general, when looking for measures of angles or sides in triangles, try methods involving simpler computations first. If these methods do not work, use the following.

1. If given two angles in a triangle, find the third angle by subtracting the total of the given angles from 180° or π radians, depending on the given units.

2. If a triangle is a right triangle, use right triangle trigonometric ratios.

3. If a triangle is not a right triangle, consider the Law of Sines. It is useful for the ASA, AAS, and SSA conditions.

4. If the Law of Sines is not helpful, use the Law of Cosines. The Law of Cosines is most directly applicable to the SAS and SSS conditions.

Notes on the Lesson
The last paragraph of this lesson summarizes Lessons 5-3 and 5-5 by listing the conditions that lead to triangle congruence and associating them with the corresponding theorem. Your students may prefer the following table.

Condition	Theorem
SAS	Law of Cosines
SSS	Law of Cosines
AAS	Law of Sines
ASA	Law of Sines
SsA	Law of Sines
SSA	Law of Sines (possibly ambiguous)

In doing the questions, encourage students to draw an accurate diagram (if none is given) as they start a question. This should help them to select an appropriate method to solve the problem. A diagram should also help students to recognize when they are dealing with an ambiguous case.

Additional Example
Example 3 In △*PQR*, *PQ* = 7, *QR* = 4 and m∠*P* = 20°. Find m∠*QRP* and draw a picture of △*QRP*. m∠*QRP* ≈ 36.765° or m∠*QRP* ≈ 143.235°. △*PQR₁* and △*PQR₂*, shown here, both satisfy the conditions of the problem.

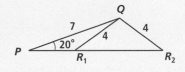

Extension

Use the Law of Sines to prove that if a triangle has two angles of the same measure, then it is isosceles. If m∠*A* = m∠*B*, then sin *A* = sin *B*. If ∠*A* and ∠*B* are in the same triangle, then $\frac{\sin A}{a} = \frac{\sin B}{b}$.

So $\frac{\sin A}{a} = \frac{\sin A}{b}$, and thus *b* sin *A* = *a* sin *A*, from which *b* = *a*, so the triangle is isosceles.

Recommended Assignment

- Questions 1–11
- • Questions 12–25
- • Question 26 (extra credit)
- Reading Lesson 5-6
- Covering the Ideas 5-6
  (Questions 1–8)

Notes on the Questions

Question 4 In any given triangle, the ratio of any side to the sine of the opposite angle equals the diameter of the circumcircle of the triangle. So each of the ratios in Part b equals that diameter. (See Question 26.)

Questions 10 and 11 The results of these questions can be generalized. If the conditions given are sufficient for triangle congruence, then it is not possible for two noncongruent triangles to be determined.

Question 12 Some students may know or remember the formula $A = \frac{\sqrt{3}}{4} s^2$ for the area of an equilateral triangle. This is easily proved by the SAS Triangle Formula by substituting $\frac{\sqrt{3}}{2}$ for sin 60° in $A = \frac{1}{2} s \cdot s \cdot \sin 60°$.

Questions

1. Find the area of △ABC where $a = 35$, $b = 26$, and m∠C = 117°.

2. Without a calculator, find the area of △DEF where $d = 40$, $f = 20$, and m∠E = 30°. **200**

3. In any triangle, the ratio of the sine of any angle to __?__ is constant.

4. Tell whether the statement is equivalent to the Law of Sines for △ABC.
   a. $\frac{A}{a} = \frac{B}{b} = \frac{C}{c}$ **no**
   b. $\frac{a}{\sin A} = \frac{b}{\sin B} = \frac{c}{\sin C}$ **yes**
   c. $\frac{a}{b} = \frac{\sin A}{\sin B}, \frac{b}{c} = \frac{\sin B}{\sin C}, \frac{a}{c} = \frac{\sin A}{\sin C}$ **yes**
   d. $ab \sin C = bc \sin A = ac \sin B$ **yes**

5. In △XYZ at the right, find x to the nearest tenth. **about 9.2**

6. In △EFG below, find m∠F to the nearest tenth of a degree. **about 4.9°**

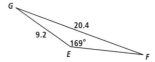

7. In △ABC, suppose m∠C = 45°, m∠A = 30°, and $c = 10$. Find the lengths of the other two sides to the nearest hundredth. **a ≈ 7.07, b ≈ 13.66**

8. The Costas want to check the survey of a plot of land they are thinking of buying. The plot is triangular with one side on the lakefront, with dimensions as shown at the right.
   a. Find the measure of the angle between the lakeshore and the 452-foot side. **about 34.4°**
   b. About how many feet of lake frontage does the plot have? **about 565 ft**

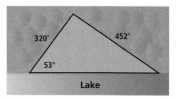

9. In △XYZ, $x = 2$ cm, $z = 3$ cm, and m∠X = 40°.
   a. Find the two possible measures of ∠Z. **about 74.6° or 105.4°**
   b. Draw two noncongruent triangles satisfying these conditions.

In 10 and 11, **True or False**.

10. When given SSA conditions, it is possible for two different triangles to be determined. **true**

11. When given ASA conditions, it is possible for two different triangles to be determined. **false**

12. Use the SAS Triangle Formula to find the area of an equilateral triangle with sides of length 20. **100√3**

13. A piston driven by a 3-cm radial arm has length 9 cm. As the radial arm moves from 80° to 70° off its axis, how much does x change?

---

1. about 405.4

3. its opposite side

9b.

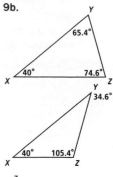

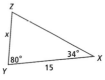

13. about 0.55 cm

14. Richard spots a tornado 40° S of W. He calls Joanne who lives 1.4 miles due south of his house. She sees the cloud at 25° S of W. How close are Richard and Joanne to the tornado?

15. In $\triangle WXY$, $WX = 100$ and $m\angle W = 45°$. What values of XY will yield the following number of possible measures for $\angle Y$?
   a. exactly two   b. exactly one   c. none

REVIEW

In 16 and 17, evaluate in degrees and radians without a calculator. (Lesson 5-4)

16. $\sin^{-1}(0)$ **0°; 0**

17. $\sin^{-1}\left(\frac{1}{2}\right)$ **30°, $\frac{\pi}{6}$**

In 18–20, find the exact value. (Lesson 4-6)

18. $\cos 45°$ **$\frac{\sqrt{2}}{2}$**

19. $\sin\left(\frac{2\pi}{3}\right)$ **$\frac{\sqrt{3}}{2}$**

20. $\tan \pi$ **0**

In 21 and 22, $\sin \theta = t$. Evaluate without a calculator. (Lesson 4-3)

21. $\sin(-\theta)$ **$-t$**

22. $\sin(180° - \theta)$ **t**

23. The graph at the right is a translation or scale-change image of the graph of $y = |x|$. Write an equation for the graph. (Lessons 3-5, 3-2) **$y + 4 = |x + 3|$**

24. A *wind chill* is an index of how cold it feels when the wind is blowing on a cold day. The data at the right give the wind chills for an actual temperature of 0° F at various wind speeds. **See margin.**
   a. Identify the independent and dependent variables in this case.
   b. Construct a scatterplot of these data.
   c. Find a suitable quadratic model for the data. (Lessons 2-6, 2-2)

25. **Skill Sequence** Suppose $X_1 = 56$, $X_2 = 73$, $X_3 = 68$, $X_4 = 65$, $X_5 = 58$, $X_6 = 91$, and $X_7 = 79$. Evaluate. (Lesson 1-2)
   a. $\sum_{i=1}^{7} 8X_i$ **3920**   b. $\sum_{i=1}^{7} kX_i$ **490k**   c. $\sum_{i=1}^{7}\left(\frac{X_i}{k}\right)$ **$\frac{490}{k}$**   d. $\sum_{i=1}^{7}(X_i - 8)$ **434**

EXPLORATION

26. $\triangle ABC$ is inscribed in $\odot O$. Prove that the diameter of $\odot O$ is $\frac{a}{\sin A}$.
   See margin.

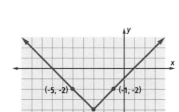

Wind Chill (°F)	Wind Speed (mph)
−11	5
−16	10
−19	15
−22	20
−24	25
−26	30
−27	35
−29	40
−30	45

Source: National Oceanic and Atmospheric Administration

14. Richard lives about 4.9 miles away, Joanne lives about 4.1 miles away.

15a. $50\sqrt{2} < XY < 100$

15b. $100 \le XY$ or $XY = 50\sqrt{2}$

15c. $0 \le XY < 50\sqrt{2}$

QY ANSWER

$h \approx 752$ m

The Law of Sines   **319**

Notes on the Questions

Question 14 This question is an example of *triangulation*, the process of using the direction of an object from the viewpoint of two or three observers in order to pinpoint the exact location of the object. This idea is used in baseball to locate the path of a home run so that the information can be used to determine how far the ball would have gone if it had not hit seats or a wall.

Question 26 This proof also could serve as a proof of the Law of Sines by just adding one step, that the other ratios $\frac{b}{\sin B}$ and $\frac{c}{\sin C}$ must equal $\frac{a}{\sin A}$ since there is no particular reason to have begun with side a and opposite angle A, and the diameter is the same regardless of the side and opposite angle from which the argument starts.

4 Wrap-Up

Ongoing Assessment

Have students work in groups. Ask each group to create and solve three different problems in which they apply the Law of Sines to the SSA condition. One problem should lead to no solution, another to one solution, and the third to two solutions. Have students include the solutions to the problems and a brief explanation of their work. **Answers vary. Check students' work.**

Project Update

Project 3, *Bond Angles in Molecules*, on page 349 and Project 5, *Application of the Law of Sines*, on page 350 relate to the content of this lesson.

Additional Answers

26. Construct the angle bisector of $\angle BOC$ and label the point where it intersects with side a as D. Since $\triangle BOC$ contains the radii $\overline{OB}$ and $\overline{OC}$, it is isosceles, so $\overline{OD} \perp \overline{BC}$ and $BD = CD$. Since $\angle A$ is an inscribed angle, $m\angle A = \frac{1}{2}m\angle BOC = m\angle BOD$. Therefore, $\sin(\angle BOD) = \sin A = \frac{\frac{a}{2}}{OB} = \frac{a}{2OB}$, so $2OB = \frac{a}{\sin A}$ = the diameter of $\odot O$.

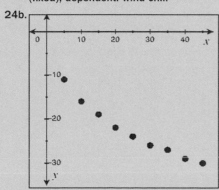

Additional Answers

24a. independent: wind speed, actual temperature (fixed); dependent: wind chill

24c. $y = 0.0087x^2 - 0.89x - 7.4$

24b.

Lesson
5-6

GOAL
Discuss the use of the inverse tangent function to solve equations of the form $\tan \theta = k$.

SPUR Objectives

B Evaluate the inverse tangent function.

D Solve equations of the form $\tan \theta = k$.

G State and use properties of the inverse tangent function.

L Graph and identify graphs of the inverse tangent function.

Materials/Resources
· Lesson Master 5-6
· Resource Masters 111– 113
· Quiz 2

HOMEWORK • **Option 1**
• Questions 1–8   • **Option 2**
• • Questions 9–23
• • Question 24 (extra credit)
  • Reading Lesson 5-7
  • Covering the Ideas 5-7
  (Questions 1–10)

Local Standards

---

1 Warm-Up

1. Give the measure of an angle whose tangent equals 1. **Answers vary. Sample: $\tan^{-1}(1) = 45°$**
2. Give the measure of an angle whose tangent is not defined. **Answers vary. Sample: 90°**
3. Give the measure of an angle whose tangent is –1. **Answers vary. Sample: $\tan^{-1}(-1) = -45°$**

Lesson
5-6   The Inverse Tangent Function

Vocabulary
inverse tangent function, $\tan^{-1}$, Arctan

▶ **BIG IDEA**   If you know $\tan \theta$, and that $-90° \leq \theta \leq 90°$, then θ is uniquely determined.

You have seen situations in which the tangent function is used. For instance, if a plane flying at an altitude of h miles begins its descent d miles from an airport, then the angle θ of the path of descent satisfies

$$\tan \theta = \frac{h}{d}.$$

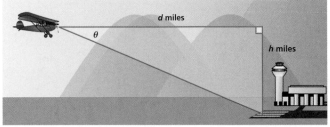

To find θ, you can use the [TAN⁻¹] key on a calculator. This key returns a single value of the function called the *inverse tangent function*.

Defining the Inverse Tangent Function

At the right is a graph of the inverse of the tangent function, $x = \tan y$. You may notice that it is a reflection image of the graph $\tan x$ over the line with equation $y = x$. Like the sine and cosine functions, the inverse of the tangent function is not a function, but it is possible to restrict the domain of the tangent function so that its inverse is a function.

Using the criteria for choosing an appropriate domain used in Lessons 5-2 and 5-4 leads to restricting the domain of the tangent function to $-\frac{\pi}{2} < x < \frac{\pi}{2}$. This **inverse tangent function**, denoted as **$\tan^{-1}$**, is the inverse of this restricted function.

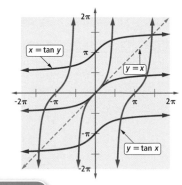

Definition of Inverse Tangent Function

$y = \tan^{-1} x$ if and only if $x = \tan y$ and $-\frac{\pi}{2} < y < \frac{\pi}{2}$.

Mental Math

Find θ if $0° \leq \theta \leq 90°$ and

a. $\tan \theta = 0$.
b. $\tan \theta = 1$.
c. $\tan \theta = \sqrt{3}$.
a. 0°
b. 45°
c. 60°

Background

This lesson continues the ideas of the inverse cosine and inverse sine functions.

The tangent function has two qualities that distinguish the discussion of the inverse tangent function from the discussion of the inverse cosine and inverse sine functions. The first is that the range of the tangent function is the set of all real numbers. Consequently, the *domain* of the inverse tangent function is the set of all reals. The second quality is that there are values for which the tangent function is undefined,

where its graph has asymptotes. Consequently, in order that the inverse tangent function is continuous, the restricted domain for the tangent function is an interval that does not contain any asymptotes.

3. a.

b

c

d

In 4–6

4. ta

In 7 a

7. a

b

c

8

APP

9. a

b

10. A

1

a

a

11. A

e

c

l

a

The restricted tangent function and inverse tangent function are graphed below. Notice that, unlike the $\sin^{-1}$ and $\cos^{-1}$ functions, the $\tan^{-1}$ function has the set of all real numbers as its domain.

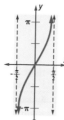

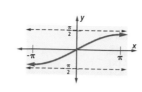

restricted tangent function
domain: $\{x \mid -\frac{\pi}{2} < x < \frac{\pi}{2}\}$
range: $\mathbb{R}$

inverse tangent function
domain: $\mathbb{R}$
range: $\{y \mid -\frac{\pi}{2} < y < \frac{\pi}{2}\}$

STOP QY

You can read $y = \tan^{-1} x$ as "y is the number (or angle) whose tangent is x." The notation **Arctan** is sometimes used in place of $\tan^{-1}$.

> **QY**

Draw a right triangle with an angle θ such that $\theta = \tan^{-1} 4$.

Finding Values of the Inverse Tangent Function

Some values of the inverse tangent function can be found exactly without using a calculator.

Example 1

Evaluate $\tan^{-1}(-1)$ in radians.

Solution If $y = \tan^{-1}(-1)$, then by definition of $\tan^{-1}$, y is the unique number in the interval $-\frac{\pi}{2} < y < \frac{\pi}{2}$ with $\tan y = -1$. So $\sin y$ and $\cos y$ are opposites. On the unit circle, this occurs in the interval desired only when $y = -\frac{\pi}{4}$.

All values of the inverse tangent function can be estimated using a calculator.

Example 2

Evaluate Arctan 4 in degrees.

Solution Apply the definition of the inverse tangent function:
$y = $ Arctan 4 if and only if $\tan y = 4$ and $-90° < y < 90°$.
Set your calculator to degree mode. Use it to get
Arctan $4 \approx 75.96°$.

tan⁻¹(4)   75.963757

Check Evaluate tan 75.96° with a calculator. This results in a display of about 3.9988... . It checks. Also, look at the drawing for the QY. The measure of angle θ is about 76°.

In 12

12. 1

14. (

The Inverse Tangent Function   **321**

---

2 Teaching

Notes on the Lesson

To clarify the discussion, you might wish to identify the domains and ranges of three functions.

Function	Domain	Range
Tangent	Set of all reals except odd multiples of $\frac{\pi}{2}$	Set of all reals
Restricted tangent	$\{x: -\frac{\pi}{2} \le x \le \frac{\pi}{2}\}$	Set of all reals
Inverse tangent	Set of all reals	$\{y: -\frac{\pi}{2} \le y \le \frac{\pi}{2}\}$

Notice that the domains of the restricted sine and restricted tangent are almost identical. This means that the range of the inverse tangent and the inverse sine functions are the same except for the endpoints, so there are negative values of the inverse tangent function (as there were with the inverse sine function) that do not correspond to angles in polygons. Example 1 has such a value.

The table below summarizes the domain and range of each of the three trigonometric functions and their corresponding restricted and inverse functions.

Function	Domain	Range
Cosine	Set of all reals	$\{y: -1 \le y \le 1\}$
Restricted cosine	$\{x: 0 \le x \le \pi\}$	$\{y: -1 \le y \le 1\}$
Inverse cosine	$\{x: -1 \le x \le 1\}$	$\{y: 0 \le y \le \pi\}$

Function	Domain	Range
Sine	Set of all reals	$\{y: -1 \le y \le 1\}$
Restricted sine	$\{x: -\frac{\pi}{2} \le x \le \frac{\pi}{2}\}$	$\{y: -1 \le y \le 1\}$
Inverse sine	$\{x: -1 \le x \le 1\}$	$\{y: -\frac{\pi}{2} \le y \le \frac{\pi}{2}\}$

Function	Domain	Range
Tangent	Set of all reals except odd multiples of $\frac{\pi}{2}$	Set of all reals
Restricted tangent	$\{x: -\frac{\pi}{2} \le x \le \frac{\pi}{2}\}$	Set of all reals
Inverse tangent	Set of all reals	$\{y: -\frac{\pi}{2} \le y \le \frac{\pi}{2}\}$

Additi

3b.

Accommodating the Learner ⬇

The table in the Notes on the Lesson summarizes information students should be able to readily give. You may wish to copy just the top row and first column of this table and have students fill in the domain and range columns themselves. Alternatively, you may have students copy the entire table and then give them a brief quiz on the contents. Either way, it is important that students demonstrate a firm grasp of each inverse trigonometric function at this point.

5-6

Notes on the Questions

Question 15 The key to answering this question is that the owners began by walking directly towards B. Otherwise there is not enough information to answer the question.

Questions 16–21 These are important review questions. Some students, having learned the Law of Cosines and the Law of Sines, forget that they do not need those theorems to solve right triangles. Other students apply the definitions of the sine or cosine to solve triangles that are not right triangles.

Question 24 Gregory's series is certainly one of the more amazing infinite series formulas for values of any function. You may need to remind students that the values of the inverse tangent function in this formula are in radians. This again points out that radian measure has very nice properties that degree measure does not have.

4 Wrap-Up

Ongoing Assessment

Have students write a simple word problem, like Questions 10 and 11, requiring the use of the inverse tangent function in the solution. Have students switch papers with a partner and solve their partner's problem. Students should then check their partner's work. **Answers vary. Check student's work.**

Administer Quiz 2 (or a quiz of your own) after students complete this lesson.

Project Update

Project 3, *Bond Angles in Molecules*, on page 349 relates to the content of this lesson.

REVIEW

15. Owners of some land wished to determine the distance from A to B. They walked 250 feet from A directly towards B but encountered a swamp. So they turned left $50°$ and walked 160 feet, then turned right $63°$ and walked directly to B. How far is it from A to B? (Lesson 5-5) **about 883.7 feet**

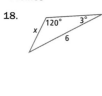

Multiple Choice In 16-21, a triangle is given with an unknown side or angle measure x. Which strategy for finding x is computationally the easiest? (Lessons 5-5, 5-3, 5-1)

A definitions of right triangle trigonometric ratios
B Law of Sines
C Law of Cosines

16. **A** 17. **B** 18. **B**

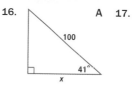

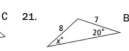

19. **C** 20. **C** 21. **B**

22. How many values of x between 0 and 2π are there such that $\tan x = -\sqrt{3}$? (Lesson 4-4) **2**

23. **Skill Sequence** Solve for x. (Previous Course)

a. $(7x - 7)(x - 3) = 0$ b. $6x^2 = 5 - 7x$ c. $6x^4 = -26x^2 - 24$

EXPLORATION

24. In 1671, James Gregory discovered that when $-1 \leq x \leq 1$,

$$\tan^{-1} x = \sum_{i=0}^{\infty} \frac{(-1)^i x^{(2i + 1)}}{2i + 1} = x - \frac{x^3}{3} + \frac{x^5}{5} - \frac{x^7}{7} + \frac{x^9}{9} - \dots .$$ In 2002, Yasumasa Kanada of Tokyo University calculated π to 1,241,100,000,000 decimal places using Gregory's series and the formula (proved from geometry) that

$$\pi = 48 \tan^{-1}\left(\frac{1}{49}\right) + 128 \tan^{-1}\left(\frac{1}{57}\right) - 20 \tan^{-1}\left(\frac{1}{239}\right) + 48 \tan^{-1}\left(\frac{1}{110,443}\right).$$

a. Use a calculator to verify that the formula for π used by Kanada seems to be correct.

b. Use the first three terms of Gregory's series to estimate each term in Kanada's formula and thus find an estimate for π. To how many decimal places is this estimate accurate?

c. Use more terms of Gregory's series to find an estimate accurate to more decimal places.

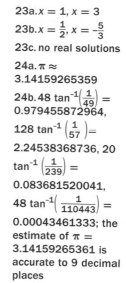

23a. $x = 1$, $x = 3$
23b. $x = \frac{1}{2}$, $x = -\frac{5}{3}$
23c. no real solutions

24a. $\pi \approx$ 3.14159265359

24b. $48 \tan^{-1}\left(\frac{1}{49}\right) = 0.979455872964$, $128 \tan^{-1}\left(\frac{1}{57}\right) = 2.24538368736$, $20 \tan^{-1}\left(\frac{1}{239}\right) = 0.083681520041$, $48 \tan^{-1}\left(\frac{1}{110443}\right) = 0.00043461333$; the estimate of $\pi =$ 3.14159265361 is accurate to 9 decimal places

24c. Answers vary. Sample: Using 5 terms, it is accurate to 16 decimal places, but your CAS may not handle that many decimal points.

QY ANSWER

Extension

Extend Question 11 by asking students to find a general formula for y in terms of x, a, and b, where a = the height of the picture and b = the height of the bottom edge above eye level. $y = \tan^{-1}\left(\frac{a + b}{x}\right) - \tan^{-1}\left(\frac{b}{x}\right)$

General Solutions to Trigonometric Equations

Vocabulary

trigonometric equation

general solution to a trigonometric equation

▶ **BIG IDEA** You can find all the solutions of a trigonometric equation using inverse trigonometric functions and the Periodicity Theorem.

A **trigonometric equation** is an equation in which the variable to be found is an argument of the sine, cosine or tangent function. Examples are $\cos \theta = 0.6$, $9 = 12 \sin(2\pi t)$, $\tan(2x) = 3$, and $2 \sin^2\theta = 1 - \sin \theta$.

Activity   Steps 1, 3. See margin.

Step 1 Graph $y = \tan(2x)$ on the interval $-\frac{\pi}{2} < x < \frac{\pi}{2}$. Use the graph to tell how many solutions the equation $\tan(2x) = 3$ has on the interval $-\frac{\pi}{2} < x < \frac{\pi}{2}$.

Step 2 Use your graph to estimate these solutions to the nearest hundredth and check each solution by substituting into the original equation.

Step 3 Use a graph to determine all solutions to the equation $\tan(2x) = 3$ on the interval $-2\pi < x < 2\pi$. Explain how you could have found all these solutions without graphing.

Step 4 Describe *all* real solutions to the equation $\tan(2x) = 3$, when x can be any real number.

The Activity shows that the number of solutions to a trigonometric equation can vary significantly depending on the domain of the variable. Three domains commonly arise:

(1) the restricted domains of the sine, cosine, and tangent functions that are used in obtaining their inverse functions;

(2) an interval equal in size to the period of the function under study;

(3) the set of all real numbers for which the function is defined.

Using the inverse trigonometric functions $\cos^{-1}$, $\sin^{-1}$, or $\tan^{-1}$ on your calculator will help you find solutions for domain (1). To find the solutions for domains (2) and (3), you may need to use the properties of the trigonometric functions studied in Chapter 4, and you will find it helpful to graph the function. For domain (3), the periodic nature of the functions generates infinitely many solutions on the set of real numbers.

The solution that arises from domain (3), considering all real values of the variable, is called the **general solution** to the trigonometric equation.

Mental Math

Describe all solutions to $\sin x = 0$ over the given domain for x.

a. $0^\circ \le x \le 90^\circ$

b. $0^\circ \le x \le 360^\circ$

c. $-720^\circ \le x \le 720^\circ$

d. set of all real numbers

a. 0°

b. $0^\circ, 180^\circ, 360^\circ$

c. $-720^\circ, -540^\circ, -360^\circ, -180^\circ, 0^\circ, 180^\circ, 360^\circ, 540^\circ, 720^\circ$

d. $180n^\circ$ for all integers n

Step 2: 0.62; $\tan(1.24) \approx 2.91$;
-0.95; $\tan(-1.9) \approx 2.93$

Step 4: $x = -0.95 + \frac{\pi n}{2}$ where n can be any integer.

GOAL

Consider and write solutions to equations over the entire set of real numbers.

SPUR Objectives

D Solve trigonometric equations.

J Write and solve equations for phenomena described by trigonometric functions.

Materials/Resources

· Lesson Master 5-7
· Resource Masters 114 and 115
· graphing utility

HOMEWORK   • Option 1

• Option 2

• Questions 1–10
• • Questions 11–23
• • Question 24 (extra credit)
  • Reading Lesson 5-8
  • Covering the Ideas 5-8 (Questions 1–10)

Local Standards

1 Warm-Up

In 1–6, give the number of real solutions to each equation.

1. $\cos x = \frac{3}{2}$ 0

2. $\sin y = -0.0004$ infinitely many

3. $\tan z = 14$ infinitely many

4. $\cos \theta = 0.5$ infinitely many

5. $\sin \phi = 3.14159$ 0

6. $\tan \mu = -\frac{\sqrt{2}}{3}$ infinitely many

Additional Answers

Activity 1

Steps 1, 3: See page 326.

Background

The approach taken in this lesson is to use inverse trigonometric functions to find or estimate one solution to a trigonometric equation. Then the periodicity and other properties of the trigonometric function involved are used to determine all others. Graphing is a powerful method of checking solutions. A CAS can obtain all solutions automatically.

Students should recall from their earlier work that odd numbers are those of the form $2n + 1$ and even numbers are those of the form $2n$, where n is any integer. Then it is a small step to the idea that $2nx$ stands for an even multiple of x and $(2n + 1)x$ stands for an odd multiple of x. If n is allowed to be negative (which is perfectly permissible and, in fact, necessary if n is any integer), then the $\pm$ symbol is not needed before $2nx$ or $(2n + 1)x$.

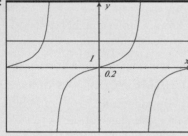

5-7

Additional Example

Example 1 Consider the equation $\sin \theta = \frac{3}{7}$. Round all solutions to the nearest thousandth.

a. Find all solutions between 0 and π.
$\theta \approx 0.443$ or ≈ 2.699

b. Solve the equation when $0 \le \theta \le 2\pi$.
$\theta \approx 0.443$ or $\theta \approx 2.699$

c. Find all real solutions.
$\theta \approx 0.443 + 2\pi n$ or
$\theta \approx 2.699 + 2\pi n$

Additional Answers

Activity

Step 1:

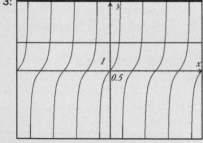

2 solutions

Step 3:

−5.66, −4.09, −2.52, −0.95, 0.62, 2.20, 3.77, 5.34; Because $y = \tan(2x)$ has a period of $\frac{\pi}{2}$, one could add or subtract $\frac{\pi}{2}$ from either of the original solutions to find the others.

The Simplest Trigonometric Equations

The simplest trigonometric equations are of the form $a \cdot f(x) = b$, where f is the sine, cosine, or tangent function.

Example 1

Consider the equation $\cos \theta = 0.6$. Round all solutions to the nearest thousandth.

a. Find all solutions between 0 and π.

b. Solve the equation when $0 \le \theta \le 2\pi$.

c. Describe the general solution.

Solution

a. By definition of the inverse cosine function, $\theta = \cos^{-1} 0.6$. In radians, $\theta \approx 0.927$.

b. On the same set of axes, graph $y = \cos \theta$ and $y = 0.6$ over the interval $0 \le \theta \le 2\pi$. Each point of intersection corresponds to a solution to the equation $\cos \theta = 0.6$.

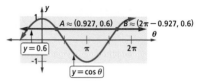

Point *A* represents the solution found in Part a. Point *B* shows another solution in the interval $0 \le \theta \le 2\pi$. The symmetry of the cosine graph shows this solution to be approximately $2\pi - 0.927$, or about 5.356. Thus, when $\cos \theta = 0.6$ and $0 \le \theta \le 2\pi$, $\theta \approx 0.927$ or $\theta \approx 5.356$.

c. The general solution follows from Part b and the Periodicity Theorem. Adding or subtracting multiples of 2π to the two solutions in Part b generates all solutions to $\cos \theta = 0.6$.

$\theta \approx 0.927 + 2\pi \qquad \theta \approx 5.356 + 2\pi$

$\theta \approx 0.927 + 4\pi \qquad \theta \approx 5.356 + 4\pi$

$\vdots \qquad\qquad\qquad \vdots$

$\theta \approx 0.927 - 2\pi \qquad \theta \approx 5.356 - 2\pi$

$\theta \approx 0.927 - 4\pi \qquad \theta \approx 5.356 - 4\pi$

$\vdots \qquad\qquad\qquad \vdots$

Thus, the general solution to $\cos \theta = 0.6$ is $\theta \approx 0.927 + 2\pi n$ or $\theta \approx 5.356 + 2\pi n$ for all integers n. These solutions represent all points of intersection of the line $y = 0.6$ and the graph of $y = \cos \theta$.

Check A CAS solution of $\cos x = 0.6$ is shown at the right. Note the CAS outputs the general solution using ± 0.9273.

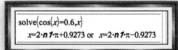

The process used in Example 1 can be employed to solve many trigonometric equations. That is, first find one solution using an inverse trigonometric function, and then use other properties of these functions, particularly the Periodicity Theorem, to find all the solutions.

Accommodating the Learner ⬆

Tell students you are thinking of a trigonometric equation of quadratic form, involving sine, which has solutions $-\frac{\pi}{6}$ and $\frac{\pi}{2}$. Lead them to come up with an equation with integer coefficients. **Answers vary. Sample:** First determine the sine of each solution: $-\frac{1}{2}$ and 1, and write: $\sin x = -\frac{1}{2}$ or $\sin x = 1$. Then write the solutions as factors in an equation: $(2 \sin x + 1)(\sin x - 1) = 0$. Expand the brackets and simplify to get: $2 \sin^2 x - \sin x - 1 = 0$.

Here is another suggestion you may wish to try: Write a trigonometric quadratic equation that involves cosine with solutions $\frac{\pi}{3}$ and π. **Answers vary. Sample:** $2 \cos^2 x + \cos x - 1 = 0$

GUIDED

Example 2

The output voltage E (in volts) of a circuit after t seconds ($t > 0$) is given by $E = 12 \sin(2\pi t)$. To the nearest 0.01 second, at which times in the first three seconds does $E = 9$?

Solution Substitute 9 for E in the given equation.

$$\underline{\quad?\quad} = 12 \sin(2\pi t) \quad \textbf{9}$$

Solve for $\sin(2\pi t)$.

$$\underline{\quad?\quad} = \sin(2\pi t) \quad \tfrac{3}{4}$$

Think of $2\pi t$ as a "chunk" representing θ and solve for $2\pi t$ to find a first quadrant solution.

$$2\pi t = \sin^{-1}\left(\tfrac{9}{12}\right) \approx 0.8481$$

So, a first solution is $\theta_1 \approx 0.8481$.

Another solution can be found using the Supplements Theorem, $\sin\theta = \sin(\pi - \theta)$. Thus,

$$\sin(2\pi t) = \sin(\pi - 2\pi t) \approx \sin(\pi - 0.8481) \approx \sin \underline{\quad?\quad}. \quad \textbf{2.2935}$$

So, $\sin \underline{\quad?\quad} \approx \tfrac{9}{12}$, from which a second solution is $\theta_2 \approx 2.2935$. **2.2935**

Because the period of the sine function is 2π, if multiples of 2π are added to or subtracted from 0.8481 and 2.2935, other solutions are generated. So the general solution is

$$2\pi t \approx 0.8481 + 2\pi n \text{ or } 2\pi t \approx 2.2935 + 2\pi n, \text{ for all integers } n.$$

Divide both sides by 2π to find that

$$t \approx 0.1350 + n \quad \text{or} \quad t \approx 0.3650 + n, \text{ for all integers } n.$$

Specifically, on the interval $0 \le t \le 3$,

$$t \approx 0.1350 + 0 \quad \text{or} \quad t \approx 0.3650 + 0$$
$$\approx 0.1350 + 1 \qquad\qquad \approx 0.3650 + 1$$
$$\approx 0.1350 + 2 \qquad\qquad \approx 0.3650 + 2$$

There are six solutions: 0.1350, $\underline{?}$, $\underline{?}$, $\underline{?}$, $\underline{?}$, $\underline{?}$. **1.1350; 2.1350; 0.3650; 1.3650; 2.3650**

Check 1 Substitute each of these six values of x in the original equation, and verify that $E \approx 9$ for each value. For instance, for the first two values,

$12 \sin(2\pi(0.1350)) \approx \underline{\quad?\quad}$ and $12 \sin(2\pi(0.3650)) \approx \underline{\quad?\quad}$. **9.00   9.00**

Check 2 Graph $y = 12 \sin(2\pi x)$ and $y = 9$. Use a window that includes the maximum and minimum values of this function, 12 and –12, respectively. Notice also that $E = 12 \sin(2\pi x)$ has period equal to $\tfrac{2\pi}{2\pi} = 1$. There are two solutions per period for a total of 6 solutions in the interval $0 \le x \le 3$.

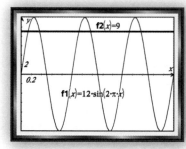

Accommodating the Learner ⬇

If students are having difficulty solving quadratic trigonometric equations, they may find it helpful to actually 'reverse engineer' an equation. For instance, begin with $\theta = \tfrac{\pi}{6}$. Ask students "What equation involving the cosine function has this solution for θ?" $\cos\theta = \dfrac{\sqrt{3}}{2}$

"What equation involving the sine function has this as a solution for θ?" $\sin\theta = \tfrac{1}{2}$; then make new equations from these. If $\cos\theta = \dfrac{\sqrt{3}}{2}$, then $\cos\theta + 1 = \underline{?} \quad \dfrac{\sqrt{3}+2}{2}$

A CAS can help students form these equations.

2   Teaching

Notes on the Lesson

Each of the examples takes up quite a bit of space. Since students often think the difficulty of a problem is measured by the amount of space devoted to it, they may think these questions are harder than they are.

Example 1 This is a basic abstract example. Note to students that most of the solution in this Example is explanatory prose and need not be written as part of a solution. Point out that, in general, the equations $\sin x = k$ and $\cos x = k$ can have at most 2 solutions between 0 and 2π because the line $y = k$ intersects the graphs of the sine and cosine functions in at most 2 points on this interval. Similarly, $\tan x = k$ has exactly one solution between $-\tfrac{\pi}{2}$ and $\tfrac{\pi}{2}$ because the graph of $y = k$ intersects the graph of the tangent function exactly once on this interval. Thus the key to finding all solutions is to find all the solutions in one cycle of the function involved and then add integer multiples of the period to describe all other solutions.

Example 2 Example 2 shows that multiple solutions can occur in real situations, just as the voltage in a circuit attains a particular value periodically. Other situations to which this idea applies are the length-of-daylight and Ferris wheel examples from Chapter 4.

Additional Example

Example 2 A merry-go-round with a 16-foot radius is designed to make a revolution every 40 seconds. Set up a coordinate system looking at the merry-go-round from above so that a point on the edge of the merry-go-round that is due east of its center at time $t = 0$ has coordinate (16, 0). The position of this point after t seconds is $\left(16 \cos\left(\tfrac{\pi t}{20}\right), 16 \sin\left(\tfrac{\pi t}{20}\right)\right)$. At what times in the first revolution is the point 10 feet east of the center of the merry-go-round?
Solve $16 \cos\left(\tfrac{\pi t}{20}\right) = 10$ to find $t \approx 5.70$ seconds or $t \approx 34.30$ seconds.

5-7

Example 3 Example 3 involves a quadratic equation in sin x, another instance of chunking (the process of thinking of a mathematical expression as a single entity) in mathematics. This equation is equivalent to the union of two linear equations in sin x, so the problem breaks down to two problems like those in Example 1. This problem could also be solved using the Quadratic Formula.

Additional Example

Example 3 Consider the equation $6 \cos^2\theta + \cos\theta = 2$.

a. Find all solutions in the interval $0 \le \theta \le 360°$.
$\theta = \cos^{-1}\left(\frac{1}{2}\right) = 60°$ or $300°$ or
$\theta = \cos^{-1}\left(-\frac{2}{3}\right) \approx 131.8°$ or $228.2°$

b. Find the general solution.
$\theta = 60° + 360°n$ or
$\theta = 300° + 360°n$ or
$\theta \approx 131.8° + 360°n$ or
$\theta \approx 228.2° + 360°n$, for all integers n.

Trigonometric Equations with Quadratic Form

In the quadratic equation $ax^2 + bx + c = 0$, where $a \ne 0$, if x is replaced by an unknown value of a trigonometric function, the resulting equation is a trigonometric equation with quadratic form.

Example 3

Consider $2\sin^2\theta = 1 - \sin\theta$.

a. Find all solutions in the interval $0 \le \theta \le 2\pi$.
b. Find the general solution.

Solution 1

a. Think of sin θ as a chunk. The equation has quadratic form, so rewrite the equation with one side equal to 0, and solve by factoring or by using the quadratic formula.

$$2\sin^2\theta = 1 - \sin\theta$$
$$2\sin^2\theta + \sin\theta - 1 = 0$$
$$(2\sin\theta - 1)(\sin\theta + 1) = 0$$

So $\quad 2\sin\theta - 1 = 0 \quad$ or $\sin\theta + 1 = 0$

$\sin\theta = \frac{1}{2} \quad$ or $\quad \sin\theta = -1$

One solution to each of these equations can be found using the inverse sine function.

$$\sin^{-1}\left(\frac{1}{2}\right) = \frac{\pi}{6} \quad \text{or} \quad \sin^{-1}(-1) = -\frac{\pi}{2}$$

So $\quad\quad\quad \theta = \frac{\pi}{6} \quad$ or $\quad\quad \theta = -\frac{\pi}{2}$.

By the Supplements Theorem, sin θ = sin $(\pi - \theta)$. Thus, $\pi - \frac{\pi}{6} = \frac{5\pi}{6}$ and $\pi - \left(-\frac{\pi}{2}\right) = \frac{3\pi}{2}$ also satisfy the given equation. Even though $-\frac{\pi}{2}$ is not in the target interval, $\frac{3\pi}{2}$ is. So the solutions to $2\sin^2\theta = 1 - \sin\theta$ for $0 \le \theta \le 2\pi$ are $\frac{\pi}{6}, \frac{5\pi}{6}$, and $\frac{3\pi}{2}$.

b. By the Periodicity Theorem, adding multiples of the period, 2π, does not change the value of the sine.

So the general solution is
$\theta = \frac{\pi}{6} + 2\pi n$, $\theta = \frac{5\pi}{6} + 2\pi n$, or $\theta = \frac{3\pi}{2} + 2\pi n$, for any integer n.

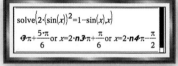

Solution 2 Use a CAS. One CAS gives the solutions $2n\pi + \frac{5\pi}{6}$ or $2n\pi + \frac{\pi}{6}$ or $2n\pi - \frac{\pi}{2}$. This looks like the Solution 1 answer except for $2n\pi - \frac{\pi}{2}$. But notice that you can add 2π to this solution without affecting its being a solution.

$2n\pi - \frac{\pi}{2} + 2\pi = 2n\pi + \frac{3\pi}{2}$, which is found in Solution 1.

Check Graph $y = (\sin x)^2$ and $y = 1 - \sin x$ on the same set of axes. Notice that there are three points of intersection on $0 \le x \le 2\pi$. The x-coordinates of these points are the solutions found in Part a.

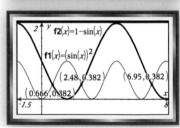

Extension

Refer students to Question 15. Suppose Mariah sits in a seat at this height but at different distances from the screen. The measure of her angle of vision is clearly quite small when she is close to the screen or far away from the screen. How is that measure related to her distance from the screen? When is the measure of the angle of vision the greatest?

Additional Answers

2. The paper solution is $\theta \approx 0.927 + 2\pi n$, or $\theta \approx 5.356 + 2\pi n$ for all integers n. The CAS solution is $x = 2\pi n + 0.927$ or $x = 2\pi n - 0.927$. Using the Opposites Theorem we can add 2π to $2\pi n - 0.927$ to get $2\pi n + 5.356$ for all integers n. These are the same answers.

Questions

COVERING THE IDEAS

1. Give the three commonly used domains for solutions to trigonometric equations.

2. The CAS solution to Example 1 does not look the same as the paper solution. Explain why it shows that the paper solution is correct.

3. Consider the equation $\cos \theta = 0.72$.
   a. Find all solutions between 0 and 2π. $\theta \approx 0.767$, or $\theta \approx 5.516$
   b. Draw a graph to illustrate the solutions in Part b.
   c. Give a general solution to the equation.

In 4 and 5, refer to Example 2.

4. Show that 2.1349 and 2.3650 are solutions to $12 \sin(2\pi t) = 9$.

5. a. How many solutions are there to the equation $12 \sin(2\pi t) = 9$ for $0 < t < 5$? **10**   **5b-c. See margin.**
   b. Use a graph to justify your answer to Part a.
   c. Give all solutions to $12 \sin(2\pi t) = 9$ for $3 < t < 5$.

6. Suppose the output voltage E (in volts) of a circuit after t seconds $(t > 0)$ is given by $E = 20 \cos(4\pi t)$. To the nearest 0.01 second, at which times in the first 2 seconds is E equal to 10? **See margin.**

In 7 and 8, find all values of θ on the interval $0 \le \theta < 2\pi$ that satisfy the equation. ≈ 3.343, or ≈ 6.082 $\dfrac{\pi}{3}, \dfrac{2\pi}{3}, \dfrac{4\pi}{3}, \dfrac{5\pi}{3}$

7. $5 \sin \theta + 1 = 0$ 8. $4 \cos^2 \theta - 1 = 0$

9. Solve $\cos \theta = 0.132$ to the nearest degree for the domain indicated.
   a. $\{\theta \mid 0° \le \theta < 90°\}$ **82°**
   b. $\{\theta \mid 0° \le \theta < 360°\}$ **82°, 278°**
   c. set of all real numbers

   **9c. 82° + 360n°
   or 278° + 360n°
   for all integers n**

10. Solve $2 \cos^2 x - 3 \cos x + 1 = 0$ for the indicated domain.
    a. $\{x \mid 0 \le x < 2\pi\}$ b. all real numbers

APPLYING THE MATHEMATICS

11. The number of hours y of daylight in Seattle x days after March 21 can be modeled by the equation
    $y = 12.25 + 3.75 \sin\left(\dfrac{2\pi x}{365}\right)$.
    a. Use the equation to find the first two times after March 21 that there will be 11.5 hours of daylight.
    b. Convert your answers in Part a to dates.

12. a. Give a general solution to $3 \cos \theta = 7$.
    b. Under what conditions will $a \cos \theta = b$ have solutions?

In 13 and 14, solve for $0 \le \theta \le 2\pi$.   **14. $\theta = \dfrac{2\pi}{3}, \dfrac{5\pi}{3}$**

13. $\tan \theta = 3$ $\theta \approx 1.25$ or 4.39 14. $\tan \theta - \sqrt{3} = 2 \tan \theta$

General Solutions to Trigonometric Equations   **329**

A battery tester is a voltage meter.

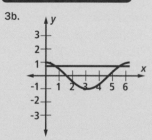

The Space Needle in Seattle is approximately 605 feet tall.

---

1. The restricted domains of the trigonometric functions used in obtaining their inverse functions; an interval equal in size to the period of the function under study; and the set of all real numbers on which the function is defined.

2, 3b–c, 4, 10, 11, 12. See margin.

---

3 Assignment

Recommended Assignment
- Questions 1–10
- •• Questions 11–23
- •• Question 24 (extra credit)
- Reading Lesson 5-8
- Covering the Ideas 5-8 (Questions 1–10)

Notes on the Questions

Question + 8 Some students may find it easier to substitute x for $\cos \theta$ and solve $4x^2 - 1 = 0$ first.

Question 10 With more frequency than Question 8, students may substitute a single letter for $\cos x$ when solving this problem.

Question 11 The conversion to dates will be more difficult for many students than the solving of the trigonometric equation.

Additional Answers

6. 0.08, 0.58, 1.08, 1.58, 0.42, 0.92, 1.42, and 1.92 seconds

10a. $x = 0, \dfrac{\pi}{3}$, or $\dfrac{5\pi}{3}$

10b. $x = 2\pi n, \dfrac{\pi}{3} + 2\pi n$, or $\dfrac{5\pi}{3} + 2\pi n$ for any integer n

11a. 194 days or 353 days

11b. October 1 or March 9

12a. no real solutions

12b. $a \ne 0$ and $-1 \le \dfrac{b}{a} \le 1$

Additional Answers

3b.
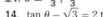

3c. $\theta \approx 0.767 + 2\pi n$, or $\theta \approx 5.516 + 2\pi n$, where n is any integer

4. $12 \sin(2\pi \cdot 2.1349) \approx 9$;
$12 \sin(2\pi \cdot 2.650) \approx 9$

5b.

5c. 3.1350, 4.1350, 3.3650, and 4.3650 seconds

5-7

Notes on the Questions

Question 17 Once Part a has been completed, Part b just involves substitution.

4 Wrap-Up

Ongoing Assessment

Refer to Example 1. Have students work in pairs to solve the example for $\cos \theta = -0.68$ and the other for $\sin \theta = 0.55$. Then have students exchange papers and use a graphing utility to check each other's work. **The general solution to $\cos \theta = -0.68$ is $\theta \approx 2.319 + 2\pi n$ or $\theta \approx 3.965 + 2\pi n$. The general solution to $\sin \theta = 0.55$ is $\theta \approx 0.582 + 2\pi n$ or $\theta \approx 2.56 + 2\pi n$.**

REVIEW

15. Mariah sits in the center seat of the first row of the Palace Movie Theater, as shown at the right. She is 8.5 feet away from the screen. When she is seated, her eyes are 3.1 feet above the floor. The bottom of the screen is 6.2 feet above the floor, and the top of the screen is 15.6 feet above the floor. Her angle of vision is formed by the bottom and top of the screen and her eyes. Find the measure of her angle of vision. (**Lesson 5-6**) $\approx 35.8°$

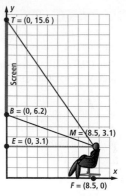

16. In $\triangle XYZ$, $x = 12$, $z = 10$, and $m\angle Z = 43°$. Find all possible values for $m\angle X$, $m\angle Y$, and XZ. (**Lesson 5-5**)

17. A portion of a roller-coaster track is to be sinusoidal as illustrated below. The high and low points of the track are separated by 60 meters horizontally and 35 meters vertically. The low point is 5 meters below ground level.

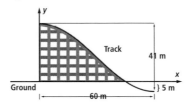

a. Write an equation for the height y in meters of a point on the track at a distance x meters from the high point.

b. The vertical timbers are to be placed every 5 meters horizontally from the foot of the high point. How long should the timbers be? (**Lesson 4-10**)

In 18–23, tell whether the function described by the equation is odd, even, or neither. (**Lessons 4-5, 3-4**)

18. $y = |x|$ **even**   19. $y = \sqrt{x}$ **neither**   20. $y = x^{10}$ **even**

21. $y = 10x$ **odd**   22. $y = \cos x$ **even**   23. $y = \tan x$ **odd**

EXPLORATION

24. a. How many solutions are there to the given equation on the interval $0 \le \theta < 2\pi$?

   i. $\cos \theta = 0.5$ ii. $\cos(2\theta) = 0.5$

   iii. $\cos(3\theta) = 0.5$ iv. $\cos(4\theta) = 0.5$

   b. Generalize your results in Part a.

   c. How many solutions are there to the equation $\sin(n\theta) = a$, where $|a| < 1$, and n is a positive integer, on the interval $0 \le \theta < 2\pi$?

---

16. $m\angle X \approx 54.9°$, $m\angle Y \approx 82.1°$, $XZ \approx 14.52$; $m\angle X \approx 125.1°$, $m\angle Y \approx 11.9°$, $XZ \approx 3.02$

17a. $y = 17.5 \cos\left(\frac{\pi x}{60}\right) + 12.5$

17b. 30, 29.40, 27.66, 24.87, 21.25, 17.03, 12.50, 7.97, 3.75, and 0.13 meters

24a.i.   2 solutions

ii.   4 solutions

iii.   6 solutions

iv.   8 solutions

24b. If n is a nonnegative integer and $k < 1$, $\cos(n\theta) = k$ has $2n$ solutions on $0 \le \theta < 2\pi$.

24c. $2n$

Lesson 5-8 — Parametric Equations for Circles and Ellipses

Vocabulary

parameter

parametric equations

equation for the unit circle in standard form

> **BIG IDEA** Parametric equations use separate functions to define coordinates x and y and to produce graphs.

A circle cannot be the graph of a function with equation $y = f(x)$ because there exist many pairs of points with the same first coordinate. However, you can write each coordinate as a function of a third variable. We call the variable t. A variable that determines other variables is called a **parameter**. When the coordinates of points on a curve (or line) are each expressed with an equation written in terms of a parameter, the equations are called **parametric equations**.

Activity 1 See margin.

Set your graphing utility to degree mode.

Step 1 Find out how you can enter parametric equations into your technology.

Enter $x_t = \cos t$ and $y_t = \sin t$.

Step 2 Choose a suitable window and graph the two equations. Describe what happens.

Step 3 If possible, animate the graph and run your animation from 0° to 1080° or from 0 to 6π.

The equations in Activity 1 are parametric equations for the unit circle. This is because any point P on the unit circle can be considered as the image of (1, 0) under a rotation of magnitude θ, and by definition, $R_\theta(1, 0) = (\cos \theta, \sin \theta)$. In this case, θ is the parameter.

Recall the Pythagorean Identity $\cos^2 \theta + \sin^2 \theta = 1$. Substituting x for $\cos \theta$ and y for $\sin \theta$, we get $x^2 + y^2 = 1$, the **equation for the unit circle in standard form**.

Activity 2 See margin.

Set your graphing utility to degree mode and choose parametric for graph type.

Step 1 Graph the equations $\begin{cases} x = 2 \cos t \\ y = 2 \sin t \end{cases}$ and $\begin{cases} x = 3 \cos t \\ y = 3 \sin t \end{cases}$, both for $0° \le t \le 360°$. What is the effect of the 2 or the 3 on the graph?

(continued on next page)

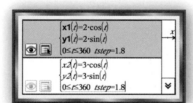

Vocabulary (right column, Mental Math)

a. negative
b. negative
c. negative
d. zero

Mental Math

Tell whether the number is positive, zero, or negative.

a. $\sin 1000°$

b. $-|-\sin 1000°|$

c. $\cos 73° - \sin 73°$

d. $\sqrt{10}\sin(10\pi)$

GOAL

Obtain parametric equations for any circle and for some ellipses.

SPUR Objectives

M Graph parametric equations of circles and ellipses.

Materials/Resources

· Lesson Master 5-8
· Resource Masters 116–118
· Graphing utility

HOMEWORK   • Option 1
• Option 2

- Questions 1–10
- • Questions 11–21
- • Question 22 (extra credit)
  • Reading Lesson 5-9
  • Covering the Ideas 5-9 (Questions 1–12)

Local Standards

1 Warm-Up

In 1–4, graph the point (x, y) when $x = \cos t$ and $y = \sin t$, for the given value of t.

1. $t = 30°$ $\left(\dfrac{\sqrt{3}}{2}, \dfrac{1}{2}\right)$

2. $t = 70° \approx (0.342, 0.940)$

3. $t = 100° \approx (-0.174, 0.985)$

4. $t = 200° \approx (-0.940, -0.342)$

Note that all points are on the unit circle.

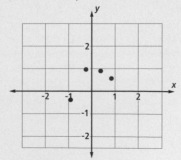

Additional Answers

See page 333 for Activity 1 and Activity 2 answers.

Background

The logic of the lesson is that we know that $\begin{cases} x = \cos \theta \\ y = \sin \theta \end{cases}$ identifies a point (x, y) on the unit circle. This point is the image of (1, 0) under a rotation of magnitude θ. Now we look at θ as a parameter, and because we are so doing we replace θ by t, only since t is a common letter for a parameter. Since the points determined by running through the values of t from 0° to 180° constitute a circle with center (0, 0) and radius 1, we say that $\begin{cases} x = \cos t \\ y = \sin t \end{cases}$ are parametric equations for this circle.

Activity 2 A size change with center (0, 0) and magnitude r multiplies coordinates by r. This size change maps the unit circle with center (0, 0) onto the circle with this center and radius r. Consequently, parametric equations for the circle with center (0, 0) and radius r are $\begin{cases} x = r \cos t \\ y = r \sin t \end{cases}$.

(continued on next page)

2 Teaching

Notes on the Lesson

It is important throughout this lesson that students have technology that can graph parametric equations so they can check the ideas as they occur.

Example 1 More generally, the ellipse with horizontal axis of length $2a$ and vertical axis of length $2b$ intersecting at $(0, 0)$ has parametric equations $\begin{cases} x = a \cos t \\ y = b \sin t \end{cases}$. Quite simple! An equation in rectangular coordinates for this ellipse is $\frac{x^2}{a^2} + \frac{y^2}{b^2} = 1$. See the notes above for an even more general equation.

Additional Examples

Example 1

a. Graph $\begin{cases} x = 4 \cos t \\ y = 0.5 \sin t \end{cases}$, $0 \le t \le 180°$.

$x = 4 \cos t$
$y = 0.5 \sin t$

b. Write an equation in rectangular coordinates for the curve in Part a.

$y = \sqrt{\dfrac{16 - x^2}{64}} = \dfrac{1}{8}\sqrt{16 - x^2}$

Example 2 Write parametric equations for the circle with center $(2, 9)$ and radius 9.

$\begin{cases} x = 2 + 9 \cos t \\ y = 9 + 9 \sin t \end{cases}$

Step 2 Generalize your observations in Step 1 to describe the graph of $\begin{cases} x = r \cos t \\ y = r \sin t \end{cases}$ for $0° \le t \le 360°$.

Activity 2 suggests that the image of the unit circle under the size change with center $(0, 0)$ and magnitude r is given by the parametric equations $\begin{cases} x = r \cos t \\ y = r \sin t \end{cases}$. This result can be proved using the Pythagorean Identity.

> ### Theorem (Parametric Equation for a Circle)
>
> The circle with center $(0, 0)$ and radius r has parametric equations $\begin{cases} x = r \cos t \\ y = r \sin t \end{cases}$, $0° \le t \le 360°$ or $0 \le t \le 2\pi$.

Proof Rewrite the parametric equations as $\begin{cases} \frac{x}{r} = \cos t \\ \frac{y}{r} = \sin t \end{cases}$.

We know $\cos^2 t + \sin^2 t = 1$, because of the Pythagorean Identity.

Substitute $\frac{x}{r}$ for $\cos t$ and $\frac{y}{r}$ for $\sin t$. $\left(\frac{x}{r}\right)^2 + \left(\frac{y}{r}\right)^2 = 1$

Use the Power of a Quotient Property. $\left(\frac{x^2}{r^2}\right) + \left(\frac{y^2}{r^2}\right) = 1$

Multiply both sides of the equation by r^2. $x^2 + y^2 = r^2$

This is an equation for the circle centered at the origin with radius r.

Notice that multiplying $\cos t$ and $\sin t$ by r makes them r times as large; however, this transformation is equivalent to replacing x with $\frac{x}{r}$ and y with $\frac{y}{r}$. This substitution is exactly what the Graph Scale-Change Theorem states: the unit circle $x^2 + y^2 = 1$ is transformed by a size change of magnitude r.

STOP QY1

Scale Changes and Parametric Equations

By multiplying x- and y-coordinates by constants, you produce a scale-change image. When the constants are not equal, the image of the unit circle under such a transformation is not a circle, but an ellipse.

> **GUIDED**
>
> **Example 1**   See margin.
> a. Graph the ellipse $\begin{cases} x = 2 \cos t \\ y = 5 \sin t \end{cases}$, $0° \le t \le 360°$.
> b. Write an equation in rectangular coordinates for the ellipse.
>
> **Solution**
> a. Make a table of values for $0° \le t \le 90°$. Also include $t = 180°$ and $t = 270°$ in the table. Some values have been filled in for you. Plot the points on a rectangular grid. Use symmetries over the axes to complete a sketch of the ellipse.

t	$x = 2\cos t$	$y = 5\sin t$
0°	2.00	0
30°	?	2.50
60°	?	?
90°	0	?
180°	?	?
270°	?	–5.00

> **▶ QY1**
> a. $x^2 + y^2 = 64$ is the image of the unit circle under a size change of what magnitude?
> b. Write parametric equations for this circle.

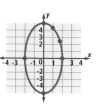

Activity 3 A translation adds a constant to x and a constant to y. So, if we want to translate the center of the circle to (h, k), we only have to add these numbers to the coordinates of each point. Thus $\begin{cases} x = \cos t + h \\ y = \sin t + k \end{cases}$ is a set of parametric equations for the circle with center (h, k) and radius 1, and $\begin{cases} x = r \cos t + h \\ y = r \sin t + k \end{cases}$ is a set of parametric equations for the circle with center (h, k) and radius r.

A side venture into scale changes in Example 1 shows how ellipses can be described using parametric equations like these. In general, $\begin{cases} x = a \cos t + h \\ y = b \sin t + k \end{cases}$ are the equations of an ellipse with center (h, k) and horizontal axis of length a and vertical axis of length b. Students familiar with the rectangular form of an equation for this ellipse, $\frac{(x - h)^2}{a^2} + \frac{(y - k)^2}{b^2} = 1$, will appreciate how much simpler the parametric form is.

b. $\cos^2 t + \sin^2 t = 1$ Pythagorean Identity

$\underline{\ ?\ } + \underline{\ ?\ } = 1$ Substitute $\frac{x}{2}$ for $\cos t$ and $\underline{\ ?\ }$ for $\sin t$.

$\underline{\ ?\ } + \underline{\ ?\ } = 1$ Apply the Power of a Quotient Property.

$\left(\frac{x}{2}\right)^2 + \left(\frac{y}{5}\right)^2; \dfrac{y}{5}; \dfrac{x^2}{4}; \dfrac{y^2}{25}$

Activity 3

Step 1 Graph the ellipse $\begin{cases} x = 2\cos t \\ y = 5\sin t \end{cases}$, $0° \le t \le 360°$, from Example 1.

Step 2 On the same grid, graph $\begin{cases} x = 2\cos t + 4 \\ y = 5\sin t - 3 \end{cases}$, for $0° \le t \le 360°$.

Describe the differences between the two graphs.

The ellipse of Step 1 of Activity 3 can be mapped onto the ellipse of Step 2 by the translation $(x, y) \to (x + 4, y - 3)$. This result suggests the following theorem.

Step 1

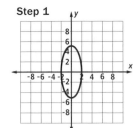

Step 2: The center of the ellipse shifts to the right 4 units and down 3 units

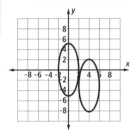

> ### Theorem (Parametric Equation for a Circle with Center (h, k))
>
> The circle with center (h, k) and radius r has parametric equations
> $\begin{cases} x = h + r\cos t \\ y = k + r\sin t \end{cases}$, $0° \le t \le 360°$ or $0 \le t \le 2\pi$.

Proof From the parametric equations,

$$\begin{cases} x - h = r\cos t \\ y - k = r\sin t \end{cases}.$$

Thus, $(x - h)^2 + (y - k)^2 = r^2\cos^2 t + r^2\sin^2 t$

$$= r^2(\cos^2 t + \sin^2 t)$$
$$= r^2 \cdot 1$$
$$= r^2.$$

GUIDED

Example 2

Write parametric equations for the circle with center $(-4, 5)$ and radius 2.

Solution The circle with radius 2 and center $(-4, 5)$ is the image of the graph of $\begin{cases} x = \cos t \\ y = \sin t \end{cases}$ first under $S: (x, y) \to (2x, 2y)$ and then the translation $T: (x, y) \to (x - 4, y + 5)$.

Under S, the equations for the image of the circle are $\begin{cases} x = \underline{\ ?\ } \\ y = \underline{\ ?\ } \end{cases}$.

To move the center to $(-4, 5)$, add $\underline{\ ?\ }$ to the x-coordinates and $\underline{\ ?\ }$ to the y-coordinates. Therefore, parametric equations for this circle are $\begin{cases} x = \underline{\ ?\ } + 2\cos t \\ y = 5 + \underline{\ ?\ } \end{cases}$.

Check Graph the parametric equations using a graphing utility.

2 cos t; 2 sin t; –4; 5; –4; 2 sin t

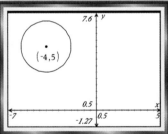

Parametric Equations for Circles and Ellipses   **333**

Additional Answers

Activity 1

Step 2: The equations graph a circle.

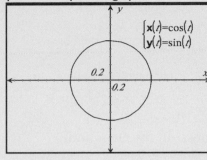

Step 3:

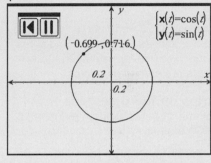

Activity 2

Step 1: The 2 or the 3 determines the radius of each circle.

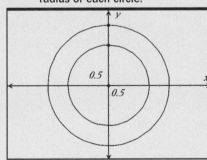

Step 2:

A graph with equation $\begin{cases} x = r\cos t \\ y = r\sin t \end{cases}$ for $0° \le t \le 360°$ will show a circle with radius r, centered about $(0, 0)$.

Additional Answers

Example 1

a.

t	$x = 2\cos t$	$y = 5\sin t$
0°	2.00	0
30°	1.73	2.50
60°	1.00	4.33
90°	0	5.00
180°	–2.00	0
270°	0	–5.00

3) Assignment

Recommended Assignment

- Questions 1–10
- • Questions 11–21
- • Question 22 (extra credit)
- • Reading Lesson 5-9
- • Covering the Ideas 5-9
  (Questions 1–12)

Notes on the Questions

Questions 5, 8 and 9 You might wish to shorten the intervals to obtain arcs on the circle.

Question 12 S and T do not commute, but the images under the composites of the two transformations in the two orders are congruent circles.

Notes on the Questions

Question 14 The desired mapping is the inverse of S.

Question 15 Since the arguments of the sine and cosine are alike, the only thing that changes is the speed with which the circles are graphed if one thinks of t as increasing or decreasing at a constant rate. This can be seen by graphing the parametric equations in trace mode.

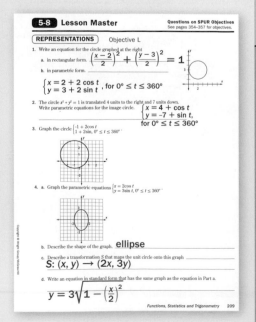

STOP QY2

Questions

COVERING THE IDEAS

In 1 and 2, write parametric equations for the circle described.

1. center (3, –2) and radius 25
2. $(x - 8)^2 + (y + 4)^2 = 9$

   1. $\begin{cases} x = 25\cos t + 3 \\ y = 25\sin t - 2 \end{cases}$ 2. $\begin{cases} x = 3\cos t + 8 \\ y = 3\sin t - 4 \end{cases}$

3. Write an equation for the ellipse $\begin{cases} x = 4\cos t \\ y = \sin t \end{cases}$ in rectangular form.

4. Write equations of the circle graphed at the right in standard rectangular and parametric form.

5. Write an equation of the circle $\begin{cases} x = 3 + 5\cos t \\ y = -2 + 5\sin t \end{cases}$, $0 \le t \le 2\pi$ in standard rectangular form. $(x - 3)^2 + (y + 2)^2 = 25$

6. Write parametric equations for the lower half of the circle with center (–4, 3) and radius 6.

7. Write parametric equations for the circles at the right.

8. a. Graph $\begin{cases} x = \cos t \\ y = \sin t \end{cases}$, $360° \le t \le 720°$. **a,b. See margin.**

   b. Compare this with the graph of $\begin{cases} x = \cos t \\ y = \sin t \end{cases}$, $0° \le t \le 360°$.

9. As t increases from 0° to 360°, what happens to the corresponding point on the graph of $\begin{cases} x = 8\cos t \\ y = 7\sin t \end{cases}$?

10. The unit circle is translated 6 units to the left and 3 units up.

    a. Write an equation in rectangular form for the transformed circle. $(x + 6)^2 + (y - 3)^2 = 1$

    b. Write parametric equations for the original circle and its image.

APPLYING THE MATHEMATICS

11. A circle with center at (8, –3) has a radius of 0.5. This circle is the image of the unit circle under what transformation?

12. Let $S(x, y) = (4x, 4y)$ and $T(x, y) = (x - 2, y + 5)$. Find equations for the image of the graph of $\begin{cases} x = \cos t \\ y = \sin t \end{cases}$ under

    a. $S \circ T$. b. $T \circ S$.

13. a. Graph the parametric equations $\begin{cases} x = 5\cos t \\ y = 3\sin t \end{cases}$.

    b. Describe the shape of the graph.

    c. What transformation has been applied to the unit circle in the horizontal direction? In the vertical direction?

    d. Describe how the graph differs from the graph of $\begin{cases} x = 5\cos t \\ y = 5\sin t \end{cases}$.

    e. Write an equation in standard form that has the same graph as the equation in Part d. **13a–e. See margin.**

    11. A size change and translation of $(x, y) \rightarrow \left(\frac{x}{2} + 8, \frac{y}{2} - 3\right)$

    12a. $\begin{cases} x = 4\cos t - 8 \\ y = 4\sin t + 20 \end{cases}$ 12b. $\begin{cases} x = 4\cos t - 2 \\ y = 4\sin t + 5 \end{cases}$

QY2

What is an equation in standard form for the circle of Example 2?

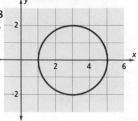

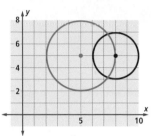

3. $\left(\frac{x}{4}\right)^2 + y^2 = 1$

4. $(x - 3)^2 + y^2 = 4$;
   $\begin{cases} x = 2\cos t + 3; \\ y = 2\sin t \end{cases}$

6. $\begin{cases} x = 6\cos t - 4 \\ y = 6\sin t + 3 \end{cases}$,
   $\pi \le t \le 2\pi$

7. $\begin{cases} x = 3\cos t + 5 \\ y = 3\sin t + 5 \end{cases}$,
   $\begin{cases} x = 2\cos t + 8 \\ y = 2\sin t + 5 \end{cases}$

9. The point moves counterclockwise on an ellipse centered at (0, 0).

10b. $\begin{cases} x = \cos t \\ y = \sin t \end{cases}$,
   $\begin{cases} x = \cos t - 6 \\ y = \sin t + 3 \end{cases}$

Extension

Ask students to use their graphing utility to investigate and describe the graph of $\begin{cases} x = t + 1 \\ y = 4t - t^2 \end{cases}$. **The graph is a parabola with vertex (3, 4) and x-intercepts 1 and 5.**

Then have them use algebra to justify their result. **The familiar form of the quadratic equation $y = -x^2 + 6x - 5$, can be obtained by solving for t in the first equation and substituting into the second equation.**

Additional Answers

8a.

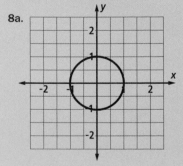

8b. **The graphs are identical.**

14. The unit circle is transformed with the mapping $S: (x, y) \rightarrow (9x, 9y)$. Find a mapping that will transform the image back to the unit circle.

15. Consider the sets of parametric equations below. Compare and contrast the curves they trace out, and how those curves are traced. (Many graphing utilities have an animation mode that shows a point moving along a parametric curve.) **See margin.**

 a. $\begin{cases} x = \cos t \\ y = \sin t \end{cases}$
 b. $\begin{cases} x = \sin t \\ y = \cos t \end{cases}$
 c. $\begin{cases} x = \cos(2t) \\ y = \sin(2t) \end{cases}$

REVIEW

16. Consider $8 \cos^2\theta = 3 - 2 \cos \theta$. **(Lesson 5-7)**
 a. Find all solutions in the interval $0 \le \theta \le 2\pi$.
 b. Find the general solution.

17. How many solutions are there to the equation $6 \sin(3\pi t) = 2$ when $0 < t < 8$? **(Lesson 5-7)**

18. A hill slopes upward at an angle of 6° with the horizontal. A tree grows vertically on the hill. When the angle of elevation of the Sun is 24°, the tree casts a shadow 41 m long. If the shadow is entirely on the hill, how tall is the tree? **(Lesson 5-5)**

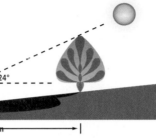
24°
6°
41 m

19. Consider the function with equation $y = -3 \cos\left(\frac{x - \pi}{6}\right) + 7$. Give the amplitude, period, vertical shift, and phase shift of the function. **(Lesson 4-9)**

20. For the function with equation $y = \tan\left(x + \frac{\pi}{4}\right)$, determine the **(Lesson 4-8)**
 a. domain.
 b. range.
 c. period.

21. Given $f(x) = |x|$ and $g(x) = 1 - x^2$, let $h(x) = f(g(x))$. **(Lesson 3-8)**
 a. Write an expression for $h(x)$.
 b. State the domain and range of h.

EXPLORATION

22. Use parametric equations to construct the picture at the right. **See margin.**

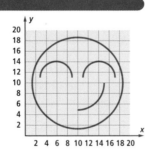

14. $(x, y) \rightarrow \left(\frac{x}{9}, \frac{y}{9}\right)$

16a. $\theta = \frac{\pi}{3}, \frac{5\pi}{3}$, 2.419, 3.864

16b. $\theta = \frac{\pi}{3} + 2n\pi, \frac{5\pi}{3} + 2n\pi$, 2.419 + 2n\pi, 3.864 + 2n\pi$ for integer n values

17. 24

18. about 13.9 ft

19. Amplitude: 3, period: 12π, vertical shift: 7 units up, phase shift: π units to the right

20a. $\{x| x \ne \frac{\pi}{4} + \pi n$, for any integer $n\}$

20b. all real numbers

20c. π

21a. $h(x) = |1 - x^2|$

21b. domain: all real numbers, range: $\{y| y \ge 0\}$

QY ANSWERS

1. a. 8
 b. $\begin{cases} x = 8 \cos t \\ y = 8 \sin t \end{cases}$
2. $(x + 4)^2 + (y - 5)^2 = 4$

Parametric Equations for Circles and Ellipses **335**

Additional Answers

13.a.
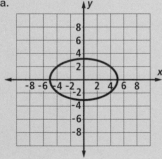

13b. The graph is an ellipse that has a semi-major axis of 5 and a semi-minor axis of 3.

13c. Horizontal scale change of $S(x, y) \rightarrow (5x, y)$; vertical scale change of $S(x, y) \rightarrow (x, 3y)$

13d. The y-intercepts of the graph are closer to the origin than the graph of the circle with radius 5.

13e. $\left(\frac{x}{5}\right)^2 + \left(\frac{y}{5}\right)^2 = 1$

Lesson 5-9

GOAL

Introduce the reciprocal trigonometric functions: secant (reciprocal of cosine), cosecant (reciprocal of sine), and cotangent (reciprocal of tangent).

SPUR Objectives

E Find secants, cosecants, and cotangents.

Materials/Resources

· Lesson Master 5-9
· Resource Masters 119–121
· Graph paper

HOMEWORK

• Option 1
• Option 2

- Questions 1–12
- • Questions 13–26
- • Question 27 (extra credit)
  • Reading Lesson 5-10
  • Covering the Ideas 5-10
  (Questions 1–10)

Local Standards

1) Warm-Up

In right triangle ABC, angle C is the right angle, $AC = 10$ and $AB = 11$. Estimate each to the nearest thousandth.

1. $\sin A$ 0.417
2. $\cos A$ 0.909
3. $\tan A$ 0.458
4. $\frac{1}{\sin A}$ 2.400
5. $\frac{1}{\cos A}$ 1.100 (exactly)
6. $\frac{1}{\tan A}$ 2.182
7. Explain why the answer to Warm-Up 6 is the answer to Warm-Up 4 divided by the answer to Warm-Up 5.

$$\frac{\frac{1}{\sin A}}{\frac{1}{\cos A}} = \frac{\cos A}{\sin A} = \frac{1}{\frac{\sin A}{\cos A}} = \frac{1}{\tan A}$$

(Warm-Ups 4, 5, and 6 ask for csc A, sec A, and cot A, respectively.)

Lesson 5-9

The Secant, Cosecant, and Cotangent Functions

Vocabulary

secant, sec
cosecant, csc
cotangent, cot
reciprocal trigonometric functions

▶ **BIG IDEA** Reciprocals of the sine, cosine, and tangent functions have special names.

Activity 1

Step 1 Six ratios can be created using two of the sides of $\triangle ABC$. Fill in the blanks with three of the ratios.

$\sin A = \underline{?} \ \frac{a}{c}$ $\qquad \cos A = \underline{?} \ \frac{b}{c}$

$\tan A = \underline{?} \ \frac{a}{b}$

Step 2 There are three other ratios that can be created from the sides of the triangle. Each one of these ratios is the reciprocal of a ratio in Step 1.

reciprocal of $\sin A = \frac{1}{\sin A} = \underline{?} \ \frac{c}{a}$

reciprocal of $\cos A = \frac{1}{\cos A} = \underline{?} \ \frac{c}{b}$

reciprocal of $\tan A = \frac{1}{\tan A} = \underline{?} \ \frac{b}{a}$

Step 3 Pick three values of a, b, and c that can be sides of a right triangle. Evaluate the three reciprocals for these values to 4 decimal places.

Step 4 Square the numbers in Step 3. Do you notice anything unusual? Compare your result with others in your class.

Naming the Reciprocal Functions

The reciprocals of the sine, cosine, and tangent functions have special names.

Definition of Secant, Cosecant, and Cotangent

Let x be any real number. Then
the **secant** of $x = \sec x = \frac{1}{\cos x}$, whenever $\cos x \neq 0$;
the **cosecant** of $x = \csc x = \frac{1}{\sin x}$, whenever $\sin x \neq 0$;
the **cotangent** of $x = \cot x = \frac{1}{\tan x} = \frac{\cos x}{\sin x}$, whenever $\sin x \neq 0$.

For example, $\cos 60° = \frac{1}{2}$, so $\sec 60° = \frac{1}{\cos 60°} = \frac{1}{\frac{1}{2}} = 2$.

 QY1

Mental Math

Give the reciprocal of each number as a fraction, decimal, or integer.

a. $-\frac{37}{99}$ $\qquad$ **b.** 0.02
c. -1 $\qquad$ **d.** 0.6

a. $-\frac{99}{37}$
b. 50
c. -1
d. $\frac{5}{3}$

Step 3: Answers vary.
Sample: $a = 3$, $b = 4$, $c = 5$
1.6667; 1.2500; 1.3333;

Step 4: Answers vary.
Sample:

$\left(\frac{1}{\sin A}\right)^2 =$
2.7777; $\left(\frac{1}{\cos A}\right)^2 =$
1.5625; $\left(\frac{1}{\tan A}\right)^2 =$
1.7777; $\left(\frac{1}{\sin A}\right)^2$
$- \left(\frac{1}{\tan A}\right)^2 = 1$

▶ **QY1**

What is the value of csc 60°?

Background

There are six ratios of different sides possible using the three sides of a right triangle. Three of these are the sine, cosine, and tangent that students have been studying before this lesson, and the other three are introduced here. They are not, however, the only trigonometric functions that have ever been studied. Among other trigonometric functions are the *versine* and *haversine*, defined as follows:

$\text{versin}(x) = 1 - \cos x = 2\sin^2\left(\frac{x}{2}\right)$, and
$\text{haversin}(x) = 0.5 \cdot \text{versin}(x) = \sin^2\left(\frac{x}{2}\right)$.

The haversine was extensively used in navigation because it appears in some formulas in spherical trigonometry. Even long before today's calculators and computers, these and other trigonometric functions based on them had gone out of fashion.

Originally, the secant and cosecant functions were employed for much the same reason as rationalizing the denominator of a radical expression—to avoid division by a decimal.

Because each of the secant, cosecant, and cotangent functions can be expressed as the reciprocal of a parent trigonometric function, these functions are sometimes called **reciprocal trigonometric functions**. Notice that since the denominator in each of the definitions can be 0, there are real numbers for which each of these functions is not defined. For instance, $\cot x = \frac{1}{\tan x}$ is not defined when $\tan x = 0$; that is, when $x = k\pi$ for any integer k.

Example 1

Find $\sec\left(\frac{7\pi}{6}\right)$ exactly.

Solution By definition of secant,

$$\sec\left(\frac{7\pi}{6}\right) = \frac{1}{\cos\left(\frac{7\pi}{6}\right)} = \frac{1}{-\frac{\sqrt{3}}{2}} = \frac{-2}{\sqrt{3}} = \frac{-2\sqrt{3}}{3}.$$

Check Use a CAS to compute $\sec\left(\frac{7\pi}{6}\right)$ or $\frac{1}{\cos\left(\frac{7\pi}{6}\right)}$.

Caution: The reciprocal of a function and the inverse of a function are different functions. For example, the reciprocal of the cosine function (the secant function) and the inverse of the cosine function ($\cos^{-1} x$) are quite different functions.

Activity 2 See margin.

MATERIALS graph paper

Step 1 Copy and complete the table below.

	0	$\frac{\pi}{6}$	$\frac{\pi}{4}$	$\frac{\pi}{3}$	$\frac{\pi}{2}$	$\frac{2\pi}{3}$	$\frac{3\pi}{4}$	$\frac{5\pi}{6}$	π	$\frac{4\pi}{3}$	$\frac{3\pi}{2}$	$\frac{5\pi}{3}$
$\sin x$	?	?	?	?	1	?	?	?	0	?	?	?
$\csc x$	?	?	?	?	?	?	?	?	undefined	?	?	?

Step 2 On graph paper, draw a horizontal axis marked in radians from $-\pi$ to 3π. Mark the vertical axis from -4 to 4.

Step 3 Graph $y = \sin x$ for $0 \le x \le 2\pi$. Use coordinates from your table. Connect the points with a smooth curve.

Step 4 Draw dotted vertical lines where $\csc x$ is undefined.

Step 5 Plot the values of the cosecant function for $0 \le x \le 2\pi$.

Step 6 Within each pair of asymptotes, connect the points with a smooth curve. You should see "U" and upside-down "U" shapes.

Step 7 Extend the graph of $y = \sin x$ to $-\pi \le x \le 3\pi$.

Step 8 Complete the graph of $y = \csc x$, $-\pi \le x \le 3\pi$. Draw asymptotes first.

STOP QY2

> **QY2**
>
> What is the range of the cosecant function?

The Secant, Cosecant, and Cotangent Functions **337**

For instance, if a ladder forms an angle of 75° with the ground and is to reach 19 feet high on a wall, then it must have length of at least $\frac{19}{\sin 75°}$ feet, but division by $\sin 75°$ is more difficult than multiplication by $\csc 75°$. Today, however, the secant and cosecant functions are seldom used for finding lengths or angle measures. They still appear in some formulas in calculus (for example, if $y = \tan x$, then $\frac{dy}{dx} = \sec^2 x$) but they have lost much of their importance.

For this reason, we restrict the study of these functions to the parents and do not devote much attention to their offspring.

The cotangent function appears a little more often in formulas than the secant or cosecant because it is the cofunction of the tangent. That is, $\tan x = \cot\left(\frac{\pi}{2} - x\right)$.

2 Teaching

Notes on the Lesson

The reciprocal functions are presented here in the same manner as the functions sine, cosine, and tangent were presented in Chapter 4 and earlier in this chapter. They are used in right-triangle situations and analyzed as functions. Students should be expected to be able to give domain, range, maximum and minimum points, and graphs of the parent reciprocal functions.

Naming the reciprocal functions The terms *secant* and *tangent* both arose from the application found in Question 27. "Cosecant" is short for "complement's secant." "Cotangent" is short for "complement's tangent."

Activity 2 The graph of the secant function can be discussed here. Its graph is a translation image and therefore congruent to the graph of the cosecant function found on page 338. The graph of the cotangent function, a reflection image of the graph of the tangent function, is found on page 339. Do not expect students to be able to make accurate graphs by hand even of these parent functions, and graphing offspring curves by hand is too time-consuming. Make use of a graphing utility. However, students should be able to draw quick sketches of these functions by hand to indicate that they understand their basic characteristics as listed in the chart on page 338.

Most of the graphing utilities we have used require entering the functions as reciprocals of sine, cosine, and tangent. Some, however, give the reciprocals as options in a menu of functions.

Caution students not to mistake the inverse functions of sine, cosine, and tangent on their calculators for the reciprocal functions. It is natural for a student to get confused and think $\sin^{-1} x$ means $\csc x$. The confusion is so likely that one rarely sees the notation $(\sin x)^{-1}$, which *is* the reciprocal of $\sin x$.

Additional Example

Example 1 Find the exact value of $\csc 135°$. $-\sqrt{2}$

Additional Answers

See page 338 for Activity 2 answers.

Additional Answers

Activity 2

Step 1:

x	$\sin x$	$\csc x$
0	0	undefined
$\dfrac{\pi}{6}$	$\dfrac{1}{2}$	2
$\dfrac{\pi}{4}$	$\dfrac{\sqrt{2}}{2}$	$\sqrt{2}$
$\dfrac{\pi}{3}$	$\dfrac{\sqrt{3}}{2}$	$\dfrac{2\sqrt{3}}{3}$
$\dfrac{\pi}{2}$	1	1
$\dfrac{2\pi}{3}$	$\dfrac{\sqrt{3}}{2}$	$\dfrac{2\sqrt{3}}{3}$
$\dfrac{3\pi}{4}$	$\dfrac{\sqrt{2}}{2}$	$\sqrt{2}$
$\dfrac{5\pi}{6}$	$\dfrac{1}{2}$	2
π	0	undefined
$\dfrac{4\pi}{3}$	$-\dfrac{\sqrt{3}}{2}$	$-\dfrac{2\sqrt{3}}{3}$
$\dfrac{3\pi}{2}$	-1	-1
$\dfrac{5\pi}{3}$	$-\dfrac{\sqrt{3}}{2}$	$-\dfrac{2\sqrt{3}}{3}$

Steps 2–4:

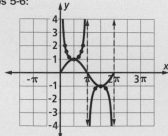

Steps 5–6:

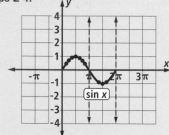

Steps 7–8:

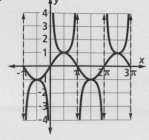

Graphs of the Reciprocal Functions

You made a graph of the cosecant function in Activity 2 by connecting points. Because the expressions $\csc x$ and $\sin x$ are reciprocals, you could also use the properties of the sine function to determine characteristics of the cosecant function.

Function Properties	Graph Characteristics
When $\sin x$ is positive, $\csc x$ is positive. When $\sin x$ is negative, $\csc x$ is negative.	For a given value of x, the graphs of $y = \sin x$ and $y = \csc x$ are on the same side of the x-axis.
When $\sin x = 0$, $\csc$ is undefined.	If $\sin k = 0$, then there is a vertical asymptote of $y = \csc x$ at $x = k$.
Because $|\sin x| \leq 1$ for all x, $|\csc x| \geq 1$ for all x. The smaller $|\sin x|$ is, the larger $|\csc x|$ is.	The closer the graph of $y = \sin x$ is to the x-axis, the farther the graph of $y = \csc x$ is.
$\csc x = \sin x$ when $\sin x = \pm 1$.	The graphs intersect when $\sin x = \pm 1$.

These properties are exhibited in the graphs below. The graph of $y = \sin x$ is in blue; the graph of $y = \csc x$ is in red.

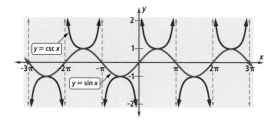

Example 2

Consider the function with equation $y = \csc x$.

a. Identify its domain and range.

b. Find its period.

c. Identify any minimum or maximum values.

Solution

a. The domain consists of all real numbers except $x = n\pi$, for any integer n. From both the definition and the graph above, you can see that the range is $\{y \mid y \leq -1 \text{ or } y \geq 1\}$.

b. The period of $y = \sin x$ is 2π. Consequently, the graph of $y = \csc x$ also has period 2π.

c. There are no maximum or minimum values of $\csc x$. However, 1 can be a relative minimum and -1 can be a relative maximum of the cosecant function.

Accommodating the Learner ↑

You may wish to have students work in groups to answer the following question.

Rewrite the following expressions in terms of the trigonometric or inverse trigonometric functions only, then use your answer to find the value.

a. $\csc^{-1} 1.5$ $\sin^{-1}\left(\dfrac{1}{1.5}\right) \approx 0.730$

b. $\cot^{-1}\left(\dfrac{1}{7}\right)$ $\tan^{-1} 7 \approx 1.429$

c. $\sec^{-1} 2.1$ $\cos^{-1}\left(\dfrac{1}{2.1}\right) \approx 1.074$

Extension

Demonstrate for students how the trigonometric identity $1 + \tan^2 x = \sec^2 x$ can be obtained by dividing both sides of the Pythagorean identity by $\cos^2 x$. Ask them to find a third trigonometric identity in a similar way and test all three identities using the values found from a right triangle with sides 3, 4, 5. **Students should find the identity $\cot^2 x + 1 = \csc^2 x$ by dividing both sides of the original Pythagorean identity by $\sin^2 x$. Answers vary. For instance, if $AB = 3$, $AC = 4$, and $BC = 5$, then $\tan B = \dfrac{4}{3}$ and $\sec B = \dfrac{5}{3}$, so $\tan^2 B = 1 + \dfrac{16}{9} = \dfrac{25}{9} = \sec^2 B$.**

Because the graph of the cosine function is a translation image of the graph of the sine function, the graph of the secant function is a translation image of the graph of the cosecant function.

The graph of $y = \cot x$ is shown below in red. It is a reflection image of the graph of $y = \tan x$ over any vertical line with equation $x = \frac{\pi}{4} + n\pi$, where n is an integer. The graph of $y = \tan x$ is drawn in blue.

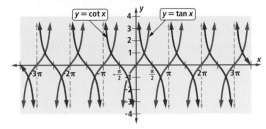

Questions

COVERING THE IDEAS

Fill in the Blank In 1 and 2, use sin, cos, tan, cot, sec, or csc.

1. $\frac{1}{\tan 36°} = \underline{\ ?\ } 36°$ **cot**

2. $\csc\left(\frac{\pi}{3}\right) = \frac{1}{\underline{\ ?\ }\left(\frac{\pi}{3}\right)}$ **sin**

3. a. Graph $y = \cos x$ for $-2\pi \leq x \leq 2\pi$.
   b. On the same axes, graph $y = \sec x$. Use dashed lines to identify asymptotes. **See margin.**

In 4–9, evaluate without technology.

4. $\csc\left(\frac{\pi}{2}\right)$ **1**

5. $\sec 210°$ $-\frac{2\sqrt{3}}{3}$

6. $\cot(-180°)$ **undefined**

7. $\sec\left(-\frac{7\pi}{6}\right)$ $-\frac{2\sqrt{3}}{3}$

8. $\cot\left(\frac{25\pi}{4}\right)$ **1**

9. $\csc\left(\frac{\pi}{4}\right)$ $\sqrt{2}$

10. Describe the asymptotes of the cotangent function in radians.

11. Give the domain, range, period, and asymptotes of $y = \csc x$.

12. Consider the triangle at the right. In terms of x, y, and z, find
    a. $\sec \theta$. $\frac{z}{x}$
    b. $\cot \theta$. $\frac{x}{y}$
    c. $\csc \theta$. $\frac{z}{y}$

APPLYING THE MATHEMATICS

13. Tell whether the equation describes an odd function.
    a. $y = \sin x$ **odd**
    b. $y = \cos x$ **not odd**
    c. $y = \cot x$ **odd**
    d. $y = \csc x$ **odd**

14. Explain why the graph of the secant function has no points between the horizontal lines with equations $y = 1$ and $y = -1$.

15. If $\sin x = 0.70$, compute.
    a. $\csc x$ $\frac{10}{7}$
    b. $\csc(-x)$ $-\frac{10}{7}$
    c. $\csc(\pi - x)$ $\frac{10}{7}$
    d. $\cos x$ $\frac{\sqrt{51}}{10}$
    e. $\sec x$ $\frac{10\sqrt{51}}{51}$
    f. $\cot x$ $\frac{\sqrt{51}}{7}$

10. multiples of π, or $x = \pi n$ for any integer n.

11. domain: all real numbers x such that $x \neq n\pi$, where n is an integer; range: all real numbers y such that $y \geq 1$ or $y \leq -1$; period: 2π; asymptotes: any vertical line with equation $x = n\pi$ where n is an integer.

14. Since the graph of the cosine function is always in the range $-1 \leq y \leq 1$, the graph of the secant function, the reciprocal of the cosine function, is always in the range $y \leq -1$ or $y \geq 1$.

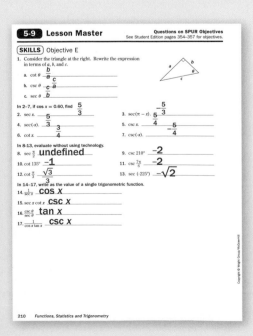

Additional Example
Example 2 Consider the function with equation $y = \cot x$.

a. Identify its domain and range. domain: $\{x : x \neq k\pi,$ for all integers $k\}$; range: the set of all real numbers

b. Give its period. π

c. Identify any minimum or maximum values. **no minimum or maximum values**

3 Assignment

Recommended Assignment
- Questions 1–12
- • Questions 13–26
- • Question 27 (extra credit)
- Reading Lesson 5-10
- Covering the Ideas 5-10 (Questions 1–10)

Notes on the Questions
Questions 11 and 13 An important generalization students can make from this lesson is that some properties of a function transfer to its reciprocal function. These properties include its period (if it is periodic) and its evenness or oddness.

Additional Answers

3a.
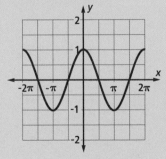

3b.
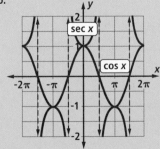

4 **Wrap-Up**

Ongoing Assessment
Have students work in pairs. Give
students three problems like Example
1, one involving secant, one involving
cosecant, and one involving cotangent.
Ask one partner to solve the problem
exactly, and the other partner to solve
the problem approximately, using a
calculator. Then have students switch
roles and give them three more
problems. **Students evaluate secant,
cosecant, and cotangent functions.**

Additional Answers

16. $\left(-\frac{9\pi}{4}, \frac{2}{\sqrt{2}}\right)\left(-\frac{7\pi}{4}, \frac{2}{\sqrt{2}}\right)\left(\frac{\pi}{4}, \frac{2}{\sqrt{2}}\right)\left(\frac{7\pi}{4}, \frac{2}{\sqrt{2}}\right)$
$\left(\frac{9\pi}{4}, \frac{2}{\sqrt{2}}\right)$

17. No. The square of secant or cosecant
each must be greater than 1 because
the absolute value of secant and
cosecant are each greater than 1. Two
numbers greater than one added will
sum to a number greater than one.

19. By the Supplements Theorem,
$\tan(\pi - x) = -\tan x$ for all x. Therefore,
$\cot(\pi - x) = \frac{1}{\tan(\pi - x)} = -\frac{1}{\tan x} = -\cot x$
for all x in the domain of the
cotangent function.

20a. In a right triangle, the tangent of a
non-right angle is the measure of the
opposite side divided by the measure
of the adjacent side. The cotangent of
a non-right angle is the measure of the
adjacent side divided by the measure of
the opposite side. Therefore, $\tan A = \frac{a}{b}$
and $\cot B = \frac{a}{b}$, thus $\tan A = \cot B$.

16. The line with equation $y = \frac{2}{\sqrt{2}}$ intersects the graph
    of $y = \sec x$ as shown at the right. One point of
    intersection is $\left(-\frac{\pi}{4}, \frac{2}{\sqrt{2}}\right)$. Find the coordinates
    of the five other points of intersection shown here.
17. The Pythagorean Identity, $\cos^2x + \sin^2x = 1$, holds
    for all values of x. Is it true that for all x,
    $\sec^2x + \csc^2x = 1$? Justify your answer.
18. Give the asymptotes of the graph of $y = \csc\left(x + \frac{\pi}{3}\right)$.
19. Explain why $\cot(\pi - x) = -\cot x$ for all values of x
    for which $\cot x$ is defined.
20. a. Explain why, in right triangle ABC with right
       angle C, $\tan A = \cot B$.
    b. What property of the graph of the tangent
       function does this explain?
21. Simplify the product $(\sin x)(\cos x)(\tan x)(\csc x)(\sec x)(\cot x)$.

REVIEW

22. Consider the circle whose parametric equations are
    $\begin{cases} x = -4 + 4\cos t \\ y = 2 + 4\sin t \end{cases}$, $0 \le t \le 360°$. (**Lesson 5-8**)
    a. Find the circle's center and radius.
    b. Write an equation for the circle in rectangular coordinates.
23. Consider the circle whose equation is $x^2 + (y + 6)^2 = 17$. Find
    parametric equations for this circle. (**Lesson 5-8**)
24. The figure at the right shows a waterwheel rotating at 4 revolutions
    per minute. The distance d of point P from the surface of the water
    as a function of time t in seconds can be modeled by a sine wave
    with equation of the form $\frac{d - k}{b} = \sin\left(\frac{t - h}{a}\right)$. (**Lessons 4-10, 4-7**)
    a. What are the amplitude and period of the distance function?
    b. After point P emerges from the water, you start a stopwatch
       when $d = 7$. Write an equation for the distance function.
    c. Approximately when does P first reach its highest point?
25. **Fill in the Blank** Under a scale change with horizontal factor 3 and
    vertical factor $\frac{1}{5}$, the image of (x, y) is ___?___. (**Lesson 3-5**)
26. The graph of $y = (x + 5)^4 + 7$ is the image of the graph of
    $y = (x - 7)^4 + 2$ under what translation? (**Lesson 3-2**)

EXPLORATION

27. In the drawing of the first quadrant of the unit circle at the right,
    $\overline{OB}$ has been extended to intersect the horizontal line $y = 1$ at G.
    Tell which segment lengths represent each of the trigonometric
    functions of θ. For example, $AB = \sin \theta$.
    $AB = \sin \theta$; $AO = \cos \theta$; $DE = \tan \theta$; $FG = \cot \theta$; $OE = \sec \theta$;
    $OG = \csc \theta$

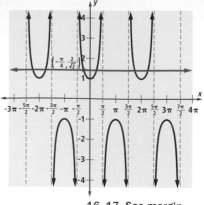

16, 17. See margin.

18. $x = -\frac{\pi}{3} + n\pi$,
    where n is an
    integer.

19, 20. See margin.

21. 1, where $x \ne \frac{\pi n}{2}$
    for any integer n

22–26. See margin.

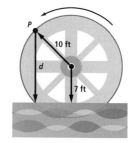

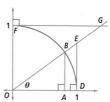

QY ANSWERS

1. $\frac{2}{\sqrt{3}}$ or $\frac{2\sqrt{3}}{3}$

2. $\{y| \, |y| \ge 1\}$

Additional Answers

20b. $\tan(x) = \cot\left(\frac{\pi}{2} - x\right)$

22a. center: $(-4, 2)$; radius: 4

22b. $(x + 4)^2 + (y - 2)^2 = 16$

23. $\begin{cases} x = \sqrt{17}\cos t \\ y = -6 + \sqrt{17}\sin t \end{cases}$

24a. amplitude: 10 ft; period: 15 seconds

24b. $\frac{d - 7}{10} = \sin\left(\frac{t - 1.8511}{\frac{15}{2\pi}}\right)$

24c. about 5.6 seconds

25. $\left(3x, \frac{y}{5}\right)$

26. $T: (x, y) \to (x - 12, y + 5)$

Lesson 5-10
From New York to New Delhi

Vocabulary

great circle

meridian

longitude

latitude

▶ **BIG IDEA** The Spherical Law of Cosines can be used to find the distance between any two points on a sphere.

In this lesson we review some geography and define "shortest distances" on a sphere. Then we use these ideas to find the shortest distance between two cities having the same longitude or latitude. Finally, we calculate the shortest distance between New York and New Delhi to illustrate how you can use trigonometry to find the shortest distance between any two cities on Earth.

Mental Math

A measure in degrees and minutes is given. Convert to degrees in decimal form.

a. 23°30' **23.5°**

b. 48°20' ≈ **48.3°**

c. 92°15' **92.25°**

d. 54°45' **54.75°**

Activity

MATERIALS Internet access

Step 1 Below is a Mollweide equal-area projection of Earth with New York and New Delhi's positions marked. Find the route that appears shortest to you. Identify a landmark along your route so you can use it later in this Activity.

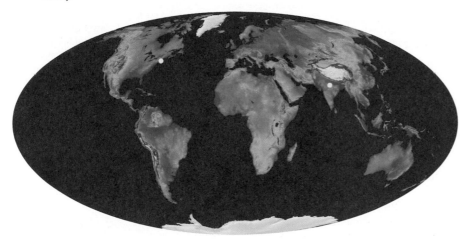

Answers vary. Sample: Cairo, Egypt

(continued on next page)

Background

A spherical triangle is a triangle whose sides are arcs of great circles on a sphere. This means that the sides and the angles can be measured in degrees or radians. Historically, the trigonometry of spherical triangles came very early due to its applications in astronomy; some people feel that it predated the trigonometry of plane triangles. In astronomy it is common to use degrees in dealing with spherical triangles, so we exclusively use degrees here.

In our dealings with spherical triangles, we continue the practice of using upper case letters to name vertices and the corresponding lower case letters to indicate the opposite sides. This convention is particularly useful in dealing with these triangles because the Spherical Law of Cosines involves cosines of two sides and an angle.

(continued on next page)

Lesson 5-10

GOAL

State the spherical Law of Cosines and apply it to the problem of finding the shortest route between two points on the surface of Earth.

SPUR Objectives

K Find the shortest distance between two points on Earth given their longitude and latitude.

Materials/Resources

· Lesson Master 5-10
· Resource Masters 122–125
· Internet access

HOMEWORK   • **Option 1**
• Questions 1–10   • **Option 2**
• • Questions 11–23
• • Question 24 (extra credit)
• • Self-Test

Local Standards

1 Warm-Up

In 1–5, give the latitude of each location.

1. a point on the equator **0°**
2. the North Pole **90°N**
3. the South Pole **90°S**
4. a place halfway between the equator and the North Pole **45°N**
5. a place one-third of the way from the equator to the South Pole **30°S**

Notes on the Lesson

This lesson is challenging, not simply because spherical trigonometry is new to students, but because the reading requires many references to complicated drawings. Students need to know some elementary concepts of geography before they can use the Spherical Law of Cosines to find the shortest distances between any two points on Earth.

We suggest that when discussing this lesson in class you have a globe available and a piece of string that you can place on the globe to show great circle routes. (If the string is fixed at two points and not allowed to be slack, and nothing is in its way, it will trace the approximate great circle route.) Once the string is taut, have students note a couple of landmarks directly on its path. Next, have them look at a wall map of the world between the same two places. Have them again note landmarks on the path. Comparing the lists of landmarks is a comparable activity if software is unavailable.

You will also need an atlas or computer in the classroom so you can look up the latitude and longitude of various cities. A road atlas is a nice source of data for comparing shortest distances to distances via roads in the United States and Canada; an almanac may give air distances between major cities in the world.

Step 2 Open a dynamic geography utility. Zoom and rotate the image until you can see New York City marked on the globe. Put a placemark on New York City so you can find it easily later.

Step 3 Find New Delhi and put a placemark there.

Step 4 Because New York City and New Delhi are so far apart, it is hard to see both on the same view of the globe. Zoom around and spin the globe to locate your landmark from Step 1. Put a placemark there and name it "Flyover."

Step 5 Use the measurement tool to find the length of the path that goes from New York to your "Flyover" location. Measure the distance from "Flyover" to New Delhi. Add the results to find the total length of your path from New York to New Delhi.

New York City

New York   New Delhi

Step 6 When rotating Earth along your path, you probably noticed that the path doesn't look as straight as it did on the Mollweide projection. Because Earth is a sphere, any flat map will distort shapes on Earth's surface. Adjust your "Flyover" point to make your entire path as straight as possible. How has the total distance changed?

Circles on a Sphere

The Activity shows that the shortest distance between two points on Earth does not always appear as a straight line on a map. If you fly from New York City to New Delhi, you might be surprised to see snowbound fjords from your window. Even though New Delhi is *south* of New York City, the shortest flight path passes over Greenland and Finland. This occurs because, on a sphere, the shortest distance between two points is the arc of a *great circle*.

Steps 2–4: Check students' work. A map should show a placemarker on New York City, New Delhi, and a selected landmark, such as Cairo, Egypt.

Step 5: Answers vary. Sample: New York to Cairo: 5,612.14 mi; Cairo to New Delhi: 2,758.14 mi. Therefore, 5,612.14 + 2,758.14 mi = 8,370.28 mi from New York to New Delhi.

Step 6: Answers vary. Sample: The new flyover is near Ufa, Russia, much farther north than Cairo. The total distance has decreased. The flight distance is now 7,314.03 mi.

The Spherical Law of Cosines is neither a generalization nor an extension of the Law of Cosines in the plane. This makes it unlike the formulas for distance between two points in 3-space, the midpoint of the segment connecting two points in 3-space, or the extensions that have been made from 2-dimensional to 3-dimensional vectors in this chapter. The Spherical Law of Cosines receives its name because, like the Law of Cosines in the plane, it obtains the third side of a triangle in terms of two sides and the included angle of the triangle. (There is an SAS Congruence Theorem for spherical triangles.)

On the other hand, there is a Spherical Law of Sines , and this theorem is an extraordinary generalization of the Law of Sines. In any spherical triangle ABC,

$$\frac{\sin a}{\sin A} = \frac{\sin b}{\sin B} = \frac{\sin c}{\sin C}.$$

This must be one of the most wonderful theorems in all of mathematics.

On a sphere, any intersection with a plane forms a circle. A **great circle** is created when that plane passes through the center of the sphere. This circle has the same center as the sphere. Thus, a great circle has the same radius and circumference as the sphere.

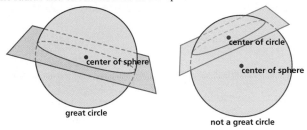

On Earth, which is approximately a sphere of radius 3960 miles, the equator is a great circle. There are infinitely many other great circles containing the north pole N and the south pole S. Each semicircle with endpoints N and S is called a "line" of longitude, or **meridian**. The meridian through Greenwich, England, is called the *Greenwich meridian* or *prime meridian*. **Longitudes** are measured using angles east or west of Greenwich, so all longitudes are between $0°$ and $180°$. In the figure at the right, the longitude of P is ϕ (the Greek letter phi). Because ϕ is east of Greenwich, ϕ measures longitude east. The meridian that is $180°$W (and $180°$E) is called the *International Date Line*.

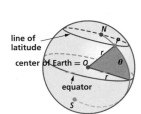

Latitudes measure the extent to which a point is north or south of the equator. They are determined by an angle whose vertex is at the center of Earth and whose sides pass through the endpoints of an arc on a line of longitude. So all latitudes are between $0°$ and $90°$. In the figure at the right, the latitude of P is θ. Because P is north of the equator, θ measures latitude north. Thus the location of P is described as $\phi°$E, $\theta°$N. Notice that each "line" of latitude is a circle, but, except for the equator, lines of latitude are *not* great circles.

Distances between Points with the Same Longitude

The position of any point on Earth can be determined by its longitude and latitude. In the figure at the right, Y represents New York City. Its location is about $74°00'$W, $40°43'$N. This means that New York is on a line of longitude $74°$ west of the Greenwich meridian and on a line of latitude $40°43'$, or $40.72°$ north of the equator. (The symbol $'$ stands for "minutes of arc"; one minute of arc is $\frac{1}{60}$ of a degree.) Since these coordinates identify a specific point on Earth, and cities cover a large area, the locations are approximate.

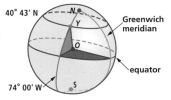

Notes on the Lesson

Activity Some students have a weak understanding of geography. Years spent looking at flat maps of a spherical world have reinforced the incorrect notion that the shortest distance between cities with the same latitude lies along that same line of latitude. The Mollweide projection corrects a major problem in the more popular Mercator projection. The Mercator Projection expands land areas as they are farther from the equator. This has led to a notion that Africa is smaller in area than North America and that North America is about twice the area of South America. Actually, Africa (area 11,720,000 mi^2) is almost 25% larger than North America (area 9,467,000 mi^2), and South America (6,880,000 mi^2) is about 75% the area of North America. Europe, which looks larger than South America on a Mercator Projection, is actually only about 60% the area of South America. The Mollweide projection shown here exhibits the entire surface of Earth and shows that Africa is larger than either North America or South America.

In Step 5, point out that the path pictured is *not* the shortest path, but a path that students might start thinking was the shortest path.

A proof of the Spherical Law of Cosines requires that students learn some theorems about spherical right triangles. These are outside the scope of this course. Our reason for this lesson is to show the power of the trigonometry of the plane in an accessible 3-dimensional situation.

Notes on the Lesson

Example 1 This Example shows students how to calculate the distance between two places on Earth that are on the same great circle of *longitude*. It does not apply to the distance between two points on the same circle of latitude, because (except for the equator) that circle is not a great circle, whereas lines of longitude are on great circles. For that, the method of Example 2 is needed.

Additional Example

Example 1 Find the distance between Labrador City, Canada, located at about 53°N and 67°W, and Caracas, Venezuela, located at about 10.5°N and 67°W. **about 2937 miles**

Because lines of longitude are arcs of great circles and all great circles on Earth are roughly congruent, the distance between two points on the same line of longitude can be found easily.

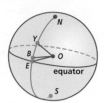

Example 1

Find the distance between New York City and Bogotá, Colombia, located at about 74°W and 4°37'N (labeled *B* in the figure at the right).

Solution Because *Y* and *B* have the same longitude, the shortest distance between them is the length of $\widehat{YB}$ on the line of longitude that is 74°W. Let *E* be the point where the equator intersects this line of longitude.

$$m\angle YOB = m\angle YOE - m\angle BOE$$
$$= 40\tfrac{43}{60}° - 4\tfrac{37}{60}°$$
$$= 36\tfrac{6}{60}° = 36.1°$$

So, the distance between New York City and Bogotá, Colombia is $\frac{36.1°}{360°}$ of the circumference of a great circle, or $\frac{36.1°}{360°} \cdot 2 \cdot \pi \cdot 3960$ mi $\approx$ 2495 mi.

Distances Between Points at the Same Latitude

Consider Tehran, Iran (35°41'N, 51°25'E), and Tokyo, Japan (35°41'N, 139°46'E). Many people think that the shortest distance between Tehran and Tokyo is along the 35°41'N line of latitude, but this is not the case, because lines of latitude are not great circles.

Let us first find the distance between Tehran (*A*) and Tokyo (*B*) along the 35°41'N line of latitude. Let *R* be the point on the Greenwich meridian at latitude 35°41'. If *Q* is the center of the circle that is this line of latitude, $\quad m\widehat{AB} = m\angle AQB$

So, $\qquad m\widehat{AB} = m\angle RQB - m\angle RQA$
$$= 139°46' - 51°25' = 88°21'$$

The distance between Tehran and Tokyo going due east is thus $\frac{88°21'}{360°}$ of the circumference of the circle of latitude they are on.

Refer to the figure at the right. To find the circumference of circle *Q*, we need the radius of circle *Q*. One radius of this circle is $\overline{RQ}$. Because $\overline{RQ} \parallel \overline{EO}$, $m\angle QRO = 35°41'$. Also,

$$\frac{RQ}{RO} = \cos(m\angle QRO).$$

Hence, $\qquad RQ = RO \cdot \cos(m\angle QRO).$

But *RO* is the radius of Earth, about 3960 miles. Therefore,

$$RQ \approx 3960 \cdot \cos 35°41' \approx 3217 \text{ mi.}$$

So the distance from Tehran to Tokyo along the line of latitude is about

$$\frac{88°21'}{360°} \cdot 2\pi \cdot 3217 \text{ mi} \approx 4961 \text{ mi.}$$

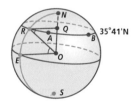

Accommodating the Learner ⬆

Have students answer the following.

1. If you started in your hometown and traveled due west, how far would you travel before you are back home again? **Answers vary. Find the latitude of your town. Then find the radius and then the circumference of the circle at a given latitude.**

2. List and describe some of the places you would go through on your journey. **Answers vary. Check students' work.**

To find the *shortest* distance between cities that have different longitudes, we need to use *spherical triangles,* that is, triangles whose sides are arcs of great circles measured in degrees, and a *Spherical Law of Cosines*, which is presented here without proof.

Theorem (Spherical Law of Cosines)

If *ABC* is a spherical triangle with arcs *a*, *b*, and *c*, then cos *c* = cos *a* cos *b* + sin *a* sin *b* cos *C*.

You can use the Spherical Law of Cosines to find the great circle distance between Tehran and Tokyo. The key is to let Tehran and Tokyo be two vertices of the spherical triangle and to let one of the poles be the third vertex. In Example 2, the North Pole is used.

Example 2

Find the length of *n*, the great circle arc from Tehran to Tokyo.

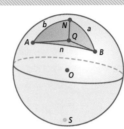

Solution Let *A* = Tehran, *B* = Tokyo, and *N* = the North Pole. In spherical △*ABN*, by the Spherical Law of Cosines,

cos *n* = cos *a* cos *b* + sin *a* sin *b* cos N.

m∠N is 88°21', the same as m∠AQB that was found before in calculating the distance from Tehran to Tokyo along the line of latitude.

Arc measures *a* and *b* are easy to find.

$$b = 90° - \text{latitude of Tehran}$$
$$= 90° - 35°41' = 54°19'$$

Because Tehran and Tokyo have the same latitude, *a* = 54°19' also. Now substitute into the Spherical Law of Cosines.

cos *n* = cos 54°19' cos 54°19' + sin 54°19' sin 54°19' cos 88°21'

$$\approx 0.3592$$

$$n = \cos^{-1}(0.3592) \approx 68.9°$$

So, the length of the great circle arc from Tehran to Tokyo is about $\frac{68.9°}{360°} \cdot 2\pi \cdot 3960$ mi ≈ 4762 mi.

Notice that this is about 200 mi shorter than the path along the line of latitude.

Tehran, Iran

Distance between Any Two Points on a Sphere

The most general and most common problem of this type is to find the shortest distance between two cities not on the same latitude or longitude, such as New York and New Delhi.

From New York to New Delhi **345**

Notes on the Lesson

Example 2 Notice what students must be able to do to find the distance between any two points on Earth: (1) From the latitudes, obtain the degree measures of two sides of the spherical triangle determined by each location and the North Pole. These sides are along meridians. (2) From the longitudes, obtain the degree measure of the angle between these meridians. (3) Since (1) and (2) give two sides and an included angle, the Spherical Law of Cosines can be applied to obtain the degree measure of the third side of the triangle, which is the shortest arc between the two original points. (4) Translate that degree measure into distance by determining what part of the circumference of a great circle it is.

In using the formula for the Spherical Law of Cosines, students will need to substitute *n* for *c*.

Additional Example

Example 2 Find the shortest distance from Delhi, India (29°N, 77.5°E) to Sidi Ifni, Morocco (29°N, 10°W).

≈ **5144 miles**

5-10

Additional Example

Example 3 Find the shortest distance between York, England (54°N, 1°W) and New York (41°N, 74°W). ≈ 3363 miles

Example 3

Find the length of n, the great circle arc from New York to New Delhi. New Delhi is located at 72°12'E, 28°38'N.

Solution Let A = New York, B = New Delhi, and N = the North Pole. In spherical $\triangle ABN$, by the Spherical Law of Cosines:

$$\cos n = \cos a \cos b + \sin a \sin b \cos N.$$

Here n is $m\widehat{AB}$, $a = m\widehat{BN}$, and $b = m\widehat{AN}$. To find $m\angle N$, extend the meridians through New York and New Delhi to points C and D on the equator. Let point E be the intersection of the prime meridian and the equator. Then

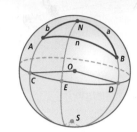

New Delhi, India

$$
\begin{aligned}
m\angle N &= m\angle COD \\
&= m\angle COE + m\angle EOD \\
&= 74°00' + 77°12' \\
&= 151°12'.
\end{aligned}
$$

Arc measures b and a are again easy to find.

$$
\begin{aligned}
b &= 90° - \text{latitude of New York} \\
&= 90° - 40°43' \\
&= 49°17'
\end{aligned}
$$

and

$$
\begin{aligned}
a &= 90° - \text{latitude of New Delhi} \\
&= 90° - 28°38' \\
&= 61°22'.
\end{aligned}
$$

Now substitute into the Spherical Law of Cosines.

$$
\begin{aligned}
\cos n &= \cos 61°22' \cos 49°17' + \sin 61°22' \sin 49°17' \cos 151°12' \\
\cos n &\approx -0.2704 \\
n &= \cos^{-1}(-0.2704) \approx 105.7°
\end{aligned}
$$

So, the length of the great circle path from New York to New Delhi is about $\frac{105.7°}{360°} \cdot 2\pi \cdot 3960 \text{ mi} \approx 7305 \text{ mi}$.

Problems involving distances in navigation and astronomy have been important for millennia and led to the development of trigonometry. Spherical trigonometry, in fact, began in ancient Greece before plane trigonometry. Euclid knew some of its fundamentals, and by the time of Menelaus (about 100 A.D.), Greek trigonometry reached its peak. Nasir-Eddin (1201–1274), an Arabian mathematician, systematized both plane and spherical trigonometry, but his work was unknown in Europe until the middle of the fifteenth century. Johannes Muller (1436–1476), also known as Regiomontanus, first enunciated the Spherical Law of Cosines given in this lesson.

Questions

COVERING THE IDEAS

In 1 and 2, tell whether the figure is *always*, *sometimes but not always*, or *never* a great circle.

1. line of longitude **always**   2. line of latitude

In 3 and 4, state the common name of the meridian.

3. 0°W   4. 180°E

5. What is the name of the great circle that is 0°N latitude?

6. Find the distance from Capetown, South Africa (18°31'E, 33°58'S) to the South Pole. **about 3873 mi**

7. Find the distance between Paris, France (2°20'E, 48°52'N) and Barcelona, Spain (2°11'E, 41°23'N). Assume that the cities are on the same meridian. **about 517 mi**

8. **True or False** An arc of a line of latitude (other than the equator) can be the side of a spherical triangle. **false**

9. In step 1 of the Activity, an apparently straight path from New York to New Delhi would take the plane over west Africa; one such path is about 8600 miles long. Using the actual distance between New York and New Delhi, estimate how much time you would save by travelling the shortest route in an airplane flying at 550 mph.

10. Find the great circle distance between Paris, Texas (95°33'W, 33°39'N), and Paris, France (2°20'E, 48°52'N).

APPLYING THE MATHEMATICS

In 11 and 12, consider Chicago, Illinois (88°W, 42°N), Providence, Rhode Island (71°W, 42°N), and Rome, Italy (12°W, 42°N).

11. a. Find the distance from Chicago to Providence along the line of latitude. **a. about 873.2 mi   b. about 871.7 mi**
    b. Find the great circle distance from Chicago to Providence.
    c. How much longer is the line of latitude distance? **about 1.5 mi**

12. a. Find the distance from Chicago to Rome along the line of latitude. **a. about 3903.6 mi   b. about 3,763.7 mi**
    b. Find the great circle distance from Chicago to Rome.
    c. How much longer is the line of latitude distance?
    d. To the nearest percent, how much longer is the line of latitude distance? **c. about 139.9 mi   d. 3.7% longer**

13. Find the great circle distance between Prague, Czech Republic (14°26'E, 50°5'N), and Rio de Janeiro, Brazil (43°12'W, 22°57'S).

14. What is the largest possible great circle distance between two points on Earth? **about 12440.7 mi**

---

2. sometimes but not always

Casa Mila, designed by Gaudi, in Barcelona

3. Greenwich meridian or prime meridian

4. International Date Line

"Paris" is the name of 15 municipalities in the U.S. Only Paris, TX, has a replica of the Eiffel Tower with a cowboy hat.

5. equator

9. about 2 hours and 21 minutes

10. about 4837 mi

13. about 6152 mi

5-10

3 Assignment

Recommended Assignment
- Questions 1–10
- • Questions 11–23
- • Question 24 (extra credit)
- • Self-Test

Notes on the Questions

Questions 10–13 If students remark about the complexity of the calculations in these questions, you might remind them that in the times of their grandparents (before 1970), sines and cosines had to be found in tables and the multiplications had to be either done by hand, with logarithms, or with slide rules.

Questions 10 and 13 These are the only questions in the set in which students are asked for the distance between two places where both latitudes and longitudes of the places differ. You might want to add a question about the distance between your school and some other place on Earth.

Question 12 Emphasize that the great circle distance is not being found here.

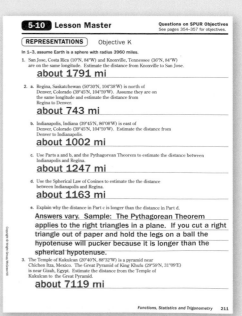

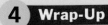

5-10

4 Wrap-Up

Ongoing Assessment
Have students pick two major cities that they think are as far away from each other as possible. Have them look up the locations of the two cities and calculate the shortest distance between them. Then have students report their distances to the class to find who picked the cities farthest apart. **Answers vary. Check students' work.**

Project Update
Project 2, *Spherical Triangles*, on page 349 and Project 4, *The Noon Day Project*, on page 350 relate to the content of this lesson.

REVIEW

15. Suppose $f(x) = \cot\left(\frac{x+\pi}{3}\right)$. **(Lessons 5-9, 4-9)**
    a. Describe a scale change and translation whose composite maps the graph of $y = \cot x$ onto the graph of $y = f(x)$.
    b. Draw a graph of $y = f(x)$.
    c. State the period and phase shift of $f(x)$.

16. If $\sec x = 2.9$, compute the five other trigonometric functions of x. Assume $0 \le x \le \frac{\pi}{2}$. **(Lesson 5-9)**

17. As t increases from 0 to 2π, what happens to the corresponding point on the graph of $\begin{cases} x = 5\sin t \\ y = 2\cos t \end{cases}$? **(Lesson 5-8)**

18. In $\triangle CAT$ below, find x to the nearest tenth. **(Lesson 5-5)**

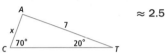

≈ 2.5

19. In $\triangle DOG$ at the right, find $m\angle G$ to the nearest tenth of a degree. **(Lesson 5-5)** $\approx 20.8°$.

20. In $\triangle ABC$, $a = 23$, $b = 17$, and $c = 33$. Find $m\angle A$. **(Lesson 5-3)**

$20. \approx 40.8°$

21. Micky lives on a lake. He wants to go from his house to Lookout Point. He can drive on County Road A for 0.9 miles, then turn onto County Road D and drive for another 1.4 miles, or he can take his power boat directly across the lake. The angle between County Roads A and B measures 57°, as shown at the right. If he drives, his average speed will be 40 mph, and if he takes the power boat, his average speed will be 20 mph. Which way will be quicker? **(Lesson 5-3)** **car**

22. Consider these data:
    12 15 14 13 17 18 30 14 19 18 15 14
    a. Find the median and the IQR. **15, 4**
    b. Compute the mean and standard deviation. $\approx 16.58, \approx 4.76$
    c. Which of these measures of central tendency and variability provides a better description of the sample? Explain your answer. **(Lessons 1-6, 1-2) See margin.**

23. **Skill Sequence** Solve. **(Previous Course)**
    a. $x(x - 6) = 0$ **$x = 0$ and $x = 6$** b. $(y + 23)(3y - 21) = 0$ **$y = -23$ and $y = 7$**
    c. $(z + 3)(z - 7)(z + 15) = 0$ **$z = -3, z = 7,$ and $z = -15$**

EXPLORATION

24. Some 3D geometry software allows you to construct points on the same line of latitude, the arc between the points along that line, and the great circle arc. Explore how the difference between the great circle and latitude path is affected by the distance between the points. **See margin.**

15a. S: $(x, y) \rightarrow (3x, y)$; T: $(x, y) \rightarrow (x - \pi, y)$; $T \circ S$: $(x, y) \rightarrow (3x - \pi, y)$

15b.
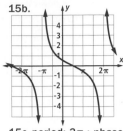

15c. period: 3π ; phase shift: $-\pi$

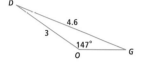

16. $\sin x \approx 0.939$, $\cos x \approx 0.345$, $\tan x \approx 2.722$, $\csc x \approx 1.065$, $\cot x \approx 0.367$

17. The point moves from $(0, 2)$ clockwise along the ellipse with equation $\frac{x^2}{25} + \frac{y^2}{4} = 1$.

Additional Answers

22c. The measures in Part a are a better description of the data because the data set contains an outlier that disproportionately affects the calculation of the measures in Part b.

24. Answers vary. Sample: The closer together the points are on the same line of latitude, the smaller the difference between the great circle and the latitude paths. This occurs because as the distance between the points decreases, the most extreme point of the great circle comes closer to the actual line of latitude.

Chapter 5 Projects

1 Determining Maximum Altitude

On its web site, the National Aeronautics and Space Administration (NASA) describes how two observers can calculate the altitude reached by a model rocket by measuring the distance L between the observers, the angles a and d of elevation to the rocket, and the angles b and c between the observers and the launch pad.

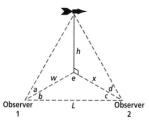

Observer 1   L   Observer 2

a. One of the equations NASA provides is
$h = \dfrac{L \tan a \tan c}{\cos b (\tan b + \tan c)}$. Explore the NASA site to find out how NASA derived this formula.

b. Use the Law of Sines to derive another formula for h in terms of a, c, e, and L.

c. Verify that the formulas in Parts a and b give similar results when $L = 200$, $a = 78°$, $d = 70°$, $b = 80°$, and $c = 35°$.

2 Spherical Triangles

When three great circular arcs intersect, they form a spherical triangle. Research the history, geometry, and 3-dimensional spherical analogs of 2-dimensional right triangle trigonometry. Make a poster displaying your findings and share these findings with your class.

3 Bond Angles in Molecules

In the methane molecule (CH_4), a single carbon atom lies at the center C of a regular tetrahedron $ABDE$ whose vertices are four hydrogen atoms, as shown both chemically and geometrically below. In this way, the hydrogen atoms achieve their maximum separation.

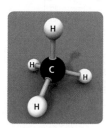

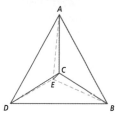

The angles with vertex at C are *bond angles*. One such bond angle is $\angle ACB$. These bond angles all have the same measure, a measure characteristic of many organic molecules.

a. Find the measure of this bond angle using geometry and trigonometry.

b. Consult a chemistry textbook to check your answer to Part a and also to find the carbon-hydrogen bond length in the methane molecule. Find the bond lengths and bond angles in the molecules ethane (C_2H_6), ethylene (C_2H_4), acetylene (C_2H_2), and cyclopropane (C_3H_6), and write a report on why bond angles are important to chemists.

Chapter 5

The projects relate to the content of the lessons of this chapter as follows:

Project	Lesson(s)
1	5-1, 5-2
2	5-10
3	5-3, 5-5, 5-6
4	5-1, 5-10
5	5-5

3 Bonds Angles in Molecules

Part (a) is quite difficult. It may be beneficial for students to summarize the various strategies they have learned and applied to determine the measure of an angle.

Sample answers for projects are in the Solution Manual in the Electronic Teacher's Edition.

Project Rubric

Advanced	Student correctly provides all of the details asked for in the project as well as additional correct independent conclusions.
Proficient	Student correctly provides all of the details asked for in the project.
Partially proficient	Student correctly provides some of the details asked for in the project or provides all details with some inaccuracies.
Not proficient	Student correctly provides few of the details asked for in the project or provides all details with many inaccuracies.
No attempt	Student makes little or no attempt to complete the project.

5 Application of the Law of Sines

The first three properties follow from the Law of Sines by general properties of proportions. A key step in the proof of (d) is to recognize that sin ∠*ADB* = sin ∠*ADC*, because these angles are supplements. The proofs of both (e) and (f) rely on properties of equality and inequality. Parts (d) to (f) are difficult partly because students may know other proofs and have to suppress them to think of how the Law of Sines might apply.

4 The Noon Day Project

This annual Internet event invites classrooms around the world to calculate the circumference of Earth from measurements of the shadow cast by a meter stick at the same time at different locations. This method was first used by Eratosthenes over 2000 years ago!

The project works by using the shadow lengths of a meter stick from two different locations to calculate a *central angle*. A sample observation is shown below.

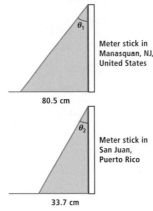

Meter stick in Manasquan, NJ, United States

80.5 cm

Meter stick in San Juan, Puerto Rico

33.7 cm

The central angle equals $\left| \theta_1 - \theta_2 \right|$.

Puerto Rico, Old San Juan,
Castillo de San Felipe del Morro

a. Use trigonometry to calculate the central angle between Manasquan and San Juan as well as between your home and a friend or family member's home somewhere else across the United States or the world.

b. How many copies of each central angle fit in a complete 360° revolution of Earth?

c. Each central angle measures the distance between the latitudes of each pair of locations. Using a dynamic geography utility, atlas, or the fact that 1 degree of latitude ≈ 111 km, approximate the circumference of Earth using each central angle calculated in Part a and each number of copies calculated in Part b.

d. Calculate the error in each of your estimates, given that the average circumference of Earth is 40,008 km.

5 Application of the Law of Sines

Use the Law of Sines to prove five of the following statements for every triangle *ABC*.

a. $\dfrac{a}{b} = \dfrac{\sin A}{\sin B}$

b. $\dfrac{a-c}{c} = \dfrac{\sin A - \sin C}{\sin C}$

c. $\dfrac{b+c}{b-c} = \dfrac{\sin B + \sin C}{\sin B - \sin C}$

d. The bisector of an interior angle of a triangle divides the opposite side into parts whose ratio is equal to the ratio of the sides adjacent to the angle bisected. That is, if $\overrightarrow{AD}$ bisects ∠*BAC*, then $\dfrac{x}{y} = \dfrac{c}{b}$.

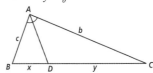

e. In a scalene triangle, the largest angle is opposite the longest side.

f. A triangle is equilateral if and only if it is equiangular.

Notes

Chapter 5 Summary and Vocabulary

- The sine, cosine, and tangent of θ, when $0° < \theta < 90°$ or $0 < \theta < \frac{\pi}{2}$, are ratios of side lengths of right triangles. In a right triangle,

$$\cos \theta = \frac{\text{adjacent leg}}{\text{hypotenuse}},$$

$$\sin \theta = \frac{\text{opposite leg}}{\text{hypotenuse}},$$

$$\tan \theta = \frac{\text{opposite leg}}{\text{adjacent leg}}.$$

These ratios can be evaluated exactly for some angles and estimated from a good drawing. Better approximations to all values can be found using a calculator or computer. These values can be used to find lengths of sides and measures of angles of right triangles.

- To find unknown sides and angles in all triangles, the following two theorems are helpful.

  Law of Cosines: In any $\triangle ABC$, $c^2 = a^2 + b^2 - 2ab \cos C$.

  Law of Sines: In any $\triangle ABC$, $\frac{a}{\sin A} = \frac{b}{\sin B} = \frac{c}{\sin C}$.

The Law of Cosines is helpful when the given information is SAS or SSS. The Law of Sines is helpful when the given information is ASA or AAS. In the case of SSA, zero, one, or two triangles may fit the given information.

- Sines and cosines may also be used to obtain arc lengths and arc measures on a sphere. One application of this idea is in finding the distance between two points on Earth given their **latitudes** and **longitudes**.

- The inverses of the parent sine, cosine, and tangent functions are not functions. However, if the domains of the parent functions (and, equivalently, the ranges of their inverses) are restricted as noted below, the inverses are functions.

$y = \cos^{-1} x$ if and only if $x = \cos y$ and is defined when $0 \le y \le \pi$.

$y = \sin^{-1} x$ if and only if $x = \sin y$ and is defined when $-\frac{\pi}{2} \le y \le \frac{\pi}{2}$.

$y = \tan^{-1} x$ if and only if $x = \tan y$ and is defined when $-\frac{\pi}{2} < y < \frac{\pi}{2}$.

The inverse trigonometric function keys on a calculator typically give values only for arguments in the above intervals.

Vocabulary

5-1
angle of depression
angle of elevation

5-2
*inverse cosine function
*$\cos^{-1}$, Arccos

5-4
*inverse sine function
*$\sin^{-1}$, Arcsin

5-6
*inverse tangent function
*$\tan^{-1}$, Arctan

5-7
trigonometric equation
general solution to a
trigonometric equation

5-8
parameter
parametric equations
equation for the unit circle
in standard form

5-9
secant, sec
cosecant, csc
cotangent, cot
reciprocal trigonometric
functions

5-10
great circle
meridian
longitude
latitude

Chapter 5

Summary and Vocabulary

The Summary gives an overview of the entire chapter and provides an opportunity for students to consider the material as a whole. Thus, the Summary can be used to help students relate and unify the concepts presented in the chapter.

Vocabulary words and symbols are listed by lesson to provide a checklist of concepts that students must know. Emphasize to students that they should read the vocabulary list carefully before starting the Self-Test on page 353. If students do not understand the meaning of a Vocabulary word, they should refer back to the indicated lesson.

Theorems and Properties covered in the chapter are listed below the Summary with page references included to lead students back to the location in the chapter where the theorem or property is stated.

◗ Equations involving the trigonometric functions are called
trigonometric equations. Solving trigonometric equations involves
the use of inverses of the trigonometric functions. This leads to
solutions in a restricted domain. Due to the periodic nature of
trigonometric functions, a **general solution** can be obtained by using
the period of the parent function and the properties of sines, cosines,
and tangents.

◗ Three other trigonometric functions are the **reciprocal trigonometric
functions**: For all θ,

$$\text{cosecant } \theta = \csc \theta = \frac{1}{\sin \theta},$$
$$\text{secant } \theta = \sec \theta = \frac{1}{\cos \theta},$$
$$\text{cotangent } \theta = \cot \theta = \frac{1}{\tan \theta}.$$

When two or more variables are defined in terms of a third variable
t, t is a **parameter** and the defining equations are called **parametric
equations**. When x and y are defined in terms of a parameter, the
points (x, y) describe a curve. The set of parametric equations
$\begin{cases} x = \cos \theta \\ y = \sin \theta \end{cases}$ defines the unit circle, while $\begin{cases} x = a \cos \theta \\ y = b \sin \theta \end{cases}$ defines an ellipse.

Theorems and Properties

Right Triangle Ratios for Sine, Cosine, and Tangent (p. 294)
Law of Cosines (p. 304)
SAS Area Formula for a Triangle (p. 315)
Law of Sines (p. 315)
Parametric Equation for a Circle (p. 332)
Parametric Equation for a Circle with Center (h, k) (p. 333)
Spherical Law of Cosines (p. 345)

Chapter 5 Self-Test

Take this test as you would take a test in class. You will need a calculator. Then use the Selected Answers section in the back of the book to check your work.

1–19. See margin.

In 1–3, consider △ABC below.

1. Find sin B exactly.
2. Find tan C exactly.
3. Find m∠B to the nearest tenth of a degree using cos⁻¹.

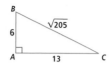

In 4–6, evaluate without a calculator.

4. $\sin^{-1}\left(\frac{1}{2}\right)$ 5. $\tan^{-1} 1$ 6. $\cot\left(\frac{3\pi}{4}\right)$

7. Explain why $\sin^{-1}\left(\sin\left(-\frac{2\pi}{3}\right)\right) \neq -\frac{2\pi}{3}$.

8. a. Draw a graph of $y = \tan^{-1} x$.
   b. Give the domain and range of the inverse tangent function.

9. Solve $\cos \theta = -0.125$ over each domain.

   a. $\{\theta \mid 0 \leq \theta \leq \pi\}$
   b. $\{\theta \mid 0 \leq \theta \leq 2\pi\}$
   c. the set of all real numbers

10. Describe the general solution to $2\cos \theta + \sqrt{3} = 0$.

11. Find x in the triangle below. Round your answer to the nearest tenth.

12. Explain why applying the Law of Cosines always leads to a situation with only one answer.

13. Find all values of θ between $-\pi$ and π such that $\cos^2\theta = 3 - 3\cos \theta$.

14. Suppose a 12-m ladder makes an angle with measure θ with the ground. Find an expression for the height h at which the ladder touches the wall in terms of θ.

20 m

15. New Orleans has about 14 hours of daylight at the summer solstice and 9.3 hours at the winter solstice. An equation for number h of hours of daylight as a function of the number d of days after March 21 is given by $h = 11.65 + 2.35 \sin\left(\frac{d}{\frac{365}{2\pi}}\right)$. Find the next four times New Orleans has 13.6 hours of daylight. Give your answer in days after March 21.

16. The diagram below shows a triangular playground that is bounded by Main Street, High Street, and Central Avenue. The city wants to erect a fence around the playground. Assume that fencing is sold by the foot. What is the minimum amount of fencing the city must buy?

17. Write equations for the circle graphed at the right in rectangular and parametric form.

18. Give two exact values of x for which sec x is undefined.

19. Estimate to the nearest mile the distance between New London, Connecticut (41.35 N, 72.11 W) and London, England (51.32 N, 0.5 W). Assume Earth is a sphere with radius 3960 mi.

Self-Test

For the development of mathematical competence, feedback and correction, along with the opportunity for practice, are necessary. The Self-Test provides the opportunity for feedback and correction; the Chapter Review provides additional opportunities for practice. We cannot overemphasize the importance of these end-of-chapter materials. It is at this point that the material gels for many students, allowing them to solidify skills and understanding. In general, student performance should improve after these pages.

Assign the Self-Test as a one-night assignment. Worked-out solutions for all questions are in the Selected Answers section of the student book. Encourage students to take the Self-Test honestly, grade themselves, and then be prepared to discuss the test in class.

Advise students to pay special attention to those Chapter Review questions (pages 354–357) that correspond to the questions they missed on the Self-Test. These are identified in the Self-Test Correlation Chart located in the Selected Answers section at the back of the book.

Additional Answers

See the Selected Answers section in the back of the book.

Chapter 5 Review

Chapter Review

The main objectives for the chapter are organized in the Chapter Review under the four types of understanding this book promotes: Skills, Properties, Uses, and Representations.

Whereas end-of-chapter material may be considered optional in some texts, in UCSMP *Functions, Statistics, and Trigonometry* we have selected these objectives and questions with the expectation that they will be covered. Students should be able to answer these questions with about 85% accuracy after studying the chapter.

You may assign these questions over a single night to help students prepare for a test the next day or you may assign the questions over a two-day period. If you work the questions over two days, we recommend assigning the evens for homework the first night so that students get feedback in class the next day, and then assigning the odds the night before the test because the answers are provided to the odd-numbered questions in the Selected Answers section at the back of the book.

It is effective to ask students which questions they still do not understand and use the day as a total class discussion of the material that the class finds most difficult.

Resources

- Assessment Resources: Chapter 5 Test

Technology Resources

Teacher's Assessment Assistant, Ch. 5
Electronic Teacher's Edition, Ch. 5

Chapter 5 Chapter Review

1, 2, 26. See margin.

SKILLS Procedures used to get answers

OBJECTIVE A Find sines, cosines, and tangents of angles. (Lesson 5-1)

In 1 and 2, find the sine, cosine, and tangent of $\angle A$.

1.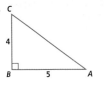

2.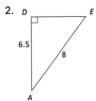

In 3–5, find the exact value without using a calculator.

3. $\sin 60°$ $\dfrac{\sqrt{3}}{2}$ 4. $\cos\left(\dfrac{\pi}{4}\right)$ $\dfrac{\sqrt{2}}{2}$ 5. $\cos\left(\dfrac{5\pi}{6}\right)$ $-\dfrac{\sqrt{3}}{2}$

In 6 and 7, approximate to the nearest thousandth.

6. $\tan\left(\dfrac{\pi}{13}\right)$ 0.246   7. $\sin 23°42'$ 0.402

OBJECTIVE B Evaluate inverse trigonometric functions. (Lessons 5-2, 5-4, 5-6)

In 8–11, evaluate without a calculator, giving answers in degrees and radians.

8. $\sin^{-1}\left(\dfrac{\sqrt{3}}{2}\right)$ $\dfrac{\pi}{3}$, 60°   9. $\text{Arctan}^{-1}\ -\dfrac{\pi}{4}$, -45°

10. $\cos^{-1}-\dfrac{\sqrt{2}}{2}$ $\dfrac{3\pi}{4}$, 135°   11. $\tan^{-1}\left(\sqrt{3}\right)$ $\dfrac{\pi}{3}$, 60°

In 12 and 13, evaluate without a calculator.

12. $\cos\left(\text{Arccos}\left(\dfrac{7}{11}\right)\right)$ 13. $\sin^{-1}\left(\sin\left(\dfrac{\pi}{3}\right)\right)$

OBJECTIVE C Use trigonometry to find lengths and angle measures in triangles. (Lessons 5-1, 5-3, 5-5)

12. $\dfrac{7}{11}$

13. $\dfrac{\pi}{3}$

14. Find, to the nearest tenth of a degree, the measures of the acute angles of an 8-15-17 right triangle. $\approx 28.1°$; $\approx 61.9°$

In 15 and 16, find x.

15. 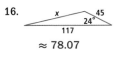 ≈ 11.46

16. 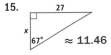 ≈ 78.07

SKILLS
PROPERTIES
USES
REPRESENTATIONS

18. $\approx 118.0°$
19. $\approx 38.9°$, $\approx 141.1°$

17. In $\triangle ABC$, m$\angle A = 37°$, m$\angle B = 72°$, and $b = 8$. Find a. $\approx 118.0°$

18. In the diagram at the right, $\overline{AB} \parallel \overline{CD}$. The circle has diameter 35 mm and $AB = CD = 30$ mm. Find θ to the nearest tenth of a degree.

19. In $\triangle KLM$, m$\angle K = 22.3°$, $k = 32$, and $\ell = 53$. Find all possible values of m$\angle L$ to the nearest tenth of a degree.

20. $\triangle ABC$ is isosceles with $AB = AC = 43$ cm and m$\angle A = 130°$. Find BC. ≈ 77.9 cm

21. $\triangle ABC$ has sides $AB = 31$, $BC = 43$, and $CA = 17$. Find all interior angles of $\triangle ABC$. $A \approx 124.6°$; $B \approx 19.02°$; $C \approx 36.38°$

OBJECTIVE D Solve trigonometric equations. (Lessons 5-2, 5-4, 5-6, 5-7)

In 22–24, find θ to the nearest hundredth, where $0 < \theta < \dfrac{\pi}{2}$.

22. $\tan \theta = 1.9$ ≈ 1.09

23. $\cos \theta = 0.43$ ≈ 1.13

24. $\sin \theta = 0.9876$ ≈ 1.41

25. Find the exact degree value of θ between 0 and $\dfrac{\pi}{2}$ such that $\sin \theta = \dfrac{\sqrt{3}}{2}$. $\dfrac{\pi}{3}$

26. Give the number of solutions to the equation, given $0 \le x \le 2\pi$. Justify your reasoning.

   a. $7 \sin x = 3$ **b.** $3 \sin x = 7$
   c. $3 \tan x = 7$

In 27–29, solve, given that $0 \le \theta \le 2\pi$.

27. $\cos \theta = -0.81$ ≈ 2.51 and ≈ 3.77

28. $\tan \theta = \sqrt{2}$ ≈ 0.96 and ≈ 4.10

29. $\sin \theta = \dfrac{4}{7}$ ≈ 0.61 and ≈ 2.53

In 30 and 31, solve, given that $2\pi \le \theta \le 4\pi$.

30. $\cos^2\theta + 2 \cos \theta + 1 = 0$ $3\pi \approx 9.42$

31. $\tan \theta = 2$ ≈ 7.39 and ≈ 10.53

Additional Answers

1. $\sin A = \dfrac{4}{\sqrt{41}}$; $\cos A \approx \dfrac{5}{\sqrt{41}}$; $\tan A = 0.8$

2. $\sin A = \dfrac{\sqrt{87}}{16}$; $\cos A = \dfrac{13}{16}$; $\tan A = \dfrac{\sqrt{87}}{13}$

26a. 2 solutions. There is one solution in the first and one in the second quadrant.

26b. No solutions. $\dfrac{7}{3}$ is not in the range of sin x.

26c. 2 solutions. There is one solution in the first and one in the third quadrant.

32. $x \approx 0.82 + 2\pi k$ and $x \approx -0.82 + 2\pi k$ for any integer k

33. $y = -\dfrac{\pi}{3} + 2\pi k$ and $y = -\dfrac{2\pi}{3} + 2\pi k$ for any integer k

34. $z \approx 0.98 + \pi k$ for any integer k

35. $w \approx 0.42 + \dfrac{\pi}{3}k$ for any integer k

36. $t \approx 0.31 + k$ or $t \approx -0.31 + k$ for any integer k

37. $\theta = \dfrac{\pi}{6} + \dfrac{2\pi}{3}k$ and $\theta = -\dfrac{\pi}{18} + \dfrac{2\pi}{3}k$ and $\theta = -\dfrac{5\pi}{18} + \dfrac{2\pi}{3}k$

44. The lengths of the corresponding sides are the same and sin 70° = sin 110° by the Supplements Theorem. Since $Area = \dfrac{1}{2}ab$ cos C, the areas are equal.

45. The Pythagorean Theorem is the Law of Cosines for a right triangle. Since $\cos \dfrac{\pi}{2} = 0$, $-2ab \cos C = 0$, leaving $c^2 = a^2 + b^2$.

32–37, 44–48, 50–55. See margin.

In 32–37, describe the general solution in radians.

32. $\cos x = 0.68$ **33.** $2 \sin y = -\sqrt{3}$

34. $6 \tan z - 9 = 0$ **35.** $\tan(3w) = 3.12$

36. $\cos(2\pi t) = -0.341$

37. $2 \sin^2(3\theta) - \sin(3\theta) = 1$

| **OBJECTIVE E** Find secants, cosecants, and cotangents. (Lesson 5-9)

38. In $\triangle URN$ at the right, identify
a. $\cot U. \frac{r}{u}$
b. $\csc R. \frac{n}{r}$

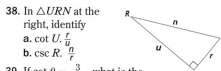

39. If $\cot \theta = \frac{3}{\sqrt{10}}$, what is the value of $\sin \theta$? $\sqrt{\frac{10}{19}}$

40. Give the exact value of $\sec\left(\frac{\pi}{3}\right).2$

41. Give the exact value of $\cot(-765°).-1$

42. If $\cos x = 0.70$, compute   **a. about 1.43**

   a. $\sec x$.   **b.** $\sec(\pi - x)$.**b. about −1.43**

43. Write $\frac{1}{\sin x \cot x}$ as the value of a single trigonometric function.**sec x**

PROPERTIES   Principles behind the mathematics

| **OBJECTIVE F** Interpret the Law of Sines, Law of Cosines, and related theorems. (Lessons 5-3, 5-5)

44. Explain why the two triangles below have the same area.

45. Explain how the Pythagorean Theorem is a special case of the Law of Cosines.

46. In $\triangle EFG$, $m\angle E = 30°$, $EF = 5$, and $FG = 8$. Alex claims that there is exactly one triangle satisfying these conditions. Keesha claims that there are two. Who is correct? Why?

47. Explain why the Law of Sines shows that no triangle ABC can have $AB = 40$, $m\angle BAC = 70°$, and $BC = 20$.

| **OBJECTIVE G** State and use properties of inverse trigonometric functions. (Lessons 5-2, 5-4, 5-6)

48. For what values of θ is this statement true? If $k = \cos \theta$, then $\theta = \cos^{-1} k$.

49. **Multiple Choice** If $\tan 3x = b$ and $-\frac{\pi}{2} < 3x < \frac{\pi}{2}$, then x equals ___?___.**D**
  A $3 \tan^{-1} b$ **B** $\tan^{-1}\left(\frac{b}{3}\right)$
  C $\tan^{-1}(3b)$ **D** $\frac{1}{3} \tan^{-1} b$

50. Why must the domain of the sine function be restricted in order to define $y = \sin^{-1} x$?

51. State the domain and range of the inverse cosine function.

52. **Fill in the Blank** The function with equation $y = \text{Arctan } x$ has range ___?___.

53. Explain why $\cos^{-1} \cos\left(-\frac{\pi}{4}\right) \neq -\frac{\pi}{4}$.

In 54 and 55, find two positive and two negative solutions.

54. Use degrees and round θ to the nearest tenth: $\sin \theta = 0.63$.

55. Use radians and round t to the nearest thousandth: $\cos t = -0.38$.

USES   Applications of mathematics in real-world situations

| **OBJECTIVE H** Use trigonometry to solve problems involving right triangles. (Lesson 5-1)

56. A ladder against a wall makes a 75° angle with the ground. If the base of the ladder is 4 feet from the wall, find the ladder's length.

57. A building casts a shadow 22 m long when the elevation of the Sun is at 51°, as shown at the right. How high is the building?

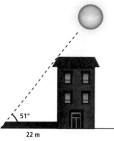

56. about 15.45 ft

57. about 27.17 m

Additional Answers

46. Usually, SSA does not uniquely determine a triangle. But if the side opposite the given angle is larger than the other given side, SsA, the triangle is unique. Alex is correct.

47. In such a triangle, $\sin \angle ACB \approx 1.55$, but since this is outside the range of sine, this triangle is not possible.

48. $\{k \mid 0 \leq k \leq \pi\}$

50. The sine function is periodic, so multiple inputs map to the same output. When the graph of the sine function is reflected over $y = x$ each input gives multiple outputs. Thus, the reflection does not result in a function. The domain is restricted in order to make sure each input gives exactly one output.

51. domain: $\{x \mid 0 \leq x \leq 1\}$; range: $\{y \mid 0 \leq y \leq \pi\}$

52. $\{y \mid -\frac{\pi}{2} < y < \frac{\pi}{2}\}$

53. Answers vary. Sample: $\cos\left(-\frac{\pi}{4}\right) = \frac{\sqrt{2}}{2}$, but $\cos^{-1}\left(\frac{\sqrt{2}}{2}\right) = \frac{\pi}{4} \neq -\frac{\pi}{4}$

54. Answers vary. Sample: –320.9°, –219.1°, 39.1°, 140.9°

55. Answers vary. Sample: –4.323, –1.961, 1.961, 4.323

Assessment

Evaluation The Assessment Resources provide a form of the Chapter 5 Test. Here are our recommendations for assigning a letter grade: 85–100 = A; 72–84 = B; 60–71 = C; 50–59 = D.

Feedback After students have taken the test for Chapter 5 and you have scored the results, return the tests to students for discussion. Class discussion on the questions that caused trouble for most students can be very effective in identifying and clarifying misunderstandings. You might want to have them note the items they missed and work either in groups or at home to correct them. It is important for students to receive feedback on every chapter test, and we recommend that students see and correct their mistakes before proceeding too far into the next chapter.

Suggestions for Assignment Assign Reading Lesson 6-1 and Covering the Ideas 6-1 for homework the evening of the test. It gives students work to do after they have completed the test and keeps the class moving. If you do not do this, you may cover one less chapter over the course of the year.

62, 64, 65. See margin.

58. Jack is steadying a 50-foot flagpole with two 60-foot-long guy wires. What acute angle θ will the wires make with the ground? **about 56.44°**

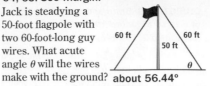

59. A sailboat sails due west from a port at 1 P.M. At 3 P.M., the bearing of a lighthouse is 42° clockwise from north.

   a. If the lighthouse is 20 miles due north of the port, how far out to sea is the sailboat? **about 18.01 miles**

   b. What is the speed of the sailboat?

   c. At what time will the lighthouse lie on a bearing of 60° (clockwise from north) to the sailboat, assuming the speed of the ship remains the same?
   b. about 9.005 mph   **c. about 4:51 P.M.**

OBJECTIVE I Solve real-world problems using the Law of Sines and the Law of Cosines. (Lessons 5-3, 5-5)

60. A team of surveyors measuring from A to B across a pond places a stake at S, a point from which they measure distances to A and B. The measures are shown in the diagram. Find AB. **about 130.3 m**

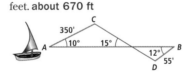

61. When the wind is directly behind a sail boat, the boat will sail faster if it tacks, or sails at an angle to the desired direction. Suppose a boat sails a course beginning at point A, going to C where it tacks, and then to D, where it tacks again, ending at B. $AC = 350'$ and $BD = 55'$. How far is point A from point B? Round your answer to the nearest ten feet. **about 670 ft**

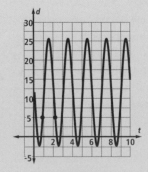

62. An airport controller notes that a plane 14° west of south and 20 miles from the airport is flying toward another plane that is 18 miles directly south of the airport. If the planes are at the same altitude, how far apart are the planes to the nearest tenth of a mile?

63. Forest lookout stations at A and B are 18 miles apart. The ranger in A spots a fire 13° east of north. The ranger at B locates the fire 27° north of west with respect to B.

   a. If B is directly northeast of A, find the distance of the fire from A. **about 17.64 mi**

   b. Find the distance of the fire from B.
     about 9.83 mi

OBJECTIVE J Write and solve equations for phenomena described by trigonometric functions. (Lessons 5-2, 5-4, 5-7)

64. The length c of chord $\overline{AB}$ in $\odot O$ depends on the magnitude of central angle θ.

   a. Use the Law of Cosines to write an equation for c in terms of θ.

   b. Solve the equation from Part a for θ.

   c. What is an appropriate domain for c?

   d. Use your equation to find the value of θ when $c = 11$.

65. The distance d in feet from the ground of a paddle on a mill wheel after t minutes can be modeled by $d = 11 + 15 \sin(\pi(t - 3))$.

   a. Graph the model for $t > 0$. Why does it dip below the t-axis?

   b. On your graph, mark the first two times that the paddle is 5′ above the ground.

   c. Find the first two times the paddle is 5′ above the ground by solving $5 = 11 + 15 \sin(\pi(t - 3))$.

Additional Answers

62. about 5.0 mi

64a. $c = \sqrt{98 - 98 \cos \theta}$

64b. $\theta = \cos^{-1}\left(\dfrac{98 - c^2}{98}\right)$

64c. domain: $\{c \mid 0 \le c \le 14\}$

64d. about 103.57°

65a. and b. When the graph is below zero the paddle is in the water.

65c. $t = \dfrac{\sin^{-1}\left(\frac{5-11}{15}\right)}{\pi} + 3$; about 0.87 and about 0.13 minutes

66. $\theta = \tan^{-1}\left(\dfrac{r}{5.9}\right)$

66. On a compass used to draw arcs, the leg that holds the pencil measures 5.9″. Find a formula for the angle θ at the top of the compass in terms of the radius of the desired circle.

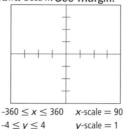
6.2″ θ 5.9″
r

67. The vertical displacement d of a mass oscillating at the end of a spring, measured in cm, is given by the equation $d = 6\sin(\pi t)$ where t is the time in seconds. **b. about 0.27 sec**
a. Solve this equation for t. $t = \dfrac{\sin^{-1}\left(\frac{d}{6}\right)}{\pi}$
b. At what time does d first equal 4.5 cm?

68. The measured voltage E in a circuit after t seconds $(t > 0)$ is given by $E = 15\cos(3\pi t)$. Find, to the nearest 0.01 second, the first five times that $E = 13$.
0.06, 0.61, 0.72, 1.28, and 1.39 sec

OBJECTIVE K Find the shortest distance between two points on Earth given their longitude and latitude. **(Lesson 5-10)**

In 69–71, assume Earth is a sphere with radius 3960 mi.

69. Jackson, Mississippi (90°12′W, 32°22′N), and St. Louis, Missouri (90°12′W, 38°35′N), are on the same meridian. Estimate the distance from Jackson to St. Louis.

70. Find the shortest distance between Ankara, Turkey (32°55′W, 39°55′N), and Beijing, China (116°25′W, 39°55′N). **about 4,245 mi**

71. Find the shortest distance between Chicago, Illinois (87°39′W, 41°51′N) and Sydney, Australia (151°13′E, 33°51′S).
69. about 430 mi   71. about 9,244 mi

REPRESENTATIONS Pictures, graphs, or objects that illustrate concepts

OBJECTIVE L Graph or identify graphs of inverse trigonometric functions. **(Lessons 5-2, 5-4, 5-6)**

72. Graph $y = \cos x$ and $y = \cos^{-1} x$ for $0 \le x \le \pi$ on the same set of axes. **See margin.**

73. **Multiple Choice** Which equation is graphed at the right? **D**

A $y = \tan^{-1} x$ **B** $y = \cos^{-1} x$
C $y = \sin x$ **D** $y = \sin^{-1} x$

74. Sarah graphed $y = \cos^{-1} x$ on her calculator in degree mode. Her screen looked like the one drawn below. **See margin.**

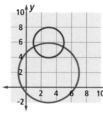

$-360 \le x \le 360$ x-scale $= 90$
$-4 \le y \le 4$ y-scale $= 1$

a. What should Sarah do to display the graph?
b. What would the display look like?

OBJECTIVE M Graph parametric equations of circles and ellipses. **(Lesson 5-8)**

75. Graph the parametric equations $\begin{cases} x = 3\cos t \\ y = 5\sin t \end{cases}$.

76. Write parametric equations for the circles graphed below.

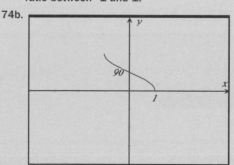

77. The unit circle is translated 7 units to the right and 5 units down.
a. Write an equation in rectangular form for the image circle.
b. Write parametric equations for the original circle and its image.

78. Find parametric equations for the circle with standard equation $(x + 3)^2 + (y - 6)^2 = 81$.
75–78. See margin.

Additional Answers

75.

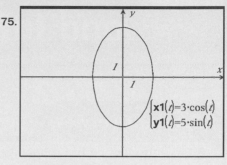

$\begin{cases} \mathbf{x1}(t) = 3\cdot\cos(t) \\ \mathbf{y1}(t) = 5\cdot\sin(t) \end{cases}$

76. $\begin{cases} x = 2\cos t + 3 \\ y = 2\sin t + 6 \end{cases}, 0 \le t \le 2\pi;$

$\begin{cases} x = 4\cos t + 3 \\ y = 4\sin t + 2 \end{cases}, 0 \le t \le 2\pi$

77a. $(x - 7)^2 + (y + 5)^2 = 1$

77b. original: $\begin{cases} x = \cos t \\ y = \sin t \end{cases}, 0 \le t \le 2\pi;$

image: $\begin{cases} x = \cos t + 7 \\ y = \sin t - 5 \end{cases}, 0 \le t \le 2\pi$

78. $\begin{cases} x = 9\cos t - 3 \\ y = 9\sin t + 6 \end{cases}, 0 \le t \le 2\pi$

Additional Answers

72.

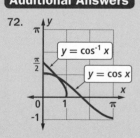

$y = \cos^{-1} x$
$y = \cos x$

74a. **Answers vary. Sample: She should change the window to $-4 \le x \le 4$, with an x-scale =**

1 and $-360 \le y \le 360$, with a y-scale $= 90$. This is because y is in degrees and x is a ratio between -1 and 1.

74b.

Chapter 6 · Counting, Probability, and Inference

Chapter Overview

	Local Standards	Pacing (in days)		
		Average	Advanced	Block
6-1 Introduction to Probability **A** Compute probabilities of events in various contexts. **G** List sample spaces and events for experiments.		1	1	0.5
6-2 Principles of Probability **A** Compute probabilities of events in various contexts. **D** Compute probabilities using the General and Mutually Exclusive Forms of the Probability of the Union of Events and the Probability of Complements.		1	1	0.5
6-3 Counting Strings with Replacement **B** Find the number of strings with replacement. **E** Determine whether events are independent or dependent. **I** Calculate probabilities in real situations. **J** Use the Multiplication Counting Principle and the Strings with Replacement Theorem to find the number of ways of arranging objects.		1	1	0.5
QUIZ 1		0.5	0.25	0.25
6-4 Counting Strings without Replacement **B** Find the number of strings without replacement. **C** Evaluate expressions using factorials. **I** Calculate probabilities in real situations. **J** Use permutations to find the number of ways of arranging objects.		1	1	0.5
6-5 Contingency Tables **H** Use a contingency table to compute percentages involving categorical variables. **M** Represent information about relative frequencies or frequencies in a contingency table.		1	1	0.5
6-6 Conditional Probability **D** Calculate probabilities using the Definition of Conditional Probability. **I** Calculate probabilities in real situations.		1	1	0.5
QUIZ 2		0.5	0.25	0.25
6-7 Designing Simulations **K** Design and conduct simulations with or without technology.		1	1	0.5
6-8 Two "Laws," but Only One Is Valid **A** Compute expected counts of events in various contexts. **F** Discuss the Law of Large numbers and the "law of averages."		1	1	0.5
6-9 The Chi-Square Test **L** Use the chi-square statistic to determine whether or not an event is likely.		1	1	0.5
Self-Test		1	0.5	0.5
Chapter Review		2	1	0.5
Test		1	1	0.5
TOTAL		13	11	6.5

Technology Resources

Teacher's Assessment Assistant, Ch. 6

Electronic Teacher's Edition, Ch. 6

Differentiated Options Universal Access

	Accommodating the Learner	Vocabulary Development	Ongoing Assessment	Materials
6-1	p. 363	p. 362	p. 366	
6-2	p. 370		p. 373	a pair of fair six-sided dice
6-3	p. 377	p. 376	p. 380	
6-4	pp. 382, 383		p. 386	
6-5		p. 390		
6-6			p. 401	
6-7	p. 404	p. 403	p. 409	
6-8			p. 416	coin, paper and pencil, spreadsheet application
6-9			p. 425	chi-square web applet

Objectives

Ⓢkills		Lessons	Self-Test Questions	Chapter Review Questions
A	Compute probabilities and expected counts of events in various contexts.	6-1, 6-2, 6-8	4, 10	1–10
B	Find the number of strings with or without replacement.	6-3, 6-4	3	11–15
C	Evaluate expressions using factorials.	6-4	2	16–23
D	Calculate probabilities using the General and Mutually Exclusive Forms of the Probability of the Union of Events, the Probability of Complements, and the Definition of Conditional Probability.	6-2, 6-6	7, 9	24–28

Ⓟroperties				
E	Determine whether events are independent or dependent.	6-3	11	29–32
F	Discuss the Law of Large Numbers and the "law of averages."	6-8	16	33–35

Ⓤses				
G	List sample spaces and events for experiments.	6-1	1	36–39
H	Use a contingency table to compute percentages involving categorical variables.	6-5	14	40–42
I	Calculate probabilities in real situations.	6-3, 6-4, 6-6	5, 8	43–47
J	Use the Multiplication Counting Principle, the Strings with Replacement Theorem, and permutations to find the number of ways of arranging objects.	6-3, 6-4	6	48–51
K	Design and conduct simulations with or without technology.	6-7	15	52–54
L	Use the chi-square statistic to determine whether or not an event is likely.	6-9	12	55–57

Ⓡepresentations				
M	Represent information about relative frequencies or frequencies in a contingency table.	6-5	13	58, 59

Resource Masters Chapter 6

None of the generic Resource Masters apply to this chapter.

Resource Master 127 Lesson 6-1

Resource Master 126 Lesson 6-1

Warm-Up

A drawer contains r red socks, b blue socks, and w white socks. Assume that you draw a sock randomly from the drawer.

1. What is the probability that it is red?
2. What is the probability that it is not white?
3. What is the probability that it is green?

Additional Examples

1. A small box contains 30 blue, 30 green, and 25 red paper clips. Two paper clips are taken from the box and their colors recorded.
   a. List all possible outcomes for this experiment.
   b. How many outcomes are in the sample space for this experiment?

2. In the situation of Additional Example 1, which of the six outcomes are equally likely?

3. Assume that births of boys and girls are equally likely.
   a. How many outcomes are in the same sample space?
   b. Find the probability that a family of four children has one girl and three boys.

Resource Masters for Lesson 6-1

Resource Master 129 Lesson 6-2

Resource Master 128 Lesson 6-2

Warm-Up

According to Nielsen Media Research in October 2008, of the 113.1 million U.S. households that owned at least one TV set, 82% had 2 or more TV sets and 88% received basic cable. From this information, what are the largest and smallest percents of households that might have both 2 or more TV sets and also have basic cable?

Additional Examples

1. Jameel and Rhonda had to take a make-up test after school. Their teacher told them they could come in no earlier than 3:00 and leave no later than 4:00. Jameel took 38 minutes on the test and Rhonda 51 minutes. For at least how many minutes were Jameel and Rhonda taking the test at the same time?

2. A pair of six-sided dice is thrown. If the dice are fair, what is the probability that the dice show a sum of 7 or 11?

3. In the situation of Additional Example 2, what is the probability that the dice show doubles (two numbers alike) or a sum of 8?

4. In the situation of Additional Example 2, what is the probability that the dice show a product between 7 and 31?

Resource Masters for Lesson 6-2

Resource Master 130 Lesson 6-2

Page 369

F S

Experiment	Sample Space	Event	Complement
tossing a coin	{heads, tails}	{tails}	{heads}
tossing two coins	{HH, HT, TH, TT}	getting no heads {TT}	getting 1 or 2 heads {HH, HT, TH}
picking an integer from 1 to 100	$\{n \in \mathbb{Z} : 1 \leq n \leq 100\}$	picking a prime number	picking 1 or a composite number

Theorem (Probability of Complements)

If A is any event, then $P(\text{not } A) = 1 - P(A)$.

ABO and Rh Blood Type Relative Frequencies in the United States

ABO Type	Rh Type	Relative Frequency
O	positive	38%
O	negative	7%
A	positive	34%
A	negative	6%
B	positive	9%
B	negative	2%
AB	positive	3%
AB	negative	1%

Resource Master for Lesson 6-2

Resource Master 132 Lesson 6-3

Resource Master 131 Lesson 6-3

Warm-Up

1. Write down all the three-letter combinations that begin with D using the letters A, B, C, D, and E only once.

2. How many three-letter combinations are there using the letters A, B, C, D, and E only once?

Additional Examples

1. A lottery game played in some states involves picking 3 digits from 0 to 9 in order. Describe a sample space for this experiment and determine the number of elements in the sample space.

2. Three of the questions on a science test are multiple choice with four choices each.
   a. How many ways are there to answer these questions?
   b. If you guess randomly on each of these questions, what is the probability of answering all these correctly?

3. Some states allow license plates with 3 letters followed by 4 digits from 0 through 9. How many license plates are possible?

4. In a certain spinning wheel, there are 20 sectors of equal size. In 18 of these sectors, you win a prize, but in the other 2, you lose all your winnings. If the wheel spins randomly, what is the probability of winning five prizes and then losing on the sixth spin?

5. In Additional Example 4, is losing on the 6th spin independent of what happens on the first 5 spins? Why or why not?

Resource Masters for Lesson 6-3

Resource Master 133 Lesson 6-3

Example 4

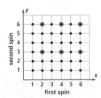

Definition of Independent Events

Events A and B are **independent events** if and only if $P(A \cap B) = P(A) \bullet P(B)$.

Resource Master for Lesson 6-3

Resource Master 135 Lesson 6-4

Resource Master 134 Lesson 6-4

Warm-Up

Ten permutations of the letters AELST are legal words in the game of Scrabble® using the *Official Scrabble® Players Dictionary, 4th Edition*.

1. Name as many as you can.

2. If the letters AELST are ordered at random, what is the probability that the ordering forms a legal word in Scrabble®?
   (Note: 12 legal words in Scrabble® can be formed from AEPRS, the most prolific set of 5 letters.)

Additional Examples

1. In volleyball, a team plays 6 players at a time, three at the net and three behind. How many different ways are there to arrange three at the net from the six who are playing?

2. An art gallery has 12 paintings by Renaissance painters but only enough room to show 8 of them. In how many ways can they arrange 8 of the 12 paintings in the 8 places they have for them?

3. Suppose $_nP_r = 110 \bullet {}_nP_{r-2}$. What are n and r?

4. Refer to Example 4 in this lesson.
   a. If Kerry Okie decided to put the 6 girls in his class first and then the 11 boys, how many different orders would he have?
   b. Is the answer to Part a greater than, equal to, or less than the answer to Example 4 in the lesson?

Resource Masters for Lesson 6-4

Resource Master 137 Lesson 6-5

Resource Master 136 Lesson 6-5

Warm-Up

In 1–4, use this information. Willie Fielder hurt himself two games into the 2047 baseball season and only batted 6 times with 1 hit, for a batting average of .167. Scott ("Scruffy") Scrub played the entire season but was a second-stringer, so was up only 100 times and got 19 hits, for a batting average of .190, better than Willie's average. In the 2048 season, Willie was well and got 201 hits in 600 at-bats. Scott still remained a second-stringer and was up only 100 times again, but got 35 hits.

1. What was Willie's batting average for the 2048 season?
2. What was Scott's batting average for the 2048 season?
3. What was Willie's combined batting average for the 2047 and 2048 seasons?
4. What was Scott's combined batting average for the 2047 and 2048 seasons?

Additional Examples

1. Use Titanic Table 1 in the lesson. Round each answer to the nearest percent.
   a. Out of all the people on the ship, what percent died?
   b. What percent of passengers in third class died?
   c. What percent of passengers in first or second class died?
2. Use the data from Example 2 in the lesson. Answer to the nearest tenth of a percent.
   a. What percent of people in the study did not have a tattoo?
   b. What percent of people in the study with no tattoo had Hepatitis C?
   c. What percent of people in the study with a tattoo had Hepatitis C?
   d. What can you conclude from the answers to Parts b and c?
3. Use the data from Example 3 in the lesson. Suppose the 5th-grade class contains 117 girls and 125 boys. Did more boys than girls prefer Lemony Snicket?

Resource Masters for Lesson 6-5

Resource Master 139 Lesson 6-5

Resource Master 138 Lesson 6-5

Example 2

	Tattoo Done in Commercial Tattoo Parlor	Tattoo Done Elsewhere	No tattoo	Totals
Has Hepatitis C	17	8	18	43
No Hepatitis C	35	53	495	?
Totals	52	?	?	626

Example 3

	Harry Potter	Animorphs	Lemony Snicket	Lord of the Rings	Other
Boys	42%	15%	23%	11%	9%
Girls	51%	8%	28%	5%	8%

Program	Men		Women		Overall	
	Applicants	% Admitted	Applicants	% Admitted	Applicants	% Admitted
A	825	62%	108	82%	933	64%
B	560	63%	25	68%	585	63%
C	325	37%	593	34%	918	35%
D	417	33%	375	35%	792	34%
E	191	28%	393	24%	584	25%
F	373	6%	341	7%	714	6%
Total	2691	44.5%	1835	30.4%	4526	38.8%

Resource Masters for Lesson 6-5

Resource Master 141 Lesson 6-6

Resource Master 140 Lesson 6-6

Warm-Up

Suppose 60% of the singers in a school play are in the school choir. In the school as a whole, suppose 10% of the students are in the choir and 5% are in the school play. Finally, suppose there are 600 students in the school.

a. If a student in the play is randomly chosen, what is the probability that student is in the choir?
b. If a student in the choir is randomly chosen, what is the probability that student is in the play?
c. If a student in the school is randomly chosen, what is the probability that student is in both the play and the choir?

Additional Examples

1. Let B = a person eats a good breakfast; let L = a person eats a good lunch. Suppose, in a group of 80 people, 43 eat good breakfasts and good lunches, 21 eat a good breakfast but not a good lunch, 12 eat a good lunch but not a good breakfast, and the rest eat neither a good lunch nor a good breakfast.
   a. Find $P(L \cap B)$.
   b. Find $P(L \mid B)$.
   c. Find $P(B \mid L)$.
2. Suppose that 1 in 500 airline passengers carry some hazardous material on them when on a plane. Further suppose that an airport screening device accurately identifies 98% of people with hazardous materials that pass through it, and accurately identifies 99% of people without hazardous materials. If a person is identified by the machine as having hazardous materials, what is the probability that the person actually has these kinds of materials?

Resource Masters for Lesson 6-6

Resource Master 142 Lesson 6-6

Example 2

	D	not D
A	0.98 • 0.005 = ?	? • ? = ?
not A	? • 0.005 = ?	0.95 • ? = ?
Total	0.5% of total	? % of total

Question 12, 13

	Airline A			Airline B		
	On Time	Delayed	% Delayed	On Time	Delayed	% Delayed
LA	497	62		694	117	
Phoenix	221	12		4840	415	
San Diego	212	20		383	65	
San Francisco	503	102		320	129	
Seattle	1841	305		201	61	
Total						

Question 14

	Level of Satisfaction		
Owners of	High	Medium	Low
American	80	100	45
Japanese	40	30	20
European	25	35	25

Resource Master for Lesson 6-6

Resource Master 144 Lesson 6-7

Resource Master 143 Lesson 6-7

Warm-Up

Toss a coin until you get 3 heads and 3 tails. How many tosses did it take? Compare your results with two others in your class and try to determine what you think is the number of tosses that it takes on average to get 3 heads and 3 tails. (This simulates trying to find a sample of 3 men and 3 women by randomly picking names of men and women.)

Additional Example

1. Suppose that, in the past, 95% of people who reserve a seat on a particular flight actually show up. If the plane holds 118 passengers, describe how you could use a simulation to estimate how many passengers will show up.

2. Assuming a 95% probability that a given passenger shows up for a flight, estimate how many tickets should be sold in order to fill all 118 seats in Additional Example 1.

Resource Masters for Lesson 6-7

Resource Master 146 Lesson 6-8

Resource Master 145 Lesson 6-8

Warm-Up

You toss a coin 8 times and get 8 heads.

1. Explain why heads and tails might be equally likely the next time you toss.

2. Explain why heads might be more likely than tails the next time you toss.

3. Explain why tails might be more likely than heads the next time you toss.

Additional Examples

1. Suppose a town has about 25,000 adults in its population. If the unemployment rate in the town is 5%, and you sampled 200 adults from the town at random, what is your expected count of unemployed?

2. Consider the following experiment. Two 6-sided dice are thrown 1000 times and the sum of the numbers on the dice are recorded. A sum of 7 occurred 175 times. Assume that the dice are fair.
   a. What is the expected number of 7s?
   b. What is the difference between the observed and the expected number of 7s?
   c. What is the relative frequency of 7s?
   d. What is the difference between the relative frequency of 7s and the probability of 7s?

Resource Masters for Lesson 6-8

Resource Master 148 Lesson 6-9

Resource Master 147 Lesson 6-9

Warm-Up

In a certain metropolitan area, 250,000 people live in the city and 400,000 live in the suburbs. When the basketball playoffs started, there were 32 teams. Of those teams, 14 were from the city and 18 were from the suburbs. How many would have been expected to be from the city and how many from the suburbs if the numbers of teams were proportional to the population?

Additional Examples

1. To test if a coin is fair, calculate the chi-square statistic for a coin that shows 85 heads in 150 tosses.

2. Compute the chi-square statistic to test whether a coin that comes up heads 93 times in 150 tosses is fair.

Resource Masters for Lesson 6-9

Resource Master 149 Lesson 6-9

Passengers	First	Second	Third	Crew	Total
Survived	203	118	178	212	711
Died	122	167	528	673	1490
Totals (Percent)	325 14.8%	285 12.9%	706 32.1%	885 40.2%	2201

Activity 2

	First	Second	Third	Crew	Total
Actual (Observed) Number of Survivors	203	118	178	212	711
Expected Number of Survivors	105	e_i	e_i	e_i	711
Contribution to Chi-square	91.5	?	?	?	?

Resource Master for Lesson 6-9

Resource Master 150 Lesson 6-9

Question 11, 12

Team won, lost, or tied	First Quarter	Second Quarter	Third Quarter	Fourth Quarter
L	30	26	18	27
W	22	31	28	29
L	24	22	19	26
W	24	28	24	16
T	26	32	26	23
T	23	22	37	25
T	32	30	19	33
T	23	35	26	30
W	32	15	24	34
L	24	27	23	15
L	20	26	22	23
W	29	19	14	41
L	21	24	28	15
W	14	13	29	36
W	25	20	24	26
L	10	22	27	11
L	24	19	31	20
W	19	20	29	31
L	24	22	18	20
W	25	24	20	21
T	31	16	26	24
T	28	29	25	15
L	26	29	32	18
W	34	30	32	26

Resource Master for Lesson 6-9

Pacing

Each lesson in this chapter is designed to be covered in 1 day. At the end of the chapter, you should plan to spend 1 day to review the Self-Test, 1 to 2 days for the Chapter Review, and 1 day for a test. You may wish to spend a day on projects, and possibly a day will be needed for quizzes. This chapter should therefore take 12 to 15 days. We strongly advise you not to spend more than 16 days on this chapter.

Students should be expected to do the equivalent of a complete set of Questions from a lesson nearly every day. Two Assignment Options are identified in each lesson. At times you may want to save a few questions to be done by students in class.

Overview

Students are familiar with descriptive statistics such as measures of center and spread. In this chapter they will be introduced to an inferential statistic, the chi-square value that compares a distribution of collected data with a theoretical distribution deduced from probability. The table on page 359 is an example of a distribution of collected data. The question it immediately raises is whether the difference between 33 out of 200,745 and 115 out of 201,229 is large enough to conclude that the Salk vaccine was effective.

The scientists concluded that the difference was large enough because the experiment was a double-blind experiment, in which neither the patients nor the people administering the shots of vaccine knew whether the patient was getting the vaccine or a placebo. Thus the results were trusted. The Salk vaccine study was one of the first double-blind studies ever conducted, and such experiments are now considered the gold standard of all medical work. However, it is very difficult to administer such a study and some studies do not lend themselves to double-blind designs.

Chapter

6 Counting, Probability, and Inference

> ### Contents

6-1   Introduction to Probability

6-2   Principles of Probability

6-3   Counting Strings with Replacement

6-4   Counting Strings without Replacement

6-5   Contingency Tables

6-6   Conditional Probability

6-7   Designing Simulations

6-8   Two "Laws," but Only One Is Valid

6-9   The Chi-Square Test

People are always wondering whether one way to improve health, learning, or some other aspect of living is better than another. Is it better to exercise daily, or is every other day enough? Does eating a good breakfast help a person score higher on a test? Does taking a particular vitamin lower your risk of getting a particular disease?

In these kinds of situations, the treatment in question rarely works all the time. It will help some people but not everyone. Those people who benefit will say that their treatment worked, while others will say that another method worked. Which should you choose?

This is a typical problem in which *inferential statistics* plays an important role. Inferential statistics works from real data to determine whether events are different from what might be expected randomly.

One important historical example of the use of inferential statistics is the research and development process that led to the first polio vaccine. In the first half of the 20th century, polio crippled large numbers of people annually in the United States. The president at the time, Franklin D. Roosevelt, survived an attack of polio in 1921 that left him permanently paralyzed from the waist down. He set a national policy to fight the disease.

Chapter 6 Overview

The intent of this chapter is to review certain concepts, tackle some important types of questions of counting and probability, and introduce the use of statistics to make decisions regarding cause and effect.

We begin by reviewing basic principles of probability in Lessons 6-1 and 6-2, as these principles provide the rationale for many of the counting situations to follow. We delay the discussion of combinations until Chapter 10 when we discuss the binomial theorem and binomial distributions, so students do not confuse them with permutations.

In Lessons 6-3 and 6-4 we present the basic properties of counting, which should be familiar to most students, but may be new to some even at this level. If your students have no background in probability you may need to spend an extra day on these lessons.

In Lesson 6-5, contingency tables are studied both for their importance in understanding results of experiments and to set up Lesson 6-6, in which such tables are examined to determine the probability that they could result from particular situations. Lesson 6-7 introduces probability simulations, in

Ask students: Would *you* have concluded (from the data in the table) that the vaccine was successful? You might ask them to defend why their answer. To answer the question, one needs to know how many children would have developed paralytic polio in each group if there were no difference between the groups. Since 148 children out of 401,974 developed the disease, the relative frequency of the disease was 0.000368 (or about 368 per million children). About 74 in each group would have gotten the disease.

Is the difference between 33 and 74 enough to say that the vaccine was successful? Most people would say yes. But what is enough of a difference? Suppose 70 vaccinated children and 78 unvaccinated children had developed paralytic polio. Is that enough? If that is not enough of a difference, suppose 65 vaccinated children and 83 unvaccinated had children developed paralytic polio. The chi-square test in this chapter provides a way to find out.

Notice that the table is 2×3 but the left column is the sum of the entries in the two right columns, so the table is essentially 2×2.

Chapter 6 Projects

At the end of each chapter, you will find projects related to the chapter. At this time you might want to have students look over the projects on pages 426 and 427. You might want to have students tentatively select a project on which to work. Then, as students read and progress through the chapter, they can finalize their project choices.

Sometimes students might work alone. At other times, you might let them collaborate with classmates for a presentation and discussion. We recommend that you allow for diversity and encourage students to use their imaginations when presenting their projects. As students work on projects throughout the year, they should see many uses of mathematics in the real world.

Scientists knew that a virus caused polio, but they had no cure. In the early 1950s, Jonas Salk of the University of Pittsburgh developed a vaccine that seemed to prevent polio. But how could one know? There were tens of thousands of polio cases, but they represented only a small percentage of the population. The study to show the vaccine worked had to be quite large. The table below summarizes the data that Salk and his team collected. All the children were 6–9 years old.

From these data, would you conclude that the vaccine was successful? The scientists did, and despite vocal criticism, the Salk vaccine

was put into widespread production. After some false starts, polio vaccinations became standard for children in the U.S., and after a few years, the more effective Sabin vaccine replaced Salk's. The number of polio cases declined precipitously, and today polio has been nearly eradicated in the U.S. and many other countries world wide.

The analysis of this and other similar experiments is based on randomization. In this chapter, you will study the concepts that underlie this kind of analysis and work with an inferential statistic that allows you to draw conclusions from certain kinds of data.

	Total	Developed Paralytic Polio	Did Not Develop Paralytic Polio
Vaccinated Children	200,745	33	200,712
Unvaccinated Children	201,229	115	201,114

Source: Journal of the American Statstical Association, December 1965

359

preparation for understanding the last two lessons of the chapter, in which simulations are very helpful. Lesson 6-8 covers the (valid) Law of Large Numbers, relating probability with relative frequency, and the (invalid) "Law of Averages." The chapter closes with a lesson on the use of a chi-square test to determine whether a particular distribution of frequencies or relative frequencies is reasonable to expect given particular hypotheses in a situation.

Some of the contexts discussed in this chapter are used in more than one lesson. This makes the discussion more efficient and less frustrating for students. Consequently, we discourage skipping lessons in this chapter.

Lesson 6-1

GOAL

Introduce the basic vocabulary and principles of probability. Calculate probabilities for events in which the sample space is small and finite and the outcomes are equally likely.

SPUR Objectives

The SPUR Objectives for all of Chapter 6 are found in the Chapter Review on pages 432–435.

A Compute probabilities of events in various contexts.

G List sample spaces and events for experiments.

Materials/Resources

· Lesson Master 6-1
· Resource Masters 126 and 127

HOMEWORK
• Option 1
• Option 2

• Questions 1–9
• • Questions 10–20
• • Question 21 (extra credit)
• Reading Lesson 6-2
• Covering the Ideas 6-2 (Questions 1–9)

Local Standards

---

1 Warm-Up

A drawer contains *r* red socks, *b* blue socks, and *w* white socks. Assume that you draw a sock randomly from the drawer.

1. What is the probability that it is red?
$\frac{r}{r+b+w}$

2. What is the probability that it is not white? $1 - \frac{w}{r+b+w}$

3. What is the probability that it is green? **0**

Lesson 6-1 Introduction to Probability

> **BIG IDEA** When outcomes of a situation are equally likely, the probability of an event is the percent or fraction of outcomes that fit the event.

Probability theory is the branch of mathematics that studies situations in which there is an element of chance. In this lesson we review the basic ideas of probability you have likely seen in previous courses.

The Outcomes and Sample Space of an Experiment

A situation with several possible results is called an **experiment**. Probabilities are a measure of how relatively often the results occur. Each result of an experiment is called an **outcome**. The set of all possible outcomes of an experiment is the **sample space** for the experiment. Here are a few experiments and their sample spaces.

Experiment	Sample Space
flipping a coin	{heads, tails}
tossing a six-sided die	{1, 2, 3, 4, 5 6}
taking an antibiotic for a sore throat	{sore throat cured, sore throat continues}
picking an integer from 1 to 100	{n ∈ ℤ	1 ≤ n ≤ 100}

Notice that an experiment does not have to take place in a laboratory!

Example 1

Two six-sided dice, one red and one green, are thrown, and both numbers are recorded.

a. List all possible outcomes for the experiment.

b. How many outcomes are in the sample space for this experiment?

Solution

a. Each one of the six possible outcomes for the red die can occur with any one of the six possible outcomes for the green die. The outcomes are pictured on the next page. Instead of drawing the dice, you might list the outcomes using ordered pairs (red, green), from right to left, top to bottom: (1, 1), (2, 1), (3, 1), (4, 1), (5, 1), (6, 1), (1, 2), (2, 2), and so on, until (6, 6).

Vocabulary

probability theory
experiment
outcome
sample space
event
probability of an event, *P(E)*
fair, unbiased
randomly, at random
empty set, null set

Mental Math

At the intersection of Large Avenue and Busy Street, the lights are timed as follows.

Large Ave	Busy Street	Time (s)
Green	Red	20
Yellow	Red	5
Red	Green	30
Red	Yellow	5

a. For a driver on Busy Street, what fraction of the time is the light red?

b. For a driver on Large Avenue, what percent of the time is the light green?

c. If you are a person who drives every day on Large Avenue through this intersection, what are the chances of the light being green today and tomorrow?

a. $\frac{5}{12}$
b. ≈ 33.33%
c. 1 out of 9

Background

The lesson is review for students who have taken UCSMP courses previously. Probably the most imposing thing about it is the number of definitions and the cryptic formulas. Don't let students be dissuaded by this.

The outcomes and sample space of an experiment The language of set theory is particularly appropriate for studying probability. The sample space is the set of possible outcomes of an experiment; an event is a subset of the sample space. There is a nice analogy with geometry: the sample space is the entire space; an outcome is a point; an event is a figure.

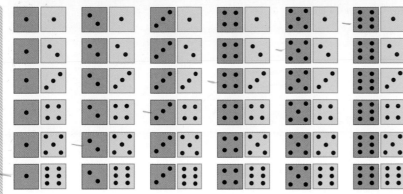

b. The list and picture show that there are 36 outcomes in the sample space.

 QY1

> ▶ **QY1**
>
> A person tosses a penny, nickel, and dime and records if each is heads or tails. List all possible outcomes.

Events and Probabilities

When two dice are thrown, people are often concerned with the sum of the dots that show on the dice. For example, they may want to get a sum of 7. This is an *event*. In general, an **event** is any subset of the sample space of an experiment. Here are some possible events in the experiment of tossing the two dice from Example 1.

Event description	Outcomes in the event
tossing "doubles"	(1, 1), (2, 2), (3, 3), (4, 4), (5, 5), (6,6)
tossing a sum of 10	(4, 6), (5, 5), (6, 4)
tossing a 3 on the red die	(3, 1), (3, 2), (3, 3), (3, 4) (3, 5), (3, 6)
tossing a sum of 1	none

 QY2

> ▶ **QY2**
>
> In the experiment of tossing two six-sided dice from Example 1, list the outcomes in the event "tossing a difference of 4".

The *probability of an event* is a number from 0 to 1 that measures the likelihood, or chance, that the event will occur. Probabilities may be written as fractions, decimals, percents, or relative frequencies. An event that is expected to happen one-quarter of the time has a probability that may be written as $\frac{1}{4}$, $\frac{2}{8}$, 0.25, 25%, or any other way equivalent to these.

Let $N(E)$ be the number of outcomes in an event E, and $N(S)$ be the number of outcomes in the sample space S. For the experiment "tossing two dice," $N(S) = 36$. If $E_1 =$ "tossing a sum less than 4," then $E_1 = \{(1, 1), (1, 2), (2, 1)\}$ and $N(E_1) = 3$. So if all outcomes in S were *equally likely*, you would expect to roll a sum less than 4 $\frac{3}{36}$ or $\frac{1}{12}$ of the time. "Equally likely" means each outcome has an equal chance of happening.

Introduction to Probability **361**

---

2 Teaching

Notes on the Lesson

The outcomes and sample space of an experiment The sample space of an experiment is not always unique. For instance, in tossing two dice, one could make the case that the sample space consists of the 36 ordered pairs (1, 1) through (6, 6). However, since the sum of the numbers is recorded and the dice are not distinguishable, if you were interested in the sum, you could choose to consider the 11 sums as the sample space. In Example 1, the sample space is viewed as having 36 outcomes, because it is easier to calculate the probability when the outcomes are equally likely.

Additional Example

Example 1 A small box contains 30 blue, 30 green, and 25 red paper clips. Two paper clips are taken from the box and their colors recorded.

a. List all possible outcomes for this experiment. **BB, BG, BR, GG, GR, RR**

b. How many outcomes are in the sample space for this experiment? **6**

Relative frequencies and probabilities Throughout UCSMP texts, we are careful to distinguish between *relative frequencies*, which are ratios calculated from data, and *probabilities*, which are values hopefully close to relative frequencies that are either (1) hypothesized on the basis of an educated guess, (2) calculated on the basis of some assumptions such as randomness or equal likelihood, or (3) estimated from known relative frequencies.

We do not use the term "theoretical probability" for "probability," or the term "experimental probability" for "relative frequency," because to have two different kinds of probability confuses what comes from assumptions (probability) with what comes from data (relative frequency).

6-1

Additional Examples

Example 2 In the situation of Additional Example 1, which of the six outcomes are equally likely?
BR and GR are equally likely (with probability $\frac{15}{119}$), as are BB and GG (with probability $\frac{29}{238}$).

Example 3 Assume that births of boys and girls are equally likely.

a. How many outcomes are in the same sample space for a family with four children? **16**

b. Find the probability that a family of four children has one girl and three boys. **0.25**

This idea is generalized in the definition of probability.

Definition of Probability of an Event

Let E be an event in a finite sample space S. Let $N(E)$ and $N(S)$ be the numbers of elements in E and S, respectively. If each outcome in S is equally likely, then the probability that E occurs, called the **probability of E** and denoted $P(E)$, is given by

$$P(E) = \frac{N(E)}{N(S)} = \frac{\text{number of outcomes in event}}{\text{number of outcomes in the sample space}}.$$

STOP QY3

When a sample space has n outcomes all of which are equally likely, then the experiment is called **fair** or **unbiased** and each outcome has probability $\frac{1}{n}$. The outcomes are said to occur **randomly** or **at random**.

▶ **QY3**

In the tossing of two fair dice from Example 1, what is the probability of a sum of 4?

GUIDED

Example 2

An experiment consists of tossing two fair coins and counting the number of heads. Consider the events 1 head in all, 2 heads in all, and 0 heads in all. Are these events equally likely?

Solution Begin by listing all possible outcomes using a tree diagram. Let H = heads, T = tails.

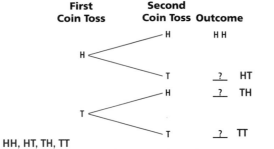

First Coin Toss — **Second Coin Toss** — **Outcome**

H — H — H H
H — T — _?_ HT
T — H — _?_ TH
T — T — _?_ TT

HH, HT, TH, TT
The sample space is { _?_ , _?_ , _?_ , _?_ }.

There is/are _?_ outcome(s) in the event 0 heads, _?_ **1 2** outcome(s) in the event 1 head, and _?_ outcome(s) in the event **1** 2 heads. These events _?_ (are/are not) equally likely. **are not**

Caution: You must know or be told that outcomes are equally likely before you can apply the definition of probability.

ENGLISH LEARNERS

Vocabulary Development

The language of probability can be confusing because all the terms involve words such as *experiment*, *trial*, *sample*, *space*, and *event* that have other meanings to students. Be careful to clarify the meanings of all these terms.

Example 3

A researcher is studying the number of boys and girls in families with three children. Assume that the birth of a boy or a girl is equally likely.

a. List the sample space.

b. Find the probability that a family of three children has exactly one boy.

Solution Let B represent a boy, G represent a girl, and a triple of letters stand for the genders of the children from oldest to youngest.

a. The sample space is the set of all possible outcomes:
{BBB, BBG, BGB, __?__, __?__, __?__, __?__, __?__}   BGG; GBB; GBG; GGB; GGG

b. There are __?__ outcomes in the sample space. __?__ outcomes are in the event "exactly one boy." So P(one boy) = $\frac{?}{?}$.   8; 3; $\frac{3}{8}$

For the situation in Example 3, the probability was found by listing the outcomes in the sample space. This was possible because there are only a few outcomes, and because it was assumed there is an equal chance of a boy or a girl being born. In more complicated situations, a *simulation* can be used to answer questions. You will learn about simulations later in this chapter.

If an event contains no possible outcomes, then it cannot occur and it has probability 0. For instance, in Example 3, the event "four boys" has probability 0. Recall from earlier courses that a set with no elements is called the **empty set** or the **null set** and is denoted either by the symbol { } or Ø. With this notation, we write $P(\{\ \}) = P(Ø) = 0$. If an event is certain to happen, then it contains all the possible outcomes in the sample space, and has probability 1. That is, $N(E) = N(S)$, so $P(E) = \frac{N(E)}{N(S)} = 1$. These properties are summarized in the theorem below.

> **Theorem (Basic Properties of Probability)**
>
> Let S be the sample space associated with an experiment. Then, for any outcome or event E in S,
> (i) $0 \leq P(E) \leq 1$.
> (ii)   if $E = S$, then $P(E) = 1$.
> (iii)   if $E = Ø$, then $P(E) = 0$.

Relative Frequencies and Probabilities

When tossing a coin, you might *assume* that heads and tails are equally likely. From this, it follows that the probability of a head is $\frac{1}{2}$ and the probability of a tail is $\frac{1}{2}$. In 2500 tosses of the coin, you would expect about 1250 heads. If you have some reason to expect that a particular coin is biased, you might toss the coin a large number of times and take the long-term *relative frequency* of heads as an estimate of the probability.

Have students consider a sample space consisting of equally likely outcomes. Suppose an event E consists of x of these outcomes and there are y outcomes in the sample space that are in E', the set of outcomes not in E. Then the odds in favor of E are $\frac{x}{y}$ and the odds against E are $\frac{y}{x}$.

Have students explore the relationship between odds and probability with the following questions.

1. Give a formula for odds in favor of an event E in terms of $P(E)$ and $P(E')$. $\frac{P(E)}{P(E')}$

2. Give a formula for odds against an event E in terms of $P(E)$ and $P(E')$. $\frac{P(E')}{P(E)}$

Notes on the Lesson

Example 3 This example can be used to illustrate the difference between a relative frequency and a probability. In this example, we *assume* that the births are equally likely even though it is known from birth certificate data that the relative frequencies are significantly different from $\frac{1}{2}$.

Basic Properties of Probability Theorem It may seem as if (ii) and (iii) could both be written as "*if and only if*" statements. The question is whether one wishes to allow impossible outcomes in the sample space. For instance, one could ask, "What is the probability of getting a 13 as the sum of numbers in the tosses of two dice?" While 13 is not a possible outcome, it could be given as an outcome in the sample space. Then we would have $P(\{13\}) = 0$, but $\{13\}$ is not the null set. It is for this reason that we do *not* write the statements in *if-and-only-if* form.

In function terms, the Properties of Probabilities are properties of the domain and range of a probability function P. The fact that the independent variable in this function (an event) may be the occurrence of one *or more* of the outcomes listed in the domain makes a probability function more complicated than most of the functions students have studied up to this point. For this reason we do not discuss P as a function in this lesson, but use the notation in anticipation of discussing *probability distribution* functions in a later chapter.

Relative frequencies and probabilities The distinction between a relative frequency and a probability may be represented graphically. Suppose a coin is flipped 1, 2, 3,..., n times and $P(n)$ represents the relative frequency of heads. The graph of the pairs $(n, P(n))$ should theoretically approach (from both directions) the line $y = p$ as an asymptote, where p is the probability that the coin lands heads up. With each toss, the relative frequency changes a little bit, but the probability remains the same.

Recommended Assignment

- Questions 1–9
- • Questions 10–20
- • Question 21 (extra credit)
- Reading Lesson 6-2
- Covering the Ideas 6-2 (Questions 1–9)

Notes on the Questions

Questions 1–7 If students have missed any of these, you may want to clarify the definitions of the terms *sample space*, *event*, and *outcome*. A useful geometric analogy is to view the sample space as the entire space, an outcome as a point, and an event as a figure.

For instance, if 1205 heads occur in 2500 tosses, then the relative frequency of heads is $\frac{1205}{2500} = 48.2\%$. Then you are faced with a decision: Is the coin a fair coin and did the 1205 heads just occur by random chance, or is the coin slightly biased towards heads? Later in this chapter, you will see some mathematics that can help you decide.

While relative frequencies and probabilities are related, the meanings of the two values differ. The values of both range from 0 to 1. However, a relative frequency of 0 means an event *has not occurred*; for example, the relative frequency of snow on July 4th in Florida since 1900 is 0. In contrast, a probability of 0 in a finite sample space means the event *cannot occur*. For example, the probability of tossing a sum of 17 with two fair six-sided dice is 0. We say that the outcome "tossing a sum of 17" is not in the sample space.

Now consider a value of 1. A relative frequency is 1 when an event *has occurred* in each known trial. A probability is 1 when an event *must always occur*. The probability is 1 that the toss of a pair of dice gives a number less than 13. Therefore if something has a probability of 1, then the relative frequency of the event will also be 1. However, if a relative frequency is 1, this does not guarantee that the probability is 1. The same holds for 0.

Questions

COVERING THE IDEAS

1. A person guesses randomly on an "Always, Sometimes, or Never" question. The correct answer to the question is "Always."
   a. List the sample space. **{Always, Sometimes, Never}**
   b. Describe the event "getting a wrong answer".
   c. What is N("getting a wrong answer")? **2**
   d. What is P("getting a wrong answer")? $\frac{2}{3}$

In 2–5, two fair dice are rolled as in Example 1.
   a. List the outcomes of the named event.
   b. Give the probability of the event.

2. The sum of the numbers shown is 9. a.{(3, 6), (4, 5), (5, 4), (6, 3)} b. $\frac{1}{9}$
3. The absolute value of the difference of the numbers shown is 2.
4. The sum of the numbers shown is either even or odd.
5. The product of the numbers shown is 11. a. ∅ b. 0
6. An egg is dropped onto a cement floor from a height of two feet. You wonder whether it will break or not.
   a. List all the outcomes of the experiment.
   b. Are the outcomes equally likely? Explain why or why not.
   a. {egg breaks, egg doesn't break}
   b. No. We would expect the egg to break almost every time.

Oops!

1b. {Sometimes, Never}

3a. {(1, 3), (2, 4), (3, 5), (4, 6), (3, 1), (4, 2), (5, 3), (6, 4)}

3b. $\frac{2}{9}$

4a. {(1, 1), (2, 1), (3, 1), (4, 1), (5, 1),(6, 1), (1, 2), (2, 2), (3, 2), (4, 2), (5, 2), (6, 2), (1, 3), (2, 3), (3, 3), (4, 3), (5, 3), (6, 3), (1, 4), (2, 4), (3, 4), (4, 4), (5, 4), (6, 4), (1, 5), (2, 5), (3, 5), (4, 5), (5, 5), (6, 5), (1, 6), (2, 6), (3, 6), (4, 6), (5, 6), (6, 6)}

4b. 1

Extension

Ask the following: Is it possible to number the faces of two fair dice so that each of the sums from 2 to 12 is equally likely? Allow the possibility that two faces on the same die could have the same numbers.

No, there are 11 sums; each cannot occur the same number of times in 36 tosses.

Then point out that it is possible to have each of the sums from 1 to 12 be equally likely. Challenge students to find out how.

Number one die with 3 sides of 1 and 3 sides of 2; number the faces of a second die 0, 2, 4, 6, 8, and 10.

7. Two fair coins are flipped as in Example 2. {HT, TH, TT}
   a. List the outcomes of the event "At least one tail appears."
   b. Give the probability of the event "At least one tail appears." $\frac{3}{4}$

8. A closet contains w white shirts, b black shirts, and g grey shirts. One shirt is chosen at random.
   a. What is the probability a grey shirt is chosen?
   b. What is the probability a black shirt is chosen?
   c. What is the probability a white shirt is not chosen?

9. A family has four children.
   a. List the sample space for the genders of the children, using B for boy and G for girl.
   b. What is the probability that the family has 3 boys and 1 girl? $\frac{1}{4}$

APPLYING THE MATHEMATICS

10. Three fair coins are flipped.
    a. List the outcomes of the events "0 heads," "1 head," "2 heads," and "3 heads."
    b. Give the probability of each event.

11. Suppose n fair coins are flipped.
    a. Make a table showing the probability of getting all heads for $n = 1, 2, 3,$ and 4.
    b. Based on your table, predict the probability of getting all heads for $n = 5$. $\frac{1}{32}$

12. Which of (1) or (2) is possible, and why?
    (1) The relative frequency of an event is 0, but the probability of the event is not 0.
    (2) The probability of an event is 0, but the relative frequency of the event is not 0.

13. Let A be an event. If $P(A) = 0.9$ and there are 460 equally likely outcomes in the sample space, how many outcomes are in A? **414**

14. A whole number between 1 and 366 (inclusive) is chosen at random. Find the probability of each event.
    a. The number is divisible by 5. $\frac{73}{366}$
    b. The number is divisible by 6. $\frac{1}{6}$

REVIEW

15. Consider the equation $\cos \theta = -\frac{1}{2}$. (**Lesson 4-4**)
    a. Draw a unit circle and mark the two points $(\cos \theta, \sin \theta)$ for which $\cos \theta = -\frac{1}{2}$. **See margin.**
    b. Give two values of θ between $540°$ and $900°$ that make the equation true. **600°, 840°**
    c. Give a negative value of θ that makes the equation true.
       Answes vary. Sample: –120°

8a. $\dfrac{g}{w + b + g}$

8b. $\dfrac{b}{w + b + g}$

8c. $1 - \dfrac{w}{w + b + g}$
   $= \dfrac{b + g}{w + b + g}$

9a. {BBBB, BBBG, BBGB, BBGG, BGBB, BGBG, BGGB, BGGG, GBBB, GBBG, GBGB, GBGG, GGBB, GGBG, GGGB, GGGG}

10a. 0 heads: {TTT}; 1 head: {HTT, THT, TTH}; 2 heads: {HHT, HTH, THH}; 3 heads: {HHH}

10b. 0 heads: $\frac{1}{8}$; 1 head: $\frac{3}{8}$; 2 heads: $\frac{3}{8}$; 3 heads: $\frac{1}{8}$

11a.

n	$P(n)$
1	$\frac{1}{2}$
2	$\frac{1}{4}$
3	$\frac{1}{8}$
4	$\frac{1}{16}$

12. Only (1) is possible. If the probability of an outcome is nonzero, it is still plausible that the outcome does not occur (giving a relative frequency of zero). But if the probability is zero then the outcome is impossible. Thus, its relative frequency would be zero as well.

Notes on the Questions

Question 14 If you give more questions of this type, there is a general pattern that students might know or discover. The probability that a number from 1 to m is divisible by n is $\dfrac{\left\lfloor \frac{m}{n} \right\rfloor}{m}$. For example, the probability that a number from 1 to 300 is divisible by 7 is $\frac{42}{300}$.

Additional Answers

15a.

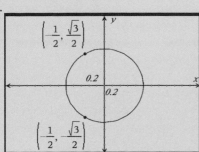

Notes on the Questions
Questions 18–20 These questions are important to review in preparation for Lesson 6-2.

4 Wrap-Up

Ongoing Assessment
Write a problem like Questions 2–5 on the board. Have each student explain orally how to find each answer, referring to the sample space pictured on page 361 as necessary. **Answers vary.** Students should explain how to compute probabilities.

Additional Answers

16a.

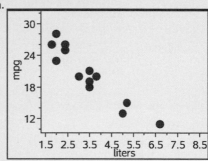

16f. –0.9444; This indicates that there is a strong negative relationship between the two variables.

19a. union

19b. union

19c. intersection

20a. {eggs, cheese}

20b. {bacon, eggs, cheese, ham}

21. Answers vary. Sample: Summary of the article "Are the Digits of Pi Random? Lab Researcher May Hold the Key" by Paul Press <http://www.lbl.gov/Science-Articles/Articles/Archive/pi-random.html>. Pi is an irrational number thought to be normal, which means its digits appear to be statistically random. In base 10 this means any single digit appears one-tenth of the time, any two-digit sequence occurs one-hundredth of the time, and so on. Pi appears to behave this way and this has been shown approximately true for one-digit strings in the decimal approximation to 6 billion decimal places.

(continued in bottom channel)

---

16. The table at the right gives the names of fourteen models of cars from the 2007 model year, their engine sizes measured in liters, and their fuel economy in miles per gallon of gas. **(Lesson 2-3)**
    a. Make a scatterplot of the data, using engine size as the independent variable. **See margin.**
    b. Describe the direction of the association between fuel economy and engine size.
    c. Find the equation of the least squares regression line. **y = –3.43x + 32.26**
    d. What is the value of the slope of your regression line? What are its units?
    e. Explain how the direction of the association is indicated in the value of the slope.
    f. What is the correlation coefficient for the model? What does it tell you about the relationship between engine size and fuel economy? **See margin.**

Car Model	Engine Size (liters)	Fuel Economy (M.P.G.)
Acura RL	3.5	19
Audi S8	5.2	15
Bentley Azure	6.7	11
BMW M6	5	13
Buick Lucerne	3.8	20
Chevrolet Optra5	2	23
Chrysler 300A WD	3.5	18
Dodge Caliber	1.8	26
Ford Taurus	3	20
Honda Accord	2.4	26
Hyundai Elantra	2	28
Kia Optima	2.4	25
Saturn Aura	3.5	21
Toyota Camry	2.4	25

Source: fueleconomy.gov

17. An alegbra teacher has 15 students who took a test in 2nd hour and 25 students each in 3rd and 7th hour who took the test. The following table summarizes the test results. **(Lesson 1-2)**

	2nd hour	3rd hour	7th hour
$\bar{x}$	72	80	83

   a. What is the mean of the scores in all three classes combined?
   b. A student in 3rd hour missed the quiz because of a field trip. When his score was averaged in, the mean for this class fell to 79.2. What was his score? **a. ≈ 79.3   b. about 59.2**

18. $x\%$ of the people who make reservations at a restaurant show up. What percent does not show up? **(Previous Course) $(100 - x)\%$**

19. **Fill in the Blanks** with "union" or "intersection." **See margin.**
    a. An angle is the ___?___ of two rays with the same endpoint.
    b. The set of all triangles is the ___?___ of the set of isosceles triangles and the set of scalene triangles.
    c. The set of multiples of 35 is the ___?___ of the set of multiples of 7 and the set of multiples of 5. **(Previous Course)**

20. If A = {bacon, eggs, cheese} and B = {eggs, cheese, ham}, **See margin.**
    a. What is $A \cap B$?   b. What is $A \cup B$? **(Previous Course)**

EXPLORATION

21. The digits of the decimal expansion of π have been conjectured as constituting a set of random digits in the sense that each digit might occur with probability 0.1; each two-digit pair might occur with probability 0.01, etc. A number with this property is called a *normal number*. Find and summarize an article about this possible property of π or other irrational numbers. **See margin.**

16b. negative linear relationship

16d. –3.43 miles per gallon per liter

16e. There is a negative association indicated by the negative slope. Thus, an increase in engine size by 1 liter results in a 3.423 MPG decrease.

QY ANSWERS

1. HHH, HHT, HTH, HTT, THH, THT, TTH, TTT

2. (5, 1); (6, 2); (1, 5); (2, 6)

3. $P(\text{sum of 4}) = \frac{4}{36} = \frac{1}{12}$

Additional Answers

However this does not prove normality in base 10 or any other base. Although many irrational mathematical constants are thought to be normal, none has been successfully proved to be normal. David H. Bailey and Richard Crandall are trying to prove normality of some of these constants by comparing them to the field of chaotic dynamics in a conjecture they refer to as "Hypothesis A." Hypothesis A was built upon a formula known as the "BBP formula," created by Bailey, Borwein, and Plouffe, used to calculate an arbitrary digit of pi without calculating any previous digit. A digit-calculation algorithm of the BBP formula yields chaotic sequences described in Hypothesis A. The hypothesis is that if the sequences are uniformly distributed between 0 and 1, the constant is normal. There is yet no proof of Hypothesis A, but this conjecture is a large step toward making a seemingly impossible problem approachable.

Principles of Probability

Vocabulary

union of sets
disjoint sets
mutually exclusive sets
intersection of sets
complementary events
complement of *A*, not *A*

▶ **BIG IDEA** The fundamental principles of probability are derived from basic principles of counting.

Because probabilities are often calculated by dividing one count by another, effective counting is essential to probability.

The Addition Counting Principle

The Addition Counting Principle is the most basic principle of counting. Addition finds the number of elements in the *union* of two *disjoint* sets. $A \cup B$, the **union of sets** *A* and *B*, contains all elements that are either in *A* or in *B*. If *A* and *B* have no elements in common, they are called **disjoint sets** or **mutually exclusive sets**.

Addition Counting Principle (Mutually Exclusive Form)

If two finite sets *A* and *B* are mutually exclusive, then
$N(A \cup B) = N(A) + N(B)$.

Activity 1

Answers vary. Sample: Step 1: 11, 7, 4, 6, 2, 2, 9, 8, 2, 8, 12, 11, 11, 5, 8, 8, 6, 9, 9, 9

MATERIALS a pair of fair six-sided dice

Step 1 Toss a pair of fair six-sided dice 20 times, recording the sum of face up numbers each time.

Step 2 Make a frequency table of each sum using the combined data for your class.

Step 3
a. What was the class's relative frequency of having a sum of 7? $\frac{1}{20}$
b. What was the class's relative frequency of having a sum of 11? $\frac{3}{20}$
c. What was the class's relative frequency of having a sum of 7 or 11? $\frac{4}{20}$

Step 4 Which of the events in Step 3 are mutually exclusive?

In the Activity, you computed relative frequencies of several events as well as the union of mutually exclusive events. This idea extends to probability in the following way. Think of *A* and *B* as events in a finite sample space *S*. Divide both sides of the equation in the Addition Counting Principle by $N(S)$.

$$\frac{N(A \cup B)}{N(S)} = \frac{N(A)}{N(S)} + \frac{N(B)}{N(S)}$$

The fractions all stand for probabilities, identified in the next theorem.

Mental Math

State as a simple fraction.
a. 2^{-5} $\frac{1}{32}$
b. 5^{-2} $\frac{1}{25}$
c. $3 \cdot 10^{-4}$ $\frac{3}{10000}$
d. $\left(\frac{1}{2}\right)^{-6}$ $\frac{1}{\left(\frac{1}{2}\right)^6} = 64$

Step 2:

Sum	Frequency
2	3
3	0
4	1
5	1
6	2
7	1
8	4
9	4
10	0
11	3
12	1

Step 4: The events "a sum of 7" and a "sum of 11" are mutually exclusive.

Background

The Addition Counting Principle

There are two Addition Counting Principles and two Probability Theorems in this lesson. They differ only in that one deals with mutually exclusive events, the other does not. They evolve from basic models for addition and subtraction that UCSMP students learned before high school: the Putting-Together Model for Addition and the Take-Away Model for Subtraction. The more complicated Addition Counting Principle simply says that to get the total number of things in two sets all you have to do is add the number in each set and subtract the number you counted twice. If the sets represent events, then divide this total by the number of outcomes in the sample space and you have a probability of either event occurring. If you can identify the events as mutually exclusive, then the process simplifies. If the events are complementary, you can compute probabilities in your head.

(continued on next page)

GOAL

Develop two forms of the Addition Counting Principle from basic principles of probability, and use them to develop theorems for finding probabilities of unions of events (mutually exclusive or not), and probabilities of complementary events.

SPUR Objectives

A Compute probabilities of events in various contexts.

D Compute probabilities using the General and Mutually Exclusive Forms of the Probability of the Union of Events and the Probability of Complements.

Materials/Resources

· Lesson Master 6-2
· Resource Masters 128–130
· A pair of fair six-sided dice

HOMEWORK   • Option 1
                 • Option 2
• Questions 1–9
• • Questions 10–23
• • Question 24 (extra credit)
• Reading Lesson 6-3
• Covering the Ideas 6-3
  (Questions 1–8)

Local Standards

1 ▶ **Warm-Up**

According to Nielsen Media Research in October 2008, of the 113.1 million U.S. households that owned at least one TV set, 82% had 2 or more TV sets and 88% received basic cable. From this information, what are the largest and smallest percents of households that might have both 2 or more TV sets and also have basic cable? **82%; 70%**

Source: *World Almanac and Book of Facts 2009*, p. 291.

2 Teaching

Notes on the Lesson

The Addition Counting Principle

While the distinction between mutually exclusive events and not mutually exclusive events is easy to make in the examples of this lesson, it seems that many people do not make the distinction so easily. For example, the number of people reported as having learning disorders or physical disabilities, or being afflicted with a disease, is sometimes overestimated because the estimator does not take into account the possibility that the same individual could have more than one disorder. The amounts of time people spend watching television is often inflated because other simultaneous activities are overlooked.

Activity 1 If you wish to use alternatives to dice problems, have the class collect statistics on eye color and hair color and calculate, for example, P(brunette and blue eyes).

Examples 1 and 4 These examples are related.

Additional Example

Example 1 Jameel and Rhonda had to take a make up test after school. Their teacher told them they could come in no earlier than 3:00 and leave no later than 4:00. Jameel took 38 minutes on the test and Rhonda 51 minutes. For at least how many minutes were Jameel and Rhonda taking the test at the same time? **29 minutes**

> **Theorem (Probability of the Union of Mutually Exclusive Events)**
>
> If A and B are mutually exclusive events in the same finite sample space, then $P(A \cup B) = P(A) + P(B)$.

Activity 2

Step 1 Write the possible sums of the face-up numbers when two fair six-sided dice are tossed. Which sums are prime?

Step 2 Let each possible sum be an event. Find the probability of each event.

Step 3 Find the probability of each of the prime number events. Add them to find the probability that, when two fair six-sided dice are tossed, the sum of the face-up numbers is a prime number.

Step 1: 2, 3, 4, 5, 6, 7, 8, 9, 10, 11, 12; possible sums that are prime: 2, 3, 5, 7, 11

Step 2: $P(2) = \frac{1}{36}$; $P(3) = \frac{1}{18}$; $P(4) = \frac{1}{12}$; $P(5) = \frac{1}{9}$; $P(6) = \frac{5}{36}$; $P(7) = \frac{1}{6}$; $P(8) = \frac{5}{36}$; $P(9) = \frac{1}{9}$; $P(10) = \frac{1}{12}$; $P(11) = \frac{1}{18}$; $P(12) = \frac{1}{36}$

Step 3: $P(\text{prime}) = P(2) + P(3) + P(5) + P(7) + P(11) = \frac{15}{36}$

Overlapping Events

When two events are not mutually exclusive, then they have outcomes in common and are said to *overlap*. The set of overlapping events is the set of elements in both A and B, called the **intersection** of the sets A and B, denoted by $A \cap B$. The table below summarizes the language of set intersections.

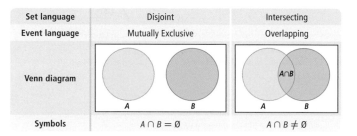

Set language	Disjoint	Intersecting
Event language	Mutually Exclusive	Overlapping
Venn diagram	(A) (B)	(A∩B) (A) (B)
Symbols	$A \cap B = \emptyset$	$A \cap B \neq \emptyset$

Example 1

Suppose at a high school, 298 students study only French, only Spanish, or both languages. The school reports 115 students study French and 209 study Spanish, but because $115 + 209 > 298$, there must be students who study both languages. How many students study both?

Solution Let F be the set of French students and S be the set of Spanish students. Then $N(F) = 115$, $N(S) = 209$, and $N(F \cup S) = 298$. Let x be the number of students who study both languages. That is, $x = N(F \cap S)$. Then the number of students who only study French is $115 - x$ and the number of students who only study Spanish is $209 - x$. The Venn diagram at the right shows this.

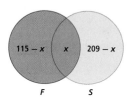

$115 - x$ | x | $209 - x$

F S

368   Counting, Probability, and Inference

Probability of the union of any two sets From (assumed) probabilities, other probabilities can be calculated using basic counting principles. Again the language of set theory is most useful. We show that
$$N(A \cup B) = N(A) + N(B) - N(A \cap B),$$
from which
$$P(A \cup B) = P(A) + P(B) - P(A \cap B).$$

Students should be able to compute the number of elements in a union of sets, and apply the theorems appropriately.

If S is the sample space, and A and B are complements, then by the definition of complement, $A \cup B = S$, from which $P(A \cup B) = 1$. Also, by the definition of complement, $A \cap B = \emptyset$, and so $P(A \cap B) = 0$. Consequently, substituting in $P(A \cup B) = P(A) + P(B) - P(A \cap B)$, we have the following theorem, not explicitly stated in the lesson:

Studying only French, only Spanish, or both languages are mutually exclusive events. By the Addition Counting Principle,

$$N(F \cup S) = (115 - x) + x + (209 - x) = 324 - x.$$

Thus $N(F \cup S)$ can be found by subtracting the overlap from the total.

So $N(F \cup S) = 298 = 324 - x.$

Solve the equation. $x = 26$

Thus, there are 26 students studying both languages.

The flag of Spain

Check

$115 - 26 = 89$ students are studying only French, and $209 - 26 = 183$ are studying only Spanish. $89 + 183 + 26 = 298$, so it checks.

 QY

This situation is a special case of a more general result.

> **QY**
>
> What is the probability that a randomly selected student in the high school of Example 1 studies both French and Spanish?

Addition Counting Principle (General Form)

For any finite sets A and B, $N(A \cup B) = N(A) + N(B) - N(A \cap B)$.

Proof If $N(A \cap B) = x$, then the number of elements in A which are not in the intersection is $N(A) - x$. Similarly, there are $N(B) - x$ elements in B which are not in the intersection, as shown at the right.

Then $N(A \cup B) = (N(A) - x) + x + (N(B) - x)$

$\qquad\qquad = N(A) + N(B) - x$

$\qquad\qquad = N(A) + N(B) - N(A \cap B)$ because $N(A \cap B) = x$.

In Question 11, you are asked to show how the general form of the Addition Counting Principle can be used to derive the theorem below.

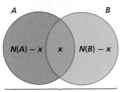

Theorem (Probability of the Union of Events, General Form)

If A and B are any events in the same finite sample space, then $P(A \text{ or } B) = P(A \cup B) = P(A) + P(B) - P(A \cap B)$.

Example 2

A pair of six-sided dice is thrown. If the dice are fair, what is the probability that the dice show doubles or a sum less than 10?

Solution Refer to the dice diagram in Example 1 of Lesson 6-1. Find the number of doubles. There are 6 doubles, so $P(\text{doubles}) = \frac{6}{36}$.

(continued on next page)

If A and B are complementary, then $1 = P(A) + P(B)$.

From this, we obtain the Probability of Complements Theorem at the top of page 371.

$P(A) = 1 - P(B)$.

These ideas are found in many of the previous UCSMP courses.

Find the number of sums less than 10. There are 30 pairs that sum less than 10, so P(sum under 10) $= \frac{30}{36}$. Find the number of doubles that sum less than 10. There are 4 doubles that sum less than 10, so P(doubles and sum under 10) $= \frac{4}{36}$. Use the Probability of the Union of Events theorem.

P(double or sum under 10)

$= $ P(doubles) $+$ P(sum under 10) $-$ P(doubles and sum under 10)

$= \frac{6}{36} + \frac{30}{36} - \frac{4}{36} = \frac{32}{36}$ or about 88.9%.

GUIDED

Example 3

A pair of fair six-sided dice is thrown. What is the probability that exactly one die shows a 3 or the sum of the numbers is greater than 9?

Solution Again, refer to the dice diagram in Example 1 of Lesson 6-1.

Count outcomes to find P(one die shows 3), P(sum > 9), and P(one die shows 3 and sum > 9). P(one die shows 3) $= \frac{?}{36}$, P(sum > 9) $= \frac{?}{36}$, and **10; 6**

P(one die shows 3 and sum > 9) $= \frac{?}{36}$. **0**

Use the Probability of the Union of Events theorem.   P(sum > 9);

P(one die shows 3 or sum > 9) $=$ P(one die shows 3) $+$ _?_ $-$ _?_ P(has 3 and sum > 9);

$= \frac{?}{36} + \frac{6}{36} - \frac{?}{36} = \frac{?}{36}$. **10; 0; 16**

Example 3 shows that the Probability of the Union of Mutually Exclusive Events Theorem is a special case of the Probability of the Union of Events Theorem. When A and B are mutually exclusive events, $A \cap B = \emptyset$ and so $P(A \cap B) = 0$. Then,

$$P(A \cup B) = P(A) + P(B) - P(A \cap B)$$

reduces to $P(A \cup B) = P(A) + P(B)$.

Complementary Events

Sometimes events are mutually exclusive and their union is the entire sample space. Such events are called **complementary events**. The **complement of an event A** is called **not A**. Here are examples of events and their complements.

Experiment	Sample Space	Event	Complement
tossing a coin	{heads, tails}	{tails}	{heads}
tossing two coins	{HH, HT, TH, TT}	getting no heads {TT}	getting 1 or 2 heads {HH, HT, TH}
picking an integer from 1 to 100	{$n \in \mathbb{Z} : 1 \le n \le 100$}	picking a prime number	picking 1 or a composite number

By the definition of complementary events, the following theorem holds.

> **Theorem (Probability of Complements)**
>
> If A is any event, then $P(\text{not } A) = 1 - P(A)$.

Example 4

Refer to the 298 students studying languages in Example 1. If a student is selected at random, what is the probability that he is not studying both languages at the same time?

Solution 1 Let event B = studying both languages, and event not B = not studying both languages. We know there are 26 students studying both languages, so $N(B) = 26$ and $P(B) = \frac{26}{298}$.

Apply the Probability of Complements Theorem.

$P(\text{not } B) = 1 - P(B) = 1 - \frac{26}{298} = \frac{272}{298}$ or about 91.3%

Check $P(B) + P(\text{not } B) = \frac{26}{298} + \frac{272}{298} = \frac{298}{298} = 1$

Solution 2 Use the symbols from Solution 1. Since $N(B) = 26$ and $N(S) = 298$, $N(\text{not } B) = 298 - 26 = 272$.

Thus $P(\text{not } B) = \frac{N(\text{not } B)}{N(S)} = \frac{272}{298}$.

Questions

COVERING THE IDEAS

In 1–3, suppose two fair six-sided dice are rolled.
   a. List the outcomes of the named event.
   b. Give the probability of the event.

1. The sum is a multiple of 3.   2. Doubles or a sum over 7.

3. The sum is a multiple of 3, but not a multiple of 2.

4. Consider the experiment of tossing 3 fair coins.
   a. Give a sample space for the experiment.
   b. Find $P(2 \text{ tails})$.   c. Find $P(\text{at least 2 tails})$.
   d. **True or False** $P(3 \text{ tails}) = P(0 \text{ tails})$

5. Assume that events A and B are in the same sample space. Under what conditions is $P(A \cup B) = P(A) + P(B)$ true?

6. Suppose two fair six-sided dice are rolled. Let X = the first die shows 1 and Y = the sum of the numbers on the dice is 5.
   a. Find $N(X \cup Y)$. **9**   b. Find $N(X \cap Y)$. **1**
   c. State whether X and Y are mutually exclusive.

Answers:

1a. {(1, 2), (2, 1), (1, 5), (2, 4), (3, 3), (4, 2), (5, 1), (3, 6), (4, 5), (5, 4), (6, 3), (6, 6)}

1b. $\frac{1}{3}$

2a. {(1, 1), (2, 2), (3, 3), (4, 4), (5, 5), (5, 4), (4, 5), (3, 5), (5, 3), (6, 6), (6, 2), (2, 6), (3, 6), (6, 3), (4, 6), (6, 4), (5, 6), (6, 5)}

2b. $\frac{1}{2}$

3a. {(1, 2), (2, 1), (3, 6), (4, 5), (5, 4), (6, 3)}

3b. $\frac{1}{6}$

4a. {HHH, HTH, HHT, HTT, THT, THH, TTH, TTT}

4b. $\frac{3}{8}$

4c. $\frac{1}{2}$

4d. true

5. when $P(A \cap B) = 0$

6c. X and Y are not mutually exclusive

Additional Example

Example 4 In the situation of Additional Example 2, what is the probability that the dice show a product between 7 and 31? $\frac{7}{12}$

3 Assignment

Recommended Assignment

- Questions 1–9
- • Questions 10–23
- • Question 24 (extra credit)
- Reading Lesson 6-3
- Covering the Ideas 6-3 (Questions 1–8)

Notes on the Questions

Questions 1–7 Again, if students have missed any of these, you may want to clarify the definitions of the terms *sample space*, *event*, *outcome*, and *mutually exclusive*. A useful geometric analogy is to view the sample space as the entire space, an outcome as a point, an event as a figure, and mutually exclusive events as figures that have no points in common.

Question 6 You might ask: In general, given two sets X and Y, when will $N(X \cap Y) = N(X \cup Y)$? **when $X = Y$** When will $N(X \cup Y) = N(X)$? **when Y is a subset of X** When will $N(X \cap Y) = N(X)$? **when X is a subset of Y**

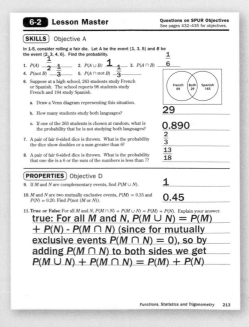

6-2

Notes on the Questions

Question 16 Here we can take the probabilities as equal to the relative frequencies because the entire population is the sample space. Relative frequencies are quite different for different races and ethnicities. For instance, among African-Americans, 49% have type O, 27% have type A, 20% have type B, and 4% have type AB.

7. **True or False** Complementary events are a special case of mutually exclusive events. Explain your answer.

8. Explain why, for any event E, $P(\text{not } E) = 1 - P(E)$.

9. It is estimated that about 10% of males in the U.S. are left-handed. Identify a complement of this event and find its probability.

APPLYING THE MATHEMATICS

10. Suppose the probability that the next test will be on a Tuesday is 0.35 and the probability that it will be on a Thursday is 0.25.
    a. What is the probability that the next test is on a Tuesday or Thursday? **0.6**
    b. What is the probability that it is not on a Tuesday? **0.65**
    c. What is the probability that the test is on neither Tuesday nor Thursday? **0.4**

11. Use the General Form of the Addition Counting Principle to derive the General Form of the Probability of the Union of Events Theorem.

In 12–15, consider tossing two fair six-sided dice and dividing the number on the first die by the number on the second to get a quotient q. Find each probability.

12. $P(q < 1)$ $\frac{15}{36}$ or $\frac{5}{12}$

13. $P(q \leq 1)$ $\frac{21}{36}$ or $\frac{7}{12}$

14. $P(q = \frac{1}{2}$ or $q = \frac{1}{3})$ $\frac{5}{36}$

15. $P(q$ is an integer) $\frac{14}{36}$ or $\frac{7}{18}$

16. All human blood can be typed as one of O, A, B, or AB, and is either Rh positive or Rh negative. Refer to the table below.
    a. What is probability that a person is Rh negative? **16%**
    b. What is the proportion of Rh negative within each blood type?
    c. Which of the four blood types has the highest proportion of Rh negative? **AB**

ABO and Rh Blood Type Relative Frequencies in the United States

ABO Type	Rh Type	Relative Frequency
O	positive	38%
O	negative	7%
A	positive	34%
A	negative	6%
B	positive	9%
B	negative	2%
AB	positive	3%
AB	negative	1%

Source: American Association of Blood Banks

Six out of the last 12 U.S. presidents, from Truman through Obama, have been left-handed.

7. true; Complimentary events never intersect. Therefore, they are always mutually exlusive.

8. not E is the complement of E, which means that the two events are mutually exclusive and their union is the entire sample space. Thus, $P(E) + P(\text{not } E) = 1$.

9. about 90% of males in the U.S. are not left-handed

11. $\frac{N(A \cup B)}{N(S)} = \frac{N(A)}{N(S)} + \frac{N(B)}{N(S)} - \frac{N(A \cap B)}{N(S)}$.
    So, $P(A \cup B) = P(A) + P(B) - P(A \cap B)$.

16b. O: $\frac{7}{45}$; A: $\frac{6}{40}$; B: $\frac{2}{11}$; AB: $\frac{1}{4}$

In **17** and **18**, refer to the Venn diagram at the right.

17. Are A and B mutually exclusive? Why or why not?

18. Calculate the following probabilities.

  a. $P(A \cap B)$ **0.05**   **b.** $P(A)$ **0.45**

  c. $P(A \cup B)$ **0.75**   **d.** $P(\text{not } B)$ **0.65**

REVIEW

19. In a game of chance, after rolling one fair six-sided die and flipping one fair coin, a player is said to win if heads and a prime number appear or if tails and the number 5 appear. (**Lesson 6-1**)

  a. Give the sample space for this experiment.

  b. Find $N(\text{loss})$ and $P(\text{loss})$ **8;** $\frac{8}{12} = \frac{2}{3}$

  c. Name an event that has three outcomes in this sample space.

20. If an experiment has only three outcomes X, Y, and Z, and $P(X) = a$ and $P(Y) = b$, what is $P(Z)$? (**Lesson 6-1**) $1 - a - b$

21. When $0 < x < 2\pi$, $\sin x = -\frac{48}{73}$, and $\cos x = -\frac{55}{73}$, find

  a. $\tan x$. $\frac{48}{55}$ **b.** $\sec x$. $-\frac{73}{55}$

  c. $\csc x$. $-\frac{73}{48}$ **d.** $\cot x$. $\frac{55}{48}$

  e. the value of x to the nearest hundredth. (**Lessons 5-9, 4-2**) ≈ 3.86

22. Give the amplitude, period, vertical shift, and phase shift of the graph of $y = 3 \cos\left(\frac{\pi - x}{6}\right)$. (**Lesson 4-9**)

23. During one day at a gas station, 60% of the gasoline sold was regular at $3.25 per gallon; 30% was premium at $3.55 per gallon; and 10% was diesel at $3.70 per gallon. What was the weighted average cost per gallon for the day? (**Lesson 1-2**) **$3.385**

EXPLORATION

24. a. Draw a Venn diagram for $A \cup B \cup C$, where A, B, and C overlap.

  b. Extend the Probability of a Union of Events Theorem to cover any three events in the same sample space. That is, give a formula for $P(A \cup B \cup C)$.

  c. Give an example of the use of the formula you found in Part b.

24. a.

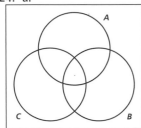

24b. $P(A \cup B \cup C) = P(A) + P(B) + P(C) - P(A \cap B) - P(A \cap C) - P(B \cap C) + P(A \cap B \cap C)$

17. No, because $P(A \cap B) = 0.05 \neq 0$.

19a. {H1, H2, H3, H4, H5, H6, T1, T2, T3, T4, T5, T6}

19c. Answers vary. Sample: heads and a number greater than 3

22. amplitude: 3; period: 12π; vertical shift: 0; phase shift: π

24c. Answers vary. Sample: If the experiment is rolling two fair dice and considering the sum of the numbers showing, $P(\text{mult. of } 4 \cup \text{multiple of } 5 \cup \text{prime}) = P(\text{mult. of } 4) + P(\text{mult. of } 5) + P(\text{prime}) - P(\text{mult. of } 4 \cap \text{mult. of } 5) - P(\text{mult. of } 4 \cap \text{prime}) - P(\text{mult. of } 5 \cap \text{prime}) + P(\text{mult. of } 4 \cap \text{mult. of } 5 \cap \text{prime})$
$= \frac{9}{36} + \frac{7}{36} + \frac{15}{36} - \frac{0}{36} - \frac{0}{36} - \frac{4}{36} + \frac{0}{36} = \frac{27}{36}$
$= \frac{3}{4}$.

QY ANSWER

$\frac{26}{298} \approx 8.7\%$

Principles of Probability   **373**

Notes on the Questions

Question 24 This is an important question to discuss in class so that all students realize the ideas of the lesson extend to more than two events.

4 Wrap-Up

Ongoing Assessment

Have students make up two probability problems and solve them. One should involve mutually exclusive events and the other should not. **Answers vary. Check students' work. Students should demonstrate understanding of mutually exclusive events and find the probability of the union of events.**

Lesson 6-3

GOAL

Apply the Multiplication Counting Principle to intuit the formulas for the number of strings with replacement of length *k* from a set *S* with *n* elements.

SPUR Objectives

B Find the number of strings with replacement.

E Determine whether events are independent or dependent.

I Calculate probabilities in real situations.

J Use the Multiplication Counting Principle and the Strings with Replacement Theorem to find the number of ways of arranging objects.

Materials/Resources

· Lesson Master 6-3
· Resource Masters 131–133
· Quiz 1

HOMEWORK
· Option 1
· Option 2
· Questions 1–8
· · Questions 9–21
· · Question 22 (extra credit)
· Reading Lesson 6-4
· Covering the Ideas 6-4
  (Questions 1–12)

Local Standards

1 Warm-Up

1. Write down all the three-letter combinations that begin with D using the letters A, B, C, D, and E only once.
   DAB, DAC, DAE, DBA, DBC, DBE, DCA, DCB, DCE, DEA, DEB, DEC

2. How many three-letter combinations are there using the letters A, B, C, D, and E only once? **60**

Lesson 6-3: Counting Strings with Replacement

Vocabulary
string
length of a string
independents events
dependent events

> ▶ **BIG IDEA** If two events are independent, the probability that both events occur is the product of the probabilities of the events.

The Multiplication Counting Principle

The Blu Yonder travel company offers package vacations with a choice of economy class or business class flights and three options for accommodation (3-star hotel, 4-star hotel or 5-star hotel). The tree diagram below shows the different possibilities.

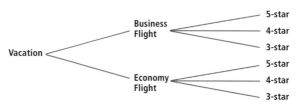

Counting the paths shows that there are six different possible options. Blu Yonder felt that there were not enough options. To try to increase sales, they decided to advertise that each vacation comes in one of five themes (adventure, sports, beaches, shopping, or sights). They knew that for each of the 6 possible vacations, there were 5 possible themes. The following tree diagram shows the 5 theme options for a vacation with a business class flight and 4-star accommodations.

If we consider each possible vacation, there are $6 \cdot 5 = 30$ total choices. This is an instance of a basic use of multiplication.

A ski resort in Savoy, France.

Multiplication Counting Principle

Let *A* and *B* be any finite sets. The number of ways to choose one element from *A* and then one element from *B* is $N(A) \cdot N(B)$.

Mental Math

Suppose that
$f(xy) = f(x) + f(y)$ **and that** $f(2) = 0.472$ **and** $f(3) = 0.295$.

a. Find $f(6)$. **0.767**

b. Find $f(12)$ **1.239**

Background

We hope that students would have seen the Multiplication Counting Principle as early as 4th grade. UCSMP students have seen it in *Transition Mathematics*, where it is used to count elements of arrays, and in *Algebra*, where it is used to count permutations of 2 objects from *n* both with and without replacement.

The Multiplication Counting Principle Tree diagrams that show visually all possible arrangements and the logic supporting the Multiplication Counting Principle are useful for small numbers, as at the beginning of the lesson, but they become less practical as the number of arrangements increases. In Lesson 6-5, tree diagrams are employed to represent situations of conditional probability that occur in contingency tables.

Ordered symbols with repetition If the first component of an ordered pair must come from a set *R* with *x* elements and the second component comes from a set *S* with *y* elements, then there are *xy* different

The Multiplication Counting Principle extends to choices made from more than two sets. In the travel situation, we chose from three sets: flight classes, hotel accommodations, and themes. There were 2 flight classes, 3 hotels, and 5 themes, and the total number of possible vacations was $2 \cdot 3 \cdot 5 = 30$. In general, the number of ordered selections with one element from set A_1, one element from set A_2, ..., and one element from set A_k is $N(A_1) \cdot N(A_2) \cdot \cdots \cdot N(A_k)$.

Ordered Symbols with Repetition

Here is a typical application of the Multiplication Counting Principle.

Example 1

A popular game show features a spinner divided into twenty-four congruent sectors and numbered something like the wheel shown at the right. The spinner cannot stop on a boundary line. You spin it twice. Describe a sample space S for this experiment, and determine the number of elements in S.

Solution There are two spins. Counting the sectors shows that each spin has twenty-four outcomes. Let x be the outcome of the first spin, and let y be the outcome of the second spin. So the sample space S consists of ordered pairs (x, y).

There are twenty-four choices for x and twenty-four for y. By the Multiplication Counting Principle, there are $24 \cdot 24 = 576$ elements in S.

In Example 1, we selected twice from the same set and found that there were 24^2 possible outcomes. If all outcomes are equally likely, the probability of each outcome is $\frac{1}{24^2}$.

 QY1

Strings

When the symbols in a problem must be ordered, it is common to refer to the ordered list of symbols as a **string**. The number of symbols in a string is the **length** of the string.

> ▶ QY1
>
> Suppose you spin the spinner in Example 1 three times.
>
> a. How many outcomes are there?
>
> b. What is the probability of each outcome?

Example 2

a. On a 28-question multiple-choice mathematics test, each question has 5 choices. How many possible completed answer sheets are there?

b. If you guess randomly on each question, what is the probability of answering all 28 questions correctly?

(continued on next page)

---

ordered pairs possible. The set of ordered pairs is called the *cross product* of R and S, written $R \times S$. When there are 3 sets R, S, and T (with z elements), we obtain xyz ordered 3-tuples. When there are n sets, we obtain ordered n-tuples.

Strings The general word for these ordered pairs, 3-tuples, and n-tuples is *string*. So the generalization to deduce the number of possible strings of k objects with replacement (n^r) is rather immediate.

Independent events We define the events A and B to be independent if and only if $P(A \cap B) = P(A) \cdot P(B)$. There is another definition of independence based on conditional probability: A and B are independent if and only if $P(B$ given $A) = P(B)$. The definition we use here directly relates to the Multiplication Counting Principle and lends itself to binomial experiments.

(Note that the answer to Warm-Up 2 is five times the number of combinations in Warm-Up 1. In Warm-Up 1, the combinations can be grouped into four groups of three. This justifies $5 \cdot 4 \cdot 3$ as the answer to Warm-Up 2.)

2 Teaching

Notes on the Lesson

We sometimes use the phrase "with repetition" and sometimes we use "with replacement." However, "with repetition" can be confusing when the original set contains repeated elements.

Do not sell the tree diagram that opens this lesson as a way to count the number of arrangements. It is too inefficient! Tree diagrams are designed (1) to emphasize the order in which selections are made when using the Multiplication Counting Principle; (2) to show that the principle is derived from the notion of multiplication as repeated addition; and (3) to introduce a representation that can be applied in situations of conditional probability.

Example 2 Students may wonder what the probability of getting half the questions correct is. Let them know that this is a more difficult question but one that has a definite answer that is discussed in a later chapter. Students need to know the binomial theorem and combinations before this more general question can be considered.

Additional Examples

Example 1 A lottery game played in some states involves picking 3 digits from 0 to 9 in order. Describe a sample space for this experiment and determine the number of elements in the sample space. **The sample space is the set of 3-digit numbers from 000 to 999, containing 1000 numbers in all.**

Example 2 Three of the questions on a science test are multiple choice with four choices each.

a. How many ways are there to answer these questions? $4^3 = 64$

b. If you guess randomly on each of these questions, what is the probability of answering all these correctly? $4^{-3} = \frac{1}{64}$

6-3

Solution

a. There are five ways to respond to each of the 28 questions. Think of each response as a choice from a set with 5 elements in it: a, b, c, d, or e. Let A_n be the set of possible responses from Question n. So
$$A_1 = A_2 = A_3 = \cdots = A_{27} = A_{28} = \{a, b, c, d, e\}.$$
The number of possible answer sheets is
$$N(A_1) \cdot N(A_2) \cdot N(A_3) \cdot \cdots \cdot N(A_{27}) \cdot N(A_{28})$$
$$= \underbrace{5 \cdot 5 \cdot 5 \cdot \cdots \cdot 5 \cdot 5}_{28 \text{ factors}} = 5^{28}$$
$$= 37{,}252{,}902{,}984{,}619{,}140{,}625.$$

b. When you guess randomly, all outcomes are equally likely. Only one of those 5^{28} outcomes is "all answers correct," so the probability of answering all questions correctly is $\frac{1}{5^{28}} = 5^{-28} \approx 0.0000000000000000000268$, which is very close to zero.

In Example 2, because there are 28 questions, each with 5 choices for an answer, finding the number of answer sheets depends on counting the number of strings of length 28. The strings are comprised of symbols from the set {a, b, c, d, e}. Each string corresponds to one possible answer sheet, assuming a student answers every question with one choice of answer. Three of the possible strings for answer sheets are listed below.

Answer Sheet Possibility: `cabdcceabcdadcbbcdacdcabecab`

Answer Sheet Possibility: `bbbbbbbbbbbbbbbbbbbbbbbbbbbb`

Answer Sheet Possibility: `abcdabcdabcdabcdabcdabcdabcd`

You saw in Example 2 that there are 5^{28} possible strings. These are *strings with replacement* because the symbols can be used over and over again.

> ### Theorem (Strings with Replacement)
>
> Let S be a set with n elements. Then there are n^k possible strings with replacement of length k with elements from S.

Proof Use the Multiplication Counting Principle. Here $N(S) = n$, so the number of possible ways to choose one element from S, each of k times, is
$$\underbrace{N(S) \cdot N(S) \cdot \cdots \cdot N(S)}_{k \text{ factors}} = \underbrace{n \cdot n \cdot \cdots \cdot n}_{k \text{ factors}} = n^k.$$

 QY2

Example 3 uses both the Strings with Replacement Theorem and the Multiplication Counting Principle.

> ▸ **QY2**
>
> How many strings with replacement are there of length 2 with 3 symbols a, b, and c?

ENGLISH LEARNERS
Vocabulary Development

Some students may be uncomfortable with the definition and usage of the word *string*; especially if they visualize a *string* as a cord or wire. It might help them to think of a "string of pearls" so they understand that we are thinking of a string as a group of objects arranged one after the next. In this case, each object is a symbol. This usage is very popular in computer logic and programming.

Example 3

In a certain state, license plates have two letters followed by 4 digits from 0 through 9. How many license plates are possible?

Solution First use the Strings with Replacement Theorem to compute the number of possibilities separately for letters and for numbers.

There are __?__ letters, so there are __?__ strings of 2 letters.

There are __?__ digits, so there are __?__ strings of 4 digits.

Now use the Multiplication Counting Principle to combine the counts for letters and numbers. 26; 26^2; 10; 10^4

So there are __?__ • __?__ = 6,760,000 possible license plates. 676; 10,000

STOP QY3

(handwritten margin notes) there are not 26 "strings," the ordered list is called a string. the length of the string is 26^2 see def'n of string p. 375

Independent Events

We think of events A and B as *independent* if the probability of A does not affect the probability of B. Selections with replacement are independent events because each selection is not affected by what has been selected previously. To find the probability that a number of independent events all occur, you can apply the Multiplication Counting Principle.

> **QY3**
>
> Refer to Example 3. Suppose each license plate is equally likely and that your family has license plate QY 1234. What is the probability that the next car you see has license plate QY 1233 or QY 1235?

Example 4

The spinner shown here is used in a carnival game. It is assumed to be fair, so the spinner has the same probability of landing in each sector. If the spinner lands on an edge, the spin does not count. The game consists of two spins. You win if the first spin stops on an even number and the second spin stops on a multiple of 3. What is the probability of winning?

Solution The sample space S for spinning twice is illustrated at the right by the 36 dots. Let event A be that the first spin stops on an even number. Let event B be that the second spin stops on a multiple of 3. One outcome that satisfies both events is (2, 3). The event $A \cap B$ consists of the six circled ordered pairs in which the first component is even and the second component is a multiple of 3. The six circled ordered pairs represent those for which both A and B are true.

So $P(A \cap B) = \dfrac{N(A \cap B)}{N(S)} = \dfrac{6}{36} = \dfrac{1}{6}$.

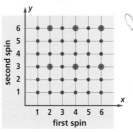

first spin

Notes on the Lesson

Independent events Words used in mathematics generally have meanings that are more precise than their definitions in everyday usage, as with *independent*. A person is considered to act independently when the person does not worry about what others do or think; two events are independent if the probability of one does not influence the probability of the other. Thus events from repeated trials with replacement can be independent because you do not know what transpired, but events from repeated trials without replacement are not independent because the first event affects what is possible for the second.

Example 4 The events are independent because the second spin is not affected by what happened on the first. However, in Example 5, event A affects event B. For instance, if the first spin is a 1, then it is impossible to have a sum of numbers on both spins equal to 8. In informal language, we would say the occurrence of B "depends on" what happens in A. The mathematical language formalizes the informal English.

Additional Examples

Example 3 Some states allow license plates with 3 letters followed by 4 digits from 0 through 9. How many license plates are possible? $26^3 \cdot 10^4 = 175,760,000$

Example 4 In a certain spinning wheel, there are 20 sectors of equal size. In 18 of these sectors, you win a prize, but in the other 2, you lose all your winnings. If the wheel spins randomly, what is the probability of winning five prizes and then losing on the sixth spin? $\dfrac{59049}{1000000} = 0.059049$ or about 6%

Ask students to simplify each of the following expressions.

1. $(k + 1)! - k!$ $k \cdot k!$

2. $\dfrac{(k + 1)! - k!}{k!}$ k

3. $\dfrac{(k + 1)! + k!}{(k + 1)! - k!}$ $\dfrac{k + 2}{k}$

4. $\dfrac{1}{k!} - \dfrac{1}{(k + 1)!}$ $\dfrac{k}{(k + 1)!}$

6-3

In Example 4, notice that $P(A) = \frac{1}{2}$ and $P(B) = \frac{1}{3}$. Thus $P(A \cap B)$ is the product of $P(A)$ and $P(B)$. This is the defining characteristic of independent events.

> **Definition of Independent Events**
>
> Events A and B are **independent events** if and only if $P(A \cap B) = P(A) \cdot P(B)$.

Events that are not independent are called **dependent events**.

GUIDED

Example 5

Refer to Example 4. If event B were changed to be "the sum of both spins is greater than 8," show that the events A and B are dependent.

Solution The sample space and $P(A)$ are the same as in Example 4.

There are 10 outcomes in which the sum of both spins is greater than 8. Thus $N(B) = \underline{\ ?\ }$ and $P(B) = \underline{\ ?\ }$. **10;** $\frac{10}{36} = \frac{5}{18}$

There are $\underline{\ ?\ }$ outcomes in which both the first spin **6** is even and the sum of the spins is greater than 8. Thus $N(A \cap B) = \underline{\ ?\ }$ and $P(A \cap B) = \underline{\ ?\ }$. The events **6;** $\frac{6}{36} = \frac{1}{6}$ A and B are dependent because $P(A) \cdot P(B) = \frac{5}{36} \neq P(A \cap B)$.

3 Assignment

Recommended Assignment

- Questions 1–8
- • Questions 9–21
- • Question 22 (extra credit)
- • Reading Lesson 6-4
- • Covering the Ideas 6-4 (Questions 1–12)

Notes on the Questions

As you go through the questions, it is useful to identify the situation as one with replacement and indicate what a corresponding situation would be without replacement, in preparation for Lesson 6-4.

Questions

COVERING THE IDEAS

1. The Blu Yonder travel company described on page 374 decides that in addition to themes, they will offer a choice of souvenir. Customers can pick a key chain, t-shirt, or canvas bag. How many different vacation packages are now offered? **90 vacations**

2. a. How many different shirt-pants-sweater outfits are possible if you have six shirts, five pairs of pants, and two sweaters, assuming all items can go with each other? **60 outfits**

   b. How many different shirt-pants-sweater outfits are possible if you have h shirts, ℓ pairs of pants, and w sweaters, assuming all items can go with each other? **$h\ell w$ outfits**

3. Suppose a 5-character ID number consists of a letter followed by 4 digits from 0 through 9. How many ID numbers are possible?

In 4 and 5, suppose you have a spinner with five congruent sectors numbered 1 through 5 and a six-sided die, both fair. Decide whether the given events are independent or dependent. Justify your answer by computing appropriate probabilities.

4. $A =$ spinner shows 4; $B =$ sum of spinner and die is over 6

5. $A =$ spinner shows 5; $B =$ die and spinner show the same number

3. 260,000 possible 5-character ID numbers

4. Dependent: $P(A) \cdot P(B) = \frac{1}{10} \neq P(A \cap B) = \frac{4}{30}$.

5. Independent: $P(A) \cdot P(B) = P(A \cap B) = \frac{1}{30}$.

---

6. A test has 12 true-false questions.

  a. How many completed answer sheets with all questions answered are possible? $2^{12} = 4{,}096$ **possible answer sheets**

  b. If you guess on all the questions, what is the probability that you will get them all correct? $\frac{1}{2^{12}} = 0.000244$

  c. If you know the answers to five questions and guess on the rest, what is the probability that you will get them all correct? $\frac{1}{2^{7}} = \frac{1}{128}$

7. How many ways are there of answering a test with 6 true-false and 12 multiple-choice questions with 4 choices each?

8. A fair six-sided die is tossed 10 times, with results written in a string. The first trial gave a string with only 5s and 6s. What is the probability of the 10 tosses giving a string that has only numbers greater than 4? $\frac{2^{10}}{6^{10}} \approx 0.000017$

APPLYING THE MATHEMATICS

9. An ice cream shop offers 34 flavors, 5 sauces, and 23 toppings. A sundae consists of one scoop of ice cream, a ladle of sauce, and a choice of one topping.

  a. How many different sundaes could be ordered? **3,910 sundaes**

  b. The shop offers 12 of its flavors in three varieties: regular, fat free, and sugar free. How many sundaes could be ordered?

  c. Suppose that a customer can omit the topping. How does that change the answer to Part a? **4,080 sundaes**

10. The teacher said there was about a one in a million chance of obtaining a perfect score by guessing on a test where all questions were true or false. Assuming the teacher was not exaggerating, about how many true-false questions were on this test?

11. A fair coin is tossed three times. Let event A be that at most one head occurs. Let event B be that both heads and tails occur at least once. Are A and B independent? Justify your answer using the definition of independence.

12. Two types of blood clotting disorders are *thrombophilia* (excessive blood clotting) and *hemophilia* (insufficient blood clotting). Suppose 51% of the age group under study is male. Assume that gender and thrombophilia are independent.

  a. One estimate is that 6.5% of the population has thrombophilia. What is the probability that a randomly selected person is male with thrombophilia? **~ 3.3%**

  b. What is the probability that a person has thrombophilia or is male? **about 0.542**

  c. Given that the relative frequency of hemophilia in the U.S. is about $\frac{1}{17{,}000}$ and the relative frequency of males with hemophilia is $\frac{1}{85{,}000}$, are these events independent? Justify your answer.

7. $2^{6} \cdot 4^{12}$
$= 1{,}073{,}741{,}824$
ways of answering

9b. 6,670 sundaes

10. at least 20 questions

11. $P(A) = \frac{1}{2}$, $P(B) = \frac{6}{8}$
$= \frac{3}{4}$, so $P(A) \cdot P(B)$
$= \frac{3}{8}$, and $P(A \cap B)$
$= \frac{3}{8}$. So A and B are independent.

We all scream for ice cream! The average American consumes 48 pints of ice cream a year.

12c. No; P(male)
$= 0.51$ and
P(hemophilia)
$= \frac{1}{17000} =$
0.000059, so
P(male) •
P(hemophilia)
$= 0.00003$.
But P(male and hemophilia)
$= \frac{1}{85000} = 0.0000118$.

6-3

Notes on the Questions

Questions 18–21 These questions prepare students for the use of factorials for permutations to be seen in Lesson 6-4.

Question 20 The maximum factorial calculators can handle and the number of digits shown can vary. One calculator gives $1.7112 \cdot 10^{98}$ for 69! and an error message for 70!. Another shows $1.711224524 \cdot 10^{98}$, more digits but no higher factorial. A third one gives $5.17346099264 \cdot 10^{499}$ for 253!, and its memory is exceeded for 254!. So students should understand that they cannot do this question by calculating the numerator, calculating the denominator, and then dividing.

4 Wrap-Up

Ongoing Assessment

Administer Quiz 1 (or a quiz of your own) after students complete this lesson.

Additional Answers

22.

Option	Number of Letters	Number of Numbers	Total Choices
1	3	0	26^3
2	4	0	26^4
3	5	0	26^5
4	6	0	26^6
5	7	0	26^7
6	3	1	$26^3 \cdot 10$
7	3	2	$26^3 \cdot 100$
8	3	3	$26^3 \cdot 1,000$
9	3	4	$26^3 \cdot 10,000$
10	4	1	$26^4 \cdot 10$
11	4	2	$26^4 \cdot 100$
12	4	3	$26^4 \cdot 1,000$
13	5	1	$26^5 \cdot 10$
14	5	2	$26^5 \cdot 100$
15	6	1	$26^6 \cdot 10$

REVIEW

13. In Mrs. William's class of 35 students, 17 students came to school by bus today, and 13 came by car. The remaining students walked.
    a. What is the probability that a randomly selected student in Mrs. William's class walked to school today? $\frac{1}{7}$
    b. What is the probability that a randomly selected student in Mrs. William's class who did not walk came by bus? (**Lesson 6-2**) $\frac{17}{30}$

14. Give an example of two mutually exclusive events that are not complementary. (**Lesson 6-2**)

15. Suppose you roll two fair six-sided dice. What is the probability that the sum is a perfect square? (**Lesson 6-1**) $\frac{7}{36}$

16. Consider the function f with $f(x) = x^2 - 1$. (**Lesson 3-5**)
    a. Sketch the graph of f under the transformation
    $S: (x, y) \rightarrow (3x, -2y)$.
    b. Give an equation for f under S. $f(x) = -\frac{2}{9}x^2 + 2$

17. Factor $8x^3 - 10x^2 - 3x$. (**Previous Course**) $x(2x - 3)(4x + 1)$

In 18–21, recall that for any positive integer n, $n!$, read "n factorial," is the product of the integers from 1 to n. (**Previous Course**)

18. Give the values of 1!, 2!, 3!, 4!, and 5!. **1; 2; 6; 24; 120**

19. Evaluate 10! with a calculator. **3,628,800**

20. Evaluate $\frac{2010!}{2009!}$ without using a calculator. **2,010**

21. Evaluate $\frac{12!}{3!9!}$. **220**

EXPLORATION

22. License plates can have both letters and digits as seen in Example 3. Different states have different restrictions on the numbers of digits and letters per license plate. Research the rules and limitations of your state's license plates and determine the number of possible license plates in your state.

22. Answers vary. Sample: In New Jersey, a personalized plate must have at least three letters, and a maximum of seven characters, letters and numbers 0-9.

By summing the rightmost column, we get 13,451,703,720 total choices.

See margin for table.

---

14. Answers vary. Sample: If you roll a die, an even roll and rolling a 5 are mutually exclusive events. These events are not complementary because the sum of their probabilities is less than 1.

16a.

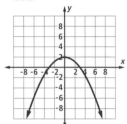

QY ANSWERS

1. **a.** $243 = 13824$
   b. $\frac{1}{243} = \frac{1}{13824} \approx 0.000072$
2. 9
3. $\frac{2}{26^2 \cdot 10^4} = \frac{2}{6760000}$

Lesson 6-4

Counting Strings without Replacement

Vocabulary

permutation

permutation of *n* objects
taken *r* at a time, $_nP_r$

▶ **BIG IDEA** The number of permutations of length *r* from a set of *n* symbols can be determined by applying the Multiplication Counting Principle.

Consider five symbols a, b, c, d, and e that will be in a string. If the symbols can be used and replaced, then the string can be as long as you wish. But if the symbols cannot be replaced, then as you use each symbol, there is one less symbol available. So the maximum length of the string is 5. That is the idea of the counting problem in Example 1.

Mental Math

Suppose $x = 24$.
Calculate:

a. $5x$. **120**

b. $6 \cdot 5x$. **720**

c. $\dfrac{6 \cdot 5x}{3 \cdot 2 \cdot 1}$. **120**

d. $\dfrac{7 \cdot 6 \cdot 5 \cdot 4 \cdot 3 \cdot 2 \cdot 1}{3 \cdot 2 \cdot 1}$.
840

Example 1

The "Big 10" athletic conference consists of 11 teams: Illinois, Indiana, Iowa, Michigan, Michigan State, Minnesota, Northwestern, Ohio State, Penn State, Purdue, and Wisconsin. You want to predict which team will finish first in a particular sport, which second, and which third. How many different predictions are possible?

Solution First, be sure that you understand the problem. You are looking for predictions, so identify one. One prediction might be that Northwestern will finish first, followed by Penn State and then Wisconsin. To find the total number of different predictions, use the Multiplication Counting Principle.

	1st	2nd	3rd
11 teams can be predicted to finish first.	11		
For each of these 11, 10 teams can be second.	11 · 10		
For each of these 11 · 10 pairs of teams, 9 teams can be third.	11 · 10 · 9		

So there are 11 · 10 · 9 = 990 possible predictions.

Example 1 illustrates that there are 990 different strings of 11 different symbols with length 3 *without replacement*. If you picked the teams blindly, the probability of predicting the first, second, and third place finishers correctly is $\frac{1}{990}$.

 QY1

Ohio State, with over 51,000 students, is the largest university in the Big Ten.

▶ **QY1**

What is the number of strings of 11 different symbols with length 3 *with* replacement?

Background

Students will have had practice with factorials and expressions containing factorials before this lesson, so the difficulty of learning the notation *and* the concept of permutations at the same time is avoided.

The application of the Multiplication Counting Principle to strings with replacement, done in Lesson 6-3, is easier than the application here, but it sets the stage for this lesson. Here, strings without replacement (called permutations) are covered, and the familiar formulas for $_nP_r$ are generated. We prefer $_nP_r$ to $P(n, r)$ notation here because it is easier to translate into words.

Lesson 6-4

GOAL

Cover the most general type of permutation without replacement, and present the familiar formulas for $_nP_r$.

SPUR Objectives

B Find the number of strings without replacement.

C Evaluate expressions using factorials.

I Calculate probabilities in real situations.

J Use permutations to find the number of ways of arranging objects.

Materials/Resources

· Lesson Master 6-4
· Resource Masters 134 and 135

HOMEWORK • Option 1
• Option 2

• Questions 1–12
• • Questions 13–24
• • Question 25 and 26 (extra credit)
• Reading Lesson 6-5
• Covering the Ideas 6-5 (Questions 1–6)

Local Standards

1 Warm-Up

Ten permutations of the letters AELST are legal words in the game of Scrabble® using the *Official Scrabble® Players Dictionary, 4th Edition*.

1. Name as many as you can. **LEAST, SETAL** (pertaining to a slender part of a plant), **SLATE, STALE, STEAL, STELA** (a carved stone slab), **TAELS** (Chinese units of weight or value), **TALES, TEALS, TESLA** (a unit of magnetic flux in the metric system named after the great Italian inventor)

(continued on next page)

6-4

2. If the letters AELST are ordered at random, what is the probability that the ordering forms a legal word in Scrabble®? $\frac{1}{12}$
(Note: 12 legal words in Scrabble® can be formed from AEPRS, the most prolific set of 5 letters.)

2 ▶ Teaching

Notes on the Lesson

In permutation problems, all of the objects may be arranged, as in Example 4, or just some of the objects may be arranged, as in Example 1, where only 3 of the 10 teams are involved in an arrangement. This is why the idea of *length* of the permutation is so important.

Example 1 Point out that in all the counting problems of this lesson, *the order of the elements being counted matters.* If 3 teams finish first, second, and third, this is different than if the order of the finish had been second, third, and first. If we were counting combinations, these would not be distinct. This idea is the difference between permutations and combinations.

Additional Examples

Example 1 In volleyball, a team plays 6 players at a time, three at the net and three behind. How many different ways are there to arrange three at the net from the six who are playing? **120**

Example 2 An art gallery has 12 paintings by Renaissance painters but only enough room to show 8 of them. In how many ways can they arrange 8 of the 12 paintings in the 8 places they have for them? **19,958,400**

An arrangement of teams, objects, or symbols without replacement is called a **permutation** of those objects. We say that the solution of Example 1 calculates the number of *permutations of 11 objects taken 3 at a time.* In general, for any positive integers n and r with $n \geq r$, the number of **permutations of n objects taken r at a time** is the number of strings of length r of n symbols without replacement. This number is denoted $_nP_r$. Generalizing the process in Example 1, we can prove the following theorem.

> **Theorem (Formula for $_nP_r$)**
>
> For any positive integers n and r with $n \geq r$, the number of permutations of n objects taken r at a time is
> $$_nP_r = n(n - 1)(n - 2) \cdot \cdots \cdot (n - r + 1).$$

Proof We want to know the number of strings of length r when n symbols are available but no symbol can be repeated. There are n possible choices for the first element of the string. Then there are $n - 1$ possible choices for the second element, $n - 2$ choices for the third element, and so on, until there are $n - (r - 1)$, or $n - r + 1$ choices for the rth element. By the Multiplication Counting Principle, the product of these numbers is the total number of possible strings.

STOP QY2

> ▶ QY2
>
> Calculate $_9P_7$.

Caution: The letter P in $_nP_r$ stands for permutation, not probability.

Example 1 shows that $_{11}P_3 = 11 \cdot (11 - 1) \cdot (11 - 2) = 11 \cdot 10 \cdot 9 = 990$. Notice that $11 \cdot 10 \cdot 9 = \frac{11 \cdot 10 \cdot 9 \cdot 8 \cdot 7 \cdot 6 \cdot 5 \cdot 4 \cdot 3 \cdot 2 \cdot 1}{8 \cdot 7 \cdot 6 \cdot 5 \cdot 4 \cdot 3 \cdot 2 \cdot 1} = \frac{11!}{8!}$, and $8 = 11 - 3$. In a similar way, any product of consecutive integers can be written as a quotient of factorials. This provides an alternate way of calculating $_nP_r$.

> **Theorem (Alternate Formula for $_nP_r$)**
>
> $$_nP_r = \frac{n!}{(n - r)!}$$

GUIDED

Example 2

How many different six-letter strings can be formed from six letters in the word PALINDROME without replacement?

Solution 1 Again first make sure that you understand the question. One possible string is DOMAIN. Other possible strings are PEORIA and DRLNPM. So the question asks for the number of permutations of __?__ objects taken **10** at a time. Use the first formula for $_nP_r$, with $n = $ __?__ and $r = $ __?__. **10, 6**

$$_{10}P_6 = \underset{6}{\underbrace{10 \cdot 9 \cdot 8 \cdot \underset{7 \cdot 6 \cdot 5}{?}}} = \underset{151,200}{\underbrace{?}}\text{ , so there are 151,200 strings.}$$
__?__ factors

Accommodating the Learner ⬆

Ask students to order the following from least to greatest without any calculations.

$_{17}P_{15}, \; _{18}P_{16}, \; _{17}P_{16},$ and $_{18}P_{15}$

$_{17}P_{15}, \; _{17}P_{16}, \; _{18}P_{15}, \; _{18}P_{16};$

Possible thought process: Do not compute, but write out the equivalent fraction containing factorials for each expression, for example $_{17}P_{15} = \frac{17!}{2!}$. We compare and see that $_{17}P_{15} < _{17}P_{16}$, they both have the same numerator (17!) but the first has a greater denominator (2! > 1!). Similarly, $_{18}P_{15} < _{18}P_{16}$.

Now if we find $_{17}P_{16}$ to be less than $_{18}P_{15}$ we will have completely determined the order. Consider $_{17}P_{16} = \frac{17!}{1!}$, and $_{18}P_{15} = \frac{18!}{3!}$.

We rewrite $_{18}P_{15}$ as $\frac{18 \cdot 17!}{3 \cdot 2 \cdot 1!} = \frac{18}{3 \cdot 2} \cdot \frac{17!}{1!} = 3 \cdot _{17}P_{16}$ to show $_{17}P_{16} < _{18}P_{15}$.

Solution 2 Use the Alternate Formula for $_nP_r$.

$$_{10}P_2 = \frac{10!}{(10 - \underline{\ ?\ })!6} = 151{,}200 \text{ strings}$$

You can solve equations involving $_nP_r$ for n or r using either formula.

Example 3

Solve $_nP_6 = 17 \cdot {_nP_5}$.

Solution 1 Use the Formula for $_nP_r$. Translate $_nP_6$ and $_nP_5$ into their polynomial equivalents.

$n(n-1)(n-2)(n-3)(n-4)(n-5)$
$\qquad = 17n(n-1)(n-2)(n-3)(n-4)$

Divide each side of the equation by $n(n-1)(n-2)(n-3)(n-4)$.

$$n - 5 = 17$$
$$n = 22$$

Solution 2 Use the Alternate Formula for $_nP_r$. Translate $_nP_6$ and $_nP_5$ into their factorial equivalents.

$$\frac{n!}{(n-6)!} = 17 \cdot \frac{n!}{(n-5)!}$$

Divide both sides by $n!$ and use the Means-Extremes Property.

$$(n-5)! = 17(n-6)!$$

Use the fact that $n! = n(n-1)!$, or, more specifically, that $(n-a)! = (n-a)(n-a-1)!$.

$$(n-5)(n-6)! = 17\ (n-6)!$$
$$n - 5 = 17$$
$$n = 22$$

Check Find the permutation function on your calculator. Then compute $_{22}P_6$ and $17 \cdot {_{22}P_5}$. It checks.

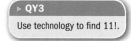

nPr(22,6)	53721360
17·nPr(22,5)	53721360

Permutations of n Objects Taken n at a Time

In many situations, the number of permutations of *all* the objects in a set is desired. For instance, in Example 1, you might want to know the number of possible rankings of all 11 teams. You know there are $11 \cdot 10 \cdot 9$ ways of selecting the first three teams. As a result, there are $11 \cdot 10 \cdot 9 \cdot 8$ ways of selecting the first four teams. Continuing the process, there will be 11 factors in the product for selecting all 11 teams, so the number of strings with *length* 11 of 11 different objects, is

$$11 \cdot 10 \cdot 9 \cdot 8 \cdot 7 \cdot 6 \cdot 5 \cdot 4 \cdot 3 \cdot 2 \cdot 1 = 11!.$$

 QY3

▶ **QY3**

Use technology to find 11!.

Permutations of n objects taken n at a time Emphasize that the the formula for $_nP_n$ is a special case of the formula for $_nP_r$. Let $r = n$ in that theorem and the formula becomes $_nP_r = n(n-1)(n-2) \cdot \ldots \cdot (n - n + 1)$. Since each factor is one less than the preceding, and the last factor is 1, $_nP_n = n!$.

There are many situations in which the number of permutations is very large and calculators are essential. In many cases some arithmetic rewriting can speed calculation, and in some cases such rewriting is necessary. For example, $_{100}P_3$ cannot be computed on most calculators in the form $\frac{100!}{97!}$, because both 100! and 97! are too large. However, the alternative $_{100}P_3 = 100 \cdot 99 \cdot 98$ is easily computed.

Additional Example

Example 3 Suppose $_nP_r = 110 \cdot {_nP_{r-2}}$. What are n and r? $_nP_r$ has two factors not in $_nP_{r-2}$, namely $(n - r + 1)$ and $(n - r + 2)$. Since they differ by 1 and their product is 110, $n - r + 1 = 10$. So any pair of positive integers n and r with $n - r = 9$ will work, for example, $n = 15, r = 6$.

Accommodating the Learner 🔽

Note the difference between arrangements with replacement and arrangements without replacement. Ask: How many four-letter arrangements are there from the letters A, B, C, D, E, and F? Students will probably in turn ask: Can we repeat letters? You could then suggest that they do it both ways. With replacements there are $6^4 = 1296$ arrangements; without replacements, there are $6 \cdot 5 \cdot 4 \cdot 3 = 360$ arrangements.

Students should know but not have to memorize the general formulas here; they can be derived quickly from the Multiplication Counting Principle.

Notes on the Lesson

It is universal to define $0! = 1$ because otherwise a number of formulas would fail. In the text it is indicated that $0! = 1$ is consistent with the formula for $_nP_r$. This value for $0!$ is the only value that satisfies the criterion that $n! = n(n-1)!$ for $n = 1$. Specifically, to satisfy that criterion, $1! = 1 \cdot 0!$, from which $1 = 1 \cdot 0!$, from which $0! = 1$. Defining $0! = 1$ is also the only value of $0!$ that works in formulas for $_nC_r$.

Some students may enjoy trying to find 5-letter permutations from BIRTHDAY that are words in the English language. Here are 19: BIRTH, RABID, BRAID, THIRD, DIARY, DAIRY, HAIRY, HABIT, HARDY, HYDRA, RHYTA, YIRTH, BAITH, DIRTY, TARDY, YAIRD, AIRTH, TABID, TRIAD.

Additional Example

Example 4 Refer to Example 4 in this lesson.

a. If Kerry Okie decided to put the 6 girls in his class first and then the 11 boys, how many different orders would he have? $6! \cdot 11! = 28{,}740{,}096{,}000$

b. Is the answer to Part a greater than, equal to, or less than the answer to Example 4 in the lesson? **less than**

The general formula for the number of permutations of n objects taken n at a time is a special case of the $_nP_r$ formula.

> ### Corollary (Formula for $_nP_n$)
>
> There are $n!$ permutations of n different elements. That is,
> $$_nP_n = n!.$$

Proof For all positive integers n and r with $n \geq r$,
$$_nP_r = n(n-1)(n-2) \cdot \cdots \cdot (n-r+1).$$
Substitute n for r.
$$_nP_n = n(n-1)(n-2) \cdot \cdots \cdot (n-n+1)$$
$$= n(n-1)(n-2) \cdot \cdots \cdot 1 = n!$$

STOP QY4

When $n = r$, the alternate formula for $_nP_r$ gives $_nP_n = \dfrac{n!}{(n-n)!} = \dfrac{n!}{0!}$. Because $_nP_n = n!$, in order to have the alternate formula for $_nP_r$ work for $_nP_n$, we must have $\dfrac{n!}{0!} = n!$. So we must define $0!$ to equal 1.

> ### Definition
>
> $$0! = 1$$

▶ **QY4**

How many ways are there for a teacher to assign a group of 3 students the jobs of erasing the boards, wiping the tables, and turning off the lights?

Example 4

Tired of hearing his 17 students argue about who gets to be first in line, first-grade teacher Kerry Okie decides to put the students in a different order every time they get in line. He decides to list all the possible orders so that he will not duplicate any of them. If it takes him 20 seconds to write each order, how long will it take him to finish his list?

Solution Calculate $_nP_n$ with $n = 17$.

$17! = 355{,}687{,}428{,}096{,}000$.

So it would take $17! \cdot 20$ seconds to list all of the possible orderings. This is over $200{,}000{,}000$ years.

Extension

Have students consider a computer spell checker. Suppose they have typed the word "oct" in their English paper when they really meant to type "cot." How many different "words" would the computer try to check if the spell checker only checks the orders of letters? **Spell checkers check more than letter order, but if they did check only letter order, they would check $3! = 6$ "words."**

Questions

COVERING THE IDEAS

1. List all the permutations of the letters in BAT.

2. Bashful, Doc, Dopey, Grumpy, Happy, Sleepy, and Sneezy go to work whistling in a different order each day. How many days can they go without repeating an order? $7! = 5{,}040$

3. Write $_{117}P_4$ in each way.
   a. as a product of integers
   b. as a ratio of two factorials

In 4 and 5, evaluate.

4. $_{14}P_8 \quad \frac{14!}{6!} = 121{,}080{,}960$

5. $_{317}P_2 \quad \frac{317!}{315!} = 100{,}172$

6. Refer to the eleven teams in the "Big Ten" football conference. In how many ways can the first 5 positions in the standings be filled?

7. a. How many 3-letter permutations are there of the letters in TRIANGLE? $_8P_3 = 336$
   b. How many of these permutations contain only consonants? $_5P_3 = 60$

8. A student's schedule consists of six class periods (in Math, English, History, Language, Science, and Physical Education), two of which meet before lunch.
   a. How many ways can those first two classes be chosen? **30**
   b. How many of these contain Math as one of the two classes? **10**

In 9 and 10, evaluate the expression and explain your answer in terms of permutations of items from a set.

9. $_nP_1$

10. $_nP_n$

11. Explain why 0! is defined to equal 1.

12. Solve for $_nP_7 = 5 \cdot {_nP_6}$ for n. $n = 11$

APPLYING THE MATHEMATICS

13. a. Some automobile door locks use five buttons numbered 1–5. A combination consists of four different buttons pressed one at a time. How many such combinations are there? $_5P_4 = 120$
    b. If a particular lock's combination is 2354 but you have forgotten it, what is the probability that you would guess it on the first try?

14. A student has textbooks in algebra, geometry, biology, chemistry, FST, and physics. These books are to be arranged on two shelves.
    a. How many different arrangements are possible if three books are on each shelf?
    b. How many different arrangements are possible if the three math books are on one shelf and the three science books are on another?
    c. How many different arrangements are possible if each shelf has at least one book?

Counting Strings without Replacement **385**

---

1. BAT; BTA; ATB; ABT; TAB; TBA

3a. $117 \cdot 116 \cdot 115 \cdot 114$

6. 55,440

9. n; There are n choices when you choose 1 element from a set with n elements.

3b. $\dfrac{117!}{113!}$

10. $n!$; By definition, there are $n!$ permutations of n different elements.

11. By one formula, $_nP_n = n!$. By the alternate formula, $_nP_n = \dfrac{n!}{(n-n)!} = \dfrac{n!}{0!}$. These formulas are only equal if $0! = 1$, so it is defined to equal 1.

13b. $\dfrac{1}{120}$

14a. $_6P_3 \cdot {_3P_3} = 720$

14b. $2 \cdot {_3P_3} \cdot {_3P_3} = 72$

14c. $_6P_1 \cdot {_5P_5} + {_6P_2} \cdot {_4P_4} + {_6P_3} \cdot {_3P_3} + {_6P_4} \cdot {_2P_2} + {_6P_5} \cdot {_1P_1} = 3{,}600$

---

3 Assignment

Recommended Assignment

- Questions 1–12
- •• Questions 13–24
- •• Question 25 and 26 (extra credit)
- Reading Lesson 6-5
- Covering the Ideas 6-5 (Questions 1–6)

Notes on the Questions

Question 2 The wording of the question is ambiguous. Do the seven dwarfs whistle in a different order each day, or do they go to work in a different order each day? However, it makes no difference: the answer is the same either way.

Question 3a You might ask how you know when to stop writing factors. (In the writing of $_nP_r$ as a product of factors, there are r factors.)

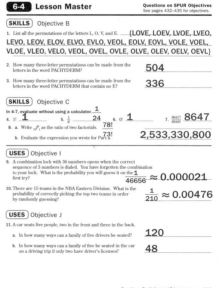

6-4

Notes on the Questions
Question 16 The skill of rewriting factorials is needed in proofs, particularly those involving combinations.

Question 17 Accept any reasonable answer.

4 Wrap-Up

Ongoing Assessment
Have students use one of the formulas for $_nP_r$ to determine how many one-letter words, four-letter words, and nine-letter words can be formed from the word EDUCATION. (The words do not have to make sense.) Then ask students to check their work using the other formula.
$_9P_1 = 9, \; _9P_4 = \frac{9!}{(9-4)!} = 3024, \; _9P_9 = 9! = 362{,}880$

---

15. Each row of an aircraft has three seats on one side of the aisle and two seats on the other. In how many different ways can a couple and their three children occupy a row of seats, if the two parents sit in the window seats?

16. a. Write $_nP_3$ as a polynomial.   b. Write $_nP_3$ using factorials.
17. a. Use algebra to show that $_nP_0 = 1$. $_nP_0 = \frac{n!}{(n-0)!} = \frac{n!}{n!} = 1$
    b. Explain why $_nP_0 = 1$ using a counting argument.

REVIEW

18. Every strand of human DNA consists of millions of nucleotides linked together to form a chain. Each nucleotide contains one of four nitrogenous bases: adenine, guanine, thymine, or cytosine. Sequences of these bases determine our genetic code. How many different possible sequences are there for a segment of DNA that is 50 nucleotides long? (**Lesson 6-3**) $4^{50} \approx 1.268 \times 10^{30}$ **possible sequences**

19. Suppose a 7-character ID number consists of a letter followed by 5 digits from 0 to 9, followed by one more letter. How many ID numbers are possible? (**Lesson 6-3**) **19. 67,600,000**

20. A pair of fair six-sided dice are thrown. What is the probability that one die shows a 5 or the sum is greater than 8? (**Lesson 6-2**) $\frac{4}{9}$

21. Give the exact value. (**Lesson 4-4**)
    a. $\tan \frac{\pi}{6}$ $\frac{\sqrt{3}}{3}$ b. $\sin 150°$ $\frac{1}{2}$
22. Convert $4\frac{1}{2}$ revolutions
    a. to degrees. **1620°**   b. to radians. (**Lesson 4-1**) **22b. 9π**
23. Let $f(x) = x^2 - 5$ and $g(x) = \frac{1}{3x-1}$. (**Lessons 3-7, 3-1**)
    a. Find a value of x that is not in the domain of g. $\frac{1}{3}$
    b. Find a value of x that is not in the domain of $g \circ f$. $\pm\frac{4\sqrt{3}}{3}$
24. If all the numbers in a data set are tripled, what happens to the standard deviation of the set? (**Lesson 3-6, 1-6**) **multiplied by 3**

EXPLORATION

25. For how many positive integers n does $n!$ end in exactly five 0s?

26. During winter, the first-grade class from Example 4 has a problem: when they put their hats on the radiator to dry out after recess, no student ever gets back his correct hat.
    a. If there are three students, how many ways are there to assign hats so that no student gets back his or her own hat? If all permutations are equally likely, what is the probability of this occurring?
    b. Repeat Part a if there are four students.
    c. In general, a derangement of a set of objects is a permutation in which no object is in its original position. Research derangements and find a method to generalize parts a and b.
    25–26. see margin

---

15. $_3P_3 \cdot _2P_2 = 12$ different seating arrangements

16a. $n(n-1)(n-2)$
16b. $\frac{n!}{(n-3)!}$

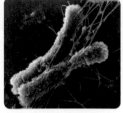

Stereoscopic photograph showing a nuclear chromosome of an eukaryote.

17b. $_nP_0$ is the number of permutations of 0 objects selected from n objects. There can only be one because there is only one empty set possible.

QY ANSWERS

1. $11^3 = 1{,}331$
2. 181,440
3. 39,916,800
4. 6

Additional Answers

25. 0; If $5 \leq n < 10$, $n!$ ends in one zero; if $10 \leq n < 15$, $n!$ ends in two zeros; etc. until 24! which ends in four zeros. However, 25! ends in six zeros.
26a. 2; $\frac{1}{3}$
26b. 9; $\frac{3}{8}$
26c. Answers vary. Sample: In a set of n elements with a certain correct order, there are d_n derangements, or arrangements such that no element is in the correct position. From the definition of derangements, we can find

that $d_n = n!\sum_{i=0}^{n}\frac{(-1)^i}{i!}$, and the probability of a derangement for large n is $\frac{1}{e} \approx 0.37$.

Lesson 6-5 Contingency Tables

Vocabulary

contingency tables

Simpson's Paradox

▶ **BIG IDEA** A careful reading of contingency tables can uncover relationships in data.

The Titanic was a luxury liner that hit an iceberg and sunk on its maiden voyage in 1912. In the movie *Titanic,* Leonardo DiCaprio plays a heroic third-class passenger who gives his life to save that of a first-class woman (played by Kate Winslet). This image agrees with a popular conception of the disaster: the rich survived, and the middle-class and poor passengers drowned. How accurate is that conception?

Titanic Table 1 below lists the number of passengers and crew who survived and died (the possible outcomes) in the sinking of the Titanic, categorized by status (first-class, second-class, third-class, and crew).

Titanic Table 1: Status and Survival

	First	Second	Third	Crew
Survived	203	118	178	212
Died	122	167	528	673

Source: British Wreck Commissioner's Inquiry Report

 QY1

Tables that divide outcomes among two or more categorical variables are called **contingency tables**. They help in analyzing complex situations.

Example 1

Refer to Titanic Table 1. Round to the nearest tenth of a percent.

a. Out of all people on the Titanic, what percent survived?

b. Find the percent of passengers in first class who survived.

c. Find the percent of passengers who survived that were in first class.

Solution

a. Add the numbers in each row. $203 + 118 + 178 + 212 = 711$ people survived and $122 + 167 + 528 + 673 = 1490$ people died. The total number of passengers was $711 + 1490 = 2201$. So $\frac{711}{2201} \approx 32.3\%$ survived.

(continued on next page)

The Titanic, pictured here on her first and last voyage, was 951 feet long.

Mental Math

Mr. Fisher has two FST classes.

	Boys	Girls
Class I	20	10
Class II	8	16

What is the probability a student is a boy if the student is randomly selected from all students

a. in Class I? $\frac{2}{3}$

b. in Class II? $\frac{1}{3}$

c. in either class? $\frac{14}{27}$

▶ **QY1**

Calculate the total number of people who survived and the total number who died.

Background

Contingency tables are to relative frequencies what conditional probability is to probability. In each case, the sample space is cut down by splitting the data into categories and we consider what happens *if* the outcome or event is in a particular category.

For example, according to the National Center for Health Statistics, 652,486 of the 2,397,615 deaths in the United States in 2004 were attributed to heart disease.

There is no contingency in that information; the relative frequency of death by heart disease was 27.2%. But if we split the data by sex and ask: what is the relative frequency of death for women by heart disease, then the splitting of the data results in a contingency table. We are speaking of the cause of death *contingent on the fact that* the person who died was a female.

(continued on next page)

GOAL

This lesson shows how to compute relative frequencies and probabilities from contingency tables.

SPUR Objectives

H Use a contingency table to compute percentages involving categorical variables.

M Represent information about relative frequencies or frequencies in a contingency table.

Materials/Resources

· Lesson Master 6-5
· Resource Masters 136–139

HOMEWORK • Option 1

• Questions 1–6 • Option 2
• • Questions 7–16
• • Question 17 (extra credit)
• Reading Lesson 6-6
• Covering the Ideas 6-6 (Questions 1–7)

Local Standards

1 Warm-Up

In 1–4, use this information. Willie Fielder hurt himself two games into the 2047 baseball season and only batted 6 times with 1 hit, for a batting average of .167. Scott ("Scruffy") Scrub played the entire season but was a second-stringer, so was up only 100 times and got 19 hits, for a batting average of .190, better than Willie's average. In the 2048 season, Willie was well and got 201 hits in 600 at-bats. Scott still remained a second-stringer and was up only 100 times again, but got 35 hits.

1. What was Willie's batting average for the 2048 season? .335

(continued on next page)

6-5

2. What was Scott's batting average for the 2048 season? **.350**

3. What was Willie's combined batting average for the 2047 and 2048 seasons? **.333**

4. What was Scott's combined batting average for the 2047 and 2048 seasons? **.270**

(This is an example of Simpson's paradox. Willie's average in both 2047 and 2048 was lower than Scott's, but his combined batting average was much higher.)

2 Teaching

Notes on the Lesson

There is no advanced mathematics here, but reading these tables and answering the questions requires care and diligence. Students would be well-served by putting frequencies into a spreadsheet when possible and letting the spreadsheet calculate the relative frequencies.

If you use the Warm-Up, you might start by having students construct a contingency table with the data from the Warm-Up.

Batter	2047		2048		Total	
	at-bats	hits	at-bats	hits	at-bats	hits
Willie	6	1	600	201	606	202
Scott	100	19	100	35	200	54

Have students try to explain why Scott has the higher batting average in both 2047 and 2048, but the lower batting average overall (by a lot!) Question 10 is similar, using actual data of two very fine Major League Baseball players.

Example 1 You might then turn to the Titanic data. Question 2 can help you get into that, and Questions 7–9 continue this theme. It is important to discuss this example, as it is used again in Lesson 6-9. There, the chi-square statistic is used as a way of determining whether the number of survivors was sufficiently different for different classes that such a difference was unlikely to happen by chance.

b. There were 203 survivors in first class. The total number of passengers in first class was $203 + 122 = 325$. Therefore, the percent of people in first class who survived is $\frac{203}{325} \approx 62.5\%$.

c. Again, there were 203 survivors in first class. The total number of people who survived was 711. Therefore, the percent of people who survived that were in first class is $\frac{203}{711} \approx 28.6\%$.

Many people find the discrepancy between the answers to Parts b and c confusing, because the questions seem so similar. As simple fractions, both answers have the same numerator, 203, which is the number of first-class survivors. But the denominators are different, because the two questions ask about different populations. Part b asks about the population of *passengers in first class*, of which there were 325. Part c asks about the population of *all passengers who survived*, of which there were 711. In forming a $\frac{part}{whole}$ ratio, you must be clear about the answer to the question "What is the whole?". For questions about ratios based on a contingency table, you must be careful to correctly identify the whole, that is, the *population* to which the question refers.

Tree diagrams can help to clarify the difference between Parts b and c above. In the diagram below at the left, the people are sorted first by status and then by who survived and who did not. In the tree diagram below at the right, the sorting is first by survival and then by status. Each of Parts b and c of Example 1 matches a different tree diagram, which isolates the population in question.

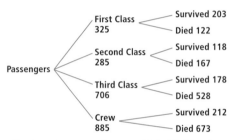

First branch separates by status: Of the 325 first class passengers, 203 survived, or $\frac{203}{325} \approx 62.5\%$.

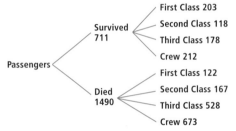

First branch separates survivors from deaths: Of the 711 people who survived, 203 were in first class, or $\frac{203}{711} \approx 28.6\%$.

STOP QY2

Other Contingency Table Formats

Because it is common to ask questions that involve totals of rows or columns, those totals are frequently included in contingency tables.

> **▶ QY2**
>
> Which is greater, the chance that a survivor was a second-class passenger, or the chance that a second-class passenger survived?

Examples 1 and 3 involve contingency tables in which the data are relative frequencies. Example 2 involves frequencies.

Averaging and Simpson's paradox

Simpson's paradox can be explained as follows: There exist positive integers a, b, c, d, e, f, g, and h such that $\frac{a}{b} > \frac{c}{d}$ and $\frac{e}{f} > \frac{g}{h}$ yet $\frac{a+e}{b+f} < \frac{c+g}{d+h}$. (For example, $\frac{19}{100} > \frac{1}{6}$ and $\frac{51}{100} > \frac{201}{400}$, yet $\frac{70}{200} < \frac{202}{406}$, as seen in the Warm-Up for this lesson.) That means that if you combine data to obtain relative frequencies (each of the first four fractions can be viewed as a relative frequency, and the combining of data gives the last two relative frequencies), the relative frequency

GUIDED

Example 2

A 2001 study by the University of Texas Southwestern Medical Center examined 626 patients to see if there was a connection between getting a tattoo and infection with Hepatitis C (HCV). The results are in the contingency table below.

	Tattoo Done in Commercial Tattoo Parlor	Tattoo Done Elsewhere	No Tattoo
Has Hepatitis C	17	8	18
No Hepatitis C	35	53	495

Source: Haley RW, Fischer RP in *Medicine*, March 2001

a. Add row and column totals to the table.

b. What does the total of the third column represent?

c. What does the total of the second row represent?

d. According to this data, is someone with a tattoo done in a commercial parlor more or less likely to have HCV than someone with a tattoo done elsewhere?

e. Give at least one reason why the result in Part d might not reflect the safety of each kind of tattoo.

Solution

a.

	Tattoo Done in Commercial Tattoo Parlor	Tattoo Done Elsewhere	No tattoo	Totals
Has Hepatitis C	17	8	18	43
No Hepatitis C	35	53	495	? 583
Totals	52	? 61	? 513	626

b. The total of the third column represents all the patients who __?__. **have no tattoo**

c. The total of the second row represents all the patients who __?__. **do not have Hepatitis C**

d. The chance that someone with a tattoo from a commercial parlor had HCV is $\frac{17}{52} \approx 33\%$. The chance that someone with a tattoo done elsewhere has HCV is $\approx$ __?__%. Therefore, someone with a tattoo done in a $\frac{8}{61} \approx 13.1$ commercial parlor is __?__ likely to have HCV than someone **more** with a tattoo done elsewhere.

e. Here is a possible explanation. **People with tattoos done in commercial tattoo parlors might have engaged in other activities that put them at risk for HCV.**

It is common to express entries in a contingency table as percents of a row or a column total. Consider the table of Titanic survivor data below.

Titanic Table 2: Column Percents

	First	Second	Third	Crew
Survived % of column	203 62%	118 41%	178 25%	212 24%
Died % of column	122 38%	167 59%	528 75%	673 76%
Totals	325	285	706	885

Sums to 100%

Notes on the Lesson

In Example 1, the difference between the two tree diagrams can be illustrated by pie charts. For the first tree diagram, use 4 charts, each one indicating number survived and number died for a particular class. For the second tree diagram, use 2 pie charts (for survived and died), each one broken down by class.

Example 2 It is surprising that tattoos done in a commercial tattoo parlor are associated with greater levels of Hepatitis C. This association may not be the result of any causal connection, for it could be due to the type of clientele who do and do not frequent tattoo parlors.

Additional Examples

Example 1 Use Titanic Table 1 in the lesson. Round each answer to the nearest percent.

a. Out of all the people on the ship, what percent died? **68%**

b. What percent of passengers in third class died? **75%**

c. What percent of passengers in first or second class died? **47%**

Example 2 Use the data from Example 2 in the lesson. Answer to the nearest tenth of a percent.

a. What percent of people in the study did not have a tattoo? **81.9%**

b. What percent of people in the study with no tattoo had Hepatitis C? **3.5%**

c. What percent of people in the study with a tattoo had Hepatitis C? **22.1%**

d. What can you conclude from the answers to Parts b and c? **People with tattoos were about 6 times more likely to have Hepatitis C than those without tattoos.**

of an event given each of two contingencies can favor one of the variables, but the combined relative frequency can favor the other.

All the data in the reading portion of the lesson are real except for Example 3. The data from the Titanic disaster and from the University of California at Berkeley admissions are quite famous.

6-5

In Titanic Table 2, each percentage represents the percent of people of a given status who survived or died. Therefore, the percentages along each column add to 100%. The percentages along each row do not add to 100% because each value is a percent of a different total: 62% represents a fraction of the 325 first-class passengers, while 41% represents a fraction of the 285 second-class passengers. If you were interested in the class breakdown of survivors, you would compute percentages of row totals instead, as in Titanic Table 3.

Titanic Table 3: Row Percents

	First	Second	Third	Crew	Totals
Survived % of row	203 29%	118 17%	178 25%	212 30%	711
Died % of row	122 8%	167 11%	528 35%	673 45%	1490

STOP QY3

> **QY3**
>
> In Titanic Table 3, what does 17% represent?

Notice that while the percentages make some comparisons easier, they make other comparisons more difficult. For example, although the 17% of survivors who were in second class is larger than the 8% of deaths in first class, the number of second-class passengers who survived is smaller than the number of first-class passengers who died. The discrepancy arises because many more people died than lived, so a smaller percentage of deaths can represent a larger number of people.

When a contingency table gives percentages but does not specify whether they are percentages of rows or columns, you should check whether rows or columns add to 100% to find out what the percentages represent.

Example 3

Fifth-grade students in a school were surveyed about their favorite book series. The results are reported in the contingency table below.

	Harry Potter	Animorphs	Lemony Snicket	Lord of the Rings	Other
Boys	42%	15%	23%	11%	9%
Girls	51%	8%	28%	5%	8%

a. What does the 23% in the first row, third column represent?

b. Which is larger: the number of boys who prefer Animorphs, or the number of girls who prefer Lemony Snicket?

Solution

a. In the first column, 42% + 51% ≠ 100%. But the total of each row is 100%. The number in the first row, third column means that 23% of all boys surveyed chose Lemony Snicket as their favorite book series.

(continued on next page)

---

b. The contingency table gives percentages of boys and percentages of girls respectively. It does not give the number of boys or girls in each cell. Nor does it give the total number of boys and of girls, from which you could compute these figures yourself. **Not enough information is given to answer this question.**

 QY4

> ▶ QY4
>
> Answer Example 3b, if you know that 500 boys and 400 girls were surveyed.

Averaging and Simpson's Paradox

When data are combined or separated, the totals may not look like the parts. Here is a famous real-world example. In the 1970s, the University of California at Berkeley was sued for gender discrimination in graduate school admissions. As a result, it examined its admissions closely. In 1973, a typical year, 35% of 4321 female applicants were admitted, while 44% of 8442 male applicants were admitted. The women's acceptance rate was noticeably smaller than the men's.

The situation was actually more complicated than it looked. Applicants for graduate school apply to specific programs, not to the university as a whole, and acceptance rates vary widely from program to program. The contingency table below shows the men's and women's acceptance rates within each program.

Program	Men		Women		Overall	
	Applicants	% Admitted	Applicants	% Admitted	Applicants	% Admitted
A	825	62%	108	82%	933	64%
B	560	63%	25	68%	585	63%
C	325	37%	593	34%	918	35%
D	417	33%	375	35%	792	34%
E	191	28%	393	24%	584	25%
F	373	6%	341	7%	714	6%
Total	2691	44.5%	1835	30.4%	4526	38.8%

Jane K. Sather Tower, University of California, Berkeley

Within each program, men were accepted at a comparable or equal rate to women. The discrepancy arises because the programs to which the most men applied (programs A and B) had higher overall acceptance rates than the two most popular women's programs (C and E). In this case, the choice of program is a *confounding variable,* that is, an extra variable associated with one of the variables in the study (gender), that causes part of the observed effect.

The discrepancy between the overall acceptance rates and the acceptance rates within each program is an example of **Simpson's Paradox**, named after Edward H. Simpson, who wrote about the paradox in 1951. Simpson's Paradox can arise whenever different categories of data are combined (or *aggregated*) to compute an average or percent. Although Simpson's Paradox arises in a variety of situations, the best way to avoid being confused by it is to separate (or *disaggregate*) the data into the original categories.

Contingency Tables **391**

Notes on the Lesson

Averaging and Simpson's Paradox This is perhaps the most-used example of Simpson's Paradox. The data were the result of an internal study *"Sex Bias in Graduate Admissions: Data from Berkeley,"* P. J. Bickel, et al (1975) Science, 187. The stratified data appeared in <u>Statistics</u> (2nd ed), D. Freedman, et al (1991), New York, W. W. Norton.

3 Assignment

Recommended Assignment

- Questions 1–6
- Questions 7–16
- Question 17 (extra credit)
- Reading Lesson 6-6
- Covering the Ideas 6-6 (Questions 1–7)

Notes on the Questions

Question 1 These data are made up.

Question 3 The percent of vaccinated children who developed polio was considerably less than the percent of unvaccinated children who developed polio. This was the key bit of data in making the decision to vaccinate the entire population. Within ten years or so, polio – a dreaded disease – was virtually eradicated in the United States. Today there are some people who are against vaccinations, somehow disbelieving or ignoring the history of common diseases that have been virtually eliminated when the entire population is vaccinated. Students might be interested in looking into the role that vaccinations played in the decline of smallpox in the world.

Questions

COVERING THE IDEAS

1. A sample of 70 students at a high school was examined to investigate patterns of enrollment in language classes.

	Freshman	Sophomore	Junior	Senior
Spanish	8	11	5	2
French	2	5	0	1
No language	5	8	10	13

   a. What percent of students who took no language were seniors?
   b. What percent of students who were seniors took no language?
   c. Copy and extend the table to include row and column totals.

2. Use Titanic Table 1 on page 387.
   a. How many first- and second-class passengers were aboard the ship when it set sail? **610**
   b. What percent of the first- and second-class passengers survived?
   c. What percent of third-class passengers survived? **about 25.2%**
   d. Do you think it is accurate to say poor passengers drowned at a disproportionate rate? Back up your response with evidence.

3. Use the table from the polio study on page 359.
   a. Give the row percents for vaccinated children.
   b. Give the column percents for those who developed paralytic polio.
   c. What percent of children who developed paralytic polio were vaccinated? **about 22.3%**

4. The contingency table for the graduate school admissions on page 391 shows that a higher percent of women than men were admitted to Program A. Find the number of men and number of women accepted to Program A. Explain how it is possible that the number of women accepted is lower when compared to men, even though the percentage of women accepted is higher.

5. The table below gives the number of motor vehicles involved in accidents in the U.S. in 2004, classified by vehicle type and severity.

	Fatality (1000s)	Injury (1000s)	No Injury (1000s)
Passenger Car	25.5	1,989.8	4,216.3
Pickup Truck	10.8	482.0	1,161.8
SUV	7.8	475.0	1085.8
Van	3.7	259.5	563.7
Other Light Truck	0.1	29.3	74.3

Source: Statistical Abstract of the United States, 2007-2008

   a. What is the total of the first row, and what does it represent?
   b. What is the total of the first column, and what does it represent?
   c. What is the chance that an SUV accident had a fatality?
   d. What is the chance that a vehicle in which there was a fatality was an SUV? **about 16.3%**

1a. about 36.1%
1b. about 81.3%
1c. See margin.
2b. about 52.6%
2d. It is accurate because about 52.6% of first- and second-class passengers survived while only about 25.2% of the third-class passengers survived.
3a. developed polio: about 0.02%; did not develop polio: about 99.98%
3b. vaccinated: about 22.3%;: unvaccinated: about 77.7%
4. 512 men and 89 women were accepted; far fewer women than men applied to Program A, so even though a higher percentage were accepted, a smaller number were accepted.
5a. 6,231.6; the number (in thousands) of passenger cars involved in accidents
5b. 47.9; the number (in thousands) of fatalities in all motor vehicle accidents
5c. about 0.5%

Additional Answers

1c.

	Freshman	Sophomore	Junior	Senior	Total
Spanish	8	11	5	2	26
French	2	5	0	1	8
No Language	5	8	10	13	36
Total	15	24	15	16	70

6-5 Lesson Master

Questions on SPUR Objectives
See Student Edition pages 432–435 for objectives.

USES Objective H

In 1-3, refer to the following data from 2,145 inline skaters in Boston.

	Amount of Protective Gear Worn		
Skill Level	No Gear	1 piece	2-4 pieces
Beginner	188	294	227
Average	314	245	123
Advanced	372	242	140

1. Of all the inline skaters, what percent wore no protective gear? $\frac{874}{2145} \approx 40.7\%$
2. Find the percent of inline skaters who were beginners and wore 2-4 pieces of protective gear. $\frac{227}{2145} \approx 10.6\%$
3. Find the percent of skaters that wore 2-4 pieces of protective gear who were beginners. $\frac{227}{490} \approx 46.3\%$
4. Consider the table at the right of Alcohol-Impaired Driving Fatalities in 2007. Drivers are considered impaired if their blood alcohol concentration (BAC) is 0.08 or higher. Explain why it is more likely that a male driver randomly chosen from all these drivers is more likely to have been impaired than a female driver randomly chosen.

Sex of the Driver	Male	Female	Not Reported
BAC < 0.08	30,789	12,244	580
BAC > 0.08	10,015	1,855	198

About 25% of the males were impaired, about 13% of the females, and about 25% of the "not reported," so it is likely that the "not reported" were predominantly male.

REPRESENTATIONS Objective M

5. Consider the following situation. A pizza parlor represented its sales for the prior month as follows.

Crust	Cheese	Veggie	Sausage	Pepperoni
Thin (58%)	34%	18%	26%	22%
Thick (42%)	27%	28%	22%	23%

   a. What percent of all pizza orders were for Sausage pizza? ≈ 24.3%
   b. What percent of all pizza orders were for Cheese pizza? ≈ 31.1%
   c. Vegetarians will not eat sausage or pepperoni pizzas. Non-vegetarians can eat any pizza. If there were equal numbers of vegetarians and non-vegetarians, [illegible]

216 *Functions, Statistics and Trigonometry*

6. An electronics store does free repairs on everything it sells for the first year. The Store sells three brands of DVD players: 50% of those sold are brand A, 30% are Brand B, and 20% are Brand C. During the first year, 25% of Brand A machines need service, 10% of Brand B need service, and 5% of Brand C need service.

a. Make a tree diagram for this situation

b. What percent of all the machines sold need service? **6b. 16.5%**

c. What percent of the machines needing service are Brand A?

APPLYING THE MATHEMATICS

In 7–9, use the data below. The British agency that conducted the inquiry into the Titanic disaster separated their findings according to gender and age, as given in the table below.

		1st Class	2nd Class	3rd Class	Steerage and crew	Total
Survived	Men	57	14	75	192	338
	Women	140	80	76	20	316
	Children	6	24	27	0	57
Died	Men	118	154	387	670	1329
	Women	4	13	89	3	109
	Children	0	0	52	0	52
Total	Men	175	168	462	862	1667
	Women	144	93	165	23	425
	Children	6	24	79	0	109

Source: British Wreck Commissioner's Inquiry Report

7. a. What percent of men in second class survived? **about 8.3%**

b. What percent of survivors were women? **about 44.4%**

c. What percent of survivors were in third class? **about 25.0%**

8. a. Who was more likely to survive: a man in first class, or a child in third class? Support your answer numerically.

b. If someone survived, how likely is it that the person was either in first class or a woman? **about 53.3%**

9. Describe the difference between the three questions below, and give each value.

a. What is the chance that a child in first class survived?

b. What is the chance that a survivor was a child in first class?

c. What is the chance that a person on the Titanic was a child who survived in first class?

6a.

Brand A 50% — Needs Service 25% / Good Condition 75%
Brand B 30% — Needs Service 10% / Good Condtion 90%
Brand C 20% — Needs Service 5% / Good Condition 95%
DVD Players

6c. about 75.8%

8a. A child in third class survives: about 34.2%; A man in first class survives: about 32.6%

9a. The population for this question is children in first class; 100%

9b. The population for this question is all survivors; about 0.8%

9c. The population for this question is all people on the Titanic; about 0.3%

Notes on the Questions

Question 5 The severity of an accident is assigned according to the worst outcome that occurs in that vehicle in the crash: if an SUV and a van are involved in a crash in which the passenger in the SUV dies and the driver of the van is injured (and nobody in the van dies), the SUV would be counted in the "fatality" category and the van would be counted in the "injury" category.

Questions 8 and 9 Note how the use of contingencies makes these questions far more interesting than those in Question 7.

6-5

4 Wrap-Up

Project Update

Project 5, *Probability Trees*, on page 427 relates to the content of this lesson.

10. The batting statistics in the table below for professional baseball players Derek Jeter and David Justice in the years 1995 and 1996 illustrate Simpson's Paradox.

	1995		1996		totals	
	at-bats	hits	at-bats	hits	at-bats	hits
Jeter	48	12	582	183	630	195
Justice	411	104	140	45	551	149

Source: Major League Baseball

a. Calculate the batting averages for Jeter and Justice in 1995 and in 1996.

b. Calculate the totals and batting averages for Jeter and Justice for the two years.

c. What is surprising about these results? What is the confounding variable?

David Justice is high-fived by teammate Derek Jeter after scoring a tying run.

REVIEW

11. Write $_{98}P_3$ in each way. (**Lesson 6-4**)

a. as a product of integers   b. as a ratio of two factorials

In 12 and 13, evaluate. (**Lesson 6-4**)

12. $_{13}P_9$ $\frac{13!}{4!} = 259,459,200$ 13. $_{212}P_3$ $\frac{212!}{209!} = 9,393,720$

14. If you must answer every question on a test, how many ways are there of answering a test with 12 true-false and 6 multiple-choice questions with 5 choices each? (**Lesson 6-3**) $2^{12} \cdot 5^6 = 64,000,000$

15. Suppose two fair six-sided dice are rolled and the sum is a multiple of 2, but not a multiple of 3. (**Lesson 6-2**)

a. List the outcomes of the event. **See margin.**

b. Give the probability of the event. $\frac{1}{3}$

16. In 2007, the population of Hungary was reported as 9,956,108 with an average annual growth rate of –0.253%. Assume this growth rate is constant. (**Lesson 2-5**)

a. Express the population P in terms of the number of years n after 2007. $P(n) = 9,956,108 \cdot (0.99747)^n$

b. Estimate the population of Hungary in 2000. **about 10,134,229**

EXPLORATION

17. Many people believe that SUVs are safer than passenger cars because they believe that when an accident occurs, occupants of an SUV are safer than occupants of passenger cars. Use the accident data given in Question 5 to either support or refute this claim. **See margin.**

10a. Jeter: (1995) .250, (1996) .314; Justice: (1995) .253, (1996) .321

10b. Jeter: .310; Justice: .270

10c. Even though Justice had a better batting average both years, Jeter has a higher overall batting average. The confounding variable is the number of total at-bats.

11a. $98 \cdot 97 \cdot 96 = 912,576$

11b. $\frac{98!}{95!} = 912,576$

QY ANSWERS

1. 711 survived; 1490 died

2. The chance that a second-class passenger survived.

3. the percent of survivors who were second-class passengers

4. the number of girls who prefer Lemony Snicket

394   Counting, Probability, and Inference

Additional Answers

15a. {(1,1), (1,3), (2,2), (3,1), (6,2), (5,3), (4,4), (3,5), (2,6), (6,4), (5,5), (4,6)}

17. Answers vary. Sample: probability of injury in SUV accident: about 30.3%; probability of fatality in SUV accident: about 0.5%; probability of injury or fatality in SUV accident: about 30.8%; probability of injury in passenger car accident: about 31.9%; probability of fatality in passenger car accident: about 0.4%; probability of injury or fatality in passenger car accident: about 32.3%; Because the percentages are so close to each other, it seems the data do not support a definitive claim that SUVs are safer than passenger cars.

Lesson 6-6 Conditional Probability

Vocabulary

conditional probability of an event, $P(B|A)$

▶ **BIG IDEA** The idea of conditional probability helps to explain and compute results from contingency tables.

Lesson 6-5 began with the following table about the numbers of people on the Titanic who survived and who died.

	First	Second	Third	Crew
Survived	203	118	178	212
Died	122	167	528	673

Source: British Wreck Commissioner's Inquiry Report

From this contingency table, you can determine probabilities that a person was in a particular row given that they were in a particular column, or vice-versa. For instance, you can determine the probability that a randomly-selected passenger survived (the first row) given that the passenger was in second class (the second column). Finding probabilities like this are the topic of this lesson.

What Is Conditional Probability?

Let A and B be events with $A = $ "the passenger was in second class" and $B = $ "the passenger survived." We want the probability of B given A. Such a probability is called a *conditional probability*. The probability is $\frac{118}{118 + 167} = \frac{118}{285}$, or about 41%. Notice that $118 = N(A \cap B)$ and $285 = N(A)$. So, the conditional probability that a randomly-selected second-class passenger survived is $\frac{N(A \cap B)}{N(A)}$, in this case $\frac{118}{285}$.

In this situation, the sample space S is the set of all passengers and crew, and $N(S) = 2201$. If we divide both numerator and denominator by $N(S)$, we obtain

$$P(B \text{ given } A) = \frac{N(A \cap B)}{N(A)} = \frac{\frac{N(A \cap B)}{N(S)}}{\frac{N(A)}{N(S)}} = \frac{P(A \cap B)}{P(A)}.$$

Thus, conditional probabilities can be defined in terms of probabilities.

Definition of Conditional Probability

The **conditional probability of an event** B given an event A, written $P(B \mid A)$, is $\frac{P(A \cap B)}{P(A)}$.

Mental Math

Write each expression as a simple fraction in lowest terms.

a. $\frac{30\% + 15\%}{50\%}$ $\frac{9}{10}$

b. $\frac{0.9 \cdot 0.3}{0.3 \cdot 0.4 + 0.7 \cdot 0.6}$ $\frac{1}{2}$

c. $\frac{2x \cdot 4x}{5x \cdot 3x + 6x \cdot 4x}$ $\frac{8}{39}$

GOAL

Introduce the language and notation of conditional probability and apply conditional probability to situations where the answers are not at all obvious.

SPUR Objectives

D Calculate probabilities using the definition of conditional probability.

I Calculate probabilities in real situations.

Materials/Resources

· Lesson Master 6-6
· Resource Masters 140–142
· Quiz 2

HOMEWORK • Option 1   • Option 2

- Questions 1–7
- • Questions 8–16
- • Question 17 (extra credit)
- • Reading Lesson 6-7
- • Covering the Ideas 6-7 (Questions 1–11)

Local Standards

1 Warm-Up

Suppose 60% of the singers in a school play are in the school choir. In the school as a whole, suppose 10% of the students are in the choir and 5% are in the school play. Finally, suppose there are 600 students in the school.

a. If a student in the play is randomly chosen, what is the probability that student is in the choir? **60%**

b. If a student in the choir is randomly chosen, what is the probability that student is in the play? $\frac{18}{60} = $ **30%**

c. If a student in the school is randomly chosen, what is the probability that student is in both the play and the choir? $\frac{18}{600} = $ **3%**

Background

What is conditional probability?

Conditional probability is the theoretical counterpart of contingency tables. In this lesson, two types of situations are offered. The first is rather simple and a matter of common sense. Suppose we ask a question such as: What is the probability that a random student in our school walked to school today? Let $W = $ the set of students who walked and $S = $ the set of all students in the school. We know that the answer is found by dividing the number $N(W)$ of

students who walked to school, by the number $N(S)$ of students in the school. So $P(\text{a random student walked}) = \frac{N(W)}{N(S)}$. There is no conditional probability in that calculation. But suppose we ask for the probability that a student who lives over 1 mile from school walked to school. Let F be the set of students who live over 1 mile from school. Then we are dealing with the probability of W given F, written $P(W \mid F)$, not the probability of W given S,

(continued on next page)

Notes on the Lesson

Warm-Up These three probabilities of the form $P(A \mid B)$, $P(B \mid A)$, and $P(A \cap B)$, each calculable from the given information, are often confused by students.)

What is conditional probability?
Conditional probability is a difficult concept for many students. You might begin either by going through the Titanic situation that begins the lesson or by going through the Warm-Up. The purpose is to have students understand the difference between $P(B \mid A)$ and $P(B \cap A)$. In the first case, the sample space has been restricted to situations in which event A occurs. In the second case, there is a larger sample space in which both events B and A are possible.

Example 1 Go through this example carefully, line by line. Point out the tree diagram solution. Then have students do Example 2 if they have not already done so as part of reading homework.

Conditional Probability and Medical Tests

You could calculate the conditional probability from the Titanic data without having a formula, by thinking clearly about the situation. A similar and very important situation involving conditional probability is in medicine. It is complex enough to require a systematic procedure for the calculation.

When a person takes a test to see if they have a particular allergy, disease, or other condition, the result is called *negative* if the test indicates the person does *not* have the condition. It is called *positive* if the test indicates the person *does* have the condition. Usually, the negative result is the one you want.

Few medical tests are 100% accurate. Taking this into account, there are two ways a test can be accurate and two ways it can be wrong. They are shown in the tree diagram below. The two ways it can be wrong are called a *false positive* (the test says you have the condition, but you don't) and *false negative* (the test says you don't have the condition, but you do.)

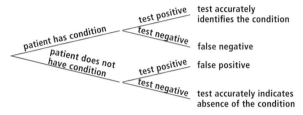

From a treatment point of view, the worst result is the false negative. Then you have a condition but the test shows you don't, so you are falsely led to believe that you do not need treatment. But false positives are also bad because they can be traumatic. A person can think they have a disease yet not have it. This is why it is useful to know how likely a false negative and false positive might be.

Example 1

An article in the Journal of the American Medical Association in 1997 reported that, when people go to their doctor's office with a sore throat and think they might have strep throat, 30% actually have strep throat. It noted that a current test for strep throat was 80% accurate if you have strep throat and 90% ccurate if you do not. What is the probability that a person who receives a positive result from this test does not have the disease?

Solution First, organize the given information into a tree diagram. We let A = "tests positive" and B = "has strep throat."

because we have cut down the sample space to considering only those students who live over 1 mile from school.
$$P(W \mid F) = \frac{N(W \cap F)}{N(F)}.$$
This probability is likely to be smaller than P(a random student walked).

Example 1 This example exhibits the second type of problem involving conditional probability. From the definition, $P(B \mid A) = \frac{P(A \cap B)}{P(A)}$, multiply both sides by $P(A)$. Then we have $P(A \cap B) = P(A) \cdot P(B \mid A)$. This gives us a way to calculate the probability that two events A and B both happen. Suppose we want $P((\text{not } B) \mid A)$. From the definition, $P((\text{not } B) \mid A) = \frac{P(A \cap \text{not } B)}{P(A)}$. By building the table, we see that $P(A) = 0.24 + 0.07 = 0.31$.

We want to calculate $P((\text{not } B) \mid A)$, the probability that a person does not have strep throat even though the test indicates that the person does. Suppose T people are tested. Then $0.30T$ have strep throat and $0.70T$ do not.

Of the 0.30T who have strep throat:

$$0.80 \cdot 0.30T = 0.24T \text{ test positive.}$$
$$0.20 \cdot 0.30T = 0.06T \text{ test negative.}$$

Of the 0.70T who do not have strep throat:

$$0.10 \cdot 0.70T = 0.07T \text{ test positive.}$$
$$0.90 \cdot 0.70T = 0.63T \text{ test negative.}$$

You can now write these percents of T on a tree diagram. Each leaf is labeled with its probability, the product of the branches that lead to it.

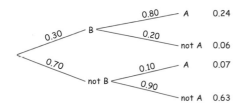

Another way to summarize these probabilities is with a table. Notice that the columns add to the totals in the bottom row.

	B = Patient has strep	not B = Patient does not have strep	Total
A = Test +	$P(A \cap B) = 0.24$	$P(A \cap \text{not } B) = 0.07$	$P(A) = 0.31$
not A = Test −	$P(\text{not } A \cap B) = 0.06$	$P(\text{not } A \cap \text{not } B) = 0.63$	$P(\text{not } A) = 0.69$
Total	$P(B) = 0.30$	$P(\text{not } B) = 0.70$	1.0

The probabilities in this table are descriptive of the population of patients who took the test.

From the definition of conditional probability,

$$P(\text{not } B \mid A) = \frac{P(A \text{ and not } B)}{P(A)} = \frac{0.07T}{0.07T + 0.24T} = \frac{0.07}{0.31} \approx 23\%.$$

Given that someone tests positive for strep, the chance he or she does not have the disease is therefore about 23%.

 QY

The answer 23% in Example 1 means that, in this situation, about 1 in 4 people for whom the test is positive do not have strep throat. In this case, a doctor may prescribe an antibiotic just to play it safe, but for a more serious disease, for which treatment may be painful and expensive, a second test may help to provide a more accurate result.

> **QY**
>
> In Example 1, what is the probability that a negative result is a false negative— that is, a person has strep but the test does not show it?

We also see that $P(A \cap (\text{not } B)) = P(\text{not } B) \cdot P(A \mid (\text{not } B)) = 0.70 \cdot 0.10 = 0.07$. In this way, $P(X \mid Y)$ has helped us obtain $P(Y \mid X)$.

Some teachers and students prefer the tree diagram solution of this problem. The calculations shown by the leaves in the tree diagram solution show the logic of the conditional probability more clearly than the table exhibited in the Solution in Example 1. A student using a tree diagram should not necessarily have to show this;

having the numbers by appropriate branches is sufficient.

Example 2 and Question 3 This real situation is the reason that doctors recommend that anyone undergoing a test for a disease that afflicts only a small percent of people (and that covers almost all diseases), if receiving a positive result on a test, should get a second opinion.

6-6

Notes on the Lesson

Example 2 and Question 3 This is an important example of the sophistication that quantitative literacy sometimes entails. Generally, people think: If I have cancer, what is the probability that the test will show it? In this case, that probability is 98%, very high. Also, the negative result of this test seems fairly reliable as only 0.01% of the negatives are false. But in Question 3 we are faced with the converse situation: If the test indicates you have cancer, what is the probability you have it? Since 91% of the positive tests are false positives, the answer is that you have a probability of about 9% of having cancer.

3 Assignment

Recommended Assignment

- Questions 1–7
- • Questions 8–16
- • Question 17 (extra credit)
  - Reading Lesson 6-7
  - Covering the Ideas 6-7 (Questions 1–5)

Notes on the Questions

Question 2 It is important to go through this diagram, because some students will prefer to do this kind of problem using a tree diagram.

Question 3b This result is discussed in the Background and Notes on the Lesson.

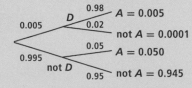

398 Chapter 6

False Negatives

In cases such as cancer, where a disease can be fatal and prompt treatment is crucial to the patient's survival, false negatives are particularly troubling.

GUIDED

Example 2

Suppose all patients are tested for a serious disease that is estimated to be found in 0.5% of people. Suppose also that the test accurately spots the disease 98% of the time and accurately indicates no disease 95% of the time. What is the probability that a negative result is a false negative?

Solution Instead of a tree diagram, construct a contingency table with the given information. Let D = "has the disease" and A = "tests positive."

0.0049   0.05, 0.995, 0.04975

	D	not D	
A	0.98 • 0.005 = __?__	__?__ • __?__ = __?__	
not A	__?__ • 0.005 = __?__	0.95 • __?__ = __?__	0.02, 0.0001
Total	0.5% of total	99.5 __?__ % of total	0.995, 0.94525

Thus, in this situation, the probability that someone who tests negative does in fact have the disease equals $P(\frac{?}{D} | \frac{?}{\text{not } A}) = \frac{P(D \cap (\text{not } A))}{P(\text{not } A)} = \frac{?}{0.0001}$.

The answer to Example 2 indicates that about 0.01% of the negatives are false negatives. It is important for tests to have a low rate of false negatives because in many cases, early detection and treatment is key to patient recovery or survival. An additional concern for doctors and hospitals is the potential liability from malpractice suits fueled by misdiagnoses. Question 3 asks for the false positive rate in the situation of Example 2, which may be quite high. This type of misdiagnosis is also troubling, considering its potential emotional, physical, and financial impact.

Questions

COVERING THE IDEAS

1. Refer to the table on page 395. What is the probability that a randomly selected passenger survived given that the passenger was in first class? **about 62.5%**

2. Refer to Example 1. For what percent of the patients is the strep throat test accurate? **87%**

3. a. Draw a tree diagram corresponding to Example 2.
   b. What is the probability that a positive result is a false positive?
   c. Your answer to Part b should surprise you. Explain why it makes sense.

398   Counting, Probability, and Inference

3a. let D = has the disease and A = tests positive. See margin for tree diagram.

3b. P(not D|A)
$= \frac{P(\text{not } D \cap A)}{P(A)}$
$= \frac{0.050}{0.50 + 0.0050} \approx 0.91$

3c. Answers vary. Sample: 91 % of positives are false positives. The reason for this surprising result is that very few people in the population have the disease, so a low percentage of false positives is enough to overtake a high percentage of true positives.

Additional Answers

3a. let D = has the disease and A = tests positive

```
                0.98
            D ──────── A = 0.005
    0.005  ╱   0.02
          ╱   ──────── not A = 0.0001
                0.05
                ──────── A = 0.050
    0.995  ╲   
         not D  0.95
              ──────── not A = 0.945
```

---

4. Your house probably has a smoke detector whose purpose is to alert you to a fire.
   a. In this context, what is a typical instance of a false positive? Why might one occur?
   b. What is a typical instance of a false negative? Why might one occur?
   c. Which is riskier: a false positive or a false negative?

In 5–7, use this information. Polygraph machines attempt to detect whether a statement is a lie by monitoring a person's skin temperature, blood pressure, breathing, and other physical symptoms believed to correlate with deception. In a lie detector test, a "positive" result means that a statement is detected as a lie. The most favorable estimates give a 90% rate of detecting lies, with 95% of truthful statements "passing" (i.e. not marked as lies). Although many studies have obtained far lower rates, true controlled experiments are both hard to create and rarely replicate "field conditions." Assume that a police department decides to use a polygraph and estimates that about 15% of people will lie at least once.

5. In this context, give the meaning of each term.
   a. false positive **A true statement detected as a lie.**
   b. false negative **A lie is undetected.**
6. a. Make a table or a tree diagram to determine how likely it is that someone who tests positive really is lying.
   b. What is the likelihood that someone who tests positive is telling the truth? **b. about 24%**   **c. about 1.8%**
   c. What is the likelihood that someone who tests negative is lying?
7. Use tree diagrams for Parts a and b. **See margin.**
   a. If the same test is used when the probability of a lie occurring is 40%, what is the likelihood a positive result is a false positive?
   b. If the test only has a 75% accuracy rate (for both true and false statements), but is used on the original applicant pool (15% lies), what is the likelihood a positive result is a false positive?
   c. Explain your result from Part b in words.

In 8–10, the standard HIV test accurately finds the condition 99% of the time and also 99% of the time accurately shows that a person does not have HIV. In the general population, the prevalence of HIV infection is about 0.5%.

8. If a test result comes back positive, what is the likelihood the person has the disease? **about 33.2%**

9. Suppose that all people who test positive are given the same test again. Also, assume that false positives are true "flukes," that is, there is no underlying condition that causes some people to receive false positive results more than others. What is the likelihood that a person who tests positive a second time actually has the disease?

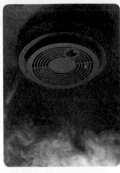

96% of U.S. households have a smoke detector. An estimated 890 lives could be saved each year if all homes had them.

4a. Answers vary. Sample: There is no fire but the alarm goes off. This might happen if the oven starts smoking.

4b. Answers vary. Sample: No alarm goes off during a fire. This might happen if the detector is out of batteries.

4c. false negative

6a. Answers vary. Sample: The probability is $\frac{0.135}{0.135 + 0.0425} \approx$ 76% that someone who tests positive is actually lying. See margin for table.

9. about 98%

Notes on the Questions

Questions 5–10 Expect it to take a good amount of time to cover these questions.

Questions 5–7 Source: Thompson, W. C., & Schumann, A. L. (1987). Interpretation of statistical evidence in criminal trials: The prosecutor's fallacy and the defense attorney's fallacy. *Law and Human Behavior*, 11, 167-187, as cited in *Calculated Risks*, by Gerd Gigerenzer (New York: Simon and Schuster, 2002).

Additional Answers

7a.

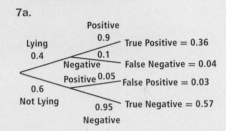

$$P(\text{false positive} \mid \text{positive test})$$
$$= \frac{0.03}{0.36 + 0.03} = 0.077 \approx 7.7\%$$

7b.

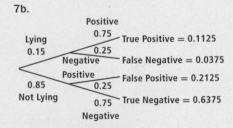

$$P(\text{false positive} \mid \text{positive test})$$
$$= \frac{0.2125}{0.2125 + 0.1125} = 0.654 = 65.4\%$$

7c. Answers vary. Sample: About 65.3% of people given a polygraph test whose result indicated a lie were actually telling the truth.

Additional Answers

6a.

	Lying	Not Lying
No Lie Detected (Negative)	0.1 · 0.15 = 0.015	0.95 · 0.85 = 0.8075
Lie Detected (Positive)	0.9 · 0.15 = 0.135	0.05 · 0.85 = 0.0425
Total	15% of total	85% of total

10. Write a few sentences explaining the results in Questions 8 and 9. First, if a test is 99% accurate, how is it that only about $\frac{1}{3}$ of positive results are actually correct? Second, how can the same test be so much more accurate if used twice?

10. See margin.

APPLYING THE MATHEMATICS

11. At a trial, a prosecutor argues that only one person in 12,000,000 matches the description of the perpetrator noted by witnesses at the scene. Therefore, the prosecutor concludes that a defendant who matches the description is guilty with probability $\frac{11,999,999}{12,000,000}$. Assume that the description is accurate, and that the accused person matches the description. Let $M =$ "a person matches the description," and let $C =$ "a person committed the crime."

   a. Which probability is represented by $\frac{1}{12,000,000}$: $P(C)$, $P(M)$, $P(C \mid M)$, or $P(M \mid C)$? **$P(M)$**

   b. Which expression in Part a represents the probability that the accused actually committed the crime, based on the description? **$P(C \mid M)$**

   c. In 2006, the population of California was about 36,000,000. If the crime was committed in California, estimate the number of people in California expected to match the description of the perpetrator. **3**

   d. Use your answer to Part c to compute $P(C \mid M)$, assuming that the perpetrator was from California. **$\frac{1}{3}$**

   e. This situation is referred to as the *prosecutor's fallacy*. Explain in ordinary terms the mistake that the prosecutor made.

11e. Answers vary. Sample: The prosecutor computed the chance of a random person matching the description, not the probability that someone who matched the description actually committed the crime. Since more than one person in California matches the description, the probability that the accused is guilty is $\frac{P(M \cap C)}{P(M)} = \frac{1}{3}$.

REVIEW

In 12 and 13, the table below shows the numbers of flights that were on time and delayed for two airlines A and B at five airports in June 1991. (Lesson 6-5)

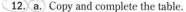

	Airline A			Airline B		
	On Time	Delayed	% Delayed	On Time	Delayed	% Delayed
LA	497	62	11.1	694	117	14.4
Phoenix	221	12	5.2	4840	415	7.9
San Diego	212	20	8.6	383	65	14.5
San Francisco	503	102	16.9	320	129	28.7
Seattle	1841	305	14.2	201	61	23.3
Total	3274	501	13.3	6438	787	10.9

12. a. Copy and complete the table.

   b. Identify the paradox contained in the table. **Simpson's Paradox**

   c. Explain why your answer in Part b is an example of this paradox.
   Airline A has a lower delay percentage at every airport, but when we combine the data Airline B has a lower total delay percentage.

400   Counting, Probability, and Inference

Additional Answers

10. Answers vary. Sample: Because very few people have HIV in this population, even a low percentage of false positives is enough to overtake the number of true positives. The second testing in essence changes the relative prevalence of HIV in the population, from 0.005 to 0.332. In this way, the number of false positives will not overtake the number of true positives.

13. a. Calculate the probability that a plane of Airline A was delayed given that it landed in Seattle. **14.2%**

   b. Calculate the probability that a plane of Airline A that was delayed landed in Seattle. **60.9%**

14. To study the connection between car owner satisfaction and origin of production, car owners were surveyed. The results are summarized in the table below. **(Lesson 6-5)**

Owners of	Level of Satisfaction		
	High	Medium	Low
American	80	100	45
Japanese	40	30	20
European	25	35	25

   a. Add appropriate row and column totals. **See margin.**

   b. What percentage of European car owners reported a medium level of satisfaction? **b. about 41.2%**   **c. about 44.4%**

   c. What percentage of Japanese car owners were highly satisfied?

15. a. How many permutations consisting of four letters each can be formed from the letters of the word CONVEX? $_6P_4 = 360$

   b. How many of the permutations in Part a begin with a vowel? **(Lesson 6-4)** $_2P_1 \cdot _5P_3 = 120$

16. Consider the data in the table below:

i	1	2	3	4	5	6	7	8	9
a_i	1	1	2	3	5	8	13	21	34

   a. Write and evaluate an expression in Σ-notation for $\sum_{i=1}^{7} a_i = 33$
   $a_1 + a_2 + a_3 + a_4 + a_5 + a_6 + a_7$.

   b. **Multiple Choice** Which expression below represents the variance of the data? **(Lessons 1-6, 1-2) C**

   A $\dfrac{\sum_{i=1}^{9} a_i}{9}$ B $\dfrac{\sum_{i=1}^{9} a_i^2}{9}$ C $\dfrac{\sum_{i=1}^{9} (a_i - \bar{a})^2}{8}$

   D $\sqrt{\dfrac{\sum_{i=1}^{9} a_i^2}{8}}$ E $\dfrac{\sum_{i=1}^{9} (a_i - \bar{a})}{8}$

EXPLORATION

17. Look for information about the accuracy of a test for a medical condition you have heard about. Use that information, and information about the prevalence of the condition, to compute the likelihood of a false positive and of a false negative.

17. Answers vary. Sample: In a test for Lyme disease, 75% of people with the disease test positive, and 81% of healthy people test negative. Suppose Lyme disease is present in about 0.04% of the population. If every person were tested, the probability of a false positive would be about 19.0% and the probability of a false negative would be about 0.01%.

4 Wrap-Up

Ongoing Assessment
Ask each student to make up a probability tree like the one in Example 1. Then have students exchange papers with a classmate and draw up a table summarizing the probabilities in their partner's tree. **Answers vary. Check student's work.**

Administer Quiz 2 (or a quiz of your own) after students complete this lesson.

Project Update
Project 5, *Probability Trees*, on page 427 relates to the content of this lesson.

QY ANSWER

$\dfrac{0.06T}{0.06T + 0.63T} = \dfrac{6}{69} \approx 8.7\%$

Conditional Probability   **401**

Additional Answers

14a.

Owners of	Level of Satisfaction			
	High	Medium	Low	Total
American	80	100	45	225
Japanese	40	30	20	90
European	25	35	25	85
Total	145	165	90	400

Lesson 6-7

Lesson 6-7

Designing Simulations

GOAL

Use a random number table to generate numbers (often called pseudo-random numbers) to simulate experiments.

SPUR Objective

K Design and conduct simulations with or without technology.

Materials/Resources

· Lesson Master 6-7
· Resource Masters 143 and 144

HOMEWORK • Option 1
• Option 2
• Questions 1–5
• • Questions 6–17
• • Questions 18 and 19 (extra credit)
• Reading Lesson 6-8
• Covering the Ideas 6-8 (Questions 1–6)

Local Standards

1 Warm-Up

Toss a coin until you get 3 heads and 3 tails. How many tosses did it take? Compare your results with two others in your class and try to determine what you think is the number of tosses that it takes on average to get 3 heads and 3 tails. (This simulates trying to find a sample of 3 men and 3 women by randomly picking names of men and women.)

> ▶ **BIG IDEA** When you do not know how to calculate the probability of an event, you may be able to use a simulation to obtain an estimate of the probability.

A **simulation** of a real situation is an experimental model that attempts to capture all aspects of the original situation that affect the outcomes. A simulation allows people to plan and predict. Crash tests, pre-election polls, and fire drills are all examples of simulations for which it would be impractical or not feasible to wait for the real event to gather data. Even college entrance tests have "trial runs." The PSAT simulates the SAT; the PLAN simulates the ACT.

In this lesson we simulate an experiment by assigning numbers to the possible outcomes. You will determine outcomes by generating *random numbers*. A set of numbers is **random** if each number has the same probability of occurring, each pair of numbers has the same probability of occurring, each triple of numbers has the same probability of occurring, etc. When an experiment or simulation is repeated, each repetition is called a **trial**.

Mental Math

Calculate.

a. log 100 **2**

b. log $\frac{1}{100}$ **–2**

c. log 1 **0**

d. log 0 **does not exist**

Using Random Numbers in a Simulation

The manufacturer of Sugar Oats cereal is promoting sales by putting a Sports Stars trading card in each box. The cards are randomly distributed so that the chance of obtaining each one is equally likely. Children are encouraged to collect a set of all four cards, which are shown below. Bobby wants his parents to buy the cereal, but they think they may need to buy many boxes in order to get all four cards.

 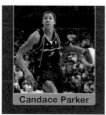  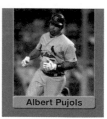

Tiger Woods   Candace Parker   Peyton Manning   Albert Pujols

How many boxes might Bobby's parents have to buy in order to get all four cards? To examine this question, we do a simulation.

Background

In order to simulate an experiment in which there is an underlying (assumed) probability distribution, since the domain variable in that distribution is a random variable, the domain values must be found by some random process. A spinner, die, or coin could be used to generate the domain values, but here we focus on the use of random numbers. The reason is that such numbers can simulate whatever probabilities we need.

For instance, if we want to simulate picking a card from a deck of playing cards, we would need 52 outcomes that occur with equal frequency. This is difficult with a coin, die, or spinner, but a random number table or technology can do it. One way is to choose pairs of numbers from the random number table, and if the pair is between 01 and 52, use that pair. If the pair is 00 or between 53 and 99, discard it. If using technology, we can specify that we want to generate random integers between 1 and 52.

First, we assign the numbers 1, 2, 3, and 4 to the four outcomes from buying a single box. Each number indicates that the box contains a card of an athlete as follows.

> 1: Tiger Woods
>
> 2: Candace Parker
>
> 3: Peyton Manning
>
> 4: Albert Pujols

Then we use the random integer command on a calculator to simulate buying boxes of cereal, and keep buying until we have at least one of each type of card.

The screen at the right shows one trial, with each digit representing the card in one cereal box. This trial produced the digits ③,④, 4,②, 2,① with the circled numbers showing boxes that contained a card that Bobby did not yet have. The set was complete after 6 boxes, when the Tiger Woods card was found.

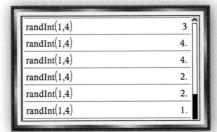

randInt(1,4)	3
randInt(1,4)	4.
randInt(1,4)	4.
randInt(1,4)	2.
randInt(1,4)	2.
randInt(1,4)	1.

Activity 1 Step 3–5. See margin.

Step 1 Perform one trial of the above simulation yourself. How many boxes did it take you to get all four Sports Stars cards? How does your result compare with those of your classmates?

Answers vary.
Sample: 5 boxes

Step 2 Bobby's parents refuse to buy dozens of boxes. Based on your results for Step 1, pick a number of boxes *B* that you think is likely to give Bobby a full set of Sports Stars cards and also satisfy his parents.

Answers vary.
Sample: *B* = 6 boxes

Step 3 Simulate buying B boxes ten times, noting each time whether you were successful in finding all four cards. Record your data in a table like the one at the right.

Step 4 Combine your data with the rest of the class. Construct a graph showing the percent of times that buying *x* boxes resulted in having all 4 cards.

Step 5 Do you think it would be worth it to buy lots of boxes to attempt to obtain all four cards? Why or why not?

Trial	Card number for each of the *B* Boxes	Success?
1		
2		
3		
4		
5		
6		
7		
8		
9		
10		

Monte Carlo Simulations

Using repeated trials to produce relative frequencies to estimate probabilities is often called a **Monte Carlo method**, named after the well-known Monte Carlo casino in the principality of Monaco. The process was developed and named by Stanislaw Ulam, a Polish-born mathematician who spent most of his career in the United States.

Designing Simulations   **403**

ENGLISH LEARNERS
Vocabulary Development

Monte Carlo simulations A Monte Carlo simulation is simply the use of random numbers to simulate an event involving repeated trials. Monte Carlo methods are an outgrowth of the ability of computers to perform calculations very quickly. However, in this lesson, random number tables are used instead of computers.

A popular meaning of the word random is "haphazard," but this is not the mathematical meaning of the term. Point out to students that a random phenomenon must have some aspect of equal probabilities with it.

2 Teaching

Notes on the Lesson

This is an appropriate lesson to begin with an open discussion (assuming students have done the reading and questions first). Ask students to summarize the major points. Go over questions that relate to the points of their summary as they mention them.

When students think of simulation, they may think of simulating accidents, or people learning to fly by using "simulators," or computer simulations of various kinds of terrain. They may not be aware of simulations that are probabilistic in nature.

Using random numbers in a simulation
With some calculators and computer programs, the random number generators start with the same value every time. If this is the case on your equipment, or if you find that you have the same random numbers as someone else, find out how you can *seed* the random number generator. Some will use the function seed() or randseed().

The text also refers to the Table of Random Numbers on page S8 as an alternative to using technology. You may need to instruct students on how to use a table like this. You may have your own method of "seeding" to start the selection randomly, or you may use the instructions below.

> To use a Table of Random Numbers, you must start randomly as well. One way to do that is to close your eyes, point to a pair of digits on the page and use that pair as the row. Then close your eyes again, point to a pair of digits on the page, and use that pair as the column. For instance, if you point to 03 and then to 12, start at the 3rd row, 12th column. Then choose to go up, down, right, or left, perhaps by rolling a die. If you point to a pair of digits which does not refer to a row or column, point again.

Additional Answers

Activity 1

Steps 3–5: See the Additional Answers section at the back of the book.

6-7

Notes on the Lesson

Designing a Monte Carlo simulation

Students may be bothered by the fact that airlines accept more reservations than seats, but point out that the alternative is to tell prospective travelers that the plane is full when the likelihood is that there will be a small number of seats available. For instance, if the company were only to accept 200 reservations on a jet seating 200 passengers, if 95% of the people showed up, there would be 10 empty seats. It is worth the risk of not satisfying a passenger with a reservation to have the opportunity to satisfy 10 more customers. Besides, if a person will be "bumped" because of overbooking (that is, not able to fly on a flight for which the person has a reservation) but must fly on the flight, then the airline offers to pay other people to get off the flight: usually a free ticket or a significant price off the next ticket.

Hotels use the same idea in booking more rooms than they have. This seems to cause problems at conventions of mathematics teachers; mathematics teachers seeem to carry through on their reservations at a much higher rate than the general public!

On the flights themselves, airlines also use Monte Carlo methods to determine how many meals of particular kinds to have for those passengers (usually only in first class) who receive meals. For instance, if the entrées are chicken and beef, they estimate the percent that might choose chicken and try to have enough more to take the random variability into account.

Ulam recognized that the power and speed of computers would allow for Monte Carlo experiments with huge numbers of trials, making this a valuable tool in science, business, and other fields. Some complex questions involving risk and decision-making that cannot be answered with other mathematical theories can be addressed with this method.

There are three steps to the Monte Carlo method.

1. Determine how the situation will be modeled.
2. Define what constitutes a trial and what will be recorded.
3. Specify the number of trials that will be run and how the estimated answer will be obtained.

A Monte Carlo method was used in Activity 1. Consider what made up a single trial. In the simulation, the numbers 1 to 4 represented the cards. A single trial involved generating B random numbers and recording whether all four Sports Stars cards had been obtained. You ran 10 trials and then calculated the percent of successful trials.

Designing a Monte Carlo Simulation

It is common for airlines to overbook, meaning that they sell more tickets for a flight than there are available seats. This compensates for the fact that many people do not show up for their scheduled flights.

But how many extra seats should be booked? If the airline sells too many tickets, it is likely that some passengers will have to be "bumped." If they sell too few tickets, many flights will depart with empty seats. Airlines use simulations to decide how many tickets to sell.

Suppose that an airline has a small commuter plane with 24 seats. Their past experience shows that 90% of passengers with tickets actually arrive at the airport. The airline must decide how many tickets to sell. To help in thinking about this decision, we use two simulations.

The first task is to decide how to assign random numbers to model the behavior of each passenger, who either shows up for the flight or does not. Unlike the simulation with the Sports Stars cards, here each outcome is *not* equally likely. So we must devise a method to assign show versus no-show to each passenger so that the outcomes are weighted 90%-10%. One way to do this is to generate random integers from 0 to 9 and call the appearance of one of the numbers a no-show. We choose to use 0 for no-show. Use either the Table of Random Numbers in the Appendix at the back of this book or technology to generate trials.

Accommodating the Learner

Some students have difficulty accurately reading a table of random numbers, or using technology to generate random numbers. The Notes on the Lesson on page 403 contain detailed instructions on how to do this.

Example 1

Suppose that 24 tickets are sold for the small plane and that the probability of arrival for each passenger is 90%. Use a simulation to estimate how many of the 24 passengers will show up.

Solution 1 A trial will consist of 24 random digits, each representing one passenger. (Listing the "passengers" in blocks of five digits makes the list easier to read.) Six trials are listed below with the no-shows indicated in red. As technology is not always available, using a table of random digits is useful. In this case, we start from some digit in the table and sequentially generate trials.

Trial 1:   89404 63870 33212 74379 7135
Trial 2:   94595 56869 69014 60045 1842
Trial 3:   57740 84378 25331 12566 5867
Trial 4:   38867 62300 08158 17983 1643
Trial 5:   56865 05859 90106 31595 7154
Trial 6:   18663 72695 52180 20847 1223

For each trial, count the no-shows (0s) and those that arrived (digits 1-9).

Trial	no-shows	arrived
1	2	22
2	3	21
3	1	23
4	3	21
5	3	21
6	2	22

The average number of arrivals is $\frac{22 + 21 + 23 + 21 + 21 + 22}{6} \approx 21.7$. The simulation estimates that when 24 tickets are sold, about 22 passengers will show up.

Solution 2 The lists of results for six trials can be generated using technology. The first trial is shown at the right. It has two no-shows. You could generate five other trials and solve the problem as you did in Solution 1.

randInt(0,9,24)
{8,9,4,0,4,6,3,8,7,0,3,3,2,1,2,7,4,3,7,9,7,▸

The results in Example 1 indicate that it is reasonable for the airline to sell more tickets than there are seats. But how many more? To get a sense of the situation, change the simulation. Remove the stipulation that 24 tickets are sold, and ask a different question: *How many tickets must be sold to have a full flight?*

Example 2

Assuming a 90% probability that a given passenger shows up for a flight, estimate how many tickets should be sold in order to fill all 24 seat

Solution Use the same plan as in Example 1, except now generate random integers until all 24 seats are full. In each trial you must generate digits until your list contains 24 nonzero digits.

(continued on next page)

Designing Simulations   **405**

Notes on the Lesson

Example 2 You might ask: If fewer than 90% of passengers show up, on average, should the airline take more reservations or fewer? **more** In fact, it seems to be the case that on well-traveled routes fewer than 90% show up because they might have traveled on different planes earlier in the day.

Additional Examples

Example 1 Suppose that, in the past, 95% of people who reserve a seat on a particular flight actually show up. If the plane holds 118 passengers, describe how you could use a simulation to estimate how many passengers will show up. **Use randInt(0, 19, 118) and count the number of 0s that show up in the list of 118 numbers from 0 to 19.**

Example 2 Assuming a 95% probability that a given passenger shows up for a flight, estimate how many tickets should be sold in order to fill all 118 seats in Additional Example 1. **Answers vary. Sample: Averaging the results of 10 trials, an estimate is that 123.8 tickets must be sold in order to have a full flight.**

Extension

Have students work in groups to simulate a board game in which players race their tokens from start to finish according to rolls of a single die. They should design and carry out their simulation using technology or a random number table and write down the results they get. **Answers vary. Check students' work.**

6-7

2. Answers vary. Sample:

	A	B	C
◆	=randint(1,6,10)	=randint(1,6	=a[]+b[]
1	6	6	12
2	1	2	3
3	4	3	7
4	3	1	4
5	5	6	11
6	1	1	2

B | =randint(1,6,10)

Trial	simulated reservations (0 means no-show)					tickets sold
1	24130	48360	22527	97265	76393 6	26
2	42167	93093	06243	61680	37856 16	27
3	37570	39975	81837	16656	06121 9	26
4	77921	06907	11008	42751	27756 534	28
5	09429	93969	52636	92737	88974	25
6	10365	61129	87529	85689	48237	25
7	07119	97336	71048	08178	77233 13	27
8	51085	12765	51821	51259	77452	25
9	82368	21382	52474	60268	89368	25
10	01001	54092	33362	94904	31273 04148	30

The last column shows the number of tickets that were sold for each flight in order to get 24 passengers who arrived. Averaging these, an estimate is that 26.4 tickets must be sold to have a full flight.

The results from Example 2 suggest that selling 25 tickets, which overbooks by 1, would not usually lead to passengers being bumped. Selling 26 tickets would lead to bumping approximately $\frac{4}{10} \approx 40\%$ of the time because of trials 5, 6, 8, and 9. However, it is important to note that these are rough estimates. While a computer would easily do millions of trials and give better estimates, such predictions only allow us to look at what usually happens. In real life, unusual situations do occur.

Using Simulations to Estimate Probabilities

Probabilities are determined in a variety of ways. In some situations, you might assume a probability, as when you assume a coin is fair. In other situations, you might conduct an experiment and use the long-term relative frequency of an event as an estimate of the probability of the event. In complicated situations, a simulation can be used to generate a relative frequency, thereby estimating the probability.

Activity 2

Two brown-eyed parents can have a blue-eyed child if they each carry a recessive gene for blue eyes. Assume that in these cases, the probability of blue eyes is $\frac{1}{4}$ and the probability of brown eyes is $\frac{3}{4}$. Design a simulation to estimate the probability of having exactly one of three children with brown eyes.

Step 1 Assign the digits 1, 2, 3, and 4 to represent the eye color when one child is born.

Step 2 Simulate forty trials of three-child families and record the results.

Step 3 Use the corresponding relative frequency to estimate the probability that a family with three children has exactly one with brown eyes.

Step 1: Answers vary. Sample: 1 represents blue eyes and 2, 3, and 4 represent brown eyes.

Step 2: Answers vary. Sample: {221, 334, 424, 322, 442, 322, 112, 313, 214, 423, 323, 124, 144, 121, 411, 344, 221, 131, 224, 143, 143, 214, 121, 142, 331, 113, 342, 124, 333, 434, 321, 341, 222, 442, 213, 131, 123, 221, 423, 224}

Step 3: $\frac{7}{40} = 17.5\%$

3b. Answers vary. Sample:

Trial #	Simulated Coupons	# needed for ice cream
1	2 1 3	3
2	3 3 1 2	4
3	2 2 2 1 1 3	6
4	1 2 1 3	4
5	3 2 3 1	4

4. Answers vary. Sample:

Trial #	No-shows	Arrived
1	1	23
2	4	20
3	4	20
4	1	23
5	7	17
6	2	22

On average 21 passengers will show up when 24 tickets are sold.

Questions

COVERING THE IDEAS

1. Define *simulation*.

2. Use the random-number generator ten times on your calculator to add two random integers, each between 1 and 6, inclusive. Record the results. This simulates tossing two dice ten times. **See margin.**

3. A local store gives away a random coupon with each visit. Coupons come in three colors: red, blue, and green. If you collect a set of three coupons, one of each color, you get a free ice cream cone. You wish to estimate how many times you must visit the store in order to get a free ice cream cone. **3b. See margin.**
   a. Describe how to assign random digits to model this situation.
   b. Perform 5 trials of your simulation and record the result.
   c. How many visits must you make in order to have a better than 50% chance to get a free ice cream cone?

4. Suppose that in Example 1, a no-show was represented by a 5 rather than by a 0. Using the same list of digits, record the number of no-shows and arrived passengers. Use the data to make another estimate of the number of passengers who will show up when 24 tickets are sold. **See margin.**

5. Suppose that 70% of adults are in favor of raising the driving age. Consider the question "If 10 adults are chosen at random. How often would all 10 be in favor of raising the driving age?" A simulation estimates the answer by assigning the digits 0-6 to "in favor" and the digits 7–9 to "against." Here are 6 trials of this simulation.

Trial 1:	09763	83473
Trial 2:	73577	88604
Trial 3:	67917	27354
Trial 4:	26575	36086
Trial 5:	15011	10536
Trial 6:	45766	96067

   5a. See margin.

   a. Give the results that would be recorded for these trials.
   b. Use the results to answer the question "How often would all 10 adults be in favor of raising the driving age?"

APPLYING THE MATHEMATICS

6. A family has four children. Assume a birth of a boy is equally likely to a birth of a girl.
   a. List the sample space for the genders of the children in birth order, using B for boy and G for girl.
   b. What is the probability that the family has 3 boys and 1 girl? $\frac{4}{16} = \frac{1}{4}$
   c. Run a simulation of 50 families of four children. How close is the relative frequency in the simulation to the actual probability?

---

1. A simulation is an experimental model that attempts to capture all aspects of the original situation that affect the outcomes.

3a. Assign 1, 2, and 3 to the coupon colors and pick them at random to represent visits to the store.

3c. Answers vary. Sample: Based on the simulation, 4 visits.

5b. Answers vary. Sample: Based off of the simulation, if 10 adults are chosen at random, about $\frac{1}{6}$ of the time all 10 would be in favor of raising the driving age.

6a, 6c. See margin.

Designing Simulations   **407**

---

3 **Assignment**

Recommended Assignment

- Questions 1–5
- • Questions 6–17
- • Question 18 and 19 (extra credit)
- Reading Lesson 6-8
- Covering the Ideas 6-8 (Questions 1–6)

Notes on the Questions

Question 4 Using a 5 should make no difference in the decision one makes regarding the number of reservations to accept, though it will generally make a slight dfference in the results that lead to the decision.

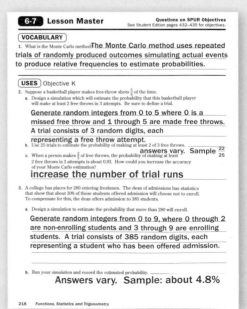

6-7 Lesson Master	Questions on SPUR Objectives

See Student Edition pages 432–435 for objectives.

VOCABULARY

1. What is the Monte Carlo method? **The Monte Carlo method uses repeated trials of randomly produced outcomes simulating actual events to produce relative frequencies to estimate probabilities.**

USES Objective K

2. Suppose a basketball player makes free-throw shots $\frac{3}{5}$ of the time.
   a. Design a simulation which will estimate the probability that this basketball player will make at least 2 free throws in 3 attempts. Be sure to define a trial.
   Generate random integers from 0 to 5 where 0 is a missed free throw and 1 through 5 are made free throws. A trial consists of 3 random digits, each representing a free throw attempt.
   b. Use 25 trials to estimate the probability of making at least 2 of 3 free throws. **answers vary. Sample $\frac{22}{25}$**
   c. When a person makes $\frac{3}{5}$ of free throws, the probability of making at least 2 free throws in 3 attempts is about 0.93. How could you increase the accuracy of your Monte Carlo estimation? **increase the number of trial runs**

3. A college has places for 280 entering freshmen. The dean of admissions has statistics that show that about 30% of those students offered admission will choose not to enroll. To compensate for this, the dean offers admission to 385 students.
   a. Design a simulation to estimate the probability that more than 280 will enroll.
   Generate random integers from 0 to 9, where 0 through 2 are non-enrolling students and 3 through 9 are enrolling students. A trial consists of 385 random digits, each representing a student who has been offered admission.
   b. Run your simulation and record the estimated probability. **Answers vary. Sample: about 4.8%**

218   *Functions, Statistics and Trigonometry*

Additional Answers

5a. Answers vary. Sample: A success equals a 10 digit number in which all the digits are less than 7 as in trial #5.

Trial #	Success?
1	No
2	No
3	No
4	No
5	Yes
6	No

6a. {BBBB, BBBG, BBGB, BBGG, BGBB, BGBG, BGGB, BGGG, GBBB, GBBG, GBGB, GBGG, GGBB, GGBG, GGGB, GGGG}

6c. Answers vary. Sample:

	A	B	C	D	E	F
◆	=rand	=rand	=rand	=rand		=e[]/50
47	1	1	1	1	0	0
48	0	0	1	1	0	0
49	1	1	0	0	0	0
50	1	0	0	0	1	1/50
51					15	3/10

$$E50 = \begin{cases} 0, a50+b50+c50+d50 \neq 1 \\ 1, a50+b50+c50+d50 = 1 \end{cases}$$

$\frac{3}{10} = 30\%$. This is 5% higher than the actual probability.

6-7

7a. The relative frequency for 10 trials was 20% in this simulation, so the probability should be about 20%.

Trial #	Man	Woman	Success?
1	82	39	No
2	94	37	No
3	50	24	No
4	10	19	Yes
5	41	24	No
6	65	79	No
7	36	46	No
8	82	34	No
9	73	72	No
10	3	95	Yes

9b. Answers vary. Sample:

Trial #	Simulated Hits	Had Hits?
1	73, 14, 38, 57, 59	Yes
2	34, 23, 28, 90, 20	Yes
3	53, 33, 71, 97, 93	No
4	65, 70, 2, 11, 80	Yes
5	37, 51, 49, 92, 40	No
6	18, 44, 99, 24, 49	Yes
7	8, 98, 32, 51, 41	Yes
8	24, 11, 97, 23, 16	Yes
9	95, 39, 39, 63, 23	Yes
10	56, 27, 74, 36, 73	Yes

10. Answers vary. Sample: Given random numbers 1–63 are neutral and 64–100 are not neutral, then about 25% of the trials were successful.

Trial #	Simulated Cars	Success?
1	41, 55, 14	Yes
2	16, 80, 43	No
3	60, 41, 16	Yes
4	39, 29, 12	Yes
5	12, 13, 54	Yes
6	24, 9, 46	Yes
7	25, 94, 53	No
8	28, 83, 26	No
9	86, 72, 2	No
10	85, 36, 23	No
11	81, 15, 1	No
12	100, 11, 8	No
13	52, 5, 83	No
14	95, 72, 93	No
15	61, 15, 100	No
16	57, 66, 78	No
17	75, 98, 83	No
18	99, 9, 42	No
19	90, 51, 36	No
20	29, 93, 51	No

---

7. A survey of a sample of people reveals the relative frequency of left-handedness to be 10% in men and 8% in women.

  a. Use a Monte Carlo simulation to estimate the probability that at least one person in a sample of one man and one woman is left-handed. **See margin for table.**

  b. Calculate the actual probability. **17.2%**

8. Suppose that a manufacturer knows that 2% of the nails produced are defective. Describe how you would design a simulation to determine each value. **See margin.**

  a. the probability that a box with 100 nails has four or more defective ones

  b. how many nails the company should put in each box in order to have at least 100 good nails in a box

9. A softball player has a batting average of 0.300. This means $\frac{\text{number of hits}}{\text{number of official at-bats}} = 0.300$. **See margin.**

  a. Design a simulation to illustrate the next five official at-bats of this player.

  b. Run at least ten trials of your simulation and record the results.

  c. Based on the data of your simulation, estimate the probability that the player gets no hits in the next five at-bats. **about 20%**

10. In 2006, most new cars in North America were a neutral color (gray, silver, black, or white). Select random integers from 1 to 100 to simulate the color of the next 3 cars you pass. Run 20 trials to estimate the probability that all 3 cars are a neutral color. **See margin.**

Colors of Cars Sold in North America

| Silver 19% | White 16% | Gray 13% | Black 13% | Blue 11% | Red 11% | Lt. Brown 7% |

Green 4%
White Pearl 3%
Yellow/Gold 3%
Others <1%

11. A diabetes test is accurate 90% of the time and gives a false result 10% of the time. In a population of ten people, one person is diabetic and the other nine are not. An accurate result for a diabetic means the test result is positive; an accurate result for a non-diabetic means the test result is negative. **See margin.**

  a. Design a simulation of giving the diabetes test to all ten people.

  b. According to fifty trials of your simulation, what is the likelihood that someone tests positive?

  c. According to fifty trials of your simulation, on average, how many non-diabetics test positive for diabetes?

Crystl Bustos of the United States softball team hits a 3-run home run at the Beijng 2008 Olympic Games.

7a. Answers vary. Sample: Generate numbers from 1 to 100, once for men and once for women in each trial. For men, numbers 1–10 are left-handed, and all others are right-handed. For women, 1–8 are left-handed, and all others are right-handed.

8a. Answers vary. Generate 100 random numbers from 1–100 where 1–2 are defective nails and 3–100 are normal. This is one trial. If a trial has four or more defective nails ("1"s or "2"s), it is a success. After some number of trials, find the percent of successful trials.

8b. Answers vary. Sample: Use the process from Part a except generate random numbers until 100 good nails are obtained. Record the total number of nails needed in that trial. After a preset number of trials, average the total nails required from each trial.

9a. Answers vary. Sample: Let a random number from 1–100 represent one official at-bat; let 1–30 represent a hit and 31–100 represent no hits. One trial is made up of five such random numbers.

11a. In one trial, generate two numbers from 1–10. The first number indicates the accuracy of the test. A 1 is a false result, and 9–10 are accurate results. The second number represents the health of the patient. A 1 means the patient is diabetic, and 9–10 mean the patient is not diabetic.

REVIEW

12. A computer software security company estimated that 87.5% of email was spam. It claimed that its software was 98.3% successful in blocking spam while properly passing 99.63% of non-spam email.

   a. What is the probability that an email that is blocked is spam?

   b. Suppose that a sample of 100,000 emails is screened for spam. Use relative frequencies along with the given probabilities to calculate the relative frequency of blocked emails that are spam and confirm your answer to Part a. **See margin.**

   c. Which method of determining the statistic was easier to compute? Explain your answer. **(Lesson 6-6)**

13. A college scholarship program awards first, second and third prize cash awards to the winners. If 700 students applied this year, how many different award outcomes are possible? **(Lesson 6-4)**

In 14 and 15, evaluate. **(Lesson 6-4)**

   $_{700}P_3 = 341,531,400$

14. $7! {}_{10}P_3$ $10! = 3,628,800$ **15.** $(n-r)! {}_nP_r$ $n!$

16. How many different Thanksgiving dinners are possible if there is 1 turkey, 2 kinds of gravy, 5 side dishes, 4 desserts and 2 kinds of biscuits and if (unfortunately) there are no "seconds" and you can have only 1 serving from each category? **(Lesson 6-3)**

17. a. Graph $f(x) = \frac{1}{x}$ and $g(x) = \frac{1}{x+3} - 2$ on the same axes. **See margin.**

   b. Find equations for the asymptotes of the function g. How are they related to the asymptotes of f?

   c. Give the domain and range of f and g. **(Lessons 3-2, 3-1)**

EXPLORATION

18. The U.S. mint has produced quarters that each bear a state's name. Each coin has a P (for Philadelphia) or D (for Denver) on it to indicate where it was minted. Suppose you want a complete collection of the 100 coins and you already have 90. If the 100 coins appear at random, conduct a simulation to determine how many quarters you would need to examine before you had all 100.

19. Monty Hall was the host of the TV game show called *Let's Make a Deal!* At the end of each show, one contestant had a chance to win a car. The contestant was told that behind one door was a car and behind the other two doors was an item of little value (such as a goat). The contestant picked a door. Then, without opening the door the contestant picked, Monty would open another door that had a goat. Now the deal: Monty would allow the contestant to take what was behind the door they had chosen or switch doors.

   a. Should the contestant switch or not?

   b. Perform a simulation to determine whether the contestant should switch. Do enough trials to convince yourself which is the better strategy or whether it makes no difference.

12a. 99.9%

Benjamin Franklin proposed the turkey as the official U.S. bird. Today, 45 million turkeys are eaten each Thanksgiving.

12c. Answers vary. Sample: Using relative frequencies, there was less abstract probabilities as chance could be associated with counts.

16. 80 possible Thanksgiving dinners

17b. $x = -3, y = -2$. These are the asymptotes of f shifted left 3 units and down 2 units.

17c.
domain of f: $\{x \mid x \neq 0\}$
range of f: $\{y \mid y \neq 0\}$
domain of g: $\{x \mid x \neq -3\}$
range of g: $\{y \mid y \neq -2\}$

18–19. See margin.

Notes on the Questions

Question 19 Marilyn vos Savant posed this probability problem in her "Ask Marilyn" column in *Parade Magazine* some years ago and it caused a furor. Judging from the mail she received, the problem confounded many people, including several mathematicians. This activity simulates the situation. Here is the theoretical solution to the problem. The probability of winning if you do not switch is $\frac{1}{3}$. Your probability of winning if you switch is $\frac{2}{3}$.

Rationale: Suppose these are the doors.

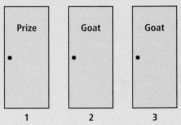

If you pick Door 1, the host will show you door 2 or 3. Either way, if you switch, you will lose. If you pick Door 2, the host will show you Door 3. If you switch, you win. If you pick Door 3, the host will show you door 2, and if you switch, you win. Hence, when you switch, you win 2 out of 3 times.

4   Wrap-Up

Ongoing Assessment

Have students write a paragraph explaining how technology or the Table of Random Numbers can be used to simulate an event. **Answers vary. Check students' work.**

Project Update

Project 1, *The Sum of Many Dice*, Project 2, *Random Walk*, and Project 4, *Probabilistic Analysis of Functions*, on pages 426 and 427 relate to the content of this lesson.

Additional Answers

11b. Answers vary. Sample: In 50 trials, the relative frequency of a positive test was $\frac{13}{50}$.

11c. Answers vary. Sample: In the same experiment, 6 non-diabetics tested positive for diabetes.

12b. Of the 87,500 spam emails in 100,000, one would expect about 0.983(87,500) $\approx$ 86,013 spam emails blocked. Of the 12,500 non-spam emails in 100,000, 0.0037(12,500) $\approx$ 46 non-spam emails blocked. Therefore, $\frac{86013}{86013 + 46} \approx 99.9\%$.

17a.

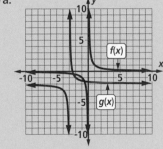

18–19. See the Additional Answers section at the back of the book.

Lesson 6-8

GOAL

Debunk the "Law of Averages." The valid Law of Large Numbers is a correct alternative.

SPUR Objectives

A Compute the expected counts of events in various contexts.

F Discuss the Law of Large Numbers and the "Law of Averages."

Materials/Resources

- Lesson Master 6-8
- Resource Masters 145 and 146
- Coin
- Paper and pencil
- Spreadsheet application

HOMEWORK

- **Option 1**
- **Option 2**

- Questions 1–6
- • Questions 7–21
- • Question 22 (extra credit)
  - Reading Lessons 6-9
  - Covering the Ideas 6-9 (Questions 1–9)

Local Standards

---

1 Warm-Up

You toss a coin 8 times and get 8 heads.

1. Explain why heads and tails might be equally likely the next time you toss. **Heads and tails will be equally likely in a fair coin regardless of the prior history of tosses.**

2. Explain why heads might be more likely than tails the next time you toss. **Since 8 heads in 8 tosses is unlikely, the coin may be weighted to favor heads. Call the bank!**

3. Explain why tails might be more likely than heads the next time you toss. **There is no justification for tails being more likely than heads the next time.**

Lesson 6-8
Two "Laws," but Only One Is Valid

Vocabulary

expected count of an outcome
expected count of an event

> ▶ **BIG IDEA** Expected counts and the Law of Large Numbers allow us to predict what happens when there are many trials of an experiment.

Expected vs. Observed Counts

In Jane Austen's famous novel *Pride and Prejudice*, the Bennet family has five daughters. Since, at that time in England, a family home could only be passed on to a male heir, the daughters faced the loss of their family home. Assuming that the probability a baby is a girl is 0.5, on average, we would expect that half of the children born would be girls, leading to an expectation of $5 \cdot \frac{1}{2} = 2.5$ girls. This is consistent with the following definition of *expected count*.

Definition of Expected Count

If an outcome in an experiment has probability p, then in n trials of the experiment, the **expected count** of the outcome is np.

Note that even though there cannot be a fraction of a child, the expected count does not have to be an integer because it measures what happens on average, not with any specific family.

Example 1

A current estimate for the proportion of left-handers in the population is 9%. What is the expected count of left-handers in a classroom of 36 students?

Solution Since $p = 0.09$ and $n = 36$ students, the expected count of the outcome is $np = 36 \cdot 0.09 = 3.24$. About 3 left-handers would be expected in a class of 36 students.

If an event contains many outcomes, then the **expected count of an event** is the sum of the expected counts of the outcomes. For instance, in many places on Earth there is a dry season and a wet season. Suppose that the wet season is 125 days long and there is a 85% probability of rain on those days, while the dry season is the other 240 days of the year and there is a 10% chance of rain on those days. Then the expected number of days of rain in a year is the sum of the expected count for each season: $125 \cdot 0.85 + 240 \cdot 0.10$, or 130.25.

Mental Math

Suppose class participation counts for 20% of a student's grade, homework counts 30%, and tests and quizzes count 50%.

a. What is the highest overall grade out of 100 that McKayla can get if she gets 75 on class participation and 85 on homework? **90.5**

b. What is her lowest possible grade? **40.5**

Background

This is a lesson in quantitative literacy, examining a belief many people have about repeated events because they do not understand the meaning of probability or because they attribute spurious causes to large events.

The Law of Large Numbers states that, if p is the probability of an event E, then $\lim_{n \to \infty} \frac{\text{number of occurences of } E}{\text{number of trials } n} = p$. If p were not the limit, we would lose our belief that p is the probability of the event, since p is supposed to describe what happens in the long run.

If you observed that it rained 144 days last year in this location, then the difference between observed and expected counts is $144 - 130.25$, or 13.75. The difference between the relative frequency of rain you observed and the probability of rain is $\frac{144}{365} - \frac{130.25}{365} = \frac{13.75}{365}$, or about 0.0377 or 3.8%. The expected count does not tell what will happen in any particular case. It tells what we expect to happen *in the long run*.

The Law of Large Numbers

Everyone expects a fair coin to come up heads 50% of the time, but does that happen in practice? During World War II, John Kerrich, a South African mathematician, was captured by the German army in Denmark and interned at a camp. To pass the time, Dr. Kerrich did experiments on chance processes. In one such experiment he tossed a coin 10,000 times and observed 5067 heads.

GUIDED

Example 2

In Kerrich's experiment, assume that the coin was fair.
a. What was the expected number of heads?
b. Find the difference between the observed and expected numbers of heads.
c. What was the relative frequency of heads?
d. What was the difference between the relative frequency and the probability of heads?

Solution

a. For a fair coin, P(heads) = __?__. Here, n = 10,000. So np = 0.5
    10,000 · __?__ = __?__. 0.5; 5000
b. observed − expected = 5067 − __?__ = __?__ 5000; 67
c. The relative frequency is $\frac{5067}{?}$ or, as a decimal, __?__. 10,000; 0.5067
d. relative frequency − probability = __?__ − __?__ = 0.0067 0.5067; 0.5

In Kerrich's experiment, he did not expect to get *exactly* 5000 heads and 5000 tails even if the coin were fair. The difference between the expected number, 5000, and the actual number, 5067, may seem like a lot. But remember that Kerrich tossed 10,000 the coin times! The relative frequency differed from the probability by only 0.0067. The relative frequency gets closer and closer to 0.5 as the number of trials increases. This idea is summarized by the following important statement about probability in the long run.

Law of Large Numbers

Suppose, in an experiment, an event E has probability p. Then if the experiment is repeated again and again, the relative frequency of the event will approach p.

Two "Laws," but Only One Is Valid   **411**

The Law of Averages is based on comparing the number of occurences of the event E with the number expected by laws of probability by *subtraction* rather than division. The Law of Averages believer thinks that the difference between the number of occurences and what is expected should become 0 (just as the ration of the relative frequency to the probability becomes 1). But this does not happen; it is more likely that the numbers diverge than that they get closer and closer.

Notes on the Lesson

The "Law of Averages" It is interesting that a habitual gambler will often say, after a run of bad luck, that his or her luck is due to change, but if the gambler has a run of good luck, he often has the view that his good run will continue in the same way.

It is possible that one reason people believe so strongly in the Law of Averages is that, in theory, if a fair coin is tossed infinitely many times (this can only happen in theory!), then, from the theory of random walks, it can be proved that there will be infinitely many places in the tossing where the number of heads equals the number of tails. So, at any time in the tossing, the number of heads will always return at some time to equal the number of tails. However, this fact does not mean that the probability of moving closer to the same number of heads and tails is greater than the probability of moving further away from the same number.

Activity We strongly encourage doing this activity to have a specific example of the use of simulation.

Additional Answers

Steps 1–2: See the Additional Answers section at the back of the book.

Step 3: Answers vary. Sample:

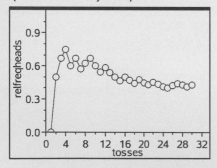

Step 4: Over the long-run the relative frequency should approach .5.

Step 5: Answers vary. Sample:

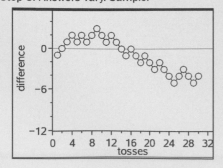

The "Law of Averages"

When a batter comes up late in the game without a hit, baseball sportscasters often say "He's due for a hit." A gambler who has had a run of bad luck will say, "My luck is due to change." Both of these statements are based on a principle often referred to as the "law of averages." But the "law of averages" is not valid.

The gambler who has had a run of bad luck may be correct that his luck has been bad, but he is no more likely to have a run of good luck now than when he began. The baseball player who has not gotten a hit is no more likely to get a hit now than before his slump.

President Ronald Reagan with baseball sportscaster Harry Caray

How do the "Laws" Differ?

Returning to a coin situation, suppose you toss a coin 10 times and 8 heads appear. What is the probability of heads on the 11th toss? The "law of averages" implies that if a fair coin is tossed and more heads have occurred, you should expect more tails to occur going forward so that the number of heads and tails will be the same in the long run. Thus, the probability of heads on the 11th toss would be less than $\frac{1}{2}$.

The Law of Large Numbers, by contrast, says that as the number of trials increases, the difference between the relative frequency of heads and the probability of heads will go to zero. The probability of heads, however, remains at $\frac{1}{2}$.

To understand why the Law of Large Numbers is true while the "law of averages" is faulty reasoning, perform the following experiment.

Activity   See margin.

MATERIALS a coin, paper and a pencil

Step 1   Toss a coin once. Observe heads or tails. Record the outcome in a spreadsheet similar to the one shown below. Your data may be different.

◇	A	B	C	D	E	F
	Toss	Heads or Tails	Cumulative Number of Heads	Cumulative Number of Tails	Relative Frequency of Heads	Cumulative Number of Heads – Cumulative Number of Tails
1	A	B	C	$D = A - C$	$E = \frac{C}{A}$	$F = C - D$
2	1	H	1	0	$\frac{1}{1}$	1
3	2	H	2	0	$\frac{2}{2}$	2
4	3	T	2	1	$\frac{2}{3}$	1
5	4	H	3	1	$\frac{3}{4}$	2
6	⋮	⋮	⋮	⋮		⋮

If B3 = "H"
 THEN C3 = C2 + 1
 ELSE C3 = C2

D[ ] = A[ ] − C[ ]

E[ ] = C[ ]/A[ ]

F[ ] = C[ ] − D[ ]

Step 2 Repeat Step 1 for a total of 30 tosses. After each toss, compute the cumulative number of heads and the relative frequency. The spreadsheet on the previous page shows how to organize and calculate the data for the first four rows if the first four tosses are H, H, T, and H.

Step 3 Graph the 30 pairs (toss number, relative frequency). A sample is at the right.

Step 4 The Law of Large Numbers says that, if the probability of heads is 0.5, then the relative frequency points on the graph in Step 3 will, in the long run, get closer and closer to the line $y = 0.5$. Do you think that would happen if you continued to toss the coin?

Step 5 Graph the 30 pairs (toss number, cumulative number of heads − cumulative number of tails). A sample graph is at the right. The "law of averages" asserts that if your graph is above the x-axis (more heads than tails have occurred), then tails is more likely, and if your graph is below the x-axis (more tails than heads have occurred) then heads is more likely. In either case, the "law of averages" asserts that the graph is more likely to come back to the x-axis than go away from it.

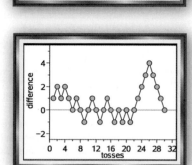

If you were to continue tossing coins, you might get results like those shown in the Activity.

In the language of expected and observed counts, as the number of trials increases, the "law of averages" incorrectly says that the difference between observed and expected values is more likely to go toward 0 than away from it.

Questions

COVERING THE IDEAS

1. Refer to the Bennet family page 410. If 72% of women are tongue curlers, what is the expected number of tongue curlers among the five Bennet daughters? **3.6**

2. Estimates of the probability that a child is left-handed range from 0.07 to 0.15. Of the 480 children in an elementary school, how many are expected to be left-handed? **Between 33.6 and 72**

3. When tossing a pair of fair dice, the probability of rolling doubles is $\frac{1}{6}$. A class experimented and tossed pairs of dice 550 times, and got doubles 84 times.
   a. What is the difference between the expected count if the dice were fair and the observed count? $\frac{23}{3} \approx 7.67$
   b. What is the difference between the probability (assuming the dice are fair) and the relative frequency? $\frac{23}{1650} \approx 0.014$
   c. Do you think the dice are fair? Why or why not?

3c. Yes, the difference between the probability and the relative frequency is not large.

It is estimated that from $\frac{2}{3}$ to $\frac{4}{5}$ of people can curl their tongue.

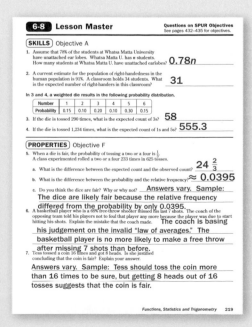

---

3 **Assignment**

Recommended Assignment

- Questions 1–6
- Questions 7–21
- Question 22 (extra credit)
- Reading Lesson 6-9
- Covering the Ideas 6-9 (Questions 1–9)

Notes on the Questions

Question 3 Emphasize that we can only *assume* that a pair of real dice are fair; we cannot ever prove fairness. By tossing, we only increase faith in our assumption.

Notes on the Questions

Qustions 7 and 8 These questions are related, though you do not need the answer to one to do the other.

Questions 11 and 12 These are important questions because these schemes are used on college entrance tests (such as the SAT and ACT). On the SAT, students need to know that, if they purely guess, their probability of raising their score from what they would have by ignoring these questions equals their probability of lowering their score. But the ACT deducts no points for wrong answers, so it's important to answer every qustion, even if just by guessing. In both cases, if students can pare down the number of choices, then the probability that they guess correctly is increased and educated guessing is a good strategy.

Additional Answers

10. The expected gain is $560.

11a. The expected count of points for 1 question is 0. Therefore, 10 questions also have an expected count of points of 0.

11b. The outcome from guessing on n random questions is 0 points.

11c. No.

4. Since there was a tie between the top two players in a golf tournament, a play-off is held. The winner will get the first prize of $80,000 and the runner-up will get a consolation prize of $35,000. The less-favored player is considered to have a 25% chance of winning. What is this player's expected winnings? **$46,250**

5. A student is playing a board game and needs to toss a 6 on a die to start. She has had five turns but still has not rolled a 6. She announces that she is due a 6 on the next couple of turns. Comment on the student's announcement.

6. A student tosses a coin 10 times and gets 8 tails.
   a. If the coin is fair, do these results contradict the Law of Large Numbers?
   b. What false conclusion would a person make following the "law of averages"?

APPLYING THE MATHEMATICS

In 7 and 8, use the fact that a field goal is worth 3 points and a touchdown is worth 6 points.

7. A football team is at the 28-yard line and it is 4th down, so there is only one more play that can be made. The coach feels that the team can successfully kick a field goal 35% of the time. The team could also try for a touchdown. The coach thinks that this would succeed 20% of the time. What should the team do?

8. When the team is at the 2-yard line, the coach feels that the team can make a touchdown 80% of the time. After the touchdown the team can get an extra point 90% of the time. What is the expected number of points the team will score in this situation? **5.7 points**

9. A commuter drives to work. When the traffic is normal, about 75% of the time, the drive averages 30 minutes. When the traffic is heavy, about 25% of the time, the drive averages 40 minutes. What is the expected travel time?

10. In investing, a general rule is that the less risk of losing principal in an investment, the lower the guaranteed interest rate. Consider a $10,000 bond that pays 10% interest annually, but with a 1 in 25 chance that the investment will lose all of its principal by the end of that year. What is the expected gain or loss in that year?

In 11 and 12, consider that some standardized multiple-choice tests with 5 choices on each question give 1 point for each correct answer and deduct $\frac{1}{4}$ of a point for each incorrect answer. **11 See margin.**

11. a. If you randomly guess on 10 questions, what is your expected point total? Explain your calculation.
    b. Generalize Part a to apply to a situation where you randomly guess on n questions.
    c. With this scoring, is it to your advantage in the long run to guess?

5. Answers vary. Sample: She is basing this prediction on the invalid "law of averages." The probability of rolling a 6 on each turn is still $\frac{1}{6}$

6a. No; the Law of Large Numbers states that as an event is repeated, its relative frequency will approach its probability. These results do not discount the Law of Large Numbers.

6b. Answers vary. Sample: A false conclusion would be if someone declares that heads are now more likely to appear because of its lack of appearance in the first ten tosses.

9. 32.5 minutes

7. They should attempt a touchdown, because the expected outcome of a field goal attempt is 1.05 points and the expected outcome of a touchdown attempt is 1.2 points.

10. See margin.

12. If on each question you can eliminate 1 of the choices, so you randomly guess from the other 4 choices, what is your expected point total on a 40 question test? Explain your calculations.

13. Leona rolls a die 10 times and gets the distribution described by the table below. She now suspects that the die is biased.

Outcome	1	2	3	4	5	6
Frequency	0	0	0	2	1	7

a. Make a relative frequency bar graph showing Leona's distribution.

b. Do the data provide evidence in support of Leona's assertion? Why or why not?

c. Leona decides to subject the die to a more complete test. She rolls it 100 times and gets the following distribution.

Outcome	1	2	3	4	5	6
Frequency	15	14	16	19	15	21

Do the new data provide evidence in support of Leona's assertion? Why or why not?

d. Which of the laws of this lesson is supported by Leona's results?

REVIEW

14. Suppose that a baseball player has a batting average of 0.300. Use your calculator to simulate his next 100 official at-bats, recording whether he gets a hit or not. What is the longest streak of hits that he gets in your simulation? (**Lesson 6-7**) **See margin.**

15. Suppose that 12% of women and 9% of men have attached ear lobes. (**Lesson 6-7**)

a. Use a Monte Carlo simulation to estimate the probability that at least one person in a sample of two women has attached ear lobes.

b. Calculate the actual probability $1 - (.88)^2 \approx 0.2256$

16. Consider the following situation. Your gym class will play football for the next 15 class days. Each class day, students are randomly assigned to one of the 11 field positions. (**Lessons 6-7, 6-1**)

a. You decide to perform a simulation to see how likely it is that you will get to play quarterback over the 15 days. Which is the better simulation strategy, (1) or (2), and why? **See margin.**

   (1) Drawing the numbers 0–10 from a box, assigning each position a number.

   (2) Taking the sum of two dice and assigning each position a number between 2 and 12.

b. What is the number of trials in this experiment? **15**

12. The expected count of points for 1 question is 0.0625. For 40 questions, the expected count is 2.5 points.

13a.

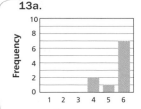

13b. No, she has only performed 10 trials, this is not enough to make any long-run conclusions.

13c. No, in fact the new data refutes her assertion because the relative frequencies are now closer to $\frac{1}{6}$.

13d. The Law of Large Numbers

15a. Answers vary. Sample: Generate numbers from 1 to 100, once for each woman. For women, numbers 1-12 have attached ear lobes and 13-100 do not. A random simulation of 10 trials returned a relative frequency of $\frac{2}{10}$ where at least one of the two has attached ear lobes.

Notes on the Questions

Question 13 This question shows why it is not useful to rely on a small number of trials.

Additional Answers

14. Answers vary. Sample: Pick random integers from 1-10, and let 1-3 stand for hits. The longest streak of hits in this simulation was 4 hits.

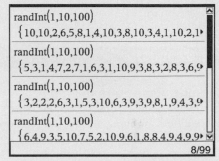

16a. (1) is the better simulation strategy, because it gives equal weight to every position, whereas not all positions have equal probability with (2).

6-8

Notes on the Questions

Question 22 The Bernoulli family contained a number of mathematicians over three generations. Furthermore, many of the members of the family had both German and French names. So students can easily think they are researching Jakob when they are researching another member of the family, or not realize that Jakob = James = Jacques. They are most likely to confuse Jakob with his younger brother Johann = Jean.

4 Wrap-Up

Ongoing Assessment

As a class (or in groups), have students discuss how the popular belief in the Law of Averages may affect the risk-taking behavior of contestants in TV game shows. **Answers vary. Check students' work.**

Project Update

Project 3, *The "Law of Averages,"* on page 427 relates to the content of this lesson.

---

17. a. How many 3-letter permutations are there in the letters in WYOMING? $_7P_3 = 210$

b. How many of the permutations in Part a contain only consonants? **(Lesson 6-4)** $_5P_3 = 60$

18. A triangle is drawn in the coordinate plane as shown.

a. Find m∠*BAC*. **57°**

b. Find the coordinates of point *B* to the nearest tenth. **(Lessons 4-4, 4-1) about (−3.8, −5.9)**

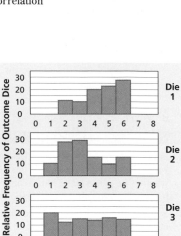

19. The graph of $y = x^2$ is transformed by $T: (x, y) \longrightarrow (x + \frac{1}{3}, y - 2)$. What is an equation for the image? **(Lesson 3-2)** $y = \left(x - \frac{1}{3}\right)^2 - 2.$

20. Put the following correlations in order from strongest correlation to weakest. **(Lesson 2-2) A, D, B, C**

A $r = -0.92$ **B** $r^2 = 0.25$

C $r = 0.4$ **D** $r^2 = 0.8$

21. The bar graphs at the right show the distributions of 100 tosses for a six-sided green die with 1, 2, 3, 4, 5 and 6 on its faces, a six-sided red die with 2, 3, 4, 5, 6 and 6 on its faces, and an eight-sided blue die with 1, 2, 2, 3, 3, 4, 5 and 6 on its faces. Match each die with its graph. **(Lesson 1-1)**

EXPLORATION

22. The Law of Large Numbers was first presented in the book *Ars Conjectandi* by Jakob Bernoulli (1654–1705). Research Bernoulli's contributions to the field of probability. **Answers vary. Sample: In *Ars Conjectandi*, Bernoulli presented alternate proofs for many problems in probability theory. He also developed the Bernoulli trial, which is a trial with two random outcomes of success and failure.**

21. Die 3 is green, die 1 is red, and die 2 is blue.

The Chi-Square Test

Vocabulary

chi-square statistic, χ^2
degree of freedom
significance level

▶ **BIG IDEA** The chi-square statistic measures the extent to which observed counts differ from expected counts.

Suppose you toss a coin 50 times. Consider the following scenarios.

(1) You think the coin is fair and heads comes up 43 times. You would suspect that the coin is not fair. The event "43 or more heads in 50 tosses" is so unlikely with a fair coin that you would be right to think the coin is biased in favor of heads.

(2) You think the coin is fair and heads comes up 30 times. Most people would conclude that the coin is fair and only the normal variability of results in such an experiment has taken place.

(3) You think the probability of heads is 80%, and heads comes up 43 times. You might pat yourself on the back for being correct about the coin being weighted, but wonder if 80% is a reasonable probability.

STOP QY1

In all three scenarios, there is an expected number and an observed number of heads. The probability that has led to the expected number is a **hypothesis** about the situation. The tossing of the coin is an experiment to test that hypothesis. This use of statistics is called **hypothesis testing**.

Chi-Square Statistic

In hypothesis-testing situations like these, the *chi-square* or χ^2 statistic (χ is the Greek letter "chi", pronounced "kai") can be used. The chi-square statistic can help you determine whether certain results are due to chance variation or whether they indicate that the hypothesis is wrong. This statistic was introduced by the English statistician Karl Pearson in 1900.

> ### Definition of Chi-square Statistic
>
> If data is collected on a variable with k outcomes, the **chi-square statistic** $\chi^2 = \sum_{i=1}^{k} \frac{(a_i - e_i)^2}{e_i}$, where a_i is the observed frequency for outcome i, and e_i is the expected count of the outcome i.

The Chi-Square Test 417

Mental Math

Find a solution to the nearest 10.

a. $\frac{523}{1681} = \frac{x}{100}$ 30

b. $\frac{74}{y} = \frac{26}{31}$ 90

> ▶ **QY1**
>
> What is the expected number of heads in each of scenarios (1), (2), (3)?

Background

The statistics that students have seen in earlier lessons and earlier courses are descriptive statistics. In this lesson, we introduce an inferential statistic, one that is used to help in decision-making. The chi-square statistic is the easiest inferential statistic to calculate. It can be calculated by hand, but is easier with a calculator. It can be used on data that are quite accessible to students, and its calculation involves only simple probability and elementary algebra.

The idea behind the chi-square statistic is a set of distributions known as chi-square distributions. In all the examples and questions in this book, the chi-square statistic compares a set of n observed values with a corresponding set of n expected values. The number of degrees of freedom in such a chi-square test is $n - 1$, because when the size of the population is known, you can calculate the nth value from any $n - 1$ values.

(continued on next page)

GOAL

Use the chi-square statistic and technology to determine if a set of discrete data differs significantly from values that would be expected when certain probabilities are given.

SPUR Objectives

L Use the chi-square statistic to determine whether or not an event is likely.

Materials/Resources

· Lesson Master 6-9
· Resource Masters 147–150
· Chi-square web applet

> **HOMEWORK** • Option 1
> • Option 2
> • Questions 1–9
> • • Questions 10–17
> • • Question 18 (extra credit)
> • • Self Test

> **Local Standards**

1 **Warm-Up**

In a certain metropolitan area, 250,000 people live in the city and 400,000 live in the suburbs. When the basketball playoffs started, there were 32 teams. Of those teams, 14 were from the city and 18 were from the suburbs. How many would have been expected to be from the city and how many from the suburbs if the numbers of teams were proportional to the population? **about 12.3 from the city and 19.7 from the suburbs**

(The calculation of these expected counts assumes that children from the suburbs go to school in the suburbs, and from the city go to schools in the city, that the schools are about the same size, and that the numbers of children are proportional to the population as a whole.)

6-9

2 Teaching

Notes on the Lesson

Examples 1 and 2 The steps in the calculation of the chi-square statistic are not very difficult. (1) Calculate the expected frequencies (= expected counts) given the assumptions that are being made about the population. (2) Calculate the square of the deviation of each observed count from the expected count, divided by the expected count. (3) Add the n numbers found in Step 2. The sum is the chi-square value. Have students do these calculations either as they read for homework or in class, each time checking their work with what is in the text.

Additional Examples

Example 1 To test if a coin is fair, calculate the chi-square statistic for a coin that shows 85 heads in 150 tosses. The observed frequencies of heads and tails are 85 and 65; the expected frequencies are 75 and 75. This leads to a chi-square value of $2\frac{2}{3}$. The table in this lesson shows that a value this large would be expected to occur more than 10% of the time, so we should not think this is enough evidence to believe the coin is unfair.

Example 2 Compute the chi-square statistic to test whether a coin that comes up heads 93 times in 150 tosses is fair. The observed frequencies of heads and tails are 93 and 57; the expected frequencies are 75 and 75. This leads to a chi-square value of 8.64. Using the table in this lesson, this value is seen to be significant at the 0.01 level.

The calculation of the chi-square statistic requires that you state hypotheses about probabilities in a situation so you can calculate the expected count. The value of the chi-square statistic is relatively small if data agrees with the model and relatively large if the data does not follow the model.

Example 1

To test if the coin is fair, compute the chi-square statistic for the coin that came up heads 43 times in 50 tosses.

Solution There are two outcomes for a coin toss, heads or tails, so $k = 2$. First determine the expected count of each: How many heads e_1 would be expected if the coin were fair? How many tails e_2 would be expected? If the coin is fair, P(heads) = 0.5 and P(tails) = 0.5. So the expected number of heads, $e_1 = 0.5 \cdot 50 = 25$. Similarly, $e_2 = 25$.

$$\chi^2 = \sum_{i=1}^{2} \frac{(a_i - e_i)^2}{e_i} = \frac{(a_1 - e_1)^2}{e_1} + \frac{(a_2 - e_2)^2}{e_2}$$

Scenario (1)	Outcome 1 HEADS	Outcome 2 TAILS
Observed Frequency	$a_1 = 43$	$a_2 = 7$
Expected Frequency	$e_1 = 25$	$e_2 = 25$
$\frac{(a_i - e_i)^2}{e_i}$	$\frac{(43 - 25)^2}{25} = 12.96$	$\frac{(7 - 25)^2}{25} = 12.96$

So, $\chi^2 = 12.96 + 12.96 = 25.92$

At this point, you have nothing with which to compare the chi-square value of 25.92. Complete Example 2 to get a comparison value and determine whether 25.92 is large or small.

GUIDED

Example 2

To test if the coin is fair, compute the chi-square statistic for the coin that came up heads 30 times in 50 tosses.

Solution Complete the table.

Scenario (2)	Outcome 1 HEADS	Outcome TAILS	
Observed Frequency	$a_1 = \underline{\ ?\ }$ 30	$a_2 = \underline{\ ?\ }$ 20	
Expected Frequency	$e_1 = \underline{\ ?\ }$ 25	$e_2 = \underline{\ ?\ }$ 25	
$\frac{(a_i - e_i)^2}{e_i}$	$\frac{(30 - 25)^2}{25} = \underline{\ ?\ }$	$\frac{(? - ?)^2}{?} = \underline{\ ?\ }$	1; $\frac{(20 - 25)^2}{25}$; 1;

The chi-square statistic is $\chi^2 = \underline{\ ?\ } + \underline{\ ?\ } = 2$.   1; 1

Notice that the chi-square value for the coin in Example 2 is much smaller than the one for the coin in Example 1. This is because the observed frequencies are closer to the expected frequencies.

There is a different chi-square distribution for each value of n, so statistics texts and other resources routinely have contained tables of chi-square statistics, indicating what values are benchmarks for 0.05, 0.01, or 0.001 probabilities.

Activity 1 Instead of going to a table to see if a chi-square value is significant, we employ a more contemporary strategy, a Monte Carlo simulation. This strategy has wide applicability and great believability because it directly determines how unusual a particular tabular distribution is. In the case of the coin, however, in Chapter 9 students will see a more mathematically precise determination of the probability of getting 30 or more heads in 50 tosses of a fair coin, using a binomial distribution.

QY2

Simulating the Likelihood of a Chi-square Value

We still have not determined how far the observed frequencies can be from expected frequencies to still be considered variation due to chance. One way to determine this is to simulate the coin-tossing experiment a large number of times, calculate the chi-square statistic for each experiment, and see how often a specific value occurs.

QY2

Can the value of the chi-square statistic be negative? Why or why not?

Activity 1 Steps 1–3. See margin.

MATERIALS chi-square application or technology file provided by your teacher

The following simulation shows how a particular χ^2 value ($\chi^2 = 2$ in Example 2) compares to 1000 generated χ^2 values. One experiment consists of a random generation of 50 heads or tails. The difference between these simulated counts of heads and tails with the expected numbers of heads and tails are used to calculate the chi-square statistic seen in Examples 1 and 2. This statistic is computed and recorded. One thousand experiments are run in one simulation.

Step 1 Consider Example 2. Record 0.5 and 0.5 in the first two cells for probabilities. These are hypothesized probabilities because that is what χ^2 is testing: how well the observed frequencies under these probabilities match the expected count.

Step 2 Put the observed counts of heads and tails in the cells for observed frequencies. For Example 2, these are 30 and 20, respectively.

Step 3 Press the "Get Chi-Square" button and record the chi-square value.

Step 4 Run the simulation. When the simulation is finished, a distribution of the chi-square values will appear on your screen graphed as a histogram. Record the percent of experiments out of the 1000 that have χ^2 larger than the original chi-square value of 2. Compare your percent to that of others in your class.

Step 5 Summarize the results of the simulation in a sentence: If the hypothesized probabilities are accurate, a chi-square value larger than the original chi-square value would occur about ___?___ of the time by chance.

Step 6 Repeat Steps 1–5 to simulate Example 1.

Step 7 Repeat Steps 1–5 to simulate scenario (3) on page 417.

Step 7. Answers vary. Sample: 22.4%
If the hypothesized probabilities are accurate, a chi-square value larger than the original chi-square value would occur about 22.4% of the time.

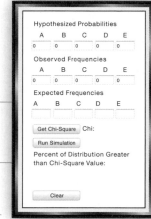

Step 4–5. Answers vary. Sample: 11.6%

Step 6. Answers vary. Sample: 0.0%
If the hypothesized probabilities are accurate, a chi-square value larger than the original chi-square value would occur about 0.0% of the time.

Notes on the Lesson

Activity 1 The larger the deviations of the observed from expected counts, the larger the chi-square value. Thus, once a chi-square value has been determined, the natural question is how unusual is a value this large? For this, the activity runs a simulation.

Additional Answers

Activity 1

Steps 1–3:

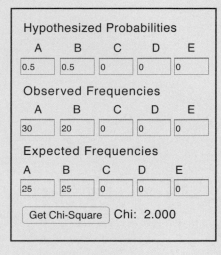

Activity 2 In this case, there is no simple distribution such as the binomial distribution to use as a comparison. After calculating the chi-square statistic, a calculator is used to determine the probability of such a distribution occurring by a chance. Alternatively, a book of tables could be used. Then, in Step 7, students simulate the data using a web applet.

The chi-square applet can be found at technical.uchicago.edu under FST Lesson 6-9.

Significance Level and the Chi-Square Table

The percent produced in the simulation of Example 2 in Activity 1 is usually between 11% and 12%. Thus, in the long run, you could expect about 12% of the experiments to have a χ^2 larger than 2 by chance. A relative frequency of 12% is about 1 in 8 and is not particularly unusual. This is not low enough to *reject* the hypothesis that the coin is fair.

It would be cumbersome to always calculate at least two chi-square values in order to compare the likelihood of one situation to another or to simulate 1000 experiments in order to estimate the likelihood of such a chi-square value. How do you decide when to reject a hypothesis? Luckily, you can compare a calculated chi-square value against a table like the one shown below. In this table, n is the number of outcomes and $n - 1$ is called the number of **degrees of freedom**. The probabilities 0.25, 0.10. 0.05, 0.01, and 0.001 indicate how likely a chi-square value that large is to occur. These are the critical probabilities we test hypotheses against, and are known as **significance levels**.

Critical Chi-Square Values

Degrees of Freedom $= n - 1$	Significance Level				
	0.25	0.10	0.05	0.01	0.001
1	1.32	2.71	3.84	6.63	10.83
2	2.77	4.61	5.99	9.21	13.82
3	4.11	6.25	7.81	11.34	16.27
4	5.39	7.78	9.49	13.28	18.47
5	6.63	9.24	11.07	15.09	20.51

Common practice is to use 0.01 or 0.05 as the significance level. If a chi-square value for the original experiment is *larger* than the chi-square value in the table at a particular significance level, then we reject the hypothesis. If the chi-square value you calculate is *less* than the chi-square value in the table, you cannot reject the hypothesis or conclude that the experiment is unlikely at the particular significance level. We say there is *insufficient evidence* to reject the hypothesis, not that the hypothesis is true.

For example, suppose we pick 0.01 as the significance level. In Example 1, $n = 2$, so look at row 1 in the table and the 0.01 column. It shows that a chi-square value as large as 6.63 would be expected to occur with a probability of 0.01. A fair coin flipped 50 times yielding 43 heads corresponds to a chi-square value of 25.92. Since $25.92 > 6.63$ at the 0.01 significance level, we reject the hypothesis that the coin is fair.

 QY3

You are not expected to know how the values in the chi-square table were calculated. The mathematics needed to calculate them is usually studied in college-level statistics courses. In fact, instead of the table, you can use a chi-square function on a statistics utility that returns the probability for the experiment in question.

> ▶ QY3
>
> Test the hypothesis that the coin is fair in Example 1 using the chi-square table at the 0.001 significance level.

We did this for Example 2. We set the lower bound to the chi-square value 2 that was calculated, the upper bound to infinity, and input 1, the degrees of freedom. The calculator computation verifies that the result in Example 2 is not unlikely. A chi-square value of 2 or larger has a probability of 15.7%. We cannot reject the hypothesis that the coin is fair.

$\chi^2\text{Cdf}(2,\infty,1)$	0.157299

More than Two Outcomes

The probabilities of getting 30 or 43 heads in 50 tosses of a fair coin can be calculated exactly. You will learn how to calculate these probabilities in Chapter 10. So simulations are not needed for coin-tossing experiments. But when there are more than two outcomes to an experiment, calculating probabilities can be quite tedious or nearly impossible, and simulating the distribution of χ^2 values is very helpful.

This is the case with the Titanic data from Lesson 6-5. Activity 2 uses the chi-square statistic to answer the question, "Was the number of survivors so unequal by class that it is unlikely to have happened by chance?" There were more passengers in first-class than in second-class, so you might expect that there would be more survivors in first class than in second. About twice as many first-class passengers survived as second class. If chance of survival was evenly distributed, is this likely?

Activity 2

MATERIALS chi-square application or technology file provided by your teacher

Step 1 Here is the first table from Lesson 6-5, with row percent totals for the number of people in each class. We consider the "crew" as a class.

Passengers	First	Second	Third	Crew	Total
Survived	203	118	178	212	711
Died	122	167	528	673	1490
Totals	325	285	706	885	2201
(Percent)	14.8%	12.9%	32.1%	40.2%	

Describe a hypothesis to test by filling in the blanks: The relative frequency of survivors by class equals the relative frequencies of all passengers by class: 14.8% first class, __?__ % second class, __?__ % third class, and __?__ % crew. **12.9; 32.1; 40.2**

Step 2 Calculate expected counts. 14.8% of people on the Titanic were traveling first class, so under the hypothesis, 14.8% of the survivors should be first class. There were 711, survivors in all, so 14.8% of 711 or about 105 survivors are expected in first class. Fill in the table below. The total number of expected survivors should add to 711.

	First	Second	Third	Crew	Total
Actual (Observed) Number of Survivors	203	118	178	212	711
Expected Number of Survivors	105	$e_2 = ?$	$e_3 = ?$	$e_4 = ?$	711

(continued on next page) **92; 228; 286**

The Chi-Square Test   **421**

(continued on next page)

Notes on the Lesson

Activity 2 An important idea to emphasize is that the chi-square statistic determines whether the *set* of observed values differs significantly from the set of expected values and not whether a particular value is significant. So, for instance, in Activity 2, the difference in the first class survivors contributes about 5 times more to the statistic than the difference in the crew survivors, and one would think that the difference in the crew survivors is not particularly large, but a look at the data indicates that fewer crew members survived than would have been expected.

If you are looking for another example, you could extend the Warm-Up. There, $n = 2$. The chi-square value is $\frac{1.7^2}{12.3} + \frac{1.7^2}{19.7} \approx 0.38$. This value is too low to be of any significance. The numbers of teams from the city and suburbs do not differ enough from the expected values to be unusually different from what would be expected if the teams were randomly chosen.

6-9

3 Assignment

Recommended Assignment

- Questions 1–9
- • Questions 10–17
- • Question 18 (extra credit)
- • Self-Test

Notes on the Questions

We suggest going through Questions 1–7 in order to cover the ideas of the lesson. Then you can pick from Questions 8–12 to discuss in class. We expect that, in all cases, students will use a calculator or other program to determine the *p*-value for a given chi-square statistic.

Question 5c To answer this question, students must calculate the *p*-value of the chi-square statistic and then compare it with a significance level of their choosing. For coin tossing, we might wish to take a tough significance level of 0.01 or 0.001.

Additional Answers

6.

$$\frac{(5067-5000)^2}{5000} + \frac{(4933-5000)^2}{5000}$$

1.7956

$\chi^2\text{Cdf}(1.7956, \infty, 1)$ 0.180245

$\chi^2 \approx 1.80$. The probability of a chi-square value as large as 1.8 is about 18%. We cannot reject Kerrich's hypothesis that the coin is fair.

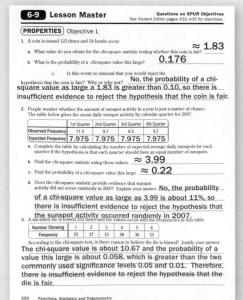

Step 3 Compute the contributions to chi-square $\frac{(a_i - e_i)^2}{e_i}$ for each of the four classes using the values for e_2, e_3, and e_4 from Step 3. Place them in a third row of the table. The contribution for first class is given.   **7.3; 11.0; 19.1**

	First	Second	Third	Crew	Total
Actual (Observed) Number of Survivors	203	118	178	212	711
Expected Number of Survivors	105	e_2	e_3	e_4	711
Contribution to Chi-square	91.5	?	?	?	128.9

Step 4 Add the 4 numbers you found in Step 3 to get the chi-square statistic.

Step 5 Check by using a statistics utility to compute the chi-square statistic for the Titanic data. Some utilities use a chi square "goodness of fit" (GOF) function, which has as inputs the list of the observed values, the list of the expected values, and the degrees of freedom. The screenshot at the right shows a χ^2 value of 128.9. The "Pval" indicates that the probability that a value as high as about 128.9 would occur is about 9.21×10^{-28}, or almost 0. That means that a chi-square as large as 128.9 would occur by chance far less than 0.001 of the time. Therefore, we reject the hypothesis that the Titanic survivors were distributed proportionally to the number of passengers in each class when tested at the 0.001 significance level. There were significantly different percents of survivors in the classes than would be expected by chance.

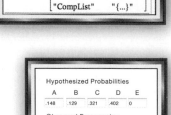

Step 6 Analyze these data using the web applet provided by your teacher to verify that the probability of such a high χ^2 value is very close to 0.

Questions

COVERING THE IDEAS

In 1–4, refer to Activity 2.

1. a. What do the a_i stand for?   b. What do the e_i stand for?
2. What equation needs to be solved to find e_3? $e_3 = 711 \cdot 0.321$
3. Show the calculation of $\frac{(a_3 - e_3)^2}{e_3}$. $\frac{(178-228)^2}{228} \approx 11.0$
4. Identify the degrees of freedom.   **3**
5. A coin is tossed 50 times and 33 heads occur.
   a. What value do you obtain for the chi-square statistic testing whether this coin is fair?   **5.12**
   b. What is the probability of chi-square value this large?   **about 0.024**
   c. Is this event so unusual that you would conclude that the coin is likely to be biased?   **Because 0.024 < 0.05, we rejected the hypothesis that the coin is fair.**

   1a. the observed number of survivors in a given class
   1b. the expected number of survivors in a given class

Step 6
Note that the chi-square value listed is different than what was calculated in Step 5 because of differences in rounding.

Additional Answers

8a.

	Commercial Tattoo Parlor	Done Elsewhere	Total
Has Hepatitis C	17	8	25
No Hepatitis C	35	53	88
Total	52	61	113

6. Recall from Lesson 6-3 that John Kerrich got 5067 heads in 10,000 tosses of a coin. Use a chi-square statistic to test the hypothesis that his coin was a fair coin at the 0.01 significance level. **See margin.**

7. A die is tossed 120 times and the values occur with the frequencies as in the table at the right. According to a chi-square test, is there reason to believe the die is biased? Justify your answer.

Number Showing	1	2	3	4	5	6
Frequency	24	17	18	21	16	24

7. There is no reason to believe the die is biased because the probability of χ^2 as large as 3.1 is about 0.685.

8. Here is part of a table from Lesson 6-5. Follow the steps to apply a chi-square test to determine whether there was a significant effect on having Hepatitis C depending on where the tattoo was done.

	Tattoo Done in Commercial Tattoo Parlor	Tattoo Done Elsewhere
Has Hepatitis C	17	8
No Hepatitis C	35	53

a. Copy the table and add totals in appropriate places. **See margin.**
b. What percent of people in this study had Hepatitis C? **about 22.1%**
c. Calculate the number of people in this study who got their tattoo in a commercial tattoo parlor who would be expected to have Hepatitis C if location had no effect. **about 11.5**

8f. about 0.027;

$\chi^2Cdf(4.87118,\infty,1\ )$	0.027309

d. Calculate the number of people in this study who did not get their tattoo in a commercial tattoo parlor who would be expected to have Hepatitis C if location had no effect. **about 13.5**
e. Calculate the chi-square statistic using the actual numbers of people who had Hepatitis C and the expected counts you found in Parts c and d. **about 4.87**
f. What is the probability of a chi-square value this large?
g. At the 0.01 significance level, does the chi-square test suggest that location had any effect on a person's chances of having Hepatitis C?

8g. Because 0.027 > 0.01, there is insufficient evidence to reject the hypothesis that the location has no effect.

9. In the years 2001–2007, 111 storms in the Atlantic, Caribbean, and Gulf of Mexico were classified as cyclones by the National Hurricane Center. A cyclone is a closed, rotating weather system that may or may not have hurricane-strength winds. The data are presented in the table below.

Year	2001	2002	2003	2004	2005	2006	2007
Number of Cyclones	15	12	16	15	28	10	15

Source: National Hurrican Center

People wonder if some years have significantly more cyclones than other years, or if the differences among years are due to chance.
a. Calculate the numbers of expected storms in these years if each year had an equal number of storms. Copy the table above and add a row for the expected counts. **See margin.**
b. Find the chi-square statistic using these values. **about 12.54**
c. Find the probability of a chi-square value this large. **about 0.0509**
d. Does the chi-square statistic provide evidence to reject the claim that cyclones occur in the same frequency over these years at the 0.05 significance level? Why or why not? **See margin.**

Aerial view of a well-defined cyclone

Notes on the Questions

Questions 6g Students should realize that the answer may depend on the significance level they have chosen. Here, because a serious disease is involved, we might want to err on the side of caution and take a significance level of 0.05.

Questions 8, 11, 12 When the data for these questions were found, we did not know whether the differences would be significant or not. That is the best kind of data on which to apply a chi-square test. You might ask students to be on the lookout for sets of data on which the chi-square test could be applied. The data should be such that the numbers in each observed and expected cell are greater than 5. (Different chi-square formulas are used when cell numbers are small, or a chi-square test may be inappropriate.)

Question 9 Emphasize that the chi-square statistic only provides a *probability* that the differences among years are significant enough not to have occurred randomly. If enough tests are done, then something that might occur only with probability 0.01 might have a good chance of occurring. Specifically, it might well be that once every 100 years one should expect 35 hurricanes in a season. While such an occurence would be unusual if it occurred in a set of five years that happened to be studied, if 20 sets of five years were being studied, it would not be so unusual.

Additional Answers

9a.

Year	2001	2002	2003	2004	2005	2006	2007	Total
Observed Number of Cyclones	15	12	16	15	28	10	15	111.0
Expected Number of Cyclones	15.86	15.86	15.86	15.86	15.86	15.86	15.86	111.0

9d. The results do not provide sufficient evidence to reject the hypothesis at the 0.05-significance level because 0.051 > 0.05.

Notes on the Questions

Questions 11 and 12 The difference between these questions is that in Question 11, we are testing whether teams *in general* tend to score more points in certain periods than others, while in Question 12 we are testing whether *winning teams* tend to score more points in certain periods than others.

APPLYING THE MATHEMATICS

10. You toss a coin 100 times. At the 0.001 significance level, if the coin is fair, the number of heads should be between which two numbers?

In 11 and 12, consider that there are 4 quarters in a professional basketball game. Do teams tend to score more points in certain periods than others? Here are the points scored by each team in the 12 NBA basketball games played on November 16, 2007. Three games went into overtime, so teams were tied (T) at the end of the 4 quarters. Other teams are indicated by who won (W) and who lost (L).

Team won, lost, or tied	First Quarter	Second Quarter	Third Quarter	Fourth Quarter
L	30	26	18	27
W	22	31	28	29
L	24	22	19	26
W	24	28	24	16
T	26	32	26	23
T	23	22	37	25
T	32	30	19	33
T	23	35	26	30
W	32	15	24	34
L	24	27	23	15
L	20	26	22	23
W	29	19	14	41
L	21	24	28	15
W	14	13	29	36
W	25	20	24	26
L	10	22	27	11
L	24	19	31	20
W	19	20	29	31
L	24	22	18	20
W	25	24	20	21
T	31	16	26	24
T	28	29	25	15
L	26	29	32	18
W	34	30	32	26

11. Add the data from all 24 teams and perform a chi-square test to determine whether, in general, teams tend to score more points in certain periods than others. Use the 0.05 significance level.

12. Add the data from the 9 teams that won before overtime and perform a chi-square test to determine whether winning teams tend to score more points in certain periods than others. Use the 0.05 significance level.

10. 34 and 66

11. The probability of a chi-square value as large as 0.38 is about 0.941 so at the 0.05-significance level there is insufficient evidence to reject the claim that point scoring by quarter is the same.

12. The probability of a chi-square value as large as 8.088 is about 0.044, which shows at the 0.05-significance level that we can reject the original claim. Because we only considered the games the teams won before overtime, we conjecture that in these games the winning team scored more at the end of the game in these games and therefore would have a higher probability of scoring in the last quarter.

REVIEW

13. A science experiment is expected to have a successful outcome 40% of the time. In 20 repetitions of the experiment, what is the expected count of the event of a failure? (**Lesson 6-8**) **12**

14. **True or False** As Dr. Kerrich tossed his coin 100,000 times, according to the Law of Large Numbers, we would expect the relative frequency of heads to approach the probability of getting heads. (**Lesson 6-8**) **true**

15. Suppose a person with a certain medical condition has probability 0.45 of recovering fully, if the person undergoes surgery. Also suppose that 100 surgeries for this condition are performed. Design a simulation for this situation and how you would run the simulation using technology. (**Lesson 6-7**)

16. Is the equation an identity? If not, change the right side of the equation to make it an identity. (**Lesson 4-3**) **no; $\cos(180° − \theta)$**
    a. $\cos(90° − \theta) = \cos \theta$ **no; $\sin \theta$** b. $−\cos \theta = \cos(360° − \theta)$
    c. $\sin(−\theta) = −\sin \theta$ **yes**   d. $\tan(180° + \theta) = \tan \theta$ **yes**

17. For a given set of data, $\bar{x} = 22$ and $s = 9$. Find the z-score for each number. (**Lesson 3-9**)
    a. 15 $-\frac{7}{9} \approx$ **-0.78**   b. 24 $\frac{2}{9} \approx$ **0.22**   c. 31 **1**

EXPLORATION

18. In *A Mathematician Reads the Newspaper*, John Paulos reports that if you spin a coin on its edge, heads will occur only about 30% of the time. Perform an experiment, spinning a penny on its edge at least 150 times. Then do a chi-square test to determine whether Paulos's report seems to be correct.
    18. Answers vary. Sample: A simulation of 150 trials results in 53 heads and 97 tails. $\chi^2 \approx 2.03$. The results of the simulation conclude that a chi-square value of 2.03 or larger would happen about 15.4% of the time. These results show that we cannot reject Paulos's hypothesis

15. Answers vary. Sample: Run a simulation with 100 trials. In each trial you generate a random number from 1 to 100, where 1-45 means the patient has recovered fully, and 46-100 means the patient has not. Add the number of successes to find the relative frequency of recovery.

QY ANSWERS

1. 25; 25; 40

2. No. Each contribution to chi-square is nonnegative because each difference in the numerator is squared and the denominator is a count.

3. $10.83 < 25.92$, so the hypothesis is rejected even at the 0.001 level.

The Chi-Square Test **425**

Ongoing Assessment
Write a problem like Question 7 on the board. Have each student explain orally how to find the answer. **Answers vary. Students should explain how to perform a chi-square test and interpret the result.**

Chapter

6

The projects relate to the content of the lessons of this chapter as follows:

Project	Lesson(s)
1	6-7
2	6-7
3	6-8
4	6-7
5	6-5, 6-6

1 The Sum of Many Dice

In Lesson 6-1, the 36 possible outcomes for a toss of two dice are listed and used to determine the probability of obtaining each possible sum. Since it becomes impractical to list all 216 outcomes for more than two dice, a simulation may be used to estimate the probabilities of getting various sums when three or more dice are tossed.

a. Simulate the sum of a toss of three fair dice 1000 times. Create a relative frequency graph of the sums obtained. Predict the probability of each.

b. Create and analyze the relative frequency graph of the sum of 10 fair dice tossed 1000 times.

c. Simulate 1000 tosses of two dice, one fair and one weighted such that a 6 occurs with probability $\frac{1}{2}$, and 1 through 5 each occur with probability $\frac{1}{10}$. Explain how you performed the simulation and display your results in a histogram.

2 Random Walk

A random walk is a trajectory generated by taking successive random steps.

a. Suppose a person stands on a north-south street at a random position marked "0." The person tosses a fair coin to determine which direction he walks. If a single toss of the coin yields heads, he takes one step north; otherwise, he takes one step south. After each step, he flips the coin again and takes one step, and so on.

   i. If the man takes 10 steps, at what possible final positions might the man stand? Of the possible positions, which do you think are most likely and why?

   ii. Simulate a walk of 10 steps 100 or more times using a spreadsheet application. Find and graph the relative frequencies of the final positions. Does this agree with your expectations?

b. The one-dimensional case of Part a can be extended to 2 or more dimensions. Describe a possible two-dimensional random walk. What are the possible final positions after 10 steps and what are the most probable positions?

Project Rubric

Advanced	Student correctly provides all of the details asked for in the project as well as additional correct independent conclusions.
Proficient	Student correctly provides all of the details asked for in the project.
Partially proficient	Student correctly provides some of the details asked for in the project or provides all details with some inaccuracies.
Not proficient	Student correctly provides few of the details asked for in the project or provides all details with many inaccuracies.
No attempt	Student makes little or no attempt to complete the project.

3 The "Law of Averages"

Lesson 6-8 discussed the invalidity of the "law of averages." Here, we test this claim.

a. Generate a sequence of 500 tosses of a fair coin.

b. Look at the sequence to find "streaks" of 3 heads in a row. For each streak, record the result of the next toss, i.e. create the set of every toss following a streak of 3 heads. What are the relative frequencies of heads and tails in this set?

c. For the same 500 tosses, look at streaks of 3 tails and create the set of tosses following each streak. What are the relative frequencies of heads and tails in this set?

d. Is a streak of heads more likely followed by tails than heads or a streak of tails more likely followed by heads than tails? Explain your answer.

4 Probabilistic Analysis of Functions

Investigate the following situation. If a, b, and c are numbers from 0 to 9, what is the probability P that the function f with equation $f(x) = ax^2 + bx + c$ has real roots?

a. Consider the case where a, b, and c are integers from 0 to 9. Calculate the probability of having real roots. (Hint: There are 1000 ways to assign values to a, b, c. Also, consider the cases when a is zero and a is nonzero separately.)

b. Consider the case where a, b, and c are real numbers from 0 to 9. Use technology to simulate this case and estimate the probability that f has real roots.

Johnny Gomes of the Tampa Bay Rays during the 2008 World Series.

5 Probability Trees

In Lesson 6-5, you used contingency tables and graphs to help you determine the probabilities involved with the diagnosis of strep throat. Graphs may be used in other situations to help determine probabilities.

A situation involving probabilities important to TV broadcasters is the World Series of Major League Baseball. Since there may be 4, 5, 6, or 7 games depending on the performance of the teams, broadcasters need to estimate the most likely length of a series in order to develop program and advertising schedules.

a. To help determine the most likely series length, a probability tree is helpful. Draw a probability tree of all possible outcomes of the World Series between two teams A and B. Assume each team has an equal chance of winning each game. (Hint: Since the series ends when one team wins 4 games, the various branches of the tree will terminate at different points.)

b. Use the tree to determine the most likely series length.

4 Probabilistic Analysis of Functions

The domain for a, b, and c can be expanded. Certainly it is reasonable to allow a, b, and c to be negative, so you might pick numbers between 9 and 9, perhaps avoiding 0. Students might also solve the quadratics to see how often the solution is rational. They would learn that even if a, b, and c are selected to be "nice numbers," only a small percentage of quadratics factor into polynomials with rational coefficients. This is the reason that factoring is not a widely applicable method for solving quadratics.

Notes

_____   _____
_____   _____
_____   _____
_____   _____
_____   _____
_____   _____
_____   _____
_____   _____

Chapter 6

Summary and Vocabulary

The Summary gives an overview of the entire chapter and provides an opportunity for students to consider the material as a whole. Thus, the Summary can be used to help students relate and unify the concepts presented in the chapter.

Vocabulary words and symbols are listed by lesson to provide a checklist of concepts that students must know. Emphasize to students that they should read the vocabulary list carefully before starting the Self-Test on pages 430–431. If students do not understand the meaning of a vocabulary word, they should refer back to the indicated lesson.

Theorems and Properties covered in the chapter are listed below the Summary with page references included to lead students back to the location in the chapter where the theorem or property is stated.

○ Probabilities are calculated from assumptions about **outcomes** in a **sample space**. If all outcomes in a finite sample space are equally likely, the **probability of an event** is the ratio of the number of individual outcomes making up the **event** to the number of outcomes in the sample space. The probability of the **union** of two events A and B satisfies $P(A \cup B) = P(A) + P(B) - P(A \cap B)$. If A and B are **mutually exclusive**, $P(A \cup B) = P(A) + P(B)$. If A and B are **complementary**, $P(B) = 1 - P(A)$.

○ The occurrence of one event may affect the probability that another event occurs. The probability of event B given that event A has occurred is written $P(B \mid A)$. If $P(B \mid A) = P(B)$, then events A and B are **independent**; this definition is equivalent to the statement $P(A \cap B) = P(A) \cdot P(B)$. **Contingency tables** help organize information in order to determine whether events are independent, to compute **conditional probabilities**, or to suggest patterns in data. It is important to be able to identify conditional probability situations clearly: for example, when a test comes back positive for a disease, the probability that you actually have the disease is a conditional probability different from the probability that an arbitrary test result is correct.

○ The number of ways to choose one element each from two finite sets A and B is $N(A) \cdot N(B)$. An ordered list of symbols is a **string**. By the Multiplication Counting Principle, the number of strings of n different items, *without* replacement, is $n!$. The number of strings of **length k** of n items with replacement is n^k. The number of strings of r items out of a given set of n *without* replacement (also called a **permutation of n objects taken r at a time**) is denoted
$$_nP_r = n(n-1) \cdot \cdots \cdot (n-r+1) = \frac{n!}{(n-r)!}.$$

○ Random numbers can be approximated manually (such as by throwing dice) or can be generated using a calculator or computer. Many real-life situations can be simulated by using **random** numbers to code experiments or events, for example, the number of people with reservations who actually show up for a flight. The use of randomness to generate relative frequencies obtained from simulated repeated trials of an experiment and then to estimate probabilities is called the **Monte Carlo method**.

Vocabulary

6-1
probability theory
experiment
*outcome
*sample space
*event
*probability of an event, $P(E)$
*fair, unbiased
randomly, at random
empty set, null set

6-2
union of sets
disjoint sets
mutually exclusive events
intersection of sets
complement of A, not A

6-3
string
length of a string
independent events
dependent events

6-4
*permutation
*permutations of n objects taken r at a time, $_nP_r$

6-5
contingency table
Simpson's Paradox

6-6
*conditional probability of an event, $P(B \mid A)$

○ It is a commonly held belief that when an event has recently occurred that the complement event is now more likely. Though the Law of Large Numbers says that over a large number of trials the relative frequency of an event approaches its probability. A particular coin toss, for instance, is not any more likely to be heads if the previous five tosses have all been tails than if they were all heads. A **chi-square statistic** can suggest whether observed counts are close to **expected counts** and can be used to estimate the probability of an observed distribution of data agreeing with a hypothesis.

Vocabulary

6-7
simulation
random
trial
Monte Carlo method

6-8
expected count of an
    outcome
expected count of an event

6-9
chi-square statistic
degrees of freedom
significance level

Properties and Theorems

Basic Properties of Probability (p. 363)
Addition Counting Principle (Mutually Exclusive Form) (p. 367)
Addition Counting Principle (General Form) (p. 369)
Probability of the Union of Mutually Exclusive Events Theorem(p. 368)
Probability of the Union of Events Theorem (General Form) (p.369)
Probability of Complements Theorem (p. 371)
Multiplication Counting Principle (p. 374)
Strings with Replacement Theorem (p. 376)
Formula for $_nP_r$ Theorem (p. 382)
Formula for $_nP_n$ Corollary (p. 384)
Alternate Formula for $_nP_r$ Theorem (p. 382)
Law of Large Numbers (p. 411)

Self-Test

For the development of mathematical competence, feedback and correction, along with the opportunity for practice, are necessary. The Self-Test provides the opportunity for feedback and correction; the Chapter Review provides additional opportunities for practice. We cannot overemphasize the importance of these end-of-chapter materials. It is at this point that the material gels for many students, allowing them to solidify skills and understanding. In general, student performance should improve after these pages.

Assign the Self-Test as a one-night assignment. Worked-out solutions for all questions are in the Selected Answers section of the student book. Encourage students to take the Self-Test honestly, grade themselves, and then be prepared to discuss the test in class.

Advise students to pay special attention to those Chapter Review questions (pages 432–435) that correspond to the questions they missed on the Self-Test. These are identified in the Self-Test Correlation Chart located in the Selected Answers section at the back of the book.

Chapter 6 Self-Test

Take this test as you would take a test in class. You will need a calculator. Then use the Selected Answers section in the back of the book to check your work.

1. Consider the experiment of tossing three different coins.
   a. Write the sample space for the experiment.
   b. List the outcomes in the event "at least two tails show up."

2. a. Evaluate $_{15}P_6$.
   b. What is meant by $_{15}P_6$?

3. How many four-letter permutations can be made from the letters in SNOWFLAKE?

4. Consider the experiment of tossing a fair coin and a fair six-sided die. The sides of the coin are marked 1 and 2. The faces of the die are marked from 1 to 6. Find the probability that the sum is less than five.

5. A consumer group reports that 15% of Brand X dental floss packages contain less than the advertised length of floss. Four packages are chosen at random. Assume that the consumer group is correct.
   a. What is the probability that all four packages contain less than the advertised amount?
   b. What is the probability that all four packages contain at least the advertised amount?

6. If you have 4 pairs of jeans, 5 t-shirts, and 2 pairs of sneakers, how many different outfits consisting of a pair of jeans, a t-shirt, and a pair of sneakers can you make?

7. Suppose $P(A \cap B) = 0.6$, $P(A) = 0.7$, and $P(B) = 0.8$.
   a. Find $P(A \cup B)$. b. Find $P(B \mid A)$.

8. The criminal justice department at a local university estimates that in 85% of the cases brought to trial in the county court the defendant is guity, that 10% of guilty defendents are found innocent, and that 5% of innocent defendants are found guilty.
   a. Make a table or tree diagram of the situation.
   b. What is the probability that a defendant who is found guilty is actually innocent?
   c. What is the probability that a defendant who is found innocent is actually guilty?

In 9 and 10, **True or False.** Explain your reasoning.

9. If A and B are complementary events and $P(A) = k$, then $P(B) = 1 - k$.

10. The expected count of the outcome 2 in 600 rolls of a fair six-sided die is 60.

11. The information booklet about a wildlife reservation park states that the probability of observing an eagle on a given day is 0.21, and the probability for a hawk is 0.17. The booklet also indicates that, based on records, 2% of the visitors observe both of these prey birds on the same day. In this park, are observing an eagle and observing a hawk independent events? Explain.

3. $_9P_4 = \frac{9!}{(9-4)!} = \frac{9!}{5!} = 9 \cdot 8 \cdot 7 \cdot 6 = 3024$ is the number of possible permutations of 9 letters taken 4 at a time.

1a. {HHH, HHT, HTH, HTT, THH, THT, TTH, TTT}

1b. HTT, THT, TTT, TTH

2a. $_{15}P_6 = \frac{15!}{(15-6)!} = \frac{15!}{9!} = 15 \cdot 14 \cdot 13 \cdot 12 \cdot 11 \cdot 10 = 3,603,600.$

2b. $_{15}P_6$ is the number of possible permutations of 15 objects taken 6 at a time.

12. A high school guidance office states that 20% of past graduates majored in science, 45% in liberal arts, and 15% in engineering. The remaining 20% were spread out among a variety of other majors. A new survey of 780 current graduates turned up 125 science majors, 312 liberal arts majors, 138 engineering majors, and 205 others. Use the chi-square statistic to test the hypothesis that the proportions by major have remainded the same..

In 13 and 14, suppose a student dormitory in a college shows the data in the table below:

	Freshmen	Sophomores	Juniors	Seniors
Own a car	70	60	70	90
Do not own a car	320	240	110	60

13. Estimate the probability that a student in the dormitory owns a car.

14. What percent of car owners are juniors?

4. Tossing the coin has 2 possible outcomes and rolling the die has 6 possible outcomes, so there are 12 possible outcomes in the sample space. There are 5 outcomes where the sum of the outcomes of the two events is less than 5: $\{1 + 3, 1 + 2, 1 + 1, 2 + 2, 2 + 1\}$. Therefore the probability is $\frac{5}{12}$.

5. a. The length of floss in each package is independent, so the probability is $(0.15)^4 \approx 0.0005$.

   b. The probability that a package has at least the advertised amount is $1 - 0.15 = 0.85$ because the two events are complements. The probability that all four packages have at least the stated amount is $(0.85)^4 \approx 0.5220$.

6. Use the Multiplication Counting Principle: $4 \cdot 5 \cdot 2 = 40$ outfits.

7a. By the Addition Counting Principle, $P(A \cup B) = P(A) + P(B) - P(A \cap B) = 0.7 + 0.8 - 0.6 = 0.9$

15. John's batting average is 0.325. Describe a simulation to estimate the probability of his getting 4 or more hits out of 8 at bats.

16. Suppose an a six-sided die is tossed 12,000 times.

   a. What is the expected number of times a 2 will appear if the die is fair?

   b. If the results of the experiment were as follows, what might you conclude?

Number	1	2	3	4	5	6
Occurrences	8271	1233	984	298	489	734

   c. Could you have this conclusion if after 10 trials you obtained three 1s, three 5s, and one each of the other outcomes? Explain why or why not.

7b. $P(B|A) = \dfrac{P(A \cap B)}{P(A)} = \dfrac{0.6}{0.7} \approx 0.86$

8a. **Answers vary. Sample:**

8b. $\dfrac{P(\text{innocent and found guilty})}{P(\text{found guilty})}$

   $= \dfrac{0.0075}{0.0075 + 0.765} \approx 0.97\%$

8c. $\dfrac{P(\text{guilty and found innocent})}{P(\text{found innocent})}$

   $= \dfrac{0.085}{0.085 + 0.1425} \approx 37.36\%$

9. true; If A and B are complementary, then they are mutually exclusive and thus make up the entire sample space. Since $P(S) = 1$, $P(A) + P(B) = 1$, and therefore $P(B) = 1 - P(A) = 1 - k$.

10. false; For a fair die, the probability of rolling a 2 is $\frac{1}{6}$. The expected number of "2"s in 600 rolls is $\frac{1}{6} \cdot 600 = 100$.

11–16. See margin.

Chapter Review

The main objectives for the chapter are organized in the Chapter Review under the four types of understanding this book promotes: Skills, Properties, Uses, and Representations.

Whereas end-of-chapter material may be considered optional in some texts, in UCSMP *Functions, Statistics, and Trigonometry* we have selected these objectives and questions with the expectation that they will be covered. Students should be able to answer these questions with about 85% accuracy after studying the chapter.

You may assign these questions over a single night to help students prepare for a test the next day or you may assign the questions over a two-day period. If you work the questions over two days, we recommend assigning the evens for homework the first night so that students get feedback in class the next day, and then assigning the odds the night before the test because the answers are provided to the odd-numbered questions in the Selected Answers section at the back of the book.

It is effective to ask students which questions they still do not understand and use the day as a total class discussion of the material that the class finds most difficult.

Resources

• Assessment Resources: Chapter 6 Test

Technology Resources

Teacher's Assessment Assistant, Ch. 6
Electronic Teacher's Edition, Ch. 6

Chapter 6 Chapter Review

SKILLS
PROPERTIES
USES
REPRESENTATIONS

SKILLS Procedures used to get answers

OBJECTIVE A Compute probabilites and expected counts of events in various contexts. (Lessons 6-1, 6-2, 6-8)

In 1 and 2, consider tossing a fair six-sided die and subtracting the number on the first toss from the number on the second, resulting in a difference d. Find each probability.

1. $P(d < 0)$ $\frac{5}{12}$ **2.** $P(d$ is an integer) **1**

In 3 and 4, two fair 6-sided dice are tossed. Find each.

3. P(doubles) $\frac{1}{6}$ **4.** P(sum is prime) $\frac{5}{12}$

In 5–7, three fair coins are tossed. Find each.

5. P(all heads) $\frac{1}{8}$ **6.** P(2 heads) $\frac{3}{8}$
7. P(at least 1 tail) $\frac{7}{8}$

8. A current estimate of color blindness in the U.S. population is 1.3%. In a high school graduating class of 1200 students, how many would be expected to be color blind?

9. When tossing a fair die 230 times, what is the expected count of the outcome "3"?

10. According to a National Center for Health Statistics survey, about 4.7% of children between the ages of 5 and 17 missed 11 or more days of school because of illness or injury in the last year. What would be the expected count of students aged 5–17 in a school of 532 students to miss 11 or more days of school because of illness or injury?

OBJECTIVE B Find the number of strings with or without replacement. (Lessons 6-3, 6-4)

11. How many possible strings are there for the letters in the word TROPICAL? $8! = 40,320$

12. How many three-letter permutations can be made from the letters in TROPICAL that contain no A? $_7P_3 = 210$

13. How many five-letter permutations can be made from the letters in CABINET? $_7P_5 = 2520$

14. How many three-letter permutations can be made from CABINET that start and end with a vowel? $_3P_1 \cdot {_5P_1} \cdot {_2P_1} = 30$

15. A coin is tossed eight times. How many possible outcomes are there? $2^8 = 256$

OBJECTIVE C Evaluate expressions using factorials. (Lesson 6–4)

In 16–18, evaluate without using a calculator.

16. 6! **720**   **17.** $\frac{9!}{5!4!3!}$ **21**   **18.** $\frac{100!}{97!} \cdot \frac{48!}{50!} \cdot \frac{8!}{11!}$

19. Write $\frac{54!}{50!}$ as a product of integers.

20. Simplify $\frac{(a+2)!}{(a+1)!}$. $a + 2$

In 21–23, evaluate.

21. $_{12}P_3$ **1320** **22.** $_7P_5$ **2520** **23.** $_nP_1$ **n**

OBJECTIVE D Calculate probabilities using the General and Mutually Exclusive Forms of the Probability of the Union of Events, the Probability of Complements, and the Definition of Conditional Probability. (Lessons 6-2, 6-6)

24. If A and B are two events where $P(A) = 0.6$ and $P(A \cap B) = 0.05$, find $P(B \mid A)$.

25. If A and B are complementary events, find $P(A \cap B)$. **0**

26. If $P(A) = 0.6$ and $P(B) = 0.7$, explain why A and B cannot be mutually exclusive.

27. A and B are two mutually exclusive events, $P(A) = 0.25$, and $P(B) = 0.3$. Find P(not (A or B)). **0.45**

28. What is the probability of a randomly chosen positive integer less than or equal to 100 being either a perfect square or a perfect cube? **0.12**

8–10, 18, 19, 24, 26. See margin.

Additional Answers

8. about 16
9. $38.\overline{3}$
10. about 25
18. $\frac{2}{5}$
19. $54 \cdot 53 \cdot 52 \cdot 51$
24. $\frac{1}{12} = 0.08\overline{3}$
26. If A and B were mutually exclusive, then $P(A) + P(B) = P(A \cup B) \le 1$, but here $P(A) + P(B) = 1.3$, so A and B cannot be mutually exclusive.

PROPERTIES Principles behind the mathematics

OBJECTIVE E Determine whether events are independent or dependent. (Lesson 6-3)

In 29–31, determine whether the events A and B are independent or dependent.

29. $P(A) = 0.4$, $P(B) = 0.25$, $P(A \cap B) = 0.1$

30. A fair coin is tossed once; A = heads occurs; B = tails occurs. **dependent**

31. A fair six-sided die is tossed twice; A = first toss is a 5; B = sum of the tosses is 7.

32. Determine if these two evens are independent. Randomly choosing two socks, one after another, from a drawer, when

   a. the first sock is replaced. **independent**

   b. the first sock is not replaced. **dependent**

OBJECTIVE F Discuss the Law of Large Numbers and the "law of averages." (Lesson 6-8)

33. The 2007–2008 NBA rookie of the year, Kevin Durant, finished the season with an 87.3% free-trow percentage during the regular season. After failing to make his first five free-throws, a radio announcer says, "Durant is due for a successful free-throw attempt." Comment on the announcer's claim.

34. A supercomputer randomly generates numbers between 0 and 9 every five seconds which are needed for an experment. After 1 day (17280 digits) the frequency distribution of digits is as shown below.

Digit	0	1	2	3	4	5	6	7	8	9
Count	1711	1741	1699	1728	1745	1795	1733	1701	1689	1738

What is the relative frequency of 2? What do you expect in the long run?

35. A state lottery costs $1 per ticket to play with a payoff of $700 and probability $\frac{1}{1000}$ of winning. Explain how the Law of Large Numbers assures the state of a profit using as an example an individual who plays this lottery every day for a year.

USES Applications of mathematics in real-world situations

OBJECTIVE G List sample spaces and events for experiments. (Lesson 6-1)

36. Consider the experiment of flipping a coin, then rolling a die.

   a. Write the sample space.

   b. List the outcomes in the event "the coin shows heads or the die shows a non-prime even number."

   c. How many outcomes are in the event "the die shows a number less than 3"?

In 37–39, describe the sample space for the given experiment.

37. finding the direction the wind is blowing to the nearest degree clockwise from north at a particular time of day

38. taking a poll of the television programs people watch at a certain time of the week

39. finding the birthdays of people in a group 366 days

OBJECTIVE H Use a contingency table to compute percentages involving categorical variables. (Lesson 6-5)

In 40–42, a city recently opened a new park and planted many new trees of three different species. Shortly thereafter, a storm knocked over some of the trees. This contingency table gives a count of trees planted and knocked down by species.

Tree Species	Maple	Oak	Ash
Trees Planted	102	68	85
Trees Knocked Down	16	8	17

40. What percentage of each species was knocked down in the storm? Which species seems to be the sturdiest?

41. What percentage of the total trees were oaks before the storm? What percentage are oaks after the storm?

42. What percentage of the total trees in the park was knocked down in the storm?

29, 31, 33–38, 40–42. See margin.

Additional Answers

29. independent

31. independent

33. The announcer is incorrectly applying the "law of averages", assuming that the observed count should approach the expected count.

34. The relative frequency of "2"s is $\frac{1699}{17280} \approx$ 0.098. Over the long-run, the Law of Large Numbers states that the relative frequency of "2"s will approach $\frac{1}{10}$.

35. expected wInnIngs: $(0)(0.999) + (700)(0.001) = \$0.70$; Someone who plays everyday has expected winnings of $(\$0.70)(365) = \$255.5$ in one year but spent $365 during the year. In the long run, the winnings will approach $0.70 per lottery ticket and therefore yield a profit of $0.30 per lottery ticket for the state.

36a. {T1, T2, T3, T4, T5, T6, H1, H2, H3, H4, H5, H6}

36b. H1, H2, H3, H4, H5, H6, T4, T6

36c. 4

37. integers from 0 to 359

38. The entire set of TV programs available at that time.

40. maple: about 15.7%, oak: about 11.8%, ash: about 20%; Oak seems to be the sturdiest species.

41. about 26.7%; about 28.0%

42. about 16.1%

Additional Answers

56.

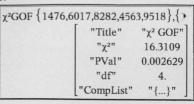

χ²GOF {1476,6017,8282,4563,9518},{ ▸

"Title"	"χ² GOF"
"χ²"	16.3109
"PVal"	0.002629
"df"	4.
"CompList"	"{...}"

The probability of a chi-square value as high as 16.31 or greater is 0.0026. Because 0.0026 > 0.001 we do not have sufficient evidence to reject the claim of the hypothesized percentages.

57.

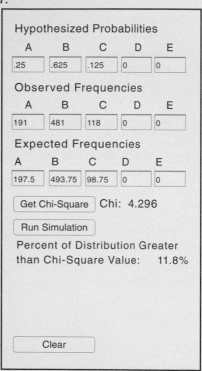

Hypothesized Probabilities

A	B	C	D	E
.25	.625	.125	0	0

Observed Frequencies

A	B	C	D	E
191	481	118	0	0

Expected Frequencies

A	B	C	D	E
197.5	493.75	98.75	0	0

Get Chi-Square | Chi: 4.296

Run Simulation

Percent of Distribution Greater than Chi-Square Value: 11.8%

Clear

The chi-square simulation web applet gives a chi-square value of 4.296 and a probability of 11.8%. Because 0.118 > 0.05, we have insufficient evidence to reject the claim of the hypothesized ratios of morning rush hour traffic.

58. a. 32.44%
   b. 34.42%
   c. about 57.19%

OBJECTIVE I Calculate probabilities in real situations. (Lessons 6-3, 6-4, 6-6)

43. What is the probability of guessing correctly on exactly four of five multiple-choice questions with four options each?

44. What is the probability of four consecutive days without rain if the probability of rain on any particular day is 0.3, regardless of whether it rained the previous day?

45. Each morning, Elliot rides his bike to the train station, where he takes the train to work. Elliot is late getting to the station 8% of the time, and the train leaves early 9% of the time and it leaves late 12% of the time. If Elliot is late getting to the train station and the train is late leaving the station, he will still be able to get to work on time. What is the probability that he will be late getting to the station but still make it to work on time?

46. In tennis, each player is allowed two serves per point. Suppose Rafael Nadal, the 2008 Wimbeldon champion, gets his first serve in 85% of the time. When this happens, he wins the point 95% of the time. If he misses his first serve, he wins the point 60% of the time.

   a. Draw a tree diagram corresponding to the situation.

   b. Find the probability that Nadal does not win the point. **10.25% of the time**

   c. Find the probability that a point that Nadal wins is from his first serve. **about 90.0%**

   d. Find the probability that he missed his first serve given he does not win the point. **about 58.5%**

47. Refer to the Titanic data in Lesson 6-5.

   a. What is the probability that someone who died on the Titanic was a crew member?

   b. What is the probability that a randomly-selected passenger survived, given that the passenger was a member of the crew?
   47a. about 45.2%
   47b. about 24.0%

   43, 44, 45, 46a, 52–54. See margin.

OBJECTIVE J Use the Multiplication Counting Principle, the Strings with Replacement Theorem, and permutations to find the number of ways of arranging objects. (Lessons 6-3, 6-4).

48. What is the probability of correctly pairing 4 locks with their keys from a box with 9 keys in it on the first try? $\frac{1}{3024}$

49. Emma's school uniform allows for three different skirts, two pairs of shoes, and six blouses. How many different outfits does the dress code allow? **36**

50. Phillip has five school subjects and he has eight different colored folders. **6720**

   a. How many ways are there for him to file his papers by subject in different folders?

   b. How many ways are there for Phillip to order his five subject folders? **120**

   c. Using your answers to Parts a and b, how many total possibilities does Phillip have for organizing his papers considering both order and folder color? **806,400**

51. How many different ways are there for a six-player volleyball team and their coach to line up in a row for a photo if the coach wants to stand at one of the ends? **1440**

OBJECTIVE K Design and conduct simulations with or without technology. (Lesson 6-7)

In 52 and 53, you are playing a game that involves six coins: three pennies, two nickels, and one dime. Each coin is flipped. If the coin shows heads, you get to keep it, but if the coin shows tails, you do not. Suppose you play the game 100 times.

52. Describe an experiment to estimate the probability of winning at least 18 cents.

53. Modify the experiment to determine the probability of winning at least 18 cents if one of the pennies is replaced with a nickel.

54. Describe how you could simulate this situation: You are going on a week-long vacation to a place where 10% of the days it rains. You want to know how many days it will rain, so you can pack accordingly.

Additional Answers

43. $\frac{15}{1024} \approx 0.015$

44. 0.2401

45. 0.96%

46a.

first serve 0.85 — win 0.95 — first and win = 0.8075
— lose 0.05 — first and lose = 0.0425
not first serve 0.15 — win 0.6 — not first and win = 0.09
— lose 0.4 — not first and lose = 0.06

52. Answers vary. Sample: Label the first 6 columns of a spreadsheet with the values of the coins. In the next row, use the spreadsheet random number function to generate a 1 (heads) or 0 (tails) in each cell. For each trial, a 7th column can total the product of each cell's coin value and random number. These cells can be copied down for *n* = 100 trials and the frequency of successful outcomes can be counted.

53. Answers vary. Sample: The experiment in 52 can be modified by changing the value of one of the penny columns to 5 and running another 100 trials.

OBJECTIVE L Use the chi-square statistic to determine whether or not an event is likely. (Lesson 6-9)

55. A sample of 6000 fruit flies contained 315, 1202, 1146, and 3337 flies of four species. A scientist claims that these four species of fruit flies should appear $\frac{1}{16}$, $\frac{3}{16}$, $\frac{3}{16}$, and $\frac{9}{16}$ of the time, respectively.

   a. Calculate the expected counts.

   b. What is the degrees of freedom in this situation?

   c. At the 0.01 significance level, is there sufficient evidence to reject the scientist's claim?

56. Below are the number of accidental injury hospitalizations in California in 2004:

Age	< 1	1-4	5-12	13-15	16-20
Injuries	1476	6017	8282	4563	9518

   Is there sufficient evidence to say that the number of injuries in the five age groups appear in the following percentages 5%, 20%, 27%, 16%, and 32% respectively? Test at the 0.001 signifiance level.

57. Three bridges into a city are hypothesized to be used by $\frac{1}{4}$, $\frac{5}{8}$, and $\frac{1}{8}$ of the cars during the morning rush hour. A highway study of a random sample of 790 cars indicated that 191, 481, and 118 cars use these bridges respectively. Run a simulation to determine whether the hypothesis should be rejected. Use a 0.05 significance level.

REPRESENTATIONS Pictures, graphs, or objects that illustrate concepts

OBJECTIVE M Represent information about relative frequencies or frequencies in a contingency table. (Lesson 6-5)

58. A poll is conducted in a local town to gauge the party affiliations of its registered voters.

Age	Democrat	Republican	Independent
18–35 (43%)	37%	31%	32%
> 35 (57%)	29%	37%	34%

   a. What percentage of the town's voters are Democrats?

   b. What percentage are Republicans?

   c. Suppose that, at the next election, each voter must decide between a Republican or Democratic candidate for mayor. Assume everyone votes according to party line. If the over-35 Independents split exactly in half between the candidates, what percentage of the 18–35 Independents must vote Democratic for there to be a tie?

59. A study of SAT preparation courses asked students to identify whether they studied more than 3 hours per week during the six-week course. School district A used a private company to conduct its course while school district B conducted its own course. Students were tested before and after the course, and the number of students who had less than or more than a 25 point increase were recorded in the following table.

School District A	Hours Studied	Performance Increase		Total
		< 25 Points	> 25 Points	
	<3	27	179	206
	>3	42	293	335

School District B	Hours Studied	Performance Increase		Total
		< 25 Points	> 25 Points	
	<3	80	197	277
	>3	21	55	76

   a. What is the relative frequency of students who went to school district A who studied more than 3 hours per week but whose scores rose less than 25 points? Studied less than 3 hours?

   b. Repeat Part a for school district B.

   c. Does number of hours of study seem to relate to test performance in each district?

   d. Make a new contingency table combining the school districts. Recalculate the performance rates for students who studied for less than 3 hours.

   e. What do these data exemplify?

55–59. See margin.

Additional Answers

54. Answers vary. Sample: Generate sets of 7 random numbers from 1–10. 1 represents a rainy date. The number of 1's in a set of 7 is the number of rainy days in a week. Do 100 trials to see the expected number of rainy days.

55a. In the same order: 375, 1125, 1125, 3375

55b. The degree of freedom is 3.

55c.

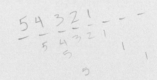

The probability of a chi-square value as high as 15.69 or greater is 0.0013. Because 0.0013 < 0.01 we can reject the geneticist's claim.

56–58. See page 434 side margin.

59a. about 12.5%, about 13.1%

59b. about 27.6%, about 28.9%

59c. No, whether a student studies more or less than three hours, the relative frequency of a score increase of less than 25 points appears to be the same. The same is true for students whose scores increased more than 25 points.

Assessment

Evaluation The *Assessment Resources* provide a form of the Chapter 6 Test. Here are our recommendations for assigning a letter grade: 85–100 = A; 72–84 = B; 60–71 = C; 50–59 = D.

Feedback After students have taken the test for Chapter 6 and you have scored the results, return the tests to students for discussion. Class discussion on the questions that caused trouble for most students can be very effective in identifying and clarifying misunderstandings. You might want to have them note the items they missed and work either in groups or at home to correct them. It is important for students to receive feedback on every chapter test, and we recommend that students see and correct their mistakes before proceeding too far into the next chapter.

Suggestions for Assignment Assign Reading Lesson 7-1 and Covering the Ideas 7-1 for homework the evening of the test. It gives students work to do after they have completed the test and keeps the class moving. If you do not do this, you may cover one less chapter over the course of the year.

Additional Answers

59d.

	< 25	> 25	Total
Less Study	107	376	483
More Study	63	348	411
Total	170	724	894

Score increase of < 25 points with less study: 22.2%; score increase of < 25 points with more study: 15.3%

59e. These data exemplify Simpson's Paradox, since there appears to be a correlation between amount of study and performance when you combine the school districts, but not when you examine them separately.

Properties

Algebra Properties from Earlier Courses

Selected Properties of Real Numbers

For any real numbers a, b, and c:

Postulates of Addition and Multiplication (Field Properties)

	Addition	**Multiplication**
Closure property	$a + b$ is a real number.	ab is a real number.
Commutative property	$a + b = b + a$	$ab = ba$
Associative property	$(a + b) + c = a + (b + c)$	$(ab)c = a(bc)$
Identity property	There is a real number 0 with $0 + a = a + 0 = a$.	There is a real number 1 with $1 \cdot a = a \cdot 1 = a$.
Inverse property	There is a real number $-a$ with $a + -a = -a + a = 0$.	If $a \neq 0$, there is a real number $\frac{1}{a}$ with $a \cdot \frac{1}{a} = \frac{1}{a} \cdot a = 1$.
Distributive property	$a(b + c) = ab + ac$	

Postulates of Equality

Reflexive property	$a = a$
Symmetric property	If $a = b$, then $b = a$.
Transitive property	If $a = b$ and $b = c$, then $a = c$.
Substitution property	If $a = b$, then a may be substituted for b in any arithmetic or algebraic expression.
Addition property	If $a = b$, then $a + c = b + c$.
Multiplication property	If $a = b$, then $ac = bc$.

Postulates of Inequality

Trichotomy property	Either $a < b$, $a = b$, or $a > b$.
Transitive property	If $a < b$ and $b < c$, then $a < c$.
Addition property	If $a < b$, then $a + c < b + c$.
Multiplication property	If $a < b$ and $c > 0$, then $ac < bc$. If $a < b$ and $c < 0$, then $ac > bc$.

Postulates of Powers

For any nonzero bases a and b and integer exponents m and n:

Product of Powers property	$b^m \cdot b^n = b^{m+n}$
Power of a Power property	$(b^m)^n = b^{mn}$
Power of a Product property	$(ab)^m = a^m b^m$
Quotient of Powers property	$\dfrac{b^m}{b^n} = b^{m-n}$
Power of a Quotient property	$\left(\dfrac{a}{b}\right)^m = \dfrac{a^m}{b^m}$

Selected Theorems of Graphing

The set of points (x, y) satisfying $Ax + By = C$, where A and B are not both 0, is a line.

The line with equation $y = mx + b$ has slope m and y-intercept b.

Two nonvertical lines are parallel if and only if they have the same slope.

Two nonvertical lines are perpendicular if and only if the product of their slopes is –1.

The set of points (x, y) satisfying $y = ax^2 + bx + c$ is a parabola.

If $A = (x_1, y_1)$ and $B = (x_2, y_2)$, then $AB = \sqrt{\left|x_2 - x_1\right|^2 + \left|y_2 - y_1\right|^2}$.

Selected Theorems of Algebra

For any real numbers a, b, c, and d (with denominators of fractions not equal to 0):

Multiplication Property of Zero	$0 \cdot a = 0$
Multiplication Property of –1	$-1 \cdot a = -a$
Opposite of an Opposite Property	$-(-a) = a$
Opposite of a Sum	$-(b + c) = -b + -c$
Distributive Property of Multiplication over Subtraction	$a(b - c) = ab - ac$
Addition of Like Terms	$ac + bc = (a + b)c$
Zero Product	$ab = 0$ if and only if $a = 0$ or $b = 0$.
Addition of Fractions	$\frac{a}{c} + \frac{b}{c} = \frac{a + b}{c}$
Multiplication of Fractions	$\frac{a}{b} \cdot \frac{c}{d} = \frac{ac}{bd}$
Equal Fractions	$\frac{ac}{bc} = \frac{a}{b}$
Means-Extremes	If $\frac{a}{b} = \frac{c}{d}$, then $ad = bc$.
Binomial Square	$(a + b)^2 = a^2 + 2ab + b^2$
Difference of Squares Factoring	$a^2 - b^2 = (a + b)(a - b)$
Extended Distributive Property	To multiply two polynomials, multiply each term in the first polynomial by each term in the second, and then add the products.
Zero Exponent	If $b \neq 0$, then $b^0 = 1$.
Negative Exponent	If $b \neq 0$, then $b^{-n} = \frac{1}{b^n}$.
Absolute Value-Square Root	$\sqrt{a^2} = |a|$
Product of Square Roots	If $a \geq 0$ and $b \geq 0$, then $\sqrt{ab} = \sqrt{a} \cdot \sqrt{b}$.
Quadratic Formula	If $ax^2 + bx + c = 0$ and $a \neq 0$, then $x = \frac{-b \pm \sqrt{b^2 - 4ac}}{2a}$.
Square Root of a Negative Number	If $k < 0$, $\sqrt{k} = i\sqrt{-k}$
Discriminant Theorem	Let $D = b^2 - 4ac$. Then $ax^2 + bx + c = 0$ has two real solutions if $D > 0$, one real solution if $D = 0$, and no real solutions if $D < 0$.
Factorial Product	For all integers $n \geq 1$, $n! = n(n - 1)!$

Geometry Properties from Earlier Courses

In this book, the following symbols are used:

a, b, c	sides	C	circumference	n	number of sides
A	area	d	diameter	p	perimeter
B	area of base	d_1, d_2	diagonals	r	radius
b_1, b_2	bases	h	height	s	side
		ℓ	length	S.A.	surface area
		ℓ	slant height (in conics)	V	volume
		L.A.	lateral area	w	width

Two-Dimensional Figures

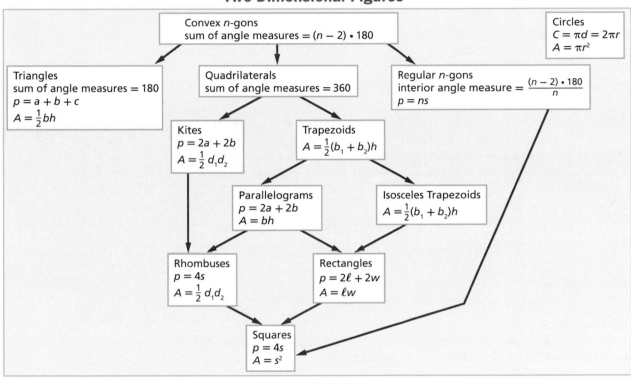

Convex n-gons
sum of angle measures $= (n - 2) \cdot 180$

Circles
$C = \pi d = 2\pi r$
$A = \pi r^2$

Triangles
sum of angle measures $= 180$
$p = a + b + c$
$A = \frac{1}{2}bh$

Quadrilaterals
sum of angle measures $= 360$

Regular n-gons
interior angle measure $= \dfrac{(n - 2) \cdot 180}{n}$
$p = ns$

Kites
$p = 2a + 2b$
$A = \frac{1}{2} d_1 d_2$

Trapezoids
$A = \frac{1}{2}(b_1 + b_2)h$

Parallelograms
$p = 2a + 2b$
$A = bh$

Isosceles Trapezoids
$A = \frac{1}{2}(b_1 + b_2)h$

Rhombuses
$p = 4s$
$A = \frac{1}{2} d_1 d_2$

Rectangles
$p = 2\ell + 2w$
$A = \ell w$

Squares
$p = 4s$
$A = s^2$

Three-Dimensional Figures

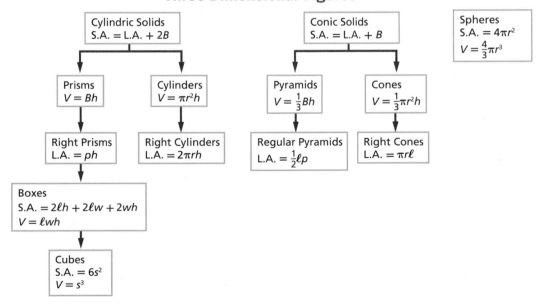

Cylindric Solids
S.A. $=$ L.A. $+ 2B$

Conic Solids
S.A. $=$ L.A. $+ B$

Spheres
S.A. $= 4\pi r^2$
$V = \frac{4}{3}\pi r^3$

Prisms
$V = Bh$

Cylinders
$V = \pi r^2 h$

Pyramids
$V = \frac{1}{3}Bh$

Cones
$V = \frac{1}{3}\pi r^2 h$

Right Prisms
L.A. $= ph$

Right Cylinders
L.A. $= 2\pi rh$

Regular Pyramids
L.A. $= \frac{1}{2}\ell p$

Right Cones
L.A. $= \pi r\ell$

Boxes
S.A. $= 2\ell h + 2\ell w + 2wh$
$V = \ell wh$

Cubes
S.A. $= 6s^2$
$V = s^3$

Selected Theorems of Geometry

Parallel Lines

Two lines are parallel if and only if:

1. corresponding angles have the same measure.
2. alternate interior angles are congruent.
3. alternate exterior angles are congruent.
4. they are perpendicular to the same line.

Triangle Congruence

Two triangles are congruent if:

SSS   three sides of one are congruent to three sides of the other.

SAS   two sides and the included angle of one are congruent to two sides and the included angle of the other.

ASA   two angles and the included side of one are congruent to two angles and the included side of the other.

AAS   two angles and a nonincluded side of one are congruent to two angles and the corresponding nonincluded side of the other.

SsA   two sides and the angle opposite the longer of the two sides of one are congruent to two sides and the angle opposite the corresponding side of the other.

Angles and Sides of Triangles

Triangle Inequality

The sum of the lengths of two sides of a triangle is greater than the length of the third side.

Isosceles Triangle

If two sides of a triangle are congruent, the angles opposite those sides are congruent.

Unequal Sides

If two sides of a triangle are not congruent, then the angles opposite them are not congruent, and the larger angle is opposite the longer side.

Unequal Angles

If two angles of a triangle are not congruent, then the sides opposite them are not congruent, and the longer side is opposite the larger angle.

Pythagorean Theorem

In any right triangle with legs a and b and hypotenuse c, $a^2 + b^2 = c^2$.

30-60-90 Triangle

In a 30-60-90 triangle, the sides are in the extended ratio $x : x\sqrt{3} : 2x$.

45-45-90 Triangle

In a 45-45-90 triangle, the sides are in the extended ratio $x : x : x\sqrt{2}$.

Parallelograms

A quadrilateral is a parallelogram if and only if:

1. one pair of sides is both parallel and congruent.
2. both pairs of opposite sides are congruent.
3. both pairs of opposite angles are congruent.
4. its diagonals bisect each other.

Quadrilateral Hierarchy

If a figure is of any type in the hierarchy pictured at the right, it is also of all types above it to which it is connected.

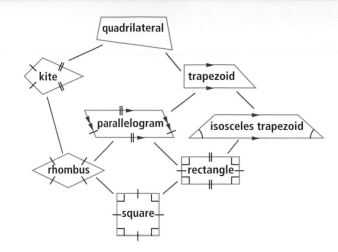

Properties of Transformations

A-B-C-D

Every isometry preserves angle measure, betweenness, collinearity, and distance.

Two-Reflection for Translations

If $m \parallel n$, the translation $r_n \circ r_m$ has magnitude two times the distance between m and n in the direction from m perpendicular to n.

Two-Reflection for Rotations

If m intersects ℓ, the rotation $r_m \circ r_\ell$ has a center at the point of intersection of m and ℓ, and has a magnitude twice the measure of an angle formed by these lines, in the direction from ℓ to m.

Isometry

Every isometry is a transformation that is a reflection or a composite of reflections.

Size-Change

Every size change with magnitude k preserves angle measure, betweenness, and collinearity; a line is parallel to its image; distance is multiplied by k.

Fundamental Theorem of Similarity

If two figures are similar with ratio of similitude k, then:

1. corresponding angle measure are equal.
2. corresponding lengths and perimeters are in the ratio k.
3. corresponding areas and surface areas are in the ratio k^2.
4. corresponding volumes are in the ratio k^3.

Triangle Similarity

Two triangles are similar if:

1. three sides of one are proportional to three sides of the other (SSS).
2. the ratios of two pairs of corresponding sides are equal and the included angles are congruent (SAS).
3. two angles of one are congruent to two angles of the other (AA).

Coordinate Plane Formulas

For all $A = (x_1, y_1)$ and $B = (x_2, y_2)$:

Distance formula
$$AB = \sqrt{(x_2 - x_1)^2 + (y_2 - y_1)^2}$$

Midpoint formula
The midpoint of $\overline{AB}$ is $\left(\dfrac{x_1 + x_2}{2}, \dfrac{y_1 + y_2}{2} \right)$.

For all points (x, y):

reflection over the x-axis $(x, y) \rightarrow (x, -y)$
reflection over the y-axis $(x, y) \rightarrow (-x, y)$
reflection over $y = x$ $(x, y) \rightarrow (y, x)$
size change of magnitude k, center $(0, 0)$ $(x, y) \rightarrow (kx, ky)$
translation h units horizontally, k units verically $(x, y) \rightarrow (x + h, y + k)$

Symbols

$\mathbb{N}$	set of natural numbers
$\mathbb{Z}$	set of integers
$\mathbb{Q}$	set of rational numbers
$\mathbb{R}$	set of real numbers
$\{...\}$	set
$\in$	is an element of
$\{\ \}, \emptyset$	null set, empty set
$\{x \mid x...\},$ $\{x : x...\}$	the set of all x such that ...
$\cup$	set union
$\cap$	set intersection
$\approx$	is approximately equal to
$\overleftrightarrow{AB}$	line containing A and B
$\overrightarrow{AB}$	ray with endpoint A and containing B
$\overline{AB}$	line segment with endpoints A and B
AB	distance between points A and B
$\|\|$	is parallel to
$\perp$	is perpendicular to
$m\angle ABC$	measure of angle ABC
$m\overset{\frown}{AB}$	measure of arc AB
A'	image of A
$T_{h,k}$	translation h units horizontally and k units vertically
r_x	reflection over the x-axis
r_y	reflection over the y-axis
r_m	reflection over the line m
R_θ	rotation of magnitude θ counterclockwise with center $(0,0)$
S_k	size change of magnitude k
$S_{a,b}$	scale change with horizontal magnitude a and vertical magnitude b
$\|x\|$	absolute value of x
$a^b, a{\wedge}b$	bth power of a
$\sqrt{}$	radical sign; square root
$\sqrt[n]{x}$	the largest real nth root of x
$\log_b a$	logarithm of a to the base b
e	2.71828...

$\ln x$	natural logarithm of x
(x, y)	rectangular coordinates
$[r, \theta]$	polar coordinates
$f: x \to y$	the function that maps x onto y
$f(x)$	the value of the function f at x
f^{-1}	inverse function of a function f
$\lim\limits_{x \to \infty} f(x)$	the limit of $f(x)$ as x gets larger and larger
$g \circ f$	composite of function f followed by g
$g(f(x))$	value at x of the composite of functions f followed by g
i	$\sqrt{-1}$
$a + bi$	a complex number, where a and b are real numbers
a_n	"a sub n"; the nth term of a sequence a
$\sum\limits_{i=1}^{n} x_i$	the sum of $x_m, x_{m+1} + ...+ x_n$
$\sin \theta$	sine of θ
$\cos \theta$	cosine of θ
$\tan \theta$	tangent of θ
$\cot \theta$	cotangent of θ
$\sec \theta$	secant of θ
$\csc \theta$	cosecant of θ
$x!$	x factorial
$N(A)$	number of elements in set A
$_nP_r$	the number of permutations of r objects from n different objects
$\binom{n}{r}, {}_nC_r$	the number of sets of r objects from n different objects
$P(E)$	probability of event E
$P(B\mid A)$	conditional probability of an event B given A has occurred
μ	population mean
$\bar{x}$	sample mean
σ^2	population variance
σ	population standard deviation
S^2	sample variance
S	sample standard deviation
Q_n	nth quartile (n = 1, 2, or 3)
r	correlation coefficient
χ^2	chi-square statistic

CAS Commands

The Computer Algebra System (CAS) commands used in this course and examples of their use are given below. Each command must be followed by a number, variable, expression, or equation, usually enclosed in parentheses.

Command	Description	Example
Define	A rule for a function is stored under the name indicated. Values of that function can then be calculated by entering the function's name followed by the value of the independent variable in parentheses.	Define $f(n)=2000 \cdot n - 1400$ Done $f(4)$ 6600
| (such that)	Variable values that appear after the symbol are substituted into an expression, inequality, or equation that appears before the symbol.	$r=\dfrac{\sqrt{v}}{\sqrt{h \cdot \pi}} \mid v=500000$ $r=\dfrac{500 \cdot \sqrt{2}}{\sqrt{h \cdot \pi}}$
solve	An equation, inequality, or system is solved for an indicated variable or variables. All real solutions are given.	$\text{solve}\left(y=\dfrac{1}{2} \cdot x - 5 \text{ and } y=2 \cdot x - 1, \{x,y\}\right)$ $x=\dfrac{-8}{3}$ and $y=\dfrac{-19}{3}$
expand	The Distributive Property is applied to products and powers of mathematical expressions.	$\text{expand}\left((72+w) \cdot (24+2 \cdot w)\right)$ $2 \cdot w^2 + 168 \cdot w + 1728$
DelVar	Any stored values for the indicated variable are deleted from memory.	DelVar a Done
cSolve	An equation or inequality is solved for an indicated variable. All complex solutions are given.	$\text{cSolve}\left(z^4=81, z\right)$ $z=3 \cdot i$ or $z=-3 \cdot i$ or $z=-3$ or $z=3$
factor	A polynomial is factored over the rational numbers. On some CAS, if ",x" is added to the end of the polynomial, it is factored over the real numbers.	$\text{factor}\left(x^4 - 14 \cdot x^2 + 45\right)$ $(x-3) \cdot (x+3) \cdot (x^2-5)$ $\text{factor}\left(x^4 - 14 \cdot x^2 + 45, x\right)$ $(x-3) \cdot (x+3) \cdot (x+\sqrt{5}) \cdot (x-\sqrt{5})$
cFactor	A polynomial is factored over the complex numbers.	$\text{cFactor}\left(x^2 + 36, x\right)$ $(x+-6 \cdot i) \cdot (x+6 \cdot i)$
propFrac	Division is applied to a rational expression to return the sum of the resulting quotient and a ratio of the remainder over the divisor.	$\text{propFrac}\left(\dfrac{x^3 + 4 \cdot x^2 - 10}{x+2}\right)$ $\dfrac{-2}{x+2} + x^2 + 2 \cdot x - 4$

A Table of Random Numbers

row	col. 1	2	3	4	5	6	7	8	9	10	11	12	13	14
1	10480	15011	01536	02011	81647	91646	69719	14194	62590	36207	20969	99570	91291	90700
2	22368	46573	25595	85393	30995	89198	27982	53402	93965	34095	52666	19174	39615	99505
3	24130	48360	22527	97265	76393	64809	15179	24830	49340	32081	30680	19655	63348	58629
4	42167	93093	06423	61680	17856	16376	39440	53537	71341	57004	00849	74917	97758	16379
5	37570	39975	81837	16656	06121	91782	60468	81305	49684	60672	14110	06927	01263	54613
6	77921	06907	11008	42751	27756	53498	18602	70659	90655	15053	21916	81825	44394	42880
7	99562	72905	56420	69994	98872	31016	71194	18738	44013	48840	63213	21069	10634	12952
8	96301	91977	05463	07972	18876	20922	94595	56869	69014	60045	18425	84903	42508	32307
9	89579	14342	63661	10281	17453	18103	57740	84378	25331	12566	58678	44947	05585	56941
10	85475	36857	43342	53988	53060	59533	38867	62300	08158	17983	16439	11458	18593	64952
11	28918	69578	88231	33276	70997	79936	56865	05859	90106	31595	01547	85590	91610	78188
12	63553	40961	48235	03427	49626	69445	18663	72695	52180	20847	12234	90511	33703	90322
13	09429	93969	52636	92737	88974	33488	36320	17617	30015	08272	84115	27156	30613	74952
14	10365	61129	87529	85689	48237	52267	67689	93394	01511	26358	85104	20285	29975	89868
15	07119	97336	71048	08178	77233	13916	47564	81056	97735	85977	29372	74461	28551	90707
16	51085	12765	51821	51259	77452	16308	60756	92144	49442	53900	70960	63990	75601	40719
17	02368	21382	52404	60268	89368	19885	55322	44819	01188	65255	64835	44919	05944	55157
18	01011	54092	33362	94904	31272	04146	18594	29852	71585	85030	51132	01915	92747	64951
19	52162	53916	46369	58586	23216	14513	83149	98736	23495	64350	94738	17752	35156	35749
20	07056	97628	33787	09998	42698	06691	76988	13602	51851	46104	88916	19509	25625	58104
21	48663	91245	85828	14346	09172	30168	90229	04734	59193	22178	30421	61666	99904	32812
22	54164	58492	22421	74103	47070	25306	76468	26384	58151	06646	21524	15227	96909	44592
23	32639	32363	05597	24200	13363	38005	94342	28728	35806	06912	17012	64161	18296	22851
24	29334	27001	87637	87308	58731	00256	45834	15398	46557	41135	10367	07684	36188	18510
25	02488	33062	28834	07351	19731	92420	60952	61280	50001	67658	32586	86679	50720	94953
26	81525	72295	04839	96423	24878	82651	66566	14778	76797	14780	13300	87074	79666	95725
27	29676	20591	68086	26432	46901	20849	89768	81536	86645	12659	92259	57102	80428	25280
28	00742	57392	39064	66432	84673	40027	32832	61362	98947	96067	64760	64584	96096	98253
29	05366	04213	25669	26422	44407	44048	37937	63904	45766	66134	75470	66520	34693	90449
30	91921	26418	64117	94305	26766	25940	39972	22209	71500	64568	91402	42416	07844	69618
31	00582	04711	87917	77341	42206	35126	74087	99547	81817	42607	43808	76655	62028	76630
32	00725	69884	62797	56170	86324	88072	76222	36086	84637	93161	76038	65855	77919	88006
33	69011	65797	95876	55293	18988	27354	26575	08625	40801	59920	29841	80150	12777	48501
34	25976	57948	29888	88604	67917	48708	18912	82271	65424	69774	33611	54262	85963	03547
35	09763	83473	73577	12908	30883	18317	28290	35797	05998	41688	34952	37888	38917	88050
36	91567	42595	27958	30134	04024	86385	29880	99730	55536	84855	29080	09250	79656	73211
37	17955	56349	90999	49127	20044	59931	06115	20542	18059	02008	73708	83517	36103	42791
38	46503	18584	18845	49618	02304	51038	20655	58727	28168	15475	56942	53389	20562	87338
39	92157	89634	94824	78171	84610	82834	09922	25417	44137	48413	25555	21246	35509	20468
40	14577	62765	35605	81263	39667	47358	56873	56307	61607	49518	89656	20103	77490	18062

Selected Answers

Chapter 1

Lesson 1-1 (pp. 6–13)

Guided Example 1 b. amount of protective gear worn.
c. 40.7% **d.** 188; 709; 26.5% **e.** 242; 754; 754 **f.** 242; 140; 382
Questions
1. Answers vary. Sample: eye color, arm span, birth month
3. population: the batch of cookies; the data is based on a
sample; number of raisins per cookie **5.** In decreasing
order: falls, motor-vehicle, and suffocation by ingestion
or inhalation **7.** A representative sample is a sample
that accurately reflects the important features of the
population. **9. a.** about 21.5% **b.** Guided Example 1d asks
for the percentage of beginner skaters in the sample who
wore no gear, whereas Part a asked for the percent of no
gear skaters who were beginners. **11. a.** categorical
b. categorical **c.** numerical **d.** numerical **13.** about 67.6%
15. Answers vary. Sample: The median income of
households headed by someone who has at least a
bachelor's degree is more than twice as high as the
median income of households headed by someone with
only a high school diploma. **17. a.** the age distribution of
trout in a certain lake **b.** sample; The population is all of
the trout in the lake. The sample is representative of the
population because the trout were captured from different
parts of the lake. **c.** about 14.6% **19. a.** $x = 20$ **b.** $x = 2000$ **c.** $x = 0.05$ **d.** $x = 0.0005$ **21. a.** Answers vary.
Sample: (0, -13), (1, 16) **b.** $y = -3x - 13$

Lesson 1-2 (pp. 14–21)

Guided Example a. 65, $65,000; 15, $1,170,000 **b.** 11
Questions
1. mean and median **3.** A weighted average is an average
calculated when some elements in the set are assigned a
larger or smaller weight. **5.** There are two employees with
salaries of $90,000 and four people with salaries of $65,000.
7. a. $\frac{3}{16}$ **b.** $75,000 **c.** $50,000 **9.** $x_4 + x_5 + x_6 + x_7 + x_8$
11. a. 28 **b.** 4 **c.** $\frac{0(4) + 1(9) + 2(7) + 3(4) + 4(2) + 5(1) + 7(1)}{28}$
$= 1.96$ **13.** about 9 **15. a.** 80.45 **b.** 85 **17.** $\sum_{i=1}^{100}(x_i + 2)$,
by 198 **19.** $n = 4$ **21.** 3,392,750 **23.** 23.9%

Lesson 1-3 (pp. 22–30)

Guided Example 2 b. 60–64 **c.** 29; 5; 13; 2020, 1980
Questions
1. Answers may vary. Sample: The graph is sharply
concentrated around the 2–3 minute time interval. The

graph also seems skewed with a tail on the right.
3. a.

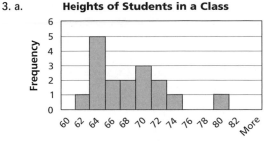

Heights of Students in a Class

b. Answers vary. Sample: A bin width of 2 was used
because it shows trends in the data accurately. **5.** 50
7. about 18% **9.** The median height of African American
males born 1920–1929 is in the $175 \leq$ height < 180 cm
interval and the median height of African American males
born 1980–1989 is in the $180 \leq$ height < 185 cm interval.
The second group has the larger median height.
11. a.

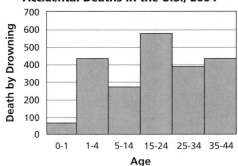

Accidental Deaths in the U.S., 2004

b. between ages 1–4 because the number of deaths per
age is the greatest. **c.** The data are organized into bins
that are not all the same size. **13.** Answers vary. Sample:
This graph might be skewed with a right tail because
most workers earn at the low end of a payroll scale.
There will likely be a long, high-paid tail. **15. a.** The
distribution is skewed with a right tail. A roll of 1 is
clearly favored. **b.** about 49% **c.** No; if the die is fair, then
each number should have appeared about 17% of the
time. **17.** about $2,528.57 **19.** -205 **21. a.** v **b.** ii **c.**
iv **d.** i

Lesson 1-4 (pp. 31–37)

Guided Example 1 a. 10; 29; 50; 37; 46 **b.** 37; 46; 29; 50
Guided Example 2 38; 157; 5; 157; 5
Questions
1. A **3.**

5. B; Because the total count is 100, the median resides in
the 5–10 bin. The only plot whose median is in this range
is plot B. **7. a.** Answers vary. Sample: the frequency
of scores in each interval **b.** Answers vary. Sample:

the values of Q_1, the median, and Q_3 **9.** Answers vary.
Sample: $\{0, 0, 0, 0, 2, 2, 4, 4, 4, 8\}$ **11. a.** about 53
b. about $\frac{100}{500}$ or $\frac{1}{5}$ **c.** about $\frac{345}{500}$ or 69%   **d.** Answers vary.
Sample: The median wait time is between 5 and 6 minutes.
The range of wait times is about 19 minutes. The data are
skewed with a tail on the right.   **13. a.** about 3.82
b. about 3.53   **c.** by about 0.28

Lesson 1-5 (pp. 38–44)

Guided Example 2 a. 14; 6; 8; 48; 34; 16

b.

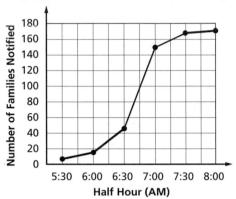

Total Number Notified of Closing

c. 85, around 6:40   **d.** 128, around 6:54

Questions

1.

Year	Number of cases	Total Cases	Relative Frequency	Cumulative Relative Frequency
2003	4	4	0.011	0.011
2004	46	50	0.131	0.142
2005	98	148	0.2792	0.4217
2006	115	263	0.3276	0.7493
2007	88	351	0.2507	1

3. a.

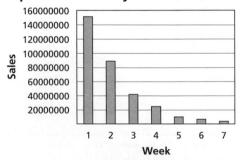

Spider-Man 3 Weekly Box Office Sales

3. b.

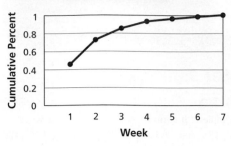

Spider-Man Cumulative Percentage of Box Office Sales

5. a. false   **b.** false   **c.** true   **7. a.** Roger Maris hits more
and more homeruns until he peaks in his 5th year, at
which point he starts hitting fewer homeruns.   **b.** The
cumulative graph increases the quickest in the middle of
Roger Maris' career, in agreement with the trend from
Part a.

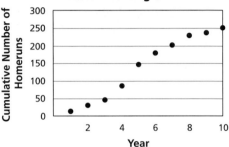

Homeruns by Roger Maris in the American League

9. Answers vary. Sample: A retailer's cumulative sales
receipts rise during the month of December, but fall
after Christmas as gifts are returned.   **11.** Answers vary.
Sample: $\{0, 0, 2, 2, 2, 2, 2, 2, 2, 2, 4, 4\}$ **13.** $65.48 per
share   **15.** 12.155   **17. a.** 13   **b.** 13   **c.** 169   **d.** 169   **e.** –2197
f. 2197

Lesson 1-6 (pp. 45–53)

Guided Example 2 10.14; 4.58; –4.86; 12; 18; 26.42; 90;
$\sum_{i=1}^{7}(x_i - \bar{x})$; 244.86; 6; $\frac{244.86}{6}$; 40.81; 40.81; 6.39
Questions
1. a. center   **b.** spread   **c.** spread   **d.** spread   **e.** spread
f. center   **3. a.** variance = 5.20; standard deviation ≈ 2.28
b. 0   **c.** 0   **d.** $3.58 - 2.28 = 1.3$ **e.** Answers vary. Sample:
The heights of the Dolphins and Sweet Peppers have the
same mean and range, but the Dolphins have a greater
standard deviation. Therefore the Dolphins' heights are
spread out more than the Sweet Peppers' heights from the
shared center, though still within the shared range.
5. 20.25 cm   **7.** $\bar{x} = 118$; $s = 5.30$ **9.** B and D   **11.** The
variance is always positive.   **13. a.** 60.84 kg^2 **b.** about
4.36 kg   **15.** $16 \leq x \leq 26$ **17.** Answers vary. Sample: The
standard deviation of $\{70, 80, 80, 150\}$ is about 36.97.
19. a. U.S. Total Imports in Goods and Services ($ billions):

Cumulative Total for Jan., 187; Feb., 373; Mar., 565; Apr., 756; May, 949; Jun., 1144; Jul., 1341; Aug., 1538; Sept., 1736; Oct., 1936; Nov., 2141; Dec., 2344

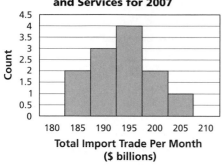

U.S. Total Import Trade in Goods and Services for 2007

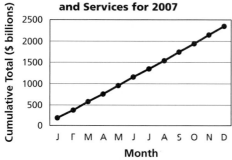

U.S. Total Import Trade in Goods and Services for 2007

19. b. 2344   **21.** Answers vary. Sample: The maximum influx of permanent legal residents into one state was between 260 and 270 thousand, and the minimum influx of residents was between 0 and 10 thousand; 30 states had the minimum level of influx. The mean value is between 30 and 40 thousand and the median is between 10 and 20 thousand. Most of the states are clustered in the 10 to 20 thousand interval, and the graph is skewed with a tail on the right.   **23. a.** about 8504 women/year **b.** about 10,548 men/year

Lesson 1-7 (pp. 54-60)

Questions

1. The variability of the Eastern states is greater than that of the Western states; the interquartile range of 299.4 is greater than 55.4. Whereas both the distributions of the Western and Eastern states have tails to the right, that of the Eastern states is longer, corresponding to its larger standard deviation of 298.3 compared to 54.4. The Eastern states also have a greater mean and median than the Western states, 301.4 and 172.3 compared to 52.4 and 38.6, respectively.   **3.** shape, center, and spread   **5.** Answers vary. Sample: The mean of the class data is 19.35 states, which is less than the mean of 24.7 for the sample. The standard deviation of the class data is 12.8893 states, which is larger than that of the sample, at 10.32 states.

Again, this shows that the variability of the states visited is greater for the class.   **7.** Answers vary. Sample: The distribution of the sample of U.S. bridge lengths appears to be bimodal. The distribution of the sample of the outside U.S. bridge lengths appears to be skewed with a tail to the left and an outlier on the right. Both the mean and median of the bridges outside the U.S. (30,864 m and 29,250 m, respectively) are higher than those inside the U.S. (19,889 m and 15,288 m). The IQR of bridges in the U.S. is 18,403 m, which is much bigger than the IQR of bridges outside the U.S., at 14,100 m. The standard deviation of bridges inside the U.S. is also higher with 11,463 instead of 10,255 outside the U.S.   **9. a.** 18.49 in^2 **b.** 3.098 in.
11. a.

◇	A	B	C
1	Score Interval	Frequency	Relative Frequency
2	50-59	1	0.033
3	60-69	6	0.200
4	70-79	10	0.333
5	80-89	6	0.200
6	90-99	7	0.233

b.

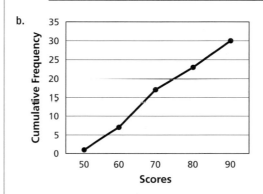

13. −18,778   **15.** $y = -\frac{\pi}{5}x + \pi$

Lesson 1-8 (pp. 61-66)

Questions

1. The Federalist papers were written between 1787 and 1788 in order to persuade the citizens of the State of New York to ratify the Constitution.   **3.** 48 papers by Hamilton and 50 papers by Madison   **5.** about 32%   **7.** Inferential reasoning gives evidence for what is likely, but does not prove findings with certainty.   **9.** This disputed paper has rates of 8.07, 3.80, and 46.04 per 1000 words for "by," "from," and "to," respectively. This pattern more closely matches Hamilton's word usage than Madison's.
11. a. Marco likely has the flu since all three data points, especially his fever, match the data for the flu better than for a cold. **b.** Annette likely has a cold since both her temperature and the magnitude of her muscle pain match the median values for a cold better than the flu. The data about coughing is inconclusive.   **13.** This is likely symmetric, centered around some average winning

score.   **15. a.** 3 **b.** 13 **c.** 64 **d.** the average of shoe ownership per person   **17. a.** Answers vary. Sample: The domain of both functions is all real numbers x and the range of both functions is $y \le 0$. Both functions have an absolute maximum at $x = 0$. **b.** Answers vary. Sample : The slope of $y = -x^2$ changes continuously, while the slope of $y = -x$ is 1 for $x < 0$, -1 for $x > 0$ and undefined at $x = 0$.

Self-Test (pp. 70-71)

1. variance: 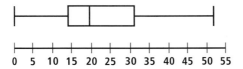 $\dfrac{\sum\limits_{i=1}^{14}(x_i - \bar{x})^2}{14} \approx \dfrac{\sum\limits_{i=1}^{14}(x_i - 21.6)^2}{14} \approx 195.245;$

standard deviation: $\sqrt{195.245} \approx 13.973$ **2.** $\dfrac{\sum\limits_{i=1}^{14} x_i}{14}$ **3.** The median is the middle value when the data are ordered, halfway between 19 and 20, so is 19.5. The box goes from the first quartile to the third quartile. The first quartile Q_1 is the median of numbers less than the median, or 14. The third quartile Q_3 is the median of numbers greater than the median, or 31. The line in the box is at the median. The whiskers go from the least to greatest value, from 0 to 52. The result is the box plot below.

High School Football Team Scores

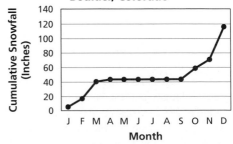

```
0   5  10  15  20  25  30  35  40  45  50  55
```

4. IQR $= Q_3 - Q_1 = 17$; $Q_1 - 1.5 \cdot 17 = -11.5$, $Q_3 + 1.5 \cdot 17 = 56.5$. No values in the data set are less than -11.5 or greater than 56.5, so there are no outliers.   **5.** The first team would have more variability since its data have a larger standard deviation.

6.

Position	Frequency	Relative Frequency
Principals	13,340	0.025
Teachers	304,311	0.563
Aides	69,201	0.128
Office/Clerical	36,116	0.067
Counselors	6640	0.012
Librarians	1218	0.002
Other	109,381	0.202

7. True, because even if there are a few extreme data points in a set the median still is the central value.
8. a. The minimum 0 is indicated by the bar to the left. Q_1 = the location of the left side of the rectangle = 2; median = location of segment splitting the rectangle ≈ 4; Q_3 = location of the right side of the rectangle ≈ 9; maximum = location of rightmost dot ≈ 57. **b.** between

Q_1 and Q_3, that is, between 2 and 9 inclusive   **9. a.** The range is the maximum minus the minimum and therefore is not calculated using the mean. **b.** The variance is the mean of squared deviations from the mean; therefore, it is calculated using the mean. **c.** The IQR is not calculated using the mean. **d.** The standard deviation is calculated with the mean because it is the square root of the variance.   **10. a.** The sum of the counts is 14. **b.** The distribution is skewed with a tail on the right.   **11. a.** Subtract the actual 2006 receipts from the estimated 2007 receipts. Personal income taxes have the largest difference: 1,168.8 − 1,043.9 = 124.9 billion dollars. **b.** For each category, subtract the estimated 2007 receipts from the estimated 2008 receipts and divide by the amount of the 2007 receipts. The greatest percent increase is for excise taxes, $\dfrac{68.1 - 57.1}{57.1} = \dfrac{11}{57.1} \approx 19\%.$

12. a.

Month	Cumulative Snowfall (inches)
January	5.5
February	5.5 + 11.4 = 16.9
March	16.9 + 23.3 = 40.2
April	40.2 + 2.9 = 43.1
May	43.1 + 0.1 = 43.2
June	43.2
July	43.2
August	43.2
September	43.2
October	43.2 + 15.2 = 58.4
November	58.4 + 12.0 = 70.4
December	70.4 + 45.5 = 115.9

b.

Cumulative Average Snowfall in Boulder, Colorado

[Graph: Cumulative Snowfall (Inches) vs Month (J F M A M J J A S O N D), y-axis from 0 to 140]

c. $\dfrac{\text{Sum of January to March}}{\text{total snowfall during year}} = \dfrac{40.2}{115.9} \approx 0.347$ or 34.7%

13. $\dfrac{(2 \cdot 3.3) + (4 \cdot 4) + (6 \cdot 2.3) + (4 \cdot 3)}{2 + 4 + 6 + 4} = 3.025$
14. Adding up the last two intervals, 15% of students scored at least 80 on the psychology test.

15. The median score for Psychology is higher than for Biology, indicating that Psychology scores are generally higher than Biology. Both distributions seem to be slightly skewed with a tail on the right, especially if the outlier in Psychology is thrown out. Lastly, the spread of the Biology scores is greater, as indicated by a higher IQR.

Self-Test Correlation Chart

Question	1	2	3	4	5	6	7	8	9	10
Objective(s)	A	C	I	E	E	B	D	I	D	H
Lesson(s)	1-6	1-2	1-4	1-4	1-6	1-2	1-2	1-4	1-6	1-3

Question	11	12	13	14	15
Objective(s)	F	J	B	H	G
Lesson(s)	1-1	1-5	1-2	1-3	1-7, 1-8

Chapter Review (pp. 72–77)

1. a. 16 **b.** 15 **c.** 6   **3. a.** 26.5 years **b.** about 28.3 years **c.** 9 and 42 years **d.** 59 years **e.** about 19.1 years
5. minimum $= 1{,}045$, $Q_1 = 49{,}372$, median $= 56{,}194$, $Q_3 = 150{,}755.5$, maximum $= 571{,}951$ (all answers in square miles)   **7.** 35 cm per month   **9.** 5.4   **11.** 89
13. a. $\dfrac{\sum\limits_{i=1}^{8} g_i}{8}$ **b.** 18.125 **c.** 75   **15. a.** $\dfrac{\sum\limits_{s=1}^{9} n_s p_s}{\sum\limits_{s=1}^{9} n_s}$ **b.** about $6.13   **17. a.** false **b.** Answers vary. Sample: Consider the data set $\{1, 1, 2, 3, 4, 5, 6, 6\}$. The mean is 3.5 and modes 1 and 6.   **19.** C   **21.** C   **23. a.** minimum: 48, Q_1: 55.5, median: 61.5, Q_3: 80, maximum: 94 **b.** $1.5 \cdot \text{IQR} = 36.75$; No values fall below 18.75 or above 116.75; therefore, there are no outliers.   **25. a.** minimum: 97.9, Q_1: 119.35, median: 165.65, Q_3: 310.6, maximum: 630 (all answers in 1000's of dollars) **b.** There is a large range of home prices in U.S. metropolitan areas.   **27. a.** mean: $188.4, median: $151.5, standard deviation: $138.16 **b.** 440, 445, 500 **c.** mean: $140.18, median: $140, standard deviation: $77.83
29. year, voting age population (millions), percent of voting age population reporting they voted, age, gender, education   **31.** 67.25 million   **33.** 65 years old and over
35. Answers vary. Sample: The mean, median, IQR and standard deviation differ very little between the males and females. These statistics, as well as the box plots and histograms, indicate little to no difference in the running times of males and females.

37.

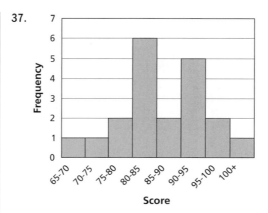

39. a. 42 **b.** false **c.** about 35.7%

41.

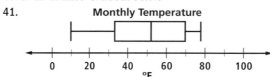

43. a. See table.
b. month 4

Month	Cumulative Wages
1	$3250
2	$7375
3	$10,125
4	$15,500
5	$20,000
6	$23,800

c.

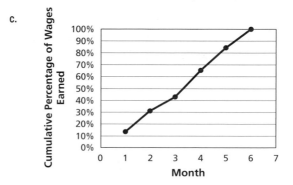

Chapter 2

Lesson 2-1 (pp. 080-086)

Guided Example 2 Answers vary. Sample:

n	Sample set (ordered)	Count of numbers larger than the median
2	{2, 5}	1
3	{24, 46, 68}	1
4	{13, 24, 35, 47}	2
5	{1, 2, 3, 4, 5}	2
6	{1, 2, 4, 6, 7, 9}	3
7	{2, 5, 6, 8, 9, 10, 15}	3
8	{1, 3, 4, 5, 7, 9, 10, 12}	4
9	{3, 4, 5, 7, 8, 10, 11, 12, 20}	4
10	{1, 2, 5, 6, 8, 11, 13, 17, 21, 30}	5

2; 2; 3; 3; 4; 4; 5

Questions

1. independent variable: number of chores completed; dependent variable: allowance earned **3.** independent variable: sunlight and water; dependent variable: tree growth **5.** The range is the set of all possible values for the dependent variable. **7. a.** f **b.** y **c.** $f(x)$ **d.** x **9. a.** $\sqrt{q+2}$ **b.** 7 **11.** function **13. a.** domain: $\{x| -2 \leq x \leq 5.9\}$ range: $\{y| -2.5 \leq y \leq 2.6\}$ **b.** −0.4 **c.** $x = 0$ or $x = 4$ **15.**

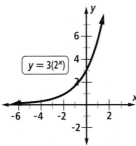

$y = 3(2^x)$

Yes, this relation passes the vertical line test and is therefore a function. domain: $\{x| x \in \mathbb{R}\}$; range: $\{y| y > 0\}$

17.

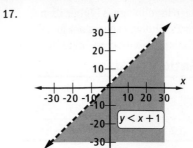

$y < x + 1$

No, this relation does not pass the vertical line test. For example, there are infinitely many y–values that satisfy the expression for $x = 0$. **19. a.** about $14,758.33 **b.** mean **21. a.** 36 **b.** $10x$ **c.** $x + 11$ **d.** $x + a$ **23.** $y - 4 = -\frac{3}{2}(x + 6)$

Lesson 2-2 (pp. 087-093)

Guided Example 1 a. $\frac{1400 - 600}{0.32 - 0.18}$; 5714.29; 600; 0.18; $5714.29x - 428.57$ **b.** 5,714.29 **c.** $1,285.72 $1,285.78 **d.** –$142.86

Questions

1. A *linear function* is a set of ordered pairs (x, y) which can be described by an equation of the form $y = mx + b$, where m and b are constants. **3.** observed; predicted **5. a.** $1,200 **b.** $90 **7.** "first square each residual and then sum the squares" **9. a.** 0.55; The number of states visited increases by 0.55 for every one year increase in age.
b.

◇	A	B	C	D
1	Age	States Visited	Predicted	Residual^2
2	16	15	12.3	7.29
3	16	18	12.3	32.49
4	40	27	25.5	2.25
5	70	42	42.0	0
6	10	9	9.0	0
7	45	19	28.25	85.56

c. 127.59 **d.** interpolation **e.** 20 states
11a and b. This line appears to model the data fairly well.

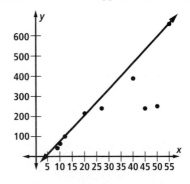

c. $y = \frac{560}{43}x - \frac{2420}{43}$

d. The average gestation period increases by about 12.8 days for every increase of one year in an animal's expected life span. **e.** −55.35 **f.** about 986 days; extrapolation **g.** about 211,453 **13. a.** about 10.59 **b.** Because there are only five data points and the range is 29, the spread is large.

Lesson 2-3 (pp. 094-101)

Questions

1. least squares line, line of best fit **3.** A **5.** C **7.** This does not affect r because swapping the data does not affect its degree of correlation. **9.** $(\bar{x}, \bar{y})$ **11.** $r \approx \pm 0.6325$ **13.** Answers vary. Sample: $\{(1, 4), (3, 4), (4, 4), (5, 4), (5.5, 4), (6, 4), (9, 4)\}$. The correlation is undefined. This is because in the equation for computing the correlation coefficient, s_y appears in the denominator, and for the chosen data set $s_y = 0$ and division by 0 is undefined. **15.** zero; There is no correlation between a person's height and how far he/she lives from school. **17.** $r = 1$ **19.** No; both likely correlate with Florida's increasing population, but an increase in the rate of sales tax would not cause an increase in shark attacks. **21.** $y = x$ **23.** $t = 3 \pm \sqrt{15}$ **25. a.** $5t^2$ **b.** $4y$ **c.** $25r^2$

Lesson 2-4 (pp. 102-109)

Guided Example 2 a. 1.053 **b.** 2500; 1.053; $2500(1.053)^t$ **c.** 1.053; $3,588.71 **d.** 1.053; 2254.67; $2,254.67 **Guided Example 3 a.** all real numbers; positive real numbers **b.** 8 **c.** $y = 0$ **d.** increasing

Questions

1. a. 4,203,000 **b.** $P(n) = 4156119(1.0113)^n$ **c.** 4,756,000 **3. a.** $A = 4,000(1.08)^t$ **b.** about $118,223.89 **c.** about $2,940.12 **5. a.** false **b.** decay **7. a.** g **b.** f **c.**

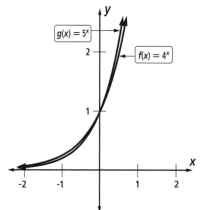

9. a. B **b.** $y = 12$ when $x = 0$ is the initial value. The growth factor is $\frac{1}{2}$ because as x increases by 1, y is divided by 2. **11. a.** 18, 16.2, and 14.53 cubic feet **b.** $20(0.9)^n$ **c.** false **13.** False, correlation does not mean causation. For

instance, both a and b may be causally related to a third variable c, and thus correlate to each other without being directly related. **15. a.** −1 **b.** 2 **c.** False; $f(1) + f(2) = -1 + 0 = -1$, but $f(1 + 2) = f(3) = \frac{3}{5}$ **d.** False; the domain is $\{x \mid x \neq -2\}$, while the range is $\{y \mid y \neq 3\}$ **e.** $\frac{3p - 15}{p - 1}$ **17.** $r = \pm \frac{20}{27}, s = \pm 3$

Lesson 2-5 (pp. 110-116)

Guided Example 2 a. $296.177(1.079)^x$
b.

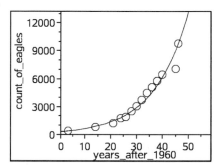

c. 296; 1960; 1.079; 7.9 **d.** 6200; 6471; 6200; 271; 9068; 7066; 9068; −2002

Questions

1. a. $\begin{cases} 20 = ab^3 \\ 156 = ab^{10} \end{cases}$ **b.** $f(t) = 8.293(1.341)^t$ **c.** $8.293 \cdot 1.341^3 \approx 20, 8.293 \cdot 1.341^{10} \approx 156$ **3. a.** $y = 47.979(1.372)^x$ **b.** about 48 **c.** 233 **5. a.** $y = 10(0.766)^x$ **b.** about 0.000001 units **7. a.** $a \approx 736, b \approx 1.398; y = 736(1.398)^t$

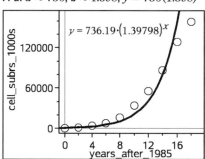

b. The model increases much more quickly than the data in the years after 1997, but otherwise fits well. **c.** 2003

9. a.

Number of Half-Lives	t	$f(t)$
0	0	3
1	1620	1.5
2	3240	0.75
3	4860	0.375

b. $y = 3(0.9995722)^x$ **c.** about 542 mg **11. a.** g **b.** f **13.** x-axis **15.** Answers vary. Sample: $y = -3^x$ domain: the set of all real numbers **17. a.** about 30,400 thousand

barrels per day **b.** about 197.3 thousand barrels per day **c.** about 67.5% **d.** The U.S. petroleum consumption is an extreme data point.

Lesson 2-6 (pp. 117-124)

Guided Example 1 **a.** -2; 3; -3; 2; -2; 2; 3; 25; 4
b. positive; $\frac{3}{4}, \frac{3}{4}, \frac{3}{4}, \frac{3}{4}$, 3; 4
Guided Example 2 **a.** 20; 15; 9.8; 20 **b.** 30.9; 30.9 **c.** 0; -0.65; 4.73; 4.73

Questions

1. $f(x) = ax^2 + bx + c$ **3.** $\{y \mid y \geq -3.125\}$
5. a. minimum **b.** minimum **c.** maximum **d.** maximum
7. $3(16) - 20(4) + 8 = -24$ **9. a.** 21.45% **b.** interpolation
11. a. $f(n) = 0.5n^2 + 0.5n + 1$ **b.** $f(5) = 16$

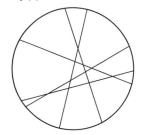

13. a.

Bar Iron Exports to England from American Colonies (1762–1774)

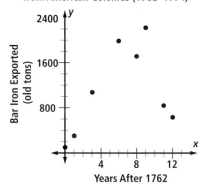

b. $f(x) = -46.393x^2 + 620.48x - 120.6$; x is the number of years after 1762 **c.** $f(14) = -526.9$ **d.** The negative value indicates that the colonies were importing iron bar from England in 1776. However, in 1776 the colonies declared war on England and active trade between the colonies and England stopped. **15. a.** $f(t) = 100(0.952)^t$ **b.** $f(13.7) \approx$ 50.87 g **17.** about 23,953,000 **19. a.** $x = 2$ or $x = 3$ **b.** $x = -1$ or $x = \frac{1}{3}$ **c.** $x = \frac{\sqrt{3}}{3}$

Lesson 2-7 (pp. 125-131)

Guided Example 1 **a.** 60; 84.6; 60; $\frac{5076}{V}$ **c.** decreasing **d.** 126.9

Questions

1. C **3. a.** $k = 450$ **b.** 225 **5.** an inverse-square

variation **7. a.** $k = 28,704 \text{ kPa} \cdot \text{mL}$ **b.** $P = \frac{28,704 \text{ kPa} \cdot \text{mL}}{V}$
c.

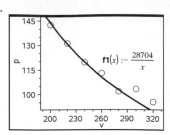

d. about 97.68 **9. a.** about $3.987 \cdot 10^8 \frac{\text{m}^3}{\text{s}^2}$ **b.** about $1.49 \frac{\text{m}}{\text{s}^2}$
c. about $0.00270 \frac{\text{m}}{\text{s}^2}$ **11. a.** $y \approx 0.021x^2 - 1.2x + 511$
b. sum of squared residuals ≈ 78.2969

13. a. interpolation **b.** The 2016 prediction would probably have a larger error since it is a result of extrapolation.
15. a. median **b.** median

Lesson 2-8 (pp. 132-139)

Questions

1. The residuals are clustered around the x-axis.

3. a.

Days (d)	Predicted Day Length (p)
1	790.62
10	764.73
20	736.95
30	710.18
40	684.39
50	659.53
60	635.57
70	612.49
80	590.24
90	568.80
100	548.14

b.

Days (d)	Predicted Day Length (p)	Computed Day Length (L)	Residual
1	790.62	793	2.38
10	764.73	766	1.27
20	736.95	739	2.05
30	710.18	711	0.82
40	684.39	684	–0.39
50	659.53	657	–2.53
60	635.57	631	–4.57
70	612.49	607	–5.49
80	590.24	586	–4.24
90	568.80	568	–0.80
100	548.14	556	7.86

c. The exponential model is not a good fit for this data because there is a distinct pattern in the residual plot.

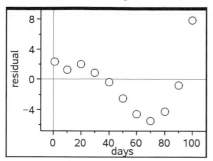

5 a. $y = (3.99866)1.0292^x$

b.

◇	A	B	C	D	E
1	Year (Y)	Year After 1790	Population (m)	Predicted Populaton (p)	Residual (R = m-p)
2	1790	0	4	3.999	0.00
3	1800	10	5	5.332	-0.33
4	1810	20	7	7.11	-0.11
5	1820	30	10	9.48	0.52
6	1830	40	13	12.646	0.35
7	1840	50	17	16.864	0.14
8	1850	60	23	22.490	0.51
9	1860	70	31	29.991	1.01
10	1870	80	40	39.995	0.01
11	1880	90	50	53.335	-3.34

c.

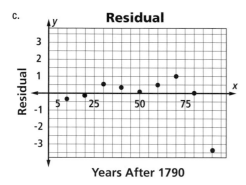

d. It seems to be appropriate for the time period because the residuals are scattered closely about the x-axis. However, the data for 1880 diverge unexpectedly, so this model probably should not be used to extrapolate into the future. **7.** Answers vary. Sample: The prices of stocks fluctuate based on many factors that cannot be accurately forecasted or predicted. **9. a.** Answers vary. Sample: The amount of driving and motor vehicle ownership generally depends on the population, so theoretically an exponential model might be a good fit. However, because there seems

to be no immediate relationship behind time and mile of motor vehicles, this would most likely be considered impressionistic and therefore have no theoretical basis.
b. Answers vary. Sample: Eyeballing the scatterplot, it seems that any of the three standard models (linear, exponential, or quadratic) might fit the data.

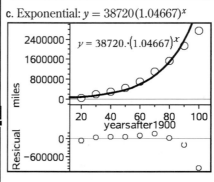

c. Exponential: $y = 38720(1.04667)^x$

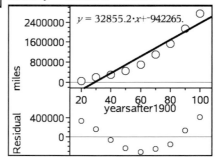

Linear: $y = 32855.2x - 942265$

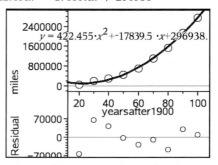

d. Quadratic: $y = 422.455x^2 - 17839.5x + 296938$

The quadratic regression model seems to fit the data best, and the residuals all lie in a relatively small range.

11. 320 N

13. a.

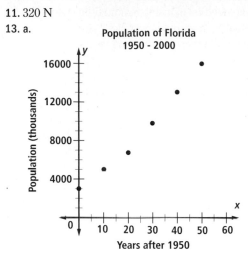

**Population of Florida
1950 - 2000**

x-axis: Years after 1950 (0, 10, 20, 30, 40, 50, 60)
y-axis: Population (thousands) (4000, 8000, 12000, 16000)

b. $y = 1.736x^2 + 178.813x + 2802.61$ **c.** about 21,760 thousand people

Self-Test pages 144-145

1. a. $f(2) = -9.8(2)^2 - 5.2(2) + 12.7 = -39.2 - 10.4 + 12.7 = -36.9$ **b.** $g(2n) = 5(2n)^2 - 3 = 20n^2 - 3$ **2.** It seems that any number can be an argument for this function, so domain $= \mathbb{R}$. The value of the function is never less than or equal to 1, so range $= \{y|y > 1\}$. **3.** x can be any real number except 0 so domain $= \{x|x \neq 0\}$; $-\frac{2}{x}$ can be any real number except 0 so range $= \{y|y \neq 0\}$. **4. a.** D and E; the points with greater x-values have or tend to have smaller y-values. **b.** C and F; C has no pattern to the data points and F is symmetric to a vertical line. **c.** A and D; all of the points are essentially on a line. **5.** residual = observed − predicted, so observed $= 17,000 + 3,424,000(1.013)^{15} \approx 4,172,999$ people. **6.** The larger the sum of the squared residuals, the farther the data points are from the line. Because Stephen's line has a smaller sum of squared residuals it is a better fit for the data. **7. a.** Substituting $h_0 = 200$, $v_0 = 44$, and $g = 32$, $h = -16t^2 + 44t + 200$. **b.** Use the Quadratic Formula on the equation $-16t^2 + 44t + 200 = 0$. $t = \frac{-44 \pm \sqrt{44^2 - 4(-16)(200)}}{2(-16)} \approx 1.378 \pm 3.793 \approx 5.168$ seconds **8. a.** The form is $y = \frac{k}{x}$ and $60 = \frac{k}{10}$, so $k = 600$. **b.** Substitute $x = 3$. $y = \frac{600}{3} = 200$ **9. a.** The form is $y = \frac{k}{x^2}$ and $60 = \frac{k}{100}$, so $k = 6000$ **b.** Substitute $x = 3$. $y = \frac{6000}{3^2} = \frac{2000}{3}$ **10.** The growth factor is greater than 1 (and a in $a(b)^x$ is positive), so the function models exponential growth. **11.** Use 115 for x and evaluate. $y = 2.51(115) + 471.1 = \$759.75$ million; The residual is observed − predicted $= 524 - 759.75 = -\$235.75$ million. **12.** Find the growth rate by using the half-life. $\frac{a}{2} = ab^{30}$ so $b \approx 0.0977$. The initial value a is 10 so the equation is $y = 10(0.0977)^x$. When $x = 20$, $y = 6.3$ g, so 6.3 g will be left after 20 years. **13.** By the graphs of

the residuals, the linear model seems to be a poor fit because the residuals are far from the x-axis. The inverse-square model seems to fit the data very well because the residuals are clustered near the x-axis and don't seem to make a pattern. Therefore, the inverse-square model is more appropriate. **14. a.** Quadratic regression on a calculator with t as the independent variable and h as the dependent variable shows $h = -15.786t^2 + 52.5t + 261$. **b.** This is a theory-based model because it is based on the theory of gravity. **c.** Substitute 4 for t and evaluate. $h = -15.786(4)^2 + 52.5(4) + 261 = 218.43$ feet **15. a.** To find the line of best fit, use linear regression on a calculator. The slope, –0.265 means that the percent of 18-24 year-olds who vote has decreased by about 0.265% per year. **b.** The correlation coefficient, –0.905, indicates that there is a strong negative correlation between the year and the percent of young people who vote.

16. a. Answers vary. Sample: A quadratic model looks appropriate for the data.

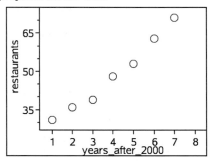

b. Linear: $y = 6.71429x + 21.8571$

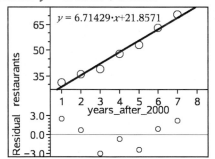

with correlation coefficient of about 0.99
Quadratic: $y = 0.5x^2 + 2.71429x + 27.8571$

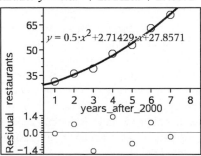

Exponential: $y = 26.7905(1.14995)^x$

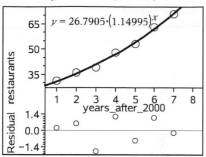

c. Answers vary. Sample: Neither theory nor an eyeball of the residual plot lead to any particular model. The linear residual plot has an almost parabolic pattern with larger residuals than the quadratic and exponential regressions. Both the quadratic and exponential regressions have very similar residual plots, so either model could be used.

Self-Test Correlation Chart

Question	1	2	3	4	5	6	7	8
Objective(s)	A	H	C	I	B	B	F	E
Lesson(s)	2-1	2-1	2-1	2-3	2-2	2-2	2-6	2-7

Question	9	10	11	12	13	14	15	16
Objective(s)	E	E	B	F	I	F	D	G
Lesson(s)	2-7	2-4	2-2	2-5	2-8	2-6	2-3	2-8

Chapter Review (pp. 146–149)

Questions

1. a. 4 b. $\frac{1}{4}$ c. 64 3. a. $x = 1$ b. no, $(4^3 + 2) - (2^3 + 2) =$
$56 \neq 2^3 + 2 = 10$

5. a.

n	$F(n)$	model	residuals
1	1	–4.82	5.82
2	1	–1.17	2.17
3	2	2.48	–0.48
4	3	6.13	–3.13
5	5	9.78	–4.78
6	8	13.43	–5.43
7	13	17.08	–4.08
8	21	20.73	0.27

b. 937.07 c. 210.206

7. a.

n	$F(n)$	model	residuals
1	1	2.521	–1.521
2	1	0.664	0.336
3	2	0.381	1.619
4	3	1.672	1.328
5	5	4.537	0.463
6	8	8.976	–0.976
7	13	14.989	–1.989
8	21	22.576	–1.576
9	34	31.737	2.263

b. 610 9. a. $\{t \mid t \in \mathbb{R}\}$ b. $\{y \mid y > 0\}$ 11. a. $\{d \mid d \neq 0\}$
b. $\{I \mid I > 0\}$ 13. $t; y$ 15. true 17. true 19. $r = 1$
21. Most of the observed data fall close to a linear model with positive slope; this indicates that the two variables have a strong positive relationship. 23. a models exponential growth, b models exponential decay
25. a. I,III b. II, IV 27. $f(x)$ decreases 29. 400
31. a. $y = 0.335(6.108)^x$ b. –2.34 33. a. $s = 0.5h - 24.5$
b. 2 35. 225.4 mg 37. exponential; Population growth is often described by exponential growth equations.
39. linear; Since peoples' body parts are proportional to each other, their measurements can be described by a linear model. 41. a. Answers vary. Sample: Cell division splits or doubles the amount of cells after each division. Exponential growth models describe this type of process.
b. The scatterplot appears to be exponentially growing. The rate of change of bacteria per hour is increasing.

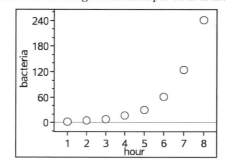

c. Exponential: $y = 1.01688(1.98128)^x$; The residual plot supports the choices made in Parts a and b.

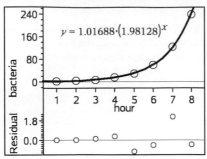

d. The theory, the scatterplot and the residual plot all support the choice of an exponential model.
43. function; $\{x| x \in \mathbb{R}\}$; $\{y| y \leq 0.5\}$ **45.** function; $\{x| x \in \mathbb{R}\}$; $\{y| y \leq 3\}$ **47. a.** 83% **b.** 81% **c.** 2%   **49.** about 8 or 9 hours; Answers vary. Sample: This might make sense because a student who studies excessively for a test may negatively affect his performance through stress or lack of sleep.   **51.** positive   **53.** negative

Chapter 3

Lesson 3-1 (pp. 152–158)

Questions

1. linear, cubic, inverse variation **3.** quadratic, inverse square, absolute value **5.** domain: $\{x|x \in \mathbb{R}\}$; range: $\{y|y \geq 12\}$ **7. a.**

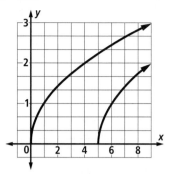

b. The graph of $y = \sqrt{x - 5}$ is the image of the graph of $y = \sqrt{x}$ under the translation 5 units to the right.

9. Answers vary. Sample: $-10 \leq x \leq 10, -10 \leq y \leq 10$

11. a.

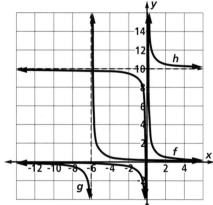

b. $x = 0, -6,$ and 0 for $f, g,$ and h, respectively **c.** $x = 0, x = -6,$ and $x = 0$ for $f, g,$ and h, respectively **d.** g is a translation of f 6 units to the left and h is a translation of f 10 units up. **13. a.** domain: $\{x|x \leq -20$ or $x \geq -10\}$

b.

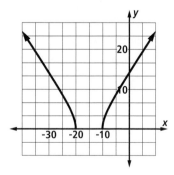

15. a.

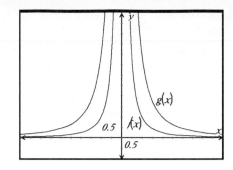

b. true **c.** The y values of g are greater than those of f in the graph above. Since $x^2 > 0$, when $x \neq 0$ and $1 < 4$, then $\frac{1}{x^2} < \frac{4}{x^2}$. So, $f(x) < g(x)$, when $x \neq 0$. **17.** not a function **19.** function

21.

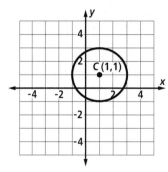

23. a.

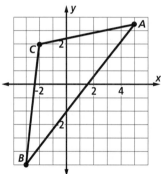

b.

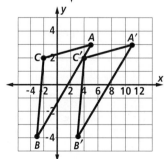

c. $\triangle A'B'C'$ is the image of $\triangle ABC$ under the translation of 6 units to the right.

Lesson 3-2 (pp. 159–164)

Guided Example 2 $y + 4; x - 5; y + 4 = \sqrt{25 - (x - 5)^2}$;
$\sqrt{-x^2 + 10x - 4}$; $(2, 0)$; $0 + 4 = \sqrt{-(2^2) + 10 \cdot 2}$; $4 = \sqrt{16}$;
$4 = 4$

Questions

1. $(-1, 1)$ 3. $(p + a, q + b)$ 5. $(r - 3, s + 4)$ 7. a. $(4, 5)$,
$(2, 3)$, $(3.5, 6)$ b. $5 - 4 = 1 = \frac{1}{4 - 3}$; $3 - 4 = -1 = \frac{1}{2 - 3}$;
$6 - 4 = 2 = \frac{1}{3.5 - 3}$ 9. $y = |x + 4| + 6$ 11. a. $T(x, y) = (x - 2, y + 1)$ b.

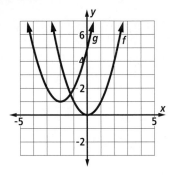

13. $h = -5, k = 2$ 15. a. about \$8,288,000,000,000
b. $N = 6.36 \cdot 10^{-72}(1.09)^t$ 17. a. $y = 1.621x + 6.413$ where
$y = $ length and $x = $ age. b. For every year that a
largemouth bass ages, it grows 1.621 inches. c. about
25.87 inches d. Answers vary. Sample: Extrapolation may
not be appropriate in this context, because largemouth
bass may stop growing in length when they are 10 years
old. e. 0.97 f. Age and length are positively correlated for
the largemouth bass.

Lesson 3-3 (pp. 165–171)

Guided Example
3 oz; 3 oz; 3 lb 5 oz; 3 oz; 3 oz; 3 lb 3.4 oz; 8 oz; 1 lb

Questions

1. translation   3. a. i. \$70 ii. \$100 iii. \$100 iv. \$90
v. \$700 vi. ≈\$26.46 b.i. \$70 ii. \$101.50 iii. \$101.50
iv. \$91.50 v. \$700 vi. ≈\$26.46   5. a. $\bar{x} + b$ b. s

7.

	Original Data	Transformed Data
cases	10	10
mean	63.5	53
sd	8.03	8.03
median	70	59.5
range	23	23
IQR	12	12

9. a.

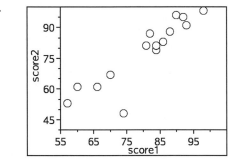

b.

	$\bar{x}$	s
score 1	80.33	12.34
score 2	77.93	16.10

c.

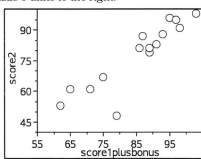

d. 0.899 e. $y = 1.173x - 16.333$ f. The points are shifted on
the x-axis 5 units to the right.

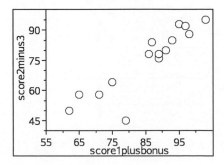

g. $r = 0.899$, $y = 1.173x - 22.2$; The correlation coefficient
and slope of the regression line are invariant; the
y-intercept changed. h. For any point (x, y) in Part c, the
point is translated to $(x + 5, y - 3)$. For the point (x, y) in
Part f, the point is translated to $(x, y - 3)$.

i. $r = 0.899$, $y = 1.173x - 25.2$ j. The correlation coefficient and slope are invariant, the y-intercept changed. **11.** 6′3″
13. a. and b.

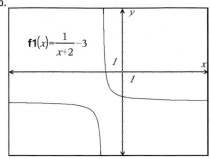

c. $T(x, y) = (x - 2, y - 3)$ **15.** $\{x \mid x \geq -99\}$
17. a.

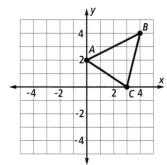

b.

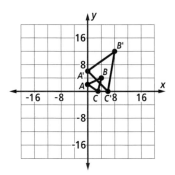

c. the scale change $S_{2,3}$

Lesson 3-4 (pp. 172–178)

Questions
1. a.

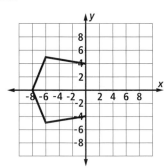

b. $(-6, -5)$ **3.** $(-4, -2)$ **5. a.** $-9 \neq 3 \mid 3 \mid$; the graph is not

symmetric with respect to the y-axis. **b.** $9 \neq -3 \mid -3 \mid$; the graph is not symmetric with respect to the x-axis.
c. $9 = 3 \mid 3 \mid$; the graph could be symmetric with respect to the origin. **7.** $f(-x) = \dfrac{8}{2 + x^2} = f(x)$, $-f(x) = -\dfrac{8}{2 + x^2} \neq f(x)$, and $-f(-x) = -\dfrac{8}{2 + x^2} \neq f(x)$, so f is only symmetric with respect to the y-axis.

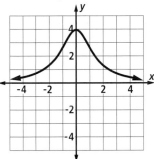

9. The function is odd.
11. a.

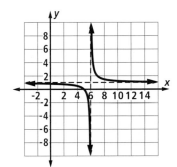

b. $x = 6$, $y = 1$ c. They are translated 6 units to the right and 1 unit up. **13.** Answers vary. Sample: The point $(2, 6)$ is on the line but the point $(-2, 6)$ is not, so f cannot be even. **15.**

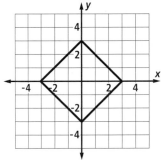

17. Suppose $f(x)$ and $g(x)$ are odd functions, then $f(-x) = -f(x)$ and $g(-x) = -g(x)$. Let $h(x) = f(x) + g(x)$. Then $h(-x) = f(-x) + g(-x) = -f(x) - g(x) = -(f(x) + g(x)) = -h(x)$, therefore, $h(x)$ is odd. Thus, the sum of two odd functions is odd. **19. a.** $\bar{x} = 71$ **b.** $s = 13$ **21. a.** $y = (x - 2)^5 - 5$
b. yes; translations preserve length and angle measure
23. $\sqrt{a^2 + b^2}$ **25.** $-b$

Lesson 3-5 (pp. 179–184)

Guided Example 1

a.

	Preimage		Image	
Point	x	y	2x	y
A	5	0	10	0
B	4	3	8	3
C	3	4	6	4
D	0	5	0	5
E	–3	4	–6	4
F	4	–3	8	–3

b.

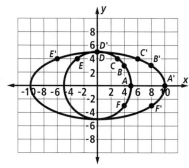

c. $\frac{x}{2}$; $\left(\frac{x}{2}\right)^2 + y^2 = 25$

Questions

1. false   **3.** If $a = 0$, every x-coordinate is mapped to 0, which maps the graph to a subset of the y-axis; if $b = 0$, every y-coordinate is mapped to 0, which maps the graph to a subset of the x-axis.   **5. a.** $f1\left(\frac{x}{3}\right) = \frac{1}{27}x^3 + \frac{1}{3}x^2 - \frac{4}{3}x$

b. $f1\left(\frac{x}{3}\right)$ is the image of $f(x)$ stretched horizontally by a factor of 3.   **7. a.** $S(x, y) = \left(x, \frac{1}{2}y\right)$ **b.** $x = -\frac{1}{2}$, 3 **c.** The y-intercept of g is $\frac{1}{2}$ the value of the y-intercept of f.
d. (1.25, 3.0625)

9.a.

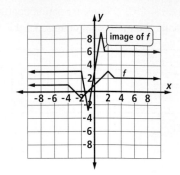

b. $x = -1.5, -0.5$; $y = 3$ **c.** (1, 9)   **11.** $S(x, y) = (12x, y)$, a vertical scale change of magnitude $\frac{1}{12}$ or a horizontal scale change of magnitude 12.   **13. a.** $y = x + \frac{4}{x}$ **b.** $y = -3x - \frac{1}{3x}$ **15.** $S(x, y) = (2x, -y)$ **17.** neither   **19.** They are reflections of each other over the x-axis.   **21. a.** The table confirms this statement: the number of injuries on children's rides decreased from 277 in 2003 to 219 to 192. **b.** The table refutes this statement: There were 613 injuries on roller coasters in 2004, more than the 504 injuries in 2003. **c.** The table partially confirms this statement: roller coasters had more injuries than children's rides in every year. On the other hand, the table cannot say whether the chance of being injured is higher on a roller coaster or on a children's ride.

Lesson 3-6 (pp. 185–192)

Guided Example

Step 1. $\frac{655.5}{496} = 1.322$ **Steps 2-6:** See below.

Guided Example, Steps 2–6

◇	A	B	C	D	E	F	G
1	Item	1998 cost	2008 cost (predicted)		1998 statistics	2008 statistics	1998 statistics × scale factor
2	Coffee 1 Pound	$4.03	$5.33	mean	$1.79	$2.36	$2.37
3	Eggs 1 dozen	$1.12	$1.48	median	$1.37	$1.80	$1.81
4	Gasoline 1 gallon	$1.13	$1.49	range	$3.01	$3.98	$3.98
5	Orange Juice 12-0z can	$1.60	$2.11	variance	$1.09	$1.91	$1.44
6	Ground Beef 1 pound	$1.82	$2.41	standard deviation	$1.04	$1.38	$1.37
7	Chicken 1 pound	$1.02	$1.35				
8							

For mean, median, standard deviation, and range, multiplying by the scale factor accurately finds the 2008 stats. Multiplying by the scale factor does not work for the variance.

Questions

1. A scale change of a set of data is a transformation that maps each x_i to ax_i, where a is a nonzero constant.

3. Between 1975 and 1980, the CPI increased by 85.36%.

5. a. $\frac{3}{4}$ **b.**

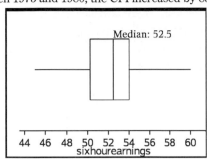

7. C **9.** For n odd, the median is the middle number when the set of numbers is put in increasing or decreasing order. If a set is $\{x_1, x_2, x_3, ..., x_n\}$, then under a scale change with scale factor a, the set becomes $\{ax_1, ax_2, ax_3, ..., ax_n\}$. Therefore, if the median of a set is x_m, the median of the set subject to the scale change is ax_m. For n even, using the same data set, the median is the mean of the middle two numbers, $\frac{x_j + x_k}{2}$. For the scaled set the median is $\frac{ax_j + ax_k}{2} = a\left(\frac{x_j + x_k}{2}\right)$, which satisfies the Centers of Scale Changes of Data Theorem. **11. a.** $\bar{x}r + b$ **b.** $(rs)^2$ **c.** rs

13. a.

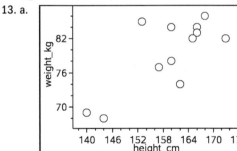

b. $w = 3.628 + 0.4746h$ **c.** $r = 0.7499$ **d.** The scatterplot appears the same but the scale of the axes is different.

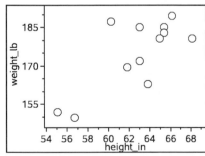

e. $w = 1.647 + 0.0848h$; $r = 0.7499$ **f. i.** invariant **ii.** not invariant **iii.** not invariant **15.** B **17.** A **19.** $g(x) = |3x|$, $h(x) = \frac{1}{3}|x|$ **21.** $6x^2(x - 3)$ **23.** $(3r - 5)(r + 1)$

Lesson 3-7 (pp. 193–198)

Guided Example 2
a. $x - 7$; $x - 7$; x^2; $14x$; $2x^2 - 25x + 77$

Guided Example 4
a. 2; translation 4 units to the right and 3 units down;
c. $x + 4$; $y - 3$; $x + 4$; $y - 3$; $2x + 8$; $y - 3$

Questions

1. maternal grandmother **3.** $f(g(0)) = f(-7) = 77$; $g(f(0)) = g(0) = -7$ **5. a.** $(M \circ N)(t) = \frac{6}{t + 1} - 1$ **b.** all real numbers except -1 **7.** 36; 14 **9. a.** -55 **b.** -1

11. a. $(x + 3, y + 1)$; $\left(x, \frac{y}{4}\right)$ **b.** $(T \circ S)(x, y) = \left(x + 3, \frac{y}{4} + 1\right)$; $(S \circ T)(x, y) = \left(x + 3, \frac{y}{4} + \frac{1}{4}\right)$ **13.** $(S \circ S)(x, y) = (-x, -y)$

15. Discounts are usually based on some percentage of the original price and rebates are usually a fixed dollar amount reduction in price. **17.** $(D \circ R)(x) = 0.9x - 90$; $(R \circ D)(x) = 0.9x - 100$; $0.9x - 90 \neq 0.9x - 100$

19. a. $m(x) = \frac{x}{5280}$ **b.** $k(x) = 1.609344x$ **c.** $(k \circ m)(x) = 0.0003048x$ **d.** 16,404.2 feet

21.

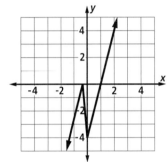

23. $y = -16x^2$

Lesson 3-8 (pp. 199–205)

Questions

1. The function found by switching the x- and y-coordinates of all points. **3. a.**

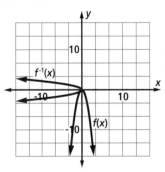

b. $f^{-1}(x)$ is equivalent to the relation $y = \pm\sqrt{\frac{x}{2}}$; therefore some x-values are assigned two y-values, which is not allowed in a function. **5.** $x = 2y - 4$; $y = \frac{x}{2} + 2$; yes **7.** $x = \sqrt{y}$; $y = x^2$ for $x \geq 0$; yes

9. $g(f(x)) = x$ for all x, $f(g(x)) = x$ for all x, therefore the functions are inverses.

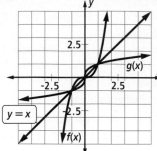

11. a. $M(x) = 10.033x$, $U(x) = \frac{x}{10.033}$ **b.** $1,993.42 **c.** yes, $M(U(x)) = \frac{10.033x}{10.033} = x$ for all real x, $U(M(x)) = \frac{10.033x}{10.033} = x$ for all real x **13. a.**

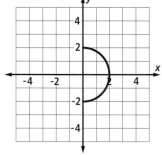

b. no **15.** To find the inverse $h^{-1}(p)$, switch p and $h(p)$: $p = \frac{1}{h(p)}$, $h^{-1}(p) = \frac{1}{p}$; $h^{-1}(h(p)) = \frac{1}{\frac{1}{p}} = p$ for all $p \neq 0$, therefore the function is its own inverse.

17. $n = \frac{w(n) - 11}{8}$ **19. a.** $39(t + 17) = 39t + 663$ **b.** $39(39t) = 1521t$ **21. a.** $p(x) = -|x| + 7$, so $p(-x) = -|-x| + 7 = -x + 7 = p(x)$. Therefore p is an even function. **b.** The graph is symmetric over the y-axis.

23. a.

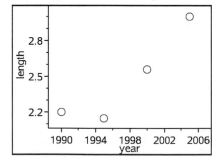

b. $y = 0.0049x^2 - 19.5193x + 19441.1$ **c.** 3.79 min
25. $\sum\limits_{i=1}^{n} p_i q_i$

Lesson 3-9 (pp. 206–210)

Guided Example 2
78, 0.7, 62, 6, 1, chemistry

Questions

1. L_2 mean = 0.0029, L_2 standard deviation = 10.7, L_3 mean = 0.014, L_3 standard deviation = 1.019 **3.** $17.57
5. Part 4b's test score of 84 is better compared to other's who took the test. **7.** for all data points x, $\frac{x - 19}{4.3}$
9. English: 2.39, Math: 0.5, Reading: -1.56, Science: -0.22
11. 6 minutes 16 seconds
13.

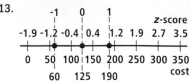

15. a. $\frac{x}{s} - \bar{x}$ **b.** mean: 20.76, standard deviation: 1 **c.** The mean is different because $T \circ S \neq S \circ T$. The standard deviations are the same because it remains invariant under translations. **17.** Physics **19.** ≈ 42 **21. a.** true **b.** false
23. false; Counterexample: $f(x) = x^3 - x$ is odd, but its inverse doesn't pass the vertical line test. **25.** B

Self-Test (p. 215)

Questions
1. The graph of h is the image of the graph of $f : x \to \frac{1}{x}$ under the translation $T(x, y) = (x + 7, y - 9)$. The asymptotes of the graph of f are the x-axis and the y-axis. By the Graph-Translation Theorem, the asymptotes of the graph of h are 7 units to the right and 9 units below, that is, $x = 7$ and $y = -9$. **2.** Under T, the graph of $y = x^2$ is translated 4 units to the right and 2 units down. So, by the Graph-Translation Theorem, an equation for the image is $y + 2 = (x - 4)^2$ **3.** Since the vertex of the graph of $y = x^2$ is $(0, 0)$, the vertex of the image is 4 units to the right and 2 units down, or $(4, -2)$. **4.** Under S, the image of $(4, 0)$ is $(8, 0)$. The image of $(-1, 2)$ is $(2, -2)$, and the image of $(-4, -4)$ is $(-8, 4)$. Connecting these points in order as in the preimage yields the graph here. **5. a.** The median is 150 larger: 3.8 + 150 = 153.8 g **b.** The range is the same: 13.6 - 0.4 = 13.2 g **c.** The IQR is the same: 4.6 - 3.6 = 1 g **6.** Convert grams to ounces. median: (153.8 g) $\left(0.035 \frac{oz}{g}\right) \approx 5.383$ oz; range: (13.2 g)$\left(0.035 \frac{oz}{g}\right) \approx 0.462$ oz; IQR: 1 g = 0.035 oz. **7.** Let $y = f(x)$ and switch x and y: $x = 4\sqrt[3]{y + 2}$. **8.** Solve the Equation in Question 7 for y : $\left(\frac{x}{4}\right)^3 = y + 2$, from which $y = \left(\frac{x}{4}\right)^3 - 2$. This is an equation for a function because each value of x yields

exactly one value of y. **9.** f and f^{-1} are reflection images of each other over the line $y = x$. **10.** $n(m(x)) = n(16 - 5x)$ $= 16 - 5x + \sqrt{16 - 5x}$ **11.** The domain of $n \circ m$ is the set of all values x in the domain of m for which $m(x)$ is in the domain of n. The domain of m is the set of all real numbers, and so is the range of m. Thus $m(x)$ can be any real number. But if $m(x)$ is negative, then $\sqrt{m(x)}$ is not real. So the domain of $n \circ m$ is the set of all x with $m(x) \geq 0$, that is, with $16 - 5x \geq 0$, the set $\left\{x \mid x \leq \frac{16}{5}\right\}$. **12.** Use the Graph Scale-Change Theorem with $a = 3$ and $b = 0.5$. An equation for the image is $\frac{y}{b} = \frac{1}{\left(\frac{x}{a}\right)^2}$. Substituting for a and b, $2y = \frac{1}{\left(\frac{x}{3}\right)^2}$ or $y = \frac{4.5}{x^2}$. **13.** Use the Graph Standardization Theorem with $\mu = 83$ and $\sigma = 7$. The transformation is $x \rightarrow \frac{x - 83}{7}$. **14.** Since $j(-x) = (-x)^2 + 5$

$= x^2 + 5 = j(x)$, j is an even function. **15. a.** The parent function is the function whose graph was transformed to get the graph of g. That is the absolute value function A with $A(x) = y = |x|$. **b.** The graph of g can be viewed as the image of the graph of A under the scale change $S_{2,\,0.5}$. So, by the Graph Scale-Change Theorem, an equation for g is $\frac{y}{0.5} = \left|\frac{x}{2}\right|$. **c.** The graph is symmetric to the y-axis. **d.** $\{y \mid y \geq 0\}$ **16.** Let T be the transformation. When a point (x, y) is reflected over the line $y = x$, its image is (y, x). So a rule is $T(x, y) = (y, x)$. **17.** Standardize these scores to compare them. For the mouse, $z = \frac{37 - 30}{3.4} \approx 2.06$; for the moose, $z = \frac{1260 - 910}{185} \approx 1.89$. Since the mouse has a higher z-score, it is heavier relative to its population than the moose.

Self-Test Correlation Chart

Question	1	2	3	4	5	6	7	8	9	10
Objective(s)	E	C	D	J	H	H	B	B	K	A
Lesson(s)	3-1	3-2	3-2	3-5	3-3	3-6	3-8	3-8	3-8	3-7

Question	11	12	13	14	15	16	17
Objective(s)	F	C	G	E	I	D	H
Lesson(s)	3-7	3-5	3-9	3-4	3-4	3-5	3-9

Chapter Review (pp. 216-219)

Questions

1. 27 **3. a.** 33 **b.** 552 **5. a.** $-\frac{1}{4}$ **b.** -24 **7. a.** $x = |y|$ **b.** The inverse is not a function. **9. a.** $\{(4, 3), (12, 4), (9, 5),$ $(0, 6), (11, 7)\}$ **b.** The inverse is a function. **11.** B **13.** $y = 12x^2$ **15.** $y = |x + 1|$ **17.** $T:(x, y) \rightarrow (x, y + 4)$ **19.** The graph of the image is translated 15.3 units down. **21.** The graph of the image is stretched by a factor of 8 vertically. **23.** true **25.** neither **27.** even **29.** $x = \frac{1}{2}$, $y = 0$ **31.** $x \geq 2$ **33.** false **35.** true **37.** false **39.** 0 **41.** The data point is 1.3 standard deviations less than the mean. **43. a.** 5 **b.** 20 **c.** Spread of Scale Changes of Data Theorem **45. a.** 46.2 mm **b.** 68.8 mm **c.** 136.52 mm^2 **47.** The porpoise is heavier relative to its group. **49.** No, this is an even function, so the inverse will not be defined for all real numbers. **51.** B **53.** A **55.** F **57.** odd **59. a.**

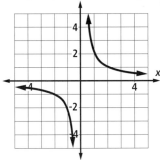

b. $x = -4$, $y = 12$ **c.** $(-3.833, 0)$ **61.** $T:(x, y) \rightarrow (x + 3, y + 2)$ **63.** $y = (x + 2)^2 + 5$ **65.** $y = \frac{1}{(x + 4)^2} + 2$ **67. a.** $y = \frac{2}{x}$ **b.**

c. The inverse is a function. **69.** They are inverses of each other. We can tell because they are symmetric over the line $y = x$, which implies that $f(g(x)) = g(f(x)) = x$.

Chapter 4

Lesson 4-1 (pp. 222–228)

Guided Example 3 12π; 12π; $\frac{5\pi}{3}$; 5.24

Questions

1. $324°$ **3. a.** π **b.** π **5. a.**

b. about $57.3°$

7.

 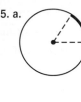

9. a. 1.5 revolutions **b.** 3π **11.** $-\frac{4\pi}{9}$ **13.** $\frac{55\pi}{2}$ **15.** about 4.398 cm **17.** about 7.3 ft **19. a.** about 4.19 in. **b.** about 40,212.4 in. **21. a.** 22π in. or about 69.1 in. **b.** 3300π in. or about 10,367.3 in. **c.** $\frac{25\pi}{8}$ mph or about 9.8 mph **23.** $y = (x-3)^2 - 2$ **25. a.** Pros mean: 3.64; Pros median: -2.5; Pros standard deviation: 21.1; Darts mean: 3.97; Darts median: 3.6; Darts standard deviation: 6.33 **b.** The Darts minimum, Q_1, and median are greater than the Pros minimum, Q_1, and median. Nearly all of the Darts data is contained between the Pros median and Q_3. The Pros Q_3 is nearly the same as the Darts maximum. The Pros range is much greater than the Darts range.

Lesson 4-2 (pp. 229–234)

Guided Example 2 a. -1; 0; 0 **b.** 0; 1; undefined

Questions

1. a. x-coordinate **b.** y-coordinate **3.** A **5.** $\tan\theta = \frac{\sin\theta}{\cos\theta}$ **7. a.** 0 **b.** -1 **c.** 0 **9. a.** Answers vary. Sample: $90°$, $270°$ **b.** Answers vary. Sample: π, 3π **11.** $(0.540, 0.841)$ **13. a.** positive **b.** negative **c.** negative **15.** 212 ft **17.** about 1.1 ft **19.** Answers vary. Sample: $180°$, $-180°$, $540°$ **21.** decreases **23.** $-300°$ **25.** $\frac{\sqrt{2}}{2}$ **27. a.** $(-x, y)$ **b.** $(x, -y)$ **c.** $(-x, -y)$

Lesson 4-3 (pp. 235–241)

Questions

1. true **3.** -3 **5.** the x-coordinates of P' and P'': c and e. **7.** false **9.** $\frac{1}{3}$ **11.** $\sin 33.5° \approx 0.552 \approx \sin 146.5°$; $\cos 33.5° \approx 0.834 \approx -\cos 146.5°$; $\tan 33.5° \approx 0.662 \approx -\tan 146.5°$ **13.** $\frac{5}{13}$ **15.** $-k$ **17.** Half-Turn Theorem and Supplements Theorem **19.** Supplements Theorem **21.** Half-Turn Theorem **23.** $\frac{\sqrt{5}-1}{4}$ **25.** $-\frac{\sqrt{5}-1}{4}$ **27.** 1 **29.** 0 **31. a.** $36°$ **b.** $2160°$

Lesson 4-4 (pp. 242–246)

Guided Example 1 PF; $\frac{1}{2}$; b

Guided Example 2 1; $\frac{1}{2}$; $\left(\frac{1}{2}\right)^2$; $\frac{3}{4}$; $\frac{\sqrt{3}}{2}$; $\left(\frac{\sqrt{3}}{2}, \frac{1}{2}\right)$; $\frac{\sqrt{3}}{2}$, $\frac{1}{2}$

Guided Example 4 $-\cos 60°$; $\sin 60°$

Guided Example 5 b. 150; $-\frac{\sqrt{3}}{2}$ **c.** $\frac{0}{-1}$; 0

Questions

1. OF **3.** RH **5. a.** $-\frac{\sqrt{3}}{2}$ **b.** $-\frac{1}{2}$ **c.** $\sqrt{3}$ **7. a.** $-\frac{1}{2}$ **b.** $\frac{\sqrt{3}}{2}$ **c.** $-\frac{\sqrt{3}}{3}$ **9.** $\frac{1}{2}$

11.

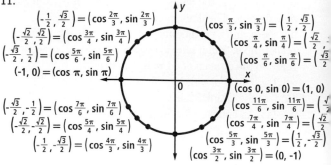
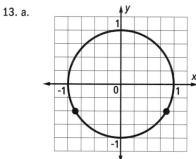

13. a.

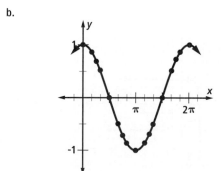

b. $210°$ and $330°$ **c.** $\frac{7\pi}{6}$ and $\frac{11\pi}{6}$ **15.** true **17. a.** -0.788 **b.** 0.788 **c.** -0.788 **d.** 0.788 **19.** -1 **21. a.** $\frac{3\pi}{4}$ **b.** $\frac{13\pi}{6}$ **c.** $-\frac{43\pi}{36}$ **d.** $-\frac{3\pi}{2}$ **23.** $(f \circ g)(t) = 3(t^2 + 1) - 1$

Lesson 4-5 (pp. 247–251)

Questions

1. a. domain: $\{x \mid x \in \mathbb{R}\}$; range: $\{y \mid -1 \leq y \leq 1\}$ **b.** Answers vary. Sample: $-\pi$, 0, π, 2π, 3π

3. a.

x	$\frac{2\pi}{3}$	$\frac{3\pi}{4}$	$\frac{7\pi}{6}$	$\frac{5\pi}{4}$	$\frac{4\pi}{3}$	$\frac{3\pi}{2}$	$\frac{5\pi}{3}$	$\frac{7\pi}{4}$	$\frac{11\pi}{6}$
$\cos x$ (exact)	$\frac{1}{2}$	$\frac{\sqrt{2}}{2}$	$-\frac{\sqrt{3}}{2}$	$\frac{\sqrt{2}}{2}$	$-\frac{1}{2}$	0	$\frac{1}{2}$	$\frac{\sqrt{2}}{2}$	$\frac{\sqrt{3}}{2}$
$\cos x$ (approx)	-0.5	-0.707	-0.866	-0.707	-0.5	0	0.5	0.707	0.866

b.

5. Answers vary. Sample: The graphs of both sin x and cos x have a cycle of length 2π (or 360°), a maximum value of 1, and a minimum value of -1. The graph of cos x crosses the y-axis at $(0, 1)$ and the graph of sin x crosses the y-axis at $(0, 0)$. The graph of cos x is symmetric about the y-axis and the graph of sin x is not. **7. a.** $\sin\left(\theta + \frac{\pi}{2}\right) = \sin\left(\frac{\pi}{2} - \theta\right)$ **b.** Answers vary. Sample: $x = \frac{3\pi}{2}$ and $x = -\frac{3\pi}{2}$ **9. a.** -1 **b.** $\frac{21\pi}{2}$ **c.** f is the sine function, because $\sin(10\pi) = 0$ whereas $\cos(10\pi) = 1$. **11.** $\left(-\frac{1}{2}, \frac{\sqrt{3}}{2}\right)$ **13.** 3π **15.** $\left(\frac{k180}{\pi}\right)$

Lesson 4-6 (pp. 252–256)

Guided Example 3 a. about 128; about 87 **b.** 11.4 to 12.5 **c.** about 0.167 seconds

Questions

1. a. 90°, 270° **b.** undefined **c.** The graph of the tangent function has a vertical asymptote at values where $\cos \theta = 0$. **3.** $\sin 495° = \sin(135° + 1 \cdot 360°) = \sin 135° = \frac{\sqrt{2}}{2}$

5. $\tan 3750° = \tan(330° + 9 \cdot 360°) = \tan 330° = -\frac{\sqrt{3}}{3}$

7. a. 2π **b.** 2π **c.** π **9.** 450° **11. a.** $x = \frac{\pi}{2}, x = -\frac{\pi}{2}$ **b.** $x = 90°, x = -90°$

13. a.

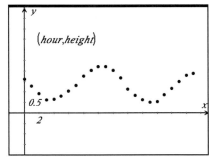

b. $\{h \mid 0.5 \le h \le 2.25\}$ where h is the height after t hours **c.** about 14 hours **15. a.** predator: $\{t \mid t > 0\}$; prey: $\{t \mid t > 0\}$ where t is months after the first measurement **b.** predator: maximum ≈ 710, minimum ≈ 500; prey: maximum $\approx 1,025$, minimum ≈ 450 **c.** predator: 20 months; prey: 20 months **17.** even; $\cos(-x) = \cos x$ **19. a.** $T(x, y) \to (x + 6, y + 5)$ **b.** $(15, 14)$

Lesson 4-7 (pp. 257–262)

Questions

1. a. true **b.** 2π **c.** $\frac{1}{5}$ **d.**

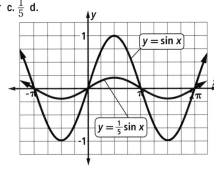

e. The graph of $y = \frac{1}{5}\sin x$ is the image of the graph of $y = \sin x$ under the scale change that maps (x, y) to $\left(x, \frac{y}{5}\right)$, a vertical shrink by a factor of $\frac{1}{5}$. **3. a.** 4 **b.** 6π **5. a.** $y = \sin\left(\frac{x}{5}\right)$ **b.** 1; 10π **7.** $y = 6\sin\left(\frac{x}{4}\right)$ **9. a.** the tone with frequency of 660 cycles per second **b.** It is one octave higher. **11.** Answers vary. Sample:

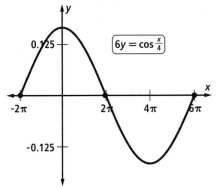

13. $y = 32\sin(880\pi x)$ **15.** f and h **17.** A **19.** -2.465; 3.815; 6.955 **21. a.** -4π **b.** $\frac{5\pi}{4}$ **c.** $\frac{7\pi}{4}$

23. a.

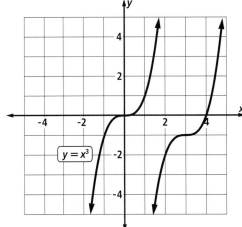

b. $y + 1 = (x - 3)^3$

Lesson 4-8 (pp. 263–268)

Guided Example 1 -60°; 60° left; -60°

Questions

1. true **3. a.** $-\frac{3\pi}{4}$ **b.** 5 **5.** Answers vary. Sample: $y = \sin x - 4$ **7.** $y = \sin\left(x + \frac{3\pi}{4}\right) - 1$ **9. a.** Answers vary. Sample: $T(x, y) = \left(x - \frac{\pi}{2}, y\right)$ **b.** Answers vary. Sample: $\cos x = \sin\left(x + \frac{\pi}{2}\right)$

11. a. π **b.** phase shift to the right by $\frac{\pi}{4}$

c. $\left(\frac{\pi}{2}, 1\right)$ **d.** $x = \frac{3\pi}{4}, x = \frac{7\pi}{4}$ **e.**

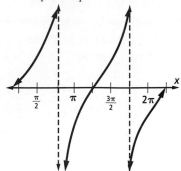

13. a. 4 **b.** 2π

15.

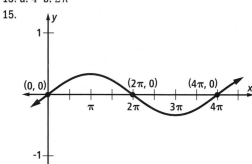

17. $225°$ **19. a. and b.**

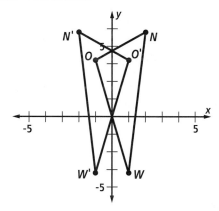

c. $(-x, y)$

Lesson 4-9 (pp. 269–275)

Questions

1. a. $(1, -2)$ **b.** $(21, 298)$ **c.** $(-19, 298)$ **3. a.** amplitude: 1; period: 6π; phase shift: π units to the right **b.** A scale change of $(x, y) \rightarrow (3x, y)$, followed by a translation of $(x, y) \rightarrow (x + \pi, y)$.   **5. a.** $\frac{y + 5}{7} = \sin\left(\frac{x}{\frac{1}{\pi}}\right)$ **b.** amplitude: 7; period: 2; phase shift: none; vertical shift: 5 units down

7. minimum: 9 ft; maximum: 271 ft   **9.** $\frac{y - 140}{131} = \sin\left(\frac{x + \frac{9}{4}}{\frac{9}{2\pi}}\right)$

11. The graphs of functions with equations $\frac{y - k}{b} = \tan\left(\frac{x - h}{a}\right)$, with $a \neq 0$ and $b \neq 0$, have vertical scale change $= b$, period $= \pi|a|$, phase shift $= h$, and vertical shift $= k$.

13. $\frac{y + 1}{5} = \sin\left(\frac{x - \frac{\pi}{4}}{3}\right)$ **15.** Answers vary. Sample: $y - 5 = 10\sin\left(x - \frac{\pi}{2}\right)$ **17.** $y - 2 = \left|x - \frac{\pi}{3}\right|$ **19.** $c = 0, \pi, 2\pi, 3\pi, 4\pi, 5\pi, 6\pi$ **21. a.** 10^5 **b.** $3 \cdot 10^8$ **c.** $2 \cdot 10^{-5}$ **d.** $\left(\frac{a}{b}\right) \cdot 10^{m-n}$

Lesson 4-10 (pp. 276–281)

Guided Example 2 a. 6; 425°F; 431°F; 419°F **b.** $\frac{20\pi}{9} \approx 7$ minutes

Questions

1. the 174th day, or June 23rd; 14.085 hours   **3.** $t = 425 + 6\cos 0.45m$ **5. a. i.** half of the range of the pendulum's distance from the motion detector; 0.75 m **ii.** the time the pendulum takes to complete a full swing; 3.8 sec. **iii.** the distance of the midpoint of the pendulum's swing from the motion detector; 1.3 m **b.** $\frac{d - 1.3}{0.75} = \sin\left(\frac{\pi t}{1.9}\right)$

7. period: about 0.033 sec., amplitude: 1.6   **9. a.** 28 ft **b.** 2 ft **c.** 30 ft **d.** 2 minutes **e.** $\frac{y - 30}{28} = \sin\left(\frac{x}{\frac{\pi}{2}}\right)$

11. a. and b.

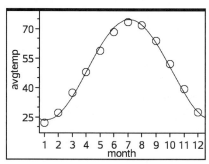

Answers vary. Sample: about 25.63 **c.** 12 **d.** B **e.** Answers vary. Sample: $\frac{y - 49}{-25.63} = \sin\left(\frac{\pi x - 3.5 + 3\pi}{6}\right)$

13. a.

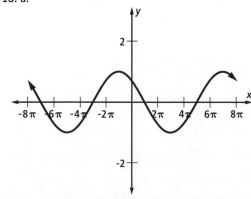

b. amplitude: 1, period: 8π, phase shift: π units to the left **c.** a scale change of $(x, y) \rightarrow (4x, y)$ followed by a translation of $(x, y) \rightarrow (x - \pi, y)$ **15. a.** $c = \frac{\sqrt{2}}{2}$ **b.** $\frac{\pi}{4}$

17. a. $-\frac{49}{340}$ **b.** $-\frac{49}{25}$

Self-Test (pp. 286–287)

1. $\frac{7}{9}$ revolution $\cdot \frac{2\pi \text{ radians}}{1 \text{ revolution}} = \frac{14\pi}{9}$ radians   **2.** $-\frac{5\pi}{2}$ radians $\cdot \frac{180°}{\pi \text{ radians}} = -450°$ **3.** $120° \cdot \frac{\pi \text{ radians}}{180°} = \frac{2\pi}{3}$ radians

4. $\sin\left(\frac{3\pi}{4}\right) = \sin\left(\pi - \frac{3\pi}{4}\right)$ by the Supplements Theorem; Therefore, $\sin\left(\frac{\pi}{4}\right) = \frac{\sqrt{2}}{2}$.   **5.** $\tan 60° = \frac{\sin 60°}{\cos 60°} = \frac{\frac{\sqrt{3}}{2}}{\frac{1}{2}} = \sqrt{3}$

6. Use a calculator; -0.3090 **7. a.** x can be any real number so domain $= \{x \mid x \in \mathbb{R}\}$ **b.** The parent sine function has range $\{y \mid -1 \le y \le 1\}$ and this sine functon is translated up 3 from the parent so its range $\{y \mid 2 \le y \le 4\}$. **c.–f.** From the Characteristics of Sine Waves Theorem, when $\frac{y-k}{b} = \sin\left(\frac{x-h}{a}\right)$, then **c.** amplitude $= b = |1| = 1$. **d.** period $= 2\pi |a| = 2\pi |1| = 2\pi$. **e.** phase shift $= k = \pi$. **f.** vertical shift $= 3$.   **8. a.** $\cos\theta$ is the x-coordinate of the rotation image of the point $(1, 0)$ by θ. This will be positive in the first and fourth quadrants. $\tan\theta = \frac{\sin\theta}{\cos\theta}$ where $\sin\theta$ is the y-coordinate of the rotation of the point $(1, 0)$ by θ. This will be positive in the first and third quadrants. Both are positive on the interval $\{\theta \mid 0 < \theta < \frac{\pi}{2}\}$. **b.** From Part a, $\cos\theta$ is negative in the second and third quadrants and $\tan\theta$ will be negative in the second and fourth quadrants. Both are negative on the interval $\{\theta \mid \frac{\pi}{2} < \theta < \pi\}$. **9.** From the diagram, $\theta = \pi + x$ where $\sin x = 0.988$. By the Half-Turn Theorem, $\sin(\pi + x) = -\sin x$. Therefore, $\sin\theta = -0.988$.   **10.** $R_{\theta + \pi}(1, 0) = (0.156, 0.988)$. Therefore $\cos(\theta + \pi) = 0.156$.   **11.** False. By the Periodicity Theorem, $\cos(\theta + 3\pi) = \cos(\theta + \pi)$ and by the Half-Turn Theorem, $\cos(\theta + \pi) = -\cos\theta \ne \cos\theta$ for all θ. **12.** $f(x) = \cos x$ because by the Periodicity Theorem, $\cos(x + 2\pi k) = \cos x$ and so $\cos(-4\pi) = \cos(0 - 4\pi) = \cos 0 = 1$.   **13.** b is the amplitude which is half of the difference between the maximum and minimum values, so $b = 2$. k is the vertical shift so $k = -3$. h is the phase shift

so $h = \frac{\pi}{2}$. $2\pi |a|$ is the period, and the period is 2π so $|a| = 1$. By checking the equation, $a = 1$.   **14.** By the Pythagorean Identity, $\cos^2\theta + \sin^2\theta = \cos^2\theta + \left(\frac{5}{13}\right)^2 = 1$. So $\cos^2\theta = \frac{144}{169}$. Thus $\cos\theta = \pm\frac{12}{13}$. Since $\frac{\pi}{2} < \theta < \pi$, θ is in the 2nd quadrant. In that quadrant, $\cos\theta$ is negative, so $\cos\theta = -\frac{12}{13}$. Since for all θ, $\cos(-\theta) = \cos\theta$, $\cos(-\theta) = -\frac{12}{13}$.   **15.** We first apply the scale change $(x, y) \rightarrow \left(\frac{x}{3}, y\right)$ resulting in an image with equation $y = \tan 3x$. Next, we apply the translation $(x, y) \rightarrow (x + \pi, y)$ resulting in the final image $y = \tan(3(x - \pi))$.   **16.** B; A vertical scale-change affects the height of a graph, which affects the amplitude.   **17. a.** The maximum is 70 and the minimum is 22 so the amplitude is $\frac{70 - 22}{2} = 24°$. **b.** The period is from minimum (January) to minimum (January), or 12 months. **c.** Answers vary. Sample: The vertical shift is about $22 + 24 = 46$ and the phase shift from the sine function is about 3 months. The equation, using the Characteristics of Sine Waves Theorem, is $\frac{T - 46}{24} = \sin\left(\frac{n - 3}{\frac{12}{2\pi}}\right)$ or $T = 24 \sin\frac{\pi}{6}(n - 3) + 46$. **d.** Substitute 1 into the equation. $T \approx 25.2°$ **18. a.** The maximum of $\cos\theta$ is 1 so the maximum of $12\cos(14\pi t)$ is 12 volts. **b.** The maximum of $\cos\theta$ is achieved when $\theta = 2n\pi$ for any integer n, so $\cos(14\pi t)$ is at a maximum when $14\pi t = 2\pi n$ for some integer n, or when $t = \frac{n}{7}$. Answers vary. Sample: $t = \frac{1}{7}, \frac{2}{7}, \frac{3}{7}$ **19.** D; The graph shows no phase shift from a cosine function with its maximum when $x = 0$. The ampitude is 5 and period is 4π, so the equation must be D. **20.** Answers vary. Sample: The frequency is the reciprocal of the period, so the period is $\frac{1}{60}$. Because no starting point is specified, either a sine or a cosine wave will work. Using the Characteristics of Sine Waves Theorem, an equation is $y = 0.1\sin(120\pi x)$ or $y = 0.1\cos(120\pi x)$.

Self-Test Correlation Chart

Question	1	2	3	4	5	6	7	8	9	10
Objective(s)	A	A	A	B	B	B	E	C	H	H
Lesson(s)	4-1	4-1	4-1	4-4	4-4	4-5	4-8	4-2	4-2	4-5
Question	11	12	13	14	15	16	17	18	19	20
Objective(s)	D	I	J	D	J	E	F	G	J	F
Lesson(s)	4-3	4-6	4-9	4-3	4-8	4-7	4-7	4-10	4-7	4-7

Chapter Review (pp. 288–291)
1. a. 144° **b.** $\frac{4\pi}{5}$ **3.** –150° **5.** $\frac{5\pi}{4}$ **7.** $\frac{1}{3}$ of a revolution
9. $\frac{\sqrt{2}}{2}$ **11.** $\frac{\sqrt{3}}{3}$ **13.** 0.996 **15.** –0.99 **17.** 2.90 **19.** $-\frac{\sqrt{3}}{2}$
21. 0 **23.** (–1, 0) **25.** $x = \frac{2\pi}{3}, \frac{4\pi}{3}$ **27.** $\frac{\pi}{2} + \pi n$, for $n \in \mathbb{Z}$
29. true; the range of the sine function is $\{x \mid -1 \le x \le 1\}$ as determined by the unit circle **31.** D **33.** By the Complements Theorem, $-\sin\left(\frac{\pi}{2} - \theta\right) = -\cos\theta$. By the Supplements Theorem, $-\cos\theta = \cos(\pi - \theta)$.
35. $-\sqrt{1 - k^2}$ **37.** $-\sqrt{1 - k^2}$ **39.** true; by the Periodicity Theorem, $\sin(\theta + 4\pi) = \sin\theta$ **41. a.** $\frac{\sqrt{15}}{4}$ and $\frac{\sqrt{15}}{4}$ **b.** $\sqrt{15}$ and $-\sqrt{15}$ **43. a.** $\frac{2}{3}$ **b.** 2 **c.** 0 **45. a.** $\frac{\pi}{3}$ **b.** does not exist **c.** 0 **47.** maximum: 15; minimum: 5 **49. a.** $y = -3\cos(4(x - 7))$ **b.** $(x, y) \rightarrow \left(\frac{x}{4} + 7, -3y\right)$ **51. a.** $\frac{1}{150}$ seconds ≈ 0.00667 seconds **b.** Answers vary. Sample: $t = \frac{1}{25}, \frac{2}{25}, \frac{3}{25}$ **53. a.** $\frac{1}{2}$ radians **b.** $\frac{3}{2\pi} \approx 0.477$ **c.** $\frac{10\pi}{3} \approx 10.472$ seconds **55. a.** $y = 2.233\sin(0.017x - 1.317) + 12.133$ **b.** about 372.9 **c.** about 9.90 hours **57. a.** $y = 3\sin(5\pi t)$ **b.** 0 cm **c.** $h = 3\cos(5\pi t) + 3\sin(5\pi t)$
59. a. g **b.** –0.940 **61. a.** f **b.** 0.342 **63.** $-b$ **65.** $-b$
67. $f(x)$ must be $-\cos(x)$ because $-\sin(20\pi) = 0$
69. a.

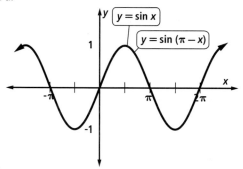

b. the graphs are identical **c.** Supplements Theorem
71. C **73.** A
75.

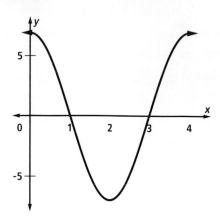

77. $y = \cos\left(\dfrac{x + \frac{\pi}{3}}{2}\right)$

Chapter 5

Lesson 5-1 (pp. 294–298)

Guided Example 1

hypotenuse; $\frac{20}{29}$; leg adjacent to A; $\frac{21}{29}$; leg opposite A; leg adjacent to A; $\frac{20}{21}$

Guided Example 3

EP; 60; 46.9; 52.1

Questions

1. $\tan\theta = \frac{\sin\theta}{\cos\theta} = \frac{\frac{\text{leg opposite }\theta}{\text{hypotenuse}}}{\frac{\text{leg adjacent to }\theta}{\text{hypotenuse}}} = \frac{\text{leg opposite }\theta}{\text{leg adjacent to }\theta}$ 3. about

10.2   5. about 290 ft   7. a. $\frac{3}{5}, \frac{3}{5}$ b. The two values are equal because the leg opposite D is the same as the leg adjacent to B.   9. $24\frac{1}{8}$ in   11. (11.3, 22.3)   13. $\cos\theta$

15. a. about 0.28   b. –0.292   c. 0.96

Lesson 5-2 (pp. 299–303)

Questions

1. Answers vary. Sample: The function does not take every value in the range of cosine.   3. Answers vary. Sample: The function is not continuous on the restricted domain.   5. $\frac{\pi}{4}$; 45°   7. $\frac{5\pi}{6}$; 150°   9. about 19.8°   11. 50°

13. Answers vary. Sample: –338°, –22°, 22°, 338°, 382°

15. about 17.2 miles north, about 24.6 miles east

17. a. $\left(400, -\frac{1}{2}\right)$ b. $\left(0, \frac{1}{8}\right)$ c. $\left(60, \frac{1}{16}\right)$

Lesson 5-3 (pp. 304–308)

Questions

1. a. $t = \sqrt{a^2 + b^2 - 2ab\cos T}$ b. $t = \sqrt{65 + 28\sqrt{2}}$ 3. A

5. a. slope of $\overline{CD} = \tan C$; slope of $\overline{CA} = \tan C$ b. The lines through both $\overline{CA}$ and $\overline{CD}$ have the same slope ($\tan C$) and y-intercept $(0, 0)$ so the points are collinear.   7. $BC =$

$15\sqrt{2 + \sqrt{3}}$ 9. about 111.4 ft   11. about 18.459 m

13. Let A be the largest angle. By the Law of Cosines, 7^2 $= 2^2 + 3^2 - 2 \cdot 3 \cdot 2 \cdot \cos A$; $36 = -12\cos A$; $\cos A = -3$ < -1. But $\cos\theta$ must lie between –1 and 1. So, the triangle cannot exist.   15. about 105 feet

17. a. $d = \sqrt{289 - 240\cos\theta}$ b. $\theta = \cos^{-1}\left(\frac{d^2 - 289}{-240}\right)$

19. a. 0° or 0 radians   b. 150° or $\frac{5\pi}{6}$

21. a.

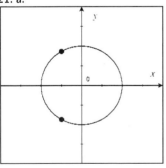

b. Two known values that satisfy the equation are 120° and –120°. By the Periodicity Theorem, adding 360° to each will result in the same cosine. Doing this twice gives us solutions 600°, 840°, which are both in the range. In radians these are $\frac{13\pi}{3}$, and $\frac{17\pi}{3}$.   c. –120° or $-\frac{\pi}{3}$

Lesson 5-4 (pp. 309–313)

Guided Example 2

46.2°; 133.8°; 46.2°

Questions

1. Answers vary. Sample: A value in the domain of the inverse sine function could have more than one value in the range, so it cannot be a function.   3.a.

Point on $y = \sin x$	$\left(-\frac{\pi}{2}, -1\right)$	$\left(-\frac{\pi}{3}, -\frac{\sqrt{3}}{2}\right)$	$\left(-\frac{\pi}{4}, -\frac{\sqrt{2}}{2}\right)$
Corresponding point on $y = \sin^{-1} x$	$\left(-1, -\frac{\pi}{2}\right)$	$\left(-\frac{\sqrt{3}}{2}, -\frac{\pi}{3}\right)$	$\left(-\frac{\sqrt{2}}{2}, -\frac{\pi}{4}\right)$

$\left(-\frac{\pi}{6}, -\frac{1}{2}\right)$	(0, 0)	$\left(\frac{\pi}{6}, \frac{1}{2}\right)$	$\left(\frac{\pi}{4}, \frac{\sqrt{2}}{2}\right)$	$\left(\frac{\pi}{3}, \frac{\sqrt{3}}{2}\right)$	$\left(\frac{\pi}{2}, \frac{1}{2}\right)$
$\left(-\frac{1}{2}, -\frac{\pi}{6}\right)$	(0, 0)	$\left(\frac{1}{2}, \frac{\pi}{6}\right)$	$\left(\frac{\sqrt{2}}{2}, \frac{\pi}{4}\right)$	$\left(\frac{\sqrt{3}}{2}, \frac{\pi}{3}\right)$	$\left(\frac{1}{2}, \frac{\pi}{2}\right)$

b.

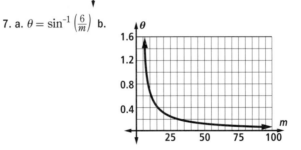

c. domain: $\{x \mid -1 \le x \le 1\}$

range: $\left\{y \mid -\frac{\pi}{2} \le y \le \frac{\pi}{2}\right\}$

d. reflection over the line $y = x$; $T(x, y) = (y, x)$ 5. $\frac{\pi}{2}$; 90°

7. a. $\theta = \sin^{-1}\left(\frac{6}{m}\right)$ b.

c. 0.2; This is the angle in radians at which the plane is descending.   9. B is false because, since the domain is restricted for the inverse sine function, there are values of θ that are not in the domain of the inverse sine function.

11. For $-1 \le x \le 1$, let $y = \sin^{-1} x$. By the definition of $\sin^{-1} x$, $\sin y = x$. Therefore, $\sin(\sin^{-1} x) = x$ for all x such that $-1 \le x \le 1$.   13. a. $t = \frac{1}{60\pi}\sin^{-1}\left(\frac{E}{4}\right)$ b. The graph of t is the image of the graph of the inverse sine function under $S: (x, y) \to \left(4x, \frac{y}{60\pi}\right)$.   15. $\frac{7\pi}{6}$ 17. about 365 yards   19. a. Answers vary. Sample: 504°   b. Answers vary. Sample: –216°   c. 36°   21. a. y-intercept: –15; x-intercepts: –3 and 2.5   b. It has a minimum at $\left(-\frac{1}{4}, -\frac{121}{8}\right)$.

Lesson 5-5 (pp. 314–319)

Guided Example 3

sin 35°; 8; 8 sin 35°; 0.7647; 0.7647; 49.89°; 49.89°; 130.11°; 49.89°, 130.11

Questions

1. about 405.4   3. its opposite side   5. about 9.2
7. $a \approx 7.07$, $b \approx 13.66$ 9. a. about 74.6° or 105.4°
b.

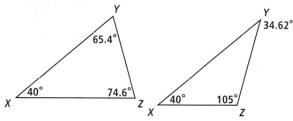

11. false   13. about 0.55 cm   15. a. $50\sqrt{2} < XY < 100$
b. $100 \le XY, XY = 50\sqrt{2}$ c. $0 \le XY < 50\sqrt{2}$ 17. 30°, $\frac{\pi}{6}$
19. $\frac{\sqrt{3}}{2}$ 21. $-t$ 23. $y + 4 = |x + 3|$ 25. a. 3920 b. $490k$
c. $\frac{490}{k}$ d. 434

Lesson 5-6 (pp. 320–324)

Questions

1. a. 4.0° b. If a plane had an altitude of 5.5 miles and was about 78.6 miles from the airport it would need to descend at an angle of about 4°.

3. a.

Point on $y = \tan x$	(−1.5, −14.1)	$\left(-\frac{\pi}{3}, -\sqrt{3}\right)$	$\left(-\frac{\pi}{4}, -1\right)$
Corresponding point on $y = \tan^{-1} x$	(−14.1, −1.5)	$\left(-\sqrt{3}, -\frac{\pi}{3}\right)$	$\left(-1, -\frac{\pi}{4}\right)$

$\left(-\frac{\pi}{6}, -\frac{\sqrt{3}}{3}\right)$	(0, 0)	$\left(\frac{\pi}{6}, \frac{\sqrt{3}}{3}\right)$	$\left(\frac{\pi}{4}, 1\right)$	$\left(\frac{\pi}{3}, \sqrt{3}\right)$	(1.5, 14.1)
$\left(-\frac{\sqrt{3}}{3}, -\frac{\pi}{6}\right)$	(0, 0)	$\left(\frac{\sqrt{3}}{3}, \frac{\pi}{6}\right)$	$\left(1, \frac{\pi}{4}\right)$	$\left(\sqrt{3}, \frac{\pi}{3}\right)$	(14.1 , 1.5)

b.

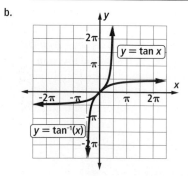

c. domain: $\{x \mid x \in \mathbb{R}\}$ range: $\left\{y \mid -\frac{\pi}{2} < y < \frac{\pi}{2}\right\}$
d. $T:(x, y) \rightarrow (y, x)$ 5. $\frac{\pi}{4}$ or 45°

7. a.

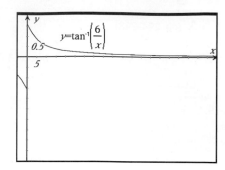

b. about 0.086

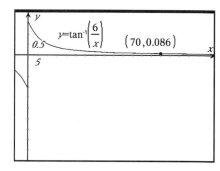

c. When $x = 70$ miles, $\tan^{-1}\left(\frac{6}{70}\right) \approx 0.086 \approx 4.9°$. The angle of descent is almost 5°.

9. a.

The slope of the line is 2, so $\frac{b}{a} = 2$ and $\tan \theta = \frac{b}{a} = 2$. Thus $\tan^{-1}(2) = \theta$.
b. If $y = mx + b$, then $\tan \theta = m$ and $\theta = \tan^{-1} m$.
11. a. $y = \tan^{-1}\left(\frac{80}{x}\right)$
b. $y = \tan^{-1}\left(\frac{110}{x}\right) - \tan^{-1}\left(\frac{30}{x}\right)$
13. $-\frac{\pi}{3}$
15. about 883.7
feet   17. B   19. C   21. B   23. a. $x = 1, x = 3$ b. $x = \frac{1}{2}$, $x = -\frac{5}{3}$ c. no real solutions

Lesson 5-7 (pp. 325–330)

Guided Example 2

9; $\frac{3}{4}$; 2.2935; 2.2935; 1.1350; 2.1350; 0.3650; 1.3650; 2.3650; 9.00; 9.00

Questions

1. The restricted domains of the trigonometric functions used in obtaining their inverse functions; an interval equal in size to the period of the function under study; and the set of all real numbers on which the function is defined.

3. a. $\theta \approx 0.767$, or $\theta \approx 5.516$

b.

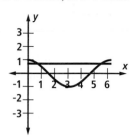

c. $\theta \approx 0.767 + 2\pi n$, or $\theta \approx 5.516 + 2\pi n$, where n is any integer   **5. a.** 10

b.

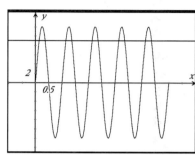

c. 3.1349, 4.1349, 3.3650, and 4.3650 seconds   **7.** ≈ 3.343, or ≈ 6.082 **9. a.** 82°   **b.** 82°, 278°   **c.** $82° + 360n°$ or $278° + 360n°$ for all integers n **11. a.** 194 days or 353 days   **b.** October 1 or March 9   **13.** $\theta \approx 1.25$ or $\theta \approx 4.39$ **15.** $\approx 35.8°$ **17. a.** $y = 17.5 \cos\left(\frac{\pi x}{60}\right) + 12.5$ **b.** 30, 29.40, 27.66, 24.87, 21.25, 17.03, 12.50, 7.97, 3.75, and 0.13 meters   **19.** neither   **21.** odd   **23.** odd

Lesson 5-8 (pp. 331–335)

Guided Example 1

a.

t	$x = 2\cos t$	$y = 5\sin t$
0°	2.00	0
30°	1.73	2.50
60°	1.00	4.33
90°	0	5.00
180°	−2.00	0
270°	0	−5.00

b. $\left(\frac{x}{2}\right)^2 + \left(\frac{y}{5}\right)^2;\ \frac{y}{5};\ \frac{x^2}{4} + \frac{y^2}{25}$

Guided Example 2

$2\cos t;\ 2\sin t;\ -4;\ 5;\ -4;\ 2\sin t$

Questions

1. $\begin{cases} x = 25\cos t + 3 \\ y = 25\sin t - 2 \end{cases}$ **3.** $\left(\frac{x}{4}\right)^2 + y^2 = 1$ **5.** $(x-3)^2 + (y+2)^2 = 25$ **7.** $\begin{cases} x = 3\cos t + 5 \\ y = 3\sin t + 5 \end{cases}, \begin{cases} x = 2\cos t + 8 \\ y = 2\sin t + 5 \end{cases}$

9. The point moves counterclockwise on an ellipse centered at $(0, 0)$.   **11.** A size change and translation of

$(x, y) \rightarrow \left(\frac{x}{2} + 8, \frac{y}{2} - 3\right)$

13. a.

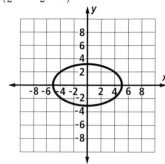

b. The graph is an ellipse that has a semi-major axis of 5 and a semi-minor axis of 3.   **c.** Horizontal translation of $S(x, y) \rightarrow (5x, y)$; vertical translation of $S(x, y) \rightarrow (x, 3y)$ **d.** The y-intercepts of the graph are closer to the origin than the graph of the circle with radius 5.   **e.** $\left(\frac{x}{5}\right)^2 + \left(\frac{y}{5}\right)^2 = 1$ **15. a.** Traces a circle by moving counterclockwise around the origin, from an original position of $(1, 0)$.   **b.** Traces a circle by moving clockwise around the origin, from an original position of $(0, 1)$.   **c.** Traces a circle by moving counterclockwise around the origin, from an original position of $(1, 0)$. Traces twice as fast as the other two graphs.   **17.** 24   **19.** Amplitude: 3, period: 12π, vertical shift: 7 units up, phase shift: π units to the right   **21. a.** $h(x) = \left| 1 - x^2 \right|$ **b.** domain: all real numbers, range: $y \geq 0$

Lesson 5-9 (pp. 336–340)

Questions

1. cot   **3. a. and b.**

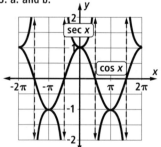

5. $-\frac{2\sqrt{3}}{3}$ **7.** $-\frac{2\sqrt{3}}{3}$ **9.** $\sqrt{2}$ **11.** domain: all real numbers x such that $x \neq n\pi$, where n is an integer; range: all real numbers y such that $y \geq 1$ or $y \leq -1$; period: 2π; asymptotes: any vertical line with equation $x = n\pi$ where n is an integer.   **13. a.** odd   **b.** not odd   **c.** odd   **d.** odd   **15. a.** $\frac{10}{7}$ **b.** $-\frac{10}{7}$ **c.** $\frac{10}{7}$ **d.** $\frac{\sqrt{51}}{10}$ **e.** $\frac{10\sqrt{51}}{51}$ **f.** $\frac{\sqrt{51}}{7}$ **17.** No. The square of secant or cosecant each must be greater than 1 because the absolute value of secant and cosecant are each greater than 1. Two numbers greater than one will sum to a number greater than one.   **19.** By the Supplements Theorem, $\tan(\pi - x) = -\tan x$ for all x.

Therefore, $\cot(\pi - x) = \frac{1}{\tan(\pi - x)} = -\frac{1}{\tan x} = -\cot x$ for all x in the domain of the cotangent function. **21.** 1, where $x \neq \pi n$ for any integer n **23.** $\begin{cases} x = \sqrt{17}\cos t \\ y = -6 + \sqrt{17}\sin t \end{cases}$ **25.** $\left(3x, \frac{y}{5}\right)$

Lesson 5-10 (pp.341–348)

Questions

1. always **3.** Greenwich meridian or prime meridian **5.** equator **7.** about 517 mi **9.** about 2 hours and 21 minutes **11. a.** about 873.2 mi **b.** about 871.7 mi **c.** about 1.5 mi **13.** about 6152 mi **15. a.** $S: (x, y) \rightarrow (3x, y)$; $T: (x, y) \rightarrow (x - \pi, y)$; $T \circ S: (x, y) \rightarrow (3x - \pi, y)$ **b.**

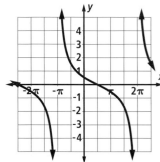

c. period: 3π; phase shift: $-\pi$ **17.** The point moves from $(0, 2)$ clockwise along the ellipse with equation $\frac{x^2}{25} + \frac{y^2}{4} = 1$. **19.** $20.8°$ **21.** car **23. a.** $x = 0$ and $x = 6$ **b.** $y = -23$ and $y = 7$ **c.** $z = -3$, $z = 7$, and $z = -15$

Self-Test (p. 353)

Questions

1. $\sin B = \frac{\text{opposite}}{\text{hypotenuse}} = \frac{13}{\sqrt{205}}$ **2.** $\tan C = \frac{\text{opposite}}{\text{adjacent}} = \frac{6}{13}$
3. $\cos B = \frac{6}{\sqrt{205}}$, so m$\angle B = \cos^{-1}\left(\frac{6}{\sqrt{205}}\right) \approx 65.2°$ **4.** This is the number y whose sine is $\frac{1}{2}$. In the restricted range $-\frac{\pi}{2} \leq y \leq \frac{\pi}{2}$, or $-90° \leq y \leq 90°$, that happens at $\frac{\pi}{6}$, or $30°$.
5. This is the number y whose tangent is 1, which happens when the sine and cosine are equal. In the restricted range $-\frac{\pi}{2} \leq y \leq \frac{\pi}{2}$, or $-90° \leq y \leq 90°$, this happens when $y = \frac{\pi}{4}$, or $45°$. **6.** This is the reciprocal of the tangent of $\frac{3\pi}{4}$. $\frac{1}{\tan\left(\frac{3\pi}{4}\right)}$ $= \frac{1}{-1} = -1$. **7.** $\sin\left(-\frac{2\pi}{3}\right) = -\frac{\sqrt{3}}{2}$. But $\sin^{-1}\left(-\frac{\sqrt{3}}{2}\right) = -\frac{\pi}{3} \neq -\frac{2\pi}{3}$. This is because $-\frac{2\pi}{3}$ is not in the range of the inverse sine function, it can never be a value of $\sin^{-1}(x)$.
8. a.

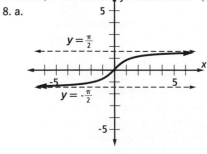

b. The graph, the domain is $\{x \mid x \in \mathbb{R}\}$, and the range is $\{y \mid -\frac{\pi}{2} \leq y \leq \frac{\pi}{2}\}$. These are the reverse of the domain and range of the tangent function. **9. a.** $\theta = \cos^{-1}(-0.125) \approx 1.696$ **b.** One solution is about 1.696, from Part a. By the Opposites Theorem, -1.696 is a solution to $\cos\theta = -0.125$, but it is not in the set of allowable values of θ. Using the Periodicity Theorem, $\theta \approx -1.696 + 2\pi \approx 4.587$ is a second solution. **c.** Each of the solutions from Part b, plus $2\pi n$ for some integer n, is a solution, so $\theta \approx 1.696 + 2\pi n$ or $\theta \approx 4.587 + 2\pi n$ for all integers n. **10.** Solving for $\cos\theta$, $\cos\theta = -\frac{\sqrt{3}}{2}$, so we are looking for the number whose cosine is $\frac{\sqrt{3}}{2}$. One solution is $\frac{5\pi}{6}$. By the Opposites Theorem, another solution is $-\frac{5\pi}{6}$. Each of these solutions plus $2\pi n$ for some integer n is a solution, so $\theta = \frac{5\pi}{6} + 2\pi n$ or $\theta = -\frac{5\pi}{6} + 2\pi n$ for all integers n. **11.** By the Law of Sines, $\frac{6}{\sin 135°} = \frac{x}{\sin 20°}$, so $x = \frac{6\sin 20°}{\sin 135°} \approx 2.90$.
12. Answers vary. Sample: The Law of Cosines finds either the square of the length of a side given SAS, or the cosine of an angle given SSS. Since these are sufficient conditions for congruence, the length and angle are uniquely determined. **13.** First use the Quadratic Formula to find $\cos\theta$. $\cos\theta = \frac{-3 \pm \sqrt{3^2 - 4(1)(-3)}}{2} = \frac{-3 \pm \sqrt{21}}{2}$. $\theta = \cos^{-1}\left(\frac{-3 \pm \sqrt{21}}{2}\right) \approx \pm 0.66$. **14.** The height of the ladder is the length of the side opposite θ, and the length of the ladder is the hypotenuse, so they are related by the sine function. $\sin\theta = \frac{h}{12}$, so $h = 12\sin\theta$. **15.** Substituting into the given equation, $13.6 = 11.65 + 2.35\sin\left(\frac{d}{\frac{365}{2\pi}}\right)$. Then solve for d. $\frac{13.6 - 11.65}{2.35} = \sin\left(\frac{d}{\frac{365}{2\pi}}\right)$, so $\left(\frac{d}{\frac{365}{2\pi}}\right) = \sin^{-1}\left(\frac{13.6 - 11.65}{2.35}\right)$, and $d = \frac{2\pi}{365}\sin^{-1}\left(\frac{13.6 - 11.65}{2.35}\right) \approx 56$ days after March 21. Using the Supplements Theorem, another solution is $\frac{2\pi}{365}\left(\pi - \sin^{-1}\left(\frac{13.6 - 11.65}{2.35}\right)\right) \approx 126$. The next two times will be one period later. A period is 365 days, so they will be $365 + 56 = 421$, and $365 + 126 = 491$ days after March 21. **16.** Use the Law of Cosines. Let the High Street side $= H$. $H^2 = 79^2 + 63^2 - 2(79)(63)\cos 86°$, so $H \approx 97.55$. The fencing needed will be $79 + 63 + 97.55 = 239.55$ ft.
17. This is the image of the unit circle under a scale change of 3 in the x- and y-directions, and then a translation of 2 in the x-direction and -3 in the y-direction. $\begin{cases} x = 3\cos\theta + 2 \\ y = 3\sin\theta - 3 \end{cases}$, $0 \leq \theta \leq 2\pi$. To turn this into rectangular form, start with the Pythagorean Identity, $\cos^2\theta + \sin^2\theta = 1$. Solve the equations to find $\cos\theta = \frac{x-2}{3}$ and $\sin\theta = \frac{y-3}{3}$ and substitute. $(x-2)^2 + (y-3)^2 = 9$.
18. Answers vary. Sample: $\sec x$ is undefined when $\cos x = 0$ because secant is the reciprocal of cosine. $\cos x = 0$

when $x = \frac{\pi}{2} + \pi k$ for any integer k. Two possible values are $\frac{\pi}{2}$ and $\frac{3\pi}{2}$. **19.** Extend meridians from the north pole N through each city to the equator as shown here. Draw the great circle that goes between the cities W and L. $m\widehat{WN} = 90° - 41.35° = 48.65°$. $m\widehat{NL} = 90° - 51.32° = 38.68°$. $m\angle N$ is the same as the angle made at the center of Earth between the two cities, and is also the same as the arc made at the equator between the two cities. This measure is $72.11° - 0.5° = 71.61°$. Using the Spherical Law of Cosines we find that $\cos n = \cos(48.65) \cos(38.68) + \sin(48.65) \sin(38.68) \cos(71.61) \approx 0.6638$. Using the inverse cosine function, $n \approx 48.41°$. This arc is a portion of

a great circle of radius 3960, so the length of the arc is $\frac{48.41°}{360°}(2\pi(3960)) \approx 3346$ mi.

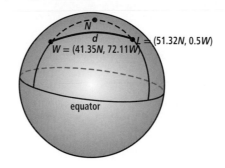

Self-Test Correlation Chart

Question	1	2	3	4	5	6	7	8	9	10
Objective(s)	A	A	C	B	B	E	G	L	D	D
Lesson(s)	5-1	5-1	5-2	5-4	5-6	5-9	5-4	5-6	5-2	5-4
Question	11	12	13	14	15	16	17	18	19	
Objective(s)	C	F	D	H	J	I	M	E	K	
Lesson(s)	5-5	5-3	5-7	5-1	5-7	5-5	5-8	5-9	5-10	

Chapter Review (pp. 354–357)

Questions

1. $\sin A = \frac{4}{\sqrt{41}}$; $\cos A \approx \frac{5}{\sqrt{41}}$; $\tan A = 0.8$ **3.** $\frac{\sqrt{3}}{2}$ **5.** $-\frac{\sqrt{3}}{2}$
7. 0.402 **9.** $-\frac{\pi}{4}$, $-45°$ **11.** $\frac{\pi}{3}$, $60°$ **13.** $\frac{\pi}{3}$ **15.** ≈ 11.46
17. ≈ 5.06 **19.** $\approx 38.9°$, $\approx 141.1°$ **21.** $A \approx 124.6°$; $B \approx$ 19.0°; $C \approx 36.4°$ **23.** ≈ 1.13 **25.** $\frac{\pi}{3}$ **27.** ≈ 2.51 and ≈ 3.77 **29.** ≈ 0.61 and ≈ 2.53 **31.** ≈ 7.39 and ≈ 10.53
33. $y = -\frac{\pi}{3} + 2\pi k$ and $y = -\frac{2\pi}{3} + 2\pi k$ for any integer k
35. $w \approx 0.42 + \frac{\pi}{3}k$ for any integer k **37.** $\theta = \frac{\pi}{6} + \frac{2\pi}{3}k$ and $\theta = -\frac{\pi}{18} + \frac{2\pi}{3}k$ and $\theta = -\frac{5\pi}{18} + \frac{2\pi}{3}k$ **39.** $\sqrt{\frac{10}{19}}$ **41.** -1
43. $\sec x$ **45.** The Pythagorean Theorem is the Law of Cosines for a right triangle. Since $\cos \frac{\pi}{2} = 0$, $-2ab \cos C = 0$, leaving $c^2 = a^2 + b^2$. **47.** In such a triangle, $\sin \angle ACB \approx 1.88$, but since this is outside the range of sine, this triangle is not possible. **49.** D **51.** domain: $\{x \mid 0 \le x \le 1\}$; range: $\{y \mid 0 \le y \le \pi\}$ **53.** Answers vary. Sample: $\cos\left(-\frac{\pi}{4}\right) = \frac{\sqrt{2}}{2}$, but $\cos^{-1}\left(\frac{\sqrt{2}}{2}\right) = \frac{\pi}{4} \ne -\frac{\pi}{4}$
55. Answers vary. Sample: -4.323, -1.961, 1.961, 4.323
57. about 27.17 m **59. a.** about 18.01 miles **b.** about 9.005 mph **c.** about 4:51 P.M. **61.** about 670 ft **63. a.** about 17.64 mi **b.** about 9.83 mi

65. a. and **b.** When the graph is below zero the paddle is in the water.

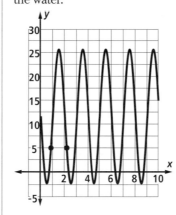

c. $t = \frac{\sin^{-1}\left(\frac{5-11}{15}\right)}{\pi} + 3$; about 0.87 and about 0.13 minutes

67. a. $t = \frac{\sin^{-1}\left(\frac{d}{6}\right)}{\pi}$
b. about 0.27 sec
69. about 430 mi
71. about 9244 mi
73. D

75.

77. a. $(x - 7)^2 + (y + 5)^2 = 1$ **b.** original: $\begin{cases} x = \cos t \\ y = \sin t \end{cases}$,

$0 \le t \le 2\pi$; image: $\begin{cases} x = \cos t + 7 \\ y = \sin t - 5 \end{cases}$, $0 \le t \le 2\pi$

Chapter 6

Lesson 6-1 (pp. 360–366)

Guided Example 2
HT; TH; TT; HH; 1; 2; 1; are not

Guided Example 3 a. GBB; BGG; GBG; GGB; GGG b. 8; 3; $\frac{3}{8}$

Questions

1. a. {Always, Sometimes, Never} b. {Sometimes, Never} c. 2 d. $\frac{2}{3}$ 3. a. {(1, 3), (2, 4), (3, 5), (4, 6), (3, 1), (4, 2), (5, 3), (6, 4)} b. $\frac{2}{9}$ 5. a. ∅ b. 0 7. a. {HT, TH, TT} b. $\frac{3}{4}$ 9. a. {BBBB, BBBG, BBGB, BBGG, BGBB, BGBG, BGGB, BGGG, GBBB, GBBG, GBGB, GBGG, GGBB, GGBG, GGGB, GGGG} b. $\frac{1}{4}$

11. a.

n	P(n)
1	$\frac{1}{2}$
2	$\frac{1}{4}$
3	$\frac{1}{8}$
4	$\frac{1}{16}$

b. $\frac{1}{32}$ 13. 414

15. a.

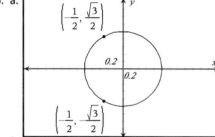

b. 600°, 840° c. Answers vary. Sample: –120°
17. a. ≈ 79.3 b. about 59.2 19. a. intersection b. union c. intersection

Lesson 6-2 (pp. 367–373)

Guided Example 3 10; 6; 0; P(sum > 9); P(has 3 and sum > 9); 10; 0; 16

Questions

1. a. {(1, 2), (2, 1), (1, 5), (2, 4), (3, 3), (4, 2), (5, 1), (3, 6), (4, 5), (5, 4), (6, 3), (6, 6)} b. $\frac{1}{3}$
3. a. {(1, 2), (2, 1), (3, 6), (4, 5), (5, 4), (6, 3)} b. $\frac{1}{6}$ 5. when $P(A \cap B) = 0$ 7. true; Complementary events never intersect. Therefore, they are always mutually exclusive.
9. about 90% of males in the U.S. are not left-handed 11. $\frac{N(A \cup B)}{N(S)} = \frac{N(A)}{N(S)} + \frac{N(B)}{N(S)} - \frac{N(A \cap B)}{N(S)}$. So, $P(A \cup B) = P(A) + P(B) - P(A \cap B)$.
13. $\frac{21}{36}$ or $\frac{7}{12}$ 15. $\frac{14}{36}$ or $\frac{7}{18}$ 17. No, because $P(A \cap B) =$

0.05 ≠ 0. 19. a. {H1, H2, H3, H4, H5, H6, T1, T2, T3, T4, T5, T6} b. 8; $\frac{8}{12} = \frac{2}{3}$ c. Answers vary. Sample: heads and a number greater than 3 21. a. $\frac{48}{55}$ b. $-\frac{73}{55}$ c. $-\frac{73}{48}$ d. $\frac{55}{48}$
e. 3.86 radians 23. $3.385

Lesson 6-3 (pp. 374–380)

Guided Example 3 26; 26^2; 10; 10^4; 676; 10,000
Guided Example 5 10; $\frac{10}{36} = \frac{5}{18}$; 6; 6; $\frac{6}{36} = \frac{1}{6}$

Questions

1. 90 vacations 3. 260,000 possible 5-character ID numbers 5. Independent: $P(A) \cdot P(B) = P(A \cap B) = \frac{1}{30}$.
7. $2^6 \cdot 4^{12} = 1,073,741,824$ ways of answering
9. a. 3,910 sundaes b. 6,670 sundaes c. 4,080 sundaes 11. $P(A) = \frac{1}{2}$, $P(B) = \frac{6}{8} = \frac{3}{4}$, so $P(A) \cdot P(B) = \frac{3}{8}$, and $P(A \cap B) = \frac{3}{8}$. So A and B are independent. 13. a. $\frac{1}{7}$
b. $\frac{17}{30}$ 15. $\frac{7}{36}$ 17. $x(2x - 3)(4x + 1)$ 19. 3,628,800
21. 220

Lesson 6-4 (pp. 381–386)

Guided Example 2 10; 6; 10; 6; 6; 7 · 6 · 5; 151,200; 6; 6

Questions

1. BAT; BTA; ATB; ABT; TAB; TBA 3. a. 117 · 116 · 115 · 114 b. $\frac{117!}{113!}$ 5. $\frac{317!}{315!} = 100,172$ 7. a. $_8P_3 = 336$ b. $_5P_3 = 60$ 9. n; There are n choices when you choose 1 element from a set with n elements. 11. By one formula, $_nP_n = n!$. By the alternate formula, $_nP_n = \frac{n!}{(n-n)!} = \frac{n!}{0!}$. These formulas are only equal if $0! = 1$, so it is defined to equal 1.
13. a. $_5P_4 = 120$ b. $\frac{1}{120}$ 15. $_3P_3 \cdot _2P_2 = 12$ different seating arrangements 17. a. $_nP_0 = \frac{n!}{(n-0)!} = \frac{n!}{n!} = 1$
b. $_nP_0$ is the number of permutations of 0 objects selected from n objects. There can only be one because there is only one empty set possible. 19. 67,600,000 21. a. $\frac{\sqrt{3}}{3}$
b. $\frac{1}{2}$ 23. a. $\frac{1}{3}$ b. $\pm \frac{4\sqrt{3}}{3}$

Lesson 6-5 (pp. 387–394)

Guided Example 2 a. 583; 61; 513 b. have no tattoo c. do not have Hepatitis C d. $\frac{8}{61} \approx 13.1$; more

Questions

1. a. about 36.1% b. about 81.3% c.

	Freshman	Sophomore	Junior	Senior	Total
Spanish	8	11	5	2	26
French	2	5	0	1	8
No Language	5	8	10	13	36
Total	15	24	15	16	70

3. a. developed polio: about 0.02%; did not develop polio: about 99.98% b. vaccinated: about 22.3%; unvaccinated: about 77.7% c. about 22.3% 5. a. 6,231.6; the number (in thousands) of passenger cars involved in accidents b. 47.9;

the number (in thousands) of fatalities in all motor vehicle accidents **c.** about 0.5% **d.** about 16.3% **7. a.** about 8.3% **b.** about 44.4% **c.** about 25.0% **9. a.** The population for this question is children in first class; 100% **b.** The population for this question is all survivors; about 0.8% **c.** The population for this question is all people on the Titanic; about 0.3% **11. a.** $98 \cdot 97 \cdot 96 = 912,576$ **b.** $\frac{98!}{95!} = 912,576$ **13.** $\frac{212!}{209!} = 9,393,720$ **15. a.** {(1,1), (1,3), (2,2), (3,1), (6,2), (5,3), (4,4), (3,5), (2,6), (6,4), (5,5), (4,6)} **b.** $\frac{1}{3}$

Lesson 6-6 (pp. 395-401)

Guided Example 0.0049; 0.05, 0.995; 0.04975; 0.02, 0.0001; 0.995, 0.94525; 99.5; D; not A; 0.0001

Questions

1. about 62.5% **3. a.** let D = has the disease and A = tests positive

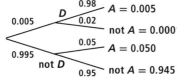

b. $P(\text{not } D|A) = \frac{P(\text{not } D \cap A)}{P(A)} = \frac{0.050}{0.50 + 0.0050} \approx 0.91$

c. Answers vary. Sample: 91 % of positives are false positives. The reason for this surprising result is that very few people in the population have the disease, so a low percentage of false positives is enough to overtake a high percentage of true positives. **5. a.** A true statement detected as a lie. **b.** A lie is undetected. **7. a.** P(false positive|positive test) $= \frac{0.03}{0.36 + 0.03} = 0.076 \approx 7.6\%$

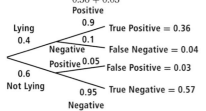

b. P(false positive|positive test) $= \frac{0.2125}{0.2125 + 0.1125} = 0.653 = 65.3\%$

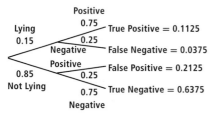

c. Answers vary. Sample: About 65.3% of people given a polygraph test whose result indicated a lie were actually telling the truth. **9.** about 98% **11. a.** $P(M)$ **b.** $P(C|M)$ **c.** 3 **d.** $\frac{1}{3}$ **e.** Answers vary. Sample: The prosecutor computed the chance of a random person matching the description, not the probability that someone who

matched the description actually committed the crime. Since more than one person in California matches the description, the probability that the accused is guilty is $\frac{P(M \cap C)}{P(M)} = \frac{1}{3}$. **13. a.** 14.2% **b.** 60.9% **15. a.** $_6P_4 = 360$ **b.** $_2P_1 \cdot _5P_3 = 120$

Lesson 6-7 (pp. 402-409)

Questions

1. A simulation is an experimental model that attempts to capture all aspects of the original situation that affect the outcomes. **3. a.** Assign 1, 2, and 3 to the coupon colors and pick them at random to represent visits to the store. **b.** Answers vary. Sample:

randInt(1,3,5)	{3,1,2,1,3}

c. 5 visits
5. a. Answers vary. Sample: A success equals a 10 digit number in which all the digits are less than 7 as in trial #5.

Trial #	Success?
1	No
2	No
3	No
4	No
5	Yes
6	No

b. Answers vary. Sample: Based off of the simulation, if 10 adults are chosen at random, about $\frac{1}{6}$ of the time all 10 would be in favor of raising the driving age.
7. a. Answers vary. Sample: Generate numbers from 1 to 100, once for men and once for women in each trial. For men, numbers 1–10 are left-handed, and all others are right-handed. For women, 1–8 are left-handed, and all others are right-handed.The relative frequency for 10 trials was 20% in this simulation, so the probability should be about 20%.

Trial #	Man	Woman	Success?
1	82	39	No
2	94	37	No
3	50	24	No
4	10	19	Yes
5	41	24	No
6	65	79	No
7	36	46	No
8	82	34	No
9	73	72	No
10	3	95	Yes

b. 17.2%

9. a. Answers vary. Sample: Let a random number from 1-100 represent one official at-bat; let 1-30 represent a hit and 31-100 represent no hits. One trial is made up of five such random numbers. **b.** Answers vary. Sample:

Trial #	Simulated Hits	Had Hits?
1	73, 14, 38, 57, 59	Yes
2	34, 23, 28, 90, 20	Yes
3	53, 33, 71, 97, 93	No
4	65, 70, 2, 11, 80	Yes
5	37, 51, 49, 92, 40	No
6	18, 44, 99, 24, 49	Yes
7	8, 98, 32, 51, 41	Yes
8	24, 11, 97, 23, 16	Yes
9	95, 39, 39, 63, 23	Yes
10	56, 27, 74, 36, 73	Yes

c. about 20% **11. a.** In one trial, generate two numbers from 1-10. The first number indicates the accuracy of the test. A 1 is a false result, and 9-10 are accurate results. The second number represents the health of the patient. A 1 means the patient is diabetic, and 9-10 mean the patient is not diabetic. **b.** Answers vary. Sample: In 50 trials, the relative frequency of a positive test was $\frac{13}{20}$. **c.** Answers vary. Sample: In the same experiment, 6 non-diabetics tested positive for diabetes. **13.** $_{700}P_3 = 341,531,400$
15. $n!$ **17. a.**

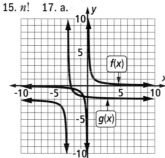

b. $x = -3, y = -2$. These are the asymptotes of f shifted left 3 units and down 2 units. **c.** domain of f: $\{x|x \neq 0\}$, range of f: $\{y|y \neq 0\}$, domain of g: $\{x|x \neq -3\}$, range of g: $\{y|y \neq -2\}$

Lesson 6-8 (pp. 410–416)

Guided Example 2 a. 0.5; 0.5; 5000 **b.** 5000; 67 **c.** 10,000; 0.5067 **d.** 0.5067; 0.5

Questions

1. 3.6 **3. a.** $\frac{23}{3} \approx 7.67$ **b.** $\frac{23}{1650} \approx 0.014$
c. Yes, the difference between the probability and the relative frequency is not large. **5.** Answers vary. Sample: She is basing this prediction on the invalid "law of averages." The probability of rolling a 6 on each turn is still $\frac{1}{6}$. **7.** They should attempt a touchdown, because the expected outcome of a field goal attempt is 1.05 points and the expected outcome of a touchdown attempt is 1.2 points. **9.** 32.5 minutes **11. a.** The expected points for 1 question is 0. Therefore, 10 questions also have an expected count of points of 0. **b.** The outcome from

guessing on n random questions is 0 points. **c.** No.
13. a.

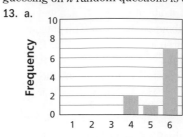

b. No, she has only performed 10 trials, this is not enough to make any long-run conclusions. **c.** No, in fact the new data refute her assertion because the relative frequencies are now closer to $\frac{1}{6}$. **d.** The Law of Large Numbers **15. a.** Answers vary. Sample: Generate numbers from 1 to 100, once for each woman. For women, numbers 1-12 have attached ear lobes and 13-100 do not. A random simulation of 10 trials returned a relative frequency of $\frac{2}{10}$ where at least one of the two has attached ear lobes. **b.** $1 - (0.88)^2 \approx 0.2256$ **17. a.** 210
b. 60 **19.** $y = \left(x - \frac{1}{3}\right)^2 - 2$. **21.** Die 3 is green, die 1 is red, and die 2 is blue.

Lesson 6-9 (pp. 417–425)

Guided Example 2 30; 20; 25; 25; 1; 20; 25; 25; 1; 1; 1
Questions
1. a. the observed number of survivors in a given class **b.** the expected number of survivors in a given class **3.** $\frac{(178 - 228)^2}{228} \approx 11.0$ **5. a.** 5.12 **b.** about 0.024
c. Because $0.024 < 0.05$, we rejected the hypothesis that the coin is fair. **7.** There is no reason to believe the die is biased because the probability of χ^2 as large as 3.1 is about 0.685 so there is no reason to believe the die is biased.
9. a.

Year	2001	2002	2003	2004	2005	2006	2007	To
Observed Number of Cyclones	15	12	16	15	28	10	15	11
Expected Number of Cyclones	15.86	15.86	15.86	15.86	15.86	15.86	15.86	11

b. about 12.54 **c.** about 0.0509 **d.** The results do not provide sufficient evidence to reject the hypothesis at the 0.05-significance level because $0.051 > 0.05$. **11.** The probability of a chi-square value as large as 0.38 is about 0.941 so because $0.941 > 0.05$, then at the 0.05-significance level there is insufficient evidence to reject the claim that point scoring by quarter is the same. **13.** 12
15. Answers vary. Sample: Run a simulation with 100 trials. In each trial you generate a random number from 1 to 100, where 1-45 means the patient has recovered fully, and 46-100 means the patient has not. Add the number of successes to find the relative frequency of recovery.
17. a. $\frac{7}{9} \approx -0.78$ **b.** $\frac{2}{9} \approx 0.22$ **c.** 1

Self-Test (pp. 430–431)

Questions

1. a. {HHH, HHT, HTH, HTT, THH, THT, TTH, TTT}
b. HTT, THT, TTT, TTH   **2. a.** $_{15}P_6 = \dfrac{15!}{(15-6)!} = \dfrac{15!}{9!} = 15$
$\cdot\,14 \cdot 13 \cdot 12 \cdot 11 \cdot 10 = 3{,}603{,}600.$ **b.** $_{15}P_6$ is the number
of all permutations of 6 objects from 15 objects.   **3.** $_9P_4$
$= \dfrac{9!}{(9-4)!} = \dfrac{9!}{5!} = 9 \cdot 8 \cdot 7 \cdot 6 = 3024$ **4.** Tossing the
coin has 2 possible outcomes and rolling the die has 6
possible outcomes, so there are 12 possible outcomes in
the sample space, by the Multiplication Counting Priciple.
In five of these outcomes, the sum of the outcomes of the
two events is less than 5: {$1+3, 1+2, 1+1, 2+2, 2+1$}.
Therefore the probability is $\dfrac{5}{12}$.   **5. a.** The lengths of
flosses in the packages are independent, so the probability
is $(0.15)^4 \approx 0.0005$. **b.** The probability that a package has
at least the advertised amount is $1 - 0.15 = 0.85$ because
the two events are complements. The probability that all
four packages have at least the stated amount is $(0.85)^4 \approx$
0.5220.   **6.** Use the Multiplication Counting Principle.
$4 \cdot 5 \cdot 2 = 40$ different outfits.   **7. a.** By the Addition
Counting Principle, $P(A \cup B) = P(A) + P(B) - P(A \cap B)$
$= 0.7 + 0.8 - 0.6 = 0.9$ **b.** $P(B|A) = \dfrac{P(A \cap B)}{P(A)} = \dfrac{0.6}{0.7} \approx 0.86$

8. a. Answers vary. Sample:

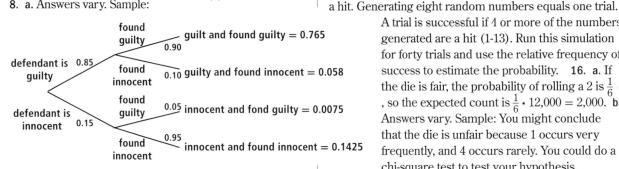

b. $\dfrac{P(\text{innocent and found guilty})}{P(\text{found guilty})} = \dfrac{0.0075}{0.0075 + 0.765} \approx 0.97\%$

c. $\dfrac{P(\text{guilty and found innocent})}{P(\text{found innocent})} = \dfrac{0.085}{0.085 + 0.1425} \approx 37.36\%$

9. true; If A and B are complementary, then they are
mutually exclusive and thus make up the entire sample
space. Since $P(S) = 1$, $P(A) + P(B) = 1$, and therefore
$P(B) = 1 - P(A) = 1 - k$.   **10.** false; For a fair die, the
probability of rolling a 2 is $\frac{1}{6}$. The expected number of
"2"s in 600 rolls is $\frac{1}{6} \cdot 600 = 100$.   **11.** No. A and B are
independent events if and only if $P(A \cap B) = P(A) \cdot P(B)$.
Here, $P(A) \cdot P(B) = 0.21 \cdot 0.17 = 0.0357 \neq P(A \cap B) =$
0.02.   **12.** Calculate the expected distribution of majors
and use this with the observed survey results to do the
chi-square test: $\chi^2 = \dfrac{(125 - 156)^2}{156} + \dfrac{(312 - 351)^2}{351} + \dfrac{(138 - 117)^2}{117}$
$+ \dfrac{(205 - 156)^2}{156} \approx 29.65$. The probability of a χ^2 value of
29.65 or larger is less than 0.001, so the new survey
yields sufficient evidence to reject the hypothesis that the
proportions by major are still what the guidance office
states.   **13.** By totaling the rows and columns we find
that the total dorm population is 1020 and the total car-
owning population is 290. $\frac{290}{1020} \approx 28.4\%$.   **14.** The total
car-owning population is 290, and there are 70 juniors who
own cars. $\frac{70}{290} \approx 24.1\%$.   **15.** Since $.325 = \frac{13}{40}$, simulate this
situation by generating random numbers between 1 and
40, where 1-13 represents a hit and 14-40 represents not
a hit. Generating eight random numbers equals one trial.
A trial is successful if 4 or more of the numbers
generated are a hit (1-13). Run this simulation
for forty trials and use the relative frequency of
success to estimate the probability.   **16. a.** If
the die is fair, the probability of rolling a 2 is $\frac{1}{6}$
, so the expected count is $\frac{1}{6} \cdot 12{,}000 = 2{,}000$. **b.**
Answers vary. Sample: You might conclude
that the die is unfair because 1 occurs very
frequently, and 4 occurs rarely. You could do a
chi-square test to test your hypothesis.
c. No, the sample is too small. By the Law of Large
Numbers, the relative frequency of each of the outcomes
should approach their probability as the number of trials
increases. A chi-square test might be inaccurate on a
sample this small.

Self-Test Correlation Chart

Question	1	2	3	4	5	6	7	8	9	10
Objective(s)	G	C	B	A	I	J	D	I	D	A
Lesson(s)	6-1	6-4	6-4	6-1	6-3	6-3	6-2, 6-6	6-6	6-2	6-8

Question	11	12	13	14	15	16
Objective(s)	E	L	M	H	K	F
Lesson(s)	6-3	6-9	6-5	6-5	6-7	6-8

Chapter Review (pp. 432–435)

Questions

1. $\frac{5}{12}$ 3. $\frac{1}{6}$ 5. $\frac{1}{8}$ 7. $\frac{7}{8}$ 9. $38.\overline{3}$ 11. $8! = 40{,}320$
13. $_7P_5 = 2520$ 15. $2^8 = 256$ 17. 21 19. $54 \cdot 53 \cdot 52 \cdot 51$
21. 1320 23. n 25. 0 27. 0.45 29. independent
31. independent   33. The announcer is incorrectly applying the "law of averages", assuming that the observed count should approach the expected count.
35. expected winnings: $(0)(0.999) + (700)(0.001) = \$0.70$; Someone who plays everyday has expected winnings of $(\$0.70)(365) = \$255.5$ in one year but spent $\$365$ during the year. In the long run, the winnings will approach $\$0.70$ per lottery ticket and therefore yield a profit of $\$0.30$ per lottery ticket for the state.   37. integers from 0 to 359
39. 366 days   41. about 26.7%; about 28.0%   43. $\frac{15}{1024} \approx 0.015$ 45. 0.96%   47. a. about 45.2% b. about 23.9%
49. 36   51. 1440   53. Answers vary. Sample: The experiment in 52 can be modified by changing the value of one of the penny columns to 5 and running another 100 trials.   55. a. In the same order: 375, 1125, 1125, 3375
b. The degree of freedom is 3.
c.

$\frac{(315-375)^2}{375} + \frac{(1202-1125)^2}{1125} + \frac{(1146-11}{1125}$	
	15.6901
$\chi^2\mathrm{Cdf}\left(15.69, \infty, 3\right)$	0.001313

The probability of a chi-square value as high as 15.69 or greater is 0.0013. Because $0.0013 < 0.01$ we can reject the geneticist's claim.

57.
The chi-square simulation web applet gives a chi-square value of 4.296 and a probability of 11.8%. Because $0.118 > 0.05$, we have insufficient evidence to reject the claim of the hypothesized ratios of morning rush hour traffic.

Hypothesized Probabilities

A	B	C	D	E
.25	.625	125	0	0

Observed Frequencies

A	B	C	D	E
191	481	118	0	0

Expected Frequencies

A	B	C	D	E
197.5	493.75	98.75	0	0

Get Chi-Square   Chi: 4.296

Run Simulation

Percent of Distribution Greater than Chi-Square Value: 11.8%

Clear

59. a. about 12.5%, about 13.1%
b. about 27.6%, about 28.9%
c. No, whether a student studies more or less than three hours, the relative frequency of a score increase of less than 25 points appears to be the same. The same is true for students whose scores increased more than 25 points.
d.

	< 25	> 25	Total
Less Study	107	376	483
More Study	63	348	411
Total	170	724	894

Score increase of < 25 points with less study: 22.2%; score increase of < 25 points with more study: 15.3% e. These data exemplify Simpson's Paradox, since there appears to be a correlation between amount of study and performance when you combine the school districts, but not when you examine them separately.

Glossary

A

absolute value of a complex number, $|z|$ The distance of the graph of a complex number from the origin or pole. Also called *modulus*. (**814**)

acceleration due to gravity The acceleration of a free-falling object toward another object caused by gravitational forces; on the surface of Earth equal to approximately 32 feet or 9.8 meters per second per second. (**120**)

Addition Counting Principle (General Form) For any finite sets A and B, $N(A \cup B) = N(A) + N(B) - N(A \cap B)$. (**367**)

Addition Counting Principle (Mutually Exclusive Form) If two finite sets A and B are mutually exclusive, then $N(A \cup B) = N(A) + N(B)$. (**367**)

Addition Formulas for the Cosine and Sine For all real numbers α and β, $\cos(\alpha + \beta) = \cos \alpha \cos \beta - \sin \alpha \sin \beta$, and $\sin(\alpha + \beta) = \sin \alpha \cos \beta + \cos \alpha \sin \beta$. (**766**)

Alternate Formula for $_nP_r$ Theorem The number of permutations of n objects taken r at a time is $_nP_r = \frac{n!}{(n-r)!}$. (**382**)

alternating harmonic sequence The sequence -1, $\frac{1}{2}$, $-\frac{1}{3}$, $\frac{1}{4}$, ... in which the nth term is $c_n = \frac{(-1)^n}{n}$. (**518**)

amplitude One-half the difference between the maximum and minimum values of a sine wave. (**257**)

angle The union of two rays (its sides) with the same endpoint (its vertex). (**Previous Course**)

angle of depression An angle measured downward from a horizontal line. (**296**)

angle of elevation An angle measured upward from a horizontal line. (**296**)

Arccos function See *inverse cosine function*.

Archimedean spiral The graph of $r = k\theta$, for $\theta > 0$, in the polar plane. (**810**)

Arcsin function See *inverse sine function*.

Arctan function See *inverse tangent function*.

area under a curve The area between the curve and the x-axis. (**688**)

Argand diagram The graphical representation of the complex number $a + bi$ as (a, b) in the coordinate plane. (**811**)

argument of a complex number For the complex number $[r, \theta]$, θ. (**814**)

arithmetic sequence A sequence in which the difference between consecutive terms is constant. Also called *linear sequence*. (**505**)

arithmetic series An indicated sum of the terms of an arithmetic sequence. (**523**)

arithmetic mean See *mean*.

asymptote A line that the graph of a function $y = f(x)$ approaches as the variable x approaches a fixed value or increases or decreases without bound. (**105**)

at random See *randomly*.

average See *mean*.

axis of symmetry In a plane, a reflecting line ℓ over which a figure can be mapped onto itself. Also called line of symmetry. (**172**)

B

bar graph A two-dimensional display of data in which one axis labels categories or variables and the other is a numerical scale typically with counts or percentages. (**10**)

base (of an exponential function) The number b in the exponential function $f : x \rightarrow ab^x$. (**103**)

base (of a logarithmic function) The number b in the logarithmic function $f : x \rightarrow \log_b x$. (**575**)

Basic Properties of Probability Theorem Let S be the sample space associated with an experiment, and let $P(E)$ be the probability of E. Then $0 \leq P(E) \leq 1$; if $E = S$, then $P(E) = 1$; and if $E = \emptyset$ then $P(E) = 0$. (**363**)

bearing An angle measured counterclockwise from due north. (**298**)

bell-shaped curve See *normal curve*.

bins Non-overlapping intervals of equal width in the range of a numerical variable. (**22**)

binomial coefficients The coefficients in the expansion of $(x + y)^n$; the combinations $_nC_k$. (**632**)

binomial distribution function The function B where $B(x) = {_nC_x}P^x(1-p)^{n-x}$, giving the probability of getting exactly x successes in n binomial trials, each of which has a probability p of success. **(651)**

binomial experiment An experiment with a fixed number of independent trials, each with only two possible outcomes, often called success and failure, and each with the same probability of success. **(645)**

binomial probability distribution See *binomial distribution function*.

Binomial Probability Theorem Suppose that in a binomial experiment with n trials, the probability of success is p in each trial, and the probability of failure is q, where $q = 1 - p$. Then p(exactly x successes) = ${_nC_x} \cdot p^x q^{n-x}$. **(647)**

Binomial Theorem For any nonnegative integer, n,
$$(x + y)^n = {_nC_0}x^n + {_nC_1}x^{n-1}y + {_nC_x}x^{n-2}y^2 + \cdots +$$
$${_nC_k}x^{n-k}y^k + \cdots + {_nC_n}y^n = \sum_{k=0}^{n} {_nC_k}x^{n-k}y^k.$$ **(632)**

birthday problem The problem of determining the probability that n people have n different birthdays. **(31)**

box plot A visual representation of the five-number summary of a data set in which a box represents the part of the data from the first to the third quartile, with another line segment crossing the box at the set's median, and two segments protruding from the box (called *whiskers*) to represent the rest of the data. **(32)**

box-and-whiskers plot See *box plot*.

C

cardioid The graph of $r = a(\cos\theta - 1)$ or $r = a(\sin\theta - 1)$ in the polar plane. **(810)**

categorical variable A variable whose values represent characteristics rather than measures. **(8)**

census A survey of an entire population; in the U.S., a survey, conducted every ten years, of the entire population of the United States. **(6)**

center of mass of a data set The point whose coordinates are the means of the corresponding coordinates of the points in the data set. **(94)**

center of symmetry for a figure The center of a rotation under which the figure is mapped onto itself. **(172)**

center of rotation A fixed point about which each point in the plane turns a fixed magnitude under a rotation. **(222)**

central angle of a circle An angle whose vertex is the center of the circle. **(226)**

Central Limit Theorem Suppose random samples of size n are selected from a population with mean μ and standard deviation σ. Then, as n increases the following occur: The mean $\mu_{\bar{x}}$ of the distribution of sample means approaches μ; the standard deviation $\sigma_{\bar{x}}$ of the distribution of sample means approaches $\frac{\sigma}{\sqrt{n}}$; and the distribution of sample means approaches a normal curve with mean μ and standard deviation $\frac{\sigma}{\sqrt{n}}$. **(710)**

Change of Base Theorem For all values of a, b, and c for which the logarithms exist, $\log_b a = \frac{\log_c a}{\log_c b}$. **(596)**

circular functions The trigonometric functions, when defined in terms of the unit circle. **(229)**

circular motion Movement of a point around a circle. **(273)**

Circular Arc Length Formula If s is the length of the arc of a central angle of θ radians in a circle of radius r, then $s = r\theta$. **(226)**

cluster In a distribution of a set of data, a place where a relatively large number of data are near each other. **(24)**

coefficient The numbers $a_n, a_{n-1}, \ldots, a_0$ of the polynomial $a_n x^n + a_{n-1}x^{n-1} + \cdots + a_1 x + a_0$; more generally, a constant factor of a variable term. **(438)**

column matrix A matrix consisting of a single column. **(745)**

combination A collection of objects in which the order of objects does not matter. **(618)**

combination of n things taken r at a time, ${_nC_r}$, $\binom{n}{r}$ A subset of r objects from a set of n objects. **(619)**

common logarithm A logarithm with base 10. **(576)**

complementary events Two events that are mutually exclusive and whose union is the entire sample space. **(370)**

Complements Theorem For all θ in radians, $\sin\left(\frac{\pi}{2} - \theta\right) = \cos\theta$ and $\cos\left(\frac{\pi}{2} - \theta\right) = \sin\theta$. **(239)**

complex conjugates A pair of complex numbers that can be written as $a + bi$ and $a - bi$. **(467)**

complex number A number that can be written in the form $a + bi$, where a and b are real numbers and $i = \sqrt{-1}$. (466)

complex plane A coordinate plane for representing complex numbers. (811)

composite The function $g \circ f$ defined by $(g \circ f)(x) = g(f(x))$, whose domain is the set of values of x in the domain of f for which $f(x)$ is in the domain of g. (194)

composition of functions The binary operation that maps two functions g and f onto their composite $g \circ f$. (194)

compounded continuously The limit of compounding interest as the number of compoundings grows larger and larger in a given time period. (583)

concave down Said of an interval that is curving downwards, that is, its slope is continuously decreasing. (687)

concave up Said of an interval that is curving upwards, that is, its slope is continuously increasing. (687)

confidence interval An interval within which a certain specified percentage (usually 90%, 95%, or 99%) of outcomes from an experiment is expected to occur. (721)

Conjugate Zeros Theorem Let $p(x) = a_n x^n + a_{n-1} x^{n-1} + \cdots + a_1 x + a_0$, where $a_n, a_{n-1}, \dots, a_1$, and a_0 are all real numbers, and $a_n \neq 0$. If $z = a + bi$ is a zero of $p(x)$, then the complex conjugate of z, $a - bi$, is also a zero of $p(x)$. (477)

constant A variable whose values do not change in the course of a problem. (Previous Course)

constant function Any function f with equation $f(x) = k$, where k is a fixed value. (Previous Course)

constant of proportionality See *constant of variation*.

constant of variation The parameter k in a direct, inverse, or joint variation. (125)

Continuous Change Model If a quantity p grows or decays continuously at an annual rate r, the amount $A(t)$ after t years is given by $A(t) = Pe^{rt}$. (583)

convergent sequence A sequence which has a finite limiting value L. If this value exists, the sequence is said to be convergent to L. (515)

convergent series A series in which the limit of the sequence of partial sums exists. (543)

correlation coefficient, r A measure of the strength of the linear relation between two variables. (96)

cos⁻¹ See *inverse cosine function*.

cosecant (csc) of a real number x For a real number x, $\csc x = \dfrac{1}{\sin x}$, when $\sin x \neq 0$. (336)

cosine (cos) of an acute angle θ in a right triangle $\dfrac{\text{leg adjacent to } \theta}{\text{hypotenuse}}$. (294)

cosine (cos) of a real number θ The first coordinate of the image of the point $(1, 0)$ under a rotation of magnitude θ about the origin. (229)

cosine function The function that maps x onto $\cos x$ for all x in its domain. (249)

cotangent (cot) of a real number x For any real number x, $\cot x = \dfrac{\cos x}{\sin x}$, when $\sin x \neq 0$. (336)

cube root For a number k, a number x that satisfies $x^3 = k$. (560)

cumulative binomial probability table A table that gives, for fixed n (number of trials) and p (probability of success), the probabilities for k or fewer successes. (694)

cycle One period of a periodic function, such as a sine wave. (254)

D

data The plural of *datum*, the Latin word for fact; a piece of information. (6)

decreasing function A function is decreasing on an interval if the segment connecting any two points on the graph of the function over that interval has negative slope. (441)

deductive reasoning Reasoning adhering to strict principles of logic. (64)

degree A unit for measuring angles, arcs, or rotations. (Previous Course)

degree of a polynomial In a polynomial with a single variable, the number n in the polynomial $a_n x^n + a_{n-1} x^{n-1} + \cdots + a_1 x + a_0$; in a polynomial in more than one variable, the largest sum of the exponents of the variables in any term. (438)

De Moivre's Theorem If $z = r(\cos \theta + i \sin \theta)$ and n is an integer, then $z^n = r^n(\cos n\theta + i \sin n\theta)$. (826)

dependent events Events A and B for which $P(A \cap B) \neq P(A) \cdot P(B)$. (378)

dependent variable The second variable in a relation. (**80**)

deviation The difference of a value in a set from the set's mean. (**46**)

dimensions of a matrix The numbers of rows and columns of the matrix. (**744**)

discriminant of a quadratic equation For the equation $ax^2 + bx + c = 0$, the number $b^2 - 4ac$. (**467**)

disjoint sets Sets with no elements in common. Also called *mutually exclusive sets*. (**367**)

distribution A function whose values are the frequencies, relative frequencies, or probabilities of mutually exclusive events. (**22**)

divergent sequence A sequence with no finite limit. (**515**)

divergent series A series in which the sequence of partial sums does not have a finite limit. (**543**)

dividend The number or expression a when a is divided by b. (**453**)

divisor The number or expression b when a is divided by b. (**453**)

domain The set of first elements of ordered pairs of a function; more generally, the set of replacement values for a variable. (**80**)

domain of an identity The set of values for which the identity is true. (**789**)

Double Angle Formulas For all real numbers θ, $\sin 2\theta = 2 \sin \theta \cos \theta$ and $\cos 2\theta = \cos^2\theta - \sin^2\theta = 2 \cos^2\theta - 1 = 1 - 2 \sin^2\theta$. (**771**)

E

e $\lim\limits_{x \to \infty} \left(1 + \frac{1}{n}\right)^n \approx 2.718$; the base of natural logarithms. (**582**)

element An object in an array. A member of a set. (**81, 744**)

end behavior In a sequence t, the behavior of the values of t_n as $n \to \infty$. (**515**)

error (in a prediction) The difference between the observed and the expected values of a variable. Also called *residual*. (**89**)

even function A function f such that for all x in its domain, $f(-x) = f(x)$. (**174**)

event Any subset of the sample space of an experiment. (**361**)

expansion of $(x + y)^n$ See *Binomial Theorem*.

expected count If an outcome in an experiment has probability p, then in n trials of the experiment, the expected count of the outcomes is np. (**410**)

expected value A value predicted by a mathematical model. Also called *predicted value*. (**410**)

expected value of a probability distribution See *mean of a random variable*.

experiment A situation that has several possible outcomes. (**360**)

explicit formula for a sequence A formula which gives the nth term of the sequence in terms of n. (**503**)

exponent The number n in the expression r^n. (**Previous Course**)

exponential decay A situation that can be modeled by $f(x) = ab^x$ with base $0 < b < 1$. (**104**)

exponential decay curve The graph of an exponential decay function. (**105**)

exponential decay function An exponential function $f(x) = ab^x$ in which $a > 0$ and $0 < b < 1$. (**104**).

exponential equation An equation to be solved for a variable in an exponent. (**594**)

exponential function with base b The exponential function with base b is a function with a formula of the form $f(x) = ab^x$, where $a \neq 0$, $b > 0$, and $b \neq 1$. (**103**)

exponential growth curve The graph of an exponential growth function. (**103**)

exponential growth function An exponential function $f = ab^x$ in which $a > 0$ and $b > 1$. (**103**)

exponential model A mathematical model of a situation in the form of an exponential function. (**110**)

exponential regression The method of fitting an exponential function to a set of data. (**111**)

exponential sequence See *geometric sequence*.

extrapolation Estimating a value beyond known values of data. (**88**)

extrema of a function The extreme values for the function, classified as either maxima or minima. (**440**)

F

f^{-1} see *inverse function.*

Factor Theorem For any polynomial $f(x)$, a number c is a solution to $f(x) = 0$ if and only if $(x - c)$ is a factor of $f(x)$. (**460**)

Factor-Solution-Intercept Equivalence Theorem
For any polynomial $f(x)$, the following are logically equivalent statements: $(x - c)$ is a factor of $f(x)$; $f(c) = 0$; c is an x-intercept of the graph of $y = f(x)$; c is a zero of f; the remainder when $f(x)$ is divided by $(x - c)$ is 0. (**461**)

failure (binomial) See *binomial experiment.*

fair experiment An experiment in which all outcomes of the sample space are equally likely. Also called *unbiased experiment.* (**361**)

***Federalist,* The** Essays written between 1787 and 1788 by James Madison, Alexander Hamilton, and John Jay under the collective pen name "Publius" to persuade the citizens of the state of New York to ratify the U.S. Constitution. (**61**)

Fibonnaci sequence The sequence beginning 1, 1, 2, 3, 5, ..., in which $t_n = t_{n-2} + t_{n-1}$, for all $n \geq 3$. (**502**)

finite arithmetic series An arithmetic series where the number of terms added is finite. (**523**)

finite series A series where the number of terms added is finite. (**523**)

first (lower) quartile In a data set, the median of the numbers less than the set's median. (**31**)

five-number summary The three quartiles, the maximum, and the minimum of a data set. (**31**)

Formula for $_nC_r$ Theorem For whole numbers n and r, with $r \leq n$, $_nC_r = \frac{n!}{(n-r)!r!}$. (**619**)

Formula for $_nP_n$ Corollary There are $n!$ permutations of n different elements. (**384**)

Formula for $_nP_r$ Theorem The number of permutations of n objects taken r at a time is $_nP_r$, $n(n-1)(n-2) \cdot \cdots \cdot (n-r+1)$. (**382**)

frequency The number of times an event occurs. (**Previous Course**) The number of cycles in a period of a periodic function. (**259**)

frequency distribution A function that maps events onto their frequencies. (**22**)

frequency histogram A histogram that displays the number of values that fall into each interval of the histogram. (**22**)

function A set of ordered pairs (x, y) in which each value of x is paired with exactly one value of y. A correspondence between two sets A and B in which each element of A corresponds to exactly one element of B. (**81**)

function notation The notation $f(x)$ for the value of a function f when the value of the independent variable is x. (**83**)

Fundamental Theorem of Algebra If $p(x)$ is any polynomial of degree $n \geq 1$ with complex coefficients, then $p(x)$ has at least one complex zero. (**475**)

full turn A rotation of 360°, 2π, or one revolution. (**222**)

G

Galton board A device, invented by Sir Francis Galton, used to illustrate binomial experiments, consisting of a box in which balls striking an array of pins form, at the bottom of the box, a normal distribution. (**616**)

general form of a polynomial in one variable
See *polynomial in x.*

general solution to a trigonometric equation The solution to a trigonometric equation for all real numbers for which the variable is defined. (**325**)

Geometric Addition Theorem If the complex numbers $a + bi$ and $c + di$ are not collinear with the origin in the complex plane, then their sum $(a + c) + (b + d)i$ is the fourth vertex of a parallelogram with consecutive vertices $a + bi$, 0, and $c + di$. (**812**)

geometric mean The geometric mean of x and y is $\sqrt{xy}$. (**511**)

geometric sequence A sequence in which the ratio of consecutive terms is constant. (**509**)

geometric series An indicated sum of the terms of a geometric sequence. (**530**)

Graph Scale-Change Theorem In a relation described by a sentence in x and y, replacing x by $\frac{x}{a}$ and y by $\frac{y}{b}$ in the sentence yields the same graph as applying the scale change $(x, y) \rightarrow (ax, by)$ to the graph of the original relation. (**181**)

Graph-Standardization Theorem In a relation described by a sentence in x and y, replacing x by $\frac{x-h}{a}$ and y by $\frac{y-k}{b}$ in the sentence yields the same graph as applying the scale change $(x, y) \rightarrow (ax, by)$, where $a \neq 0$ and $b \neq 0$, followed by applying the translation $(x, y) \rightarrow (x + h, y + k)$ to the graph of the original relation. (**270**)

Graph Translation Theorem In a relation described by a sentence in x and y, replacing x by $x - h$ and y by $y - k$ in the sentence yields the same graph as applying the translation $(x, y) \rightarrow (x + h, y + k)$ to the graph of the original relation. (**161**)

great circle A circle on a sphere that has the same center as the sphere. (**342**)

Greenwich meridian See *prime meridian*.

grouping A technique used to factor polynomials that contain groups of terms with common factors. (**486**)

growth factor In an exponential growth situation, the base of the exponential function. (**103**)

growth rate The factor by which a quantity changes during a given time period. (**102**)

H

Half-Angle Formulas For all θ, $\cos \theta = \pm \sqrt{\frac{1 + \cos 2\theta}{2}}$ and $\sin \theta = \pm \sqrt{\frac{1 - \cos 2\theta}{2}}$. The sign is determined by the quadrant in which θ lies. (**775**)

half-life The time it takes a quantity to decay to half its original amount, usually applied to exponential decay situations. (**113**)

half turn A rotation of $180°$, π, or $\frac{1}{2}$ revolution. (**222**)

Half-Turn Theorem For all θ, $\cos(\pi + \theta) = -\cos \theta$, $\sin(\pi + \theta) = -\sin \theta$, and $\tan(\pi + \theta) = \tan \theta$. (**237**)

harmonic sequence The sequence h in which $h_n = \frac{1}{n}$ for all $n \geq 1$. (**502**)

histogram A bar graph in which the range of values of a numerical variable are broken into non-overlapping intervals of equal width, and side-by-side bars display the number of values that fall into each interval. (**22**)

homogeneous population A population in which members are very similar on some measure. (**52**)

horizontal scale change A transformation that maps (x, y) to (ax, y) for all (x, y), where $a \neq 0$. (**180**)

horizontal scale factor The number a in the transformation that maps (x, y) to (ax, by). (**180**)

hypothesis In statistics, a statement to be tested. (**417**)

hypothesis testing The process of using statistics to find if a given hypothesis fits a situation within a given significance level. (**417**)

I

identity An equation that is true for all values of the variable(s) for which the expressions are defined. (**235**)

identity function, I A function that maps each element in its domain onto itself, that is, $I(x) = x$ for all x. (**202**)

image The result of a transformation. (**159**)

imaginary axis The vertical axis in a complex plane. (**811**)

imaginary numbers The number $i = \sqrt{-1}$ and its nonzero real-number multiples. (**465**)

imaginary part of a complex number The real number b in the complex number $a + bi$. (**466**)

impressionistic model A model where no theory exists that explains why the model fits the data. Also called *non-theory-based model*. (**121**)

in-phase circuit An alternating current circuit in which the voltage and current flow coincide. (**263**)

increasing function A function is increasing on an interval if the segment connecting any two points on the graph of the function over that interval has positive slope. (**441**)

independent events Events A and B such that $P(A \cap B) = P(A) \cdot P(B)$. (**378**)

independent variable The first variable in a relation. (**80**)

index A variable indicating the position of a number in an ordered list or sequence. (**15**)

inductance A property of an alternating current circuit created when the current flow lags behind the voltage. (**263**)

inferential reasoning Reasoning based on principles of probability. (**64**)

infinite series An indicated sum of the terms of an infinite sequence. (**523, 524**)

infinity, ∞ The limit of a sequence whose terms after a given point become larger than any fixed number one might choose; greater than any given number. (**516**)

inflection point A point on a graph where the graph changes concavity. (**687**)

initial condition The description of the initial term or terms in a recursive formula. (**504**)

initial side (of an angle) The side of an angle from which the angle is considered to have been generated, and from which the angle is measured. (Previous Course)

initial value In a function f modeling a situation, the value $f(0)$. (**104**)

interest rate In an investment, the percent by which the principal is multiplied to obtain the interest paid to the investor. (**536**)

International Date Line The meridian which is 180° W (and 180° E) of the prime meridian. (**343**)

interpolation Estimating a value between known values of data. (**88**)

interquartile range (IQR) The difference between the third quartile and the first quartile. (**32**)

intersection, $A \cap B$ The set of elements that are in both set A and set B. (**368**)

invariant Unchanged by a particular transformation. (**168**)

inverse cosine function, $\cos^{-1}$, Arccos The function described by $y = \cos^{-1} x = \text{Arccos } x$, if and only if $x = \cos y$ and $0 \leq y \leq \pi$. (**300**)

inverse function, f^{-1} The function which is the inverse of the function f. (**201**)

inverse of a function The relation formed by switching the coordinates of the ordered pairs of a given function. (**199**)

inverse sine function, $\sin^{-1}$, Arcsin The function described by $y = \sin^{-1} x = \text{Arcsin } x$, if and only if $x = \sin y$ and $-\frac{\pi}{2} \leq y \leq \frac{\pi}{2}$. (**310**)

inverse tangent function, $\tan^{-1}$, Arctan The function described by $y = \tan^{-1} x = \text{Arctan } x$, if and only if $x = \tan y$ and $-\pi < y < \pi$. (**320**)

Inverse Function Theorem Two functions f and g are inverse functions if and only if $f(g(x)) = x$ for all x in the domain of g, and $g(f(x)) = x$ for all x in the domain of f. (**202**)

inverse-square relationship A function with an equation the form $y = \frac{k}{x^2} = kx^{-2}$. (**123**)

inversely proportional y is inversely proportional to x if $y = \frac{k}{x}$ for all x, where k is a constant. y is inversely proportional to the square of x if $y = \frac{k}{x^2}$ for all x. (**125, 127**)

L

latitude A measure of the extent to which a point is north of south of the equator determined by the angle subtended at the center of Earth by an arc on a line of longitude. (**343**)

Law of Cosines In any triangle ABC, $c^2 = a^2 + b^2 - 2ab \cos C$. (**304**)

Law of Sines In any triangle ABC, $\frac{\sin A}{a} = \frac{\sin B}{b} = \frac{\sin C}{c}$. (**315**)

leading coefficient (of a polynomial) The coefficient of the term of the highest degree of the polynomial. (**438**)

least squares line See *line of best fit*.

limit of a sequence, $\lim\limits_{x \to \infty} s_n$ A number which the terms of a sequence approach as n increases without bound. (**515**)

line of best fit The line that fits a set of data points with the smallest value for the sum of the squares of the deviations (vertical distances) from the data points to the line. Also called *regression line* or *least-squares line*. (**94**)

line of longitude See *meridian*.

line of symmetry See *axis of symmetry*.

linear function A function with an equation of the form $y = mx + b$, where m and b are constants. (**87**)

linear model The model of one variable as a linear function of another variable. (**87**)

linear regression The method of finding a line of best fit for a given set of points. (**94**)

linear sequence See *arithmetic sequence*.

linearity A relation's degree of correlation to a linear model. (**98**)

ln See *natural logarithm*.

logarithm (log) Let $b > 0$ and $b \neq 1$. Then y is the logarithm of x to the base b, written $y = \log_b x$, if and only if $b^y = x$. (**575**)

logarithm function (with base b) The function that maps x onto $\log_b x$. (**578**)

logarithmic transformation A transformation under which a variable x is replaced by $\log_b x$. (**600**)

Logarithm of 1 Theorem For any base b, $\log_b 1 = 0$. (**587**)

Logarithm of a Power Theorem For any base b, and for any positive real number x and any real number p, $\log_b x^p = p \log_b x$. (**588**)

Logarithm of a Product Theorem For any base b, and for any positive real numbers x and y, $\log_b (xy) = \log_b x + \log_b y$. (**588**)

Logarithm of a Quotient Theorem For any base b and for any positive real numbers x and y, $\log_b \frac{x}{y} = \log_b x - \log_b y$. (**589**)

logarithmic spiral The polar graph of $r = ka^\theta$, where $a > 0$. (**810**)

longitude The number of degrees that a meridian is east or west of the prime meridian, used as a coordinate of a location on Earth. (**343**)

lower quartile See *first quartile*.

M

magnitude (of rotation) The amount by which every point in the plane is turned around the center of the rotation. (**222**)

margin of error Half the length of a confidence interval. (**722**)

mathematical model A mathematical description of a real situation, often involving some simplifications and assumptions about that situation. (**78**)

Matrices for Reflections Theorem The matrix for r_x, reflection over the x-axis, is $\begin{bmatrix} 1 & 0 \\ 0 & -1 \end{bmatrix}$. The matrix for r_y, reflection over the y-axis, is $\begin{bmatrix} -1 & 0 \\ 0 & 1 \end{bmatrix}$. The matrix for $r_{y=x}$, reflection over the line $y = x$, is $\begin{bmatrix} 0 & 1 \\ 1 & 0 \end{bmatrix}$. (**752**)

Matrices for Rotations Theorem The matrix for $R_{90°}$, the rotation of 90° around the origin, is $\begin{bmatrix} 0 & -1 \\ 1 & 0 \end{bmatrix}$. The matrix for $R_{180°}$, the rotation of 180° around the origin, is $\begin{bmatrix} -1 & 0 \\ 0 & -1 \end{bmatrix}$. The matrix for $R_{270°}$, the rotation of 270° around the origin, is $\begin{bmatrix} 0 & 1 \\ -1 & 0 \end{bmatrix}$. (**759**)

matrix A rectangular arrangement of objects into rows and columns. (**744**)

Matrix Basis Theorem Suppose T is a transformation represented by a 2×2 matrix. If $T(1, 0) = (x_1, y_1)$ and $T(0, 1) = (x_2, y_2)$, then T has the matrix $\begin{bmatrix} x_1 & x_2 \\ y_1 & y_2 \end{bmatrix}$. (**759**)

matrix multiplication An operation on an $m \times n$ matrix A and an $n \times p$ matrix B resulting in the product matrix $A \cdot B$, an $m \times p$ matrix whose element in row i and column j is the sum of the products of elements in row i of A and corresponding elements in column j of B. (**745**)

matrix representing a transformation A matrix M such that whenever F, a matrix for a geometric figure, is multiplied by M, the product is a matrix for the image of F under the transformation T. (**752**)

maximum The largest value in a set. (**31**)

maximum value of a function The largest value in the function's range. (**440**)

mean The sum of the elements of a numerical data set divided by the number of items in the data set. Also called *average* and *arithmetic mean*. (**14**)

Mean of a Binomial Random Variable Theorem The mean μ of a binomial random variable with n trials and probability p of success on each trial is given by $\mu = np$. (**659**)

mean of a random variable For the probability distribution $\{(x_1, P(x_1)), (x_2, P(x_2)), \ldots, (x_n, P(x_n))\}$, the number $\mu = \sum_{i=1}^{n} (x_i \cdot P(x_i))$. Also called *expected value of a probability distribution*. (**659**)

measure of an angle A number that represents the size and direction of rotation used to generate an angle. (**222**)

measure of center A statistic describing a typical value of a numerical data set. Measures of center include the mean and median, and sometimes the mode. Also called *measure of central tendency*. (**14**)

measure of central tendency See *measure of center*.

measure of spread A statistic that describes how far data are from a center of a distribution. (**45**)

median The middle value of a set of data placed in ascending or descending order. The median of a set with an even number of elements is the mean of the two middle values. (**14**)

member An element of a set. (**81**)

meridian A semicircle of a great circle on the surface of Earth from the north pole to the south pole. Also called *line of longitude*. (**343**)

method of least squares The process of finding the line of best fit. (**94**)

middle quartile See *second quartile*.

minimum The smallest value in a set. (31)

minimum value of a function The smallest value in the function's range. (440)

minute (of a degree) A unit for measuring angles. 60 minutes = 1 degree. (228)

mode The item(s) with the greatest frequency in a data set. (15)

mode of a distribution In a probability distribution, the value of the random variable whose probability is the highest. (639)

modulus See *absolute value of a complex number*.

Monte Carlo method The method of using random numbers and related probabilities to simulate events for the purpose of solving a problem. (404)

Multiplication Counting Principle Let A and B be any finite sets. The number of ways to choose one element from A and then one element from B is $N(A) \cdot N(B)$. (374)

multiplicity of a zero For a zero r of a polynomial, the highest power of $(x - r)$ that appears as a factor of that polynomial. (474)

mutually exclusive sets See *disjoint sets*.

N

n factorial, n! For a positive integer n, the product of the positive integers from 1 to n. In symbols, $n! = n \cdot (n - 1) \cdot (n - 2) \cdot (n - 3) \cdot \cdots \cdot 3 \cdot 2 \cdot 1$. $0! = 1$. (380)

natural logarithm, ln The logarithm of x to the base e, written $\ln x$. (584)

natural logarithm function The function that maps x to $\ln x$. (584)

$_nC_r$ See *Formula for $_nC_r$ Theorem*.

Negative Exponent Theorem For all $x \neq 0$ and n for which x^n is defined, $x^{-n} = \frac{1}{x^n}$. (571)

negative association A relation between two variables where the larger values of one variable are associated with smaller values of the other. (96)

non-theory-based model See *impressionistic model*.

normal curve The graph of a normal distribution. (686)

normal distribution A probability distribution p in which $P(x) = \frac{1}{\sqrt{2\pi}\sigma}e^{-\frac{1}{2}\left(\frac{x - \mu}{\sigma}\right)^2}$, where μ is the mean and σ is the standard deviation. (686)

not A The complement of an event A, that is, the set of outcomes of the sample space that are not in A. (370)

nth partial sum, S_n The sum of the first n terms of a sequence. (530)

nth root, $\sqrt[n]{\ }$, $x^{\frac{1}{n}}$ x is an nth root of k if and only if $x^n = k$, where n is an integer ≥ 2. The positive nth root (if there are two) or the only nth root of a real number x is denoted by $\sqrt[n]{\ }$. (560)

nth root function A function with an equation of the form $y = x^{\frac{1}{n}}$, where n is an integer with $n \geq 2$. (561)

nth roots of unity The zeros of $x^n - 1$. (479)

nth term of a sequence The term in the nth domain value of a sequence. (502)

null hypothesis, H_0 The main hypothesis used in hypothesis testing of a situation. (670)

Number of Zeros of a Polynomial Theorem A polynomial of degree $n \geq 1$ with complex coefficients has exactly n complex zeros, if multiplicities are counted. (476)

numerical variable A variable that represents a numerical value. (8)

O

observed values Data collected from sources such as experiments or surveys. (89)

odd function A function f such that for all x in its domain, $f(-x) = -f(x)$. (174)

1.5 × IQR criterion A criterion under which those elements of a data set greater than $1.5 \times$ IQR plus the third quartile or less than the first quartile minus $1.5 \times$ IQR are considered to be outliers. (33)

Opposites Theorem For all θ, $\cos(-\theta) = \cos\theta$, $\sin(-\theta) = -\sin\theta$, and $\tan(-\theta) = -\tan\theta$. (237)

oscilloscope An instrument for representing the oscillations of varying voltage or current on the fluorescent screen of a cathode-ray tube. (220)

out-of-phase circuit An alternating current circuit in which the current flow lags behind the voltage. (263)

outcome A possible result of an experiment. (360)

outlier An element of a set of numbers which is very different from most or all of the other elements. (33)

overlapping sets Two sets that have one or more elements in common. (368)

P

parabola The graph of a quadratic function. (118)

parameter A variable that is constant in a particular situation but whose value can vary from situation to situation. (331)

parametric equation Two or more equations in which different variables are written in terms of a parameter. (331)

parent function A simple form or the simplest form of a class of functions, from which other members of the class can be derived by transformations. (152)

partial sum See *nth partial sum.*

Pascal's Triangle The values of $_nC_r$, arranged in an array in the form of a triangle; the $(r + 1)$st term in row n of Pascal's Triangle is $_nC_r$. (625)

pentagonal numbers The sequence of numbers 1, 5, 12, 22, ... , in which the nth term is $\frac{n(3n - 1)}{2}$. (464)

percentile The pth percentile of a set of numbers is the value in the set such that p percent of the numbers are less than or equal to that value, or alternatively, less than that value. (40)

perfect correlation A correlation coefficient of 1 or –1; a situation in which all data points lie on the same line. (96)

periodic function A function f in which there is a positive real number p such that $f(x + p) = f(x)$ for all x. The smallest positive value of p is the period of the function. (254)

Periodicity Theorem For all θ, and for every integer n, $\sin(\theta + 2\pi n) = \sin \theta$, $\cos(\theta + 2\pi n) = \cos \theta$, and $\tan(\theta + \pi n) = \tan \theta$. (253)

permutation An arrangement of a set of objects. (382)

permutation of n objects taken r at a time, $_nP_r$ An arrangement of r objects from a set of n objects. (32)

petal curve See *rose curve.*

phase shift The least positive or the greatest negative horizontal translation that maps the graph of a circular function or its scale change image onto a given sine wave. (263)

piecewise definition A definition of a function whose domain is broken into subsets with a rule for each subset. (82)

point matrix The matrix $\begin{bmatrix} a \\ b \end{bmatrix}$ when it represents the point (a, b). (751)

point symmetry 180° rotation symmetry. (172)

polar axis A ray, usually horizontal and drawn to the right, through the pole of a polar coordinate system, from which the magnitudes of rotations are measured. (797)

polar coordinate system A coordinate system in which a point is identified by polar coordinates $[r, \theta]$, where $|r|$ is the distance of the point from a fixed point (the pole), and θ is a magnitude of rotation from the polar axis. (797)

polar form of a complex number The description of a complex number using polar coordinates. (814)

polar grid A grid of rays and concentric circles radiating from a central point, used for plotting points and sketching curves in the polar plane. (798)

pole See *polar coordinate system.*

polynomial A sum of multiples of nonnegative integer powers of a variable or variables. (439)

polynomial function A function whose rule can be written as a polynomial. (438)

polynomial in x An expression of the form $a_nx^n + a_{n-1}x^{n-1} + a_{n-2}x^{n-2} + \cdots + a_1x + a_0$ where n is a nonnegative integer and $a_n \neq 0$. Also called *general form of a polynomial in one variable.* (438)

Polynomial Difference Theorem The function $y = f(x)$ is a polynomial function of degree n if and only if, for any set of x-values that form an arithmetic sequence, the nth differences of corresponding y-values are equal and nonzero. (448)

population The set of all individuals or objects to be studied. (6)

population pyramid A double histogram with bin intervals along a central vertical axis and frequencies along the horizontal axis. (26)

Polynomial Graph Wiggliness Theorem Let $p(x)$ be a polynomial of degree $n \geq 1$. The graph of $p(x)$ can cross any horizontal line $y = d$ at most n times. (476)

population standard deviation, σ See *standard deviation.*

population variance, σ^2 See *variance.*

positive association A relation between two variables where larger values of one variable are associated with larger values of the other. (**96**)

power function A function f with an equation of the form $f(x) = ax^n$, where n is an integer greater than 1. (**128**)

predicted value See *expected value.*

preimage The domain or set of domain values of a transformation. (**159**)

prime meridian The meridian through Greenwich, England from which all other meridians are measured. (**343**)

principal Of a loan, the amount of money borrowed. Of an investment, the amount of money that is earning interest. (**536**)

probability A number which indicates the measure of certainty of an event. (**371**)

probability distribution A function that maps each value of a random variable onto its probability. (**637**)

probability of an event, $P(E)$ If E is an event in a finite sample space S, and each outcome in S is equally likely, then the probability that E occurs, $P(E)$, is given by $P(E) = \dfrac{\text{number of outcomes in the event}}{\text{number of outcomes in the sample space}}$. (**361**)

probability theory The branch of mathematics that studies chance. (**360**)

Probability of the Union of Mutually Exclusive Events Theorem If A and B are mutually exclusive events in the same finite sample space, then $P(A \cup B) = P(A) + P(B)$. (**368**)

Probability of a Union of Events Theorem (General Form) If A and B are any events in the same finite sample space, then $P(A \text{ or } B) = P(A \cup B) = P(A) + P(B) - P(A \cap B)$. (**367**)

Probability of Complements Theorem If A is any event, then $P(\text{not } A) = 1 - P(A)$. (**371**)

product matrix See *matrix multiplication.*

Product of Complex Numbers Theorem (Trigonometric Form) If $z_1 = r_1(\cos\theta_1 + i\sin\theta_1)$ and $z_2 = r_2(\cos\theta_2 + i\sin\theta_2)$, then $z_1z_2 = r_1r_2(\cos(\theta_1 + \theta_2) + i\sin(\theta_1 + \theta_2))$. (**820**)

Pythagorean identity For every θ, $\cos^2\theta + \sin^2\theta = 1$. (**235**)

quadratic function A function f with a rule of the form $f(x) = ax^2 + bx + c$ where $a \neq 0$. (**Previous Course**)

quadratic model A quadratic function used to estimate data in a set. (**117**)

quadratic regression A method of finding an equation for the best-fitting quadratic function through a data set. (**120**)

quartiles The three values which divide an ordered set into four subsets of approximately the same size. See *first (lower) quartile, second (middle) quartile,* and *third (upper) quartile.* (**31**)

quotient The answer to a division problem. For polynomials, the polynomial $q(x)$ when $f(x)$ is divided by $d(x)$, where $f(x) = q(x)d(x) + r(x)$, and either $r(x) = 0$ or the degree of $r(x)$ is less than the degree of $d(x)$. (**453**)

Quotient of Complex Numbers Theorem If $z_1 = r_1(\cos\theta_1 + i\sin\theta_1)$ and $z_2 = r_2(\cos\theta_2 + i\sin\theta_2)$, then $\dfrac{z_1}{z_2} = \dfrac{r_1}{r_2}(\cos(\theta_1 - \theta_2) + i\sin(\theta_1 - \theta_2))$. (**821**)

radian A unit for measuring an angle, arc, or the magnitude of a rotation. π radians $= 180°$. (**223**)

radical The symbol $\sqrt{}$ used to denote square roots or nth roots. (**564**)

random numbers A set of numbers such that each number has the same probability of occurring, each pair of numbers has the same probability of occurring, each trio of numbers has the same probability of occurring, and so on. (**402**)

random sample See *simple random sample.*

random variable A variable whose values are numbers determined by the outcome of an experiment. (**637**)

randomly A property of sampling a population so that every member of the population has an equal chance of being chosen. Also referred to as *at random.* (**361**)

range The difference between the highest and lowest values in a set. The set of possible values of the dependent variable in a function. (**80**)

Rational Exponent Theorem For all positive integers m and n, and all real numbers $x \geq 0$, $x^{\frac{m}{n}} = \left(x^{\frac{1}{n}}\right)^m = (\sqrt[n]{x})^m$ and $x^{\frac{m}{n}} = (x^m)^{\frac{1}{n}} = (\sqrt[n]{x})^m$. (**568**)

rational power function A function f with an equation of the form $f(x) = ax^{\frac{m}{n}}$, where m and n are nonzero integers and $a \neq 0$. **(572)**

raw data Data that has not been transformed or statistically manipulated. **(207)**

real axis The horizontal axis (axis of first coordinates) in a complex plane. **(811)**

real function A function whose domain and range is a set of real numbers. **(81)**

real part of a complex number The real number a in the complex number $a + bi$. **(466)**

reciprocal trigonometric functions The secant, cosecant, and cotangent functions. **(336)**

recurrence relation A formula for a term of a sequence in terms of preceding terms. **(504)**

recursive formula A formula for a sequence in which the first term or the first few terms are given, and then the nth term is expressed using the preceding term(s). **(504)**

reflection-symmetric figure A figure that can be mapped onto itself by a reflection over some line ℓ. **(172)**

regression line See *line of best fit*.

relation A set of ordered pairs. **(80)**

relative extrema Relative maxima or relative minima. **(440)**

relative frequency The ratio of the number of times an event occurred to the number of times it could have occurred. **(18)**

relative frequency distribution A function mapping events onto their relative frequencies. **(22)**

relative frequency histogram A histogram that displays the proportion of values that fall into each interval of the histogram. **(22)**

relative maximum A point or value at which a function has a maximum on a specified interval. **(440)**

relative minimum A point or value at which a function has a minimum on a specified interval. **(440)**

remainder (in polynomial division) The polynomial $r(x)$ when $f(x)$ is divided by $d(x)$ and $f(x) = q(x)d(x) + r(x)$ when either $r(x) = 0$ or the degree of $r(x)$ is less than the degree of $d(x)$. **(454)**

Remainder Theorem If a polynomial $f(x)$ is divided by $x - c$, then the remainder is $f(c)$. **(455)**

removable singularity A point of discontinuity of a function that can be "removed" by adding a single point to the function. **(794)**

representative sample A sample that has the same characteristics as the population. **(7)**

rescaling See *scaling*.

residual The difference between the observed value and a value predicted by a model. **(89)**

residual plot A plot of each x-value in a data set and its residual. **(133)**

revolution A unit for measuring rotations. 1 revolution (counterclockwise) $= 360°$. Also called *full turn*. **(222)**

root function A function that maps x onto some root of x, such as its square root. **(561)**

root of a polynomial function For the polynomial function $f(x) = a_n x^n + a_{n-1} x^{n-1} + \cdots + a_1 x + a_0$, any value of x such that $f(x) = 0$. Also called *zero of the function*. **(442)**

Roots of a Complex Number Theorem For any positive integer n, the n distinct roots of $z^n = r(\cos \theta + i \sin \theta)$, $r > 0$, are $z = \sqrt[n]{r}\left(\cos\left(\frac{\theta}{n} + k\frac{360°}{n}\right) + i \sin\left(\frac{\theta}{n} + k\frac{360°}{n}\right)\right)$, where $k = 0, 1, 2, \ldots, n - 1$. **(828)**

rose curve The graph of the polar equation $r = a \sin b\theta$ or $r = a \cos b\theta$, where b is a positive integer and $a \neq 0$. Also called *petal curve*. **(807)**

rotation A transformation under which each point in the plane turns a fixed magnitude around a fixed point called its center. **(222)**

Rotation Matrix Theorem The matrix for R_θ, the rotation of magnitude θ about the origin, is $\begin{bmatrix} \cos \theta & -\sin \theta \\ \sin \theta & \cos \theta \end{bmatrix}$. **(762)**

row matrix A matrix consisting of a single row. **(745)**

S

sample The subset of a population that is studied in an experiment. **(6)**

sample space The set of all possible outcomes of an experiment. **(360)**

sample standard deviation, s See *standard deviation*.

sample variance, s^2 See *variance*.

sampling distribution A distribution of the means of all samples of a fixed size from the same population. (708)

SAS Area Formula for a Triangle The area of any triangle is one-half the product of the lengths of any two sides and the sine of their included angle. (314)

scale change (of data) A transformation that maps each data value x_i in a set of data $\{x_1, x_2, \dots, x_n\}$ to ax_i, where a is a nonzero constant. (186)

scale change (in the plane) The transformation that maps (x, y) to (ax, by), where $a \neq 0$ and $b \neq 0$ are constants. (180)

scale factor The nonzero constant by which each data value is multiplied in a scale change. (186)

scale image The result of a scale change, or the point it represents. (186)

scaling Applying a scale change to a data set. Also called *rescaling*. (185)

scatterplot A graph of a finite set of ordered pairs in the coordinate plane. (Previous Course)

secant (sec) of a real number For any real number x, $\sec x = \frac{1}{\cos x}$, provided $\cos x \neq 0$. (337)

second (middle) quartile The median of a set of data. (31)

second (of a degree) A unit for measuring angles. 60 seconds = 1 minute, and 3600 seconds = 1 degree. (228)

sequence A function whose domain is a set of consecutive integers greater than or equal to a fixed integer k. (503)

sequence of partial sums The sequence whose nth term is the sum of the first n terms of a given sequence. (542)

series An indicated sum of the terms of a sequence. (523)

sides (of an angle) See *angle*.

Σ (sigma) A symbol for sum. (15)

Σ notation (sigma-notation) See *summation notation*. (15)

significance level The level of probability (often 0.05 or 0.01) that is chosen to test a hypothesis. (420, 669)

simple random sample A sample of size n chosen from a population such that every sample of size n has an equal chance of being selected. (707)

simulation An experimental model of a situation that attempts to capture all aspects of the situation that affect the outcomes. (402)

$\sin^{-1}$ See *inverse sine function*.

sine function The function that maps x onto $\sin x$ for all x in its domain. (248)

sine (sin) of an acute angle θ in a right triangle $\frac{\text{leg opposite } \theta}{\text{hypotenuse}}$. (294)

sine (sin) of a real number θ The second coordinate of the image of the point $(1, 0)$ under a rotation of magnitude θ about the origin. (229)

sine wave The image of the graph of the sine or cosine function under a composite of translations and scale changes. (257)

singularity An isolated value for which a function is undefined. (792)

sinusoidal Varying in the manner of a sine wave. (221)

size change A scale change in which the scale factors are equal; a transformation that maps (x, y) to (kx, ky), where k is a nonzero constant. (180)

slope For the segment joining (x_1, y_1) and (x_2, y_2), the number $\frac{y_2 - y_1}{x_2 - x_1}$. (Previous Course)

spherical triangle A triangle on a sphere whose sides are arcs of great circles of that sphere. (345)

Spherical Law of Cosines If ABC is a spherical triangle with sides a, b, and c, then $\cos c = \cos a \cos b + \sin a \sin b \cos C$. (345)

spread An indication of how the value of data in a set vary. (45)

square root x is a square root of k if and only if $x^2 = k$. (560)

standard deviation, s, σ The square root of the sample variance (sample standard deviation s) or the population variance (population standard deviation σ). (46, 48)

standard normal curve The graph of the function $f(x) = \frac{1}{\sqrt{2\pi}} e^{-\frac{x^2}{2}}$. (688)

standard normal distribution The probability distribution represented by the standard normal curve. (689)

standard score See *z-score*.

Standard Normal Distribution Table A table that gives the area under the standard normal curve to the left of a given positive number a. (694)

standardized data Data that has been transformed into *z*-scores. (207)

standardizing a variable The process of getting *z*-values from an original data set. (699)

statistical inference Judgments using probabilities derived from statistical tests. (64)

statistic A number used to describe a set of numbers. (6)

statistics The branch of mathematics dealing with the collection, organization, analysis, and interpretation of information, usually numerical information. (6)

Strings With Replacement Theorem Let S be a set with n elements. Then there are n^k possible arrangements of k elements from S with replacement. (376)

Strings Without Replacement Theorem Let S be a set with n elements. Then there are $n!$ possible arrangements of the n elements without replacement. (381)

strong correlation A relation for which the data in a data set falls close to a line (or another specified curve). (97)

Subtraction Formulas for the Cosine and Sine
For all real numbers α and β,
$\cos(\alpha - \beta) = \cos \alpha \cos \beta + \sin \alpha \sin \beta$, and
$\sin(\alpha - \beta) = \sin \alpha \cos \beta - \cos \alpha \sin \beta$. (767)

success (binomial) See *binomial experiment*.

sum of a series The sum of the terms of a sequence. Also called *value of a series*. (523)

sum of an infinite series, S_∞, $\sum\limits_{i=1}^{\infty} a_i$ The limit of the sequence of partial sums $S_n = \sum\limits_{i=1}^{n} a_i$ of the series, provided the limit exists and is finite. (542)

sum of squared residuals The sum of the squares of the differences between observed values and predicted values. (90)

summation notation The use of the symbol Σ to represent a summation. Also called *sigma-notation* or *Σ-notation*. (15)

Sums and Differences of Cubes Theorem For all x and y, $x^3 + y^3 = (x + y)(x^2 - xy + y^2)$ and $x^3 - y^3 = (x - y)(x^2 + xy + y^2)$. (482)

Sums and Difference of Odd Powers Theorem For all x and y and for all odd positive integers n, $x^n + y^n = (x + y)(x^{n-1} - x^{n-2}y + x^{n-3}y^2 - \cdots - xy^{n-2} + y^{n-1})$ and $x^n - y^n = (x - y)(x^{n-1} + x^{n-2}y + x^{n-3}y^2 + \cdots + xy^{n-2} + y^{n-1})$. (483)

Supplements Theorem For all θ, $\sin(\pi - \theta) = \sin \theta$, $\cos(\pi - \theta) = -\cos \theta$, and $\tan(\pi - \theta) = -\tan \theta$. (238)

survey A gathering of facts or opinions through an interview or questionnaire; to gather such facts. (6)

symmetric distribution A distribution that is, or nearly is, reflection-symmetric. (24)

symmetric to the origin A property of a relation such that if (x, y) is on its graph, then so is $(-x, -y)$. (173)

symmetric with respect to the x-axis A property of a relation such that if (x, y) is on its graph, then so is $(x, -y)$. (173)

symmetric with respect to the y-axis A property of a relation such that if (x, y) is on its graph, then so is $(-x, y)$. (173)

symmetry to a point See *point symmetry*.

T

table of random numbers A listing of (pseudo-) random numbers used to simulate random situations. (466)

tan⁻¹ See *inverse tangent function*.

tangent function The function that maps x onto $\tan x$ for all x in its domain. (252)

tangent (tan) of an acute angle in a right triangle $\dfrac{\text{leg opposite the angle}}{\text{leg adjacent to the angle}}$. (294)

tangent (tan) of a real number θ For all real numbers θ, $\dfrac{\sin \theta}{\cos \theta}$, if $\cos \theta \neq 0$. (230)

term (of a loan) The length of time a person has to pay back the entire amount of a loan. (536)

term (of a sequence) An element in the range of a sequence. (502)

tetrahedral array A three-dimensional array made up of layers of points arranged in triangular arrays. (446)

tetrahedral numbers The values $T(n)$ of the sequence defined by $\begin{cases} T(1) = 1 \\ T(n) = T(n-1) + t(n) \end{cases}$, for all integers $n > 1$, where $t(n)$ is the nth triangular number. **(446)**

theory-based model A model based on a concrete theory that explains why the model should fit the data. **(121)**

third (upper) quartile In a data set, the median of the numbers greater than the set's median. **(31)**

transformation A one-to-one correspondence between sets of points. **(150, 159)**

translation (of data) A transformation that maps each x_i of a data set to $x_i + h$, where h is some constant. **(165)**

translation (in the plane) A transformation that maps each point (x, y) to $(x + h, y + k)$, where h and k are constants. **(159)**

translation image The result of a translation. **(159)**

tree diagram A method of graphically presenting the possible outcomes of an experiment by using a network of branches, resembling a tree. **(374)**

trial One of the instances of an experiment. **(402)**

triangular numbers The values of the sequence $t(n) = \dfrac{n(n+1)}{2}$. **(446)**

trigonometric equation An equation in which the variable to be found is in an argument of a trigonometric function. **(325)**

trigonometric form of a complex number The form $r(\cos\theta + i\sin\theta)$ of the complex number $a + bi$. **(818)**

trigonometric functions The sine, cosine, tangent, cotangent, secant, and cosecant functions and their offspring. Also called *circular functions*. **(229)**

trigonometry The branch of mathematics that deals with the study of the circular functions, and the relations between sides and angles of triangles using these functions. **(229)**

U

unbiased experiment See *fair experiment*.

union, $A \cup B$ The set of all elements that are either in set A or set B, or in both **(367)**

unit circle The circle with center at the origin and radius 1. **(235)**

upper quartile See *third quartile*.

V

value One of the elements that a variable can represent. **(83)**

value (of a series) See *sum of a series*.

variable (in statistics) A characteristic of a person or thing which can be classified, counted, ordered, or measured. **(6)**

variance, s^2, σ^2 In a data set, the sum of the squared deviations of the data from the mean divided by one less than the number of elements in the set (sample variance s^2) or by the number of elements in the set (population variance σ^2). **(46, 48)**

variance of a random variable For a probability distribution $\{(x_i, P(x_i))\}$ with n outcomes and mean μ, $\sigma^2 = \sum_{i=1}^{n}(x_i^2 \cdot P(x_i)) - \mu^2$. **(640)**

Variance and Standard Deviation of a Binomial Random Variable Theorem In a binomial distribution with n trials, probability p of success and probability q of failure on each trial, the variance $\sigma^2 = npq$, and the standard deviation $\sigma = \sqrt{npq}$. **(662)**

varies inversely See *inversely proportional*.

Venn diagram A method of displaying unions and intersections of sets, using circles or ellipses. **(368)**

vertex (of an angle) See *angle*.

vertical line test A test to determine whether a set of ordered pairs in the rectangular coordinate plane is a function; if there exists a vertical line that intersects the set in more that one point, then the set is not a function. **(83)**

vertical scale change A transformation that maps (x, y) to (x, by), where $b \neq 0$ is a constant. **(180)**

vertical scale factor The number b in the transformation that maps (x, y) to (ax, by). **(180)**

viewing window The subset of the coordinate plane that appears on the screen of a graphing utility. **(105)**

W

weak correlation A relation for which, although a linear trend can be seen, many points are not very close to the line (or another specified curve). **(97)**

weighted average If x_i is a value in a data set and w_i is the weight of the value, the weighted average is $\dfrac{\sum\limits_{i=1}^{n} w_i x_i}{\sum\limits_{i=1}^{n} w_i} = \dfrac{w_1 x_1 + w_2 x_2 + \dots + w_n x_n}{w_1 + w_2 + \dots + w_n}$. **(17)**

window See *viewing window*.

whiskers Segments emanating from the box in a box-and-whiskers plot. **(32)**

Y

yield The actual percentage added to the principal in an investment annually, given by $\left(1 + \frac{r}{n}\right)^n$, where r is the annual interest rate and n is the number of compoundings per year. **(582)**

Z

z-score The value $z = \frac{x - \bar{x}}{s}$ for a member x of a data set with mean $\bar{x}$ and standard deviation s. Also called *standard score*. **(206)**

Zero Exponent Theorem If b is an nonzero real number, $b^0 = 1$. **(571)**

zero of a function For a function f, a value of x such that $f(x) = 0$. **(492)**

Index

180°- rotation-symmetric, 172
2 × 2 identity matrix, 753

A

A Mathematician Reads the Newspaper, 425
Abel, Niels, 478
absolute value function, 152-153
absolute value of a complex number, 814
acceleration due to gravity, 119, 130-131
Accommodating the Learner ☉, 8, 17, 48,
    64, 84, 89, 100, 104, 119, 129, 135, 154,
    162, 174, 182, 195, 201, 209, 225, 248,
    254, 259, 272, 297, 301, 310, 321, 327,
    383, 404
Accommodating the Learner ☋, 10, 18, 49,
    65, 83, 90, 98, 104, 113, 120, 135, 155,
    163, 167, 196, 202, 208, 244, 258. 264,
    296, 302, 305, 311, 316, 326, 338, 344,
    363, 370, 377, 382
Activities, 18, 24, 41, 45, 49, 54, 56, 62, 63, 91,
    97, 105, 133, 134, 160, 166, 172, 174,
    179, 180, 200, 210, 230, 236, 239, 244,
    247, 252, 272, 276, 311, 315, 325, 331,
    333, 336, 337, 341, 348, 367, 368, 403,
    406, 412, 419, 421, 439, 443, 448, 459,
    474, 482, 509, 511, 516, 518, 523, 538,
    543, 544, 561, 565, 570, 578, 581, 583,
    588, 590, 618, 624, 631, 646, 653, 655,
    669, 687, 688, 695, 707, 709, 710, 752,
    753, 757, 763, 771, 789, 800, 804, 807,
    812, 817, 826
Adams family tree, 193
Addition Counting Principle
    General Form, 367
    Mutually Exclusive Form,
        367-368
Addition Formulas for the Cosine and Sine
    Theorem, 766-767, 769, 787
aggregated categories, 391
algebra, properties, S1-S2
algebraic number, 492
Alternate Formula for $_nP_r$ Theorem, 382
alternating harmonic sequence, 518
amplitude, 257, 258, 271
An Inconvenient Truth, 816
angular separation of the horizon, 313
angle of depression, 296
angle of elevation, 296
antiphase, 268
applets, See *computer applications*.
applications, (Applications are found
    throughout the text. Selected
    applications are grouped here by
    context.See also *geography*.)

adult height distribution, 11
agriculture
    grain silo, 296
animation, 742-743
architecture and structures
    longest bridges, 59
    Taipei 101, 298
    tallest buildings, 66, 297
art dating, 597
computer and internet usage, 21
consumer finance/economics
    bar iron exports, 123
    car depreciation, 514
    car loans, 541
    cell-phone subscribers, 115, 205
    certificates of deposit, 510
    college loans, 525
    continuously compounded interest,
        583
    cost per share, 14
    CPI/rate of inflation, 141, 185, 212
    credit cards, 551
    diamond rings in Singapore, 87-90
    discounts, 198
    dollar-peso conversion, 203
    Dow Jones Industrial Average, 136-137
    eBay, 598
    foreign exchange, 203, 782
    garbage in U.S., 504
    gasoline cost components, 21
    interest, 581
    investment risk, 415
    loan amortization, 536-541
    median price of homes, 74, 158
    mortgage cost, 539-540
    New York Times, 228
    petroleum consumption, 116
    physician assistant income, 732
    rate, 582
    saving accounts, 504
    televisions, 91, 101
    U.S. budget, 71
    U.S. imports, 52
    U.S. national debt, 78-79, 86, 163, 565
    unemployment, 91, 101, 138
    wages, 205-206
    yield, 582
cooking, 573
copy machine maintenance, 11
demographics
    China, 30, 108
    Cleveland, OH, 566
    Dutch adult male height, 699
    Florida, 139
    Huntley, IL, 110
    India, 28, 76
    Iowa City, 130
    Ireland, 107, 586
    Japanese female
        life expectancy, 567
    Madagascar, 124

New Zealand 144
Russia, 30
Serbia/Montenegro, 703
Sri Lanka, 124
Tampa, FL, 139
United States, 25-26, 76, 135, 605, 650,
    662, 706
Vietnam, 703
education
    ACT scores, 51, 209, 717
    Advanced Placement examinations, 53
    California public schools, 70
    grade-point average, 16-17
    income and education, 9
    public school revenues, 70
    SAT scores, 27, 36, 464, 705
    University of California-Berkeley
        admissions, 391-392
energy
    automobile fuel economy, 366
    electricity, voltage output, 327
    natural gas reserves, 77
    oven temperature, 278
    petroleum consumption, 116
entertainment
    78 RPM-record, 251
    auditorium seating, 525
    Dark Knight, The, 548
    1893 Ferris wheel, 234, 273-274
    Oscar winners, 32
    Pride and Prejudice, 410
    rollercoasters, 58, 184
    Seven Samurai, The, 458
    Spider-Man 3 box office, 42
    television game show, 10
    Texas Star Ferris wheel, 232
games and puzzles
    bridge, 639
    chess, 529-530
    darts, 663
    dominoes, 452
    game show, 375
    lottery, 463
    superball, 535
genealogy
    ancestors, 532-533
    family tree, 193
government
    Adams family tree, 193
    Bureau of Labor Statistics, 141, 210
    Dewey/Truman election, 734
    elections, 734, 737
    Environmental Protection Agency, 50
    Houses of Parliament, 227
    representatives in Congress, 23, 748
    The Federalist papers, 61-64
    state areas, 72
    voters, 74, 145, 166
Hawaiian language, 650
health/safety
    access ramp, 322

accidents, 4, 5, 27, 184, 392, 435
AIDS, 796
Avian Influenza, 42
blood pressure, 254
blood type, 372
calories in food, 139
CAT scan, 114
ELISA test, 796
false negatives/false positives, 396-400
heights, 43, 700, 711, 765
hepatitis C and tattoos, 389, 423
high school smoking, 123
HIV, 399-400
inline skating, 7-8, 11
motor vehicle accidents, 4-5, 398
polio, 359
smoking trends, 123
strep throat, 396-397
tattoo, 389
tidal volume, 280
Titanic, 387-390, 393, 395, 421-422
human biology, 58
axial symmetry, 211
births in U.S., 662
blood pressure, 254
blood types, 372, 664
DNA, 386
hemophilia and thrombophilia, 379
left-handedness, 413
memory, 599-601
polio vaccine, 558
tidal volume of lungs, 280
velocity of blood, 123
weight and height, 614
wrist and neck circumferences, 157
law, 391-392, 400
literature
Pride and Prejudice, 410
St. Ives, 500
marine salvage, 295
music
chromatic scale, 569-570, 574
metronome, 227
sound waves, 220-221,
257-262
tuning fork, 260
nature
bald eagles, 111-112, 151
carbon dioxide concentration, 816
catfish, 599
chambered nautilus, 138
earthworms, 48
fish, 99
flowers, 784
gannet, 308
gestation, 93
Keeling Curve, 816
largemouth bass, 164
lifespan of mammals, 93
natural gas reserves, 42
tides, 255, 267, 791

predator-prey, 250, 256
mountains, 70
navigation
aircraft, 289, 312, 322
great circle, 343
ships, 356
opinion polling, 704, 726, 732, 734, 737,
770
pencil, 704
pets, 737
physical sciences
acceleration due to gravity, 119,
130-131
alternating current, 262, 267
atmospheric pressure, 585, 613
Boyle's Law, 126, 129
circuits, 471
earthquake, 580
electrical fields, 127, 139
electrical force, 127
gear, 290
half-life, 14, 113-115, 124, 145, 596-598,
606, 611
impedence, 471, 485
inductance, 263-264
Kepler's Laws, 573, 608
light, 141
light intensity, 148, 614
length of a day, 133-134, 137
molecules, 349
pendulum, 277, 279, 281
pH level, 580
radio signal, 580
Richter scale, 580
sizes of objects, 558
sound, 260
pizza cutting, 122
polygraph, 399, 664
population
China, 30
density, 57
Florida, 139
growth, 110
Hong Kong, 394
India, 28
Ireland, 107, 586
Madagascar, 124
New Zealand, 144
Russia, 36, 452
Sri Lanka, 124
United States, 25-26, 76, 135
space/astronomy
altitude of a rocket, 319
black hole, 794
international space station, 302
Jovian day, 228
Jupiter, 228
Kepler's Laws, 573, 608
Landsat, 7, 301, 313
Mars, 256, 573
Moon, 298

rocket velocity, 586
satellite orbit, 301
sizes of objects, 558
sports
archery, 673
"Big 10" athletic conference, 381
baseball, 43, 308, 394, 644
championship series, 623
discus throw, 304-306
golf, 313, 771
handicaps, 211
heights of NBA and NFL players, 54
high school participation, 12-13
NBA, 54-56, 425, 433
NFL, 54-56
Olympic long jump, 131
Roger Maris home runs, 43
rowing, 606
soccer, 774
softball, 774
shotput, 308
springboard diving, 154
tennis, 434, 774
track and field records, 109, 602-605
surveying, 318
transportation
airline bookings, 404-406
airline reservations, 11
automobile fuel economy, 366
bicycle, 228, 303
bridges, 59
car color, 408
marine navigation, 298
motor vehicle mileage, 138
ship power, 566
text messaging while driving, 672
water wheel, 290, 340
weather
cyclones, 428
daylight, 276, 281, 329
dry and rainy seasons, 410
length of a day, 353
precipitation, 38-39
rainfall in London, 6
snowfall, 71
sunrise, sunset, 283, 291
temperature, 75, 256, 280, 287
wind chill, 319
arc length, 222, 226
arc measure, 222
Arccos, 300
Archimedian spiral, 810
Archimedes, 810
Arcsin, 310
Arctan, 321
Argand diagrams, 811
Argand, Jean Robert, 811
argument of a complex number, 814
arithmetic mean, 510-511
arithmetic sequence, 505-508,
510-512

nth term, 505-506
arithmetic series, 522-528
  sum, 523-525
Arithmetica Logarithmica, 576
arrangement, 814
Ars Conjectandi, 416
Ars Magna, 475
ASA Condition, 315-316
Assessment
  Chapter Test, 70-71, 144-145, 215, 286-287,
    353, 430-431
  Ongoing Assessment, 30, 53, 60, 86, 93,
    101, 109, 116, 124, 131, 139, 158, 164,
    171, 178, 184, 192, 198, 205, 210, 228,
    234, 241, 246, 251, 256, 262, 268, 275,
    281, 298, 303, 308, 313, 319, 324, 330,
    335, 340, 348, 366, 373, 380, 386, 401,
    409, 425
Associated Press poll, 740
Associated Press-Ipsos poll, 737
asymptote, 105-106, 126, 128,
  155-156
at random, 262
Austen, Jane, 410
Austin, Thomas, 148
average, 14
  weighted, 16-19
axis,
  imaginary, 811
  of symmetry, 172
  real, 811

B

bar graph, 10-11
base, 105
Basic Properties of Probability Theorem, 363
bearing, 289
Bernoulli, Jakob, 416
Bernoull trials, 650
biased coin, 666-669
bin, 22-24
binomial coefficient, 632-635
binomial distribution, 617
binomial expansion, 632-635
binomial experiment, 645-649
  failure, 645
  success, 645
  trials, 645
binomial probability distribution, 651-659,
  666-667, 692, 701-702
  approximating with a normal
    distribution, 701-702
  cumulative, 658
  mean, 652
  parameters, 651
  standard deviation, 640
  variance, 640
Binomial Probability Theorem,
  647-648
Binomial Theorem, 632-636
Boone, Steven, 591

box plot, 31-36, 54-57
box-and-whiskers plot, 32
box problem, 439
Briggs, Henry, 576

C

Cardano, Girolamo, 475
cardioid, 810, 831
Catalan, Eugene Charles, 514
Catalan number, 514
categorical variable, 8
cause and effect, 98
census, 6
center, measures of, 14-16, 167-168, 188-191
center of mass, 94
center of rotation, 222
center of symmetry, 172-178
Central Limit Theorem, 710-711, 713-718
Central Limit Theorem Corollary, 710-711
Change of Base Theorem, 596-598
Chapter Test, 70-71, 144-145, 215, 286-287,
  353, 430-431
Characteristics of Sine Waves Theorem, 271
Chebychev, Pafnuti L., 53
Chebychev's Inequality, 53
chi-square statistic, 417-425
Chu Shih-Chieh, 628
chunking, 486-487
circle
  chords, 452
  graph, 20
  great, 596
  on a sphere, 342-345
  parametric equation for, 331-334,
  unit, 229-231, 233-246, 248-249
circle arc length formula, 226
circular functions, See *trigonometric functions.*
cissoid of Diocles, 831
Clinton, Hillary, 737
cliometrics, 61
cochleoid, 831
coefficient, 438, 633
  binomial, 632-635
  correlation, 95-101
  leading, 438
column matrix, 745
combination, 618-630
common logarithm, 576-577,
  579-580
commutative group, 212
commutativity, 194
comparing numerical distributions, 54
complement of event A, 370
complementary events, 370
Complements Theorem, 234
**Complex Conjugate Multiplication
    Theorem**, 469
complex conjugates, 467-470,
  477-478
complex factoring, 469
complex number, 466, 471,

  474-478, 492, 814-830
  absolute value, 814
  argument, 814
  conjugates, 467-470, 477-478
  imaginary part, 466
  modulus, 814
  operations with, 467-469
  power, 825-827
  nth root, 827-829
  polar form, 814
  graphing, 811-815, 826-829
  real part, 466
  trigonometric form, 817-823
Complex Number Operations Theorem, 468
complex plane, 811
composite of functions 194-198
  domain of, 195-196
composition of functions, 192-198, 202-203
composition of transformations, 196-197
  757-758, 760-761
Compound Interest Formula, 510, 581-583
compounded continuously, 583-584, 595
computer algebra systems (CAS), S7
  complex numbers, 469, 478, 492,
  composition of functions, 195
  defining functions, 84, 120, 161, 175, 455,
    462
  division of polynomials, 454, 456-457, 478,
    481-482, 487, 489
  extrema, 443
  factoring of polynomials, 459-460, 469
  geometric series, 530
  inverse functions, 201-203
  limit, 519
  logarithms, 593, 597
  matrices, 747
  multiplication of polynomials, 486, 489,
    631
  odd function, 175
  trigonometric functions, 241, 244, 337,
    767, 819
  x-intercepts, 118
  solving with complex numbers, 467, 478
  solving exponential equations, 532
  solving quadratic equations, 467, 488
  solving systems, 111, 120, 449
  solving trigonometric equations, 306,
    326-328
  trigonometric identities, 789, 793
  zeros, 443
computer applications (applets)
  binomial probability distributions, 653
  chi-square, 419, 421
  distribution of sample means, 707-708
  Graph-Standardization Theorem, 272
  normal distribution, 688
  polar coordinates, 800
  polar curves, 807
  transformation matrices, 752, 753, 757,
    763

trigonometric form of complex numbers, 817-818
window, 158
concave down, 687, 690
concave up, 687, 690
conditional probability, 395-401
cone, 562, 613
confidence interval, 721-724, 726-730
confidence level, 721-723,
confounding variable, 391
conjugate complex numbers, 467-470
Conjugate Zeros Theorem, 477-478
constant of proportionality, 125-126
constant of variation, 125-126
constant polynomial, 438
contingency table, 387-395
Continuous Change Model, 583-584, 594-595
continuous compounding, 583-585
convergent sequence, 515-521
convergent series, 543
Cooper, Curtis, 591
correlation
    coefficient, 95-101
    direction, 96
    does not imply causation, 98
    negative, 97
    perfect, 96
    positive, 97
    strength, 96
    strong, 97
    weak, 97
cosecant (csc), 336-340, 792
cosine (cos), 229-231, 235-251
    function, 249-250
    domain, 249
    exact values, 242-245, 250
    graph, 249
    in right triangles, 294-298
    inverse, 300
    of complements, 239
    of opposites, 237
    of supplements, 238
cotangent (cot), 336-337, 339-340, 772
cube (geometry), 566, 572, 613
cubes, factoring sums and differences, 482
cube root, 199, 481,560, 827-828
cubic function, 152, 159
cubic model, 450
cubic polynomial, 438
cubing function 159
cumulative binomial probability table, 658
cumulative data, 38-43
cumulative distribution, 38-43
cycle, 248

D

data (datum)
(Data collected by a variety of sources are found throughout the text. See *applications* and *geography*.)
    center of mass, 96
    comparing distributions, 54-57
    cumulative, 38-43
    raw, 207
    scale change of, 185-191
    standardized, 207-208
    translation of, 165-171
da Vinci, Leonardo 597
de Moivre, Abraham, 825
de Moivre's Theorem, 785, 826-827, 829-830
decimal, infinite, 546
decreasing function, 441
degree
    measure, 222-225
    minutes, 228
    of a polynomial, 438
degrees of freedom, 420
del Ferro, Scipione 475
Delos, altar at, 566
density, 57, 76
dependent events, 378
Descartes, Rene, 797
deviation, 46
Dewey, Thomas, 734
DiCaprio, Leonardo, 387
dimensions of a matrix, 744
disaggregated categories, 392
discontinuity, 155, 792, 794
discriminant, 467, 473
disjoint, 367
displays (statistical), See also *distribution*.
    bar graph, 10-11
    box plot, 31-36, 54-57
    comparing data sets, 54, 56-57
    histogram, 22-28, 30, 34-36, 54-57
    standard window, 153
distribution, 22, 24, 38-41, 54-57, 62-63
    binomial probability, 651-659, 666-667, 692, 701-702
    comparing, 54-57
    cumulative, 38-43
    five-number summary, 31-33
    frequency, 62-63, 684
    mode, 639
    multinomial, 675
    normal, 663, 684-690, 692-704
    outlier, 33
    probability, 637-639, 642-643, 651-659, 666-667
    relative frequency, 684
    sample means, 707-711
    sampling, 708-711, 714-716
    shape, 54-57
    skewed, 24
    symmetric, 24
divergent sequence, 515-521

divergent series, 543
dividend, 453
division of complex numbers, 468-469
division of polynomials, 453-457
divisor, 453
domain, 80, 128, 249, 789, 792-795
Double Angle Formulas Theorem 771-775, 785, 787
dragon curve, 551
Durant, Kevin, 433
Dynamic Geometry Systems (DGS)
    complex numbers, 817-818
    transformations, 752-753, 763, 817-818
    trigonometric functions, 236-237, 239
    unit circle, 236-237, 239

E

e, 582, 586
Ekman, Paul, 211
Electronic Frontier Foundation, 591-592
element of a matrix, 744
element of a set, 81
Elements (of Euclid), 306
ellipse, 332-334, 614
empty set, 363
end behavior of a sequence, 515-517
equations, See also *functions* and *models*.
    exponential, 594-596
    for a circle, 235, 333
    for a line, 87-88
    logarithmic, 577-580, 585, 591-593, 600-606
    parametric, 331-335
    polynomial, 439-440, 461-463, 467, 473, 488-489
    quadratic, 466-467, 473-474, 490
    trigonometric, 301, 306, 316-317, 322-323, 325-329
Equivalent Polar-Coordinates Theorem, 799
error, 133
Euclid, 306, 346
Euler, Leonhard, 582
Euler's Theorem, 831
even function, 174-177
event(s), 361
    complementary, 370-371
    conditional probability, 395-401
    dependent, 378
    expected count, 361
    independent, 377-378
    mutually exclusive, 367-368, 370-371
    overlapping, 368-370
    probability, 361-365
expanded form of a polynomial, 459
expansion of $(x + y)^n$, 632-635
expected count, 410-411
experiment, 361, 370
    fair, 362
    unbiased, 362

explicit formula for a sequence, 503
Exploration questions, 13, 21, 30, 37, 44, 53, 60, 66, 86, 93, 101, 109, 116, 124, 131, 139, 158, 164, 171, 178, 184, 192, 198, 205, 210, 228, 234, 241, 246, 251, 256, 262, 268, 275, 281, 298, 303, 308, 313, 319, 324, 330, 335, 340, 366, 373, 380, 386, 394, 401, 409, 416, 425, 445, 452, 458, 463, 472, 480, 485, 490, 508, 567, 574, 580, 586, 593, 599, 606, 623, 630, 636, 644, 650, 658, 665, 673, 691, 697, 705, 712, 718, 725, 731, 750, 756, 761, 765, 770, 775, 791, 803, 810, 816, 824, 830
exponent
    negative, 571
    rational, 558-561, 564-566, 568-574, 675
    zero, 571, 574
exponential equation, 594-596
exponential function, 102-107, 110-115, 584
    decay, 102-104
    growth, 102, 103
    growth factor, 103, 110-112
    half-life, 113-115
    initial value, 103
    properties of, 106
exponential growth curve, 103
exponential growth function, 103
exponential model, 110-115, 134
exponential regression, 111-112
exponential sequence,
    See *geometric sequence*.
Extensions, 19, 85, 106, 121, 183, 196, 226, 232, 244, 265, 317, 324, 328, 334, 338, 364, 384, 405
extrapolation, 88, 138
extreme values (extrema), 440

F

factor, 453, 459-461, 473, 481-484, 486-490
Factor Theorem, 460-462
factoring of polynomials, 459-461, 469, 481-490
Factor-Solution-Intercept Equivalence Theorem, 461, 464
factorial, ! , 380, 619-621
Fahrenheit-Celsius conversion, 204
failure, 645
fair coin, 666-669
fair experiment, 361
false negative, 396-400
false positive, 396-400
Family Circus, The, 486
Federalist Papers, *The,* 61-64
Ferrari, Ludovico, 475
Fibonacci sequence, 502
figurate numbers, 446, 449-451, 464, 472, 496
finite arithmetic series, 523

finite geometric series, 530
finite series, 523
first (lower) quartile, 31
five-number summary, 31-33
    box plot, 32
    box-and-whiskers plot, 32
folium of Descartes, 831
formula
    1.5 IQR criterion for outliers, 34
    Algorithm for Matrix Multiplication, 746
    Alternate Formula for Variance of a Random Variable, 641
    Arithmetic Sequences, 505
    Benchmarks for Normal Distributions, 719
    Central Limit Theorem Rule of Thumb, 710
    circular arc length, 226
    compound interest, 583
    Continuous Change Model, 583
    explicit, 503
    Geometric Sequences, 509
    gravitational force, 592
    half-angle, 773
    height of a projectile, 119
    Kepler's Third Law, 608
    $_nC_n$, 619
    $_nC_r$ Theorem, 614
    $_nP_n$, 384
    $_nP_r$, 382
    $_nP_r$, alternate, 382
    $_nP_r$ Theorem, 382
    Pearson, 96
    Periodic Installment for a Loan, 537
    Polar-Rectangular Conversion, 801
    population standard deviation, 46-48
    population variance, 46-48
    Quadratic, 118
    recursive, 504
    sample standard deviation, 48-49
    sample variance, 48-49
    SAS Area for a Triangle, 315
    Sum of an Infinite Geometric Series, 545
    sum of squared residuals, 90
    variance of a random variable, 640
    velocity of a rocket, 586
Foucault, Léon, 281
Foucault pendulum, 281
Four Numbers game, 550
Foxtrot, 135
fractal, 465, 551, 832
Franklin, Benjamin, 115
frequency, 17-18, 61-63
    histogram, 22, 63
    of a periodic function, 259-260
frieze pattern, 252
full turn, 222
Fuller, Buckminster, 774
function, 80-83, See also *distributions, sequences, and transformations.*
    absolute value, 152-153

    as a correspondence, 81
    as a set of ordered pairs, 80
    asymptote, 105, 155
    composite composition, 193-198
    cosecant, 336-340
    cosine, 249-250
    cotangent, 336-337, 334-340
    cubic, 152, 159
    decreasing, 441
    description of, 82
    discontinuity, 155
    domain, 80, 128, 249, 299-306, 309-310
    even, 174
    exponential, 102-107, 110-115, 584
    extreme values (extreme), 440
    $f(x)$, 83
    graphing, 82-83
    identity function, 202
    increasing, 441
    inverse cosine, 299-302
    Inverse Function Theorem, 202
    inverse of, 199-204
    inverse sine, 309-313
    inverse-square, 152
    inverse tangent, 320-324
    linear, 87-91, 95
    logarithm, 578, 602
    maximum value, 440
    minimum value, 440
    natural logarithm, 584
    negative, 441
    notation, 83
    nth power, 563
    nth root, 560, 602
    odd, 73
    parent, 152, 155-156
    periodic, 254-259
    periodicity, 253
    piecewise definition, 82
    polynomial, 436-437, 439-452, 473-480
    positive, 441
    power, 128, 602
    quadratic, 117-123, 473
    range, 80, 249
    real, 81
    reciprocal power, 128-130
    reciprocal trigonometric, 336-340
    relative extremum, 440
    relative maximum, 440
    relative minimum, 440
    restricted cosine, 299-300
    restricted sine, 309-310
    restricted tangent, 320-321
    secant, 336-337, 338-340
    sine, 247-250
    square root, 560
    tangent, 252
    trigonometric, 229-283
    value, 83
    vertical line test, 83

zeros, 249, 442-443, 473-480
Fundamental Theorem of Algebra 475, 488

G

Gallup poll, 730, 740
Galton board, 616, 674
Galton, Sir Francis, 674
Gauss, Karl Friedrich, 475, 523-524, 825
general solution to the trigonometric
    equation, 325
generating function, 491
Geography, See also *applications* and
    demographics.
    Ankara, Turkey, 357
    Barcelona, Spain, 346
    Beijing, China, 357
    Bogota, Columbia, 344
    Boulder, CO, 71
    Cape Town, South Africa, 346
    Caribou, ME, 140
    Cheyenne, WY, 749
    Chicago, IL, 280, 347, 357
    circumference of Earth, 350
    Cleveland, OH, 566
    Delos, Greece, 566
    Denver, CO, 140, 749
    equator, 343-345
    Florida, 139
    Grand Rapids, MI, 228, 287
    Great Falls, MT, 140
    Greenwich, England, 343
    Greenwich meridian, 343-344
    Herculaneum, 596
    Huntley, IL, 110
    Iceland, 614
    International Dateline, 343
    International Falls, MN, 281
    Iowa City, IA, 130
    Jackson, MS, 357
    Jacksonville, FL, 276
    Juneau, AK, 75
    Kansas City, MO, 140, 749
    latitude, 343-347
    London, England, 36, 227, 353
    longitude, 343-347
    Los Angeles, CA, 38, 290
    Madagascar, 124
    meridian, 343
    Mexico City, Mexico, 140
    Minneapolis-St. Paul, MN, 75
    Mollweide equal-area projection, 341
    Montgomery, AL, 228
    Mount Vesuvius, 596
    New Delhi, India, 341-342,
        345-347
    New London, CT, 353
    New Orleans, LA, 148, 353
    New York, NY, 341-347
    North Pole, 343-346
    Omaha, NE, 749
    Ottawa, Canada, 140

Pago Pago, American Samoa, 255
    Paris, France, 281, 346
    Paris, TX, 347
    Pompeii, 596
    Prague, Czech Republic, 347
    Providence, RI, 347
    Rio de Janeiro, Brazil, 347
    Rome, Italy, 347
    Salt Lake City, UT, 140
    San Francisco, CA, 140
    Sarasota, FL, 713
    Seattle, WA, 140
    South Pole, 346
    Sri Lanka, 124
    St. Louis, MO, 357
    Sydney, Australia, 357
    Taipei, Taiwan, 297
    Tampa, FL, 139
    Tehran, Iran, 344
    temperature vs. latitude, 140
    Toyko, Japan, 344
    Trujillo, Peru, 252
    Washington, DC, 140
Geometric Addition Theorem,
    812-813
geometric mean, 511, 514, 550
geometric sequence, 501, 509-514
    nth term, 509
geometric series
    finite, 529-535, 537
    infinite, 543-548
    nth partial sum, 530
geometry
    AAS condition, 315-316
    arc length, 223
    ASA condition, 315-316
    complex numbers, 811
    cube, 566, 572, 613
    great circle on a sphere, 342-347
    point matrix, 751
    properties, S3
    Pythagorean Theorem, 235, 306
    radian measure, 223
    right triangle, 294, 298, 336
    SAS Area Formula for a Triangle, 314
    similar triangles, 295
    sphere, 341-347, 565
    SSA condition, 316-317
    symmetry, 172
    triangles, 294
    volume of a cone, 562
GIMPS, 591
Gore, Al, 816
graph, polar coordinate, 804-810, 813, 814
graph, rectangular coordinate
    amplitude, 257
    circular function, 229
    complex numbers, 811, 816
    cosine function, 248
    exponential function, 103-107
    imaginary numbers, 811

logarithm function, 575
    parent function, 152, 155-156
    period, 253
    phase shift, 263
    polynomials, 439
    sine function, 248
    tangent function, 253
    vertical shift, 161-165, 253, 271
    window, 153-154
Graph Scale-Change Theorem, 181
Graph-Standardization Theorem, 270-272
graph-standardized form, 271
graph, statistical
    bar, 10, 11
    histogram, 22-28, 30, 34-36, 54-57
    box plot, 31-36, 54-57
    line, 5-6
    outliers on, 33-34
Graph-Translation Theorem, 161-165, 175-176
Graphing utilities
    absolute value functions, 153
    asymptotes, 155-156, 196
    discontinuities, 155
    domain, 153-155, 196
    exponential functions, 105, 578
    extrema, 154-155, 439, 443
    harmonic series, 548
    inverse functions, 203
    inverse variation, 126
    logarithm functions, 578, 588
    nth root functions, 561
    parametric equations, 331-333
    polar graphs 800, 804, 805
    polynomial functions,
    quadratic functions,
    range, 153-155
    symmetry of graphs, 175
    transformations, 179-180
    trigonometric functions, 248, 259, 265,
        272, 327, 789
    window, 156
great circle, 342-347
Greek letters
    alpha (α), 766
    beta (β), 766
    mu (μ), 46
    pi (π), 224
    sigma, lowercase (σ), 46
    sigma, uppercase (Σ), 15
    theta (θ), 229
Greenwich (Prime) Meridian, 343
group, 212
group theory, 478
grouping, 486
growth factor of exponential function, 103
growth rate, 103

H

half turn, 222
half-angle formula, 775
half-life, 113-115, 596-598

actinium, 147
barium, 114
carbon-14, 596-597, 606
cesium, 145
polonium, 113
radium, 115
strontium-90, 611
thorium, 124
Half-Turn Theorem, 237
Hall, Monty, 409
Hamilton, Alexander, 61
harmonic motion, 277
harmonic sequence, 502, 516-517
    alternating, 518
harmonic series, 548
Harris poll, 737
heptagonal number, 496
histogram, 22-28, 30, 34-36, 54-57
    analyzing, 24
    cumulative, 39-41
    drawing, 23
    frequency, 23
    relative frequency, 23
history of mathematics, See *mathematicians*
homogeneous population, 52
horizontal asymptote, 125
horizontal scale change, 180
horizontal scale factor, 180
horizontal shift 159-165
hyperbola, 126
hypotenuse, 294
hypothesis, 417, 668-671
hypothesis testing, 417, 669-671
    null hypothesis, 670
    significance level, 420, 669

I

identity, 235, 786-795
identity function, 202
identity matrix, 753
identity transformation, 753
image, 159
imaginary axis, 811
imaginary number, 465
imaginary part, 466
impressionistic model, 121, 135
increasing function, 441
independent events, 378-379
independent variable, 80
index, 15
inductance, 264
inferential statistics, 358-359, 667-673, 714-732
infinite decimal, 546
infinite series, 501, 523, 542-549
infinite geometric series, 543-548
inflection points, 687, 689-690
Infratest poll, 726, 728
initial value for exponential model, 105
integer, 469
interest rate, 536
International Date Line, 343

interpolation, 88, 136
interquartile range, 32
intersection, 368
invariant, 168
inverse, 199
inverse cosine function, 299-302
Inverse Function Theorem, 202
inverse of a function, 199
inverse operations, 560
inverse proportionality, 125, 127
inverse sine function, 309-313
inverse square relationship, 127
inverse tangent function, 320, 324
inverse-square function, 125
inverse variation, 125, 130
IQR, 32
irrational number, 469

J

Jay, John, 61
Jeter, Derek, 394
Justice, David, 394

K

Keeling curve, 816
Kelvin temperatures 204
Kepler, Johannes 608
Kepler's Laws, 573, 608
Kerrich, John, 411, 713, 731
Khayyam, Omar, 628

L

Laplace, Pierre-Simon, 713
latitude, 140
"Law of Averages", 412-414
Law of Cosines, 304-308, 314
    Spherical, 345-346
Law of Large Numbers, 412-414
Law of Sines, 314-319, 350
leading coefficient, 438
least squares, 94
leg, 294
Leibniz harmonic triangle, 674
lemniscate of Bernoulli, 831
length (of a string), 375-376
Let's Make a Deal 409
Liberty Bell, 184
limit, 515-521
    harmonic sequence, 516
    properties, 516-521
Limit of a Sum Property, 518
Limit of a Difference Property, 518
Limit of a Product Property, 518
Limit of a Quotient Property, 518
linear polynomial, 438
linear sequence, See *arithmetic sequence*.
line of best fit, 94-96
line of symmetry, 172
linear function, 87-91, 95
linear model, 87-101
    regression, 96-101

linearity, 98
linearizing, 601, 603
lituus, 831
Litvinenko, Alexander, 113, 595
local maximum, 440
local minimum, 440
logarithm 575-581, 583-608
    common, 576-577, 579-580
    function, 578, 584
    models, 600-602
    natural, 584-585
    properties, 587-590, 596
Logarithm of a Power Theorem,
    590-591
Logarithm of a Product Theorem, 588, 592
Logarithm of a Quotient Theorem, 589, 592
Logarithm of 1 Theorem, 587
logarithmic equations, 577-580, 585, 591-593,
    600-606
logarithmic spiral, 810, 827
longitude, 343

M

Madison, James, 61
Mandelbrot, Benoit, 832
Mandelbrot Set, 832
margin of error, 721-724
Maris, Roger, 43
mathematical model, 78
mathematicians
    Abel, Niels, 478
    Argand, Jean Robert, 811
    Bernoulli, Jakob, 416, 797
    Boone, Steven, 591
    Briggs, Henry, 576
    Cardano, Girolamo, 475
    Catalan, Eugene Charles, 514
    Chu Shih-Chieh, 628
    Cooper, Curtis, 591
    del Ferro, Scipione, 475
    de Fermat, Pierre, 797
    De Moivre, Abraham, 825
    Descartes, Rene, 797
    Euclid, 306, 346
    Euler, Leonhard, 83
    Ferrari, Ludovico, 475
    Galileo, 119
    Galton, Sir Francis, 674
    Gauss, Karl Friedrich, 475,
        523-524, 825
    Gregory, James, 324
    Kanada, Yasumasa, 324
    Kepler, Johannes, 608
    Kerrich, John, 411, 713, 731
    Khayyam, Omar, 628
    Laplace, Pierre-Simon, 710
    Mandelbrot, Benoit, 832
    Menelaus, 346
    Mosteller, Frederick, 61-64

Muller, Johannes (Regiomontanus), 346
Napier, John, 587
Nasir-Eddin, 346
Newton, Isaac, 119, 675, 797
Pascal, Blaise, 625
Paulos, John, 425
Pingala, 628
Pythagoras, 235
Sally, Paul, 550
Smith, Edison, 592
Tartaglia, Niccolo, 475
Ulam, Stanislaw, 403
Wallace, David, 61-64
Wessel, Caspar, 811
Wilf, Herbert S., 491
mathematics in other disciplines (Examples of mathematics in other disciplines are found throughout the text. See *applications* and *geography*.)
Matrices for Reflections Theorem, 752
Matrices for Rotations Theorem, 762
matrix (matrices), 742-749, 751-765, 767, 776-777
  2×2 identity, 753
  column, 754
  dimension, 744-746
  element, 744
  for composites of transformations, 757-758, 760-761
  for reflections, 752, 774
  for rotations, 757-764
  for transformations, 751-764
  for translations, 777
  for scale changes, 753-754
  identity, 753
  multiplication, 745-749
  point, 757
  product, 746-749
  row, 745
  square, 749
Matrix Basis Theorem, 759-760
maximum, 31
Maximum Numbers of Zero Theorem, 476
maximum point, 117
maximum value, 249, 440
mean, 14
  arithmetic, 510
  as a weighted average, 17
  geometric, 511
  of a binomial random variable, 659-664
  of a random variable, $\bar{x}$, 638-642
    of sample means, $\mu_{\bar{x}}$, 708-711, 720-721
  of z-scores, 207
  population, μ, 46, 48, 708, 720-721
  sample, x, 48, 708
Mean of a Binomial Random Variable Theorem, 659
measures of center, 14-16
  mean, 14
  median, 14

measures of central tendency, See *measures of center*
measures of spread, 45
  quartiles, 31
  range, 45
  standard deviation, 46
  variance, 46
median, 14, 31-33
member of a set, 81
Mental Math, 6, 14, 22, 31, 38, 45, 54, 61, 80, 87, 94, 102, 110, 117, 125, 132, 152, 159, 165, 172, 179, 185, 193, 199, 206, 222, 229, 235, 242, 247, 252, 257, 263, 269, 276, 294, 299, 304, 309, 314, 320, 325, 331, 336, 341, 360, 367, 374, 381, 387, 395, 402, 410, 417, 438, 446, 453, 459, 465, 473, 481, 486, 502, 509, 515, 522, 529, 536, 542, 560, 568, 575, 581, 587, 594, 600, 618, 624, 631, 637, 645, 651, 659, 666, 686, 692, 698, 706, 714, 719, 726, 744, 751, 757, 762, 766, 771, 786, 792, 797, 804, 811, 817, 825
meridian, 343
Mersenne prime, 591, 593
method of least squares, 94
minimum, 31
minimum point, 117
minimum value, 249, 440
minute (unit), 228, 248, 298
Miritici logarithmorum canonis descriptio, 587
mode, 15, 639
model
  comparison, 133-139
  cubic, 450
  exponential, 110-115, 134
  impressionistic, 121
  inverse variation, 125-131
  linear, 87-101, 133
  linear regression, 96-101, 133
  logarithmic, 600-602
  mathematical, 78
  non-theory-based, 121
  polynomial, 446-451
  quadratic, 117, 119-123, 135
  trigonometric, 276-281
modulus, 814
Monte Carlo method, 404-408
Mosteller, Frederick, 61-64
MSN-Zogby poll, 731
Multiplication Counting Principle, 374-377
multinomial distribution, 675
multinomial experiment, 675
multiplicity of a zero, 474-476
mutually exclusive, 267

N

Napier, John, 580, 587
Nasir-Eddin, 346
natural logarithm, 584-585
natural logarithm function, 584
natural number, 469

negative correlation, 97
Negative Exponent Theorem, 571
negative function on an interval, 441
Newton, Isaac, 119, 675, 797
non-theory-based model, 121
normal curve, 686-690, 692-698
  standard, 688
normal distribution, 663, 684-690, 692-704
  benchmarks, 719-720
  mean, 692
  standard deviation, 692
not A, 370
notation (page of first introduction)
  χ^2, chi-square, 417
  ${}_nC_r$, combinations, 619
  $\circ$, composition of functions, 194
  $^\circ$, degree, 228
  e, 582
  $\in$ is an element of, 81
  $f(x)$, 83
  f^{-1}, inverse functions, 125
  !, factorial, 380
  i, complex number, 15
  i, index, 15
  k, constant of variation, 125
  limit, 515
  mapping, for functions, 159
  minutes, 228
  μ, mu, population mean, 46
  $\mathbb{N}$, set of natural numbers, 81
  $\varnothing$, null set, 363
  ${}_nP_r$, permutations, 382
  σ^2, population variance, 46
  $\mathbb{Q}$, set of rational numbers, 81
  Q_1, first quartile, 31-34
  Q_2, second quartile, 31
  Q_3, third quartile, 31-33
  $\mathbb{R}$, set of rational numbers, 81
  r, correlation, 96
  $\sqrt{}$, radical, 564
  s, sample standard deviation, 48
  s^2, sample variance, 48
  $\{x|...\}$, set builder, 81
  $\{x:...\}$, set builder, 81
  σ, sigma, population standard deviation, 46
  Σ, summation, 15
  $\bar{x}$ sample mean, 48
  $\mathbb{Z}$, set of integers, 81
  nth power functions, 563
nth root, 559-570, 827-830
  of a complex number, 827-830
  function,
    of unity, 489-490
  radical notation, 564-565
null set, $\varnothing$, 363
Number of Real Roots Theorem, 564
number of solutions, 563

Number of Zeros of a Polynomial Theorem, 476
number
 algebraic, 492
 Catalan, 514
 complex, 466-471, 474-478, 492
 heptagonal, 496
 imaginary, 465
 integer, 469
 natural, 469
 pentagonal, 464
 pronic, 674
 rational, 469
 real, 469
 tetrahedral, 446
 transcendental, 492
 triangular, 475
 tribonacci, 550
numerical analysis, 8
numerical variable, 478

O

Obama, Barack, 740
observed values, 89-90, 411
odd function, 174-177
Ohring, George, 256
Ongoing Assessment, 30, 53, 60, 86, 93, 101, 109, 116, 124, 131, 139, 158, 164, 171, 178, 184, 192, 198, 205, 210, 228, 234, 241, 246, 251, 256, 262, 268, 275, 281, 298, 303, 308, 313, 319, 324, 330, 335, 340, 348, 366, 373, 380, 386, 401, 409, 425
Opposites Theorem, 237
outcomes, 360
outlier, 33

P

Panthéon, 281
parabola, 117-121
parallelogram, 514
parameter, 331, 651
parametric equations, 331-335
parent function, 152, 155-156, 269
parent normal curve, 686
partial sums, 530
Pascal, Blaise, 625
Pascal's Triangle, 617, 624-631
Pascal Triangle Symmetry Theorem, 627
Peanuts, 644
pendulum, 277, 279, 281
pentagonal numbers, 464
Peppermint Patty, 644
percentile, 40-41
perfect correlation, 96
period, 254, 258, 271, 282
periodic function, 254-259
Periodicity Theorem, 253
permutation, 381-385, 618, 622
phase shift, 263-267, 271
Phase Shift Identity, 264

pi, π, 492
piecewise definition of a function, 82
Pingala, 628
point matrix, 751
point symmetry, 172-178
polar axis, 797-789
polar coordinate system, 784-785, 797
polar coordinate(s), 797-810, 813-814
polar form, 814
polar grid, 798
Polar-Rectangular Conversion Formula, 801
pole, 797
polygon, 472, 549
polynomial, 436, 438
 coefficient, 438
 degree, 438
 differences, 447-451
 division, 453-457
 expanded form, 459
 factored form, 459
 factoring, 481-490
 leading coefficient, 438
 model, 446-451
 regression, 450
 standard form, 438
Polynomial Difference Theorem, 448
polynomial function, 436-437, 439-452, 473-480
 graph, 437, 439-444, 460-464, 476-477
 roots, 442
Polynomial Graph Wiggliness Theorem, 476
polynomial in x, 438
population, 6
 mean (μ), 46, 48, 708, 720-721
 standard deviation (σ), 46, 48
 variance (σ^2), 46, 48
 density, 57
 pyramid, 25-26, 28, 30
positive correlation, 97
positive function on an interval, 441
positive relation, 128
power, 558-562, 568-574,
 rational, 568-574, 675
 properties, 570-571
 zero, 571
 negative, 571
power function, 128
Power of a Power Property, 570
Power of a Product Property, 570
Power of a Quotient Property, 570
predicted values, 89-90
 extrapolation, 88
 interpolation, 88
preimage, 159
Pride and Prejudice, 410
prime meridian, 343
principal (of a loan), 536
Probability of Complements Theorem, 371
probability, 360-373
 binomial, 647-648, 651-659, 666-667

Central Limit Theorem, 710-711, 713-718
complementary events, 371
dependent events, 378
distribution, 637-639, 642-643, 651-659, 666-667, 684
expected count, 410
experiment, 360
from simulations, 406, 408
independent events, 378
Multiplication Counting Principle, 374
mutually exclusive events, 368
normal distribution, 684-690
of an event, 361-365
outcome, 360-362
permutations, 382
probability distribution, 637-639, 642-643, 651-659, 666-667
random variable, 637
sample space, 360
sampling distribution, 708
simulation, 402-408, 419
standard normal distribution, 693
union of events, 367
with replacement, 374
without replacement, 381
Probability of the Union of Events-General Form Theorem, 367
Probability of the Union of Mutually Exclusive Events Theorem, 368
probability of an event, $P(E)$, 361, 362
probability theory, 360
product matrix, 746
Product of Complex Numbers Theorem
 Polar Form, 821
 Trigonometric Form, 820
Product of Powers Property, 570
Projects
 A test for convergence, 550
 Algebraic and transcendental numbers, 492
 Application of the Law of Sines, 350
 Automobile survey, 67
 Beat matching and Djing 101, 282
 Bell curve, 734
 Binomial theorem for rational exponents, 675
 Bond angles in molecules, 349
 Bug walk, 776
 Class survey, 68
 Class survey data revisited, 141
 Class survey, yet again, 212
 Coin circulation, 67
 CPI/rate of inflation, 212
 Determining maximum altitude, 349
 Dewey defeats Truman!!, 734
 Disputed *Federalist Papers*, 68
 Euler's Theorem, 831
 Facial symmetry and asymmetry, 211
 Famous polar equations, 831
 Five years from now, 141
 Four number game, 550

Generating functions: the crazy dice problem, 491
Geometric mean, 550
Graphic design using polar equations, 832
Graphing complex numbers, 491
Graphing and interpreting statistical data, 68
How common is a particular letter?, 733
How do credit cards work?, 551
Is your class typical?, 733
Jar of pennies, 733
Kepler's Third Law and log-log graphs, 608
"Law of averages", 426
Leibniz's harmonic triangle, 674
Light intensity, 141
Logarithmic timelines, 608
Mandelbrot set, 832
Multinomial probability distribution, 675
Noncircular functions, 283
Noon day project, 350
Probabilistic analysis of functions, 427
Probabilities and the lottery, 675
Probability trees, 427
Properties of cubics, 492
Quincunx, 674
Random walk, 426
Recursively defined curves, 551
Sabermetrics: the fastest player, 67
Semilog graphing paper, 607
Shear mapping, 776
Sierpinski sieve, 675
Spherical triangles, 350
Sports handicaps, 211
Square waves, 283
Sum of many dice, 426
Sums of random digits, 734
Sums of sine waves with the same period, 282
Sunrise and sunset times, 283
Temperature vs. latitude, 140
Transformation groups, 212
Translation using matrix multiplication, 777
Trigonometric identities, 777
Using logs to calculate - the old way, 607
Properties and Theorems (page of statement)
$\frac{1}{n}$ Exponent Theorem, 560
Addition Counting Principle (General Form), 368
Addition Counting Principle (Mutually Exclusive Form), 367
Addition Formulas for the Cosine and Sine, 766
Basic Properties of Probability, 363
Binomial Probability Theorem, 647
Binomial Theorem, 632
Centers of Scaled Data, 188
Centers of Translated Data, 167
Change of Base Theorem, 596
Characteristics of Sine Waves, 271

Complements Theorem, 239
Complex Conjugate Multiplication, 469
Complex Number Operations, 468
Conjugate Zeros Theorem, 477
Continuous Change Model, 583
De Moivre's Theorem, 826
Double Angle Formulas, 771
Equivalent Polar Coordinates Theorem, 799
Euler's Theorem, 831
Factor Theorem, 460
Factor-Solution-Intercept Theorem, 461
Formula for Arithmetic Sequences, 505
Formula for Geometric Sequences, 509
Formula for $_nC_r$, 619
Formula for $_nP_n$, Corollary, 384
Formula for $_nP_r$, 382
Formula for $_nP_r$, Alternate, 382
Formulas for the Sum of an Arithmetic Series, 524
Formulas for the Sum of a Geometric Series, 530
Fundamental Theorem of Algebra, 475
Geometric Addition Theorem, 812
Graph Scale-Change Theorem, 181
Graph-Standardization Theorem, 270
Graph-Translation Theorem, 161
Half-Turn Theorem, 237
Inverses of Functions Theorem, 181
Law of Cosines, 304
Law of Sines, 315
Limit of a Difference Property, 519
Limit of a Product Property, 519
Limit of a Quotient Property, 519
Limit of a Sum Property, 519
Limit of Harmonic Sequences Property, 516
Logarithm of 1, 587
Logarithm of a Power of the Base, 587
Logarithm of a Quotient, 589
Logarithm of the Base, 587
Logarithm of a Product, 588
Logarithm of a Power, 588
Matrices and Composites, 758
Matrices for Reflections, 752
Matrices for Rotations, 759
Matrix Basis Theorem, 759
Mean and Standard Deviation of z-scores, 207
Mean of a Binomial Random Variable, 659
Multiplication Counting Principle, 374
Negative Exponent Theorem, 571
Number of Real Roots Theorem, 564
Number of Zeros of a Polynomial, 476
Opposites Theorem, 237
Parametric Equation for a Circle, 332
Parametric Equation for a Circle with Center (h, k), 333
Pascal Triangle Symmetry Theorem, 627
Periodic Installment Formula for a Loan, 537

Periodicity Theorem, 253
Phase Shift Identity, 264
Polar-Rectangular Conversion Formula, 801
Polynomial Difference Theorem, 448
Polynomial Graph Wiggliness Theorem, 476
Probability of Complements, 371
Probability of the Union of Events, 367
Probability of the Union of Mutually Exclusive Events, 368
Product of Complex Numbers Theorem (Polar Form), 821
Product of Complex Numbers Theorem (Trigonometric Form), 820
Properties of Limits and Constants, 517
Properties of Limits on Operations with Sequences, 518
Properties of Powers, 570
Properties of Sine Waves, 258
Pythagorean Identity, 235
Quotient of Complex Numbers Theorem (Polar Form), 821
Quotient of Complex Numbers Theorem (Trigonometric Form), 821
Rational Exponent Theorem, 568
Remainder Theorem, 455
Right Triangle Ratios for Sine, Cosine, and Tangent, 294
Roots of a Complex Number Theorem, 828
Rotation Matrix Theorem, 762
SAS Area Formula for a Triangle, 315
Spherical Law of Cosines, 344
Spread of Scaled Data, 188
Spread of Translated Data, 168
Standardization Theorem, 699
Strings with Replacement Theorem, 376
Subtraction Formulas for the Cosine and Sine, 768
Sums and Differences of Cubes, 482
Sums and Differences of Odd Powers, 483
Supplements Theorem, 238
Symmetry over the x-axis, 173
Symmetry over the y-axis, 173
The Central Limit Theorem, 710
The Sum of an Infinite Geometric Series, 545
Variance and Standard Deviation of a Binomial Random Variable, 662
Zero Exponent Theorem, 571
pronic number, 674
pth percentile, 40
Pythagorean Identity, 235, 786-787
Pythagorean Theorem, 235, 306, 508

Q

quadratic equation
  complex number solutions,
      466-467, 473-474
  sum and product of roots, 473, 490
Quadratic Formula, 18, 467, 473
quadratic function, 117-123, 473
  x-intercepts, 118
  zeros, 473-474
quadratic model, 117, 119-123
  residuals of, 136
quadratic polynomial, 438
quadratic regression, 120-123
quarter turn, 222
quartic polynomial, 436-438, 474
quartiles, 31-34
  first, Q1, 31-34
  interquartile range, IQR, 32
  second, Q2, 31
  third, Q3, 31-33, 41
quincunx, 674
Quinnipiac University, 704, 726-729
quintic polynomial, 438
quotient, 453, 455-457
Quotient of Complex Numbers Theorem
  Polar Form, 821-823
  Trigonometric Form, 821-823
Quotient of Powers Property, 570

R

radian, 224
radian measure, 223-227
radical, 564-565
random number, 402, S8
random outcomes, 362
random variable, 637-642, 651, 659-664
range
  interquartile, 32
  measure of spread, 45
  of a function, 80, 126
rate, 582
Rational Exponent Theorem, 568
rational exponent, 568-574, 675
rational number, 469
rational power, 568-574
raw data, 207
raw scores, 207
real axis, 811
real function, 81
real number, 469
real part, 465
reciprocal power function, 128
reciprocal trigonometric functions, 337
rectangular coordinates, 800-802, 807-808,
      811-813, 817
recursive formula for a sequence, 504-505,
      509
recurrence relation, 504
reflection, 752, 774
reflection symmetry, 172-178
regression

cubic, 450
direction, 96
exponential, 111
line, 94-96
linear, 94-98, 601-603
quadratic, 120
relation, 80
  dependent variable, 80
  function, 80
  independent variable, 80
relative extrema, 440
relative frequency, 18-19, 363-364, 367, 726
relative frequency histogram, 18
relative maximum, 440
relative minimum, 440
remainder, 454-457, 461
Remainder Theorem, 455
removable discontinuity, 794
removable singularity, 794
repeated factoring, 487
representative sample, 7
residual, 89
  error, 132
  exponential model, 134
  linear model, 89-95, 133, 603
  plot, 132-133
  quadratic model, 135
restricted cosine function, 299-300
restricted sine function, 309-310
restricted tangent function, 320-321
restriction, 792
Review Questions, 13, 21, 29, 37, 44, 52-53,
      60, 65-66, 86, 93, 100-101, 108-109, 116,
      124, 130-131, 139, 157-158, 163-164,
      171, 178, 184, 191-192, 198, 204-205,
      228, 234, 241, 246, 251, 255-256, 262,
      267-268, 275, 281, 298, 303, 308, 313,
      319, 324, 330, 335, 340, 348, 365-366,
      373, 380, 386, 394, 400-401, 409, 415-
      416, 425, 445, 452, 458, 463, 471-372,
      480, 485, 490, 508, 514, 521, 528, 535,
      541, 548-549, 566-567, 574, 580, 586,
      593, 598-599, 606, 623, 630, 636, 644,
      650, 657-658, 664-665, 673, 691, 697,
      705, 712, 717-718, 724-725, 731
revolution, 222-224
Richter scale, 580
right triangle, 294, 508
right triangle trigonometry, 294-298
Roosevelt, Franklin D., 358
Roots of a Complex Number Theorem, 828-
      830
roots of a polynomial function, 442
rose curve, 784-785, 806-809
rotation, 220-234
  center, 222
  image, 222
  magnitude, 222
  matrix for, 757-759, 762-764
Rotation Matrix Theorem, 762
row-by-column multiplication, 745

row matrix, 745
Rule of 72, 599

S

sabermetrics 67
St. Ives, 500
Sally, Paul, 550
Salk, Jonas, 359
sample, 6
  distribution, 706
  mean, 708
  representative, 7
  simple random, 707
  space, 360, 370
  standard deviation, 48
  variance, 48
sampling distribution, 708-711, 714-716
**SAS Area Formula for a Triangle
      Theorem**, 314-315
scale change, 180-191, 270-274, 332-333,
      753-754
  Graph Scale-Change Theorem, 181-184
  horizontal, 180, 182-183
  matrix for, 753-754
  of data, 185-191
  size change, 180
  vertical, 179, 182-183
  with parametric equations, 332
scale factor, 180, 182-186
  horizontal, 180, 182-183
  negative, 182-184
  vertical, 180, 182-183
scale image, 186
scaling, 180
scatterplot, 91, 601-603
scores
  data, 207
  standardized, 207
Scratch Live, 282
secant (sec), 336-337, 339-340, 792
second (middle) quartile, 31
sequence, 501-522
  alternating harmonic, 518
  arithmetic, 505-508, 510-512
  arithmetic operations on,
      510-516
  convergent, 543
  divergent, 543
  end behavior, 515-517
  explicit formula, 503
  Fibonacci, 502
  geometric, 509-514
  harmonic, 502
  initial condition, 504
  limits, 516-520
  of partial sums, 542
  recursive formula, 504-505, 509
  recurrence relation, 504
  term, 502
series, 522-535
  arithmetic, 522-528

finite, 523
geometric, 530-535, 537
infinite, 523, 542-549
sum, 523, 524
set
  disjoint, 367, 368
  element, 81
  intersection, 368, 370
  member, 81
  mutually exclusive, 367, 368
  union, 367-370
shear, 776
Seven Samurai, The 88
Sierpinski quilt, 675
Sierpinski sieve, 675
sigma (Σ), 15
sigma-notation, 15
significance level, 420, 608-671
significance test, 669-671
simple harmonic motion, 277
simple random sample, 707
Simpson, Edward H., 391
Simpson's Paradox, 391, 344
simulation, 402, 408
sine (sin), 229-232, 235-251, 294
  domain, 249
  exact values, 242-245, 247
  function, 247-250
    of complements, 239
    of opposites, 237
    of supplements, 238
  graph, 249, 805-806
  inroght triangles, 244-248
  inverse, 310
sine wave, 257-267, 271-274, 282
singularity, 792, 794
size change, 180
skewed distribution, 24
sliders, 179-180, 272, 492, 578, 588, 688
sound waves, 220
Smith, Edson, 592
sphere, 341-347, 565, 613
Spherical Law of Cosines, 345-346 spherical
  triangles, 345-346, 348
spherical trigonometry, 345-347
spiral, 804, 810, 827
spread
  measure of, 45-51, 167-166,
    185-191
  of a distribution, 45, 54
spreadsheets, See also *statistical packages*
  binomial probability, 669
  Central Limit Theorem, 709
  continuous compounding, 581
  e, 581
  histogram, 24
  Law of Large Numbers, 412-413
  limits 516, 518,
  loans, 537-539
  logarithmic modeling, 603
  mean, 19, 186-187, 641

Monte Carlo simulation, 687
  polynomial differences, 448
  quadratic regression, 121
  residuals, 90-92. 127, 133-134
  scaling, 186-187
  sequences, 503-505, 516, 518
  series, 532, 544, 548
  standard deviation, 186-187, 641
  summation, 15-16, 19
  variance, 46-47, 49, 186-187
square matrix, 749
square root, 153, 465-466, 560
SSA condition, 316-317
standard deviation, 46, 207
  binomial distribution, 692
  of binomial random variable, 659, 661-664
  of random variable, 640-642
  of sample mean, 710-712
  of z-scores, 207
  population, 46, 48
  sample, 48
standard form of a polynomial, 438
standard normal curve, 688-690, 692-701
standard normal distribution,
    688-690, 692-701
  mean, 692
  standard deviation, 692
Standard Normal Distribution Table, 693
Standardization Theorem, 699
standardized data, 207-208
standardized scores, 208, 699-700
standardizing, 699
*Statistical Abstract of the
    United States,* 68
statistical inference, 714
statistical packages, See also *spreadsheets.*
  box plot, 33-34, 166
  Central Limit Theorem, 709
  chi-square, 420-422
  correlation, 95
  cubic regression, 450
  cumulative distribution, 41
  exponential regression, 111-112
  five-number summary, 33
  histogram, 24
  line of fit, 91, 93, 95, 601, 603
  linear regression, 95
  models, 95, 111-112, 120-121, 127, 450,
    601, 603
  normal distribution, 695-696, 700-701, 716
  quadratic regression, 120-121
  random numbers, 403, 405
  scatterplot, 91
  sinusoidal regression, 276
  standard deviation, 46-47, 49
  variance, 46-47
statistics, 6
  center, measure of, 14-16, 167, 186-187
  confidence interval, 721-724, 726-730
  chi-square, 417-425, 668
  correlation coefficient, 95-101

data, 6
deviation, 46
first quartile, 31
five-number summary, 31-33
graphs, 10
histogram, 22
hypothesis testing, 669
line of best fit, 94
linear regression, 98
maximum, 31
mean, 14
median, 14, 31-33
minimum, 31
mode, 15
null hypothesis, 715
outliers, 33
percentile, 40-41
population, 6
quadratic regression, 120
quartiles, 31
range, 45
sample, 6
second quartile, 31
significance level, 668
skewness, 24
spread, measure of, 45-51,
  167-168, 188-191
standard deviation, 45-51
sum of squared residuals, 90
third quartile, 31
variance, 45-51
weighted average, 16
stemplot, 20
string, 375-377, 381-383
Strings with Replacement Theorem, 376-377
strings without replacement, 381
strong correlation, 99
strophoid, 831
subscripted variable, 15
Subtraction Formula for the Cosine and Sine
  Theorem, 767-768, 787
success, 645
sum of an arithmetic series, 524
sum of squared residuals, 90
summation notation, 15
Sums and Differences of Odd Powers
  Theorem, 483
Sums and Differences of Cubes Theorem, 482
Supplements Theorem, 238
survey, 6
symbols, list of, S6
symmetric distribution, 24
symmetry, 172, 236
  center of, 172
  facial, 211
  line of, 172
  point, 172-178
  reflection, 172-178
  to a point, 172-178
  to the origin, 173
  to the x-axis, 173-175

to the *y*-axis, 173-175
symmetry identities, 236-239
system of equations, 449-451

T

table, 7-10
   contingency, 387-395
   critical chi-square. 420
   random numbers, S8
tail of a distribution, 24-25
tangent (tan), 230-231, 234, 253
   domain, 253
   exact values, 242-245
   function, 252-254, 792
   graph, 253
   in right triangles, 294-297
   inverse, 320
   of opposites, 237
   of supplements, 238
Tartaglia, Niccolo, 475
Technology, (The use of calculator and
   computer technology beyond scientific
   calculators is found throughout. For
   some locations, see *Computer Algebra
   Systems, computer applications,
   graphing utilities, sliders, spreadsheets,*
   and *statistical packages*.)
tendency, 14
term of a loan, 536
term of a sequence, 502
tetrahedral number, 446-467,
   449-451
tetrahedron, 446
***The Federalist* papers,** 61-64
third (upper) quartile, 31
Thorpe, Jim, 304
***Titanic*,** 387-390, 393, 421-422
transcendental number, 492
transformation, 150, 159, 751-752
   composite, 196-197, 757-758, 760-761
   group, 212
   identity, 753
   image, 150-151
   matrices for, 751-764
   preimage, 159
   reflection, 752
   rotation, 220-234, 757-759,
      762-764
   scale change, 180-191, 220-234, 323-333,
      753-754
   shear, 776
   size change, 180
   translation, 151, 159-171,
      175-176, 263-265, 777
translation, 151, 159-171, 175-176, 263-265,
   777
tree diagram, 374, 388, 396-397
trial, 402
triangular number, 446-447
tribonacci number, 550
trigonometric equation, 301, 306, 316-317,

322-323, 325   -329
   general solution, 325-326
   with quadratic form, 328
trigonometric form of a complex number, 817-
   823
trigonometric function, 220-221, 229, 247-283
trigonometric identity, 766-768, 771, 777,
   786-795
trigonometry, 292
   addition formulas for cosine and sine, 766
   Complements Theorem, 239
   complex numbers, 817
   cosecant, 337
   cosine, 229
   cotangent, 337
   Double Angle Formula, 771
   Half-Turn Theorem, 273
   identities, 766-768, 771, 777, 786-795
   inverse cosine, 300
   inverse sine, 310
   inverse tangent, 320
   Law of Cosines, 304
   Law of Sines, 315
   periodic function, 254
   Pythagorean Identity, 235
   right triangle, 294-298, 336
   secant, 337
   sine, 224
   Supplements Theorem, 230
   tangent, 230
   unit circle, 229
Triple-Angle Formulas, 776
Truman, Harry, 734

U

Ulam, Stanislaw, 403
unbiased experiment, 362
union, 367
unit circle, 229-231, 233-246, 248-249
Universal Access
   Accommodating the Learner ◑, 8, 17, 48,
      64, 84, 89, 100, 104, 119, 129, 135, 154,
      162, 174, 182, 195, 201, 209, 225, 248,
      254, 259, 272, 297, 301, 310, 321, 327,
      383, 404
   Accommodating the Learner ◑, 10, 18, 49,
      65, 83, 90, 98, 104, 113, 120, 135, 155,
      163, 167, 196, 202, 208, 244, 258. 264,
      296, 302, 305, 311, 316, 326, 338, 344,
      363, 370, 377, 382
   Vocabulary Development, 9, 16, 32, 57, 83,
      89, 96, 105, 118, 128, 161, 195, 201, 224,
      231, 239, 260, 300, 362, 376, 390, 403
University of California-Berkeley, 391-392
**University of Texas Southwestern Medical
   Center,** 389

V

values
   observed, 89
   of a function at *x*, 83
   predicted, 89
variable, 6
   categorical, 8
   confounding, 391
   dependent, 80
   independent, 80
   numerical, 8
   random, 637-642, 651
   subscripted, 15
variance
   binomial distribution, 640
   of binomial random variable, 661-664
   of random variable, 640-643
   population, 46-48
   sample, 48-49
**Variance and Standard Deviation of
     a Binomial Random Variable
     Theorem,** 662
Venn diagram, 368
vertex of a parabola, 117
vertical asymptote, 126
vertical line test, 83
vertical scale change, 179
vertical scale factor, 180
vertical shift, 159-165, 271
vertical translation, 159
viewing window, 153
Vocabulary Development, 9, 16, 32, 57, 83, 89,
   96, 105, 118, 128, 161, 195, 201, 224,
   231, 239, 260, 300, 362, 376, 390, 403
volume, 439

W

Wallace, David, 61-64
***Weather on the Planets*,** 256
weak correlation, 97
weighted average, 16-19
Wessel, Caspar, 811
whiskers, 32
Wilf, Herbert S., 491
window, 153-154
Winslet, Kate, 387

X

$\bar{x}$, mean, 48
x-intercept, 118, 461

Y

yield, 582
y-intercept, 117

Z

Zero Exponent Theorem, 571
zero
   of a function, 249, 442-443,
     473-480

of a polynomial, 442, 459,
461-463, 476
of a polynomial function,
442-443, 473-480
zero power, 571, 574
z-score, 207-210, 692-696, 698-703
mean, 207
standard deviation, 207

Photo Credits

Photo Credits

Cover, back: ©Digital Vision/Getty Images; **vi** (l) ©Peter Ginter/Science Faction, (r) ©Michael G. Smith/Shutterstock; **vii** (l) ©Michael S. Quinton/National Geographic/Getty Images, (r) ©PHOTO 999/Shutterstock; **viii** (l) ©Don Smith/Photodisc, (r) ©Per-Anders Pettersson/Reportage/Getty Images; **ix** ©Ivan Cholakov/Shutterstock; **x** (l) ©Micheal Simpson/Taxi, (r) ©Mitchell Funk/Photographer's Choice; **xi** ©Richard Bloom/GAP Photos; **xii** ©Digital Vision/Getty Images; **4-5** (t) ©Peter Ginter/Science Faction; **5** (b) ©National Safety Council; **6** Photo by Scott Bauer, USDA/ARS; **7** ©Royalty Free/Corbis; **10** ©University of Chicago; **11** ©Ingram Publishing/Alamy; **17** ©Charles Siegel; **22** ©Chip Somodevilla/Getty Images; **32** ©Chepe Nicoli/Shutterstock; **39** ©Comstock Images/Alamy; **44** ©TongRo Image Stock/Alamy; **47** ©SW Productions/Brand X/Corbis; **49** ©The McGraw-Hill Companies, Inc./Ken Cavanagh, photographer; **50** ©Ingram Publishing/SuperStock; **53** ©Photodisc/PunchStock; **55** (t) ©Bill Baptist/NBAE/Getty Images, (b) ©Larry French/Getty Images; **58** ©Matthew Bernard/Time & Life Pictures/Getty Images; **59** ©China Photos/Getty Images; **61** ©Jack Zehrt/Taxi/Getty Images; **65** ©Royalty Free/Corbis; **67** ©Stockbyte/Getty Images; **68** ©The McGraw-Hill Companies/Kefover/Opatrany; **78-79** ©Michael G. Smith/Shutterstock; **81** ©Photolink/Getty Images; **85** ©Charles Siegel; **88** ©Comstock Images/PunchStock; **93** ©Royalty Free/Corbis; **94** ©Brand X Pictures; **98** ©Stockbyte/Getty Images; **102** ©Digital Vision/PunchStock; **107** ©Artur Bogacki/Shutterstock; **108** ©Doug Menuez/Getty Images; **109** ©Keystone/Hulton Archive/Getty Images; **110** ©Robin F. Pendergrast Photography, Inc.; **111** ©Photodisc Collection/Getty Images; **113** ©Ryan McVay/Getty Images; **116** ©Creatas/PunchStock; **119** ©Brand X Pictures; **121** ©Royalty Free/Corbis; **123** ©The McGraw-Hill Companies; **124** ©Travel Ink/Gallo Images/Getty Images; **126** ©Royalty Free/Corbis; **129** ©Janis Christie/Getty Images; **130** ©Photodisc/Getty Images; **131** ©Clive Brunskill/Getty Images; **133** ©Charles Siegel; **135** Foxtrot ©2002 Bill Amend. Reprinted with permission of UNIVERSAL PRESS SYNDICATE. All rights reserved; **136** ©Digital Vision/Getty Images; **138** ©Getty Images; **139** ©Royalty Free/Corbis; **140** ©Image Source; **141** ©Comstock/PunchStock; **150-151** ©Michael S. Quinton/National Geographic/Getty Images; **154** ©Stockbyte/Getty Images; **157** ©Leonard McLane/Digital Vision/Getty Images; **164** ©Lawrence M. Sawyer/Getty Images; **165** ©Karl Weatherly/Getty Images; **168** ©Lisa Romerein/Taxi/Getty Images; **169** ©Photodisc/Getty Images; **170** ©The McGraw-Hill Companies; **178** ©DAJ/Getty Images; **184** ©BananaStock/PunchStock; **185** ©Index Stock/Getty Images; **186** ©Comstock/PunchStock; **188** ©Nancy R. Cohen/Getty Images; **189** ©Dennis Sabo/Shutterstock; **190** ©Comstock/PunchStock; **193** (t, b) ©Stock Montage/Hulton Archives/Getty Images; **198** ©Creatas/PunchStock; **199** ©Arthur S. Aubry/Getty Images; **203** ©Royalty Free/Corbis; **204** (t) ©Royalty Free/Corbis, (b) ©The McGraw-Hill Companies, Inc.; **205** ©Jose Luis Pelaez, Inc./Blend Images/Corbis; **206** ©Comstock Images; **208** ©Purestock/SuperStock; **210** ©Steve Cole/Getty Images; **211** (bl) ©Royalty Free/Corbis, (tr) ©UCSMP; **212** ©image100/PunchStock; **220** (t) ©Don Farrall/Getty Images, (b) ©Medioimages/Alamy; **220-221** ©PHOTO 999/Shutterstock; **223** ©Ian Shaw/Alamy; **226** ©Purestock/PunchStock; **227** ©Photodisc Collection/Getty Images; **231** ©Ingram Publishing/Alamy; **232** ©Texas State Fair; **234** ©Special Collections Research Center, University of Chicago; **241** ©Photodisc/Getty Images; **246** ©The McGraw-Hill Companies, Inc./Ken Karp, photographer; **251** ©Ingram Publishing/Alamy; **252** ©Tom Cockrem/Lonely Planet Images/Getty Images; **254** ©Brand X/Punchstock; **257** ©Gerrit/Shutterstock; **260** ©Stockbyte/Punchstock; **261** ©Steve Cole/Getty Images; **263** ©Corbis/Punchstock; **267** ©Doug Sherman/Geofile; **268** ©2007 Getty Images, Inc.; **273** ©Special Collections Research Center, University of Chicago; **276** ©Thinkstock/Corbis; **278** ©Blend Images/PunchStock; **280** ©Royalty Free/Corbis; **282** ©Ingram Publishing/age fotostock; **283** ©Digital Vision/Getty Images; **292-293** ©Don Smith/Photodisc/Getty Images; **303** ©Brand X Pictures/Getty Images; **304** ©Hulton Archive/Getty Images; **316** ©Galyna Andrushko/Shutterstock; **322** ©Royalty Free/Corbis; **327** ©Vince Clements/Shutterstock; **329** (t) ©Comstock/Jupiter Images, (b) ©Robert Glusic/Getty Images; **341** ©Cartesia/Getty Images; **342** (tr) ©NASA, (c) ©Stefano Maccari/Shutterstock; **345** ©Travel Ink/Gallo Images/Getty Images; **346** ©Galina Mikhalishina/Shutterstock; **347** (t) ©Jack Hollingsworth/Corbis, (b) ©Lori Martin/Shutterstock; **349** ©bouzou/Shutterstock; **350** ©Mark Lewis/Stone/Getty Images; **358-359** ©Per-Anders Pettersson/Reportage/Getty Images; **362** ©James Steidl/Shutterstock; **363** ©Big Cheese Photo/PunchStock; **364** ©Postnikova Kristina/Shutterstock; **366** ©Burke/Triolo/Brand X Pictures; **369** ©Photodisc/Getty Images; **372** ©Dynamic Graphics Group/PunchStock; **374** ©Goodshoot/PunchStock; **375** ©Cindy Hughes/Shutterstock; **376** ©Mike Flippo/Shutterstock; **379** ©Photodisc/PunchStock; **381** ©aceshot1/Shutterstock; **382** ©Charles Siegel; **384** ©Per-Anders Pettersson/Getty Images; **385** ©Tetra Images/Getty Images; **386** (t) ©G. Wanner/ScienceFoto/Getty Images, (b) ©Jose Luis Pelaez/Iconica/Getty Images; **387** ©Hulton Archive/Getty Images; **391** ©Tom Holdford/UC Regents, May 12, 2008; **394** ©Doug Kanter/AFP/Getty Images; **396** ©Jonatan Fernstrom/Cultura/Getty Images; **399** ©Wanke/PhotoLink/Getty Images; **400** ©Brand X Pictures; **402** (l) ©Kyle Auclair/Getty Images, (lc) ©Barry Gossage/NBAE/Getty Images, (rc) ©Cut and Deal Ltd./Alamy, (r) ©Steve Grayson/WireImage/Getty Images; **404** ©Elena Elisseeva/Shutterstock; **407** ©Lisa F. Young/Shutterstock; **408** ©Clive Rose/Getty Images; **409** ©Spike Mafford/Getty Images; **412** ©Diana Walker/Time & Life Picture/Getty Images; **413** ©The McGraw-Hill Companies, Inc./Ken Karp, photographer; **414** ©PhotoLink/Getty Images; **423** ©Stocktrek/age fotostock; **425** ©Photos.com/Jupiter Images; **426** ©Lawrence Manning/Corbis; **427** ©Rob Tringall/Sportschrome/Getty Images; **436-437** ©Ivan Cholakov/Shutterstock; **445** ©Joseph Angert; **446** ©The McGraw-Hill Companies, Inc./Ken Cavanagh, photographer; **452** ©Klaus

Additional Answers

Chapter 1

Lesson 1-2
Activity Pages 18–19

Step 1

A salary	B	C	D	E	F
1 380000					
2 35000					
3 150000					
4 30000					
5 90000					
6 27000					

A	**salary**

Step 2

A salary	B freq	C	D	E
1 380000	1			
2 35000	1			
3 150000	1			
4 30000	3			
5 90000	2			
6 27000	1			

B	**freq**

Step 3

A salary	B freq	C	D	E
1 380000	1	380000		
2 35000	1	35000		
3 150000	1	150000		
4 30000	3	90000		
5 90000	2	180000		
6 27000	1	27000		

C1	$=a1 \cdot b1$

Step 4

A salary	B freq	C	D	E
5 90000	2	180000		
6 27000	1	27000		
7 24000	2	48000		
8 65000	4	260000		
9	15	1170000		
10				

C9	$=\text{sum}(c1{:}c8)$

Step 5

A salary	B freq	C	D
7 24000	2	48000	
8 65000	4	260000	
9	15	1170000	
10		78000	
11			

C10	$=\dfrac{c9}{b9}$

Step 6

A salary	B freq	C	D relfreq	E
1 380000	1	380000	.066667	
2 35000	1	35000	.066667	
3 150000	1	150000	.066667	
4 30000	3	90000	.2	
5 90000	2	180000	.133333	

D1	$=\text{approx}\left(\dfrac{b1}{15}\right)$

Step 7

$83,000;

new mean: $\dfrac{\sum\limits_{i=1}^{15}(x_i + 5000)}{15} = \dfrac{\sum\limits_{i=1}^{15} x_i + \sum\limits_{i=1}^{15} 5000}{15}$

$=$ old mean $+ 5000$

Lesson 1-5
Activity Page 41

Step 1

A scores	B freq	C	D
1	0	0	
2	2	3	
3	5	18	
4	8	54	
5	11	81	
6	14	148	

B1	0

Step 2

A scores	B freq	C cumfreq	D
1	0	0	0
2	2	3	3
3	5	18	21
4	8	54	75
5	11	81	156
6	14	148	304

C2	=c1+b2

Step 3

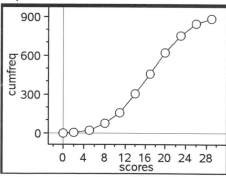

Step 4

cores	B freq	C cumfreq	D relfreq
1	0	0	0	0.
2	2	3	3	0.003405
3	5	18	21	0.020431
4	8	54	75	0.061294
5	11	81	156	0.091941

D1	$=\dfrac{b1}{881.}$

The 19-21 score range has the highest relative frequency, about 0.183882.

Step 5

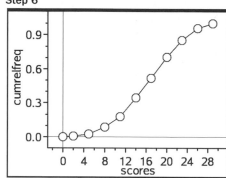

eq	C cumfreq	D relfreq	E cumre...
1	0	0	0.	0.
2	3	3	0.003405	0.003405
3	18	21	0.020431	0.023837
4	54	75	0.061294	0.085131
5	81	156	0.091941	0.177072
6	148	304	0.167991	0.345062

E2	=e1+d2

Step 6

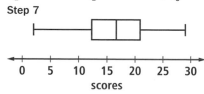

Q_1: about 12.3; Q_2: about 16.64; Q_3: about 20.9

Step 7

Lesson 1-5
Questions Page 42

1.

Year	Number of cases	Total Cases	Relative Frequency	Cumulative Relative Frequency
2003	4	4	0.011	0.011
2004	46	50	0.131	0.142
2005	98	148	0.2792	0.4217
2006	115	263	0.3276	0.7493
2007	88	351	0.2507	1

2c.

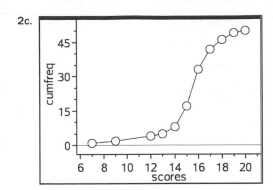

2d.

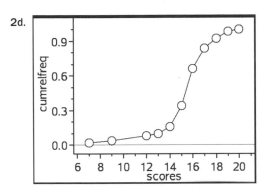

4a.

score	frequency	relative frequency
26	1	0.033
30	2	0.067
32	1	0.033
33	1	0.033
34	2	0.067
36	1	0.033
37	3	0.1
38	3	0.1
39	3	0.1
40	2	0.067
42	2	0.067
43	1	0.033
44	1	0.033
45	2	0.067
46	1	0.033
47	2	0.067
48	2	0.067

4b.

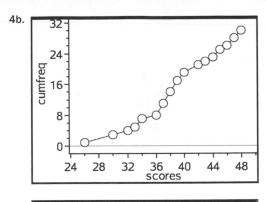

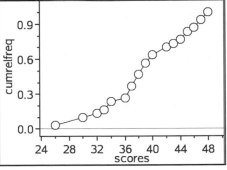

4c. Q_1: 36; Q_3: 44; median: 39

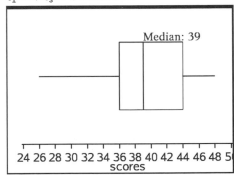

Median: 39

Lesson 1-7
Activity 2 Page 56

Step 2

mean	median	IQR	standard deviation	range
19.35	16	18	12.8893	46

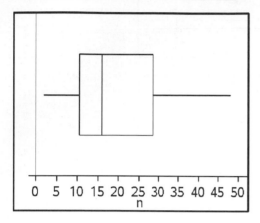

Lesson 1-8
Activity 2 Page 63-64

Step 2

Rate	Relative Frequency
23-26	0.167
26-29	0.167
29-32	0.167
32-35	0.25
35-38	0.083
38-41	0.167
41-44	0
44-47	0
47-50	0
50-53	0
53-56	0
56-59	0

Step 3

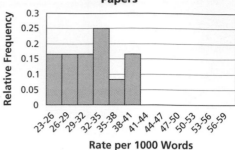

Step 4

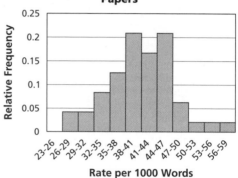

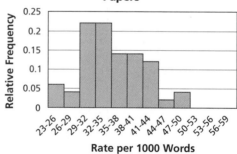

Step 5

Using the graphs, we can conclude that it is more likely that Madison wrote the disputed papers.

Chapter 2

Lesson 2-1
Questions Page 86

20a. The range between the highest and lowest value is 1,000. Since standard deviation measures the spread from the mean of a given data set, the measure of spread from the mean will necessarily be smaller than 500.

Lesson 2-4
Questions Page 107

2a. exponential; $a = 11$, $b = 4$

b. not exponential

c. not exponential

d. exponential; $a = 1$, $b = 0.6$

Lesson 2-6
Questions Page 123–124

14a.

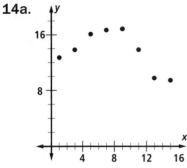

16c.

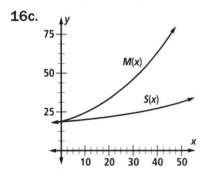

Lesson 2-8
Activity 1 Pages 133–134

Step 3

◇	A	B	C	D
1	Days (D)	Observed Days Length (L)	Predicted Days Length (p)	Residual (R = L − p)
2	0	793	784.05	6.95
3	10	766	761.53	4.47
4	20	739	737.01	1.99
5	30	711	712.49	-1.49
6	40	684	687.97	-3.97
7	50	657	663.45	-6.45
8	60	631	638.93	-7.93
9	70	607	614.41	-7.41
10	80	586	589.89	-3.89
11	90	568	565.37	2.63
12	100	556	540.85	15.15

Step 4

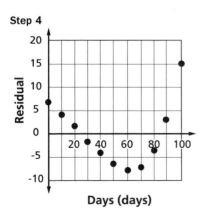

Step 5

The residuals show that the model differs significantly from the observed data. Furthermore, there is a pattern to the residuals, which indicates that another model might be better.

Activity 2 Page 134

Step 3

◇	A	B	C	D	E
1	Year	Year After 1790 (y)	Population (m)	Predicted Populaton (p)	Residual (R = m-p)
2	1790	0	4	6.03	-2.03
3	1800	10	5	7.39	-2.39
4	1810	20	7	9.04	-2.04
5	1820	30	10	11.07	-1.07
6	1830	40	13	13.55	-0.55
7	1840	50	17	16.58	0.42
8	1850	60	23	20.30	2.70
9	1860	70	31	24.85	6.15
10	1870	80	40	30.42	9.58
11	1880	90	50	37.24	12.76
12	1890	100	63	45.59	17.41
13	1900	110	76	55.81	20.19
14	1910	120	92	68.32	23.68
15	1920	130	106	83.63	22.37
16	1930	140	123	102.38	20.62
17	1940	150	132	125.32	6.68
18	1950	160	151	153.41	-2.41
19	1960	170	179	187.80	-8.80
20	1970	180	203	229.89	-26.89
21	1980	190	227	281.42	-54.42
22	1990	200	249	344.50	-95.50
23	2000	210	281	421.72	-140.72

Step 4

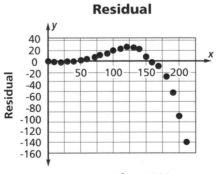

Years After 1790

Step 5

The exponential model is not a fit for this data because it increasingly diverges from the data with time.

Questions Pages 137–138

5b.

◇	A	B	C	D	E
	Year (Y)	Year After 1790	Population (m)	Predicted Populaton (p)	Residual (R = m-p)
2	1790	0	4	4.00	0.00
3	1800	10	5	5.33	-0.33
4	1810	20	7	7.11	-0.11
5	1820	30	10	9.48	0.52
6	1830	40	13	12.64	0.36
7	1840	50	17	16.86	0.14
8	1850	60	23	22.49	0.51
9	1860	70	31	29.98	1.02
10	1870	80	40	39.98	0.02
11	1880	90	50	53.32	-3.32

9b. Answers vary. Sample: Eyeballing the scatterplot, it seems that any of the three standard models (linear, exponential, or quadratic) might fit the data.

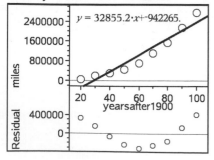

c. Exponential: $y = 38720(1.04667)x$

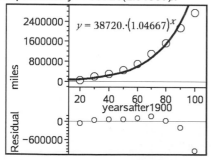

Linear: $y = 32855.2x - 942265$

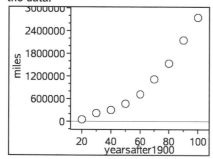

d. Quadratic: $y = 422.455X^2 - 17839.5X + 296938$

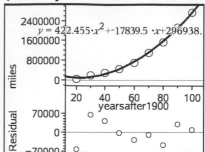

The quadratic regression model seems to fit the data best, and the residuals all lie in a relatively small range.

Chapter Review
Questions Pages 146–149

5b. 937.07

49. about 8 or 9 hours; Answers vary. Sample: This might make sense because a student who studies excessively for a test may negatively affect his performance through stress or lack of sleep.

50. The quadratic model is more appropriate because the data points are clustered closer to the x-axis, so the sum of its squared residuals is less than the sum of the squared residuals for the linear model.

Chapter 3

Lesson 3-1
Questions Pages 156–158

10a.

i.

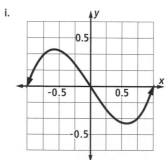

ii.

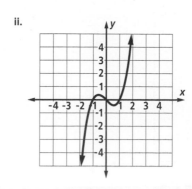

iii.

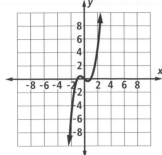

iv.

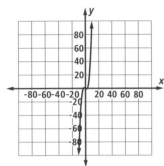

12a.

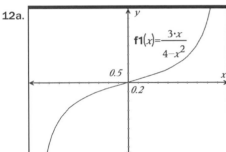

$$f1(x) = \frac{3 \cdot x}{4 - x^2}$$

0.5

0.2

b.

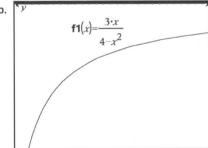

$$f1(x) = \frac{3 \cdot x}{4 - x^2}$$

15a.

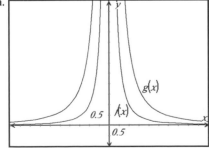

$g(x)$

0.5 $f(x)$

0.5

c. The y values of g are greater than those of f in the graph above. Since $x^2 > 0$, when $x \neq 0$ and $1 < 4$, then $\frac{1}{x^2} < \frac{4}{x^2}$. So, $f(x) < g(x)$, when $x \neq 0$.

24a. $10 < x < 40$, $10 < y < 40$

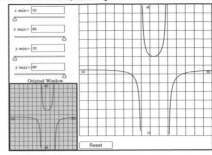

b. Answers vary. Sample: parabola:

$22 \leq x \leq 32$, $25 \leq y \leq 40$

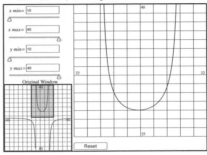

c. Answers vary. Sample: line:

$37 \leq x \leq 40$, $18 \leq y \leq 27$

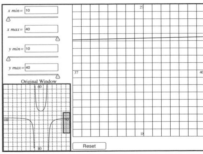

d. Answers vary. Sample: inverse-square:

$10 \leq x \leq 40$, $10 \leq y \leq 28$

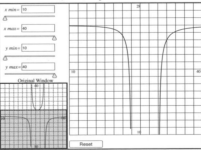

e. Answers vary. Sample: exponential:

$28 \le x \le 31$, $28 \le y \le 40$

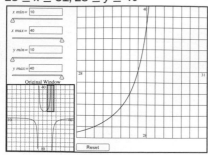

240°	270°	300°	315°	330°	360°
$\dfrac{4\pi}{3}$	$\dfrac{3\pi}{2}$	$\dfrac{5\pi}{3}$	$\dfrac{7\pi}{4}$	$\dfrac{11\pi}{6}$	2π
$-\dfrac{\sqrt{3}}{2}$	-1	$-\dfrac{\sqrt{3}}{2}$	$-\dfrac{\sqrt{2}}{2}$	$-\dfrac{1}{2}$	0
-0.866	-1	-0.866	-0.707	-0.5	0

Lesson 3-6
Guided Example Page 186

Guided Example, Steps 2–6

◇	A	B	C	D	E	F	G
1	Item	1998 cost	2008 cost (predicted)		1998 statistics	2008 statistics	1998 statistics × scale factor
2	Coffee 1 Pound	$4.03	$5.33	mean	$1.79	$2.36	$2.37
3	Eggs 1 dozen	$1.12	$1.48	median	$1.37	$1.80	$1.81
4	Gasoline 1 gallon	$1.13	$1.49	range	$3.01	$3.98	$3.98
5	Orange Juice 12-oz can	$1.60	$2.11	variance	$1.31	$2.28	$1.73
6	Ground Beef 1 pound	$1.82	$2.41	standard deviation	$1.14	$1.51	$1.51
7	Chicken 1 pound	$1.02	$1.35				
8							

For mean, median, standard deviation, and range, multiplying by the scale factor accurately finds the 2008 stats. Multiplying by the scale factor does not work for the variance.

Chapter 4

Lesson 4-5
Activity 1 Pages 247–248

Step 1:

θ (degrees)	0°	30°	45°	60°	90°
θ (radians)	0	$\dfrac{\pi}{6}$	$\dfrac{\pi}{4}$	$\dfrac{\pi}{3}$	$\dfrac{\pi}{2}$
$\sin \theta$ exact	0	$\dfrac{1}{2}$	$\dfrac{\sqrt{2}}{2}$	$\dfrac{\sqrt{3}}{2}$	1
$\sin \theta$ approx	0	0.5	0.707	0.866	1

120°	135°	150°	180°	210°	225°
$\dfrac{2\pi}{3}$	$\dfrac{3\pi}{4}$	$\dfrac{5\pi}{6}$	π	$\dfrac{7\pi}{6}$	$\dfrac{5\pi}{4}$
$\dfrac{\sqrt{3}}{2}$	$\dfrac{\sqrt{2}}{2}$	$\dfrac{1}{2}$	0	$-\dfrac{1}{2}$	$-\dfrac{\sqrt{2}}{2}$
0.866	0.707	0.5	0	−0.5	−0.707

Activity 2 Page 249

	sine function (degrees)	sine function (radians)
Domain	$\{\theta \mid \theta \in \mathbb{R}\}$	$\{\theta \mid \theta \in \mathbb{R}\}$
Range	$\{y \mid -1 \le y \le 1\}$	$\{y \mid -1 \le y \le 1\}$
Zeros	$\sin \theta = 0$ when $\theta = $ 0°, 180°, 360°, …	$\sin \theta = 0$ when $\theta = 0, \pi, 2\pi, …$
Maxima	$\sin \theta = 1$ when $\theta = $ 90°, 450°, 810°, …	$\sin \theta = 1$ when $\theta = \dfrac{\pi}{2}, \dfrac{5\pi}{2}, \dfrac{9\pi}{2}, …$
Minima	$\sin \theta = -1$ when $\theta = $ 270°, 630°, 990°, …	$\sin \theta = -1$ when $\theta = \dfrac{3\pi}{2}, \dfrac{7\pi}{2}, \dfrac{11\pi}{2}, …$

	cosine function (degrees)	cosine function (radians)
Domain	$\{\theta \mid \theta \in \mathbb{R}\}$	$\{\theta \mid \theta \in \mathbb{R}\}$
Range	$\{y \mid -1 \leq y \leq 1\}$	$\{y \mid -1 \leq y \leq 1\}$
Zeros	$\cos\theta = 0$ when $\theta =$ $90°, 270°, 450°, \dots$	$\cos\theta = 0$ when $\theta = \frac{\pi}{2}, \frac{3\pi}{2}, \frac{5\pi}{2}, \dots$
Maxima	$\cos\theta = 1$ when $\theta =$ $0°, 360°, 720°, \dots$	$\cos\theta = 1$ when $\theta = 0, 2\pi, 4\pi, \dots$
Minima	$\cos\theta = -1$ when $\theta =$ $180°, 540°, 900°, \dots$	$\cos\theta = -1$ when $\theta = \pi, 3\pi, 5\pi, \dots$

Lesson 4-10
Activity Page 277

Step 1:

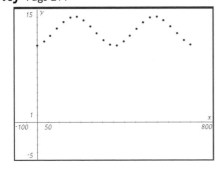

Step 2:

a. about 2 hours; maximum hours of daylight is about 14 and minimum is about 10

b. 365 days; number of days in a year

c. about 12 units up; average number of hours of daylight is 12

d. $\frac{365}{4}$ units to the right; The first day of at least 12 hours of sunlight is around April 4.

Step 3: $\dfrac{y - 12.155}{1.925} = \dfrac{\sin x - \frac{365}{4}}{\frac{365}{2\pi}}$

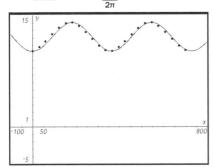

Step 4: $y = 1.91 \sin(0.017x - 1.39) + 12.17$

Chapter 5

Lesson 5-3 Page 308

23. Extend $\overline{BA}$ and draw an altitude from C to this line. Label the intersection point D. Then $\triangle ACD$ is a 30-60-90 right triangle with $m\angle DAC = 30°$ and $AC = 15$. So $DC = \frac{15}{2} = 7.5$ and $AD = \frac{15\sqrt{3}}{2} = 7.5\sqrt{3}$. $\triangle BDC$ is a right triangle with $DC = 7.5$ and $BD = 15 + 7.5\sqrt{3}$. By the Pythagorean Theorem, $BC^2 = 7.5^2 + (15 + 7.5\sqrt{3})^2 = 15^2(2 + \sqrt{3})$. Therefore, $BC = 15\sqrt{2 + \sqrt{3}} \approx 28.98$ cm.

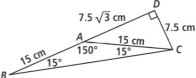

Lesson 5-6 Page 323

9a.

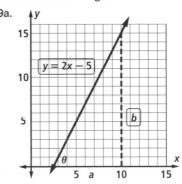

The slope of the line is 2, so $\frac{b}{a} = 2$ and $\tan\theta = \frac{b}{a} = 2$. Thus $\tan^{-1}(2) = \theta$.

9b. If $y = mx + b$, then $\tan\theta = m$ and $\theta = \tan^{-1}m$.

10. $\theta = \tan^{-1}\left(\frac{a}{2}\right)$

11a. $y = \tan^{-1}\left(\frac{80}{x}\right)$

11b. $y = \tan^{-1}\left(\frac{110}{x}\right) - \tan^{-1}\left(\frac{30}{x}\right)$

14a.

a	b	$\tan^{-1}\left(\frac{a}{b}\right) + \tan^{-1}\left(\frac{b}{a}\right)$
1	3	90°
2	2	90°
3	4	90°
1	5	90°
4	7	90°

14b. $\tan^{-1}\left(\frac{a}{b}\right) + \tan^{-1}\left(\frac{b}{a}\right) = 90°$; Consider the arbitrary angle $0 < A < 90°$ such that $A = \tan^{-1}\left(\frac{a}{b}\right)$, and $\tan A = \frac{a}{b}$. By the definition of $\tan A$, $\tan A = \frac{\sin A}{\cos A} = \frac{a}{b}$. By the Complements Theorem we have $\frac{a}{b} = \frac{\cos(90° - A)}{\sin(90° - A)}$. Taking the reciprocal of each side we have $\frac{b}{a} = \frac{\sin(90° - A)}{\cos(90° - A)} = \tan(90° - A)$. Then $\tan^{-1}\left(\frac{b}{a}\right) = (90° - A)$, so $\tan^{-1}\left(\frac{a}{b}\right) + \tan^{-1}\left(\frac{b}{a}\right) = A + (90° - A) = 90°$.

14c. In right triangle ABC with $m\angle C = 90°$, $\tan^{-1}\left(\frac{a}{b}\right) = m\angle A$ and $\tan^{-1}\left(\frac{b}{a}\right) = m\angle B$. Since the angles are complementary, $m\angle A + m\angle B = \tan^{-1}\left(\frac{a}{b}\right) + \tan^{-1}\left(\frac{b}{a}\right) = 90°$.

Chapter 6

Lesson 6-7 Page 403

Step 3:

Trial #	Card Numbers	Success?
1	4, 4, 1, 3, 2, 1	Yes
2	3, 1, 2, 4, 2, 4	Yes
3	1, 4, 4, 1, 2, 1	No
4	4, 4, 2, 2, 1, 1	No
5	2, 2, 4, 1, 4, 3	Yes
6	1, 4, 3, 2, 2, 1	Yes
7	1, 4, 4, 1, 1, 3	No
8	1, 4, 1, 2, 1, 1	No
9	3, 1, 1, 1, 3, 3	No
10	1, 2, 4, 3, 3, 2	Yes

Step 4: Answers vary. Sample:

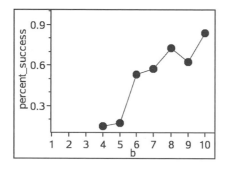

Step 5: Answers vary. Sample: According to the class data, it would take buying at least 7 boxes to get the complete set of 4 cards only 60% of the time. Buying almost twice as many boxes as there are cards in the set for only a 60% chance of obtaining the complete set is left to parents to decide.

Questions Pages 407 and 409

6c. Answers vary. Sample:

	A	B	C	D	E	F
◆	=rand	=rand	=rand	=rand		=e[]/50
47	1	1	1	1	0	0
48	0	0	1	1	0	0
49	1	1	0	0	0	0
50	1	0	0	0	1	1/50
51					15	3/10

$$E50 = \begin{cases} 0, a50+b50+c50+d50 \neq 1 \\ 1, a50+b50+c50+d50 = 1 \end{cases}$$

For this simulation we define girl = 1 and boy = 0. We have chosen a random integer 0 or 1 for 4 children in each of 50 families using the function randInt(0,1,50) in the first 4 columns. In the fifth column, the number of girls are summed and if there is 1 girl in the family the cell displays 1, else it displays 0. This is summed and divided by 50 for the relative frequency.

18. Answers vary. Sample: Generate a large number of random integers from 1-100. A success is when you get an integer between 91-100 (but only count the first instance). The set is complete when you have all of the numbers. In this simulation, you had to examine about 494 quarters before you had all 100.

	A	B	C	D
◆	=randint(0			
491	39			
492	80			
493	53			
494	97			
495	9			
496	2			
A494	=97			

19a. Answers vary. Sample: The contestant should switch.

b. Answers vary. Sample: We can simulate this using a die to randomly determine the door. Let 1 and 2 = door #1, 3 and 4 = door #2, and 5 and 6 = door #3.

Use 3 cups labeled 1 to 3 to stand for the doors. Choose an object for a prize. One trial is one roll of the die. Put the prize under a particular cup. The player makes a guess as to which cup the prize is in. The host then shows the "unchosen" door with no prize. The player gets to choose to either switch or stick with the original cup. Play the Monty Hall Game 20 times and record the number of wins with a stick or a switch. When comparing the sticking strategy versus the switching strategy, make sure to compare the same number of sticking situations with switching situations.

14. The total car-owning population is 290, and there are 70 juniors who own cars. $\frac{70}{290} \approx 24.1\%$.

15. Since $.325 = \frac{13}{40}$, simulate this situation by generating random numbers between 1 and 40, where 1-13 represents a hit and 14-40 represents not a hit. Generating eight random numbers equals one trial. A trail is successful if 4 or more of the numbers generated are a hit (1-13). Run this simulation for forty trials and use the relative frequency of success to estimate the probability.

16a. If the die is fair, the probability of rolling a 2 is $\frac{1}{6}$, so the expected count is $\frac{1}{6} \cdot 12{,}000 = 2{,}000$.

  b. Answers vary. Sample: You might conclude that the die is unfair because 1 occurs very frequently, and 4 occurs rarely. You could do a chi-square test to test your hypothesis.

  c. No, the sample is too small. By the Law of Large Numbers, the relative frequency of each of the outcomes should approach their probability as the number of trials increases. A chi-square test might be inaccurate on a sample this small.